Intervention and Reflection

Customized for Anoka Ramsey Community College

Ronald Munson

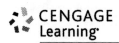 CENGAGE
Learning·

Australia • Brazil • Japan • Korea • Mexico • Singapore • Spain • United Kingdom • United States

CENGAGE
Learning·

**Intervention and Reflection
Customized for Anoka Ramsey
Community College**

Intervention and Reflection: Basic Issues in Bioethics, 9th Edition
Ronald Munson
© 2012 Cengage Learning. All rights reserved.

Senior Project Development Manager:
Linda deStefano

Market Development Manager:
Heather Kramer

Senior Production/
Manufacturing Manager:
Donna M. Brown

Production Editorial Manager:
Kim Fry

Sr. Rights Acquisition Account Manager:
Todd Osborne

For product information and technology assistance, contact us at
Cengage Learning Customer & Sales Support, 1-800-354-9706
For permission to use material from this text or product,
submit all requests online at **cengage.com/permissions**
Further permissions questions can be emailed to
permissionrequest@cengage.com

This book contains select works from existing Cengage Learning resources and was produced by Cengage Learning Custom Solutions for collegiate use. As such, those adopting and/or contributing to this work are responsible for editorial content accuracy, continuity and completeness.

Compilation © 2012 Cengage Learning

ISBN-13: 978-1-285-54843-2

ISBN-10: 1-285-54843-4

Cengage Learning
5191 Natorp Boulevard
Mason, Ohio 45040
USA

Cengage Learning is a leading provider of customized learning solutions with office locations around the globe, including Singapore, the United Kingdom, Australia, Mexico, Brazil, and Japan. Locate your local office at:
international.cengage.com/region.
Cengage Learning products are represented in Canada by Nelson Education, Ltd.
For your lifelong learning solutions, visit **www.cengage.com /custom.**
Visit our corporate website at **www.cengage.com.**

Printed in the United States of America

Brief Contents

Ronald Munson is Professor of the Philosophy of Science and Medicine at the University of Missouri–St. Louis. He received his Ph.D. from Columbia University and was a Postdoctoral Fellow in Biology at Harvard University. He has been a Visiting Professor at University of California, San Diego, Johns Hopkins School of Medicine, and Harvard Medical School.

A nationally acclaimed bioethicist, Munson is a medical ethicist for the National Eye Institute and a consultant for the National Cancer Institute. He is also a member of the Washington University School of Medicine Human Studies Committee.

His other books include *Raising the Dead: Organ Transplants, Ethics, and Society* (named one of the "Best Science and Medicine Books of 2002" by the National Library Association), *Reasoning in Medicine* (with Daniel Albert and Michael Resnik), *Elements of Reasoning* and *Basics of Reasoning* (both with David Conway), and *Outcome Uncertain: Cases and Contexts in Bioethics.* He is also author of the novels *Nothing Human, Fan Mail,* and *Night Vision.*

Foundations of Bioethics: Ethical Theories, Moral Principles, and Medical Decisions

Foundations of Bioethics: Ethical Theories, Moral Principles, and Medical Decisions

CHAPTER CONTENTS

"He's stopped breathing, Doctor," the nurse said. She sounded calm and not at all hysterical. By the time Dr. Sarah Cunningham had reached Mr. Sabatini's bedside, the nurse was already providing mouth-to-mouth resuscitation. But Mr. Sabatini still had the purplish blue color of cyanosis, caused by a lack of oxygen in his blood.

Dr. Cunningham knew that, if Mr. Sabatini was to survive, he would have to be given oxygen fast and placed on a respirator. But should she order this done?

Mr. Sabatini was an old man, almost ninety. So far as anyone knew, he was alone in the world and would hardly be missed when he died. His health was poor. He had congestive heart disease and was dying slowly and painfully from intestinal cancer.

Wouldn't it be a kindness to Mr. Sabatini to allow him this quick and painless death? Why condemn him to lingering on for a few extra hours or weeks?

The decision that Sarah Cunningham faces is a moral one. She has to decide whether she should take the steps that might prolong Mr. Sabatini's life or not take them and accept the consequence that he will almost surely die within minutes. She knows the medical procedures that can be employed, but she has to decide whether she should employ them.

This kind of case rivets our attention because of its immediacy and drama. But there are many other situations that arise in the context of medical practice and research that present problems that require moral decisions. Some are equal in drama to the problem facing Dr. Cunningham, while others are not so dramatic but are of at least equal seriousness. There are far too many to catalog, but consider this sample: Is it right for a woman to have an abortion for any reason? Should children with serious birth defects be put to death? Do people have a right to die? Does everyone have a right to medical care? Should physicians ever lie to their patients? Should people suffering from a genetic disease be allowed

to have children? Can parents agree to allow their children to be used as experimental subjects?

Most of us have little tolerance for questions like these. They seem so cold and abstract. Our attitude changes, however, when we find ourselves in a position in which we are the decision makers. It changes, too, when we are in a position in which we must advise those who make the decisions. Or when we are on the receiving end of the decisions.

But whether we view the problems abstractly or concretely, we are inclined to ask the same question: Are there any rules, standards, or principles that we can use as guides when we are faced with moral decisions? If there are, then Dr. Cunningham need not be wholly unprepared to decide whether she should order steps taken to save Mr. Sabatini. Nor need we be unprepared to decide issues like those in the questions above.

The branch of philosophy concerned with principles that allow us to make decisions about what is right and wrong is called *ethics* or *moral philosophy*. *Bioethics* is specifically concerned with moral principles and decisions in the context of medical practice, policy, and research. Moral difficulties connected with medicine are so complex and important that they require special attention. Medical ethics gives them this attention, but it remains a part of the discipline of ethics. Thus, if we are to answer our question as to whether there are any rules or principles to use when making moral decisions in the medical context, we must turn to general ethical theories and to a consideration of moral principles that have been proposed to hold in all contexts of human action.

In the first section, we will discuss five major ethical theories that have been put forward by philosophers. Each of these theories represents an attempt to supply basic principles we can rely on in making moral decisions. We'll consider these theories and examine how they might be applied to moral issues in the medical context. We will discuss the reasons that have been offered to persuade us to accept each theory, but we will also point out some of the difficulties each theory presents.

In the second section, we will examine and illustrate several moral principles that are of special relevance to medical research and practice. These principles are frequently appealed to in discussions of practical ethical problems and are sufficiently uncontroversial to be endorsed in a general way by any of the ethical theories mentioned in the first section. (Those who defend theories without principles do not, of course, endorse them as principles.)

In the third and last section, we will consider the basic concepts of three ethical theories usually offered as theories that are free of principles: virtue ethics, care ethics, and feminist ethics. We will consider how these theories might be used in making moral decisions, but we will also call attention to some of the criticisms urged against each of them.

The three sections are not dependent on one another, and it is possible to profit from one without reading the others. (The price for this independence is a small amount of repetition.) Nevertheless, reading all three sections is recommended. The Case Presentations and Social Contexts presented in the majority of this book can most easily be followed by someone who has at least some familiarity with basic moral theories.

Also, some points in discussions turn upon questions about the applicability of certain familiar moral principles or whether it is possible to operate without any principles. Being acquainted with those principles makes it easier to understand and evaluate such discussions.

BASIC ETHICAL THEORIES

Ethical theories attempt to articulate and justify principles that can be employed as guides for making moral decisions and as standards for the evaluation of actions and policies. In effect, such theories define what it means to act morally, and in doing so, they stipulate in a general fashion the duties or obligations that fall upon us.

Ethical theories also offer a means to explain and justify actions. If our actions are guided by a particular theory, then we can explain them by demonstrating that the principles of the theory required us to act as we did. In such cases, the explanation also constitutes a justification. We justify our actions by showing that, according to the theory, we had an obligation to do what we did. (In some cases, we may justify our actions by showing that the theory *permitted* our actions—that is, didn't require them, but didn't rule them out as wrong.)

Advocates of a particular ethical theory present what they consider to be good reasons and relevant evidence in its support. Their general aim is to show that the theory is one that any reasonable individual would find persuasive or would endorse as correct. Accordingly, appeals to religion, faith, or nonnatural factors are not considered to be either necessary or legitimate to justify the theory. Rational persuasion alone is regarded as the basis of justification.

In this section, we will briefly consider four general ethical theories and one theory of justice that has an essential ethical component. In each case, we will begin by examining the basic principles of the theory and the grounds offered for its acceptance. We will then explore some of the possibilities of applying the theory to problems that arise within the medical context. Finally, we will mention some of the practical consequences and conceptual difficulties that raise questions about the theory's adequacy or correctness.

Utilitarianism

The ethical theory known as utilitarianism was given its most influential formulation in the nineteenth century by the British philosophers Jeremy Bentham (1748–1832) and John Stuart Mill (1806–1873). Bentham and Mill did not produce identical theories, but both of their versions have come to be spoken of as "classical utilitarianism." Subsequent elaborations and qualifications of utilitarianism are inevitably based on the formulations of Bentham and Mill, so their theories are worth careful examination.

The Principle of Utility

The foundation of utilitarianism is a single apparently simple principle. Mill calls it the "principle of utility" and states it this way: *Actions are right in proportion as they tend to promote happiness, wrong as they tend to produce the reverse of happiness.*

The principle focuses attention on the *consequences* of actions, rather than upon some feature of the actions themselves. The "utility" or "usefulness" of an action is determined by the extent to which it produces happiness. Thus, no action is *in itself* right or wrong. Nor is an action right or wrong by virtue of the actor's hopes, intentions, or past actions. Consequences alone are important. Breaking a promise, lying, causing pain, or even killing a person may, under certain circumstances, be the right action to take. Under other circumstances, the action might be wrong.

We need not think of the principle as applying to just one action that we are considering. It supplies the basis for a kind of cost–benefit analysis to employ in a situation in which several lines of action are possible. Using the principle, we are supposed to consider the possible results of each action. Then we are to choose the one that produces the most benefit (happiness) at the least cost (unhappiness). The action we take may produce some unhappiness, but it

is a balance of happiness over unhappiness that the principle tells us to seek.

Suppose, for example, that a woman in a large hospital is near death: she is in a coma, an EEG shows only minimal brain function, and a respirator is required to keep her breathing. Another patient has just been brought to the hospital from the scene of an automobile accident. His kidneys have been severely damaged, and he is in need of an immediate transplant. There is a good tissue match with the woman's kidneys. Is it right to hasten her death by removing a kidney?

The principle of utility would probably consider the removal justified. The woman is virtually dead, while the man has a good chance of surviving. It is true that the woman's life is threatened even more by the surgery. It may in fact kill her. But, on balance, the kidney transplant seems likely to produce more happiness than unhappiness. In fact, it seems better than the alternative of doing nothing. For in that case, both patients are likely to die.

The principle of utility is also called the "greatest happiness principle" by Bentham and Mill. The reason for this name is clear when the principle is stated in this way: *Those actions are right which produce the greatest happiness for the greatest number of people.* This alternative formulation makes it obvious that, in deciding how to act, it is not just my happiness or the happiness of a particular person or group that must be considered. According to utilitarianism, every person is to count just as much as any other person. That is, when we are considering how we should act, everyone's interest must be considered. The right action, then, will be the one that produces the most happiness for the largest number of people.

Mill is particularly anxious that utilitarianism not be construed as no more than a sophisticated justification for crude self-interest. He stresses that, in making a moral decision, we must look at the situation in an objective way. We must, he says, be a "benevolent spectator" and then act in a way that will bring about the best results for all concerned. This view is summarized in a famous passage:

> *The happiness which forms the utilitarian standard of what is right in conduct is not the agent's own happiness, but that of all concerned. As between his own happiness and that of others, utilitarianism requires him to be as strictly impartial as a disinterested and benevolent spectator. In the golden rule of Jesus of Nazareth, we read the complete spirit of the ethics of utility. To do as you would be done by, and to love your neighbor as yourself, constitute the ideal perfection of utilitarian morality.*

The key concept in both formulations of the principle of utility is "happiness." Bentham simply identifies happiness with pleasure—pleasure of any kind. The aim of ethics, then, is to increase the amount of pleasure in the world to the greatest possible extent. In furtherance of this aim, Bentham recommends the use of a "calculus of pleasure and pain," in which characteristics of pleasure such as intensity, duration, and number of people affected are measured and assigned numerical values. To determine which of several possible actions is the right one, we need only determine which one receives the highest numerical score. Unfortunately, Bentham does not tell us what units to use or how to make the measurements.

Mill also identifies happiness with pleasure, but he differs from Bentham in a major respect. Unlike Bentham, he insists that some pleasures are "higher" than others. Thus, pleasures of the intellect are superior to, say, purely sensual pleasures. This difference in the concept of pleasure can become significant in a medical context. For example, in the choice of using limited resources to save the life of a lathe operator or of an art historian, Mill's view might assign more value to the life of the art historian. That person, Mill might say, is capable of "higher pleasures" than the lathe

operator. (Of course, other factors would be relevant here for Mill.)

Both Mill and Bentham regard happiness as an intrinsic good. That is, it is something good in itself or for its own sake. Actions, by contrast, are good only to the extent to which they tend to promote happiness. Therefore, they are only instrumentally good. Since utilitarianism determines the rightness of actions in terms of their tendency to promote the greatest happiness for the greatest number, it is considered to be a *teleological* ethical theory. (*Teleological* comes from the Greek word *telos*, which means "end" or "goal.") A teleological ethical theory judges the rightness of an action in terms of an external goal or purpose—"general happiness" or utility for utilitarianism. However, utilitarianism is also a *consequentialist* theory, for the outcomes or consequences of actions are the only considerations relevant to determining their moral rightness. Not all teleological theories are consequentialist.

Some more recent formulations of utilitarianism have rejected the notion that happiness, no matter how defined, is the sole intrinsic good that actions or policies must promote. Critics of the classical view have argued that the list of things we recognize as valuable in themselves should be increased to include ones such as knowledge, beauty, love, friendship, liberty, and health. According to this *pluralistic* view, in applying the principle of utility we must consider the entire range of intrinsic goods that an action is likely to promote. Thus, the right action is the one that can be expected to produce the greatest sum of intrinsic goods. In most of the discussion that follows, we will speak of the greatest happiness or benefit, but it is easy enough to see how the same points can be made from a pluralistic perspective.

Act and Rule Utilitarianism

All utilitarians accept the principle of utility as the standard for determining the rightness of actions. But they divide into two groups over the matter of the application of the principle.

Act utilitarianism holds that the principle should be applied to particular acts in particular circumstances. *Rule utilitarianism* maintains that the principle should be used to test rules, which can in turn be used to decide the rightness of particular acts. Let's consider each of these views and see how it works in practice.

Act utilitarianism holds that an act is right if, and only if, no other act could have been performed that would produce a higher utility. Suppose a child is born with severe impairments. The child has an open spine, severe brain damage, and dysfunctional kidneys. What should be done? (We will leave open the question of who should decide.)

The act utilitarian holds that we must attempt to determine the consequences of the various actions that are open to us. We should consider, for example, these possibilities: (1) Give the child only the ordinary treatment that would be given to a normal child; (2) give the child special treatment for its problems; (3) give the child no treatment—allow it to die; (4) put the child to death in a painless way.

According to act utilitarianism, we must explore the potential results of each possibility. We must realize, for example, that when such a child is given only ordinary treatment, it will be worse off, if it survives, than if it had been given special treatment. Also, a child left alone and allowed to die is likely to suffer more pain than one killed by a lethal injection. Furthermore, a child treated aggressively will have to undergo numerous surgical procedures of limited effectiveness. We must also consider the family of the child and judge the emotional and financial effects that each of the possible actions will have on them. Then, too, we must take into account such matters as the "quality of life" of a child with severe brain damage and multiple defects, the effect on physicians and nurses in killing the child or allowing it to die, and the financial costs to society in providing long-term care.

After these considerations, we should then choose the action that has the greatest utility. We should act in the way that will produce the most benefit for all concerned. Which of the possibilities we select will depend on the precise features of the situation: how impaired the child is, how good its chances are for living an acceptable life, the character and financial status of the family, and so on. The great strength of act utilitarianism is that it invites us to deal with each case as unique. When the circumstances of another case are different, we might, without being inconsistent, choose another of the possible actions.

Act utilitarianism shows a sensitivity to specific cases, but it is not free from difficulties. Some philosophers have pointed out that there is no way that we can be sure that we have made the right choice of actions. We are sure to be ignorant of much relevant information. Besides, we can't know with much certainty what the results of our actions will really be. There is no way to be sure, for example, that even a severely impaired infant will not recover enough to live a better life than we predict.

The act utilitarian can reply that acting morally doesn't mean being omniscient. We need to make a reasonable effort to get relevant information, and we can usually predict the probable consequences of our actions. Acting morally doesn't require any more than this.

Another objection to act utilitarianism is more serious. According to the doctrine, we are obligated to keep a promise only if keeping it will produce more utility than some other action. If some other action will produce the same utility, then keeping the promise is permissible but not obligatory. Suppose a surgeon promises a patient that only he will perform an operation, then allows a well-qualified resident to perform part of it. Suppose all goes well and the patient never discovers that the promise was not kept. The outcome for the patient is exactly the same as if the surgeon had kept the promise. From the point of view of act utilitarianism, there is nothing wrong with the surgeon's failure to keep it. Yet critics charge that there is something wrong—that, in making the promise, the surgeon took on an obligation. Act utilitarianism is unable to account for obligations engendered by such actions as promising and pledging, critics say, for such actions involve something other than consequences.

A third objection to act utilitarianism arises in situations in which virtually everyone must follow the same rules in order to achieve a high level of utility, but even greater utility can be achieved if a few people do not follow the rules. Consider the relationship between physicians and the Medicaid program. The program pays physicians for services provided to those poor enough to qualify for the program. The program would collapse if nearly all physicians were not honest in billing Medicaid for their services. Not only would many poor people suffer, but physicians themselves would lose a source of income.

Suppose a particular physician believes that the requirements to qualify for Medicaid are too restrictive and that many who urgently need medical care cannot afford it. As an act utilitarian, she reasons that it is right for her to get money to open a free clinic under the program. She intends to bill for services she does not provide, then use that money to treat those not covered by Medicaid. Her claims will be small compared to the entire Medicaid budget, so it is unlikely that anyone who qualifies for Medicaid will go without treatment. Since she will tell no one what she is doing, others are not likely to be influenced by her example and make false claims for similar or less worthy purposes. The money she is paid will bring substantial benefit to those in need of health care. Thus, she concludes, by violating the rules of the program, her actions will produce greater utility than would be produced by following the rules.

The physician's action would be morally right, according to act utilitarians. Yet, critics say, we expect an action that is morally right to be one that is right for everyone in similar circumstances. If every physician in the Medicaid program acted in this way, however, the program would be destroyed and thus produce no utility at all. Furthermore, according to critics, the physician's action produces unfairness. Although it is true that the patients she treats at her free clinic gain a benefit they would not otherwise have, similar patients must go without treatment. The Medicaid policy, whatever its flaws, is at least prima facie fair in providing benefits to all who meet its requirements. Once again, then, according to critics, more seems to be involved in judging the moral worth of an action than can be accounted for by act utilitarianism.

In connection with such objections, some critics have gone so far as to claim that it is impossible to see how a society in which everyone was an act utilitarian could function. We could not count on promises being kept nor take for granted that people were telling us the truth. Social policies would be no more than general guides to action, and we could never be sure that people would regard themselves as obligated to adhere to the provisions of those policies. Decisions made by individuals about each individual action would not obviously lead to the promotion of the highest degree of utility. Indeed, some critics say, such a society might collapse, for communication among individuals would be difficult, if not impossible, social cohesion would be weakened, and general policies and regulations would have very uncertain effects.

The critics are not necessarily right, of course, and defenders of act utilitarianism have made substantial efforts to answer the criticisms we have presented. Some have denied that the theory has those implications and argued that some of our generally accepted moral perceptions should be changed. In connection with this last point, Carl Wellman provides an insight into the sort of conflict between moral feelings and rational judgment that the acceptance of act utilitarianism can produce. Concerning euthanasia, Wellman writes,

> *Try as I may, I honestly cannot discover great hidden disutilities in the act of killing an elderly person suffering greatly from an incurable illness, provided that certain safeguards like a written medical opinion by at least two doctors and a request by the patient are preserved. In this case I cannot find any way to reconcile my theory with my moral judgment. What I do in this case is to hold fast to act-utilitarianism and distrust my moral sense. I claim that my condemnation of such acts is an irrational disapproval, a condemnation that will change upon further reasoning about the act. . . . That I feel wrongness is clear, but I cannot state to myself any rational justification for my feeling. Hence, I discount this particular judgment as irrational.*

Rule utilitarianism maintains that an action is right if it conforms to a rule of conduct that has been validated by the principle of utility as one that will produce at least as much utility as any other rule applicable to the situation. A rule like "Provide only ordinary care for severely brain damaged newborns with multiple impairments," if it were established, would allow us to decide about the course of action to follow in situations like that of our earlier example.

The rule utilitarian is concerned with assessing the utility not of individual actions, but of particular rules. In practice, then, we do not have to go through the calculations involved in determining in each case whether a specific action will increase utility. All that we have to establish is that following a certain rule will in general result in a situation in which utility is maximized. Once rules are established, they can be relied on to determine whether a particular action is right.

The basic idea behind rule utilitarianism is that having a set of rules that are always observed produces the greatest social utility. Having everyone follow the same rule in each case of the same kind yields more utility for everybody in the long run. An act utilitarian can agree that having rules may produce more social utility than not having them. But the act utilitarian insists that the rules be regarded as no more than general guides to action, as "rules of thumb." Thus, for act utilitarianism it is perfectly legitimate to violate a rule if doing so will maximize utility in that instance. By contrast, the rule utilitarian holds that rules must generally be followed, even though following them may produce less net utility (more unhappiness than happiness) in a particular case.

Rule utilitarianism can endorse rules like "Keep your promises." Thus, unlike act utilitarianism, it can account for the general sense that, in making promises, we are placing ourselves under an obligation that cannot be set aside for the sake of increasing utility. If "Keep your promises" is accepted as a rule, then the surgeon who fails to perform all of an operation himself when he has promised his patient he would do so has not done the right thing, even if the patient never learns the truth.

Rule utilitarians recognize that circumstances can arise in which it would be disastrous to follow a general rule, even when it is true that, *in general*, greater happiness would result from following the rule all the time. Clearly, we should not keep a promise to meet someone for lunch when we have to choose between keeping the promise and rushing a heart-attack victim to the hospital. It is consistent with the theory to formulate rules that include appropriate escape clauses. For example, "Keep your promises, unless breaking them is required to save a life" and "Keep your promises, unless keeping them would lead to a disastrous result unforeseen at the time the promise was made" are rules that a rule utilitarian might regard as more likely to lead to greater utility than "Always keep your promises no matter what the consequences may be." What a rule utilitarian cannot endorse is a rule like "Keep your promises, except when breaking a promise would produce more utility." This would in effect transform the rule utilitarian into an act utilitarian.

Of course, rule utilitarians are not committed to endorsing general rules only. It is compatible with the view to offer quite specific rules, and in fact there is no constraint on just how specific a rule may be. A rule utilitarian might, for example, establish a rule such as "If an infant is born with an open spine, severe brain damage, and dysfunctional kidneys, then the infant should receive no life-sustaining treatment."

The possibility of formulating a large number of rules and establishing them separately opens this basic version of rule utilitarianism to two objections. First, some rules are likely to conflict when they are applicable to the same case and basic rule utilitarianism offers no way to resolve such conflicts. What should a physician do when faced both with a rule like that above and with another that directs him to "Provide life-sustaining care to all who require it"? Rules that, when considered individually, pass the test of promoting utility, may express contradictory demands when taken together. A further objection to basic rule utilitarianism is that establishing rules to cover many different circumstances and situations results in such an abundance of rules that employing the rules to make moral decisions becomes virtually impossible in practice.

Partly because of such difficulties, rule utilitarians have taken the approach of establishing the utility of a set of rules or an entire moral code. The set can include rules for resolving possible conflicts, and an effort can be made to keep the rules few and simple to minimize the practical difficulty of employing them. Once again, as with individual actions or rules, the principle of utility is employed to determine which set of rules, out of the various sets considered, ought to be accepted.

In this more sophisticated form, rule utilitarianism can be characterized as the theory that an action is right when it conforms to a set of rules that has been determined to produce at least as much overall utility as any other set. It is possible to accept the present forms of social and economic institutions, such as private property and a market economy, as constraints and then argue for the set of rules that will yield the most utility under those conditions. However, it is also possible to be more radical and argue for a particular set of rules that would lead to the greatest possible utility, quite apart from present social forms. Indeed, such a set of rules might be proposed and defended in an effort to bring about changes in present society that are needed to increase the overall level of utility. Utilitarianism, whether act or rule, is not restricted to being a theory about individual moral obligation. It is also a social and political theory.

We have already seen that rule utilitarianism, unlike act utilitarianism, makes possible the sort of obligation we associate with making a promise. But how might rule utilitarianism deal with the case of the physician who files false Medicaid claims to raise money to operate a free clinic? An obvious answer, although certainly not the only one possible, is that any set of rules likely to be adopted by a rule utilitarian will contain at least one rule making fraud morally wrong. Without a rule forbidding fraud, no social program that requires the cooperation of its participants is likely to achieve its aim. Such a rule protects the program from miscalculations of utility that individuals may make for self-serving reasons, keeps the program focused on its goal, and prevents it from becoming fragmented. Even if some few individuals commit fraud, the rule against it is crucial in discouraging as many as possible. Otherwise, as we pointed out earlier, such a program would collapse. By requiring that the program operate as it was designed, rule utilitarianism also preserves prima facie fairness, because only those who qualify receive benefits.

The most telling objection to rule utilitarianism, according to some philosophers, is that it is inconsistent. The justification of a set of moral rules is that the rules maximize utility. If rules are to maximize utility, then it seems obvious that they may require that an act produce more utility than any other possible act in a particular situation. Otherwise, the maximum amount of utility would not result. But if the rules satisfy this demand, then they will justify exactly the same actions as act utilitarianism. Thus, the rules will consider it right to break promises, make fraudulent claims, and so on. When rule utilitarianism moves to block these possibilities by requiring that rules produce only the most utility overall, it becomes inconsistent: the set of rules is said to maximize utility, but the rules will require actions that do not maximize utility. Thus, rule utilitarianism seems both to accept and reject the principle of utility as the ultimate moral standard.

Preference Utilitarianism

Some philosophers have called into question the idea of using happiness or any other intrinsic value (e.g., knowledge or health) as a criterion of the rightness of an action. The notion of an intrinsic value, they have argued, is too imprecise to be used as a practical guide. Furthermore, it is not at all clear that people share the same values, and even if they do, they are not committed to them to the same degree. Someone may value knowledge more than health, whereas someone else may value physical pleasure over knowledge or health. As a result, there can be no clear-cut procedure for determining what action is likely to produce the best outcome for an individual or group.

The attempt to develop explicit techniques (such as those of decision theory) to help resolve questions about choosing the best action or policy has led some thinkers to replace considerations of intrinsic value with considerations of actual preferences. What someone wants, desires, or prefers can be determined, in principle, in an objective way by consulting the person directly. In addition,

people are often able to do more than merely express a preference. Sometimes they can rank their preferences from that which is most desired to that which is least desired.

Such a ranking is of special importance in situations involving risk, for people can be asked to decide how much risk they are willing to take to attempt to realize a given preference. A young woman with a hip injury who is otherwise in good health may be willing to accept the risk of surgery to increase her chances of being restored to many years of active life. By contrast, an elderly woman in frail health may prefer to avoid surgery and accept the limitations that the injury imposes on her physical activities. For the elderly woman, not only are the risks of surgery greater because of her poor health, but even if the surgery is successful, she also will have fewer years to benefit from it.

By contrast, the older woman may place such a premium on physical activity that she is willing to take the risk of surgery to improve her chances of securing even a few more years of it. Only she can say what is important to her and how willing she is to take the risk required to secure it.

These considerations about personal preferences can also be raised about social preferences. Statistical information about what people desire and what they are willing to forgo to see their desires satisfied becomes relevant to institutional and legislative deliberations about what policies to adopt. For example, a crucial question facing our own society is whether we are willing to provide everyone with at least a basic minimum of health care, even if this requires increasing taxes or reducing our support for other social goods, such as education and defense.

Employing the satisfaction of preferences as the criterion of the rightness of an action or policy makes it possible to measure some of the relevant factors in some situations. The life expectancy of infants with particular impairments at birth can be estimated by statistics; a given surgical procedure has a certain success rate and a certain mortality rate. Similarly, a particular social policy has a certain financial cost, and if implemented, the policy is likely to mean the loss of other possible benefits and opportunities.

Ideally, information of this kind should allow a rational decision maker to calculate the best course of action for an individual or group. The best action will be the one that best combines the satisfaction of preferences with other conditions (e.g., financial costs and risks) that are at least minimally acceptable. To use the jargon of the theorists, the best action is the one that maximizes the utilities of the person or group.

A utilitarianism that employs preferences has the advantage of suggesting more explicit methods of analysis and rules for decision making than the classical formulation. It also has the potential for being more sensitive to the expressed desires of individuals. However, preference utilitarianism is not free from specific difficulties.

Most prominent is the problem posed by preferences that we would generally regard as unacceptable. What are we to say about those who prefer mass murder, child abuse, or torturing animals? Obviously, subjective preferences cannot be treated equally, and we must have a way to distinguish acceptable from unacceptable ones. Whether this can be done by relying on the principle of utility alone is doubtful. In the view of some commentators, some other moral principle (or principles) is needed. (See the discussion of justice immediately following.)

Difficulties with Utilitarianism

Classical utilitarianism is open to a variety of objections. We will concentrate on only one, however, for it seems to reveal a fatal flaw in the structure of the entire theory. This most serious of all objections is that the principle of utility appears to justify the imposition of great suffering on a few people for the benefit of many people.

Certain kinds of human experimentation forcefully illustrate this possibility. Suppose an investigator is concerned with acquiring a better understanding of brain functions. She could learn a great deal by systematically destroying the brain of one person and carefully noting the results. Such a study would offer many more opportunities for increasing our knowledge of the brain than those studies which use as subjects people who have damage to their brains in accidental ways. We may suppose that the experimenter chooses as her subject a person without education or training, without family or friends, who cannot be regarded as making much of a contribution to society. The subject will die from the experiment, but it is not unreasonable to suppose that the knowledge of the human brain gained from the experiment will improve the lives of countless numbers of people.

The principle of utility seems to make such experiments legitimate because the outcome is a greater amount of good than harm. One or a few have suffered immensely, but the many have profited to an extent that far outweighs that suffering.

Clearly, what is missing from utilitarianism is the concept of *justice*. It cannot be right to increase the general happiness at the expense of one person or group. There must be some way of distributing happiness and unhappiness and avoiding exploitation.

Mill was aware that utilitarianism needs a principle of justice, but most contemporary philosophers do not believe that such a principle can be derived from the principle of utility. In their opinion, utilitarianism as an ethical theory suffers severely from this defect. Yet some philosophers, while acknowledging the defect, have still held that utilitarianism is the best substantive moral theory available.

Kant's Ethics

For utilitarianism, the rightness of an action depends upon its consequences. In stark contrast to this view is the ethical theory formulated by the German philosopher Immanuel Kant (1724–1804) in his book *Fundamental Principles of the Metaphysics of Morals*. For Kant, the consequences of an action are morally irrelevant. Rather, an action is right when it is in accordance with a rule that satisfies a principle he calls the "categorical imperative." Since this is the basic principle of Kant's ethics, we can begin our discussion with it.

The Categorical Imperative

If you decide to have an abortion and go through with it, it is possible to view your action as involving a rule. You can be thought of as endorsing a rule to the effect "Whenever I am in circumstances like these, then I will have an abortion." Kant calls such a rule a "maxim." In his view, all reasoned and considered actions can be regarded as involving maxims.

The maxims in such cases are personal or subjective, but they can be thought of as being candidates for moral rules. If they pass the test imposed by the categorical imperative, then we can say that such actions are right. Furthermore, in passing the test, the maxims cease to be merely personal and subjective. They gain the status of objective rules of morality that hold for everyone.

Kant formulates the categorical imperative in this way: *Act only on that maxim which you can will to be a universal law.* Kant calls the principle "categorical" to distinguish it from "hypothetical" imperatives. These tell us what to do if we want to bring about certain consequences—such as happiness. A categorical imperative prescribes what we ought to do without reference to any consequences. The principle is an "imperative" because it is a command.

The test imposed on maxims by the categorical imperative is one of generalization or "universalizability." The central idea of the test is that a moral maxim is one that can be generalized to apply to all cases of the same kind. That is, you must be willing to see your rule

adopted as a maxim by everyone who is in a situation similar to yours. You must be willing to see your maxim universalized, even though it may turn out on some other occasion to work to your disadvantage.

For a maxim to satisfy the categorical imperative, it is not necessary that we be agreeable in some psychological sense to seeing it made into a universal law. Rather, the test is one that requires us to avoid inconsistency or conflict in what we will as a universal rule.

Suppose, for example, that I am a physician and I tell a patient that he has a serious illness, although I know that he doesn't. This may be to my immediate advantage, for the treatment and the supposed cure will increase my income and reputation. The maxim of my action might be phrased as, "Whenever I have a healthy patient, I will lie to him and say that he has an illness."

Now suppose that I try to generalize my maxim. In doing so, I will discover that I am willing the existence of a practice that has contradictory properties. If "Whenever any physician has a healthy patient, she will lie to him and say he has an illness" is made a universal law, then every patient will be told that he has an illness. Trust in the diagnostic pronouncements of physicians will be destroyed, while my scheme depends on my patients' trusting me and accepting the truth of my lying diagnosis.

It is as if I were saying, "Let there be a rule of truth telling such that people can assume that others are telling them the truth, but let there also be a rule that physicians may lie to their patients when it is in the interest of the physician to do so." In willing both rules, I am willing something contradictory. Thus, I can will my action in a particular case, but I can't will that my action be universal without generating a logical conflict.

Kant claims that such considerations show that it is always wrong to lie. Lying produces a contradiction in what we will. On one hand, we will that people believe what we say—that they accept our assurances and promises. On the other hand, we will that people be free to give false assurances and make false promises. Lying thus produces a self-defeating situation, for, when the maxim involved is generalized, the very framework required for lying collapses.

Similarly, consider the egoist who seeks only his self-interest and so makes "Never show love or compassion for others" the maxim of his actions. When universalized, this maxim results in the same kind of self-defeating situation that lying does. Since the egoist will sometimes find himself in need of love and compassion, if he wills the maxim of his action to be a universal law, then he will be depriving himself of something that is in his self-interest. Thus, in willing the abolition of love and compassion out of self-interest, he creates a logical contradiction in what he wills.

Another Formulation

According to Kant, there is only one categorical imperative, but it can be stated in three different ways. Each is intended to reveal a different aspect of the principle. The second formulation, the only other we will consider, can be stated in this way: *Always act so as to treat humanity, either yourself or others, always as an end and never as only a means.*

This version illustrates Kant's notion that every rational creature has a worth in itself. This worth is not conferred by being born into a society with a certain political structure, nor even by belonging to a certain biological species. The worth is inherent in the sheer possession of rationality. Rational creatures possess what Kant calls an "autonomous, self-legislating will." That is, they are able to consider the consequences of their actions, make rules for themselves, and direct their actions by those self-imposed rules. Thus, rationality confers upon everyone an intrinsic worth and dignity.

This formulation of the categorical imperative perhaps rules out some of the standards

that are sometimes used to determine who is selected to receive certain medical resources (such as kidney machines) when the demand is greater than the supply. Standards that make a person's education, accomplishments, or social position relevant seem contrary to this version of the categorical imperative. They violate the basic notion that each person has an inherent worth equal to that of any other person. Unlike dogs or horses, people cannot be judged on "show points."

For Kant, all of morality has its ultimate source in rationality. The categorical imperative, in any formulation, is an expression of rationality, and it is the principle that would be followed in practice by any purely rational being. Moral rules are not mere arbitrary conventions or subjective standards. They are objective truths that have their source in the rational nature of human beings.

Duty

Utilitarianism identifies the good with happiness or pleasure and makes the production of happiness the supreme principle of morality. But, for Kant, happiness is at best a conditional or qualified good. In his view, there is only one thing that can be said to be good in itself: a good will.

Will is what directs our actions and guides our conduct. But what makes a will a "good will"? Kant's answer is that a will becomes good when it acts purely for the sake of duty.

We act for the sake of duty (or from duty) when we act on maxims that satisfy the categorical imperative. This means, then, that it is the motive force behind our actions—the character of our will—that determines their moral character. Morality does not rest on results—such as the production of happiness—but neither does it rest on our feelings, impulses, or inclinations. An action is right, for Kant, only when it is done for the sake of duty.

Suppose that I decide to donate one of my kidneys for transplanting. If my hope is to gain approval or praise, or even if I am moved by pity and a genuine wish to reduce suffering, and there is no other consideration behind my action, then, although I have done the morally right thing, my action has no inner moral worth. I may have acted *in accordance with duty* (done the same thing as duty would have required), but I did not act *from duty*.

This view of duty and its connection with morality captures attitudes we frequently express. Consider a nurse who gives special care to a severely ill patient. Suppose you learned that the nurse was providing such extraordinary care only because he hoped that the patient or her family would reward him with a special bonus. Knowing this, you would be unlikely to say that the nurse was acting in a morally outstanding way. We might even think the nurse was being greedy or cynical, and we would say that he was doing the right thing for the wrong reasons.

Kant distinguishes between two types of duties: perfect and imperfect. (The distinction corresponds to the two ways in which maxims can be self-defeating when tested by the categorical imperative.) A *perfect duty* is one we must always observe; an *imperfect duty* is one that we must observe only on some occasions. I have a perfect duty not to injure another person, but I have only an imperfect duty to show love and compassion. I must sometimes show it, but when I show it and which people I select to receive it are entirely up to me.

My duties determine what others can legitimately claim from me as a right. Some rights can be claimed as perfect rights, while others cannot. Everyone can demand of me that I do him or her no injury. But no one can tell me that I must make him or her the recipient of my love and compassion. In deciding how to discharge my imperfect duties, I am free to follow my emotions and inclinations.

For utilitarianism, an action is right when it produces something that is intrinsically valuable (happiness). Because actions are judged by their contributions to achieving a goal, utilitarianism is a teleological theory. By contrast, Kant's ethics holds that an action has features in itself that make it right or in accordance with duty. These features are distinct from the action's consequences. Such a theory is called *deontological*, a term derived from the Greek word for "duty" or "obligation."

Kant's Ethics in the Medical Context

Four features of Kant's ethics are of particular importance in dealing with issues in medical treatment and research:

1. No matter what the consequences may be, it is always wrong to lie.

2. We must always treat people (including ourselves) as ends and not as means only.

3. An action is right when it satisfies the categorical imperative.

4. Perfect and imperfect duties give a basis for claims that certain rights should be recognized.

We can present only two brief examples of how these features can be instrumental in resolving medical ethical issues, but these are suggestive of other possibilities.

Our first application of Kant's ethics bears on medical research. The task of medical investigators would be easier if they did not have to tell patients that they were going to be made part of a research program. Patients would then become subjects without even knowing it, and more often than not their risk would be negligible. Even though no overt lying would be involved, on Kantian principles this procedure would be wrong. It would require treating people as a means only and not as an end.

Likewise, it would never be right for an experimenter to deceive a potential experimental subject. If an experimenter told a patient, "We would like to use this new drug on you because it might help you" and this were not really so, the experimenter would be performing a wrong action. Lying is always wrong.

Nor could the experimenter justify this deception by telling herself that the research is of such importance that it is legitimate to lie to the patient. On Kant's principles, good results never make an action morally right. Thus, a patient must give voluntary and informed consent to become a subject of medical experimentation. Otherwise, the patient is being deprived of autonomy and treated as a means only.

We may volunteer because we expect the research to bring direct benefits to us. But we may also volunteer even though no direct personal benefits can be expected. We may see participation in the research as an occasion for fulfilling an imperfect duty to improve human welfare.

But, just as Kant's principles place restrictions on the researcher, they place limits on us as potential subjects. We have a duty to treat ourselves as ends and act so as to preserve our dignity and worth as humans. Therefore, it would not be right for us to volunteer for an experiment that threatened our lives or threatened to destroy our ability to function as autonomous rational beings without first satisfying ourselves that the experiment was legitimate and necessary.

Our second application of Kant's ethics in a medical context bears on the relationship between people as patients and those who accept responsibility for caring for them. A physician, for example, has only an imperfect duty to accept me as a patient. He has a duty to make use of his skills and talents to treat the sick, but I cannot legitimately insist on being the beneficiary. How he discharges his duty is his decision.

If, however, I am accepted as a patient, then I can make some legitimate claims. I can demand that nothing be done to cause me pointless harm, because it is never right to injure a person. Furthermore, I can demand that I never be lied to or deceived. Suppose, for example, I am given a placebo (a harmless but inactive substance) and told that it is a powerful and effective medication. Or suppose that

a biopsy shows that I have an inoperable form of cancer, but my physician tells me, "There's nothing seriously wrong with you." In both cases, the physician may suppose that he is deceiving me "for my own good": the placebo may be psychologically effective and make me feel better, and the lie about cancer may save me from useless worry. Yet, by being deceived, I am being denied the dignity inherent in my status as a rational being. Lying is wrong in general, and in such cases as these it also deprives me of my autonomy, of my power to make decisions and form my own opinions. As a result, such deception dehumanizes me.

As an autonomous rational being, a person is entitled to control over his or her own body. This means that medical procedures can be performed on me only with my permission. It would be wrong even if the medication were needed for my "own good." I may voluntarily put myself under the care of a physician and submit to all that I am asked to, but the decision belongs to me alone.

In exercising control over my body, however, I also have a duty to myself. Suppose, for example, that I refuse to allow surgery to be performed on me, although I have been told it is necessary to preserve my life. Since I have a duty to preserve my life, as does every person, my refusal is morally unjustifiable. Even here, however, it is not legitimate for others to force me to "do my duty." In fact, in Kantian ethics it is impossible to force another to do his or her duty because it is not the action, but the maxim involved, that determines whether or not one's duty has been done.

It is obvious even from our sketchy examples that Kantian ethics is a fruitful source of principles and ideas for working out some of the specific moral difficulties of medical experimentation and practice. The absolute requirements imposed by the categorical imperative can be a source of strength and even of comfort. By contrast, utilitarianism requires us to weigh alternative courses of actions by anticipating their consequences and deciding whether what we are considering doing can be justified by those results. Kant's ethics saves us from this kind of doubt and indecision: we know we must never lie, no matter what good may come of it. Furthermore, the lack of a principle of justice that is the most severe defect of utilitarianism is met by Kant's categorical imperative. When every person is to be treated as an end and never as only a means, the possibility of legitimately exploiting some for the benefit of others is wholly eliminated.

Difficulties with Kantian Ethics

Kant's ethical theory is complex and controversial. It has problems of a theoretical sort that manifest themselves in practice and lead us to doubt whether the absolute rules determined by the categorical imperative can always provide a straightforward solution to our moral difficulties. We will limit ourselves to discussing just three problems.

First, Kant's principles may produce resolutions to cases in which there is a conflict of duties that seems intuitively wrong. I have a duty to keep my promises, and I also have a duty to help those in need. Suppose, then, that I am a physician and I have promised a colleague to attend a staff conference. Right before the conference starts, I am talking with a patient who lapses into an insulin coma. If I get involved in treating the patient, I'll have to break my promise to attend the conference. What should I do?

The answer is obvious: I should treat the patient. Our moral intuition tells us this. But for Kant, keeping promises is a perfect duty, while helping others is an imperfect one. This suggests, then, that according to Kantian principles, I should abandon my patient and rush off to keep my appointment. Something is apparently wrong with a view that holds that a promise should never be broken—even when the promise concerns a relatively trivial matter and the consequences of keeping it are disastrous.

Another difficulty with the categorical imperative arises because we are free to choose how we formulate a maxim for testing. In all likelihood, none of us would approve a maxim such as "Lie when it is convenient for you." But what about one like "Lie when telling the truth is likely to cause harm to another"? We would be more inclined to make this a universal law. Now consider the maxim "Whenever a physician has good reason to believe that a patient's life will be seriously threatened if she is told the truth about her condition, then the physician should lie." Virtually everyone would be willing to see this made into a universal law.

Yet these three maxims could apply to the same situation. Since Kant does not tell us how to formulate our maxims, it is clear that we can act virtually any way we choose if we are willing to describe the situation in detail. We might be willing to have everyone act just as we are inclined to act whenever they find themselves in exactly this kind of situation. The categorical imperative, then, does not seem to solve our moral problems quite so neatly as it first appears to.

A final problem arises from Kant's notion that we have duties to rational beings or persons. Ordinarily, we have little difficulty with this commitment to persons, yet there are circumstances, particularly in the medical context, in which serious problems arise. Consider, for example, a fetus developing in its mother's womb. Is the fetus to be considered a person? The way this question is answered makes all the difference in deciding about the rightness or wrongness of abortion.

A similar difficulty is present when we consider how we are to deal with an infant with serious birth defects. Is it our duty to care for this infant and do all we can to see that it lives? If the infant is not a person, then perhaps we do not owe him the sort of treatment it would be our duty to provide a similarly afflicted adult. It's clear from these two cases that the notion of a person as an autonomous rational being is both too restrictive and arbitrary. It begs important moral questions.

Another difficulty connected with Kant's concept of a rational person is the notion of an "autonomous self-regulating will." Under what conditions can we assume that an individual possesses such a will? Does a child, a mentally retarded person, or someone in prison? Without such a will, in Kant's view, such an individual cannot legitimately consent to be the subject of an experiment or even give permission for necessary medical treatment. This notion is very much in need of development before Kant's principles can be relied on to resolve ethical questions in medicine.

The difficulties that we have discussed require serious consideration. This does not mean, of course, that they cannot be resolved or that, because of them, Kant's theory is worthless. As with utilitarianism, there are some philosophers who believe the theory is the best available, despite its shortcomings. That it captures many of our intuitive beliefs about what is right (not to lie, to treat people with dignity, to act benevolently) and supplies us with a test for determining our duties (the categorical imperative) recommends it strongly as an ethical theory.

Ross's Ethics

The English philosopher W. D. Ross (1877–1971) presented an ethical theory in his book *The Right and the Good* that can be seen as an attempt to incorporate aspects of utilitarianism and aspects of Kantianism. Ross rejected the utilitarian notion that an action is made right by its consequences alone, but he was also troubled by Kant's absolute rules. He saw not only that such rules fail to show sensitivity to the complexities of actual situations, but also that they sometimes conflict with one another. Like Kant, Ross is a deontologist, but with an important difference: Ross believes that it is necessary to consider consequences in making

a moral choice, even though he believes that it is not the results of an action taken alone that make it right.

Moral Properties and Rules

For Ross, there is an unbridgeable distinction between moral and nonmoral properties. There are only two moral properties—rightness and goodness—and these cannot be replaced by, or explained in terms of, other properties. Thus, to say that an action is right is not at all the same as saying that it causes pleasure or increases happiness, as utilitarianism claims.

At the same time, however, Ross does not deny that there is a connection between moral properties and nonmoral ones. What he denies is the possibility of establishing an identity between them. Thus, it may be right to relieve the suffering of someone, but right is not identical with relieving suffering. (More exactly put, the rightness of the action is not identical with the action's being a case of relieving suffering.)

Ross also makes clear that we must often know many nonmoral facts about a situation before we can legitimately make a moral judgment. If I see a physician injecting someone, I cannot say whether she is acting rightly without determining what she is injecting, why she is doing it, and so on. Thus, rightness is a property that depends partly on the nonmoral properties that characterize a situation. I cannot determine whether the physician is doing the right thing or the wrong thing until I determine what the nonmoral properties are.

Ross believes that there are cases in which we have no genuine doubt about whether the property of rightness or goodness is present. The world abounds with examples of cruelty, lying, and selfishness, and in these cases we are immediately aware of the absence of rightness or goodness. But the world also abounds with examples of compassion, reliability, and generosity in which rightness and goodness are clearly present. Ross claims that our experience with such cases puts us in a position to come to know rightness and goodness with the same degree of certainty as when we grasp the mathematical truth that a triangle has three angles.

Furthermore, according to Ross, our experience of many individual cases puts us in a position to recognize the validity of a general statement like "It is wrong to cause needless pain." We come to see such rules in much the same way that we come to recognize the letter A after having seen it written or printed in a variety of handwritings or typefaces.

Thus, our moral intuitions can supply us with moral rules of a general kind. But Ross refuses to acknowledge these rules as absolute. For him, they can serve only as guides to assist us in deciding what we should do. Ultimately, in any particular case we must rely not only on the rules but also on reason and our understanding of the situation.

Thus, even with rules, we may not recognize what the right thing to do is in a given situation. We recognize, he suggests, that there is always some right thing to do, but what it is may be far from obvious. In fact, doubt about what is the right way of acting may arise just because we have rules to guide us. We become aware of the fact that there are several possible courses of action, and all of them seem to be right.

Consider the problem of whether to lie to a terminally ill patient about his condition. Let us suppose that, if we lie to him, we can avoid causing him at least some useless anguish. But then aren't we violating his trust in us to act morally and to speak the truth?

In such cases, we seem to have a conflict in our duties. It is because of such familiar kinds of conflicts that Ross rejects the possibility of discovering absolute, invariant moral rules like "Always tell the truth" and "Always eliminate needless suffering." In cases like the one above, we cannot hold that both rules are absolute without contradicting ourselves. Ross says that we have to recognize that every rule

has exceptions and must in some situations be overridden.

Actual Duties and Prima Facie Duties

If rules like "Always tell the truth" cannot be absolute, then what status can they have? When our rules come into conflict in particular situations, how are we to decide which rule applies? Ross answers this question by making use of a distinction between what is actually right and what is prima facie right. Since we have a duty to do what is right, this distinction can be expressed as one between *actual duty* and *prima facie duty*.

An actual duty is simply what my real duty is in a situation. It is the action that, out of the various possibilities, I ought to perform. More often than not, however, I may not know what my actual duty is. In fact, for Ross, the whole problem of ethics might be said to be the problem of knowing what my actual duty is in any given situation.

Prima facie literally means "at first sight," but Ross uses the phrase to mean something like "other things being equal." Accordingly, a prima facie duty is one that dictates what I should do when other relevant factors in a situation are not considered. If I promised to meet you for lunch, then I have a prima facie duty to meet you. But suppose I am a physician, and just as I am about to leave for an appointment, the patient I am with suffers cardiac arrest. In such circumstances, according to Ross's view, I should break my promise and render aid to the patient. My prima facie duty to keep my promise doesn't make that fact obligatory. It constitutes a moral reason for meeting you, but there is also a moral reason for not meeting you. I also have a prima facie duty to aid my patient, and this is a reason that outweighs the first one. Thus, aiding the patient is both a prima facie duty and, in this situation, my actual duty.

The notion of a prima facie duty permits Ross to offer a set of moral rules stated in such a way that they are both universal and free from exceptions. For Ross, for example, lying is always wrong, but it is wrong prima facie. It may be that in a particular situation my actual duty requires that I lie. Even though what I have done is prima facie wrong, it is the morally right thing to do if some other prima facie duty that requires lying in the case is more stringent than the prima facie duty to tell the truth. (Perhaps only by lying am I able to prevent a terrorist from blowing up an airplane.) I must be able to explain and justify my failure to tell the truth, and it is of course possible that I may not be able to do so. It may be that I was confused and misunderstood the situation or failed to consider other alternatives. I may have been wrong to believe that my actual duty required me to lie. However, even if I was correct in my belief, that I lied is still prima facie wrong. It is this fact (and for Ross it is a fact) that requires me to explain and justify my action.

We have considered only a few simple examples of prima facie duties, but Ross is more thorough and systematic than our examples might suggest. He offers a list of duties that he considers binding on all moral agents. Here they are in summary form:

1. *Duties of fidelity:* telling the truth, keeping actual and implicit promises, and not representing fiction as history

2. *Duties of reparation:* righting the wrongs we have done to others

3. *Duties of gratitude:* recognizing the services others have done for us

4. *Duties of justice:* preventing a distribution of pleasure or happiness that is not in keeping with the merit of the people involved

5. *Duties of beneficence:* helping to better the condition of other beings with respect to virtue, intelligence, or pleasure

6. *Duties of self-improvement:* bettering ourselves with respect to virtue or intelligence

7. *Duties of nonmaleficence:* avoiding or preventing an injury to others

Ross doesn't claim that this is a complete list of the prima facie duties that we recognize. However, he does believe that the duties on the list are all ones that we acknowledge and are willing to accept as legitimate and binding without argument. He believes that if we simply reflect on these prima facie duties, we will see that they may be truly asserted. As he puts the matter:

> *I . . . am claiming that we know them to be true. To me it seems as self-evident as anything could be, that to make a promise, for instance, is to create a moral claim on us in someone else. Many readers will perhaps say that they do not know this to be true. If so I certainly cannot prove it to them. I can only ask them to reflect again, in the hope that they will ultimately agree that they also know it to be true.*

Notice that Ross explicitly rejects the possibility of providing us with reasons or arguments to convince us to accept his list of prima facie duties. We are merely invited to reflect on certain kinds of cases, like keeping promises, and Ross is convinced that this reflection will bring us to accept his claim that these are true duties. Ross, like other intuitionists, tries to get us to agree with his moral perceptions in much the same way as we might try to get people to agree with us about our color perceptions. We might, for example, show a paint sample to a friend and say, "Don't you think that looks blue? It does to me. Think about it for a minute."

We introduced the distinction between actual and prima facie duties to deal with those situations in which duties seem to conflict. The problem, as we can now state it, is this: What are we to do in a situation in which we recognize more than one prima facie duty and it is not possible for us to act in a way that will fulfill them? We know, of course, that we should act in a way that satisfies our actual duty. But that is just our problem. What, after all, is our actual duty when our prima facie duties are in conflict?

Ross offers us two principles to deal with cases of conflicting duty. The first principle is designed to handle situations in which just two prima facie duties are in conflict: *That act is one's duty which is in accord with the more stringent prima facie obligation.* The second principle is intended to deal with cases in which several prima facie duties are in conflict: *That act is one's duty which has the greatest balance of prima facie rightness over prima facie wrongness.*

Unfortunately, both these principles present problems in application. Ross does not tell us how we are to determine when an obligation is "more stringent" than another. Nor does he give us a rule for determining the "balance" of prima facie rightness over wrongness. Ultimately, according to Ross, we must simply rely upon our perceptions of the situation. There is no automatic or mechanical procedure that can be followed. If we learn the facts in the case, consider the consequences of our possible actions, and reflect on our prima facie duties, we should be able to arrive at a conclusion as to the best course of action—in Ross's view, something that we as moral agents must and can do.

To return to specific cases, perhaps there is no direct way to answer the abstract question, Is the duty not to lie to a patient more stringent than the duty not to cause needless suffering? So much depends on the character and condition of the individual patient that an abstract determination of our duty based on balance or stringency is useless. However, knowing the patient, we should be able to perceive what the right course of action is.

Ross further believes that there are situations in which there are no particular difficulties about resolving the conflict between prima facie duties. For example, most of us would agree that, if we can save someone from serious injury by lying, then we have more of an obligation to save someone from injury than we do to tell the truth.

Ross's Ethics in the Medical Context

Ross's moral rules are not absolute in the sense that Kant's are; consequently, as with utilitarianism, it is not possible to say what someone's duty would be in an actual concrete situation. We can discuss in general, however, the advantages that Ross's theory brings to medical–moral issues. We will mention only two for illustration.

First and most important is Ross's list of prima facie duties. The list of duties can serve an important function in the moral education of physicians, researchers, and other medical personnel. The list encourages each person who is responsible for patient care to reflect on the prima facie obligations that the person has toward those people and to set aside one of those obligations only when morally certain that another obligation takes precedence.

The specific duties imposed in a prima facie way are numerous and can be expressed in terms relevant to the medical context: do not injure patients; do not distribute scarce resources in a way that fails to recognize individual worth; do not lie to patients; show patients kindness and understanding; educate patients in ways useful to them; do not hold out false hopes to patients; and so on.

Second, like utilitarianism, Ross's ethics encourages us to show sensitivity to the unique features of situations before acting. Like Kant's ethics, however, Ross's also insists that we look at the world from a particular moral perspective. In arriving at decisions about what is right, we must learn the facts of the case and explore the possible consequences of our actions. Ultimately, however, we must guide our actions by what is right, rather than by what is useful, what will produce happiness, or anything of the kind.

Since, for Ross, actions are not always justified in terms of their results, we cannot say unequivocally, "It's right to trick this person into becoming a research subject because the experiment may benefit thousands." Yet, we cannot say that it is always wrong for a researcher to trick a person into volunteering. An action is right or wrong regardless of what we think about it, but in a particular case circumstances might justify an experimenter in allowing some other duty to take precedence over the duty of fidelity.

Fundamentally, then, Ross's ethics offers us the possibility of gaining the advantages of utilitarianism without ignoring the fact that there seem to be duties with an undeniable moral force behind them that cannot be accounted for by utilitarianism. Ross's ethics accommodates not only our intuition that certain actions should be performed just because they are right but also our inclination to pay attention to the results of actions and not just the motives behind them.

Difficulties with Ross's Moral Rules

The advantages Ross's ethics offers over both utilitarianism and Kantianism are offset by some serious difficulties. To begin with, it seems false that we all grasp the same principles. We are well aware that people's beliefs about what is right and about what their duties are result from the kind of education and experience that they have had. The ability to perceive what is good or right does not appear to be universally shared. Ross does say that the principles are the convictions of "the moral consciousness of the best people." In any ordinary sense of "best," there is reason to say that such people don't always agree on moral principles. If "best" means "morally best," then Ross is close to being circular: the best people are those who acknowledge the same prima facie obligations, and those who recognize the same prima facie obligations are the best people.

Some have objected that Ross's list of prima facie duties seems incomplete. For example, Ross does not explicitly say that we have a prima facie obligation not to steal, but most people would hold that if we have any prima facie duties at all, the duty not to steal must surely be counted among them. Of course, it is possible to say that stealing is covered by some other obligation—the duty of fidelity, perhaps, since stealing may violate a trust. Nevertheless, from a theory based on intuition, the omission of such duties leaves Ross's list peculiarly incomplete.

Further, some critics have claimed that it is not clear that there is always even a prima facie obligation to do some of the things Ross lists. Suppose that I promise to lie about a friend's physical condition so that she can continue to collect insurance payments. Some would say that I have no obligation at all to keep such an unwise promise. In such a case, there would be no conflict of duties, because I don't have even a prima facie duty to keep such a promise.

Finally, Ross's theory, some have charged, seems to be false to the facts of moral disagreements. When we disagree with someone about an ethical matter, we consider reasons for and against some position. Sometimes the discussion results in agreement. But, according to Ross's view, this should not be possible. Although we may discuss circumstances and consequences and agree about the prima facie duties involved, ultimately I arrive at my judgment about the duty that is most stringent or has the greatest degree of prima facie rightness, and you arrive at yours. At this point, it seems, there can be no further discussion, even though the two judgments are incompatible. Thus, a choice between the two judgments about what act should be performed becomes arbitrary.

Few contemporary philosophers would be willing to endorse Ross's ethical theory without serious qualifications. The need for a special kind of moral perception (or "intuition") marks the theory as unacceptable for most philosophers. Yet many would acknowledge that the theory has great value in illuminating such aspects of our moral experience as reaching decisions when we feel the pull of conflicting obligations. Furthermore, at least some would acknowledge Ross's prima facie duties as constituting an adequate set of moral principles.

Rawls's Theory of Justice

In 1971, the Harvard philosopher John Rawls (1921–2002) published a book called *A Theory of Justice*. The work continues to attract a considerable amount of attention and has been described by some as the most important book in moral and social philosophy of the twentieth century.

One commentator, R. P. Wolfe, points out that Rawls attempts to develop a theory that combines the strengths of utilitarianism with those of the deontological position of Kant and Ross, while avoiding the weaknesses of each view. Utilitarianism claims outright that happiness is fundamental and suggests a direct procedure for answering ethical–social questions. But it is flawed by its lack of a principle of justice. Kant and Ross make rightness a fundamental moral notion and stress the ultimate dignity of human beings. Yet neither provides a workable method for solving problems of social morality. Clearly, Rawls's theory promises much if it can succeed in uniting the two ethical traditions we have discussed.

The Original Position and the Principles of Justice

For Rawls, the central task of government is to preserve and promote the liberty and welfare of individuals. Thus, principles of justice are needed to serve as standards for designing and evaluating social institutions and practices. They provide a way of resolving conflicts among the competing claims that individuals make and a means of protecting the legitimate interests of individuals. In a sense, the principles of justice constitute a blueprint for the development of a just society.

But how are we to formulate principles of justice? Rawls makes use of a hypothetical device he calls "the original position." Imagine a group of people like those who make up our society. These people display the ordinary range of intelligence, talents, ambitions, convictions, and social and economic advantages. They include both sexes and members of various racial and ethnic groups.

Furthermore, suppose that this group is placed behind what Rawls calls "a veil of ignorance." Assume that each person is made ignorant of his or her sex, race, natural endowments, social position, economic condition, and so on. Furthermore, assume that these people are capable of cooperating with one another, that they follow the principles of rational decision making, and that they are capable of a sense of justice and will adhere to principles they agree to adopt. Finally, assume that they all desire what Rawls calls "primary goods": the rights, opportunities, powers, wealth, and such that are both worth possessing in themselves and are necessary to securing the more specific goods an individual may want.

Rawls argues that the principles of justice chosen by such a group will be just if the conditions under which they are selected and the procedures for agreeing on them are fair. The original position, with its veil of ignorance, characterizes a state in which alternative notions of justice can be discussed freely by all. Since the ignorance of the participants means that individuals cannot gain advantage for themselves by choosing principles that favor their own circumstances, the eventual choices of the participants will be fair. Since the participants are assumed to be rational, they will be persuaded by the same reasons and arguments. These features of the original position lead Rawls to characterize his view as "justice as fairness."

We might imagine at first that some people in the original position would gamble and argue for principles that would introduce gross inequalities in their society. For example, some might argue for slavery. If these people should turn out to be masters after the veil of ignorance is stripped away, they would gain immensely. But if they turn out to be slaves, then they would lose immensely. However, since the veil of ignorance keeps them from knowing their actual positions in society, it would not be rational for them to endorse a principle that might condemn them to the bottom of the social order.

Given the uncertainties of the original situation, there is a better strategy that these rational people would choose. In the economic discipline known as game theory, this strategy is called "maximin," or maximizing the minimum. When we choose in uncertain situations, the maximin strategy directs us to select, from all the alternatives, the one whose worst possible outcome is better than the worst possible outcome of the other alternatives. (If you don't know whether you're going to be a slave, you shouldn't approve a set of principles that permits slavery when you have other options.)

Acting in accordance with this strategy, Rawls argues that people in the original position would agree on the following two principles of justice:

1. Each person is to have an equal right to the most extensive total system of equal basic liberties compatible with a similar system of liberty for all.

2. Social and economic inequalities are to be arranged so that they are both (a) to the greatest benefit of the least advantaged. . . and (b) attached to offices and positions open to all under conditions of fair equality of opportunity.

For Rawls, these two principles are taken to govern the distribution of all social goods: liberty, property, wealth, and social privilege. The first principle has priority. It guarantees a system of equal liberty for all. Furthermore, because of its priority, it explicitly prohibits

the bartering away of liberty for social or economic benefits. (For example, a society cannot withhold the right to vote from its members on the grounds that voting rights damage the economy.)

The second principle governs the distribution of social goods other than liberty. Although society could organize itself in a way that would eliminate differences in wealth and abolish the advantages that attach to different social positions, Rawls argues that those in the original position would not choose this form of egalitarianism. Instead, they would opt for the second principle of justice. This means that, in a just society, differences in wealth and social position can be tolerated only when they can be shown to benefit everyone and to benefit, in particular, those who have the fewest advantages. A just society is not one in which everyone is equal, but one in which inequalities must be demonstrated to be legitimate. Furthermore, there must be a genuine opportunity for acquiring membership in a group that enjoys special benefits. Those not qualified to enter medical schools because of past discrimination in education, for example, can claim a right for special preparation to qualify them. (Of course, in a Rawlsian society, there would be no discrimination to be compensated for.)

Rawls argues that these two principles are required to establish a just society. Furthermore, in distributing liberty and social goods, the principles guarantee the worth and self-respect of the individual. People are free to pursue their own conception of the good and fashion their own lives. Ultimately, the only constraints placed on them as members of society are those expressed in the principles of justice.

Yet Rawls also acknowledges that those in the original position would recognize that we have duties both to ourselves and to others. They would, for example, want to take measures to see that their interests are protected if they should meet with disabling accidents, become seriously mentally disturbed, and so on. Thus, Rawls approves a form of paternalism: others should act for us when we are unable to act for ourselves. When our preferences are known to them, those acting for us should attempt to follow what we would wish. Otherwise, they should act for us as they would act for themselves if they were viewing our situation from the standpoint of the original position. Paternalism is thus a duty to ourselves that would be recognized by those in the original position.

Rawls is also aware of the need for principles that bind and guide individuals as moral decision makers. He claims that those in the original position would reach agreement on principles for such notions as fairness in our dealings with others, fidelity, respect for persons, and beneficence. From these principles, we gain some of our obligations to one another.

But, Rawls claims, there are also "natural duties" that would be recognized by those in the original position. Among those Rawls mentions are (1) the duty of justice—supporting and complying with just institutions; (2) the duty of helping others in need or jeopardy; (3) the duty not to harm or injure another; and (4) the duty to keep our promises.

For the most part, these are duties that hold between or among people. They are only some of the duties that would be offered by those in the original position as unconditional duties.

Thus, Rawls in effect endorses virtually the same duties as those that Ross presents as prima facie duties. Rawls realizes that the problem of conflicts of duty was left unsolved by Ross and so perceives the need for assigning priorities to duties—ranking them as higher and lower. Rawls believes that a full system of principles worked out from the original position would include rules for ranking duties. Rawls's primary concern, however, is with justice in social institutions, and he does not attempt to establish any rules for ranking.

Rawls's Theory of Justice in the Medical Context

Rawls's "natural duties" are virtually the same as Ross's prima facie duties. Consequently, most of what we said earlier about prima facie duties and moral decision making applies to Rawls.

Rawls endorses the legitimacy of paternalism, although he does not attempt to specify detailed principles to justify individual cases. He does tell us that we should consider the preferences of others when they are known to us and when we are in a situation in which we must act for them because they are unable to act for themselves. For example, suppose we know that a person approves of electroconvulsive therapy (shock treatments, or ECT) for the treatment of severe depression. If that person should become so depressed as to be unable to reach a decision about his own treatment, then we would be justified in seeing to it that he received ECT.

To take a similar case, suppose you are a surgeon and have a patient who has expressed to you her wish to avoid numerous operations that may prolong her life six months or so but will be unable to restore her to health. If, in operating, you learned that she has a form of uterine cancer that had spread through her lower extremities and if, in your best judgment, nothing could be done to restore her to health, then it would be your duty to her to allow her to die as she chooses. Repeated operations would be contrary to her concept of her own good.

The most important question in exploring Rawls's theory is how the two principles of justice might apply to the social institutions and practices of medical care and research. Most obviously, Rawls's principles repair utilitarianism's flaw with respect to human experimentation. It would never be right, in Rawls's view, to exploit one group of people or even one person for the benefit of others. Thus, experiments in which people are forced to be subjects or are tricked into participating are ruled out. They involve a violation of basic liberties of individuals and of the absolute respect for persons that the principles of justice require.

A person has a right to decide what risks she is willing to take with her own life and health. Thus, voluntary consent is required before someone can legitimately become a research subject. However, society might decide to reward research volunteers with money, honors, or social privileges to encourage participation in research. Provided that the overall structure of society already conforms to the two principles of justice, this is a perfectly legitimate practice, so long as it brings benefits (ideally) to everyone and the possibility of gaining the rewards of participation is open to all.

Regarding the allocation of social resources in the training of medical personnel (physicians, nurses, therapists, and so on), one may conclude that such investments are justified only if the withdrawal of the support would work to the disadvantage of those already most disadvantaged. Public money may be spent in the form of scholarships and institutional grants to educate individuals who may then derive great social and economic benefits from their education. But, for Rawls, the inequality that is produced is not necessarily unjust. Society can invest its resources in this way if it brings benefits to those most in need of them.

The implication of this position seems to be that everyone is entitled to health care. First, it could be argued that health is among the "primary goods" that Rawls's principles are designed to protect and promote. After all, without health, an individual is hardly in a position to pursue other, more specific goods, and those in the original position might be imagined to be aware of this fact and to endorse only those principles of justice that would require providing at least basic health care to those in the society. Furthermore, it could be argued that the inequalities of the health care system can be justified only if those in most need can benefit from them. Since this is not obviously the case with the present

system, Rawls's principles seem to call for a reform that would provide health care to those who are unable to pay.

However, it is important to point out that it is not at all obvious that a demand to reform our health care system follows from Rawls's position. For one thing, it is not clear that Rawls's principles are intended to be directly applied to our society as it is. Our society includes among its members people with serious disabilities and people with both acute and chronic diseases. If Rawls's principles are intended to apply only to people with normal physical and psychological abilities and needs, as he sometimes suggests, then it is not clear that those who are ill can be regarded as appropriate candidates. If they are considered appropriate, then the results may be unacceptable. The principles of justice may require that we devote vast amounts of social resources to making only marginal improvements in the lives of those who are ill.

Furthermore, Rawls does not explicitly mention the promotion of health as one of the primary goods. It may seem reasonable to include it among them, given the significance of health as a condition for additional pursuits, but this is a point that requires support. Norman Daniels argues considering health a primary good seems the most promising position to take if Rawls's principles are to be used as a basis for evaluating our current health policies and practices.

It seems reasonable to hold that Rawls's principles, particularly the second, can be used to restrict access to certain kinds of health care. In general, individuals may spend their money in any way they wish to seek their notions of what is good. Thus, if someone wants cosmetic surgery to change the shape of his chin and has the money to pay a surgeon, then he may have it done. But if medical facilities or personnel should become overburdened and unable to provide needed care for the most seriously afflicted, then the society would be obligated to forbid cosmetic surgery. By doing this, it would then increase the net access to needed health care by all members of society. The rich who desired cosmetic surgery would not be permitted to exploit the poor who needed basic health care.

These are just a few of the possible implications that Rawls's theory has for medical research and practice. It seems likely that more and more applications of the theory will be worked out in detail in the future.

Difficulties with Rawls's Theory

Rawls's theory is currently the subject of much discussion in philosophy. The debate is often highly technical, and a great number of objections have been raised. At present, however, there are no objections that would be acknowledged as legitimate by all critics. Rather than attempt to summarize the debate, we will simply point to two aspects of Rawls's theory that have been acknowledged as difficulties.

One criticism concerns the original position and its veil of ignorance. Rawls does not permit those in the original position to know anything of their own purposes, plans, or interests—of their conception of the good. They do not know whether they prefer tennis to Tennyson, pleasures of mind over pleasures of the body. They are allowed to consider only those goods—self-respect, wealth, social position—which Rawls puts before them. Thus, critics have said, Rawls has excluded morally relevant knowledge. It is impossible to see how people could agree on principles to regulate their lives when they are so ignorant of their desires and purposes. Rawls seems to have biased the original position in his favor, and this calls into question his claim that the original position is a fair and reasonable way of arriving at principles of justice.

A second criticism focuses on whether Rawls's theory is really as different from utilitarianism as it appears to be. Rawls's theory may well permit inequalities of treatment under certain conditions in the same way

that the principle of utility permits them. The principles of justice that were stated earlier apply, Rawls says, only when liberty can be effectively established and maintained. Rawls is very unclear about when a situation may be regarded as one of this kind. When it is not, his principles of justice are ones of a "general conception." Under this conception, liberties of individuals can be restricted, provided that the restrictions are for the benefit of all. It is possible to imagine, then, circumstances in which we might force individuals to become experimental subjects both for their own benefit and for that of others. We might, for example, require that all cigarette smokers participate in experiments intended to acquire knowledge about lung and heart damage. Since everyone would benefit, directly or indirectly, from such knowledge, forcing their participation would be legitimate. Thus, under the general conception of justice, the difference between Rawls's principles and the principle of utility may in practice become vanishingly small.

Natural Law Ethics and Moral Theology

The general view that the rightness of actions is something determined by nature itself, rather than by the laws and customs of societies or the preferences of individuals, is called *natural law theory*. Moral principles are thus regarded as objective truths that can be discovered in the nature of things by reason and reflection. The basic idea of the theory was expressed succinctly by the Roman philosopher Cicero (103–43 B.C.): "Law is the highest reason, implanted in Nature, which commands what ought to be done and forbids the opposite. This reason, when firmly fixed and fully developed in the human mind, is Law." The natural law theory originated in classical Greek and Roman philosophy and has immensely influenced the development of moral and political theories. Indeed, all the ethical theories we have discussed are indebted to the natural law tradition. The reliance upon reason as a means of settling upon or establishing ethical principles and the emphasis on the need to reckon with the natural abilities and inclinations of human nature are just two of the threads that are woven into the theories that we have discussed.

Purposes, Reason, and the Moral Law as Interpreted by Roman Catholicism

The natural law theory of Roman Catholicism was given its most influential formulation in the thirteenth century by St. Thomas Aquinas (1225–1274). Contemporary versions of the theory are mostly elaborations and interpretations of Aquinas's basic statement. Thus, an understanding of Aquinas's views is important for grasping the philosophical principles that underlie the Roman Catholic position on such issues as abortion.

Aquinas was writing at a time in which a great number of the texts of Aristotle (384–322 B.C.) were becoming available in the West, and Aquinas's philosophical theories incorporated many of Aristotle's principles. A fundamental notion borrowed by Aquinas is the view that the universe is organized in a teleological way. That is, the universe is structured in such a way that each thing in it has a goal or purpose. Thus, when conditions are right, a tadpole will develop into a frog. In its growth and change, the tadpole is following "the law of its nature." It is achieving its goal.

Humans have a material nature, just as a tadpole does, and in their own growth and development they, too, follow a law of their material nature. But Aquinas also stresses that humans possess a trait that no other creature does: reason. Thus, the full development of human potentialities—the fulfillment of human purpose—requires that we follow the direction of the law of reason, as well as being subjected to the laws of material human nature.

The development of reason is one of our ends as human beings, but we also rely upon reason to determine what our ends are and how we can achieve them. It is this function of reason that leads Aquinas to identify reason as the source of the moral law. Reason is practical in its operation, for it directs our actions so that we can bring about certain results. In giving us directions, reason imposes an obligation on us, the obligation to bring about the results that it specifies. But Aquinas says that reason cannot arbitrarily set goals for us. Reason directs us toward our good as the goal of our action, and what that good is, is discoverable within our nature. Thus, reason recognizes the basic principle "Good is to be done and evil avoided."

But this principle is purely formal, or empty of content. To make it a practical principle, we must consider what the human good is. According to Aquinas, the human good is that which is suitable or proper to human nature. It is what is "built into" human nature in the way that, in a sense, a frog is already "built into" a tadpole. Thus, the good is that to which we are directed by our natural inclinations as both physical and rational creatures.

Like other creatures, we have a natural inclination to preserve our lives; consequently, reason imposes on us an obligation to care for our health, not to kill ourselves, and not to put ourselves in positions in which we might be killed. We realize through reason that others have a rational nature like ours, and we see that we are bound to treat them with the same dignity and respect that we accord ourselves. Furthermore, when we see that humans require a society to make their full development possible, we realize that we have an obligation to support laws and practices that make society possible.

For example, as we have a natural inclination to propagate our species (viewed as a "natural" good), reason places on us an obligation not to thwart or pervert that inclination. As a consequence, to fulfill this obligation within society, reason supports the institution of marriage.

Reason also finds in our nature grounds for procedural principles. For example, because everyone has an inclination to preserve his life and well-being, no one should be forced to testify against himself. Similarly, because all individuals are self-interested, no one should be permitted to be a judge in his own case.

Physical inclinations, under the direction of reason, point us toward our natural good. But, according to Aquinas, reason itself can also be a source of inclinations. For example, Aquinas says that reason is the source of our natural inclination to seek the truth, particularly the truth about the existence and nature of God.

Just from the few examples we have considered, it should be clear how Aquinas believed it was possible to discover natural goods in human nature. Relying upon these as goals or purposes to be achieved, reason would then work out the practical way of achieving them. Thus, through the subtle application of reason, it should be possible to establish a body of moral principles and rules. These are the doctrines of natural law.

Because natural law is founded on human nature, which is regarded as unchangeable, Aquinas regards natural law itself as unchangeable. Moreover, it is seen as the same for all people, at all times, and in all societies. Even those without knowledge of God can, through the operation of reason, recognize their natural obligations.

For Aquinas and for Roman Catholicism, this view of natural law is just one aspect of a broader theological framework. The teleological organization of the universe is attributed to the planning of a creator: goals or purposes are ordained by God. Furthermore, although natural law is discoverable in the universe, its ultimate source is divine wisdom and God's eternal law. Everyone who is rational is capable of grasping natural law. But because passions and irrational inclinations may corrupt human nature and because some people lack the abilities or time to work out the demands of natural law, God also chose to reveal our duties to us in explicit ways. The major source of revelation, of course, is taken to be the biblical scriptures.

Natural law, scriptural revelation, the interpretation of the Scriptures by the Church, Church tradition, and the teachings of the Church are regarded in Roman Catholicism as the sources of moral ideals and principles. By guiding one's life by them, one can develop the rational and moral part of one's nature and move toward the goal of achieving the sort of perfection that is suitable for humans.

This general moral–theological point of view is the source for particular Roman Catholic doctrines that have special relevance to medicine. We will consider just two of the most important principles.

The Principle of Double Effect. A particular kind of moral conflict arises when the performance of an action will produce both good and bad effects. On the basis of the good effect, it seems it is our duty to perform the action; but on the basis of the bad effect, it seems our duty not to perform it.

Let's assume that the death of a fetus is in itself a bad effect and consider a case like the following: A woman who is three months pregnant is found to have a cancerous uterus. If the woman's life is to be saved, the uterus must be removed at once. But if the uterus is removed, then the life of the unborn child will be lost. Should the operation be performed?

The principle of double effect is intended to help in the resolution of these kinds of conflicts. The principle holds that such an action should be performed only if the intention is to bring about the good effect and the bad effect will be an unintended or indirect consequence. More specifically, four conditions must be satisfied:

1. The action itself must be morally indifferent or morally good.

2. The bad effect must not be the means by which the good effect is achieved.

3. The motive must be the achievement of the good effect only.

4. The good effect must be at least equivalent in importance to the bad effect.

Are these conditions satisfied in the case that we mentioned? The operation itself, if this is considered to be the action, is at least morally indifferent. That is, in itself it is neither good nor bad. That takes care of the first condition. If the mother's life is to be saved, it will not be *by means of* killing the fetus. It will be by means of removing the cancerous uterus. Thus, the second condition is met. The motive of the surgeon, we may suppose, is not the death of the fetus but saving the life of the woman. If so, then the third condition is satisfied. Finally, since two lives are at stake, the good effect (saving the life of the woman) is at least equal to the bad effect (the death of the fetus). The fourth condition is thus met. Under ordinary conditions, then, these conditions would be considered satisfied, and such an operation would be morally justified.

The principle of double effect is most often mentioned in a medical context in cases of abortion. But, in fact, it has a much wider range of application in medical ethics. It bears on cases of contraception, sterilization, organ transplants, and the use of extraordinary measures to maintain life.

The Principle of Totality. The principle of totality can be expressed in this way: an individual has a right to dispose of his or her organs or to destroy their capacity to function only to the extent that the general well-being of the whole body demands it. Thus, it is clear that we have a natural obligation to preserve our lives, but, by the Roman Catholic view, we also have a duty to preserve the integrity of our bodies. This duty is based on the belief that each of our organs was designed by God to play a role in maintaining the functional integrity of our bodies—that each has a place in the divine plan. As we are the custodians of our bodies, not their owners, it is our duty to care for them as a trust.

The principle of totality has implications for a great number of medical procedures. Strictly speaking, even cosmetic surgery is morally right only when it is required to maintain or ensure the normal functioning of the rest of the body. More important, procedures that are typically employed for contraceptive purposes— vasectomies and tubal ligations—are ruled out. After all, such procedures involve "mutilation" and the destruction of the capacity of the organs of reproduction to function properly. The principle of totality thus also forbids the sterilization of the mentally retarded.

As an ethical theory, natural law theory is sometimes described as teleological. In endorsing the principle "Good is to be done and evil avoided," the theory identifies a goal with respect to which the rightness of an action is to be judged. As the principle of double effect illustrates, the intention of the individual who acts is crucial to determining whether the goal is sought. In a sense, the intention of the action— what the individual wills—defines the action. Thus, "performing an abortion" and "saving a woman's life" are not necessarily the same action, even in those instances in which their external features are the same. Unlike utilitarianism, which is also a teleological theory, natural law theory is not consequentialist: the outcome of an action is not the sole feature to consider in determining the moral character of the action.

Applications of Roman Catholic Moral–Theological Viewpoints in the Medical Context

Roman Catholic ethicists and moral theologians have written and developed a body of widely accepted doctrine. We will consider only four topics.

First, the application of the principle of double effect and the principle of totality have definite consequences in the area of medical experimentation. Since we hold our bodies in trust, we are responsible for assessing the degree of risk present in an experiment in which we are asked to be a subject. Thus, we need to be fully informed of the nature of the experiment and the risks that it holds for us. If, after obtaining this knowledge, we decide to give our consent, it must be given freely and not as the result of deception or coercion.

Because human experimentation carries with it the possibility of injury and death, the principle of double effect and its four strictures apply. If scientific evidence indicates that a sick person may benefit from participating in an experiment, then the experiment is morally justifiable. If, however, the evidence indicates that the chances of helping that person are slight and he or she may die or be gravely injured, then the experiment is not justified. In general, the likelihood of a person's benefiting from the experiment must exceed the danger of that person's suffering greater losses.

A person who is incurably ill may volunteer to be an experimental subject, even though she or he cannot reasonably expect personal gain in the form of improved health. The good that is hoped for is good for others, in the form of increased medical knowledge. Even here, however, there are constraints imposed by the principle of double effect. There must be no likelihood that the experiment will seriously injure anyone, and the probable value of the knowledge expected to result must balance the risk run by the patient. Not even the incurably ill can be made subjects of trivial experiments.

The good sought by healthy volunteers is also the good of others. The same restrictions mentioned in connection with the incurably ill apply to experimenting on healthy people. In addition, the principle of totality places constraints on what a person may volunteer to do with his or her body. No healthy person may submit to an experiment that involves the probability of serious injury, impaired health, mutilation, or death.

A second medical topic addressed by Roman Catholic theologians is whether "ordinary" or "extraordinary" measures are to be taken in the preservation of human life. While

it is believed that natural law and divine law impose on us a moral obligation to preserve our lives, Catholic moralists have interpreted this obligation as requiring that we rely upon only ordinary means. In the medical profession, the phrase "ordinary means" is used to refer to medical procedures that are standard or orthodox, in contrast with those that are untried or experimental. But from the viewpoint of Catholic ethics, "ordinary" used in the medical context applies to "all medicines, treatments, and operations which offer a reasonable hope of benefit for the patient and which can be obtained and used without excessive expense, pain, or other inconvenience." Thus, by contrast, extraordinary means are those which offer the patient no reasonable hope or whose use causes serious hardship for the patient or others.

Medical measures that would save the life of a patient but subject her to years of pain or produce in her severe physical or mental incapacities are considered extraordinary. A patient or her family are under no obligation to choose such measures, and physicians are under a positive obligation not to encourage their choice.

The third medical topic for consideration is euthanasia. In the Roman Catholic ethical view, euthanasia in any form is considered immoral. It is presumed to be a direct violation of God's dominion over creation and the human obligation to preserve life. The Ethical Directives for Catholic Hospitals is explicit on the matter of taking a life:

> The direct killing of any innocent person, even at his own request, is always morally wrong. Any procedure whose sole immediate effect is the death of a human being is a direct killing. . . . Euthanasia ("mercy killing") in all its forms is forbidden. . . . The failure to supply the ordinary means of preserving life is equivalent to euthanasia.

According to this view, it is wrong to allow babies suffering from serious birth defects to die. If they can be saved by ordinary means, there is an obligation to do so. It is also wrong to act to terminate the lives of those hopelessly ill, either by taking steps to bring about their deaths or by failing to take steps to maintain their lives by ordinary means.

It is never permissible to hasten the death of a person as a direct intention. It is, however, permissible to administer drugs that alleviate pain. The principle of double effect suggests that giving such drugs is a morally justifiable action even though the drugs may indirectly hasten the death of a person.

Last, we may inquire how Roman Catholicism views abortion. According to the Roman Catholic view, from the moment of conception, the conceptus (later, the fetus) is considered to be a person with all the rights of a person. For this reason, direct abortion at any stage of pregnancy is regarded as morally wrong. Abortion is "direct" when it results from a procedure "whose sole immediate effect is the termination of pregnancy." This means that what is generally referred to as therapeutic abortion, in which an abortion is performed to safeguard the life or health of the woman, is considered wrong. For example, a woman with serious heart disease who becomes pregnant cannot morally justify an abortion on the grounds that the pregnancy is a serious threat to her life. Even when the ultimate aim is to save the life of the woman, direct abortion is wrong.

We have already seen, however, that the principle of double effect permits the performance of an action that may result in the death of an unborn child if the action satisfies the four criteria for applying the principle. Thus, *indirect* abortion is considered to be morally permissible. That is, the abortion must be the outcome of some action (for example, removal of a cancerous uterus) that is performed for the direct and total purpose of treating a pathological condition affecting the woman. The end sought in direct abortion is the destruction of life, but the end sought in indirect abortion is the preservation of life.

Difficulties with Natural Law Ethics and Moral Theology

Our discussion has centered on the natural law theory of ethics as it has been interpreted in Roman Catholic theology. Thus, there are two possible types of difficulties: those associated with natural law ethics in its own right and those associated with its incorporation into theology. The theological difficulties go beyond the scope of our aims and interests. We will restrict ourselves to considering the basic difficulty that faces natural law theory as formulated by Aquinas. Since it is this formulation that has been used in Roman Catholic moral theology, we shall be raising a problem for it in an indirect way.

The fundamental difficulty with Aquinas's argument for natural law is caused by the assumption, borrowed from Aristotle, that the universe is organized in a teleological fashion. (This is the assumption that every kind of thing has a goal or purpose.) This assumption is essential to Aquinas's ethical theory, for he identifies the good of a thing with its natural mode of operation. Without the assumption, we are faced with the great diversity and moral indifference of nature. Inclinations, even when shared by all humans, are no more than inclinations. There are no grounds for considering them "goods," and they have no moral status. The universe is bereft of natural values.

Yet, there are many reasons to consider this assumption false. Physics surrendered the notion of a teleological organization in the world as long ago as the seventeenth century: the rejection of Aristotle's physics also entailed the rejection of Aristotle's teleological view of the world. This left biology as the major source of arguments in favor of teleology. But contemporary evolutionary theory shows that the apparent purposive character of evolutionary change can be accounted for by the operation of natural selection on random mutations. Also, the development and growth of organisms can be explained by the presence of genetic information that controls the processes. The tadpole develops into a frog because evolution has produced a genetic program that directs the sequence of complicated chemical changes. Thus, no adequate grounds seem to exist for asserting that the teleological organization of nature is anything more than apparent.

Science and "reason alone" do not support teleology. It can be endorsed only if one is willing to assume that any apparent teleological organization is the product of a divine plan. Yet, because all apparent teleology can be explained in nonteleological ways, this assumption seems neither necessary nor legitimate.

Without its foundation of teleology, Aquinas's theory of natural law ethics seems to collapse. This is not to say, of course, that some other natural law theory—one not requiring the assumption of teleology—might not be persuasively defended.

MAJOR MORAL PRINCIPLES

Making moral decisions is always a difficult and stressful task. Abstract discussions of issues never quite capture the feelings of uncertainty and self-doubt we characteristically experience when called upon to decide what ought to be done or to judge whether someone did the right thing. There are no mechanical processes or algorithms we can apply in a situation of moral doubt. There are no computer programs to supply us with the proper decision when given the relevant data.

In a very real sense, we are on our own when it comes to making ethical decisions. This does not mean that we are without resources and must decide blindly or even naively. When we have the luxury of time, when the need to make a decision is not pressing, we may attempt to work out an answer to a moral question by relying upon a general ethical theory like those discussed earlier. However, in ordinary life we rarely have the opportunity or time to engage in an elaborate process of reasoning and analysis.

A more practical approach is to employ moral principles that have been derived from and justified by a moral theory. A principle such as "Avoid causing needless harm" can serve as a more direct guide to action and decision making than, say, Kant's categorical imperative can. With such a principle in mind, we realize that if we are acting as a physician, then we have a duty to use our knowledge and skills to protect our patients from injury. For example, we should not expose a patient to the needless risk of a diagnostic test that does not promise to yield useful information.

In this section, we will present and illustrate five moral principles. All are ones of special relevance to dealing with the ethical issues presented by decisions concerning medical care. The principles have their limitations. For one thing, they are in no sense complete. Moral issues arise, even in the context of medicine, for which they can supply no direct guidance. In other situations, the principles themselves may come into conflict and point toward incompatible solutions. (How can we both avoid causing harm and allow a terminally ill patient to die?) The principles themselves indicate no way such conflicts can be resolved, for, even taken together, they do not constitute a coherent moral theory. To resolve conflicts, it may be necessary to employ the more basic principles of such a theory.

It is fair to say that each of the five basic moral theories we have discussed endorses the legitimacy of these principles. Not all would formulate them in the same way, and not all would give them the same moral weight. Nevertheless, each theory would accept them as expressing appropriate guidelines for moral decision making.

Indeed, the best way to think about the principles is as guidelines. They are in no way rules that can be applied automatically. Rather, they express standards to be consulted in attempting to arrive at a justified decision. As such, they provide a basis for evaluating actions or policies as well as for making individual moral decisions.

The principles help guarantee that our decisions are made in accordance with them and not according to our whims or prejudices. By following the principles, we are more likely to reach decisions that are reasoned, consistent, and applicable to similar cases.

The Principle of Nonmaleficence

"Above all, do no harm" is perhaps the most famous and most quoted of all moral maxims in medicine. It captures in a succinct way what is universally considered to be an overriding duty of anyone who undertakes the care of a patient. We believe that, in treating a patient, a physician should not by carelessness, malice, inadvertence, or avoidable ignorance do anything that will cause injury to the patient.

The maxim is one expression of what is sometimes called in ethics the principle of nonmaleficence. The principle can be formulated in various ways, but here is one relatively uncontroversial way of stating it: *We ought to act in ways that do not cause needless harm or injury to others.* Stated in a positive fashion, the principle tells us that we have a duty to avoid maleficence—that is, to avoid harming or injuring other people.

In the most obvious case, we violate the principle of nonmaleficence when we intentionally do something we know will cause someone harm. For example, suppose that, during the course of an operation, a surgeon deliberately severs a muscle, knowing that, by doing so, he will cripple the patient. Then the surgeon is guilty of maleficence and is morally (as well as legally) blameworthy for his action.

The principle may also be violated when no malice or intention to do harm is involved. A nurse who carelessly gives a patient the wrong medication and causes the patient to suffer irreversible brain damage may have had no intention of causing the patient any injury. However, the nurse was negligent in his actions and failed to exercise due care in

discharging his responsibilities. His actions resulted in an avoidable injury to his patient. Hence, he failed to meet his obligation of nonmaleficence.

The duty imposed by the principle of nonmaleficence is not a demand to accomplish the impossible. We realize that we cannot reasonably expect perfection in the practice of medicine. We know that the results of treatments are often uncertain and may cause more harm than good. We know that the knowledge we have of diseases is only partial and that decisions about diagnosis and therapy typically involve the exercise of judgment, with no guarantee of correctness. We know that an uncertainty is built into the very nature of things and that our power to control the outcome of natural processes is limited. Consequently, we realize that we cannot hold physicians and other health professionals accountable for every instance of death and injury involving patients under their care.

Nevertheless, we can demand that physicians and others live up to reasonable standards of performance. In the conduct of their professions, we can expect them to be cautious and diligent, patient and thoughtful. We can expect them to pay attention to what they are doing and to deliberate about whether a particular procedure should be done. In addition, we can expect them to possess the knowledge and skills relevant to the proper discharge of their duties.

These features and others like them make up the standards of performance that define what we have a right to expect from physicians and other health professionals. In the language of the law, these are the standards of "due care," and it is by reference to them that we evaluate the medical care given to patients. Failure to meet the standards opens practitioners (physicians, nurses, dentists, therapists) to the charge of moral or legal maleficence.

In our society, we have attempted to guarantee that at least some of the due-care standards are met by relying upon such measures as degree programs, licensing laws, certifying boards, and hospital credentials committees. Such an approach offers a way of ensuring that physicians and others have acquired at least a minimum level of knowledge, skill, and experience before undertaking the responsibilities attached to their roles. The approach also encourages such values as diligence, prudence, and caution, but there is of course no way of guaranteeing that in a particular case a physician will exhibit those virtues. Haste, carelessness, and inattention are always possible, and the potential that a patient will suffer an injury from them is always present.

The standards of due care are connected in some respects with such factual matters as the current state of medical knowledge and training and the immediate circumstances in which a physician provides care. For example, in the 1920s and 1930s, it was not at all unusual for a general practitioner to perform relatively complicated surgery, particularly in rural areas. In performing surgery, he would be acting in a reasonable and expected fashion and could not legitimately be charged with violating the principle of nonmaleficence.

However, the change in medicine from that earlier time to the present has also altered our beliefs about what is reasonable and expected. Today, a general practitioner who has had no special training and is not board certified and yet performs surgery on her patients may be legitimately criticized for maleficence. The standards of due care in surgery are now higher and more exacting than they once were, and the general practitioner who undertakes to perform most forms of surgery causes her patients to undergo an unusual and unnecessary risk literally at her hands. Their interest

would be better served if their surgery were performed by a trained and qualified surgeon.

Such a case also illustrates the idea that no actual harm or injury must occur for someone to be acting in violation of the principle of nonmaleficence. The general practitioner performing surgery may not cause any injury to his patients, but he puts them in a position in which the possibility of harm to them is greater than it needs to be. It is in this respect that he is not exercising due care in his treatment and so can be charged with maleficence. He has subjected his patients to *unnecessary risk*—risk greater than they would be subject to in the hands of a trained surgeon.

It is important to stress that the principle of nonmaleficence does not require that a physician subject a patient to no risks at all. Virtually every form of diagnostic testing and medical treatment involves some degree of risk to the patient, and to provide medical care at all, a physician must often act in ways that involve a possible injury to the patient. For example, a physician who takes a thorough medical history, performs a physical examination, and then treats a patient with an antibiotic for bacterial infection cannot be held morally responsible if the patient suffers a severe drug reaction. That such a thing might happen is a possibility that cannot be foreseen in an individual case.

Similarly, a serious medical problem may justify subjecting the patient to a serious risk. (Gaining the consent of the patient is an obvious consideration, however.) A life-threatening condition, such as an occluded right coronary artery, may warrant coronary-bypass surgery with all its attendant dangers.

In effect, the principle of nonmaleficence tells us to avoid needless risk and, when risk is an inevitable aspect of an appropriate diagnostic test or treatment, to minimize the risk as much as is reasonably possible. A physician who orders a lumbar puncture for a patient who complains of occasional headaches is acting inappropriately, given the nature of the complaint, and is subjecting his patient to needless risk. By contrast, a physician who orders such a test after examining a patient who has severe and recurring headaches, a fever, pain and stiffness in his neck, and additional key clinical signs is acting appropriately. The risk to the patient from the lumbar puncture is the same in both cases, but the risk is warranted in the second case and not in the first. A failure to act with due care violates the principle of nonmaleficence, even if no harm results, whereas acting with due care does not violate the principle, even if harm does result.

The Principle of Beneficence

"As to diseases, make a habit of two things—to help or at least to do no harm." This directive from the Hippocratic writings stresses that the physician has two duties. The second of them ("at least to do no harm") we discussed in connection with the principle of nonmaleficence. The first of them ("to help") we will consider here in connection with the principle of beneficence.

Like the previous principle, the principle of beneficence can be stated in various and different ways. Here is one formulation: *We should act in ways that promote the welfare of other people.* That is, we should help other people when we are able to do so.

Some philosophers have expressed doubt that we have an actual duty to help others. We certainly have a duty not to harm other people, but it has seemed to some that there are no grounds for saying that we have a duty to promote their welfare. We would deserve praise if we did, but we would not deserve blame if we did not. From this point of view, being beneficent is beyond the scope of duty.

We need not consider whether this view is correct in general. For our purposes, it is enough to realize that the nature of the relationship between a physician and a patient does impose the duty of acting in the patient's welfare. That is, the duty of beneficence is inherent in the role of physician. A physician who was not acting

for the sake of the patient's good would, in a very real sense, not be acting as a physician.

That we recognize the principle of beneficence as a duty appropriate to the physician's role is seen most clearly in cases in which the physician is also a researcher and her patient is also an experimental subject. In such instances, there is a possibility of a role conflict, for the researcher's aim of acquiring knowledge is not always compatible with the physician's aim of helping the patient. (See Chapter 1 for a discussion of this problem.)

The duty required by the principle of beneficence is inherent in the role not only of physicians but of all health professionals. Nurses, therapists, clinical psychologists, social workers, and others accept the duty of promoting the welfare of their patients or clients as an appropriate part of their responsibilities. We expect nurses and others to do good for us, and it is this expectation that leads us to designate them as belonging to what are often called "the helping professions."

The extent to which beneficence is required as a duty for physicians and others is not a matter easily resolved. In practice, we recognize that limits exist to what can be expected from even those who have chosen to make a career of helping others. We do not expect physicians to sacrifice completely their self-interest and welfare on behalf of their patients. We do not think their duty demands that they be totally selfless. If some do, we may praise them as secular saints or moral heroes, but that is because they go beyond the demands of duty. At the same time, we would have little good to say of a physician who always put his interest above that of his patients, who never made a personal sacrifice to service their interests.

Just as there are standards of due care that explicitly and implicitly define what we consider to be right conduct in protecting patients from harm, so there seem to be implicit standards of beneficence. We obviously expect physicians to help patients by providing them with appropriate treatment. More than this, we expect physicians to be prepared to make *reasonable* sacrifices for the sake of their patients. Even in the age of "health care teams," a single physician assumes responsibility for a particular patient when the patient is hospitalized or treated for a serious illness. It is this physician who is expected to make the crucial medical decisions, and we expect her to realize that discharging that responsibility may involve an interruption of private plans and activities. A surgeon who is informed that her postoperative patient has started to bleed can be expected to cancel her plan to attend a concert. Doing so is a reasonable duty imposed by the principle of beneficence. If she failed to discharge the duty, then, in the absence of mitigating circumstances, she would become the object of disapproval by her patient and by her medical colleagues.

It would be very difficult to spell out exactly what duties are required by the principle of beneficence. Even if we limit ourselves to the medical context, there are so many ways of promoting someone's welfare and so many different circumstances to consider that it would be virtually impossible to provide anything like a catalog of appropriate actions. However, such a catalog is hardly necessary. Most people most often have a sense of what is reasonable and what is not, and it is this sense that we rely on in making judgments about whether physicians and others are fulfilling the duty of beneficence in their actions.

The principles of nonmaleficence and beneficence impose social duties also. In the most general terms, we look to society to take measures to promote the health and safety of its citizens. The great advances made in public health during the nineteenth century were made because the society recognized a responsibility to attempt to prevent the spread of disease. Water treatment plants, immunization programs, and quarantine as restrictions were all in recognition of society's duty of nonmaleficence.

These and similar programs have been continued and augmented, and our society has also recognized a duty of beneficence in connection with health care. The Medicaid program for the poor and Medicare for the elderly are major efforts to see to at least some of the health needs of a large segment of the population. Prenatal programs for expectant mothers and public clinics are among the other social responses we have made to promote the health of citizens.

Less obvious than programs that provide direct medical care are ones that support medical research and basic science. Directly or indirectly, such programs contribute to meeting the health needs of our society. Much basic research is relevant to acquiring an understanding of the processes involved in both health and disease, and much medical research is specifically aimed at the development of effective diagnostic and therapeutic measures.

In principle, social beneficence has no limits, but in practice it must. Social resources like tax revenues are in restricted supply, and the society must decide how they are to be spent. Housing and food for the poor, education, defense, the arts, and the humanities are just some of the areas demanding support in the name of social beneficence. Medical care is one among many claimants, and we must decide as a society what proportion of our social resources we want to commit to it. Are we prepared to guarantee to all whatever medical care they need? Are we willing to endorse only a basic level of care? Do we want to say that what is available to some (the rich or well insured) must be available to all (the poor and uninsured)? Just how beneficent we wish to be—and can afford to be—is a matter still under discussion. (See Chapter 8.)

The Principle of Utility

The principle of utility can be formulated in this way: *We should act in such a way as to bring about the greatest benefit and the least harm.* As we discussed earlier, the principle is the very foundation of the moral theory of utilitarianism. However, the principle need not be regarded as unique to utilitarianism. It can be thought of as one moral principle among others that present us with a prima facie duty, and, as such, it need not be regarded as always taking precedence over others. In particular, we would never think it was justified to deprive someone of a right, even if by doing so we could bring benefit to many others.

We need not repeat the discussion of the principle of utility presented earlier, but it may be useful to consider here how the principle relates to the principles of nonmaleficence and beneficence. When we consider the problem of distributing social resources, it becomes clear that acting in accordance with the principles of nonmaleficence and beneficence usually involves trade-offs. To use our earlier example, as a society we are concerned with providing for the health care needs of our citizens. To accomplish this end, we support various programs—Medicare, Medicaid, hospital-building programs, medical research, and so on.

However, there are limits to what we can do. Medical care is not the only concern of our society. We are interested in protecting people from harm and in promoting their interests, but there are many forms of harm and many kinds of interest to be promoted. With finite resources at our disposal, the more money we spend on health care, the less we can spend on education, the arts, the humanities, and so on.

Even if we decided to spend more money on health care than we are currently spending, there would come a point at which we would receive only a marginal return for our money. General health would eventually reach such a level that it would be difficult to raise it still higher. To save even one additional life, we would have to spend a vast sum of money. By contrast, at the start of a health care program, relatively little money can make a relatively big difference. Furthermore, money spent for marginal improvements would be directed away from other needs that had become even more crucial because of underfunding. Thus, we could not spend all our resources on health care without ignoring other social needs.

The aim of social planning is to balance the competing needs of the society. Taken alone, the principles of nonmaleficence and beneficence are of no help in resolving the conflicts among social needs. The principle of utility must come into play to establish and rank needs and to serve as a guide for determining to what extent it is possible to satisfy one social need in comparison with others. In effect, the principle imposes a social duty on us all to use our resources to do as much good as possible. That is, we must do the most good *overall*, even when this means we are not able to meet all needs in a particular area.

The application of the principle of utility is not limited to large-scale social issues, such as how to divide our resources among medical care, defense, education, and so on. We may also rely on the principle when we are deliberating about the choice of alternative means of accomplishing an aim. For example, we might decide to institute a mandatory screening program to detect infants with PKU but decide against a program to detect those with Tay–Sachs. PKU can often be treated successfully if discovered early enough, whereas early detection of Tay–Sachs makes little or no difference in the outcome of the disease. Furthermore, PKU is distributed in the general population, whereas Tay–Sachs occurs mostly in a special segment of the population. In general, then, the additional money spent on screening for Tay–Sachs would not be justified by the results. The money could do more good, produce more benefits, were it spent some other way.

The principle of utility is also relevant to making decisions about the diagnosis and treatment of individuals. For example, as we mentioned earlier, no diagnostic test can be justified if it causes the patient more risk than the information likely to be gained is worth. Invasive procedures are associated with a certain rate of injury and death (morbidity and mortality). It would make no sense to subject a patient to a kidney biopsy if the findings were not likely to affect the course of treatment or if the risk from the biopsy were greater than the risk of the suspected disease itself. Attempts are well under way in medicine to employ the formal theories of decision analysis to assist physicians in determining whether a particular mode of diagnosis, therapy, or surgery can be justified in individual cases. Underlying the details of formal analysis is the principle of utility, which directs us to act in a way that will bring about the greatest benefit and the least harm.

Principles of Distributive Justice

We expect (and can demand) to be treated justly in our dealings with other people and with institutions. If our insurance policy covers up to thirty days of hospitalization, then we expect a claim against the policy for that amount of time to be honored. If we arrive in an emergency room with a broken arm before the arrival of someone else with a broken arm, we expect to be attended to before that person.

We do not always expect that being treated justly will work to our direct advantage. Although we would prefer to keep all the money we earn, we realize that we must pay our share of taxes. If a profusely bleeding person arrives in the emergency room after we do, we recognize that he is in need of immediate treatment and should be attended to before we are.

Justice has at least two major aspects. Seeing to it that people receive that to which they are entitled, that their rights are recognized and protected, falls under the general heading of *noncomparative justice*. By contrast, *comparative justice* is concerned with the application of laws and rules and with the distribution of burdens and benefits.

The concern of comparative justice that is most significant to the medical context is *distributive justice*. As the name suggests, distributive justice concerns the distribution of such social benefits and burdens as medical services, welfare payments, public offices, taxes, and military service. In general, the distribution of income has been the focus of recent discussions of distributive justice. In medical ethics, the focus has been the distribution of health care. Are all in the society entitled to receive health care benefits, whether or not they can pay for them? If so, then is everyone entitled to the same amount of health care? (See Chapter 8 for a discussion of this issue.)

Philosophical theories of justice attempt to resolve questions of distributive justice by providing a detailed account of the features of individuals and society that will justify our making distinctions in the ways we distribute benefits and burdens. If some people are to be rich and others poor, if some are to rule and others serve, then there must be some rational and moral basis for such distinctions. We look to theories of justice to provide us with such a basis. (See the earlier discussion of John Rawls's theory for an outstanding recent example.)

Theories of justice differ significantly, but at the core of all of them is the basic principle that "Similar cases ought to be treated in similar ways." The principle expresses the notion that justice involves fairness of treatment. For example, it is manifestly unfair to award two different grades to two people who score the same on a multiple-choice exam. If two cases are the same, then it is arbitrary or irrational to treat them differently. To justify different treatment, we would have to show that the cases are also dissimilar in some relevant respect.

This fairness principle is known as the *formal* principle of justice. It is called "formal" because, like a sentence with blanks, it must be filled in with information. Specifically, we must be told what factors or features are to be considered *relevant* in deciding whether two cases are similar. If two cases differ in relevant respects, we may be justified in treating them differently. We may do so without being either irrational or arbitrary.

Theories of distributive justice present us with *substantive* (or *material*) principles of justice. The theories present us with arguments to show why certain features or factors should be considered relevant in deciding whether cases are similar. The substantive principles can then be referred to in determining whether particular laws, practices, or public policies can be considered just. Further, the substantive principles can be employed as guidelines for framing laws and policies and for developing a just society.

Arguments in favor of particular theories of justice are too lengthy to present here. However, it is useful to consider briefly four substantive principles that have been offered by various theorists as ones worthy of acceptance. To a considerable extent, differences among these principles help explain present disagreements in our society about the ways in which such social "goods" as income, education, and health care should be distributed. Although the principles themselves direct the distribution of burdens (taxation, public service, and so on) as well as benefits, we will focus on benefits. The basic question answered by each principle is "Who is entitled to what proportion of society's goods?"

The Principle of Equality

According to the principle of equality, all benefits and burdens are to be distributed equally. Everyone is entitled to the same sized slice of the pie, and everyone must bear an equal part of the social load. The principle, strictly interpreted, requires a radical egalitarianism: everyone is to be treated the same in all respects.

The principle is most plausible for a society not too far above the margin of production. When there is enough to go around but not much more, then it is manifestly unfair for some to have more than they need and for others to have less than they need. When a society is more affluent, the principle may lose some of its persuasiveness. When greater efforts by a few produce more goods than the efforts of the ordinary person, it may be unfair not

to recognize the accomplishments of a few by greater rewards. Rawls's theory remains an egalitarian one, while providing a way to resolve this apparent conflict. According to Rawls, any departure from equality is arbitrary, unless it can be shown that the inequality will work out to *everyone's* advantage.

The Principle of Need

The principle of need is an extension of the egalitarian principle of equal distribution. If goods are parceled out according to individual need, those who have greater needs will receive a greater share. However, the outcome will be one of equality. Since the basic needs of everyone will be met, everyone will end up at the same level. The treatment of individuals will be equal, in this respect, even though the proportion of goods they receive will not be.

What is to count as a need is a significant question that cannot be answered by a principle of distribution alone. Obviously, basic biological needs (food, clothing, shelter) must be included, but what about psychological or intellectual needs? The difficulty of resolving the question of needs is seen in the fact that—even in our affluent society, the richest in the history of the world—we are still debating the question of whether health care should be available to all.

The Principle of Contribution

According to the principle of contribution, people should get back that proportion of social goods that is the result of their productive labor. If two people work to grow potatoes and the first works twice as long or twice as hard as the second, then the first should be entitled to twice as large a share of the harvest.

The difficulty with this principle in an industrialized, capitalistic society is that contributions to production can take forms other than time and labor. Some people risk their money in investments needed to make production possible, and others contribute crucial ideas or inventions. How are comparisons to be made? Furthermore, in highly industrialized societies it is the functioning of the entire system, rather than the work of any particular individual, that creates the goods to be distributed. A single individual's claim on the outcome of the whole system may be very small.

Nonetheless, it is individuals who make the system work, so it does seem just that individuals should benefit from their contributions. If it is true that it is the system of social organization itself that is most responsible for creating the goods, then this is an argument for supporting the system through taxation and other means. If individual contributions count for relatively little (although for something), there may be no real grounds for attempting to distinguish among them in distributing social benefits.

The Principle of Effort

According to the principle of effort, the degree of effort made by the individual should determine the proportion of goods received by the individual. Thus, the file clerk who works just as hard as the president of a company should receive the same proportion of social goods as the president. Those who are lazy and refuse to exert themselves will receive proportionally less than those who work hard.

The advantage of the principle is that it captures our sense of what is fair—that those who do their best should be similarly rewarded, while those who do less than their best should be less well rewarded. The principle assumes that people have equal opportunities to do their best and that if they do not, it is their own fault. One difficulty with this assumption is that, even if the society presents equal opportunities, nature does not. Some people are born with disabilities or meet with accidents, and their misfortunes may make it difficult for them to want to do their best, even when they are given the opportunity.

Each principle has its shortcomings, but this does not mean that adjustments cannot be made to correct their weaknesses. A complete

theory of justice need not be limited in the number of principles that it accepts, and it is doubtful that any theory can be shown to be both fair and plausible if it restricts itself to only one principle. Although all theories require adjustment, theories fall into types in accordance with the principles they emphasize. For example, Marxist theories select need as basic, whereas libertarian theories stress personal contribution as the grounds for distribution. Utilitarian theories employ that combination of principles which promises to maximize both private and public interests.

Joel Feinberg, to whom the preceding discussion is indebted, may be mentioned as an example of a careful theorist who recommends the adoption of a combination of principles. Feinberg sees the principle of equality based on needs as the basic determination of distributive justice. After basic needs have been satisfied, the principles of contribution and effort should be given the most weight.

According to Feinberg, when there is economic abundance, the claim to "minimally decent conditions" can reasonably be made for every person in the society. To have one's basic needs satisfied under such conditions amounts to a fundamental right. However, when everyone's basic needs are taken care of and society produces a surplus of goods, considerations of contribution and effort become relevant. Those who contribute most to the increase in goods or those who work the hardest to produce it (or some combination) can legitimately lay claim to a greater share.

The principles of justice we have discussed may seem at first to be intolerably abstract and so irrelevant to the practical business of society. However, it is important to keep in mind that it is by referring to such principles that we criticize our society and its laws and practices. The claim that society is failing to meet some basic need of all of its citizens and that this is unfair or unjust is a powerful charge. It can be a call to action in the service of justice. If the claim can be demonstrated, it has more than rhetorical power. It imposes upon us all an obligation to eliminate the source of the injustice.

Similarly, in framing laws and formulating policies, we expect those who occupy the offices of power and influence to make their decisions in accordance with principles. Prominent among these must be principles of justice. It may be impossible in the conduct of daily business to apply any principle directly or exclusively, for we can hardly remake our society overnight. Yet if we are committed to a just society, then the principles of justice can at least serve as guidelines when policy decisions are made. They remind us that it is not always fair for the race to go to the swift.

The Principle of Autonomy

The principle of autonomy can be stated this way: *Rational individuals should be permitted to be self-determining.* According to this formulation, we act autonomously when our actions are the result of our own choices and decisions. Thus, autonomy and self-determination are equivalent.

Autonomy is associated with the status we ascribe to rational beings as persons in the morally relevant sense. We are committed to the notion that persons are by their very nature uniquely qualified to decide what is in their own best interest. This is because, to use Kant's terms, persons are ends in themselves, not means to some other ends. As such, they have an inherent worth, and it is the duty of others to respect that worth and avoid treating them as though they were just ordinary parts of the world to be manipulated according to the will of someone else. A recognition of autonomy is a recognition of that inherent worth, and a violation of autonomy is a violation of our concept of what it is to be a person. To deny someone autonomy is to treat that individual as something less than a person.

This view of the nature of autonomy and its connection with our recognition of what is involved in being a person is shared by several significant moral theories. At the core of each theory is the concept of the rational individual as a moral agent who, along with other moral agents, possesses an unconditional worth. Moral responsibility itself is based on the assumption that such agents are free to determine their own actions and pursue their own aims.

Autonomy is significant not only because it is a condition for moral responsibility, but because it is through the exercise of autonomy that individuals shape their lives. We might not approve of what people do with their lives. It is sad to see talent wasted and opportunities for personal development rejected. Nevertheless, as we sometimes say, "It's his life." We recognize that people are entitled to attempt to make their lives what they want them to be and that it would be wrong for us to take control of their lives and dictate their actions, even if we could. We recognize that a person must "walk to heaven or hell" by her own freely chosen path.

Simply put, to act autonomously is to decide for oneself what to do. Of course, decisions are never made outside of a context, and the world and the people in it exert influence, impose constraints, and restrict opportunities. It is useful to call attention to three interrelated aspects of autonomy in order to get a better understanding of the ways in which autonomy can be exercised, denied, and restricted. We will look at autonomy in the contexts of actions, options, and decision making.

Autonomy and Actions

Consider the following situations: A police officer shoves a demonstrator off the sidewalk during an abortion protest. An attendant in a psychiatric ward warns a patient to stay in bed or be strapped down. A corrections officer warns a prison inmate that if he does not donate blood he will not be allowed out of his cell to eat dinner. A state law requires that anyone admitted to a hospital be screened for the HIV antibody.

In each of these situations, either actual force, the threat of force, or potential penalties are employed to direct the actions of an individual toward some end. All involve some form of coercion, and the coercion is used to restrict the freedom of individuals to act as they might choose. Under such circumstances, the individual ceases to be the agent who initiates the action as a result of his or her choice. The individual's initiative is set aside, wholly or partially, in favor of someone else's.

Autonomy is violated in such cases even if the individual intends to act in the way that is imposed or demanded. Perhaps the prison inmate would have donated blood anyway, and surely some people would have wanted to be screened for HIV. However, the use of coercion makes the wishes or intentions of the individual partly or totally irrelevant to whether the act is performed.

Autonomy as the initiation of action through one's own intervention and choice can clearly be restricted to a greater or lesser degree. Someone who is physically forced to become a subject in a medical experiment, as in a Nazi concentration camp, is totally deprived of autonomy. The same is true of someone tricked into becoming a subject without knowing it. In the infamous Tuskegee syphilis studies, some participants were led to believe they were receiving appropriate medical treatment when in fact they were part of a control group in the experiment. The situation is somewhat different for someone who agrees to become a subject in order to receive needed medical care. Such a person is acting under strong coercion, but the loss of autonomy is not complete. It is at least possible to refuse to participate, even if the cost of doing so may be extremely high.

In situations more typical than these, autonomy may be compromised rather than denied. For example, someone who is by nature nonassertive or someone who is poor and uneducated may find it very difficult to preserve his power of self-determination when he becomes a patient in a hospital. Medical authority, represented by physicians and the hospital staff, may be so intimidating to such

a person that he does not feel free to exercise his autonomy. In such a case, although no one may be deliberately attempting to infringe on the patient's autonomy, social and psychological factors may constitute a force so coercive that the patient feels he has no choice but to do what he is told.

Autonomy and Options

Autonomy involves more than freedom from duress in making decisions. There must be genuine possibilities to decide among. A forced option is no option at all, and anyone who is in the position of having to take what he can get can hardly be regarded as self-determining or as exercising free choice.

In our society, economic and social conditions frequently limit the options available in medical care. As a rule, the poor simply do not have the same choices available to them as the rich. Someone properly insured or financially well off who might be helped by a heart transplant can decide whether or not to undergo the risk of having one. That is an option not generally available to someone who is uninsured and poor.

Similarly, a woman who depends on Medicaid and lives in a state in which Medicaid funds cannot be used to pay for abortions may not have the option of having an abortion. Her choice is not a genuine one, for she lacks the means to implement it. The situation is quite different for a middle-class woman faced with the same question. She may decide against having an abortion, but whatever she decides, the choice is real. She is autonomous in a way that the poor woman is not.

Those who believe that one of the goals of our society is to promote and protect the autonomy of individuals have frequently argued that we must do more to offer all individuals the same range of health care options. If we do not, they have suggested, then our society cannot be one in which everyone has an equal degree of autonomy. In a very real sense, those who are rich will have greater freedom of action than those who are poor.

Autonomy and Decision Making

More is involved in decision making than merely saying yes or no. In particular, relevant information is an essential condition for genuine decision making. We are exercising our autonomy in the fullest sense only when we are making *informed* decisions.

It is pointless to have options if we are not aware of them; we can hardly be said to be directing the course of our lives if our decisions must be made in ignorance of information that is available and relevant to our choices. These are the reasons that lying and other forms of deception are so destructive of autonomy. If someone with a progressive and ordinarily fatal disease is not told about it by her physician, then she is in no position to decide how to shape what remains of her life. The lack of a crucial piece of information—that she is dying—is likely to lead her to make decisions different from the ones she would make were she in possession of the information.

Information is the key to protecting and preserving autonomy in most medical situations. A patient who is not informed of alternative forms of treatment and their associated risks is denied the opportunity to make his own wishes and values count for something in his own life. For example, someone with coronary artery disease who is not told of the relative merits of medical treatment with drugs but is told only that he is a candidate for coronary-artery bypass surgery is in no position to decide what risks he wishes to take and what ordeals he is prepared to undergo. A physician who does not supply the patient with the information the patient needs is restricting the patient's autonomy. The principle of autonomy requires *informed* consent, for consent alone does not involve genuine self-determination.

Making decisions for "the good" of others (paternalism), without consulting their wishes, deprives them of their status as autonomous agents. For example, some people at the final stages of a terminal illness might prefer to be allowed to die without heroic intervention, while others might prefer to prolong their lives as long as medical skills and technological powers make possible. If a physician or family undertakes to make a decision in this matter on behalf of the patient, then no matter what their motive, they are denying to the patient the power of self-determination.

Because autonomy is so bound up with informed consent and decision making, special problems arise in the case of those unable to give consent and make decisions. Patients who are comatose, severely brain damaged, psychotic, or seriously mentally impaired are not capable of making decisions on their own behalf. The nature of their condition has already deprived them of their autonomy. Of course, this does not mean that they have no status as moral persons or that they have no interests. It falls to others to see that their interests are served.

The situation is similar for those, such as infants and young children, who are incapable of understanding. Any consent that is given must be given by others. But what are the limits of consent that can legitimately be given for some other person? Consenting to needed medical care seems legitimate, but what about rejecting needed medical care? What about consenting to becoming a subject in a research program? These questions are as crucial as they are difficult to resolve.

Restrictions on Autonomy

Autonomy is not an absolute or unconditional value. We would regard it as absurd for someone to claim that she was justified in committing a murder because she was only exercising her power of self-determination. Such a defense would be morally ludicrous.

However, we do value autonomy and recognize a general duty to respect it and even to promote its exercise. We demand compelling reasons to justify restricting the power of individuals to make their own choices and direct their own lives.

We will briefly examine four principles that are frequently appealed to in justifying restrictions on autonomy. The principles have been discussed most in the context of social and legal theory, for it is through laws and penalties that a society most directly regulates the conduct of its citizens. However, the principles can also be appealed to in justifying policies and practices of institutions (such as hospitals) and the actions of individuals that affect other people.

Appealing to a principle can provide, at best, only a prima facie justification. Even if a principle can be shown to apply to a particular case in which freedom of action is restricted, we may value the lost freedom more than what is gained by restricting it. Reasons suggested by the principle may not be adequately persuasive. Furthermore, the principles themselves are frequently the subjects of controversy, and, with the exception of the harm principle, it is doubtful that any of the principles would be universally endorsed by philosophers and legal theorists.

The Harm Principle. According to the harm principle, we may restrict the freedom of people to act if the restriction is necessary to prevent harm to others. In the most obvious case, we may take action to prevent violence like rape, robbery, killing, or assault. We may act to protect someone who is at apparent risk of harm from the action of someone else. The risk of harm need not be the result of the intention to harm. Thus, we might take steps to see that a surgeon whose skills and judgment have been impaired through drug use is not permitted to operate. The risk that he poses to his patients warrants the effort to keep him from acting as he wishes.

The harm principle may also be used to justify laws that exert coercive force and so restrict freedom of action. Laws against homicide and assault are clear examples, but the principle extends also to the regulation of institutions and practices. People may be robbed at the point of a pen, as well as at the point of a knife, and the harm produced by fraud may be as great as that produced by outright theft. Careless or deceptive medical practitioners may cause direct harm to their patients, and laws that regulate the standards of medical practice restrict the freedom of practitioners for the protection of patients.

The Principle of Paternalism. In its weak version, the principle of paternalism is no more than the harm principle applied to the individual himself. According to the principle, we are justified in restricting someone's freedom to act if doing so is necessary to prevent him from harming himself. Thus, we might force an alcoholic into a treatment program and justify our action by claiming that we did so to prevent him from continuing to harm himself by his drinking.

In its strong version, the principle of paternalism justifies restricting someone's autonomy if by doing so we can benefit her. In such a case, our concern is not only with preventing the person from harming herself, but also with promoting her good in a positive way. The principle might be appealed to even in cases in which our actions go against the other's known wishes. For example, a physician might decide to treat a patient with a placebo (an inactive drug), even if she has asked to be told the truth about her medical condition and her therapy. He might attempt to justify his action by claiming that if the patient knew she was receiving a placebo, then the placebo would be less likely to be effective. Since taking the placebo while believing that it is an active drug makes her feel better, the physician may claim that by deceiving her he is doing something to help her.

Paternalism may be expressed in laws and public policies, as well as in private actions. Some have suggested the drug laws as a prime example of governmental paternalism. By making certain drugs illegal and inaccessible and by placing other drugs under the control of physicians, the laws aim to protect people from themselves. Self-medication is virtually eliminated, and the so-called recreational use of drugs is prohibited. The price for such laws is a restriction on individual autonomy. Some have argued that the price is too high and that the most the government should do is warn and educate the individual about the consequences of using certain drugs.

The Principle of Legal Moralism. The principle of legal moralism holds that a legitimate function of the law is to enforce morality by turning the immoral into the illegal. Hence, the legal restrictions placed on actions are justified by the presumed fact that the actions are immoral and so ought not to be performed.

To a considerable extent, laws express the values of a society and the society's judgments about what is morally right. In our society, homicide and theft are recognized as crimes, and those who commit them are guilty of legal, as well as moral, wrongdoing. Society attempts to prevent such crimes and to punish offenders.

The degree to which the law should embody moral judgments is a hard question. It is particularly difficult to answer in a pluralistic society like ours, in which there may be sharp differences of opinion about the moral legitimacy of some actions. Until quite recently, for example, materials considered obscene could not be freely purchased, birth-control literature could not be freely distributed nor contraceptives legally prescribed in some states, and the conditions of divorce were generally stringent and punitive. Even now, many states outlaw homosexual solicitation and acts, and prostitution is generally illegal. The foundation for such laws is the belief by many that the practices proscribed are morally wrong.

The current heated debate over abortion reflects, in some of its aspects, the conflict between those who favor strong legal moralism and those who oppose it. Many who consider abortion morally wrong would also like to see it made illegal once more. Others, even though they may oppose abortion, believe that it is a private moral matter and that the attempt to regulate it by law is an unwarranted intrusion of state power.

The Welfare Principle. The welfare principle holds that it is justifiable to restrict individual autonomy if doing so will result in providing benefits to others. Those who endorse this principle are not inclined to think that it demands a serious self-sacrifice for the welfare of others. Rather, in their view, an ideal application of the principle would be the case in which we give up just a little autonomy to bring about a great deal of benefit to others.

For example, transplant organs are in short supply at the moment because their availability depends mostly on their being freely donated. The situation could be dramatically changed by a law requiring that organs from the recently dead be salvaged and made available for use as transplants.

Such a law would end the present system of voluntary donation, and by doing so it would restrict our freedom to decide what is to be done with our bodies after death. However, it would be easy to argue that the tremendous value that others might gain from such a law easily outweighs the slight restriction on autonomy that it would involve.

These four principles are not the only ones that offer grounds for abridging the autonomy of individuals, but they are the most relevant to decision making and policy planning in medicine. It is important to keep in mind that merely appealing to a principle is not enough to warrant a limit on autonomy. A principle points in the direction of an argument, but it is no substitute for one. The high value we place on autonomy gives its preservation a high priority, and compelling considerations are required to justify compromising it. In the view of some philosophers who endorse the position taken by Mill, only the harm principle can serve as grounds for legitimately restricting autonomy. Other theorists find persuasive reasons to do so in other principles.

THEORIES WITHOUT PRINCIPLES

Most of traditional Western ethics is based on the assumption that ethical beliefs are best represented by a set of rules or abstract principles. Kant's categorical imperative, Mill's principle of utility, and Ross's list of prima facie duties attempt to supply guides for moral action and decision making that apply in all circumstances.

Moral decisions thus typically involve bringing a case under a rule, in much the same way that law courts apply statutory laws to cases brought before them. Much ethical dispute, like much legal dispute, is over whether an abstract rule does or does not apply in a concrete case.

In recent decades, some ethical theorists have turned away from the principle-governed, legalistic approach to ethics in favor of another approach from the Western tradition. Some of the new theorists have emphasized the importance of character as the source of moral action, whereas others have stressed the central role of shared concerns and the crucial importance of social practices and institutions in shaping our moral lives.

We will present brief sketches of ethical theories that (according to their proponents) cannot be reduced to sets of abstract principles. Although moral theorists debate such questions as whether the virtue of being a truthful person (a character trait) isn't ultimately derived from the duty to tell the truth (a principle), we will steer clear of these issues. Rather, as with theories based on principles, we will restrict ourselves to a general statement of each theory, indicate how it might be applied in a medical context, and then discuss some of the difficulties it faces as a moral theory.

The three theories discussed here have been presented by their proponents in a variety of versions, some of them quite elaborate and philosophically sophisticated. Keep in mind that we are presenting only sketches.

Virtue Ethics

J. D. Salinger's character Holden Caulfield dislikes "phonies" and dreams of standing in a field and keeping little kids from running off the edge of the cliff beyond. He wants to be a "catcher in the rye."

Millions of us who have read *The Catcher in the Rye* have admired Holden and wanted to be like him in some ways. We, too, would like to avoid phoniness, particularly in ourselves, and we would like to do something to make the world a better place, particularly for children. Holden isn't a perfect person, but even so, he's a moral hero, a sort of icon or example of what we wish we could be in some respects.

Every culture is populated by real and fictional characters representing the sort of people we should try to become. Some characters are seen as perfect, while others are people who, despite their flaws, show what they were capable of in confronting life's problems and struggles. To name only a few historically important people, consider Socrates, Jesus, Gautama Buddha, Moses, Florence Nightingale, Confucius, Martin Luther King, Susan B. Anthony, Anne Frank, Gandhi, and Mother Teresa. It would be easy to make an even longer list of fictional characters who evoke our admiration and make us feel that we would be better people if we could be more like them.

Virtue ethics is ethics based on character. Its fundamental idea is that a person who has acquired the proper set of dispositions will do what is right when faced with a situation involving a moral choice. Thus, virtue ethics doesn't involve invoking principles or rules to guide actions.

The virtuous person is both the basic concept and the goal of virtue ethics. The virtuous person is one who acts right, because she is just that sort of person. Right actions flow out of character, and the virtuous person has a disposition to do the right thing. Rules need not be consulted, calculations need not be performed, abstract duties need not be considered.

People become virtuous in the way they become good swimmers. Upbringing, education, the example of others, reflection, personal effort, and experience all play a role. As with swimming, some people may be more naturally inclined to become virtuous than others. Those who are naturally patient, reflective, and slow to anger may find it easier than those who are impatient, impulsive, and possessed of a fiery temper.

Families and social institutions—like schools, clubs, and athletic teams, as well as religious institutions—play a role in shaping our moral character. They tell us how we should behave when we lose a school election or win a softball game. They teach us what we should do when we have a chance to take money without anyone's finding out, when we witness a case of discrimination, when we ourselves are treated unfairly.

Quite apart from explicit teachings or doctrines, the lives of historical figures like Jesus, Mohammed, and Buddha have served as examples of what it is possible for a person to become. Perhaps no one believes that he can achieve the level of moral perfection such people represent, but they offer us models for fashioning ourselves. In the way a swimmer may study the backstroke, we can study the way moral heroes have dealt with the moral questions that face us.

When a Christian asks, "What would Jesus do?" it is not typically an attempt to call on divine guidance. Rather, it is an occasion for reflection, of attempting to imagine what someone trying to live a life like Jesus's would do. We try to improve our character by becoming more like those who are admirable. Hence, in addition to education and social influences, we must engage in self-criticism and make deliberate efforts to improve.

The Virtues

The virtuous person is disposed to demonstrate virtues through behavior. *Virtue* is a translation of the Greek word *arete*, which also has much the same meaning as *excellence*. (Virtue ethics is also called *aretaic ethics*.) The excellent tennis player demonstrates in playing tennis that he possesses characteristics needed to play the game well. Similarly, the virtuous person demonstrates through living that she possesses the appropriate range of excellences.

Virtues have traditionally been divided into moral and practical, or nonmoral, virtues:

> Moral virtues: *benevolence, compassion, honesty, charity, sincerity, sympathy, respect, consideration, kindness, thoughtfulness, loyalty, fairness, and so on*

> Nonmoral virtues: *rationality (or intelligence), tenacity, capability, patience, prudence, skillfulness, staunchness, shrewdness, proficiency, and so on*

The distinction between moral and nonmoral virtues is far from clear, but the rough idea is that those in one set are associated with living a good (moral) life, whereas those in the other are associated with the practical aspects of living. A thief can be patient (a nonmoral virtue), but not honest (a moral one). By contrast, an honest (moral virtue) person may lack patience. (How to classify *courage* has always been a problem. A courageous thief may be more successful than a cowardly one, but a benevolent person lacking the courage to put his views into practice will be ineffective.)

Virtue Ethics in the Medical Context

Consider Dr. Charles Holmes, an emergency-room trauma surgeon who chose his specialty because the money is good and the hours reasonable. He treats the patients, and then he goes home. Holmes is technically expert, but he lacks compassion for his patients and is not interested in their worries or fears. He shows no tact in dealing with patients and barely acknowledges that they are people.

Dr. Holmes is far removed from our notion of what a physician as a compassionate healer should be. In treating his patients as broken machines, he may help them in important ways, but his skills as a physician are deficient. Holmes, we might say, lacks the disposition necessary to be a good physician.

From at least the time of the ancient Greeks, the Western tradition has expected physicians to be virtuous, and more recently we have broadened that expectation to include nurses, medical technicians, and all who care for patients. The tradition is resplendent with stories of those who behaved in ways that make them moral examples for all who commit themselves to providing patient care. Scores of European physicians at the time of the Black Death (the bubonic plague) in the fourteenth century tended to their patients, even though they knew they risked infection themselves. The eighteenth-century American physician Benjamin Rush did his best to help cholera sufferers, although he knew that he was likely to get the disease. Florence Nightingale, braving harsh conditions and the risk of sickness, helped care for British troops during the Crimean War and fought to establish nursing as a profession.

Virtue ethics calls attention to the strength of medicine at its moral (and practical) best. Courage, loyalty, integrity, compassion, and benevolence, along with determination and intelligence, are virtues associated with physicians and others who provide what we consider the right sort of care for their patients. We expect everyone involved in patient care to display in their behavior a similar constellation of virtues. Virtue ethics, with its emphasis on character and behavioral dispositions, comes closer to capturing our concept of the ideal health professional than does a rule-based view of moral decision making such as Kant's ethics or utilitarianism.

Difficulties with Virtue Ethics

A fundamental difficulty with virtue ethics is that it provides us with no explicit guidance in deciding how to act in particular circumstances. Suppose someone is terminally ill, in great pain, and asking for assistance in dying. Should we agree to help? We may ask, "What would Jesus do?" and the answer may be "I don't know." If we have been brought up to be virtuous, perhaps we should have no need to ask such questions. But how are we to know who among us has been properly brought up, and for those of us who aren't sure, what should we do?

Medicine is repeatedly faced with the problem of deciding about what actions ought to be taken, but virtue ethics is about character and dispositions. However, even a benevolent person (one disposed to act benevolently) may not know how to distribute organs that are in scarce supply. Further, virtue ethics does not supply any clear way to resolve moral conflicts. What if Assiz thinks it would be wrong to abort a fetus twenty-four weeks after conception, but Puzo does not. How can they go about resolving their dispute? The answer is not clear.

Also, virtues, like duties, can be incompatible when they are translated into action. If I am a transplant coordinator and try to express my gratitude to my physics teacher by allowing her to jump to the head of the waiting list for a new liver, this will conflict with my commitment to fairness. But if virtues are not ranked, how do I decide what to do in such a case? Surely we don't think it would be right for me to put my teacher at the head of the list, but on what grounds can virtue ethics say that it would be wrong?

Care Ethics

Care ethics is an outgrowth of feminist ethics or, perhaps more accurately, is a particular strand of feminist ethics. Care ethics is not a unified doctrine that can be captured in a set of abstract statements. Indeed, care ethics, like feminist ethics in general, rejects abstract principles as the basis for ethics. It is perhaps best characterized as a family of beliefs about the way values should be manifested in character and in behavior. It is unified by a set of shared concerns and commitments, as well as by the rejection of the traditional philosophical view that ethics can be adequately represented by rules and principles.

Much of the philosophical work in care ethics has been developed on the basis of psychologist Carol Gilligan's research on moral development. Lawrence Kohlberg's earlier studies suggest that women are "less developed" in their moral reasoning skills than men because they are not as adept at applying moral principles to particular cases. Gilligan does not conclude that Kohlberg is wrong but, rather, that women have a *style* of moral reasoning that is entirely different from the style employed by men. The title Gilligan gave to her book, *In a Different Voice*, is an allusion to the impression she formed, in listening to women discuss how they would resolve moral difficulties, that she was hearing a voice different from the strident and judgmental male voice of traditional ethical theory.

Gilligan claims that when women are presented with cases of moral conflict, they focus on the details of the people involved in the situation and their personal relationships. They then try to find a way to resolve the conflict that will avoid causing harm to anyone and satisfy, to the extent possible, the interests of everyone concerned. To accomplish such a resolution, women are prepared to look for compromises and points of agreement, to be flexible in their demands, and to take novel approaches to find resolutions that all parties to the dispute will accept.

Unlike the approach taken by women, Gilligan claims, when men are presented with a case of moral conflict, they focus on analyzing the situation with the aim of deciding what abstract rule it would be appropriate to follow to resolve the case. They take little interest in the people as individuals who have their own concerns and needs. Once men have identified

a rule they believe fits the case at hand, they act (and try to make others act) in a way that most closely conforms to it. Men are prepared to follow rules in the interest of justice, even if securing justice involves sacrificing the interests of some of the people involved in the conflict.

Gilligan characterizes the way women respond to situations of moral conflict as expressing an *ethic of care* and the way in which men respond as expressing an *ethic of justice.* She emphasizes, however, that there isn't a perfect correlation between these types of response and gender. Ideally, according to Gilligan, moral agents should employ both approaches in moral decision making. Not only is there room for both, but there is also a need for both.

Some philosophers have refined Gilligan's original distinction and divided "feminist ethics" from "care ethics." *Feminist ethics*, they emphasize, involves acknowledging the validity of women's experience in dealing with people and society, expressing a commitment to social equality, and exploring ways to empower women. (See the discussion of feminist ethics later in this chapter.) *Care ethics* need not have such explicit feminist concerns, although it shares the same general aims and point of view.

Even so, most feminists see the question of whether care ethics should be distinguished from feminist ethics as less important than the need to make sure that women's perspectives and concerns are represented within ethics. According to them, the tradition of philosophical ethics has concentrated on the development of comprehensive abstract theories that fail to acknowledge the importance of values prized by women; as a result, traditional ethicists assign those values no role in moral decision making or the moral life. Care ethics is a means of bringing women's concerns about the lives of individual women, children, families, and the society into ethics.

Values, Not Principles

Ethical theories as diverse as utilitarianism and Kantian ethics have in common a reliance upon abstract principles both as an expression of the theory and as a means of resolving moral conflicts. Thus, to decide whether an action is morally legitimate, we can appeal to the principle of utility or to the categorical imperative. Moral theories can be viewed as providing a decision procedure for arriving at morally justified conclusions in particular cases: to justify an action, bring it under a rule.

Care ethics holds that it is not even appropriate to think in terms of rules or principles where certain kinds of relationships are concerned. Do we need to perform a utilitarian calculation before giving a friend a ride to the hospital? Should parents consult the categorical imperative before deciding whether to immunize their children against polio? Of course not. These relationships require that we give of ourselves and provide assistance and care of an appropriate sort. Such a requirement is bound up with the nature of being a friend or a parent. Other relationships—being a nurse, physician, teacher, manager, therapist, or trainer—have similar requirements bound up with them. In general, rules and principles seem both inappropriate and unnecessary where certain human relationships are concerned.

Care ethics rejects outright the idea that abstract principles can capture everything relevant to making moral decisions. Hence, feminist/care ethics explicitly denies there can be a decision procedure consisting only in bringing a case "under a rule" or showing it to be an "instance" of a general principle. What is crucial for care ethics, rather, is an understanding of the complexities of the particular situation in which a moral problem has occurred. It requires a deep and detailed understanding of the people and their interests and feelings. Only then is it possible to resolve the problem in a way that is sensitive to everyone's needs.

In understanding a complex situation, we must use intelligence to grasp relationships and details about the people, the circumstances, and the problem. But equally important, we must use *empathy* to understand the concerns and feelings of the people involved. We must identify with those in need or conflict, see what is at stake from their point of view, and ascertain their worries and concerns. We must also bring to the situation of moral conflict or doubt such traditional "women's values" as caring, consideration, kindness, concern for others, compassion, understanding, generosity, sympathy, helpfulness, and a willingness to assume responsibility.

These are the very values we must rely on to resolve moral conflicts and see to the needs of the people involved. The point is not to show who is in the wrong or being treated unfairly. Rather, the point is to find a way out of the conflict that takes into account the concerns and feelings of those involved.

According to care ethics, the traditional ethical model of a disinterested, detached, and dispassionate judge reviewing the objective facts in a case and then issuing an impartial decision about the moral acceptability of an action is inappropriate and mistaken. It excludes the very values that are most relevant to moral situations and most important to the people who are involved. Moral decisions should not be impartial, in an abstract and bloodless way; rather, they should show partiality to *everyone* involved.

Like virtue ethics, care ethics emphasizes the development of an appropriate character. As a society, we should make an effort, by teaching and example, to develop individuals, male and female, who respond appropriately to moral situations. They should be people who recognize the importance of personal relationships, respect individuals, and accept responsibility. In their dealings with others, if they have acquired the proper character, they will bring to bear the values (see earlier) we associate with caring for and about people.

Care Ethics in the Medical Context

Suppose the parents of a severely impaired newborn boy are told by the child's physicians that his treatment ought to be discontinued and he should be given only "comfort care" and allowed to die. The parents' initial response is to reject the recommendation and insist that everything possible be done to continue the life of their child. How might such a conflict be resolved by the approach advocated by care ethics?

The parties to the conflict must discuss each of their positions freely and openly. (We need not assume that only two positions are involved.) The physicians must explain in detail the baby's medical condition, discuss the therapy they may be able to offer, and be forthcoming about its limitations. If they believe the baby will die in a few hours or days, no matter what they do, they must be frank about their expectation. They might point out that the only therapy possible involves extensive and painful surgery, that it is almost certain to be unsuccessful, that it will be expensive, and that it will demand the resources of the hospital, the society, and the parents themselves.

For their part, the parents might talk about their hopes for the child and their willingness to love and nurture even a child with severe physical and mental problems. They might discuss the guilt they would feel about giving up the struggle and allowing the child to die. They might discuss their experiences with other children or talk about the difficulties they had conceiving the one who is now not expected to live.

No particular outcome can be predicted from such a discussion. We might imagine education taking place and compromises developing among all the participants. We might imagine the physicians coming to a greater appreciation of what the child means to the parents and why they are so reluctant to allow the child to die. The parents, for their part, might come to understand that the physicians are concerned with their child and are also frustrated and saddened by their inability to help the child get better.

The outcome might involve adjustments on the part of all participants. The parents might come to realize that their child is almost sure to die no matter what is done. The physicians might realize that they might make the child's death easier for the parents to bear by allowing the parents to hold the child and spend time with him.

Other moral conflicts or questions might be approached in a similar fashion. Should Ladzewell's request that he be assisted in dying be followed? Should Terema's request for an abortion in the second trimester of pregnancy be honored? Dozens of similar questions arise in the area of health care, and care ethics suggests that the proper approach is not to invoke principles, but instead to deal with the people involved as individuals and behave in accordance with the values of care.

Medicine, nursing, and allied areas have traditionally been associated with the values of caring. We have expected practitioners to manifest, in their character and conduct, concern, compassion, sympathy, kindness, and a willingness to take responsibility and to help patients in their charge. In this respect, care ethics is asking us to recognize a traditional approach to patients. However, care ethics also reassures us that this approach is legitimate, even though no abstract principles are involved. More than this, though, it tells us to rely on those same values and dispositions when we are faced with moral conflicts in medicine. Again, care ethics reassures us that we can put our trust in the values of care and need not reach for principles to resolve the conflict.

Difficulties with Care Ethics

A frequent criticism of care ethics is that Gilligan's empirical claims about the differences between the moral reasoning of women and men do not stand up to the challenge of more recent data. Without taking a stand on this question, it is enough to observe that Gilligan's empirical claims are not crucial to care ethics. It is enough for the care ethics theorist to demonstrate the importance of the values that belong to the ethic of care by showing how they can play a role in the moral life of individuals and society and how they can be employed as guides in resolving cases of moral doubt and conflict.

Also, not all care advocates have accepted a radical division between two "ethics." Some critics have pointed out, for example, that the principle of beneficence ("Act so as to promote the good of others") can be construed as implying the need for caring. Hence, according to this line of criticism, care ethics can be seen as a part of the traditional enterprise of philosophical ethics. Care ethics usefully emphasizes values and approaches that are relatively ignored or unappreciated in traditional ethical theory, but it does not stand as an alternative to a moral theory like utilitarianism or even Ross's intuitionism.

A more important criticism may be that, like virtue ethics, which also rejects principles as necessary to ethics, care ethics provides us with no obvious way to resolve moral conflicts. We may bring to a conflict the ethics of care, but we may still not know how to make a decision. When a number of people are in need of the same kidney for transplant, how should we decide who gets the kidney? Should we, in the manner suggested by care ethics, have a discussion with them all, assess their needs and feelings, and then make a decision? It seems unlikely that such a group could reach a consensus, particularly in the short time allowed under such circumstances. If we make the decision affecting them, then most would probably claim that they had been treated unfairly. Such cases suggest that the abstract principle of justice may yield more satisfactory results than the values of care ethics alone.

Finally, values, like virtues and duties, can be incompatible when they have to be translated into action. While I may be moved by sympathy and want the mother with two young children to receive the bone marrow

that may save her life, I may also be moved by my compassion for the sufferings of a six-year-old boy who might have a long life ahead of him and want him to receive it. If I am forced to choose who gets the bone marrow, even if I learn much more about the people involved, my choice ultimately seems arbitrary.

These objections might be answered satisfactorily by a care ethics theorist. Even so, they are prima facie shortcomings that require serious responses.

Feminist Ethics

Feminist ethics in general, like care ethics in particular, rejects the traditional notion that ethics can be represented by a set of abstract rules or principles and that the morality of actions and policies can be assessed by reference to them.

From the feminist perspective, the "principlism" of traditional ethics is compromised by the facts of the social world. The unequal distribution of political and social power and the inequalities attached to the accidents of birth, race, and gender mean that even such an apparently basic principle as the autonomy (self-directedness) of the individual is restricted in its application. In some states, for example, a woman who cannot pay for an abortion is not free to get one. Thus, her autonomy as an abstract right is meaningless in practical terms. The focus of ethics, according to feminist philosophers, must be on social arrangements, practices, and institutions, not abstract principles. Further, the overall aim of ethics must be to eliminate (or at least reduce) the oppression of women, races, and other subordinate groups in societies throughout the world.

Although care ethics originated in feminism, some feminists regard associating it with feminism as a threat to feminism. They fear that caring will be seen as a uniquely female trait and that feminist ethics will be undercut. First, it may be dismissed as based on an inferior form of reasoning (Gilligan's "ethic of care") more appropriate to the largely female "helping" professions of nursing and social work than to the predominantly male profession of medicine. Second, the view that caring is a woman's way of thinking may reinforce the stereotypes that confine women to the lower ranks of the health care hierarchy. Caring has a legitimate place in feminist ethics, but it must be seen as a disposition desirable for all people to have across all divisions of gender, race, and class.

For many feminist philosophers, *equality* lies at the core of ethics. Their primary concern is with gender equality, and their aim is to critique the institutions and practices of society to expose the ways in which they keep women subjected to men. More broadly, though, most feminists support an effort to expose and eradicate the domination of any one group by another. They recognize that women may suffer compound injustices because they belong to races and classes that have been subordinated. A woman who is Asian, sick, and old needs to have all the ways she is subordinated addressed by ethics and redressed by society.

For feminists, ethics is part of the ongoing effort to uncover and eliminate the sources of social inequality. As Susan Sherwin puts the point, feminist ethics cannot be satisfied just by calculating increases in happiness and invoking moral principles. Rather, it must also ask *whose* happiness is increased and how the principles affect the oppressed as well as the oppressor. In the final analysis, she writes, "Positive moral value attaches to actions or principles that help relieve oppression, and negative value attaches to those that fail to reduce oppression or actually help to strengthen it."

Traditional ethics is among the practices scrutinized by feminist philosophers. As discussed earlier, the concept of individuals as self-directing, or autonomous, is compromised by social realities. Equality is necessary for the exercise of autonomy, and under present conditions, most people are not autonomous. Thus, appealing to the principle of autonomy is more

a way of saying that those who are socially privileged and economically and politically powerful may do as they wish than a way of putting power into the hands of people who are oppressed. People limited by social disadvantages, dependence on others, or responsibility for the care of others are not equal to those who are free of such burdens, and thus lack their autonomy.

Because of the importance feminists attach to social equality, they are concerned with the ways medicine as a social institution tends to subordinate women to men. They point to the fact that most nurses are still female while most physicians are male. Also, some feminists tend to see the "medicalization" of women's reproductive lives—through assisted-reproduction procedures such as in vitro fertilization, hospitalized deliveries by obstetricians, or hormone-replacement therapy at menopause—as ways for men to exercise control over women. Further, some feminists view the techniques of assisted reproduction as a means for powerful males to produce genetically connected offspring at the expense of subordinated females.

Various feminists also question some of society's fundamental assumptions about the value of medicine. For example, some have argued that providing expensive health care for the very sick is not the best way to pursue health. It could be more effectively pursued by the equal distribution of resources like food, shelter, security, and education that help keep people healthy. We could get (as it were) more health by redistributing our resources than we could by treating sick people with expensive drugs, equipment, and expertise.

Feminist Ethics in the Medical Context

Because feminist ethics can't be represented by a set of principles and isn't a unified set of beliefs, it's not likely that particular examples of how feminist doctrines might be put into practice would be accepted as accurate by most feminists. Nevertheless, we can at least suggest in a general way how a few cases might be approached from the perspective of feminist ethics.

Feminist ethics, because of its views about how reproduction and child rearing have been employed to keep women subordinate to men, supports the idea that women must have unfettered access to abortion. Without such access, women cannot control their own lives and are forced to submit to regulation by others. They are therefore in a state of subjection. On the question of when abortions are permissible—whether late-term abortions are acceptable or whether abortions are permitted when contraception has not been used, when it has been used, or only when a rape has occurred—feminist theorists differ. Even on the topic of abortion, not all feminists agree; some argue that the ready availability of abortion deprives women of the strongest support for saying no to male sexual aggression.

Assisted reproduction is another area in which feminists disagree among themselves. Some hold that the new technologies which allow women who would otherwise be infertile (even postmenopausal women) to have a child empower women. Others hold, however, that reproductive technology is dangerous to women and an instrument of male dominance, a way of forcing women to have children. Women who seem to seek out such technology on their own may simply have been misled by our male-dominated society to believe that their choice is free.

A feminist ethics approach to a particular case might involve asking questions about the power relations among those involved. For example, suppose a seventy-two-year-old woman with leukemia is considering whether she should refuse a second course of chemotherapy and wait for death with only home care and no further medical intervention. Feminist ethics would want us to ask (1) whether the attitude of the mostly male hospital staff that an old woman has no useful life is influencing her decision; (2) whether her experience of caring for others is making her reluctant to impose a burden on her daughter or daughter-in-law, whereas an old man might simply feel entitled to care; and (3) whether society's view that an old woman has no function might not result in her thinking of herself in the same way—thus ignoring herself as a repository of wisdom and a link with the past or (assuming that she regains her health) as someone able to exercise her skills in whatever way she sees fit. In sum, from the perspective of feminist ethics, instead of regarding the decision to discontinue treatment as a straightforward matter of exercising autonomy, we are enjoined to look at the hidden factors that may be influencing the woman's decision and making it less than free.

Difficulties with Feminist Ethics

Proponents of traditional ethical theories question whether feminist ethics can be of much use in actual cases in which decisions must be made. What does it mean to promote gender equality when deciding whether life support should be terminated or late-term abortion allowed? How do we go about practical decision making? Even asking a feminist doesn't seem to be of much use, because they differ among themselves on how such questions should be answered.

The multiplicity of feminist views has led some critics to charge that feminist ethics is not a unified and coherent ethical theory in the way that, say, utilitarianism is. Feminists respond that they reject the notion of moral knowledge as essentially theoretical and deny that the role of ethics is to tell us what to do. (Those in power may believe or wish this were so, but that is only because traditional ethics allows them to employ principles to subjugate women.) Rather, ethics is about people, and it has the aim of facilitating their mutual understanding and adjusting the differences among them. Working together, they resolve conflicts and find a solution to their problems.

One problem with this view of ethics is that, like care and virtue ethics, it appears to provide us with no way to resolve moral conflicts. Suppose someone who is HIV positive claims that he has no responsibility to warn sexual partners of his HIV status or to practice safe sex. "It's their lookout," he says. What, from the point of view of feminist ethics, might he be told to persuade him that he has an obligation not to put others at risk of a deadly disease by his behavior? Or what grounds could be offered to support his position? The answer is not clear. And if the approach assumed in these questions (asking for "grounds") is wrong, what is the right approach to resolve the problem of someone's acting in ways that will endanger others needlessly?

A second difficulty of this view of ethics is that it seems to open feminist ethics to the charge of relativism. If ethics is (in Margaret Urban Walker's phrase) "socially embodied" and can facilitate agreement only among those who accept the values of a particular culture, how can feminist ethics criticize the culture? More to the point, even if the culture is one that subjugates women, feminist ethics seems to be committed to going along with its practices and values.

In fact, some cultural practices, such as so-called female circumcision (genital mutilation) in some countries, have divided feminists. Many want to condemn it, but the feminist view of ethics doesn't seem to provide a means for doing so. As with virtue ethics and care ethics, the commitment to doing without principles or rules doesn't seem to offer a way of assessing actions, policies, and practices from the outside.

RETROSPECT

The two major tasks of this chapter have been to provide information about several important ethical theories and to formulate and illustrate several generally accepted moral principles. One aim in performing these tasks was to make it easier to follow the arguments and discussions in this book.

Another, and ultimately more serious, aim has been to call attention to ethical theories and principles you may wish to consider adopting. From this standpoint, the problems and issues raised in the Case Presentations and Social Contexts can be considered tests of the theories and principles. You may find that some of the theories that we have discussed are inadequate to deal with certain moral issues in the medical context, although they may seem satisfactory in more common or simpler cases. Or you may discover that certain commonly accepted moral principles lead to contradictory results or to conclusions that you find difficult to accept. Other theories or principles may appear to give definite and persuasive answers to medical–moral problems, but you may find that they rest on assumptions that it does not appear reasonable to accept. Such a dialectical process of claims and criticism is slow and frustrating. Yet it offers the best hope of settling on theories and principles that we can accept with confidence and employ without misgivings.

During the last quarter century, a great amount of effort has been expended addressing the moral problems of medical practice and research. Without question, progress has been made in developing a better understanding of a number of issues and securing agreement about how they are to be dealt with. Nevertheless, a large number of moral issues in medicine remain unsettled or even unexplored. Even in the absence of moral consensus on these issues, the demands of practical decision making generate a force that presses us for immediate solutions.

In such a situation, we cannot afford to try to settle all doubts about moral principles in an abstract way and only then apply them to problems in medicine. The dialectical process must be made practical. Formulating and testing theories and principles must go on at the same time as we are actually making moral decisions. We must do our best to discover the principles of aerodynamics while staying aloft.

To a considerable extent, that is what this book is about. Bioethics is still an area in which there are more legitimate questions than there are satisfactory answers, but the answers that we do have are better supported and better reasoned than those available even twenty years ago.

Part I

Rights

Chapter 1

Physicians, Patients, and Others: Autonomy, Truth Telling, and Confidentiality

CHAPTER CONTENTS

CASES AND CONTEXTS

CASE PRESENTATION

Donald (Dax) Cowart Rejects Treatment—and Is Ignored

The man stretched out on the steel platform of the sling with his knees drawn up is thin to the point of emaciation. His face and numerous patches of bare, raw flesh are slathered with layers of thick white salve. A pad covers one eye, and the eyelid of the other is sewn shut. Bandages wrapped around his legs and torso give him the look of a mummy in a low-budget horror movie.

In obvious pain, he writhes on the platform. With rock music playing in the background, white-uniformed attendants in gauze masks raise the sling and lower him into a steel tank of clear liquid.

The real horror began for Donald Cowart in July of 1973. The previous May he had left active duty in the Air Force after three years of service, including a tour of duty in Vietnam, to take a slot in the Air Force Reserve. He returned to his family home in east Texas to wait for an opening as a commercial airline pilot. He was twenty-five years old, a college graduate, unmarried, and in excellent health and top physical condition. A high school athlete who had played football and basketball and run track, he had stayed athletic. He played golf, surfed when he could, and rodeoed. As a pilot for a large airline, he'd be busy, but not too busy to continue the active life he was used to. But in 1973 the airlines weren't looking for new pilots,

and while Don waited for them to start hiring again, he decided to join his father as a real estate broker. The two had always been close, so working together was a pleasure for both of them.

And then everything changed forever.

One hot Wednesday afternoon in July, Don and his father drove out to the country to take a look at a piece of land Don thought might be a good buy. They parked the car in a shady, cool spot at a low place in the road beside a bridge. They took a walking tour of the land, but when they returned to the car, it wouldn't start.

Mr. Cowart got out, raised the hood, and tinkered with the carburetor. Don, in the driver's seat, turned the key repeatedly, grinding the engine around so much, he got afraid he would run down the battery. Then after three or four minutes of trying, a blue flame suddenly shot from the carburetor, and a tremendous explosion rocked the car, throwing Don sideways onto the passenger seat. A huge ball of live fire enveloped the car.

Don managed to get the door open; then, still surrounded by fire, he ran three steps toward the woods, the only place that wasn't on fire. But seeing that the undergrowth was so thick that he was likely to get trapped in it and burn to death, he turned away and ran straight down the road. He hurtled through three thick walls of fire, and when he cleared the last one, he threw himself to the ground and rolled to smother the flames.

Getting to his feet, he ran again, shouting for help. He noticed his vision was blurred, as if he were looking at everything from under water, and he realized his eyes had been seared by the fire. *This can't be happening*, he thought as he ran. But the pain assured him that it was. He heard a voice shouting, "I'm coming!" and only then did he stop running and lie down beside the road.

He thought at the time that the car's gas tank had exploded, and only after he had been in a hospital for several days did he learn that the blast and fire were caused by a leak in a propane gas transmission line. Seeping from the line, the gas had collected in the hollow by the bridge, saturating the air to such an extent that the car wouldn't start because the engine couldn't get enough oxygen. The spark from the starter had ignited the gas.

When the farmer who had heard Don's shouts arrived, he said, "Oh, my God." Then Don knew for the first time that he was burned more badly than he had thought. After the farmer came back from looking for Mr. Cowart, Don asked him to get him a gun. "Why?" the man asked.

"Can't you see I'm a dead man?" Don told him. "I'm going to die anyway."

"I can't do that," the farmer said gently.

When the first ambulance arrived, Don sent it to pick up his father. When the second came, he didn't want to go to the hospital. "All I wanted to do was die and to die as quickly as possible," he recalled nine years later. Despite his protest, the attendants put him in the ambulance. He asked them to pick him up by his belt, because his burns were so excruciating he couldn't bear to be touched.

Don and his father were taken to a small nearby hospital, but because of the extent of their injuries, they were soon transported to the burn unit of Parkland Hospital in Dallas, 140 miles away. "I'm sorry, Donny boy," his father told him as they were placed in the ambulance. Mr. Cowart died on the way to Parkland. Don continued to insist that he be allowed to die.

Charles Baxter, Don's attending physician, estimated that Don had extremely deep burns over about sixty-five percent of his body. His face, upper arms, torso, and legs had suffered severe third-degree burns, and both ears were virtually destroyed. His eyes were so damaged that his left eye had to be surgically removed, and he eventually lost

the vision in his right eye. His fingers were burned off down to the second joint, making it impossible for him to pick up anything. The pain was tremendous, and even though he was given substantial doses of narcotics, it remained unbearable for more than a year.

Don's mother had heard about an accidental explosion on the radio, but she learned her husband and son were involved only when the police called her out of an evening church service to tell her. After rushing to Dallas to be with Don, she was approached by his physicians to sign consent forms for surgery and treatment. Knowing nothing about burn therapies, she took the advice offered to her by the physicians. She knew of Don's protest against being treated, but she expected his wish to be allowed to die to pass as soon as he began to recover.

Rex Houston, the family's attorney and close friend, filed a lawsuit with the owners of the propane transmission line for damages resulting from the explosion. He was concerned with going to trial as soon as possible. Don was unmarried and had nobody depending on him, so if he died before the case was heard, the lawsuit would be likely to produce little money. But with Don as a living plaintiff and a young man who had lost the use of both hands and both eyes, the suit had the potential to be of tremendous value. "I had to have a living plaintiff," Houston said years later. Dr. Baxter later said he had discussed the legal and moral aspects of Don's treatment with Mr. Houston.

Don continued to want to die. He asked a nurse with whom he had developed a rapport to give him a drug that would kill him or at least to help him do something to take his own life. As sympathetic as she was, she was forced to refuse his request. Don also asked a family friend to get a gun for him, but then, even while he was asking, he observed that getting him a gun would be pointless, because he had no fingers to pull the trigger.

Dr. Baxter's initial response to Don's request to die was dismissive: "Oh, you don't want to do that," he would say. For a while, though, Don convinced Dr. Baxter he was serious and not simply reacting out of the immediate pain and shock. But eventually Dr. Baxter decided Don talked about wanting to die only to manipulate the people around him and gain control over his environment. Don later rejected this interpretation.

Mrs. Cowart considered her son's medical condition too serious to allow him to make decisions about accepting or rejecting treatment. "Everything was discussed with her in detail," Dr. Baxter recalled. "She was most co-operative and most helpful. We approached the problem of his desire to die very openly." Also, Dr. Baxter remembered, "Even the possibility that it could be allowed was discussed with her. She was never in favor of it, because basically she thought he did not have this desire."

When his burns had healed enough that he was out of danger, Don was moved to the Texas Institute of Rehabilitation in Houston. He agreed to give the program a try, but after about three weeks, he began to refuse treatment again. He had learned that rehabilitation would take years of pain and suffering. The doctors at the Institute honored his request that he not be treated, and in a few days, the burns on his legs became infected again, and the grafted skin peeled away. He came near death.

Dr. Robert Meier, a rehabilitation specialist responsible for Don's care, called a meeting with Don's mother and attorney. They decided that because Don's burns had become infected again due to his refusal to have his dressings changed, he should be hospitalized in an acute care center again.

Don was transferred to the University of Texas Medical Branch at Galveston in April of 1974. Once there, he again refused treatment. Psychiatrist Robert B. White was called in by the surgeons in charge of Don's case, because they thought Don's refusal might be the result of clinical depression or some form of mental illness. If he were found incompetent, a legal guardian could be appointed to give permission for the additional surgery he needed. After examining Don and with the concurrence of a second psychiatrist, Dr. White concluded that Don was fully competent and not suffering from any kind of mental illness. He was, moreover, intelligent, self-aware, and highly articulate.

To control the many infected areas on his body, Don had to be submerged daily in a tank of highly chlorinated water to destroy the microorganisms breeding on the surface of his wounds. The experience was excruciatingly painful, and despite Don's protests and refusals, the "tankings" were carried out anyway. He refused to give his permission for surgery on his hands, which had become more clawlike due to scarring and contracture. Eventually, he consented, with his surgeon's assurance that he would give Don enough drugs to control the pain.

Don wanted to leave the hospital so he could go home and die. But he couldn't leave without help, and neither his physicians nor his mother would agree to

help. His mother wanted him taken care of, and moving him home to die of massive infection was more than she could accept. Don accused her of being responsible for prolonging his hopeless condition.

Surgeon Duane Larson was puzzled by Don's ongoing insistence that he wanted to die. Don wasn't on the verge of death and would surely recover some degree of normalcy. He would find new ways to enjoy life. "In essence he was asking people to participate in his death," Dr. Larson recalled.

One alternative Dr. Larson mentioned to Don was for him to be treated until he was well enough to leave the hospital; then he could kill himself, if he still wanted to. Another alternative was to get Don to see that new things could be done to lessen his pain and make him more comfortable. But Dr. Larson also thought Don might be brought to see that some of his outbursts were merely angry "little boy feelings" anyone would experience after going through such a terrible ordeal.

The tankings were by far the worst treatments. "It was like pouring alcohol on an open wound," Don remembered. Being lifted out of the tank was even worse, because the room was freezing, and every nerve in the damaged parts of his body produced agony. "All I could do was scream at the top of my lungs until I would finally pass out with exhaustion. The tankings took place seven days a week—week after week after week."

"Don't ask us to let you die," Dr. Meier had told Don at the rehabilitation center, "because in a sense what that means is we're killing you. If you want to die, then let me fix your hands, operate on them and open them up so at least you can do something with them, and if you want to commit suicide then, you can. But don't ask us to stand here and literally kill you."

"The argument that not treating a patient is the same as killing borders on the ridiculous," Don said years later. "If letting the patient die is characterized as playing God, then treating the patient to save his life has to be as well. In the final analysis, I was nothing but a hostage to the current state of medical technology." Just a few years earlier he would have died, but the management of burns had advanced sufficiently to keep him alive. He was, he said, "forced to receive treatment," because he was "too weak to resist and unable to walk out on my own." Ironically, as Don later saw the situation, what was happening to him was taking place when the country was emphasizing the importance of individual liberties and freedom of choice by the individual.

Don was treated for ten months. He lost all ten fingers, was blind, and terribly scarred and disfigured. He had to have help with everything and was unable to take care of even his most basic bodily needs. His pain was still constant and he couldn't walk.

Discharged from the hospital, he took up residence in his mother's house. At first he was relieved to be out of the hospital, but in a few weeks he fell into a deep depression. Frustration built up as he experienced his loss of independence, grew bored, and worried about what he was going to do with the rest of his life. Marriage seemed at best a remote possibility.

Because of his disfigurement, he thought about never going out in public, but eventually he began to go to stores and restaurants, protected by his blindness from the stares and reactions of others. Money from the court settlement gave him the financial independence to do what he wanted and was able to do.

Starting law school, he lived with a married couple and learned to do some things for himself. But in the spring of that year, beset by a sleep disturbance and upset by the breakdown of a personal relationship, he tried to kill himself with an overdose of sleeping pills and tranquilizers. He was found in time for him to be taken to the hospital and have his stomach pumped. Despite what Dr. Larson and others had told him while his burns were being treated, he wasn't going to be allowed to kill himself. Don was rehospitalized for depression and insomnia for about a month and eventually returned to law school.

After graduating, Don—who was now called Dax—set up a practice in Corpus Christi. He married Karen, someone he had known in high school, in 1983.

His mother is sure she made the right decision in signing the consent forms for treatment, particularly now that her son's life is filled with the satisfactions of marriage and a job he likes. She wishes she had asked the doctors to give him more pain medication, though. They hadn't told her it was possible.

Dax doesn't blame his mother for her decisions. He blames his doctors for putting her in the position of having to make them. *He* should have been the one asked. "The individual freedom of a competent adult should never be restricted," he says, "except when it conflicts with the freedom of some other individual." For him the individual should be able to decide what minimum quality of life is acceptable to him or her. This is not a decision that should be made by physicians or anyone else on behalf of another person.

Now that Donald Cowart is living a satisfactory life, is he glad his physicians and his mother continued his treatment against his wishes? "I'm enjoying life now, and I'm glad to be alive," Cowart says. "But I still think it was wrong to force me to undergo what I had to, to be alive."

Nor would the assurance of pulling through be enough to make him change his mind. "If the same thing were to occur tomorrow, knowing I could reach this same point, I still would not want to undergo the pain and agony that I had to undergo to be alive now. I should want that choice to lie entirely with myself and not others."

SOCIAL CONTEXT
Autism and Vaccination

Autism spectrum disorders (ASDs) are a group of developmental disabilities. The disorders involve difficulties (often severe) in learning language and in communicating and interacting with others.

Spectrum

The spectrum of disorders is wide, and the behaviors of the people who fall within it can range from withdrawn and passive to highly agitated, violent, and potentially self-destructive. ASDs are often accompanied by abnormalities in cognitive abilities, learning, attention, and sensory processing.

The behavioral symptoms typically appear before a child turns three. Parents may watch their baby develop in expected ways for a period of months or even years, then notice that the child stops making eye contact and seems to lose interest in them and in the surrounding world. These changes in behavior may be signs that the child is no longer following the path of normal development and needs to be evaluated.

The term *spectrum* indicates that a range and variety of behaviors can be considered autistic. Disorders within the spectrum are given specific diagnoses by experts who test the child, observe the child's behavior, and compare it with what might be expected given the child's age. Included in the spectrum are *autistic disorder* (autism), *Asperger syndrome*, and *pervasive developmental disorder—not otherwise specified* (PDD-NOS).

People with Asperger disorder or PDD-NOS have fewer symptoms compared with people with autism, and in terms of language, intelligence, and social skills, they are usually only mildly impaired. In the discussion here, however, unless there is a reason to be more specific, we will use **autism** to refer to the entire autistic disorders spectrum.

Numbers and Facts

The Centers for Disease Control estimates that an average of one out of every 110 children has autism. Given that four million children are born every year in the U.S., about 36,500 a year will be diagnosed with the disorder. If the prevalence has been the same over the last twenty years, about 730,000 people ages 21 or younger can be considered autistic. This means that about thirteen percent of the children in the U.S. have a developmental disability that ranges from mild (language problems) to severe (cognitive difficulties, cerebral palsy, and severe autism).

Generally accepted facts about autism also include the following:

- Males are three to four times more likely than females to be autistic.

- Autism occurs in all races and in all parts of the world.

- A sibling of someone with autism is twenty-five times more likely to be autistic than someone in the general population.

- If one identical twin has autism, the other twin has autism sixty to ninety percent of the time. If one fraternal twin has autism, the other has autism up to twenty-four percent of the time.

- Parents who have a child with autism have a two to eight percent chance of having a second child with autism.

- Families with an autistic child are more likely to have a family member with a neurological disorder or a chromosomal disorder than families in the general population.

- About ten percent of children with autism have an identifiable genetic, neurological, or metabolic disorder. As more is learned about autism, this number is likely to increase.

- About forty-one percent of children with autistic spectrum disorders have an intellectual disability (defined as an IQ of 70 or lower).

- About forty percent of children with autistic spectrum disorders do not talk at all. About thirty percent acquire a few words at age twelve to eighteen months, then lose them.

- Autism is a lifelong disorder that cannot be "cured."

- Lifetime costs to care for a person with autism are $3.2 million.

Causes

The causes of autism are unknown. The disorder almost certainly has a genetic component, but it is not a genetic disease in the way that sickle cell anemia or cystic fibrosis are genetic diseases. Autism, instead of being produced by a single inherited gene, may result from the interaction of a group of genes. Even if this is so, however, some genetically predisposed infants may not develop the disorder, because they don't encounter some unknown environmental factor that acts as a trigger. It may also be possible that there is not "a cause" of autism, but that different sets of conditions may result in behavior that falls within the autism spectrum.

During the 1950s and 1960s, a favorite theory was that autism is the result of psychodynamic processes in the individual. Mothers who are cold and rejecting, those Bruno Bettleheim called "refrigerator mothers," were held to be responsible for producing children who lacked language and empathy and withdrew from the world. No one accepts such a view today.

Increase In Autism?

Before the 1980s, the term *autism* was used in a rigorous way to diagnose behavior now considered limited to the *autistic disorder* part of the ASD spectrum. The disorder was a rare diagnosis, and only 0.5 percent of children (10 in 2,000) received it.

Autism is now only one of three disorders in the ASD spectrum. Applying the diagnostic criteria in use since the 1990s, 0.7 percent of children (7 in 1000) are estimated to have an autism spectrum disorder. These estimates are about ten times higher than those relying on the older diagnostic criteria.

Some recent evidence based on studies of particular populations shows that more than 1 percent of the children in the U.S., Japan, Sweden, and the United Kingdom have one of the disorders in the spectrum. (A study in Norway found that 2.7 percent of the children in the population had symptoms of autism.)

Most scientists don't think the increase in the number of *reported cases* of autism represents a genuine increase in the number of *actual cases* of autism. Rather, the change in diagnostic criteria and social factors may account for the amazing increase in the number of reported cases. For example, (1) once we might have considered a child a little odd, but now we classify him as autistic; (2) the old criteria classified only "low-functioning" children as autistic, but now "high-functioning" children are also included in the category; (3) physicians are now sensitive to the need to look for early signs of autism, so overdiagnose it; (4) parents are more attentive to their children and more medically

sophisticated, and to satisfy them, pediatricians diagnose as autism cases they would not have a decade earlier; (5) the rise in special-education and social-benefit programs gives parents and school districts an incentive to pressure pediatricians to give children with difficulties a diagnosis of autism.

All these factors may be responsible for some of the increase in the number of *reports* of autism. No one doubts that autism is a real disorder, or that cases of autism are picked up now that once would have been missed. Nor does anyone doubt the need to find ways to reduce the occurrence of autism. It seems doubtful, however, that the occurrence of autism is on the rise. That is, the disorder does not appear to have increased in frequency in the population.

Vaccines and Autism: First Shot

A crucial assumption of those who believe that vaccines cause autism is that the rise in the number of reported cases represents the rise in actual cases. An increase in the use of vaccines has been paralleled by an increase in cases of autism, so proponents of this view argue that the vaccines are responsible for the autism.

The debate started in 1998 with observations about the MMR vaccine—a combination of vaccines to protect children against the viral diseases measles, mumps, and rubella (German measles)—and autistic symptoms.

Pediatrician Andrew Wakefield and his collaborators published a paper that year in *The Lancet* in which they reported that a dozen children in London's Royal Free Hospital who had intestinal symptoms (pain, bloating, and inflammation) also displayed autism-like symptoms. Furthermore, eight of the twelve had started displaying autistic symptoms within days of being injected with the MMR vaccine.

The paper did not claim that the MMR vaccine was the cause of autism. The authors suggested, however, that the exposure to the measles virus in the vaccine might have been a contributing factor. Later, Wakefield, speaking only for himself, expressed the view that the virus in the vaccine might cause inflammation in the gut and the inflammation might affect brain development. Thus, the MMR vaccine would be the initiating event in the causal chain leading to autism.

Thimerosal

As writer Alice Park points out, parents of autistic children had already been primed to suspect vaccines might cause autism. Beginning in the 1930s, a mercury compound called thimerosal was used in vaccines as a preservative to keep molds and bacteria from growing in them. That mercury and other heavy metals can cause brain damage was already a familiar fact. It was also understood that children are particularly susceptible to damage from heavy metals because their brains are still undergoing development.

It made intuitive sense to many people that thimerosal was responsible for autism. Not only was the substance known to destroy brain tissue, but the timing was right. Children are given several vaccines by their second year, and it is around this time that the first symptoms of autism typically appear. Thus, it seems that a vaccine causes brain damage, which produces the symptoms of autism.

As obvious as this conclusion may appear, it is the result of fallacious post-hoc reasoning. That the symptoms of autism appear after vaccinations does not prove that vaccines cause the symptoms. (After you put on your winter coat, the geese fly south, but putting on your coat doesn't make them fly south.) Evidence of a different kind is needed.

This evidence seemed to be at hand in 2001 when the FDA released the results of a study showing that six-month-old children who received all five of their recommended vaccinations were being given twice the amount of mercury the Environmental Protection Agency considered safe for people who eat fish as a regular part of their diet. Prompted by this startling finding, the FDA and vaccine makers went into overdrive, and by the end of 2001,

thimerosal-free versions of all five vaccines were available for use. These included DPT (diphtheria, pertussis, and tetanus), hepatitis-B, and HiB (*Haemophilus influenzae*, type B). The thimerosal content dropped from a total of 187.5 micrograms to no more than trace amounts. Thus, six-month-old babies who received all five of the recommended vaccinations would have virtually no exposure to thimerosal.

Proponents of what had become known as the "vaccine hypothesis" expected the rates of autism to drop dramatically: no thimerosal, no autism. But the opposite happened. The rate of autism has *increased* since thimerosal was removed from vaccines, so that its occurrence among eight-year-olds (those vaccinated after 2001) is one in 150.

In 2003, the Centers for Disease Control and the National Institutes of Health assembled a panel to review and evaluate the scientific literature concerning the connection between thimerosal and autistic symptoms. The panel concluded that there was no evidence to support such a link. Furthermore, the panel noted that it did not consider the use of more resources to investigate the possibility of such a link a wise investment. Instead, the panel held, the money should be spent on investigating the genetics and developmental biology of the disease.

The National Institute of Medicine also conducted a scientific review of the potential connection between thimerosal and autism. Its conclusion was that "The evidence favors rejection of a causal relationship between thimerosal-containing vaccines and autism." The CDC endorsed this conclusion.

MMR Vaccine

What about the claim made by Wakefield and his collaborators that the MMR vaccine may be responsible for triggering inflammatory processes in the gut that result in autism? In 2004, ten of Wakefield's thirteen collaborators published a retraction of their paper in *The*

Lancet, stating that their evidence was not adequate to support such a claim.

Wakefield himself was said to have an undisclosed conflict of interest connected with his plans to market another measles vaccine, something he could not do with much hope of success so long as the MMR vaccine was standard. A 1993 paper by Wakefield on the role of the measles virus in causing autism reported results that could not be reproduced, and a 2002 study on the same topic has been criticized as being poorly designed.

In 2010, after years of investigation, the British General Medical Council concluded that in gathering data used in the original 1998 *Lancet* paper, Wakefield violated ethical principles. He had subjected eleven children to invasive tests such as lumbar punctures and colonoscopies that were irrelevant to their treatment, and he performed these tests without informed consent. Wakefield had shown, the panel said, a "callous disregard" for the suffering of the children involved in his research. After the release of the panel's report, *The Lancet* retracted the 1998 paper that had connected vaccines with autism.

Since the initial suggestion was made in the 1998 Wakefield paper, at least twenty-five studies have been conducted to explore the connection between the MMR vaccine and the development of autism. None of the studies, all published in peer-reviewed scientific journals, has established such a link. The scientific community has rejected the MMR vaccine as a causal factor responsible for autism just as decisively as it has rejected the link between thimerosal and autism.

Court Rulings

The scientific findings have formed the basis for court decisions involving vaccines and claims of harm. In 2002, the U.S. Court of Federal Claims combined the cases of 5,000 families with autistic children seeking compensation from the federal Vaccine Injury Compensation Trust Fund. The fund, which is supported by a 75-cent tax on vaccines, was established to deal with death and injury claims alleged to be connected with vaccines administered after October 1, 1988. Families with children who can be shown to have died or been injured by the vaccines receive compensation from the fund, in exchange for surrendering their right to sue the vaccine manufacturers.

The Omnibus Autism Proceedings began in 2002 with a court composed of three judges acting as Special Masters. (Special Masters are civil court officers appointed because of their expertise in areas relevant to issues about which the courts must decide.) The court heard nine cases based on three different theories about the causes of autism.

In three separate cases decided in March 2010, the Masters all ruled that thimerosal did not cause autism in the children whose families made claims for compensation. One Master found it "extremely unlikely" that vaccines caused autism in the cases under consideration, and another expressed the view that many parents "relied upon practitioners and researchers who peddled hope, not opinions grounded in science and medicine." In three earlier cases decided in February 2009, the Special Masters had made the same rulings, and their decisions had been upheld on appeal.

The Coalition for Vaccine Safety, an organization that claims to represent 75,000 families, was scornful of the decisions. "The deck is stacked against families in vaccine court," said a member of the group's steering committee. "Government attorneys defend a government program using government-funded science before government judges. Where's the justice in that?"

The opposite view was expressed by Paul Offit, who developed a rotavirus vaccine from which he receives royalties. The hypothesis that vaccines cause autism "has already had its day in scientific court," he said. "But in America we like to have our day in literal court. Fortunately, we now have these rulings."

"Vaccines Weaken the Immune System"

Perhaps because the rise in the number of reported cases of autism has been paralleled by an increase in the number of vaccinations children receive, some parents cannot believe vaccines are not in some way responsible for the disorder.

The idea behind any vaccine is that injected antigens (proteins) will trigger the immune response. The immune system will turn out antibodies against the antigen, and should the immune system encounter the antigen again (be exposed to a virus, for example), the pre-existing antibodies will respond immediately. Vaccines build up the body's immunity to the antigens.

The most recent form of the vaccine hypothesis is that the proteins in vaccines damage the immune system. Current recommendations are that babies be inoculated against as many as fifteen diseases and get twenty-eight vaccinations before they are six months old. Thus, vaccine critics claim, the number of antigens in the vaccines overwhelm the child's immune system, and this results in whatever brain changes may be responsible for autism.

This hypothesis is supported by no more evidence than that the number of vaccines given to infants has increased. This is, again, an instance of post-hoc reasoning. Besides, the idea of an immune-system overload is not one with any scientific validity. Indeed, its very meaning is unclear.

Perhaps the more important flaw in the hypothesis is that it rests on the mistaken assumption that the increase in the number of vaccines has meant an increase in the number of antigens to which an infant is exposed. The original smallpox vaccine given to people now ages 30 years or older when they were infants contained 200 different antigens, and it did not cause a rise in autism cases. By contrast with the smallpox vaccine the total number of antigens in all fifteen of the standard vaccines is only 150. Scientists are now able to identify just those proteins (antigens) that trigger the immune response and provide immunity from the disease.

Finally, critics of the protein-overload hypothesis point out that infants are exposed to thousands of new proteins every day. They eat new foods, breathe in dust, and are exposed to pollen, dirt, and cat dander. There is no obvious reason why exposing them to additional antigens should trigger some process leading to autism.

Vaccines Can Harm

Human biology is amazingly complex, and individuals vary widely in multiple subtle ways. Some infants are born with a genetic predisposition to react badly to gluten in their diet, but gluten allergies are comparatively rare. It should be no surprise, though, that some infants may have a genetic predisposition to react badly to some of the substances in vaccines.

In 2008 a Georgia girl with a preexisting cellular disease developed a severe allergic reaction to the vaccines she received as an infant and later developed autism-like symptoms. She is the first, and so far the only, case in which it is plausible to say that the vaccines caused autism.

The case shows that in rare instances vaccines can cause harm of the sort that defenders of the vaccine hypothesis fear. Rare cases are important for prompting additional scientific inquiry, but they don't prove that all or even a significant number of cases of autism can be ascribed to vaccines. Rare cases should certainly not become the basis for rewriting public health policies.

Protection

The traditional childhood diseases of diphtheria, whooping cough (pertussis), polio, measles, rubella, and mumps are now rare in developed countries. Yet, hardly more than a generation ago these diseases, which now seem as exotic to most people as the bubonic plague, were common in almost every American household. All are serious diseases that cause not only suffering, but death, among infants and children.

(To get a sense of how dangerous the diseases still are, consider that in 2008 (the most recent figures), 164,000 people died—eighteen every hour—from measles alone. Nearly all deaths were in children under five in countries in which children are not routinely vaccinated.)

The importance of immunization to individuals is obvious, but having such a high percentage immunized has a general benefit as well. Newborn infants and people (including children) who have compromised immune systems because of certain illnesses (e.g., HIV infection) or treatments (e.g., chemotherapy) cannot be vaccinated because of the harm it would cause them. They depend on the immunity of those around them to protect them.

The greater the percentage of people in a population who are immunized against a given disease, the less likely it is that an infectious agent will establish itself within the population and threaten the lives of those who are most vulnerable. This phenomenon is known to immunologists as *herd immunity.*

Herd Immunity

Herd immunity serves as a barrier to protect a population from the ravages of infectious diseases. The higher the percentage of people inoculated, the stronger the barrier. When the percentage starts to decline, the barrier grows weaker and more porous. Those who are most susceptible to the disease have a greater likelihood of becoming its victims.

The story of what happened with polio in Nigeria in 2001–2007 is a prime example of what occurs when the barrier weakens. In 2001, some sixty-six people in Nigeria died most likely because of the live (although weakened) virus they received in the oral polio vaccine during a vaccination campaign. These deaths convinced the country's Muslim and political leaders that the planned campaign to eradicate polio in Nigeria was actually a Western

attempt to sterilize Muslims. The campaign was cancelled, and Nigerian children were unprotected against the virus.

The rate of polio infection in Nigeria afterward increased by a factor of 30. Because viruses don't recognize political boundaries, the outbreak of polio in Nigeria spread to a dozen other countries. Some had previously been free of the disease. The breakdown of Nigeria's herd immunity led to a significant loss of life, an increase in suffering, and lifelong disability for thousands of people.

Public health officials in the U.S. have long recognized the importance of herd immunity to the well-being of the country, and it has not been left to voluntary decisions by individuals. All states have laws requiring that children be vaccinated before they are enrolled in school, and more than seventy-seven percent of children are immunized by their first day. The rewards are obvious. The CDC estimates that vaccinating all U.S. children born in a given year from birth to adolescence saves 33,000 lives, prevents fourteen million infections, and saves $10 billion in medical costs.

The laws requiring vaccination are not ironclad, however. Physicians can issue waivers for children with compromised immune systems, and in forty-eight states, when parents object to vaccination on religious grounds, those states grant their children waivers. At least twenty states permit parents to seek waivers on personal philosophical grounds. In all, about six percent of U.S. children enter school unvaccinated on a waiver of some sort: one percent medical and five percent religious or "philosophical."

Parents who believe that vaccines are likely to cause harm to their children are responsible for the decline in the inoculation rate during recent years. Quite often, their fear is based on the belief that vaccines are responsible for an increase in autism. (They are not persuaded that only the *reports* of autism have increased, not actual cases.) Hence, they believe their children should not be vaccinated and that other parents should not be required to vaccinate their children either.

Parents who decide not to vaccinate their child must depend on herd immunity for their child's protection. Sometimes, however, this defense fails disastrously. Alice Park reported in *Time* (May 21, 2008) the case of Kelly Lacek, who decided to stop vaccinating her two-month-old son Matthew when her chiropractor expressed doubts about the safety of thimerosal vaccines.

All was well until Matthew turned three. Lacek returned home to find him suffering from a high fever and gasping for breath. Physicians at the ER were puzzled, until one experienced physician asked Lacek if Matthew had been fully vaccinated.

Matthew was infected with *Haemophilius-b*, a bacterium that produces fever and a swelling of the tissues of the throat, which makes breathing difficult. Hib also causes meningitis, a brain infection that, untreated, can lead to death. Matthew survived, and his mother made sure that he and his siblings received all recommended immunizations.

Parents' Perception of Best Interest

Parents, with rare exceptions, want to do what is in the best interest of their child. We have no reason to believe that parents who refuse to vaccinate their children on the basis of their beliefs about the risk posed by vaccines or their religious beliefs are acting in bad faith. They believe they are entitled to make decisions about the welfare of their child and that it is violation of their right for the state to order them to take measures they believe are wrong.

This is a view ordinarily supported by the society. We leave it up to parents to decide how much time their children spend online, whether they get the shoes they want, and whether they have to eat their spinach. We expect parents to follow the "best interest" principle in making decisions about children, and we usually allow parents to exercise their judgment about what counts as their child's best interest.

The view becomes problematic, however, when the beliefs of the parents conflict with standards generally accepted within the society. If parents believe, for example, that their child will not die if they recite a certain incantation while plunging a knife into his chest, we try to prevent that from happening. The parents may not be mentally ill, but their beliefs cannot be justified in terms of accepted standards of evidence, and the society has an obligation to protect the child.

The situation becomes especially vexed when the religious beliefs of the parents are shared by a significant number of people, yet those beliefs are at odds with what society believes to be in the best interest of the child. These conflicts occur, for the most part, with respect to not seeking medical treatment for an ailing child. Although we support religious freedom, we also support the view that a child's best interest should be served according to society's accepted standards. Hence, such conflicts will continue to arise in our society, unless we decide that one should always take precedence over the other. The issue has been long debated, but it is not yet resolved.

Another sort of problem arises when the decisions of parents affect the welfare of the society. This is what happens when parents refuse to have their children immunized. The drop in the rate of immunizations, as in the example of Nigeria, weakens herd immunity and, as a consequence, the barrier between infectious diseases and the most vulnerable population in the society—the youngest, the oldest, and many of the sickest. Not having one's child immunized thus has a consequence for others, as well as for the child.

Various outbreaks of infectious diseases in the U.S. in recent years can be attributed to the lack of immunization. Four states have already experienced measles outbreaks that can be traced to unvaccinated children. The more parents refuse to vaccinate their children, the more likely it is that there will be an increase in the number of cases of infectious diseases. This means more death, suffering, and disability that could have been avoided.

Whose Choice?

Should parents be free to decide whether vaccinations are in the best interest of their children? This may be a case in which parents who reject vaccination for their children are not acting in their child's best interest, judged by the accepted standards (scientific and medical) of society. Further, such parents are not only putting their own child at risk; they are also putting others in the society at risk.

In 1905, the U.S. Supreme Court, in *Jacobson vs. Massachusetts*, addressed the issue of whether the state's requirement that everyone be vaccinated for smallpox violated Jacobson's "inherent right" to "care for his own body and health in such way as seems to him best." The Court pointed out that, in general, the state has the right to impose burdens and restraints on citizens for the good of all. Jacobson, the Court ruled, could not expect to enjoy the benefits of living in a community in which people have been vaccinated without accepting the risks of vaccination himself. What's more, even if some scientists questioned the efficacy of vaccination, the legislature had the right to adopt and enforce one of the competing scientific views.

With respect to beliefs about vaccination and autism, we are in a situation similar to that in the Jacobson case: If we prize the right of parents to make decisions about their child on the basis of their beliefs about the child's best interest, then we must pay a double price. We must accept that, on the basis of the knowledge we have, the child will run a serious risk of dying from an infectious disease that could have been prevented. We must also accept that the herd immunity protecting us from a number of diseases will be reduced. Thus, other people are also likely to die.

* * *

On March 1, 2010, the journal *Pediatrics* reported the results of a survey of 1500 parents of children ages 17 or younger. Despite all evidence to the contrary, one out of four parents say they think some vaccines cause autism in healthy children. Nearly one in eight have refused at least one recommended vaccination.

The controversy over vaccination will continue, but the debate will not be over science. The scientific evidence is now sufficient to show that there is no causal link between autism and vaccinations. The debate will be about how we as a society should deal with parents who believe that the causal link is real and don't want their child to be vaccinated.

CASE PRESENTATION
Suffer the Little Children?

Eleven-year-old Kara Neumann began to feel tired and sick, then became progressively weaker. She lost her ability to walk, and eventually she could no longer speak. "Kara laid down and was unable to move her mouth," the police report later said, " and merely made moaning sounds and moved her eyes back and forth."

Kara's parents, Lelani and Dale Neumann, were worried about their daughter and prayed for her recovery. They did not call a doctor or take Kara to a hospital ER for treatment, though. The Neumanns were adherents of the doctrines of an online faith outreach organization called Unleavened Bread Ministries. The group's website presents stories of healing through faith and prayer alone. According to the testimonies, all diseases, whether of people or animals, can be cured by prayer and divine intervention. "Jesus never sent anyone to a doctor or hospital," says an essay by "Pastor Bob" posted on the site and quoted by reporter Dirk Johnson. "Jesus offered healing by one means only! Healing was by faith."

Kara's aunt in California did not share the Neumann's belief that faith and prayer could cure their daughter. When she learned from them how sick Kara was and that they intended to do no more than pray for her, she phoned the sheriff's department in Kara's hometown of

Wenton, Wisconsin, and implored them to intervene and save Kara's life. The department dispatched an ambulance to the Neumanns' house, and Kara was rushed to the nearest hospital. Kara was pronounced DOA—dead on arrival.

She died from ketoacidosis, the result of her undiagnosed and untreated Type I (juvenile-onset) diabetes. The islet cells in her pancreas had failed to produce the hormone insulin in sufficient quantities, and as a result, glucose couldn't enter muscle cells to be converted into energy. Needing energy, her body then began to break down fats, producing toxic fatty acids known as ketones. Ketoacidosis is characterized by severe dehydration and nausea, followed by the impairment of muscle, lung, and heart function. The last stage is irreversible coma and death.

Thousands of children each year are diagnosed with Type I diabetes, and the overwhelming majority are successfully treated with diet, exercise, and insulin injections. Kara was examined by a doctor when she was three, but that had been her last visit. Her death could have been prevented by appropriate medical care.

Number of Cases

Rita Swan, director of Children's Health Care is a Legal Duty, estimates that in the last twenty-five years about 300 children have died because their parents refused to get medical treatment for them for religious reasons. (Swan's own sixteen-month-old son died after she failed to take him to be treated for what turned out to be meningitis. This led her to renounce her Christian Science religion and become an advocate for children's health care.) Nearly all states, forty-four by some estimates, thirty according to Swan's group, have laws that permit parents who believe in healing by faith or in the unreality of disease to withhold medical treatment from their children.

No year passes without a case in which a child dies or is put at serious risk of death because parents reject standard medical treatments in favor of prayer or some religious ceremony based on faith. In May of 2009, for example, Colleen Hauser fled her home in New Ulm, Minnesota, with her son Daniel so that Daniel wouldn't have to submit to court-ordered chemotherapy for Hodgkin's lymphoma. Daniel had a cancerous tumor in his chest likely to be fatal without the standard treatment, but Colleen Hauser and her husband wanted Daniel to have natural healing treatments based on American Indian

traditions. A warrant was issued for Ms. Hauser's arrest, but she eventually returned home and agreed to allow Daniel to be treated at a Minneapolis hospital.

In 2008, two sets of parents in Oregon refused to get medical care for their children on religious grounds, and both children died. One couple was charged with manslaughter in the death of their fifteen-month-old daughter who died of pneumonia. The other couple was charged with criminally negligent homicide when their fifteen-year-old son died a painful death from a urinary tract infection. Both children had diseases that were easily treated, and both most likely would have made a full recovery.

Each time a child dies because of the parent's religious beliefs and the case becomes public, lawyers, physicians, and ethicists talk about the need to change the laws to protect children. This has not happened yet, but it seemed most likely to happen as a response to events in the case of Robyn Twitchell. The Twitchells were educated and middle class, unlike many of the parents whose religious beliefs lead them to avoid getting medical help for their children.

The Death of Robyn Twitchell

Two-year-old Robyn Twitchell ate very little for dinner on April 3. Then, shortly after eating, he began to cry. The crying was soon replaced by vomiting and screaming. Robyn lived in Boston, the city where the Christian Science religion was founded, and both his parents, David and Ginger Twitchell, were devout Christian Scientists. The tenets of the religion hold that disease has no physical being or reality but, rather, is the absence of being. Because God is complete being, disease is an indication of the absence of God, of being away from God. Healing must be mental and spiritual, for it consists in bringing someone back to God, of breaking down the fears, misperceptions, and disordered thinking that stand in the way of having the proper relationship with God. When someone is ill, the person may need help getting to the root cause of the estrangement from God. The role of a Christian Science practitioner is to employ teaching, discussion, and prayer to assist someone suffering from an illness to discover its spiritual source.

Acting on the basis of their beliefs, the Twitchells called in Nancy Calkins, a Christian Science practitioner, to help Robyn. She prayed for Robyn and sang hymns, and, although she visited him three times during the next five days, he showed no signs of getting better. A Christian Scientist nurse was brought in to help feed and bathe Robyn, and on her chart she described him as "listless at times, rejecting all food, and moaning in pain" and "vomiting." On April 8, 1986, Robyn began to have spasms, and his eyes rolled up into his head. He finally lost consciousness, and that evening he died.

Robyn was found to have died of a bowel obstruction that could have been treated by medicine and surgery. Medical experts were sure that he wouldn't have died had his parents sought medical attention for him.

Manslaughter Charges

David and Ginger Twitchell were charged with involuntary manslaughter. In a trial lasting two months, the prosecution and defense both claimed rights had been violated. The Twitchells' attorneys appealed, in particular, to the First Amendment guarantee of the free exercise of religion and claimed that the state was attempting to deny it to them.

Prosecutors responded by pointing out that courts have repeatedly held that not all religious practices are protected. Laws against polygamy and laws requiring vaccinations or blood transfusions for minors, for example, have all been held to be constitutional.

The prosecutors also claimed that Robyn's rights had been violated by his parents' failure to seek care for him as required by law. They also cited the 1923 Supreme Court ruling in *Prince v. Massachusetts,* which held that "Parents may be free to become martyrs of themselves, but it does not follow they are free to make martyrs of their children."

Guilty

The Jury found the Twitchells guilty of the charge, and the judge sentenced them to ten years' probation. John Kiernan, the prosecutor, had not recommended a jail sentence. "The intent of our recommendation was to protect the other Twitchell children." Judge Sandra Hamlin instructed the Twitchells that they must seek medical care for their three children if they showed signs of needing it, and they must take the children to a physician for regular checkups.

"This has been a prosecution against our faith," David Twitchell said. Although, speaking of Robyn, at one point he also said, most sadly, "If medicine could have saved him, I wish I had turned to it."

The prosecutor called the decision "a victory for children." However, Stephen Lyons, one of the defense attorneys, said it was wrong to "substitute the imperfect and flawed judgment of medicine for the judgment of a parent." A spokesman for the Christian Science church said it was not possible to combine spiritual and medical healing as the ruling required. "They're trying to prosecute out of existence this method of treatment," he said.

During the last several years a number of children have died because religious beliefs kept their parents from getting them necessary medical care. Christian Science parents have been convicted of involuntary manslaughter, felony child abuse, or child endangerment in California, Arizona, and Florida.

The Twitchell case was one of several initially successful prosecutions. The case directly challenged the First Church of Christ Scientist (the official name of the church) in the city where it was founded and has its headquarters, and the church recognized the challenge and helped in providing leading attorneys to defend the case. "The message has been sent," John Kiernan said after the Twitchells were sentenced. "Every parent of whatever religious belief or persuasion is obligated to include medical care in taking care of his child."

Appeal

The Twitchells' attorneys immediately announced they would appeal the decision on the grounds that the ruling rested on the judge's misinterpretation of a Massachusetts child-neglect law, which explicitly exempts those who believe in spiritual healing. Because of this, legal authorities considered it possible that the Twitchell decision would be overturned on appeal.

A spiritual-healing exemption is found in similar laws in almost all states. Such exclusions make it difficult to successfully prosecute Christian Scientists or others on the grounds of child neglect. The American Academy of Pediatrics is one of several groups that have campaigned to eliminate the exceptions from child-protection laws, but so far only South Dakota has actually changed its laws.

Despite legal exemptions, parents belonging to religious groups like the Church of the First Born, Faith Assembly, and True Followers of Christ have been convicted and imprisoned for failing to provide their children with medical care. However, so far no Christian Scientist has gone to jail. When a Christian Scientist has been convicted, the sentence has been suspended or has involved probation or community service and the promise to seek medical care for their children in the future.

Critics claim Christian Scientists have been treated more leniently than members of more fundamentalist groups, because a high proportion of church members are middle to upper-middle class and occupy influential positions in business, government, and the law. They also suggest that the legal exceptions for spiritual healing in child-protection laws are there because of the influence of the Christian Science church and its members.

Some legal observers initially believed that the Twitchell case would spur wider and more intense efforts to eliminate the spiritual-healing exception, and groups representing the rights of children consider such a change to be long overdue. However, the Twitchell conviction was overturned on appeal in 1993, and it did not turn out to have the impact on the law many hoped it would.

Neumann Sentences

Lelani and Dale Neumann were convicted of second-degree reckless homicide in August 2009. In October, they were ordered to do thirty days in jail each year for the next six years and were placed on ten years' probation. For the crime of which they were convicted, the Neumanns could have received a maximum prison term of twenty-five years. The prosecutor in their case had asked for a three-year sentence.

The Neumanns' attorney announced that he would appeal their conviction, on the grounds that the state law is not clear on the issue of using spiritual means to treat children. Perhaps the Neumanns, like the Twitchells, will have their convictions overturned.

If so, it will fall into a familiar pattern. Since 1982, at least fifty convictions have been handed down by courts in cases in which children have died because medical care was withheld for religious reasons. The convictions usually have been overturned on appeal. Almost no one has done jail time, and those who have are people who, like the Neumanns, belong to fringe religions groups.

In our society, except in exceptional cases, the religious beliefs of parents continue to take precedence over the medical welfare of their children.

SOCIAL CONTEXT
The HPV Vaccine: Hope or Hype?

HPV—human papillomavirus—is the world's most common sexually transmitted infection. Some twenty millions Americans are infected with HPV at any given time, and almost seven million new infections occur every year. Nearly eighty percent of all sexually active women and men are infected at some time during their lives.

HPV is transmitted through genital contact. Most often this is through vaginal and anal sex, but transmission through genital-to-genital contact or oral sex is also possible. The majority of HPV infections cause no symptoms, and the virus can be present and undetected for years. Most people who are infected don't know it, so they don't realize they are transmitting the virus to a sexual partner.

HPV infections are most often eventually eliminated by the body's immune system. More than 100 strains of the virus have been identified, and some of them cause genital warts in both males and females. At least sixteen strains cause cervical cancer, as well as cancers of the vulva, vagina, penis, anus, and head and neck (including the tongue, tonsils, and throat).

Cervical Cancer

Cervical cancer is the most common of the cancers caused by HPV. (The cervix is the opening at the end of the uterus.) Each year in the U.S., about 12,000 women are diagnosed with cervical cancer, and about 4000 die from the disease. However, this represents only a small fraction of women who are infected with HPV. Very little is known about the links between an HPV infection in a young woman and the development of cervical cancer decades later. No one can now predict which woman infected with HPV will develop cervical cancer or explain why some develop it and others do not.

Cervical cancer rates in the U.S. have decreased because of the widespread use of the Papanicolaou test ("Pap smear"). The test consists of a microscopic examination of cells from the cervix so that precancerous changes can be detected and surgery performed before the changed cells become cancerous and life threatening. Cervical cancer usually doesn't have symptoms until it is very advanced. Thus, in countries where the Pap test is not routinely performed, the death rate due to cervical cancer is considerably higher. According to the World Health Organization, 470,000 women are diagnosed each year with cervical cancer and 233,000 die from the disease.

Gardasil

Two strains of HPV (6 and 11) are known to cause seventy percent of all cervical cancers, and two other strains (16 and 18) are known to cause ninety percent of all genital warts. In March 2007 the pharmaceutical company Merck announced the availability of a new FDA-approved vaccine called Gardasil that is effective against these four strains. Gardasil doesn't work once someone becomes infected with the viruses, but the vaccine is highly effective in preventing infection.

The vaccine is produced by using recombinant techniques to splice the DNA that encodes L1 into the genetic material of yeast cells. L1 is the major protein forming the capsule around the virus. The yeast cells produce virus like particles that contain L1. The particles don't cause an HPV infection, but they trigger the immune system to produce antibodies against it.

Vaccination

Vaccinating women with Gardasil before they are infected with HPV would in theory,

eliminate up to seventy percent of the cases of cervical cancer. This would mean preventing as many as 84,000 cases a year and saving the lives of almost 3000 women. Cervical cancer caused by other strains of the HPV virus would not be prevented by vaccination, so even women who were vaccinated would need to continue to have a regular Pap test.

HPV is sexually transmitted, so the obvious way to reduce the incidence of infection and reduce the occurrence of cervical cancer would be to vaccinate girls and women before they are likely to become sexually active. This was the position taken by the Centers for Disease Control's Advisory Committee on Immunization Practices. Reviewing the research conducted to gain FDA approval, the committee concluded that, on the basis of the evidence available, Gardasil was safe for use in girls and women nine to twenty-six years old.

The committee recommended that girls be vaccinated between ages 11 and 12. Because Gardasil had just become available, the committee also recommended that females ages 13 to 26 be vaccinated. The reasoning was that, although older females may have been sexually active, they may have escaped infection by the HPV strains the vaccine can prevent. Thus, vaccination might benefit them.

The vaccine, to be effective, requires three injections given six-months apart. The costs amount to $300–$400, and the vaccine is considered to be effective for five to seven years. The side effects are ordinarily nothing more than temporary pain and soreness at the site of the injection (usually the arm), but some people experience headache, fever, nausea, dizziness, or vomiting. Some receiving the vaccine fainted. The number of serious adverse events reported from the clinical trails of the vaccine were not enough for the FDA to withhold its approval.

Require HPV Vaccination?

The advent of Gardasil was treated by the national media as a major medical story. The possibility of reducing the occurrence of a potentially deadly form of cancer by a significant percentage was regarded as important news, and medical experts and ethicists were interviewed about the impact the vaccine would likely have on the disease and society.

Vaccination with Gardasil to reduce the chance of HPV infection became the topic of a national debate. Should the CDC recommendation be followed and girls ages 11 to 12 vaccinated? Wouldn't it make more sense to wait until someone became sexually active? Should vaccination be required? Should boys be vaccinated also? Was the vaccine sufficiently safe? Shouldn't parents be the ones to make the decision about when their daughters are vaccinated?

The underlying theme of most discussions about the use of the vaccine was that, because it has the potential to prevent cancer, it should be used. Either parents ought to encourage their daughter to be vaccinated, or school systems ought to require vaccinations.

Governor Rick Perry of Texas was among the first officials to act. In April 2007, he issued an executive order requiring that sixth-grade girls be vaccinated with Gardasil by the start of the next school year. Parents, acting on behalf of their daughters, would be able to opt out of the vaccination program. "The governor believes we should protect as many young women as possible—rich and poor, insured and uninsured—while maintaining parent's rights to opt their daughters out of receiving the vaccine," a representative of Governor Perry said in a statement.

Texas would have become the first state to comply with the CDC recommendation, but the governor's order met with immediate criticism and eventual legislative action. In April 2007, in a 135–2 vote, the legislature barred the vaccination policy from going into effect until 2011. By then, it might be reviewed by the legislature and set aside.

Critics of Governor Perry claimed he had abused his executive authority in ordering the vaccinations. The legislative process should

have been followed and the issues debated and voted on. Moreover, Merck was represented in the state capital by the lobbyist Mike Toomey. Toomey had also been the chief of staff for Governor Perry from 2002 to 2004, so some legislators suspected that Perry's action may have been prompted by something more than the wish to protect the health of the women of Texas. This suspicion was reinforced by the fact that, at the time, Merck was lobbying state legislatures around the country to adopt policies requiring vaccinations with Gardasil.

Texas was not the only state with a governor who thought it was important to mandate that sixth-grade girls be vaccinated with Gardisil. Timothy M. Kaine of Virginia stated that he would sign the vaccination bill that had been submitted to him, and the state budget would include $4 million to help make sure that girls from low-income families got the vaccine. In addition, Governor Bill Richardson of New Mexico promised to sign the HPV-vaccine bill that had already been approved by the state legislature. The New Mexico legislation, like the Texas proposal, included a clause allowing parents to opt out on behalf of their children. Eventually, however, the governor vetoed the bill.

A number of other states considered implementing the CDC's Immunization Advisory Committee recommendation and mandating HPV vaccination for girls ages 12 to 13. So far, however, only Virginia has required such vaccinations. Other states have either made no decision or left the choice up to parents.

The New York Times, in a February 6, 2007, editorial, had congratulated Texas for "becoming the first state to mandate vaccinating young schoolgirls" against HPV and observed that "Other states would be wise to follow the same path."

Although it looked for a while as if many other states would, this point of view was far from universally shared. Some critics argued that requiring girls to be vaccinated would encourage sexual activity at an early age and increase promiscuity. Girls, starting in their early teens, would get the false impression that they would be protected from any harmful consequences associated with sex. Focus on the Family, a Christian advocacy group, expressed the view that women should avoid HIV infection by not having sex before marriage. (Opponents pointed out that this would require the partner also to have avoided sex before marriage, and that was not something a young woman ought to stake her health on.) The organization did not oppose voluntary HPV vaccination, however.

Other critics objected to any policy that would require girls to be vaccinated before they could attend school. Unlike diseases such as measles and mumps, they pointed out, HPV is not an infection that can be spread by casual contact. There is no justification, then, for requiring girls to be vaccinated in order to protect other people.

The choice should be left up to individuals and their famlies. Also, those questioning the safety of all vaccines said that number of childhood vaccinations is already too large and we should not add to it.

Some critics were struck by what they regarded as the unfairness of requiring that girls be vaccinated but not boys. Although only females develop cervical cancer, males are as much responsible for spreading HPV as females. Thus, they claimed, boys and men should be vaccinated also.

Merck and Marketing

Researchers Sheila and David Rothman, in a 2009 article in the *Journal of the American Medical Association (JAMA)* on the sales promotion of Gardasil by Merck, pointed out that Merck had taken a new approach in marketing a vaccine. Traditionally, a vaccine had been identified by the disease it prevented (e.g., the "measles vaccine") or by its developer (e.g., the "Salk vaccine"). Merck, however, named the HPV vaccine Gardasil and promoted it to "guard against" cervical cancer, rather than reduce the risks of acquiring an HPV infection: Promoted in this way, Gardasil's worldwide sales from 2006–2008 were $1.4 billion. The trade publication *Pharmaceutical Executive* named Gardasil the 2006 "brand of the year" for generating a market "out of thin air."

Merck's marketing strategy required the company to promote Gardasil as if every girl and young woman in the country were at equal risk of developing cervical cancer. This meant concentrating marketing on major population cernters, rather than on areas of the country where the population density is lower, but the risks of cervical cancer are greater.

Black women in the south, Latino women in the southwest, and white women in Appalachia have much higher rates of cervical cancer than women in other parts of the country. Thus, the use of the vaccine in these areas might be expected eventually to reduce the number of deaths from the disease. The promotion of Gardasil in these areas would not be as cost effective, however, as promoting it in population centers.

The Rothmans call attention to the way that Merck provided grants to professional medical organizations to develop educational programs and speaker's bureaus to promote the use of Gardasil. The Rothmans observe that "much of the material [in the educational programs and preparations for speakers] did not address the full complexity of the issues surrounding the vaccine and did not provide balanced recommendations on risks and benefits." Merck not only overstressed both the benefits of the vaccine and the risks of cervical cancer, but succeeded in turning a large and influential segment of the medical establishment into Gardasil advocates.

Merck, as it had done in Texas, also lobbied heavily in state legislatures to get lawmakers to require that girls ages 11 to 12 be vaccinated with Gardasil. Once again, the major theme pressed by Merck in its marketing messages was that Gardasil is a vaccine against cervical cancer, and several professional medical groups (including the one performing biopsies for Pap tests) supported that message. Many state legislators were eager to show that they favored legislation that would benefit women in their state, so long as any vaccination requirements contained an opt-out provision.

Safety Concerns

In August 2009, three years after Gardasil was introduced, the CDC's Vaccine Adverse Event Reporting System listed more than 700 "very serious" adverse events associated with the use of the HPV vaccine. The adverse events included blood clots, neurological disorders such as Guillain-Barré syndrome, and death. Some twenty-three to twenty-five million doses of Gardasil had been distributed during the period covered by the reports. The total number of adverse events reported averaged about sixty per 100,000 doses of Gardasil, and 6.2 percent of the adverse events were classified as serious. They included thirty-two deaths.

What is not clear, experts agree, is whether the adverse events reported were caused by the HPV vaccine. Without knowing how many of the events would have occurred independently of the vaccine, it is not possible to conclude that the vaccine caused them. Would the person who was vaccinated and then died of a stroke caused by a blood clot have died anyway? Was the timing only accidental? A 2009 study, also published in *JAMA*, showed that ninety percent of those reporting problems with blood clots already had risk factors for developing blood clots (using birth-control pills or smoking) before getting the vaccine. How many other preexisting conditions were responsible for the adverse events reported? No one knows.

Futhermore, the adverse event reports themselves may not contain reliable data. The Vaccine Adverse Events Reporting System is voluntary, and the reports submitted are neither assessed for quality nor verified. Some of the adverse events are most likely real, yet no vaccine is 100 percent safe, and there is not

reason enough at present to claim that Gardasil is less safe than other widely used vaccines. "There are 732 serious problems identified in twenty-four million doses of the HPV vaccine," Keven Ault, professor of gynecology at Emory University, told a reporter. "I usually tell my patients that these serious events are tragic, rare, and likely unrelated to the vaccine."

This is not a view endorsed by all physicians. Dr. Jacques Moritz, director of gynecology at New York's St. Luke's–Roosevelt Hospital, told the same reporter that he saw no reason to offer Gardasil to patients, given the availability of good screening techniques like the Pap test and good treatments. He said he didn't plan to vaccinate his eleven-year-old daughter.

Dr. Charlotte Haug, in a *JAMA* editorial accompaning the articles mentioned earlier, is particularly critical of Gardasil. She points out that it was approved by the FDA on the basis of clinical trails that focused on whether it prevented HPV infections by the two strains, and it wasn't until almost a year later that the results of the Phase 3 trials were reported. These trials focused on the prevention of precancerous changes, and although the results were promising, no longer term results from the studies have been published since then. So far, the vaccine has not been proven to reduce cervical cancer.

Also, the adverse events that have been reported since the vaccine has come into use need to be investigated in a scientific fashion. The reports don't prove that the vaccine is unsafe, but we also can't conclude that the reports are groundless and that the vaccine is safe. We simply don't know enough to be sure in the absence of more systematic studies.

Whether a risk is worth taking depends on comparing the potential benefit and the potential risk. In Haug's view, the "net benefit to a woman of the HPV vaccine is uncertain." Even a woman who is infected with HPV for many years is unlikely to develop cancer if she has regular screening tests. Rationally, then, when it comes to the HPV vaccine, she should be willing to take only a small risk that it will cause her harm.

Hope or Hype?

The development of a new vaccine for an infectious disease is rare good news, and if the vaccine also protects against cancer, the news seems even better. It is no wonder that the announcement that Gardasil had been approved by the FDA for vaccinating girls and women was met with such enthusiasm. Even if the promotional efforts of Merck were instrumental in stirring up that enthusiasm and in encouraging states to consider requiring HPV vaccination for schoolgirls, this does not mean that Gardasil shouldn't be considered a potentially important weapon in the war against HPV and cervical cancer.

As more studies are done and data about the use of Gardasil accumulate, researchers will be able to make a more accurate assessment of its potential risks and benefits. Women will then be in a better position to decide whether they want to take the risks to get the benefits. It does not seem likely, however, that many states will pass legislation requiring that schoolgirls be vaccinated against HPV. Even if current doubts about the safety of the vaccine are resolved in its favor, people have come to realize that the great majority of women, even though infected for decades with HPV, will never develop cervical cancer and that they can ensure their safety by regular Pap tests. Because the vaccine protects against only two cancer-causing strains of HPV, even those who are vaccinated must still be regularly tested for precancerous changes in cervical cells. Thus, many people will see no compelling reason to subject themselves or their children to whatever slight risks the vaccine may pose. Finally, because the HPV virus is spread by sexual contact and not merely by closeness in a crowd, legislators are unlikely to believe that they have an obligation to require vaccination for the protection of others.

The HPV vaccine is far from being nothing but hype, but the hope that it offers seems less substantial than it did at first.

Placebos and Transparency

Jane Hunter (as we will call her) was convinced that she had a serious, perhaps fatal, illness. She was constantly fatigued, and she felt so tired in the mornings that it was all she could do to get out of bed. Despite all her efforts, she seemed unable to get enough rest. She also ached all over, and various places on her body were extraordinarily tender. If she pressed a finger against the side of her neck, she would have to bite her lip to keep from crying. Points of pain were also located between her shoulder blades and behind her knees. Sometimes she seemed to hurt all over.

Jane didn't think of herself as a whiner and complainer, but she had been to see Dr. Jerrold Chang, her family doctor three times during the eight months she had been having problems. He had examined her and ordered a variety of tests to rule out diabetes, lupus, lung cancer, kidney disease, leukemia, and other sorts of blood disorders.

"I can't find anything wrong with you," Dr. Chang had told her. "I want you get a second opinion, though. So I'm going to ask you to see Dr. Ellen Deutch. She's a rheumatologist, and they specialize in diseases that involve inflammation. I think you probably have fibromyalgia."

"I've never heard of it." Jane felt a wave of panic pass through her. "How serious is it?"

"We're not sure it's a disease," Dr. Chang told her. "But it's what we call the group of symptoms like yours. About two percent of the population, mostly women, complain of constant fatigue, poor sleep, generalized aches and pains, and several painfully sensitive places on their bodies." Dr. Chang shrugged. "No one knows how to treat fibromyalgia or even if it's real."

"It seems real to me." Jane felt annoyed.

Jane's symptoms didn't improve during the four weeks she had to wait before she was able to get in to see Dr. Deutch. When she was finally able to tell her story, Dr. Deutch gave her another physical exam. She explained to Jane that she was checking in particular to see if Jane's thyroid had any nodules. Dr. Deutch then looked at the laboratory results from the numerous tests Dr. Chang had ordered.

"I agree with Dr. Chang that you most likely have fibromyalgia," Dr. Deutch told her. "I don't see a reason to perform any more tests at the moment, but I would like you to make an appointment to return in a month so I can check on your progress."

"You aren't going to give me any drugs or anything?" Jane felt her heart sink. She was both surprised and disappointed. She had convinced herself that her new doctor would be able to help her escape from the prison of fatigue and pain her life had become.

Dr. Deutch looked thoughtful a moment. "We can try something that might help. I'm going to give you some tablets that are a combination of dextrose and a small amount of sodium chloride. Some people with your condition have found them helpful." Dr. Deutch began writing on a prescription pad. "I want you to take two tablets three times a day, then let me know next time if you think they are helping."

Traditional Practice

Scenes like these are played out in the consulting rooms of physicians every day. Patients with vague complaints go to their doctors and ask them for help. Their doctors examine them thoroughly and give them a range of tests, but find nothing abnormal. Yet wanting to get their patients to feel better, the doctors prescribe something they hope will help.

The tablets Dr. Deutch prescribed for Jane are nothing but sugar mixed with a trace of table salt. They are essentially harmless, but they also cannot be considered to be an active drug. Jane would probably get similar amounts of the contents of the tablets by eating a small candy bar. Dr. Deutch has prescribed a placebo to treat Jane's condition.

The word *placebo* is Latin for "I shall please." Over the centuries, people who feel ill have consulted physicians with the expectation that their doctors will give them something to make them feel better. Doctors have always tried to oblige. Before the current era, this might have meant prescribing a particular diet, letting the patient's blood, administering enemas, or giving drugs to cause vomiting. But these procedures were part of legitimate medical practice based on accepted theory. (The theory dominant for about two thousand years was that disease results from an imbalance in the four humors—blood, phlegm, black bile, and yellow bile—so the aim of treatment was to restore the balance.)

Even if a doctor believed nothing was wrong with the patient, the patient still expected to be treated. Typically, this meant giving the patient some sort of medicine. Thus, the doctor might prescribe an emetic like nux vomica or a laxative like syrup of figs just to satisfy the patient. Such substances have definite and unpleasant effects, however, so the doctor might prefer to give the patient a box of pills made from sugar or bread dough. These pills would be harmless, produce no side effects, and assure the patient that his doctor was taking his medical complaint seriously and treating it appropriately.

Every traditional doctor learned during his apprenticeship that placebos were often successful in treating patients with vague complaints. Hence, prescribing placebos in such cases became a standard part of medical practice. Even in the current era, the patient dismissively described as "LOL-NAD" ("a little old lady in no apparent distress") who showed up in an emergency department or a doctor's office would often, after examination, be sent away with a prescription for a two-week course of sugar pills. So, too, would a patient who seemed to be a hypochondriac or mildly to moderately depressed. Just receiving medical attention might be all the patient needed to begin to feel better.

Tradition Challenged

During the 1960s and the 1970s, many of the customary practices of physicians were called into question. In particular, the paternalism prevalent in the medical community was severely criticized. Until the 1960s, for example, it was common for a doctor not to tell a patient that he had cancer. But, critics charged, what gave the doctor the right to withhold such information? And why should the doctor decide whether the patient should be treated? That decision should be left up to the patient.

Informed consent was not a new idea in medical practice, but most often it was sought in only a formal fashion and used as a means to protect surgeons from lawsuits. During the 1960s and 1970s, however, in response to pressure from patient advocates and ethicists, the medical community began to acknowledge the importance of the autonomy of patients. This meant recognizing that informed consent is essential to protecting autonomy in cases in which a patient's interest is concerned. The doctor informs and advises, but it is the patient who makes the final decision about whether to accept a treatment.

The consequence of the recognition of autonomy and the incorporation of informed consent into medical practice was that physicians had to change many of their traditional patterns of behavior. Patients could no longer be kept in ignorance "for their own good." They had to be provided with information so that they could participate in making decisions directly affecting them.

Patients had to rely on their doctors to educate them and to tell them the truth. Doctors and patients were seen to be partners working together to do what was in the best interest of the patient. This requires transparency on the part of both patient and doctor. The patient shouldn't hide anything from her doctor, because the doctor needs reliable information to make a diagnosis and decide what to recommend as the best course of treatment. The doctor shouldn't hide anything from his patient, because the patient needs reliable information to exercise her autonomy and make a decision about what treatments she is willing to accept. Both effective medical practice and informed consent require trust and openness.

The transparency required by the doctor–patient relationship doesn't prima facie seem compatible with the use of placebos. Prescribing placebos can be viewed as engaging in a deceptive practice. The doctor is, in effect, telling the patient "You have a medical problem, and this is a drug I think will be effective in treating it." If the patient doesn't have a problem that fits into a recognized diagnostic category, doesn't the patient have a right to know this? If the patient's problem is like Jane's and fits into a category like fibromyalgia that isn't recognized as a disease and has no established treatment, shouldn't the patient be told this?

Placebos, in the view of many, are also relics of the time when medicine had available virtually no effective drugs. This time extended into the early part of the twentieth century. Hundreds—even thousands—of drugs and compounds were listed in the pharmacopoeia and prescribed by doctors, but almost none had been tested for effectiveness and safety. Now, however, we insist that drugs be shown to be safe and effective before they are prescribed. (By some estimates, however, only about twenty percent of drugs in use have been tested.) The use of placebos, critics say, undercuts our commitment to scientific medicine and is an implicit endorsement of a medical practice than can no longer be justified.

Placebos in Practice

Despite the new emphasis on transparency in the doctor–patient relationship, a recent survey of physicians in the specialties of internal medicine and rheumatology showed that about half (46–58%, depending on the phrasing of the question) regularly prescribe placebo treatments and most (62%) believe that the practice is ethically permissible. (The survey was about practices during the previous year, but it seems reasonable to assume that year was typical.)

Contemporary physicians don't usually prescribe such traditional placebos as sugar pills or saline (saltwater) solutions, however. (This may be because pharmacies no longer compound drugs to order.) Rather, most of them (41%) give their patient analgesics (aspirin or acetaminophen, for example) or vitamins (38%). A few (13%) prescribe antibiotics or sedatives. Whatever placebo they prescribe, most physicians (68%) accompany it by saying something like "This is a potentially beneficial medicine not typically used for your condition." Only rarely (5%) do doctors describe the treatment they prescribe as a placebo.

The practice of using placebos isn't confined to U.S. physicians. Another survey showed that 86% of general practitioners in Denmark use placebos, and surveys in Sweden, Israel, New Zealand, and the United Kingdom produced similar results.

The motivation of doctors who prescribe placebo treatments for their patients is most likely the desire to get their patients to feel better. Various studies have shown that a significant number of patients (perhaps as many as 12–20%) gain medical benefit from whatever treatment they receive. (It is for this reason that double-blind clinical trials with a large number of patients have become the standard for determining the effectiveness of a drug.) Thus, when a doctor gives a placebo to a patient with a vague complaint who shows no evidence of having a particular disease, the placebo has a reasonable chance of benefiting the patient.

The doctor who prescribes a placebo is not honoring the presumed commitment to transparency. However, the doctor may be benefiting the patient. If the primary duty of the physician is to benefit the patient—to relieve the patient's suffering—then the case can be made that the physician is sometimes justified in setting aside or violating the implicit commitment to being completely honest with the patient. Cases in which it is appropriate for a physician to prescribe a placebo may be ones in which paternalism can be justified.

Even if such a case can be made in general, it is harder to make the case for physicians who prescribe active placebos—that is, drugs given as placebos that have significant pharmacological consequences. Sugar pills are harmless, but people may have serious and potentially fatal allergic reactions to antibiotics. Similarly, sedatives may produce disturbed sleep, arrthymias, or life-threatening respiratory distress. A physician who prescribes an active placebo would most likely be hard pressed to come up with an adequate explanation for putting a patient at risk for what, by definition, has to be a situation in which the patient displays no signs of a disease for which an appropriate drug should be prescribed.

Bottom Line

The routine use of placebos in medical practice always raises ethical questions. Prescribing a placebo can be a physician's way of getting rid of a troublesome patient whose problem she can't solve. In the worst case, it can be a physician's way of shirking the responsibility for diagnosis or helping the patient understand that what is bothering him is not the symptom of a disease. In the best case, prescribing a placebo can be the physician's way of relieving a patient's worry and distress without causing harm.

Physicians prescribed placebos, in part, because they felt patients' expectations that their doctor will do something to help. Traditionally and even now, "doing something" has usually been construed to mean prescribing a drug. (This is one reason antibiotics have been overprescribed.) What patients should most appropriately expect from their physicians is an informed judgment about their complaint and symptoms. Were patients able to accept the judgment that sometimes medicine has nothing to offer to make them feel better, then physicians would most likely not be so inclined to prescribe placebos.

SOCIAL CONTEXT
Health Cops: How Much Regulation Is Too Much?

Obesity is causally associated with these disorders: Type-2 diabetes, hypertension, heart disease, stroke, kidney failure blindness, and unhealing wounds leading to foot and leg amputations. Someone with a body-mass index (BMI) of 30 or more is, by definition, obese. (BMI is the ratio of height to weight. Thus, someone who is six feet tall is obese when he reaches 221 pounds; someone five feet, six inches, tall is obese when she reaches 186 pounds.) As the number of obese people in the population rises, the number of diseases caused by obesity also rises, and each disease is associated with high medical costs, disability, and death.

Longevity in Reverse

A 2005 *New England Journal of Medicine* study concludes that, because of obesity, for the first time in the nation's history life expectancy is growing shorter rather than longer. Current life expectancy for adults is seventy-seven years, but if deaths attributable to obesity were subtracted, an additional four to nine months would be added. However, the effect obesity has on life expectancy now is small compared to the effect it is likely to have as the current crop of children grows into adulthood. The adults of tomorrow may live from two to five years less than adults do now.

To put these figures into perspective, the four to nine months now lost to the effects of obesity mean that obesity is shortening the life span at a greater rate than the combined effects of accidents, homicides, and suicides. The effects on the children of today will to be to shorten their life spans to a greater extent than the *combined* effects of cancer and coronary artery disease.

Some experts estimate that 300,000–400,000 people die each year from obesity-related causes. The number of cases of disability and sickness associated with obesity is likely to be several times this number. Even so, as an author of the report, David Ludwig, observed, society is now in the lull before the real storm breaks. "There is an unprecedented increase in the prevalence of obesity at younger and younger ages without much public heath impact," he says. "But when they start developing heart attacks, stroke, kidney failure, amputations, blindness, and ultimately death at younger ages, then that could be a huge effect on life expectancy." When this starts happening, it will have a serious impact on health care costs, insurance, Social Security, and the productivity of the economy. Even if advances in medicine soften the blow obesity can be expected to deliver, the amount of suffering and sadness will rise as life expectancy falls and millions of individuals sicken and die.

Obesity Rates Level Off

During the period 2005–2010, Americans apparently reached the peak of obesity. The rates of obesity remained constant, but the rate was very high. Some thirty-four percent of adults are obese—double the 1980 percentage. During the same period, the percentage of obese children tripled, to reach seventeen percent.

Why did the rates level off? Some experts believe it is partly because women, who most often buy and prepare the food for families, became more aware of the need to feed their families a better diet. Also, the food served in schools improved, and children and the population in general were educated about the high-fat, high-salt, and high-calorie contents of fast food.

Not everyone is convinced that the halt in the increase is due to better eating habits or an increased awareness of the importance of a healthful diet. David Ludwig, the author of the 2005 report, thinks the plateau may be because the population has reached the biological limit of how obese it is possible to be. When people eat more, they gain weight, and an increasing number of calories go toward maintaining and

moving around the additional weight. "A population doesn't keep getting heavier and heavier indefinitely," Ludwig says. Also, "It could be that most of the people who are genetically susceptible or susceptible for psychological or behavioral reasons have already become obese."

The leveling off of obesity is a statistical feature of the population, but some groups within the population have not leveled off. From 1999 to 2008, boys who were the heaviest (mostly white) became even heavier. African-American adults have the highest obesity rates (37% of men, 50% of women), and 43% of Hispanic women count as obese. Weight in the general population has continued to increase, so 68% of adults and almost 75% of children are now overweight, defined as having a body-mass index of 25 or more.

Obesity rates have plateaued, but the problems posed by obesity are still with us. They will require considerable resources to deal with for decades to come. Even if the conveyor belt that has been moving people into the obese category were suddenly to stop, so many people are already obese that their problems will occupy at least another generation.

Soaring Costs

Type-2 diabetes, which most commonly results from obesity, is estimated to cost the nation $174 billion a year in medical bills, disability payments, and lost productivity. (Direct medical costs are $116 billion; $58 billion are for disability, work loss, and premature mortality.) Almost twenty-four million adults and children (nearly eight percent of the population) have diabetes, and almost two million new cases are diagnosed each year. Every 24 hours, 4100 people are diagnosed with the disease, and due to it, 55 people go blind, 120 develop end-stage kidney disease, and 230 amputations are performed. About ninety-five percent of diagnosed cases of diabetes are Type 2.

Genetic factors are now known to be involved in producing at least some cases of Type-2 diabetes. In January 2006, researchers at Decode Genetics announced that they had identified a variant gene that increases the risk of developing diabetes in those who inherit the gene. The variant, designated TCF7L2, is a regulatory gene that controls a metabolic pathway. It was found in the population of Iceland, and its existence was later confirmed in the populations of both Denmark and the United States. An estimate 38% of those possessing one copy (allele) of the variant gene have a 45% greater than usual risk of developing the disease, and the 7% of the population who possess two copies have a 141% greater risk.

The variant gene is responsible for 21% of all cases of diabetes in the U.S. population, and it is likely that other variant genes are involved in other cases. The immediate hope is that knowledge about TCF7L2 can be used to develop a genetic test to identify people who are at risk for developing the disease. They can then be encouraged to modify their lifestyle to avoid developing the disease. The longer term hope is that treatments can be found that act on the metabolic pathways influenced by the variant gene and thus prevent the development of the disease.

While a genetic predisposition is likely in every case of Type-2 diabetes even though not all the genes have been identified, obesity and a lack of physical activity appear to trigger the disease. People can show prediabetic conditions for seven to ten years before the disease is finally diagnosed, and by that time, significant damage may already be occurring in the patient's body. Numbness and tingling in the hands and feet may signal damage to the nervous system, bleeding in the retina can cause significant vision loss, poor circulation can lead to unhealing wounds that are prone to infection or to the death of tissues in the toes or feet, requiring amputation. (About seventy percent of limb amputations are due to diabetes.) High blood pressure caused by the disease can damage the kidneys, requiring dialysis or a transplant.

Obese people may face these problems one at a time, but often two, three, or even more problems occur in a cluster. Obesity triggers Type-2 diabetes, which raises blood pressure and causes a stroke, damages the kidneys so severely that they shut down, and causes blood vessels in the eye to leak blood and damage the retina. Hospitalization and lack of activity may slow circulation, causing tissues in the toes or feet to die, thus requiring amputation. The life of a diabetic is one of constant vigilance and relentless efforts to stave off the ravages of the disease.

The medical costs for caring for someone who develops Type-2 diabetes are staggering. Given that twenty-one million people are now being treated for diabetes, it is not surprising that the annual medical costs add up to $174 billion. Here are typical per-patient charges: stroke care, $40,200; limb amputation, $30,400; end-stage kidney disease, $37,000. With the rise of obesity causing an increase in the number of Type-2 diabetics, the annual cost of care for this group of patients can be expected to soar.

Public Health or Private Choice

If only we could keep people from being obese, the costs of health care would decrease and people would live longer and healthier lives. But what would we have to do to slow or perhaps halt the increase in overweight kids and adults? And how far are we as a society prepared to go in regulating the weight of our citizens? Should we even be thinking about intruding on this area of privacy and autonomy?

Researchers tend to regard obesity as a public health issue. They view it as a problem that, like smoking, should be addressed by using laws and public policies as tools to bring it under control. Obesity, like smoking, has a high economic cost attached to it, and that cost must be paid by society. The money spent on coping with Type-2 diabetes might be better spent on prenatal care, on providing health care for the poor or uninsured, or on education or scientific research. Type-2 diabetics typically develop the disease because they are significantly overweight, and the disease causes the problems discussed earlier, and treating these problems drives up the cost of medical care. Therefore, society is justified in taking measures to keep people from becoming obese.

West Virginia introduced a wellness program for Medicaid patients that asks them to sign a pledge to "do my best to stay healthy," to attend "health improvement programs as directed," to go for regularly scheduled checkups, to take the medicines that are prescribed, and to go to an emergency room only for an event like a heart attack, stroke, or seizure. West Virginia has some of the country's highest rates of smoking, obesity, diabetes, and heart disease. A state commissioner of health services said, "We want to reach people before they get chronic and debilitating diseases that will keep them on Medicaid for the rest of their lives."

Those who stick to the plan will receive such "enhanced benefits" as diabetes management, cardiac rehabilitation, mental health counseling, and prescription drugs and home-health visits from a nurse as needed. Those who do not sign up will receive only the benefits mandated by the federal government. (Medicaid is a joint federal–state program.) They will not be eligible for the advanced benefits, and their prescriptions will be limited to four a month.

Pressure has been building for years to provide children with school lunches that are nutritionally sound. Although steps have been taken in this direction, many state and local governments have decreased the amount of physical activity built into the school day. Recess has been eliminated or shortened to add extra classes, and athletic programs have been cut to reduce costs. A school without physical education (P.E.) doesn't require a P.E. teacher, and one without competitive teams doesn't require a coach.

Reversing the current practices of governments and schools could do much to prevent obesity and to promote children's health. Yet this would often require increasing the amount of funding that schools receive, and the public is generally not enthusiastic about increasing school taxes.

Some states have taken some tentative steps toward reducing the obesity crisis. The Arkansas State Board of Education now requires that schools send home with each child a weight report card along with the academic report card. The hope is that when the report is accompanied by nutritional education and advice, children, with the help of their parents, will be able to maintain their weight within limits compatible with good health. Local school districts in a number of states—California, Massachusetts, and Oregon among them—have initiated similar programs.

The federal government, after much pressure from consumer groups, now requires the labels on foods to provide more nutritional information than ever before. Labels display data about the calories, carbohydrates, fats, transfats, fiber, and vitamins in a specified serving of the food, to guide consumers in their decisions. Similarly, fast-food restaurants are required to make available to their customers nutritional information about the items they serve. Knowing that one bacon cheese double hamburger, fries, and a large milk shake can contain more than half the calories an average person should consume in a day ought to help people make sensible choices.

In 2010, the Food and Drug Administration proposed a new requirement for food manufacturers. They would have to start providing nutritional information about realistic serving sizes on the front of many packaged foods. Cereals, cookies, chips, and ice cream now print the information on the back or sides of packages, and the serving sizes manufacturers use do not reflect the amounts of the product that people typically consume as a serving. Frosted Flakes, for example, lists its serving size as ¾ cup (110 calories), but two cups (293 calories) is more likely to be an actual serving.

The FDA proposal is thus intended to give people a better sense of what they are eating. If people don't understand that "one serving" is a smaller amount than they are likely to eat, they won't understand how many calories and nutrients or how much fat they are consuming. Current serving sizes, the FDA contends, are often misleading. A fourteen-ounce bowl-shaped container of soup intended to be heated in a microwave looks as if constitutes a single serving, but the label says the bowl contains two servings. Thus, someone may be unknowingly consuming 680 mg of sodium, rather than 424 mg. The label on a small bag of potato chips says the chips are 100 calories per serving, but the bag is actually 132 calories. The difference may be small case by case, but the effects are cumulative.

How Far Is Too Far?

But just how far should the government go in the name of protecting the public health by preventing obesity and its consequences? Should all restaurants be required to put nutritional information about their dishes on their menus? Should unhealthful transfats like hydrogenated vegetable oils be outlawed as ingredients in food products? Should, as has been proposed in New York, limits be placed on the addition of salt to restaurant foods?

Is West Virginia justified in rewarding Medicaid beneficiaries to sign up for programs to control their weight and help them quit smoking? Should employers be required to provide nutritional and fitness programs for their employees? Should employees be required to maintain their weight within specified limits, or suffer a penalty, or even lose their jobs? Should the sale and consumption of high-fat or high-sugar products be licensed and regulated like liquor? Should the taxes on foods that contribute to obesity (e.g., soft drinks, high-sugar cereals) be treated like cigarettes, and should those foods be heavily taxed to discourage their consumption?

The fundamental question is, to what extent are we prepared to charge our government with the task of regulating our weight or our health in general? Some people may want a government agency to take over the difficult job of getting them to lose weight or, at the least, keeping them from gaining more. They may want a government-mandated exercise program. But are we ready to surrender some of our autonomy to gain the beneficial results that doing so offers?

Many people answer this question with a resounding no. In their view, what people eat, how much they eat, how much or how little they exercise, and how fat or thin they become is a purely private matter. Government is not justified in interfering with the nutritional aspect of their lives, anymore than it would be justified in interfering with the religious aspect. Providing information is acceptable, in a general way, but it may not be acceptable to require restaurants to inform people about the contents of their meals. People are smart enough to know that if they eat the grilled fish fillet and green salad, they are not going to be consuming as many calories as they would if they eat the double cheeseburger and fries.

Critics of proposals to involve the government in personal health insist that it certainly is not acceptable for the government to constrain or regulate people's behavior with the idea of keeping them from becoming obese. This is, they say, a direct violation of the autonomy of individuals, and what is more, such attempts are likely to increase the prejudice already shown toward overweight people in our society. Also, any talk of firing people or penalizing them for avoiding required exercise sessions or for being obese is a plan to violate individual rights. Besides, individuals vary in their genetic makeup, and we don't know enough about what predisposes people to becoming obese to hold those who do responsible for their condition.

A Medical Matter

Obesity is a problem with serious and expensive health consequences for the individual and for society. As more and more children become obese and as Type-2 diabetes and other obesity-related diseases increase, the society will face a public health crisis. The obesity epidemic will not be wholly unlike the HIV/AIDS epidemic of the 1980s and 1990s: relatively young people will face life-threatening, difficult-to-treat, and expensive medical problems, and so many will die that the longevity of the population will be significantly reduced for the first time since the advent of modern clinical medicine.

A major difference between the AIDS epidemic and the obesity epidemic is that we don't have to await some medical breakthrough in order to prevent or treat obesity. We know that, in almost every case, diet and exercise can bring weight under control. Even so, it is clear that many people have a complex and perhaps even addictive relationship with food, so that merely exhorting them to eat less and exercise more is not likely to help them achieve a normal weight. Obesity is better regarded as a medical problem than a moral one caused by a lack of willpower, but how to solve the problem is not well understood.

Without interfering with autonomy, government can help people acquire a better understanding of nutrition, and we can make it easier for people to seek medical advice about programs to reduce their weight. Most obese people aren't happy with their condition and would welcome appropriate help in changing it. They would not welcome being threatened with losing their jobs if they don't lose weight.

Even slight changes in our health-care system could do much to reduce the incidence of Type-2 diabetes. Most insurance plans pay little or nothing for preventive care of any sort, although they pay considerable amounts for expensive treatments. Hence, nutritional counseling, exercise programs, monitoring by a specialist in metabolic medicine, or care of the feet by a podiatric physician are not likely to be covered by most insurance policies. Yet these same policies may cover stroke care, laser therapy for retinal bleeding, and foot amputation—all treatments for conditions caused by diabetes. Mandating coverage for preventive care is a modest form of government intervention that might pay off for insurers as well as the insured.

SOCIAL CONTEXT
Medical Tourism

Jeju Island, South Korea, is not a travel destination as well known as Paris, London, or Rome, but for a certain kind of tourist, it has more to offer. These are tourists who are looking for a medical bargain: first-class medical care at rock-bottom prices.

Jeju is a resort island off the coast of South Korea where the government is building Health Care Town, a 370-acre medical complex of hospitals, clinics, and luxury apartments. The complex will be accompanied by an eighteen-hole golf course and shops filled with high-priced merchandise. The aim is to lure tourist patients from the U.S., Japan, Russia, and the Middle East.

Jeju is only the most recent destination for medical tourists. Other Asian nations are already in the business of trying to attract people with medical needs who are prepared to spend what counts as a great deal of money locally. Singapore, Thailand, and India are currently the most popular destinations for medical tourists, so South Korea will have to offer its visitor patients a lot if it expects to compete with those countries.

Mostly Surgery

The medical care sought at the more established tourist destinations is mostly surgery, and the list of surgeries available is almost as extensive as the menu of a Greek diner: face-lifts, tummy tucks, liposuction, eyelid and brow lifts, chin implants, nose jobs, dermabrasion, breast augmentation or reduction, stomach bypass, laparoscopic banding, knee and shoulder ligament repairs, spinal fusion, coronary-artery bypasses, and kidney and liver transplants. (Dentistry of all sorts is also available, the most popular being procedures like multiple dental implants and extensive reconstructions.)

When these operations are carried out at U.S. hospitals, they range in price from tens of thousands of dollars for cosmetic surgery to hundreds of thousands for kidney or liver transplants. These are prices that even people with insurance are often unable to pay. Either their policy doesn't cover the operation (almost always the case with cosmetic procedures and sometimes the case with transplants), or it pays only a small fraction of the costs. Operations performed at foreign centers are typically sixty to ninety percent lower in costs than those performed in U.S. hospitals. It is no mystery, then, why in recent years increasing numbers of Americans have sought medical care at foreign destinations.

One study indicates that in 2009 almost a million Americans traveled to another country to seek cheaper medical treatments. A report from the Deloite Center for Health Solutions suggests that in the next few years this number will increase to more than six million.

Appeal

Low price is not the only appeal of Asian medical centers. The physicians and surgeons have usually received at least part of their training at medical schools and hospitals in the U.S. or Western Europe, and everyone who deals with patients speaks English. The centers are also newly built modern complexes of steel and glass outfitted with the latest medical equipment—MRI machines, CAT and PET scanners, monitoring equipment, and operating microscopes. Patients' rooms are private and furnished like rooms in luxury hotels, with cable TV, broadband access, bathrooms, and often an extra bed so that a family member can stay with the patient. Meals are specially prepared, and patients may be able to convalesce in a resort-like setting, with swimming pools,

terraces, and gardens. Doctors and nurses are attentive and responsive, and the overall experience is reported by most patients as far better than that at even the best U.S. hospitals.

Some insurance companies have seen the advantage of allowing their clients to become medical tourists. If a company sees an opportunity to save money on expensive surgery such as a hip replacement or stomach-bypass surgery, it may agree to pay part of a patient's travel expenses, provided that the patient goes to a foreign hospital that is approved by the company.

Although some foreign hospitals that are tourist destinations are not rated by any agency, more than 200 of them are accredited by Joint Commission International, a branch of the organization that accredits American hospitals. Thus, these hospitals appear to meet the quality standards of most U.S. hospitals.

Duty to Treat?

So why shouldn't everyone who needs surgery and wants to save money, while being treated and convalescing in a resort setting, not become a medical tourist? The main difficulty for patients is not the surgery but the follow-up care after the surgery. Major surgery requires a recovery period of several weeks to several months, and during that time, it is usually necessary for a physician to fine-tune the recovery and determine the need for any additional treatment. For example, surgical wounds must be observed for infection, and hip and back function must be evaluated.

Physicians stress the importance of continuity of care—of examining the patient over time. But continuity of care is not possible when patients are treated overseas, then sent back home before they are fully healed.

Also, many American physicians and hospitals are reluctant to accept patients who have been operated on abroad. Some physicians claim that they should not be expected to take responsibility for patients with postoperative problems that may be the result of some other surgeon's negligence. In addition, some say, why should they risk being sued when they were not responsible for the original surgery. Some physicians maintain that they have no duty to treat such patients.

Critics of this view hold that physicians have a duty to treat the problems patients present, no matter what produced those problems. Besides, not every post-surgical complication is the result of negligence. Even the best surgeons can't guarantee a trouble-free result.

Critics also point out that in many cases patients sought offshore treatment because they couldn't get the treatment they needed under the American health-care system. Thus, the complications patients develop after they return home are, in effect, the price our society pays for not providing health care for all who need it. The debate over whether physicians have a duty to treat patients who were initially treated abroad is tied up with the concern of both physicians and hospitals with a patient's ability to pay. Someone who sought surgery abroad, then developed complications, is most likely not someone who has the financial resources required to cover any needed postoperative treatment in this country.

Who should pay for that treatment? Should such patients be turned away without treatment? Should the U.S. pass laws forbidding medical tourism? Some physicians and hospitals would answer the first question by saying that the patient needs to find someone who will pay for him if he has no resources. Some would also favor restricting traveling for the purpose of getting inexpensive surgery.

Turning away patients in need of care is not a practice that our society applauds. Even so, we do not require physicians or hospitals to provide patients with the medical care they need. We require only that they stabilize patients before discharging them.

But restricting medical tourism is not likely to happen. One reason is that the U.S. is itself a destination for medical tourists with substantial financial means. Many major medical centers welcome foreign nationals as patients because they are likely to be paying for their treatment in cash and at the nominal billing rate, not at the discounted rate that insurance companies establish by bargaining. Also, forbidding Americans to travel abroad for the purpose of taking advantage of a legal service offered in a foreign country would most likely be condemned as unconstitutional by the courts.

Unknown Risks, Uncertain Remedies

Not all hospitals that draw medical tourists are strictly monitored, so patients may be running risks that are hard to determine. Surgeons and other hospital personnel may not be as well qualified as they appear to be. Also, it is hard to be sure that the materials and medicines meet the highest standards. Hip implants come in a variety of grades, and a patient is typically not in a position to determine whether he is getting hardware of high quality. Similarly, even generic drugs may vary in quality, and once more, patients are rarely in a position to make sure that they are receiving products of the best quality. Physicians worry about whether they might be sued for treating a patient first operated on abroad, but for patients the risk is that they would have no substantial legal remedy for an operation gone wrong.

The most serious drawback for some unlucky patients is that if their surgery has a bad outcome, they may have little legal recourse, even if they believe the outcome was due to negligence. The laws in most Asian countries make it difficult to file lawsuits against physicians or to receive financial compensation. Malpractice suits and large monetary settlements for medical harm are an almost exclusively American phenomenon.

Comparative Results?

The natural question when comparing U.S. surgery with surgery performed at Asian hospitals catering to medical tourists is how the results of the surgery compare. Unfortunately, this is not a question that can be given a definitive answer. We don't have data about the surgical outcomes of the Asian hospitals, and even more surprising, we don't have data about the surgical outcomes at American hospitals either.

We don't know, for example, the complication rates for spinal-fusion surgery in Indian hospitals or Thai hospitals, so not only can we not compare hospitals in those countries, but we can't compare them with hospitals in our own. Indeed, we can't compare the outcomes at any two hospitals in the U.S. for most surgical procedures. Patients are thus in the position of having to rely on reputation and anecdotal information to make what might be one of the most important decisions in their lives.

Bad for the Countries?

Countries, like South Korea that promote medical tourism do it for financial reasons. The hospitals, operating rooms, examination and recovery rooms, rehabilitation suites, clinics, laboratories, pharmacies, cafeterias, restaurants, swimming pools, shops, and golf courses that are found in the new medical complexes employ hundreds of people and generate thousands of jobs in other sectors of the economy.

Some of those employed are highly educated physicians, surgeons, and nurses, but the majority are people with lower level skills. The medical center will need pharmacists, physical therapists, and operating-room technicians, but it will also require people to clean the rooms, do the laundry, and cook the meals. The medical center will also buy some or most of its supplies from local or national manufacturers and producers. The medical center is supposed to generate income from foreign sources to benefit the overall economy in much the same way as a factory manufacturing computers for export is supposed to.

Because wages are comparatively low in countries that court medical tourists, they can provide high-quality care and luxurious accommodations at extremely low prices. The same economic principles that led clothing manufacturers to close their plants in New York and Los Angeles and open new ones in China and Honduras allow low-wage countries to offer medical care at bargain prices.

Critics of medical tourism charge that the analogy is a bad one. The countries that depend on medical tourism to improve their economies are typically comparatively poor, with populations that have limited access to health care. The medical centers catering to foreigners depend for their success on the expertise of some of the country's most highly educated citizens. This means, however, that the physicians who are employed to produce income for the country are not available to address the medical needs of the citizens. Physicians and surgeons represent a social investment for any society (e.g., they must be educated), and it is wrong (the argument goes) not to use that investment to benefit citizens in need of medical help. Medical tourism is thus seen as a practice in which poor countries subsidize the health-care costs of rich countries.

CASE PRESENTATION
Healing the Hmong

The Hmong are a Southeast Asian mountain people who were American allies during the Vietnam war. At the end of the war, whole families of Hmong were airlifted to the United States to protect them from reprisals. Most of the Hmong settled in California, and more than 35,000 now live in or near Fresno.

The Hmong (pronounced "mung") brought their culture with them and have not abandoned it in favor of the general Western or American culture. This is unproblematic so far as matters like dress, food preferences, and modes of worship are concerned. But some Hmong practices have brought them into conflict with the law. Over the years, the Fresno police have been required to deal with complaints about the Hmong slaughtering pigs and other animals in their apartments. The police have also raided patches of ground where the Hmong were growing opium poppies. The police mounted an educational campaign to discourage Hmong men from engaging in their traditional practice of abducting teenage girls to be brides.

Hmong beliefs about illness, its causes, and its treatment have led to even more conflicts, with sometimes tragic results. Adhering to their traditional beliefs, the Hmong don't accept the view of the world depicted by Western science. They are animists who see the everyday world as a place shared with spirits, and they regard the interactions between spirits and humans as factors that shape the course of life. Spirits can be angered or seek revenge for insults or wrongs, and often the vengeful actions of the spirits are manifested as diseases. Propitiating the spirits may involve praying, performing healing rituals, burning incense, or carrying out animal sacrifices.

Hmong and Western cultures come into sharp conflict over the treatment of sick children. Hmong parents of a child with clubfeet, an observer reported, avoided getting the child treated, because they thought the child's feet were deformed as punishment for an ancestor's wrongdoing. To try to correct the problem might result in another family member's becoming sick.

Other Hmong parents have refused to have surgery for their child, because they believe surgery maims the body and makes it impossible for the child to be reincarnated. But two cases of conflict between Hmong cultural beliefs and the Western notion of the legal and moral responsibility to provide children with appropriate medical care have been at the focus of concern and debate.

Lee Lor

Lee Lor, a fifteen-year-old girl, was admitted to Valley Children's Hospital in late September of 1994 with a complaint of severe abdominal pains. Her physicians made a diagnosis of acute appendicitis and operated on her immediately. During the operation, however, the surgeon discovered that Lee Lor had a cancerous abdominal tumor. To remove the tumor, he also had to take out an ovary and part of one of her fallopian tubes. Her family later claimed that it wasn't until three days afterward that

they were told about the cancer and the surgery to remove it. A hospital spokesman said they were told, but he suggested that they may have not have understood what they were told because of problems with the translation.

Chemo

Failing to get permission from Lee Lor's family to initiate chemotherapy, the hospital notified the Fresno County Department of Social Services of the situation. The agency obtained a court order requiring Lee Lor to submit to chemotherapy. The police, facing a barrage of stones hurled by a group of Hmong, removed Lee Lor from her home, strapped to a stretcher. Her father was so upset that a police officer had to wrestle a knife out of his hand to keep him from killing himself. A guard was posted outside Lee's room in the hospital.

To protest Lee Lor's forced treatment, several hundred Hmong marched through the city twice. At a town meeting, they accused the county and the hospital of racism.

Lee Lor was given chemotherapy for a week, then allowed to return home. On the day of her discharge, a court hearing was initiated to determine whether she should be placed in a foster home until the completion of her course of chemotherapy. Her physicians estimated that with treatment she had an eighty percent chance of survival, but without it her chances dropped to ten percent.

Lee Lor made her own decision by running away from home on October 28. Her parents saw her sleeping on a couch with her eight siblings, but the next morning she was gone. She left with little or no money, but she took with her a supply of herbal medicines. Her parents notified the police, but they also called in the family shaman. The shaman reported that she had a vision of Lee Lor out in the open and well.

Some two months later, Lee Lor returned home. She had spent the time wandering around the state and was apparently no worse for the wear. While she was gone, the Department of Social Services had dropped its efforts to get a court order to continue her chemotherapy. In one sense, Lee Lor and her parents and the Hmong community had won their battle against Western medicine.

Lia Lee

Anne Fadiman, in *The Spirit Catches You and You Fall Down*, follows the experiences of a Hmong family, the Lees, in Merced, California, as they encounter the people and institutions of Western medicine in seeking help for their infant daughter Lia.

At the county medical center, Lia was diagnosed with a severe seizure disorder. The Lee family, in accordance with Hmong tradition, believed it was caused by spirits call *dabs* catching hold of Lia and throwing her down, then holding her there, despite her struggles to get up. The only remedy, the Lees thought, was to sacrifice animals and persuade the *dabs* to turn her soul loose. Once they did, she would be free of seizures forever.

Lia's physicians at the hospital where she was evaluated prescribed a drug regimen to bring her seizures under control. Her family, however, believing her seizures had nothing to do with anything that could be helped by medications, refused to give her the drugs.

Brain Damage

Uncontrolled by medications, Lia's seizures became worse over time. Lia eventually suffered irreversible brain damage caused by the seizures. Her physicians attributed her worsened condition to her parent's failure to give her the drugs that could have helped her, while her parents attributed it to the drugs her physicians gave her during several hospital stays.

"You can't tell them somebody is diabetic because their pancreas doesn't work," said one of her physicians. "They don't have a word for pancreas. They don't have an *idea* for pancreas." Two conceptual worlds were in collision.

Are Good Intentions Enough?

The Lees were devoted to their daughter, but like the parents of Lee Lor, they were caught within the conceptual framework of the Hmong culture. They found the conceptual framework of Western scientific medicine unintelligible and came to distrust it and the doctors who represented it.

Both sets of parents did what they believed best for their children. Even so, the practices and treatments of Western medicine are more effective in dealing with cancer and seizure disorders than are those based on the Hmong's animistic view of the world.

If parents are doing what they think best for their child, does a respect for the beliefs of others require us to refrain from interfering when a sick child is given a treatment we consider ineffective? Or, instead, does our knowledge of what is more likely to be effective require us to intervene to make sure that the child receives the treatment we think will benefit her—even if this means acting against the wishes of her parents?

These questions are not prompted just by "alien" cultures like that of the Hmong. We need only to think of Jehovah's Witnesses or Christian Scientists (see the Case Presentation "Suffer the Little Children") to realize that even in our own culture, when the best treatment for a child's illness is at issue, the beliefs of parents can come into conflict with the beliefs of scientific medicine.

Our society is committed to both individual autonomy and recognizing the responsibility of parents in caring for their children. Hence, we are ambivalent about setting aside parental decisions. When the beliefs of an entire culture like that of the Hmong are concerned, we become even more ambivalent. No one wants to be thought guilty of cultural chauvinism or arrogance.

We recognize, however, that allowing a competent adult to choose a treatment with little or no chance of success is quite different from allowing an adult to make that choice for a child. Children are dependent on their parents and are expected to submit to whatever their parents decide is best for them.

Does society, recognizing this difference, have a duty to intervene when parents make what is generally acknowledged to be the wrong choice about their child's medical treatment? Were California officials right to try to protect the welfare of Lee Lor and Lia Lee, the two Hmong girls, by making sure that they got what we consider proper medical care?

CASE PRESENTATION
The Vegan Baby

Joseph and Silva Swinton's daughter Ilce (pronounced "ice") Swinton was born on July 21, 2000, in Queens, New York. She was delivered in a house shared with relatives, without a doctor, nurse, or midwife in attendance. Ilce was three months premature, weighed three pounds (less than half that of the average baby), and suffered from respiratory problems due to underdeveloped lungs. She received no medical attention for her breathing difficulties.

Silva Swinton, who was 32 at the time of Ilce's birth, had once weighed more than 300 pounds. She had dropped to a normal weight by sticking to a strict vegan diet—no meat, fish, milk, or cheese—nothing but vegetables, grains, fruits, and nuts. She and her husband, who was the same age, had followed their vegan diet for several years, and both believed it had improved their health and helped prevent the various chronic ailments Silva had suffered from when she was so overweight.

Silva decided not to breast feed Ilce. Instead, she and Joseph agreed that the baby should be fed the same diet that they followed. This meant no milk or milk-based infant formula. They gave her pureed organic vegetables, ground nuts, fruit juices, and vitamins. Silva read labels on jars of baby food and tried to match the contents while avoiding any additives. Although Ilce did not do well on the diet she was fed, her parents stuck to it. For whatever reason, they didn't give her the soy-based baby formula favored by strict vegetarians.

When Ilce was fifteen months old, an anonymous caller tipped off the Administration for Children's Services that the baby wasn't being properly cared for. The agency intervened, and Ilce was taken to a hospital on November 16, 2001. When the physicians examined her, they found that her body was wasted from severe malnourishment, and she weighed only ten pounds, half as much as a baby her age should weigh. Also, her teeth had not started to grow, and she suffered from rickets, a bone disorder due to a vitamin D deficiency that is rarely seen in developed countries. Ilce's bones were soft and brittle from a lack of calcification, and some were broken. Her internal organs had also failed to develop as they should.

Ilce was kept in the hospital for four months and fed a medically prescribed diet, including doses of vitamin D. She was eventually released into the care of Silva Swinton's aunt. The aunt was already taking care of the Swintons' second child, Ini Free Swinton, who was born in 2003. Both children were fed a vegetarian diet approved by physicians, and Ms. Swinton was allowed supervised visits twice a week.

The Queens District Attorney's office charged both Swintons with first-degree assault, claiming that they either knew or should have known that the strict diet would endanger their child's life. Prosecutors in court also claimed that the Swintons had failed to seek medical care for Ilce, even though it was obvious that she was starving to death, failing to grow, and displaying symptoms of poor health.

Ms. Swinton's lawyer, Christopher Shella, argued that Ilce's premature birth was the cause of most of her medical problems and that her parents were trying to do their best for her. Their treatment of their child, he claimed, was not due to malice, and they should not be found guilty of a criminal offense and sent to prison. They were not sufficiently knowledgeable about infant nutrition to know that they were endangering their child.

Mr. Swinton's lawyer, Rona Gordon-Galcus, described the Swintons as "loving and attentive" parents who "did nothing knowingly to harm their child." She moved that the case be dismissed because there was no evidence of criminal intention. The motion was denied.

On April 4, 2003, a jury of the New York State Supreme Count found Silva and Joseph Swinton guilty of first-degree assault and the lesser charges of first-degree reckless endangerment and endangering the welfare of a child. They were immediately taken into police custody and faced with prison terms of five to twenty-five years.

"I don't see any justice here," Ms. Swinton's lawyer said. "That they made the wrong choice doesn't make it depraved, given how much they cared about their child." To be guilty of first-degree assault, the law requires that a perpetrator display "depraved intentions."

"We were brand-new parents trying to do everything we could for her," Ms. Swinton said at the end of the trial.

Nutritionists had testified during the trial that both breast feeding and the feeding of soy baby formula are permitted in the usual vegan diet. Had Ilce been fed either, the chances were good that she would not have become malnourished.

"This community spoke through the jury and indicated that the weakest will be protected," prosecutor Eric Rosenbaum said. "The law protects children."

By the time Ilce was three years old, she was round faced and well nourished. She was beginning to develop more normally, even though her doctors feared she would always suffer from some neurological deficits. Permanent neurological damage can result from either prematurity or malnutrition. Ilce had experienced both.

BRIEFING SESSION

Consider the following cases:

1. A state decides to require that all behavioral therapists (that is, all who make use of psychological conditioning techniques to alter behavior patterns) be either licensed psychologists or psychiatrists.

2. A member of the Jehovah's Witnesses religion, which is opposed to the transfusion of blood and blood products, refuses to consent to a needed appendectomy. But when his appendix ruptures and he lapses into unconsciousness, the surgical resident operates and saves his life.

3. A physician decides not to tell the parents of an infant who died shortly after birth that the cause of death was an unpredictable birth defect, because he does not wish to influence their desire to have another child.

4. A janitor employed in an elementary school consults a psychiatrist retained by the school board and tells her that he has molested young children on two occasions. The psychiatrist decides that it is her duty to inform the school board.

5. A six-year-old develops a high fever accompanied by violent vomiting and convulsions while at school. The child is rushed to a nearby hospital. The attending physician makes a diagnosis of meningitis and telephones the parents for permission to initiate treatment. Both parents are Christian Scientists, and they insist that no medical treatment be given to her. The physician initiates treatment anyway, and the parents later sue the physician and the hospital.

6. A thirty-year-old woman who is twenty-four-weeks pregnant is involved in an automobile accident that leaves her with a spinal cord injury. Her physician tells her that she would have a greater chance of recovery if she were not pregnant. She then requests an abortion. The hospital disagrees with her decision and gets a court order forbidding the abortion.

There is perhaps no single moral issue that is present in all these cases. Rather, there is a complex of related issues. Each case involves acting on the behalf of someone else—another individual, the public at large, or a special group. And each action comes into conflict with the autonomy, wishes, or expectations of some person or persons. Even though the issues are related, it is most fruitful to discuss them under separate headings. We will begin with a brief account of autonomy, then turn to a discussion of paternalism and imposed restrictions on autonomy.

Autonomy

We are said to act autonomously when our actions are the outcome of our deliberations and choices. To be autonomous is to be self-determining. Hence, autonomy is violated when we are coerced to act by actual force or by explicit and implicit threats or when we act under misapprehension or under the influence of factors that impair our judgment.

We associate autonomy with the status we ascribe to rational agents as persons in the moral sense. Moral theories are committed to the idea that persons are, by their nature, uniquely qualified to decide what is in their own best interest. This is because they are ends in themselves, not means to some other end. As such, persons have inherent worth, rather than instrumental worth. Others have a duty to recognize this worth and to avoid treating persons as though they were only instruments to be employed to achieve a goal chosen by someone else. To treat someone as if she lacks autonomy is thus to treat her as less than a person.

All the cases previously listed may be viewed as involving violations of the autonomy of the individuals concerned. (1) Laws requiring a license to provide therapy restrict the actions of individuals who do not qualify for a license. (2) The Jehovah's Witness is given blood he does not want. (3) Information crucial to decision making is withheld from the parents of the child with the genetic disease, so their future decision cannot be a properly informed one. (4) By breaking confidentiality, the psychiatrist is usurping the prerogative of the janitor to keep secret information that may harm him. (5) By treating the girl with meningitis, the physician is violating the generally recognized right of parents to make decisions concerning their child's welfare. (6) By refusing the woman's request for an abortion, the hospital and the court are forcing her to remain pregnant against her will.

The high value we place on autonomy is based on the realization that without it we can make very little of our lives. In its absence, we become the creatures of others, and our lives assume the forms others choose for us. Without being able to act in ways that shape our own destiny by pursuing our aims and making our own decisions, we are not realizing the potential we have as rational agents. Autonomy permits us the opportunity to make decisions ourselves; even if we are dissatisfied with the result, we have the satisfaction of knowing that the mistakes were our own. We at least acted as rational agents.

One of the traditional problems of social organization is to structure society in such a way that the autonomy of individuals will be preserved and promoted. However, autonomy is not an absolute or unconditional value, but just one among others. For example, few would wish to live in a society in which you could do what you wanted only if you had enough physical power to get your way. Because one person's exercise of autonomy is likely to come into conflict with another's, we are willing to accept some restrictions to preserve as much of our own freedom as possible. We value our own safety, the opportunity to carry out our plans in peace, the lives of other rational beings, and perhaps even their welfare.

Because autonomy is so basic to us, we usually view it as not requiring any justification. However, this predisposition in favor of autonomy means that to violate someone's autonomy, to set aside that person's wishes and render impotent her power of action, requires that we offer a strong justification. Various principles have been proposed to justify conditions under which we are warranted in restricting autonomy.

The most relevant principle in discussing the relationships among physicians, patients, and society is that of paternalism. The connection of paternalism with the physician–patient relationship and with truth telling and confidentiality in the medical and social context is discussed in the next section. (For a fuller account of autonomy, as well as the principles invoked to justify restricting its exercise, see Part V, "Foundations of Bioethics." The harm principle is of particular relevance to the topics presented here.)

Paternalism

Exactly what paternalism is, is itself a matter of dispute. Roughly speaking, we can say that paternalism consists in acting in a way that is believed to protect or advance the interest of a person, even if acting in this way goes against the person's own immediate desires or limits the person's freedom of choice. Oversimplifying, paternalism is the view that "Father knows best." (The word "parentalism" is now sometimes preferred to "paternalism" because of the latter's gender association. See Part V for the distinction between the weak and strong versions of the principle of paternalism.) Thus, the first three cases presented on page 38 are instances of paternalistic behavior.

It is useful to distinguish what we can call "state paternalism" from "personal paternalism." State paternalism, as the name suggests, is the control exerted by a legislature, agency, or other governmental body over particular kinds of practices or procedures. Such control is typically exercised through laws, licensing requirements, technical specifications, and operational guidelines and regulations. (The first case listed is an example of state paternalism.)

By contrast, personal paternalism consists in an individual's deciding, on the basis of his own principles or values, that he knows what is best for another person. The individual then acts in a way that deprives the other person of genuine and effective choice. (Cases 2 and 3 are examples of this.) Paternalism is personal when it is not a matter of public or semipublic policy but is a result of private, moral decision making.

The line between public and private paternalism is often blurred. For example, suppose a physician on the staff of a hospital believes a pregnant patient should have surgery to improve the chances for the normal development of the fetus. The physician presents his view to the hospital's attorney, and, agreeing with him, the attorney goes to court to request a court order for the surgery. The judge is persuaded and issues the order. Although the order is based on arguments that certain laws are applicable in the case, the order itself is neither a personal decision nor a matter of public policy. The order reflects the judgment of a physician who has succeeded in getting others to agree.

Despite the sometimes blurred distinction between state and personal paternalism, the distinction is useful. Most important, it permits us to separate issues associated with decisions about public policies affecting classes of individuals (for example, people needing medication) from issues associated with decisions by particular people affecting specific individuals (for example, a Dr. Latvia explaining treatment options to a Mr. Zonda).

State Paternalism in Medical and Health Care

At first sight, state paternalism seems wholly unobjectionable in the medical context. We are all certain to feel more confident in consulting a physician when we know that she or he has had to meet standards of education, competency, and character set by a state licensing board and medical society. We feel relatively sure that we aren't putting ourselves in the hands of an incompetent quack.

Indeed, that we can feel such assurance can be regarded as one of the marks of the social advancement of medicine. As late as the early twentieth century in the United States, the standards for physicians were low, and licensing laws were either nonexistent or poorly enforced. It was possible to qualify as a physician with as little as four months' formal schooling and a two-year apprenticeship.

Rigorous standards and strictly enforced laws have undoubtedly done much to improve medical care in this country. At the very least, they have made it less dangerous to consult a physician. At the same time, however, they have also placed close restrictions on individual freedom of choice. In the nineteenth century, a person could choose among a wide variety of medical viewpoints. That is no longer so today.

We now recognize that some medical viewpoints are simply wrong and, if implemented, may endanger a patient. At the least, people treated by those who espouse such views run the risk of not getting the best kind of medical care available. Unlike people in the nineteenth century, we are confident that we know (within limits) what kinds of medical therapies are effective and what kinds are useless or harmful. The scientific character of contemporary medicine gives us this assurance.

Secure in these beliefs, our society generally endorses paternalism by the state in the regulation of medical practice. We believe it is important to protect sick people from quacks and charlatans, from those who raise false hopes and take advantage of human suffering. We generally accept, then, that the range of choice of health therapy ought to be limited to what we consider to be legitimate and scientific.

This point of view is not one that everyone is pleased to endorse. In particular, those seeking treatment for cancer have sometimes wanted to try drugs rumored to be effective but not approved by the Food and Drug Administration. Such drugs cannot be legally prescribed in the United States, and those wishing to gain access to them must travel to foreign clinics, often at considerable discomfort and expense. Some have claimed that FDA regulations make it impossible for them to choose the therapy they wish and that this is an unwarranted restriction of their rights. It should be enough, they claim, for the government to issue a warning if it thinks one is called for. But after that, people should be free to act as they choose.

The debate about unapproved therapies raises a more general question: To what extent is it legitimate for a government to restrict the actions and choices of its citizens for their own good? It is perhaps not possible to give a wholly satisfactory general answer to this question. People don't object that they are not permitted to drink polluted water from the city water supply or that they are not able to buy candy bars contaminated with insect parts. Yet some do object if they have to drink water that contains fluorides or if they cannot buy candy bars that contain saccharine. But all such limitations result from governmental attempts to protect the health of citizens. Seeing to the well-being of its citizens certainly must be recognized as one of the legitimate aims of a government. And this aim may easily include seeing to their physical health. State paternalism with respect to health seems, in general, to be justifiable. Yet the laws and regulations through which the paternal concern is expressed are certain to come into conflict with the exercise of individual liberties. Perhaps the only way in which such conflicts can be resolved is on an issue-by-issue basis. Later, we will discuss some of the limitations that moral theories place on state paternalism.

State paternalism in medical and health-care matters may be more pervasive than it seems at first sight. Laws regulating medical practice, the licensing of physicians and medical personnel, regulations governing the licensing and testing of drugs, and guidelines that must be followed in scientific research are some of the more obvious expressions of paternalism. Less obvious is the fact that government research funds can be expended only in prescribed ways and that only certain approved forms of medical care and therapy will be paid for under government-sponsored health programs. For example, it was a political and social triumph for chiropractors and Christian Science readers when some of their services were included under Medicare coverage. Thus, government money, as well as laws and regulations, can be used in paternalistic ways.

Personal Paternalism in Medical and Health Care

That patients occupy a dependent role with respect to their physicians seems to be true historically, sociologically, and psychologically. The patient is sick; the physician is well. The patient is in need of the knowledge and skills of the physician, but the physician does not need those of the patient. The patient seeks out the physician to ask for help, but the physician does not seek out the patient. The patient is a single individual, while the physician represents the institution of medicine with its hospitals, nurses, technicians, consultants, and so on. In his dependence on the physician, the patient willingly surrenders some of his autonomy. Explicitly or implicitly, he agrees to allow the physician to make certain decisions for him that he would ordinarily make for himself.

The physician tells him what to eat and drink and what to avoid, what medicine he should take and when to take it, how much exercise he should get and what kind it should be. The patient consents to run at least part of his life by "doctor's orders" in the hope that he will regain his health or at least improve his condition.

The physician acquires a great amount of power in this relationship. But she also acquires a great responsibility. It has been recognized at least since the time of Hippocrates that the physician has an obligation to act in the best interest of the patient. The patient is willing to transfer part of his autonomy because he is confident that the physician will act in that way. If this analysis of the present form of the physician–patient relationship is roughly correct, two questions are appropriate.

First, should the relationship be one in which the patient is so dependent on the pateralism of the physician? Perhaps it would be better if patients did not think of themselves as transferring any of their autonomy to physicians. Physicians might better be thought of as people offering advice rather than as ones issuing orders. Thus, patients, free to accept or reject advice, would retain fully their power to govern their own lives. If this is a desirable goal, it is clear that the present nature of the physician–patient relationship needs to be drastically altered.

The problem with this point of view is that the patient is ordinarily not in a position to judge the advice that is offered. The reason for consulting a physician in the first place is to gain the advantage of her knowledge and judgment. Moreover, courses of medical therapy are often complicated ones involving many interdependent steps. A patient could not expect the best treatment if he insisted on accepting some of the steps and rejecting others. As a practical matter, a patient who expects good medical care must to a considerable extent put himself in the hands of his physician.

For this reason, the second question is perhaps based on a more realistic assessment of the nature of medical care: How much autonomy must be given up by the patient? The power of the physician over the patient cannot be absolute. The patient cannot become the slave or creature of the physician—this is not what a patient consents to when he agrees to place himself under the care of a physician. What,

then, are the limits of the paternalism that can be legitimately exercised by the physician?

Informed Consent and Medical Treatment

Traditionally, many physicians believed they could do almost anything to a patient so long as it was in the patient's best interest. Indeed, many thought they could act even against the patient's wishes because they considered themselves to know the patient's interest better than the patient himself and thought that eventually the patient would thank them for taking charge and making hard decisions about treatment. (See the Dax Cowart Case Presentation that begins this chapter for what has become the standard example of this way of thinking.)

Although some physicians may still wish to press treatments on patients for the patients' own good, patients need not choose to do as they are advised. Some people refuse to take needed medications, change their diets, quit smoking, exercise more, or undergo surgical procedures that promise to improve the quality of their lives, if not lengthen them. Valuing autonomy, we now realize, requires recognizing that people do not always do what is good for them in a medical way, and accepting this outcome as a consequence of the exercise of autonomy.

People may even choose to reject treatment necessary to save their lives. Over the past two decades, the courts have recognized repeatedly and explicitly that the right to refuse or discontinue medical treatment has a basis in the Constitution and in common law. To receive medical treatment, people must first give their consent, and if they wish to reject treatment, even after it has been started, they are legally and morally entitled to do so.

Free and Informed Consent

Both ethicists and the courts have understood *consent* (in the context of agreeing to treatment) to mean that several specific conditions must be fulfilled. For consent to be morally and legally meaningful, individuals must be (1) competent to understand what they are told about their condition and capable of exercising judgment; (2) provided with relevant information about their illness and the proposed treatment for it in an understandable form and allowed the opportunity to ask questions; (3) given information about alternative treatments, including no treatment at all; and (4) allowed the freedom to make a decision about their treatment without coercion. (For a fuller discussion of consent in the context of becoming an experimental subject, see the Orientation in the next chapter.)

Most public, legal, and philosophical attention on the topic of refusing treatment has focused on cases in which terminally ill patients wished to have respirators disconnected or the guardians of patients in chronic vegetative states wanted nutrition and hydration to be discontinued. The issues have concerned the rights of patients themselves, and in this respect the questions were more or less straightforward. (See Chapter 11, "Euthanasia and Physician-Assisted Suicide," for detailed discussions.)

The matter of refusing treatment becomes more complicated when the interest of someone other than or in addition to the patient is involved. Two sorts of cases, in particular, present difficulties: cases in which parents' beliefs cause them to deny their children necessary medical attention and cases in which a pregnant woman's behavior results in damage to her fetus.

Parents and Children

First is the situation in which parents, acting on the basis of their beliefs, refuse to authorize needed medical treatment for their child. The duty of the physician is to provide the child the best medical care possible. The duty of the parent is to protect and promote the welfare of the child. Ordinarily, in the medical context, these two duties are convergent with respect to the line of action they lead to. The parents ask the physician to "do what is best" for their child,

and the physician discusses the options and risks with the parents and secures their consent on behalf of the child. (See the earlier discussion of informed consent and children for details.)

However, this convergence of duties leading to agreement about action is dependent on physicians and parents sharing some fundamental beliefs about the nature of disease and the efficacy of medical therapy in controlling it. When these beliefs are not shared, the outcome is a divergence of opinion about what should be done in the best interest of the child. The actions favored by the physician will be incompatible with the actions favored by the parents.

As in the Case Presentation "Suffer the Little Children" and example 5 in the Briefing Session, some parents are adherents of religions like Christian Science that teach that disease has no reality but is a manifestation of incorrect or disordered thinking. Adherents of other religions endorse the idea that prayer alone has healing powers. People with such beliefs thus think that the appropriate response to illness is to seek spiritual healing rather than to employ medical modalities.

What about the children of those with such beliefs? Their parents can legitimately claim that by refusing to seek or accept medical treatment for their children, they are doing what they consider best. It is a recognized principle that parents should decide the best interest of their children except in very special circumstances. We don't think, for example, that a psychotic or clinically depressed parent should be allowed to decide a child's welfare. Should Christian Scientists and others with similar beliefs be put into the category of incompetent parents and forced to act against their beliefs and seek medical care for their children?

A strong case can be made for answering yes. If mentally competent adults wish to avoid or reject medical treatment for themselves, the principle of autonomy supports a public policy permitting this. However, when the interest of someone who lacks the abilities to deliberate and decide for himself is concerned, it is reasonable to favor a policy that will protect that person from harm. This is particularly so when matters as basic as the person's health and safety are at stake.

Hence, to justify restricting the generally recognized right of parents to see to the welfare of their children, we can appeal to the harm principle. We might say that if a parent's action or failure to take action tends to result in harm to a child, then we are justified in restricting his or her freedom to make decisions on behalf of the child. We could then look to someone else—a court or an appointed guardian—to represent the child's best interest.

In general, we consider a legitimate function of the state to be the protection of its citizens. When parents fail to take reasonable steps to secure the welfare of their children, doing so becomes a matter of interest to the state.

Pregnancy and Autonomy

The second kind of case is one that involves an actual or potential conflict between the actions of a pregnant woman and the interest of the fetus she is carrying. (This kind of case is illustrated in example 6 on page 38.)

An obvious way of dealing with an alleged conflict between what a pregnant woman wants or does and the interest of her fetus is to deny that conflict is possible. If one holds that the fetus, at every developmental stage, is a part of the woman's body and that she is free to do with her body as she pleases, then there can be no conflict. The woman is simply deciding for herself, and it would be an unjustifiable violation of her autonomy to regulate her actions in ways that the actions of men or nonpregnant women are not regulated.

However, a number of difficulties are associated with this position. The most significant one is that as a fetus continues to develop, it becomes increasingly implausible to hold that it is no different from any other "part" of a woman's body. The problem of when the fetus is a person in the moral sense is one that plagues

the abortion dispute (see Chapter 9), and it is no less relevant to this issue.

Furthermore, even if one is not prepared to say that the fetus has the status of a person, particularly at the very early stages of pregnancy, it seems prima facie wrong to act as if the fetus (barring miscarriage or abortion) were not going to develop into a child.

Suppose a woman knows that she is pregnant and knows that continuing to drink alcohol even moderately is likely to cause the child who will be born to suffer from birth defects. Most people would consider it wrong for her to disregard the consequences of her actions. Once she has decided against (or failed to secure) an abortion, it seems she must accept the responsibility that goes with carrying a child to term. For even a moderate view, this would imply avoiding behavior she knows will be likely to cause birth defects.

However, another aspect of the question of whether a pregnant woman has any responsibility to protect the welfare of the fetus is to what extent, if any, we are justified in regulating the woman's actions. Should a pregnant woman retain her autonomy intact? Or is it legitimate for us to require her, by virtue of being pregnant, to follow a set of rules or laws not applicable to other people?

Once again, the status of the fetus as a person makes such a question hard to answer. Should we regard cases of "fetal neglect" or "fetal abuse" as no different from cases of child neglect or abuse? If the answer is yes, then the pregnant woman does not differ from the parent of a minor child. In the same way the state might order a Christian Science parent to seek medical help for a sick child, we might consider ourselves justified in insisting that a pregnant woman get prenatal care and avoid drugs and alcohol. Just as parents are subject to laws and rules that don't apply to other people, so then are pregnant women.

Assuming this answer is accepted, the question becomes one of how far we should go in prescribing behavior for a pregnant woman.

Should we require a basic minimum, or should we establish an obtainable ideal? Even the basic questions surrounding the issue of pregnancy and responsibility remain unanswered by our society. We have yet to develop a social policy to reduce the incidence of fetal alcohol syndrome and drug-damaged babies while also protecting the autonomy of pregnant women.

Truth Telling in Medicine

The question of the limits of paternalism arises most forcefully when physicians deceive patients. When, if ever, is it justifiable for a physician to deceive his patient?

The paternalistic answer is that deception by the physician is justified when it is in the best interest of the patient. Suppose, for example, that a transplant surgeon detects signs of tissue rejection in a patient who has just received a donor kidney. The surgeon is virtually certain that within a week the kidney will have to be surgically removed and the patient put on dialysis again. Although in no immediate clinical danger, the patient is suffering from postoperative depression. It is altogether possible that if the patient is told at this time that the transplant appears to be a failure, his depression will become more severe. This, in turn, might lead to a worsening of the patient's physical condition, perhaps even to a life-threatening extent.

Eventually the patient will have to be told of the need for another operation. But by the time that need arises, his psychological condition may have improved. Is the surgeon justified in avoiding giving a direct and honest answer to the patient when he asks about his condition? In the surgeon's assessment of the situation, the answer is likely to do the patient harm. His duty as a physician, then, seems to require that he deceive the patient, either by lying to him (an act of commission) or by allowing him to believe that his condition is satisfactory and the transplant was successful (an act of omission).

Yet doesn't the patient have a right to know the truth from his physician? After all, it is his life

that is being threatened. Should he not be told how things stand with him so that he will be in a position to make decisions that affect his own future? Is the surgeon not exceeding the bounds of the powers granted to him by the patient? The patient surely had no intention of completely turning over his autonomy to the surgeon.

The issue is one of truth telling. Does the physician always owe it to the patient to tell the truth? Some writers make a distinction between lying to the patient and merely being nonresponsive or evasive. But is this really a morally relevant distinction? In either case, the truth is being kept from the patient. Both are instances of medical paternalism.

Some insight into the attitudes of physicians and patients with respect to disturbing medical information can be gathered from a 2005 study by the Rand Corporation and Harvard Medical School. Researchers asked 509 oncologists how candid they were in giving a prognosis to cancer patients whom they expected to die in six to twelve months. Some ninety-eight percent said they told these patients that their cancer would eventually kill them, but only five percent gave their patients an estimate of their remaining time. Yet seventy-five percent of these oncologists said that they themselves would want an estimate. This might be viewed prima facie as the expression of a paternalistic attitude toward their patients by the oncologists.

Placebos

The use of placebos (from the Latin *placebo*, meaning "I shall please") in medical therapy is another issue that raises questions about the legitimate limits of paternalism in medicine. The "placebo effect" is a well-documented psychological phenomenon: even patients who are seriously ill will sometimes show improvement when they are given any kind of medication (a sugar pill, for example) or treatment. This can happen even when the medication or treatment is irrelevant to their condition.

The placebo effect can be exploited by physicians for the (apparent) good of their patients.

Many patients cannot accept a physician's well-considered judgments. When they come to a physician with a complaint and are told that there is nothing organically wrong with them, that no treatment or medication is called for, they continue to ail. They may then lose confidence in their physician or be less inclined to seek medical advice for more serious complaints.

One way to avoid these consequences is for the physician to prescribe a placebo for the patient. Since the patient (we can assume) suffers from no organic disease, he is not in need of any genuine medication. And because of the placebo effect, he may actually find himself relieved of the symptoms that caused him to seek medical help. Moreover, the patient feels satisfied that he has been treated, and his confidence in his physician and in medicine in general remains intact.

Since the placebo effect is not likely to be produced if the patient knows he is being given an ineffective medication, the physician cannot be candid about the "treatment" prescribed. She must either be silent, say something indefinite like "I think this might help your condition," or lie. Since the placebo effect is more likely to be achieved if the medication is touted as being amazingly effective against complaints like those of the patient, there is a reason for the physician to lie outright. Because the patient may stand to gain a considerable amount of good from placebo therapy, the physician may think of herself as acting in the best interest of her patient.

Despite its apparent advantages, placebo therapy may be open to two ethical criticisms. First, we can ask whether giving placebos is really in the best interest of a patient. It encourages many patients in their belief that drugs can solve their problems. Patients with vague and general complaints may need some kind of psychological counseling, and giving them placebos merely discourages them from coming to grips with their genuine problems. Also, not all placebos are harmless (see the discussion in the Social Context on page 22). Some contain active chemicals that produce side effects (something likely to enhance the placebo effect),

so the physician who prescribes placebos may be subjecting her patient to some degree of risk.

Second, by deceiving her patient the physician is depriving him of the chance to make genuine decisions about his own life. Because the person is not genuinely sick, it does not seem legitimate to regard him as having deputized his physician to act in his behalf or as having transferred any of his power or autonomy to the physician. In Kant's terms, the physician is not acknowledging the patient's status as an autonomous rational agent. She is not according him the dignity that he possesses simply by virtue of being human. (A utilitarian who wished to claim that telling the truth to patients is a policy that will produce the best overall benefits could offer essentially the same criticism.)

Some of the traditional ethical problems about using placebos as a form of treatment rest, in part, on the assumption that placebos can be an effective form of therapy. At least one recent study analyzing investigations employing placebos as part of the experimental design casts doubt on the so-called placebo effect. Yet, even assuming the result is correct, we still must deal with the issue of whether it is ever morally legitimate to mislead a patient by giving her an inactive substance in the guise of an effective medication.

Dignity and Consent

Deception is not the only issue raised by the general question of the legitimacy of medical paternalism. Another of some importance is difficult to state precisely, but it has to do with the attitude and behavior of physicians toward their patients. Patients often feel that physicians deal with them in a way that is literally paternalistic—that physicians treat them like children.

The physician, like the magician or shaman, is often seen as a figure of power and mystery, one who controls the forces of nature and, by doing so, relieves suffering and restores health. Some physicians like this role and act in accordance with it. They resent having their authority questioned and fail to treat their patients with dignity and respect.

For example, many physicians call their patients by their first names, while expecting patients to refer to them as "Dr. X." In our society, women in particular have been most critical of such condescending attitudes displayed by physicians.

More serious is the fact that many physicians do not make a genuine effort to educate patients about the state of their health, the significance of laboratory findings, or the reasons that medication or other therapy is being prescribed. Patients are not only expected to follow orders but to do so without questioning them. Patients are, in effect, denied an opportunity to refuse treatment; consent is taken for granted.

The amount of time that it takes to help a patient understand his medical condition and the reason for the prescribed therapy is, particularly in this era of managed care, one reason that physicians do not attempt to provide such information. A busy physician in an office practice may see thirty or forty patients a day, and it is difficult to give each of them the necessary amount of attention. Also, patients without a medical background obviously can find it hard to understand medical explanations—particularly in the ways in which they are often given.

The result, for whatever reasons, is a situation in which physicians make decisions about patients without allowing patients to know the basis for them. Explanations are not given, physicians sometimes say, because patients "wouldn't understand" or "might draw the wrong conclusions about their illness" or "might worry needlessly." Patients thus not only are not provided information but are also discouraged from asking questions or revealing their doubts.

The moral questions here concern the responsibility of the physician. Is it ultimately useful for patients that physicians should play the role of a distant and mysterious figure of power? Do patients have a right to ask that physicians treat them with the same dignity as physicians treat one another? Should a physician attempt to educate her patients about their illnesses? Or is a physician's only real responsibility to provide patients with needed medical treatment?

Furthermore, is it always obvious that the physician knows what will count as the all-around best treatment for a patient? Patients, being human, have values of their own, and they may well not rank their best chance for effective medical treatment above all else. A woman with breast cancer, for example, may wish to avoid having a breast surgically removed (mastectomy) and so prefer another mode of treatment, even though her physician may consider it less effective. Can her physician legitimately withhold from her knowledge of alternative modes of treatment and so allow her no choice? Can he make the decision about treatment himself on the grounds that it is a purely medical matter, one about which the patient has no expert knowledge?

If patients have a right to decide about their treatment, physicians have an obligation to provide them with an account of their options and with the information they need to make a reasonable choice. Thus, treating patients with dignity requires recognizing their status as autonomous agents and securing their free and informed consent.

Confidentiality (Privacy)

"Whatever I see or hear, professionally or privately, which ought not be divulged, I will keep it secret and tell no one," runs one of the pledges in the Hippocratic Oath.

The tradition of medical practice in the West has taken this injunction very seriously. That it has done so is not entirely due to the high moral character of physicians, for the pledge to secrecy also serves an important practical function. Physicians need to have information of an intimate and highly personal sort to make diagnoses and prescribe therapies. If physicians were known to reveal such personal information, then patients would be reluctant to cooperate, and the practice of medicine would be adversely affected.

Furthermore, because psychological factors play a role in medical therapy, the chances of success in medical treatment are improved when patients can place trust and confidence in their physicians. This aspect of the physician–patient relationship actually forms a part of medical therapy. It is particularly so for the "talking cures" characteristic of some forms of psychiatry and psychotherapy.

Breaching Confidentiality

A number of states recognize the need for "privileged communication" between physician and patient and have laws to protect physicians from being compelled to testify about their patients in court. Yet physicians are also members of a society, and the society must attempt to protect the general interest. This sometimes places the physician in the middle of a conflict between the interest of the individual and the interest of society.

For example, physicians are often required by law to act in ways that force them to reveal certain information about their patients. The clearest instance of this is the legal obligation to report to health departments the names of those patients who are carriers of such communicable diseases as syphilis and tuberculosis. This permits health authorities to warn those with whom the carriers have come into contact and to guard against the spread of the diseases. Thus, the interest of society is given precedence over physician–patient confidentiality.

Confidentiality may also be breached in cases when the interest of the patient is at stake. Thus, a woman seeking medical attention for trauma resulting from abuse by a husband or boyfriend may have no choice about whether the police are notified. State laws may give the physician no choice about whether to report a suspected case of assault.

Similarly, physicians usually have no discretion about whether to report cases of suspected child abuse. Although the parents of the child may deny responsibility for the child's injuries, if the physician suspects the parents of abuse, she must make a report notifying police of her suspicions.

Few people question society's right to demand that physicians violate a patient's confidence when protecting the health of great numbers of people is at stake. More open to question are laws that require physicians to report gunshot wounds or other injuries that might be connected with criminal actions. (In some states, before abortion became legal, physicians were required to report cases of attempted abortion.) Furthermore, as citizens, physicians have a legal duty to report any information they may have about crime unless they are protected by a privileged-communication law.

Thus, the physician can be placed in a position of conflict. If he acts to protect the patients' confidences, then he runs the risk of acting illegally. If he acts in accordance with the law, then he must violate the confidence of his patients. What needs to be decided from a moral point of view is to what extent the laws that place a physician in such a situation are justified.

The physician who is not in private practice but is employed by a government agency or a business organization also encounters similar conflicts. Her obligations run in two directions: to her patients and to her employer.

Should a physician who works for a government agency, for example, tell her superiors that an employee has confided in her that he is a drug addict? If she does not, the employee may be subject to blackmail or bribery. If she does, then she must violate the patient's confidence.

Or what if a psychiatrist retained by a company decides one of its employees is so psychologically disturbed that she cannot function effectively in her job? Should the psychiatrist inform the employer, even if it means going against the wishes of the patient? (Consider also the fourth case cited on page 38.)

Duty to Warn?

Even more serious problems arise in psychiatry. Suppose that a patient expresses to his psychiatrist feelings of great anger against someone and even announces that he intends to go out and kill that person. What should the psychiatrist do? Should he report the threat to the police? Does he have an obligation to warn the person being threatened?

This is the fundamental issue dealt with by the California Supreme Court in the *Tarasoff* case. The court ruled that therapists at the student health service of the University of California, Berkeley, were negligent in their duty to warn Tatiana Tarasoff that Prosenjit Poddar, one of their patients, had threatened her life. The therapists reported the threat orally to the police, but they did not warn Tarasoff. Two months later, after her return from a trip to Brazil, she was murdered by Poddar.

Poddar was tried and convicted of second-degree murder. The conviction was overturned on appeal, on the grounds that the jury had not been properly instructed. The state decided against a second trial, and Poddar was released on condition that he return to India.

The parents of Tatiana Tarasoff sued the university for damages and eventually won a favorable judgment in the California Supreme Court. The court ruled that not only were the therapists justified in breaking the confidentiality of a patient, but they had a duty to warn her that her life was in danger. Since this ruling many psychiatrists and other therapists have argued that the court went too far in its demands.

Managed Care

A worrying trend with the rise of managed care is the availability of intimate information about patients that the patients provided to their physicians on the assumption that it would remain confidential. For patients to have their medical bills paid, their physicians may have to reveal to the insurer information concerning such matters as a patient's sexual history and practices, drug use, and troubling psychological problems. Most observers now believe that the assumption that what one tells one's physician will remain private no longer holds. The result is that patients are becoming less willing to

tell their physicians anything that might cause them harm if it were known to their spouse, employer, or insurance company.

HIPA Regulations

On April 14, 2003, the first comprehensive federal rules governing medical privacy went into effect. The Health Insurance Portability and Accountability Act of 1996 (HIPA) was originally conceived to protect information about patients as it is transferred from one computer database to another when a patient changes insurers or physicians.

The proposed legislation required patients to give written consent before physicians and hospitals released any information about them. When the proposed rules were made public, however, insurers, hospitals, and some medical organizations condemned the proposals as unrealistic and unworkable.

Critics claimed that a physician wouldn't even be able to question a patient about her symptoms without first securing her written consent and that pharmacies wouldn't be able to fill a called-in prescription. The health-care industry said the rules would impose an unrealistically heavy burden of paperwork on it and that this, in turn, would cause the cost of medical care to soar.

The written-consent requirement was dropped, and HIPA rules now require only that health-care providers notify patients of their legally acknowledged rights with respect to privacy and make a "good-faith effort" to obtain from patients a written acknowledgment that they have been notified.

The rights and policies acknowledged by HIPA, even in its modified form, include a number of important ones:

* Patients have a right to examine their medical records, secure copies, and correct errors.

* Medical information from a patient's records cannot be disclosed to an employer without the patient's explicit authorization.

- Researchers may use medical records for epidemiological studies, but they must remove all uniquely identifying information such as names, addresses, and Social Security numbers.

- Pharmacists are forbidden to use data about a patient for marketing purposes (e.g., selling prescription information to a pharmaceutical company that may try to get patients to ask their doctors to switch them from drugs produced by a rival company).

- The rules guarantee that parents will have "appropriate access" to the medical records of their minor children, including information about abortion, psychotherapy, and drug use.

- Hospital staff and those involved in treating a patient are restricted to knowing the minimum amount of personal information necessary to performing their tasks.

- Medical consultants, laboratories, lawyers, and business associates connected with the care of patients must sign contracts agreeing to protect the patients' confidentiality.

The law doesn't require that physicians secure the consent of patients before releasing information about them, so long as the release is for a medical purpose. Thus, a physician can solicit an opinion from another physician, tell a physical therapist why the patient needs treatment, or call in a prescription to a pharmacy.

HIPA has imposed some additional costs on hospitals and forced them to abandon longstanding practices. Even a moderate-sized hospital may have to negotiate confidentiality contracts with 400–500 business associates. Also, people can no longer be listed as patients in the hospital without their permission. Thus, hospitals may not be able to tell family members who call that their mother was taken to the emergency room with a stroke, was stabilized, and is now unconscious in the ICU.

Defenders of the HIPA rules as originally proposed claim that without the written-consent requirement, the rules are inadequate to protect patients from the breaches of privacy made possible by computers and the electronic storage of information. Even if this is true, HIPA has undeniably done a great deal to protect and promote the medical privacy of individuals. It has made everyone involved in health care, including patients, aware of the importance of confidentiality and the legitimacy of demanding it.

A 2005 ruling by the U.S. Department of Justice, however, raises a doubt about whether HIPA rules will protect privacy. The Justice Department decided that the HIPA law applies only to such "covered entities" as physicians, hospitals, and medical laboratories, and not to people who work for these "entities." This seems to mean that a physician may be fined as much as $250,000 or sent to prison for up to ten years for selling a mailing list of her patients who take drugs for heart problems, but her insurance clerk who does the same thing is not liable to prosecution.

The basic question about confidentiality concerns the extent to which we are willing to go to protect it. It is doubtful that anyone would want to assert that confidentiality should be absolutely guaranteed. But, if not, then under what conditions is it better to violate it than to preserve it?

Ethical Theories: Autonomy, Truth Telling, Confidentiality

What we have called state paternalism and personal paternalism are compatible with utilitarian ethical theory. But whether they are justifiable is a matter of controversy. According to the principle of utility, if governmental laws, policies, practices, or regulations serve the general interest, then they are justified. It can be argued that they are justified even if they restrict the individual's freedom of choice or action, because, for utilitarianism, autonomy has no absolute value. Personal paternalism is justified in a similar way. If a physician believes that she can protect her patient from unnecessary suffering or relieve his pain by keeping him in ignorance, by lying to him, by giving him placebos, or by otherwise deceiving him, these actions are morally legitimate.

However, John Stuart Mill did not take this view of paternalism. Mill argued that freedom of choice (autonomy) is of such importance that it can be justifiably restricted only when it can be shown that unregulated choice would cause harm to other people. Mill claimed that compelling people to act in certain ways "for their own good" is never legitimate. This position, Mill argued, is one that is justified by the principle of utility. Ordinarily, then, people have the freedom to decide what is going to be done to them, so free and informed consent is a prerequisite for medical treatment. Clearly, utilitarianism does not offer a straightforward answer to the question of the legitimacy of paternalism.

What we have said about paternalism applies also to confidentiality. Generally speaking, if violating confidentiality seems necessary to produce a state of affairs in which happiness is increased, then the violation is justified. This might be the case when, for example, someone's life is in danger or someone is being tried for a serious crime and the testimony of a physician is needed to help establish her innocence. Yet it also might be argued from the point of view of rule utilitarianism that confidentiality is such a basic ingredient in the physician–patient relationship that, in the long run, more good will be produced if confidentiality is never violated.

The Kantian view of paternalism, truth telling and confidentiality is more clearcut. Every person is a rational and autonomous agent. As such, he is entitled to make decisions that affect his own life. This means that a person is entitled to receive information relevant to making such decisions and is entitled to the truth,

no matter how painful it might be. Thus, for treatment to be justified, the informed consent of the individual is required.

The use of placebos or any other kind of deception in medicine is morally illegitimate in a Kantian view, because this would involve denying a person the respect and dignity to which she is entitled. The categorical imperative also rules out lying for the maxim involved in such an action produces a contradiction. (There are special difficulties in applying the categorical imperative that are discussed in Part V, "Foundations of Bioethics." When these are taken into account, Kant's view is perhaps not quite so straightforward and definite as it first appears.)

It can be argued that Kant's principles also establish that confidentiality should be regarded as absolute. When a person becomes a patient, she does so with the expectation that with regard to what she tells her physician, there is an implicit promise of confidentiality. The physician implicitly promises that he will not reveal any information about his patient, either what he has been told or what he has learned for himself. If this analysis is correct, then the physician is under an obligation to preserve confidentiality, because keeping promises is an absolute duty. Here, as in the case of lying, there are difficulties connected with the way a maxim is stated. (See Part V, "Foundations of Bioethics," for a discussion.)

Ross's principles recognize that everyone has a moral right to be treated as an autonomous agent who is entitled to make decisions affecting his own life. Thus, free and informed consent to medical treatment is required. Also, everyone is entitled to know the truth and to be educated in helpful ways. Similarly, if confidentiality is a form of promise keeping, everyone is entitled to expect that it will be maintained. Thus, paternalism, lying, and violation of confidence are prima facie morally objectionable.

But, of course, it is possible to imagine circumstances in which they would be justified. The right course of action that a physician must follow is one that can be determined only on the basis of the physician's knowledge of the patient, the patient's problem, and the general situation. Thus, Ross's principles rule out paternalism, deception, and violations of confidence as general policies, but they do not make them morally illegitimate in an absolute way.

Rawls's theory of social and political morality is compatible with state paternalism of a restricted kind. No laws, practices, or policies can legitimately violate the rights of individuals. At the same time, however, a society, viewing arrangements from the original position, might decide to institute a set of practices that would promote what they agreed to be their interests. If, for example, health is agreed to be an interest, then they might be willing to grant to the state the power to regulate a large range of matters connected with the promotion of health. Establishing standards for physicians would be an example of such regulation.

But they might also go so far as to give the state power to decide (on the advice of experts) what medical treatments are legitimate, what drugs are safe and effective to use, what substances should be controlled or prohibited, and so on. So long as the principles of justice are not violated and so long as the society can be regarded as imposing these regulations on itself for the promotion of its own good, then such paternalistic practices are unobjectionable.

With respect to personal paternalism, consent, deception, and confidentiality, Rawl's general theory offers no specific answers. But since Rawls endorses Ross's account of prima facie duties (while rejecting Ross's intuitionism), it seems reasonable to believe that Rawls's view on these matters would be the same as Ross's.

The natural law doctrine of Roman Catholicism suggests that paternalism in both its forms is legitimate. If the state is organized to bring about such "natural goods" as health, then laws and practices that promote those goods are morally right. Individuals do have a worth in themselves and should be free to direct and organize their own lives. Thus, they generally should be informed and should make their own medical decisions. Yet at the same time, individuals may be ignorant of sufficient relevant information, lack the intellectual capacities to determine what is really in their best interest, or be moved by momentary passions and circumstances. For these reasons, the state may act so that people are protected from their own shortcomings, and yet their genuine desire—their "natural ends"—are satisfied.

Thus, natural law doctrine concludes that because each individual has an inherent worth, she is entitled to be told the truth in medical situations (and others) and not deceived. But it reasons, too, that because a physician has superior knowledge, he may often perceive the interest of the patient better than the patient herself. Accordingly, natural law doctrine indicates that although the physician should avoid lying, he is still under an obligation to act for the best interest of his patient. That may mean allowing the patient to believe something that is not so (as in placebo therapy) or withholding information from the patient. In order for this to be morally legitimate, however, the physician's motive must always be that of advancing the welfare of the patient.

In the matter of confidentiality, the natural law doctrine recognizes that the relationship between physician and patient is one of trust, and a physician has a duty not to betray the confidences of her patients. But the relationship is not sacrosanct and the duty is not absolute. When the physician finds herself in a situation in which a greater wrong will be done if she does not reveal a confidence entrusted to her by a patient, she has a duty to reveal the confidence. If, for example, the physician possesses knowledge that would save someone from death or unmerited suffering, then it is her duty to make this knowledge available, even if by doing so she violates a patient's trust.

We have only sketched an outline of the possible ways in which ethical theories might deal with the issues involved in paternalism, consent to treatment, truth telling, and confidentiality. Some of the views presented are open to challenge, and none has been worked out in a completely useful way. That is one of the tasks that remains to be performed.

Autonomy, paternalism, truth telling, and confidentiality are bound together in a complicated web of moral issues. We have not identified all the strands of the web, nor have we traced out their connections with one another.

We have, however, mentioned enough difficulties to reveal the seriousness of the issues.

As the cases and contexts that follow illustrate, some of the issues are social ones and require that we decide about the moral legitimacy of certain kinds of laws, practices, and policies. Others are matters of personal morality that concern our obligations to society and to other people. Our ethical theories, we can hope, will provide us with the means of arriving at workable and justifiable resolutions of the issues. But before this point is reached, much intellectual effort and ingenuity will have to be invested.

READINGS

Section 1: Consent and Medical Treatment

Paternalism and Partial Autonomy

Onora O'Neill

O'Neill argues that traditional views of autonomy in medical ethics fail to recognize that most patients fall short in varying degrees of the ideal rationality assumed as the basis of genuinely informed consent. Serious respect for autonomy, she claims, requires more than getting patients to sign consent forms. Physicians must make it possible for patients to understand the basics of their diagnosis and the proposed treatment, then make sure that they are secure enough to refuse the treatment or insist that it be changed.

Autonomous action, understood literally, is self-legislated action. It is the action of agents who can understand and choose what they do. When cognitive or volitional capacities, or both, are lacking or impaired, autonomous action is reduced or impossible. Autonomy is lacking or incomplete for parts of all lives (infancy, early childhood), for further parts of some lives (unconsciousness, senility, some illness and mental disturbance) and throughout some lives (severe retardation). Since illness often damages autonomy, concern to respect it does not seem a promising fundamental

principle for medical ethics. Medical concern would be strangely inadequate if it did not extend to those with incomplete autonomy. Concern for patients' well-being is generally thought a more plausible fundamental principle for medical ethics.

But it is also commonly thought implausible to make beneficence the only fundamental aim of medical practice, since it would then be irrelevant to medical treatment whether patients possessed standard autonomy, impaired autonomy or no capacity for autonomous action. All patients, from infants to the most autonomous, would be treated in ways judged likely to benefit them. Medical practice would be through and through paternalistic, and would treat patients as persons only if beneficence so required.

Recurrent debates about paternalism in medical ethics show that the aim of subordinating concern for autonomy to beneficence remains controversial. The group of notions invoked in these debates—autonomy, paternalism, consent, respect for persons, and treating others as persons—are quite differently articulated in different ethical theories. A consideration of various ways in which they can be articulated casts some light on issues that lie behind discussions of medical paternalism.

1. Paternalism and autonomy in result-oriented ethics

Most consequential moral reasoning does not take patients' autonomy as a fundamental constraint on medical practice. Utilitarian moral reasoning takes the production of welfare or well-being (variously construed) as the criterion of right action. Only when respect for patients' autonomy (fortuitously) maximises welfare is it morally required. Paternalism is not morally wrong; but some acts which attempt to maximise welfare by disregarding autonomy will be wrong if in fact non-paternalistic action (such as showing respect for others or seeking their consent to action undertaken) would have maximised welfare. Only some 'ideal' form of consequentialism, which took the maintenance of autonomy as an independent value, could regard the subordination of autonomy to beneficence as wrong. In utilitarian ethical thinking autonomy is of marginal ethical importance, and paternalism only misplaced when it reflects miscalculation of benefits.

This unambiguous picture is easily lost sight of because of an historical accident. A classical and still highly influential utilitarian discussion of autonomy and paternalism is John Stuart Mill's *On Liberty*[1]. Mill believed both that each person is the best judge of his or her own happiness and that autonomous pursuit of goals is itself a major source of happiness, so he thought happiness could seldom be maximised by action which thwarted or disregarded others' goals, or took over securing them. Paternalists, on this view, have benevolent motives but don't achieve beneficent results. They miscalculate.

Mill's claims are empirically dubious. Probably many people would be happier under beneficent policies even when these reduce the scope for autonomous action. Some find autonomous pursuit of goals more a source of frustration and anxiety than of satisfaction. In particular, many patients want relief from hard decisions and the burden of autonomy. Even when they don't want decisions made for them they may be unable to make them, or to make them well. The central place Mill assigns autonomy is something

of an anomaly in result-oriented ethical thought[2]. It is open to challenge and shows Mill's problem in reconciling liberty with utility rather than any success in showing their coincidence.

2. Paternalism and autonomy in action-oriented ethics

Autonomy can have a more central place only in an entirely different framework of thought. Within a moral theory which centres on action rather than on results, the preconditions of agency will be fundamental. Since autonomy, of some degree, is a presupposition of agency, an action-centred ethic, whether its fundamental moral category is that of human rights, or of principles of obligation or of moral worth, must make the autonomy of agents of basic rather than derivative moral concern. This concern may be expressed as concern not to use others, but to respect them or 'treat them as persons', or to secure their consent and avoid all (including paternalistic) coercion.

A central difficulty for all such theories is once again empirical. It is obvious enough that some human beings lack cognitive and volitional capacities that would warrant thinking of them as autonomous. But where autonomous action is ruled out what can be the moral ground for insisting on respect or support for human autonomy[3]? The question is sharply pointed for medical ethics since patients *standardly* have reduced cognitive and volitional capacities.

Yet most patients have some capacities for agency. Their impairments undercut some but not all possibilities for action. Hence agent-centred moral theories may be relevant to medical ethics, but only if based on an accurate view of human autonomy. The central tradition of debate in agent-centred ethics has not been helpful here because it has tended to take an abstract and inaccurate view of human autonomy. The history of these discussions is revealing.

Enlightenment political theory and especially Locke's writings are classical sources of arguments against paternalism and for respect for human autonomy. Here the consent of citizens to their governments is held to legitimate government action. In consenting citizens become, in part, the authors of government action: the notion of the sovereignty of the people can be understood as the claim that they have consented to, and so authorised, the laws by which they are ruled. In obeying such laws they are not mere subjects but retain their autonomy.

This picture invited, and got, a tough focus on the question 'What constitutes consent?' An early and perennial debate was whether consent has to be *express*—explicitly declared in speech or writing—or can be *tacit*—merely a matter of going along with arrangements. In a political context the debate is whether legitimate government must have explicit allegiance, or whether, for example, continued residence can legitimate government action. A parallel debate in medical ethics asks whether legitimate medical intervention requires explicit consent, recorded by the patient's signing of consent forms, or whether placing oneself in the hands of the doctor constitutes consent to whatever the doctor does, provided it accords with the standards of the medical profession[4].

The underlying picture of human choice and action invoked by those who advocate the 'informed consent' account of human autonomy is appropriate to a contractual model of human relations. Just as parties to commercial contracts consent to specific action by others, and have legal redress when this is not forthcoming, and citizens consent to limited government action (and may seek redress when this is exceeded), so patients consent to specified medical procedures (and have cause for grievance if their doctors do otherwise). Those who argue that informed consent criteria are not appropriate in medical practice sometimes explicitly reject the intrusion of commercial and contractual standards in medical care.

The contractual picture of human relations is clearly particularly questionable in medicine. We may think that citizenship and commerce are areas where we are autonomous decision-makers, enjoying what Mill would have called 'the maturity of our faculties'. In these areas, if anywhere, we come close to being fully rational decision-makers. Various well-known idealisations of human rationality— 'rational economic man', 'consenting adults', 'cosmopolitan citizens', 'rational choosers'—may seem tolerable approximations. But the notion that we could be 'ideal rational patients' cannot stand up to a moment's scrutiny. This suggests that we cannot plausibly extend the enlightenment model of legitimating consent to medical contexts. Where autonomy is standardly reduced, paternalism must it seems be permissible; opposition to medical paternalism appears to reflect an abstract and inaccurate view of human consent which is irrelevant in medical contexts.

3. The opacity of consent: a reversal of perspective

However, the same picture might be seen from quite a different perspective. Human autonomy is limited and precarious in many contexts, and the consent given to others' actions and projects is standardly selective and incomplete. *All* consent is consent to some proposed action or project *under certain descriptions*. When we consent to an action or project we often do not consent even to its logical implications or to its likely results (let alone its actual results), nor to its unavoidable corollaries and presuppositions. Put more technically, consenting (like other proposition attitudes) is *opaque*. When we consent we do not necessarily 'see through' to the implications of what we consent to and consent to these also. When a patient consents to an operation he or she will often be unaware of further implications or results of that which is consented to. Risks may not be understood and post-operative expectations may be vague. But the opacity of patients' consent is not radically different from the opacity of all human consenting. Even in the most 'transparent', highly-regulated, contractual arrangements, consent reaches only a certain distance. This is recognised whenever contracts are voided because of cognitive or volitional disability, or because the expectations of the 'reasonable man' about the further implications of some activity do not hold up. Medical cases may then be not so much anomalies, with which consent theory cannot adequately deal, as revealing cases which highlight typical limits of human autonomy and consent[5].

Yet most discussions of consent theory point in the other direction. The limitations of actual human autonomy aren't taken as constraints on working out the determinate implications of respect for autonomy in actual contexts, but often as *aberrations* from ideally autonomous choosing. The rhetoric of the liberal tradition shows this clearly. Although it is accepted that we are discussing the autonomy of '*finite* rational beings', finitude of all sorts is constantly forgotten in favour of loftier and more abstract perspectives.

4. Actual consent and 'ideal' consent

There are advantages to starting with these idealised abstractions rather than the messy incompleteness of human autonomy as it is actually exercised. Debates on consent theory often shift from concern with dubious consent actually given by some agent to a proposed activity or arrangement to concern with consent that would hypothetically be given by an ideally autonomous (rational and free) agent faced with that proposal. This shift to hypothetical consent allows us to treat the peculiar impairments of autonomy which affect us when ill as irrelevant: we can still ask what the (admittedly hypothetical) ideally autonomous patient would consent to. This line of thought curiously allows us to combine ostensible concern for human autonomy with paternalistic medical practice. Having reasoned that some procedure would be consented to by ideally autonomous patients we may then feel its imposition on actual patients of imperfect autonomy is warranted. But by shifting focus from what has (actually) been consented to, to what would (ideally) be consented to, we replace concern for others' autonomy with concern for the autonomy of hypothetical, idealised agents. This is not a convincing account of what it is not to use others, but rather to treat them as persons[6].

If we don't replace concern for actual autonomy with concern for idealised autonomy, we need to say something definite about when actual consent is genuine and significant and when it is either spurious or misleading, and so unable to legitimise whatever is ostensibly consented to. Instead of facing the sharp outlines of idealised, hypothetical conceptions of human choosing we may have to look at messy actual choosing. However, we don't need to draw a sharp boundary between genuine, morally significant consent and spurious, impaired consent which does not legitimate. For the whole point of concern for autonomy and hence for genuine consent is that it is not up to the *initiator* of action to choose what to impose: it is up to those affected to choose whether to accept or to reject proposals that are made. To respect others' autonomy requires that we make consent *possible* for them[7], taking account of whatever partial autonomy they may have. Medical practice respects patients' autonomy when it allows patients as they actually are to refuse or accept what is proposed to them. Of course, some impairments prevent refusal or acceptance. The comatose and various others have to be treated paternalistically. But many patients can understand and refuse or accept what is proposed over a considerable range. Given some capacities for autonomous action, whatever can be made comprehensible to and refusable by patients, can be treated as subject to their consent—or refusal. This may require doctors and others to avoid haste and pressure and to counteract the intimidation of unfamiliar, technically bewildering and socially alien medical environments. Without such care in imparting information and proposing treatment the 'consent' patients give to their treatment will lack the autonomous character which would show that they have not been treated paternally but rather as persons.

5. 'Informed consent' and legitimating consent

There is a long-standing temptation, both in medical ethics and beyond, to find ways in which consent procedures can be formalised and the avoidance of paternalism guaranteed and routinised. But if the ways in which human autonomy is limited are highly varied, it is not likely that any set procedures can guarantee that consent has been given. Early European colonialists who 'negotiated treaties' by which barely literate native peoples without knowledge of European moral and legal traditions 'consented' to sales of land or cession of sovereignty reveal only that the colonialists had slight respect for others' autonomy. Medical practice which relies on procedures such as routine signing of 'consent forms' may meet conditions for avoiding litigation, but does not show concern for human autonomy as it actually exists. Such procedures are particularly disreputable given our knowledge of the difficulties even the most autonomous have in assimilating distressing information or making unfamiliar and hard decisions.

Serious respect for autonomy, in its varied, limited forms, demands rather that patients' refusal or consent, at least to fundamental aspects of treatment, be made possible. The onus on practitioners is to see that patients, as they actually are, understand what they can about the basics of their diagnosis and the proposed treatment, and are secure enough to refuse the treatment or to insist on changes. If the proposal is accessible and refusable for an actual patient, then (but only then) can silence or going along with it reasonably be construed as consent. The notions of seeking consent and respecting autonomy are brought into disrepute when the 'consent' obtained does not genuinely reflect the patient's response to proposed treatment.

6. Partial autonomy, coercion and deception

Once we focus on the limited autonomy of actual patients it becomes clear that consent to *all* aspects and descriptions of proposed treatment is neither possible nor required. Only the ideally, unrestrictedly autonomous could offer such consent. In human contexts, whether medical or political, the most that we can ask for is consent to the more *fundamental* proposed policies, practices and actions. Patients can no more be asked to consent to every aspect of treatment than citizens can be asked to consent to every act of government. Respect for autonomy requires that consent be possible to *fundamental* aspects of actions and proposals, but allows that consent to trivial and ancillary aspects of action and proposals may be absent or impossible.

Treatment undertaken without consent when a patient could have reached his or her own decisions if approached with care and respect may fail in many ways. In the most serious cases the action undertaken uses patients as tools or instruments. Here the problem is not just that some partially autonomous patient couldn't (or didn't) consent, but that the treatment precluded consent even for ideally autonomous patients. Where a medical proposal hinges fundamentally on coercion or deception, not even the most rational and independent can dissent, or consent. Deceivers don't reveal their fundamental proposal or action; coercers may make their proposal plain enough but rob *anyone* of choice between consent or dissent. In deception 'consent' is spurious because cognitive conditions for consent are not met: in coercion 'consent' is spurious because volitional conditions for consent are not met.

However, some non-fundamental aspects of treatment to which consent has been given may have to include elements of deception or coercion. Use of placebos or of reassuring but inaccurate accounts of expected pain might sometimes be non-fundamental but indispensable and so permissible deceptions[8]. Restraint of a patient during a painful procedure might be a non-fundamental but indispensable and so permissible coercion. But using patients as unwitting experimental subjects or concealing fundamental aspects of their illness or prognosis or treatment from them, or imposing medical treatment and ignoring or preventing its refusal, would always use patients, and so fail to respect autonomy. At best such imposed treatment might, if benevolent, constitute impermissible paternalism; at worst, if non-benevolent, it might constitute assault or torture.

7. Partial autonomy, manipulation and paternalism

Use of patients is an extreme failure to respect autonomy; it precludes the consent even of the ideally autonomous, let alone of those with cognitive or volitional impairments. Respect for partial autonomy would also require medical practice to avoid treatment which, though refusable by the ideally autonomous, would not be refusable by a particular patient in his or her present condition. Various forms of manipulation and of questionable paternalism fail to meet these requirements. Patients are manipulated if they are 'made offers they cannot refuse', given their actual cognitive and volitional capacities. For example, patients who think they may be denied further care or discharged without recourse if they refuse proposed treatment may be unable to refuse it. To ensure that 'consent' is not manipulated available alternatives may have to be spelled out and refusal of treatment shown to be a genuine option. 'Consent' which is achieved by relying on misleading or alarmist descriptions of prognosis or uninformative accounts of treatment and alternatives does not show genuine respect. Only patients who are quite unable to understand or decide need complete paternalist protection. When there is a relationship of unequal power, knowledge or dependence, as so often [exists] between patients and doctors, avoiding manipulation and unacceptable paternalism demands a lot.

Avoiding unacceptable paternalism demands similar care. Manipulators use knowledge of others and their weaknesses to impose their own goals; paternalists may not recognise either others' goals, or that they are *others'* goals. Patients, like anyone with limited understanding and capacity to choose, may be helped by advice and information, and may need help to achieve their aims. But if it is not the patients' but others' aims which determine the limits and goals of medical intervention, the intervention (even if neither deceptive nor coercive) will be unacceptably paternalistic. Handicapped patients whose ways of life are determined by others may not be deceived or coerced—but they may be unable to refuse what others think appropriate for them. This means that patients' own goals, medical and non-medical, and their plans for achieving these, are constraints on any medical practice which respects patients' autonomy. Since return to health is often central to patients' plans, this constraint may require little divergence from the treatment that paternalistic medical practice would select, except that patients would have to be party to fundamental features of their treatment. But where patients' goals differ from doctors' goals—perhaps they value quality of life or avoiding pain or dependence more than the doctor would—respect for the patient requires that these goals not be overridden or replaced by ones the patient does not share and that the patient's own part in achieving them not be set aside.

Debates on medical paternalism often assume that the goals of medical action can be determined independently of patients' goals. But in action-oriented ethical thinking morally required goals are not given independently of agents' goals. Paternalism in this perspective is simply the imposition of others' goals (perhaps those of doctors, nursing homes or relatives) on patients. These goals too must be taken into account if we are to respect the autonomy of doctors, nursing homes and relatives. But imposing their goals on patients capable of some autonomy does not respect patients. The contextually-sensitive, action-oriented framework discussed here does not reinstate a contractual or consumer-sovereignty picture of medical practice, in which avoiding deceit and coercion is all that respect requires. On the contrary, it insists that judgements of human autonomy must be contextual, and that what it takes to respect human autonomy will vary with context. When patients' partial autonomy constrains medical practice, respect for patients may demand action which avoids not only deceit and coercion but also manipulation and paternalism; but where autonomy is absent there is no requirement that it be respected.

8. Respecting limited autonomy

Medical paternalism has been considered within three frameworks. Within a result-oriented framework of the standard utilitarian type it is not only permissible but required that concern for human autonomy be subordinated to concern for total welfare. Within an action-oriented framework that relies on an abstract, 'idealising' account of human autonomy, medical practice is too readily construed as ruling out all paternalism and permitting only treatment that would be consented to by 'idealised' autonomous agents. Within an action-oriented framework that takes account of the partial character of human autonomy we can sketch patterns of reasoning which draw boundaries in given contexts between permissible and impermissible forms of paternalism. This account yields no formula, such as the requirement to avoid coercion and deception may be thought to yield for abstract approaches. But the inadequacies of that formula for guiding action when impairment is severe speak in favour of a more accurate and contextual view of human autonomy.

By trying to incorporate concern for actual, partial capacities for autonomous action into an account of respect for patients and medical paternalism we find that we are left without a single boundary-line between acceptable and unacceptable medical practice. What we have are patterns of reasoning which yield different answers for different patients and for different proposals for treatment. One patient can indeed be expected to come to an informed and autonomous (if idiosyncratic) decision; another may be too confused to take

in what his options are. A third may be able to understand the issues but too dependent or too distraught to make decisions. Attempts to provide uniform guidelines for treating patients as persons, respecting their autonomy and avoiding unacceptable medical paternalism are bound to be insensitive to the radical differences of capacity of different patients. A theory of respect for patients must rely heavily and crucially on actual medical judgements to assess patient's current capacities to absorb and act on information given in various ways. But it does not follow that 'professional judgement' or 'current medical standards' *alone* can provide appropriate criteria for treating patients as persons. For if these do not take the varying ways in which patients can exercise autonomy as constraints on permissible treatment, they may institutionalise unjustifiable paternalism. Professional judgement determines what constitutes respect for patients only when guided by concern to communicate effectively what patients can understand and to respect the decisions that they can make.

9. Issues and contexts

Sections 1, 2 and 3 above discussed some ways in which treatment of autonomy, paternalism and respect for patients are articulated in result-oriented ethics and in action-oriented approaches which take an abstract view of cognition and volition, and hence of autonomy. The alternative account proposed in sections 4 to 8 is that only consideration of the determinate cognitive and volitional capacities and incapacities of particular patients at particular times provides a framework for working out boundaries of permissible medical paternalism. If such judgements are contextual, there is no way to demarcate unacceptable paternalism in the abstract. The following headings only point to contexts in which these issues arise and have to be resolved. Which resolutions are justifiable will depend not only on following a certain pattern of reasoning but on the capacities for autonomous action particular patients have at the relevant time.

A. Temporarily Impaired Capacity For Autonomy

If respect for autonomy is morally fundamental, restoring (some) capacities is morally fundamental. Survival is necessary for such restoration; but not sufficient. If patients' autonomy constrains practice, survival can never be foregone in favour of autonomy, but it is an open question whether survival with no or greatly reduced capacities for autonomy can be a permissible goal. Risky surgery may sometimes reasonably be imposed for the sake of restoring capacities, even when mere survival would be surer without surgery.

Temporary loss of autonomy offers grounds for paternalistic intervention to restore autonomy—but not for all paternalistic interventions. It might be better for an unconscious sportsman if advantage were taken of his temporary incapacity to perform some non-urgent operation or to make some non-medical intervention—in his affairs. But if restoration of autonomy is likely, an action-oriented ethic offers no ground for such paternalism.

B. Long Term Or Permanent Impairment Of Autonomy

This is the standard situation of children, and so the original context of paternalism. Those with long and debilitating illnesses, physical as well as mental, may suffer very varied impairments of autonomy. Hence consideration of parental paternalism may illuminate these cases. While the law has to fix an age to end minority, parents have to adapt their action to a constantly altering set of capacities for autonomous action. Choices which cannot be made at one stage can at another; autonomy develops in one area of life and lags in another[9]. Unfortunately, medical trajectories may not be towards fuller capacities. Medical and other decisions may then have to be to some extent imposed. But there is no general reason to think that those who are unable to make some decisions are unable to make any decisions, and even when full return of capacities is unlikely, patients, like children, may gain in autonomy when an optimistic view is taken of their capacities.

C. Permanent Loss Of Autonomy

Here decisions have (eventually) to be made that go beyond what is needed for restoring (some) autonomy. Sometimes medical staff and relatives may be able to make some use of a notion of hypothetical consent. But what they are likely to be asking is not 'What would the ideally autonomous choose in this situation?', but rather 'What would this patient have chosen in this situation?' If this can be answered, it may be possible to maintain elements of respect for the particular patient as he or she was in former times. But usually this provides only vague indications for medical or other treatment, and respect for absent autonomy can be at best vestigial.

D. Lifelong Incapacity For Autonomy

For those who never had or will have even slight capacities for autonomous action the notion of respect

is vacuous. There is no answer to the hypothetical question 'What would he or she have chosen if able to do so?' and the hypothetical question 'What would the ideally autonomous choose in this situation?' may have determinate answer. Here, unavoidably, paternalism must govern medical practice indefinitely and the main questions that arise concern the appropriate division of authority to make paternalistic decisions between relatives and medical staff and legally appointed guardians.

References and Notes

1. Mill J S. On liberty. In: Warnock M, ed. *Utilitarianism and on liberty*, etc. London: Fontana, 1972.

2. This has been a recurrent criticism of Mill from Stephen J F, *Liberty, equality, fraternity*, London: Smith, Elder, 1873, to Dworkin G. Paternalism. *The monist* 1972;56: 64–84 and reprinted in Sartorius R, ed., *Paternalism*, Minneapolis: University of Minnesota Press, 1983: section IV.

3. Broader worries mushroom here too: what grounds the moral status of non-autonomous humans in action oriented ethics? For recent discussion see Haksar V. *Liberty, equality, perfectionism*. Oxford: Clarendon Press, 1979; Clark S, *The moral status of animals*. Oxford: Clarendon Press, 1977; Dennett D Conditions of personhood. In: Rorty A, ed. *The identity of persons*. Berkeley and Los Angeles: University of California Press, 1976, and reprinted in Dennett D. *Brainstorms*. Hassocks, Sussex: The Harvester Press, Ltd 1979.

4. Here US and British practice differ. US legislation and debates often stress the need to secure informed consent from patients (or their guardians). Cf. discussions and bibliography in Veatch R M. *Case studies in medical ethics*. Cambridge Mass: Harvard University Press, 1977. British law holds that 'what information should be disclosed, and how and when, is very much a matter of professional judgement', and that 'there is no ground in English law for extending the limited doctrine of informed consent outside the field of property rights'. See Sidaway v Board of Governors of the Bethlem Royal Hospital and the Maudsley Hospital and Others, Law Report, *The Times*, 1984 Feb 24. However, medical paternalism may be more practised in the US than it is praised by those who write on medical ethics. See Buchanan A E Medical paternalism. *Philosophy and public affairs* 1978;7: 371–390, and reprinted in Sartorius, see reference (2).

5. For further comments on the limitations of 'normal' abilities see Wilder D. Paternalism and the mildly retarded. Reprinted in Sartorius, see reference (2).

6. A point made long since by Isaiah Berlin in Two concepts of liberty. *Four essays on liberty*. Oxford: OUP, 1969.

7. For the interpretation of Kantian ethics offered here see also O'Neill O. Kant after virtue. *Inquiry* 1984;26: 387–405; Consistency in action. In: Potter N, Timmons M, eds. *New essays in ethical universalizability*. Dordrecht, the Netherlands: Reidel publishing company, forthcoming, and Between consenting adults, unpublished.

8. Bok S. *Lying: moral choice in public and private life*. New York: Harvester Press, Random House, 1978: 234. Bok points out that sometimes the use of placebos may be more than ancillary (61–68), and also discusses fundamental forms of deception such as hiding from the patient that the illness is terminal. On the latter point see also Kubler-Ross E. *On*

death and dying. New York: Macmillan 1969, and the bibliography in Veatch, reference (4).

9. For discussions of some distinctive features of children's partial autonomy see Leites E. Locke's liberal theory of fatherhood; Slote M A. Obedience and illusions and Katz S N, Schroeder W A, Sidman L. Emancipating our children—coming of legal age in America. In: O'Neill O, Ruddick W, eds. *Having children: philosophical and legal reflections on parenthood*. New York: OUP, 1979.

Paternalism

Gerald Dworkin

Gerald Dworkin attempts to show that even if we place an absolute value on individual choice, a variety of paternalistic policies can still be justified. In consenting to a system of representative government, we understand that it may act to safeguard our interests in certain ways. But, Dworkin asks, what are the "kinds of conditions which make it plausible to suppose that rational men could reach agreement to limit their liberty even when other men's interests are not affected?"

Dworkin suggests that such conditions are satisfied in cases in which there is a "good" such as health involved—one that everybody needs to pursue other goods. Rational people would agree that attaining such a good should be promoted by the government even when individuals don't recognize it as a good at a particular time. There is a sense, Dworkin argues, in which we are not really imposing such a good on people. What we are really saying is that if everyone knew the facts and assessed them properly, this is what they would choose. Also, we are sometimes influenced by immediate alternatives that look more attractive, or we are careless or depressed and so do not act for what we acknowledge as a good. Thus, we might approve of laws against cigarette smoking because we know we should not smoke cigarettes.

It is plausible, Dworkin suggests, that rational people would grant to a legislature the right to impose such restrictions on their conduct. But the government has to demonstrate the exact nature of the harmful effects to be avoided. Also, if there is an alternative way of accomplishing the end without restricting liberty, then the society should adopt it.

Neither one person, nor any number of persons, is warranted in saying to another human creature of ripe years, that he shall not do with his life for own benefit what he chooses to do with it.   MILL

I do not want to go along with a volunteer basis. I think a fellow should be compelled to become better and not let him use his discretion whether he wants to get smarter, more healthy or more honest.   GENERAL HERSHEY

From Gerald Dworkin "Paternalism" Reprinted from *The Monist*, LaSalle, IL, Vol. 56, no. 1, (1973): 64–84. Copyright © *The Monist: An International Quarterly Journal of General Philosophical Inquiry*, Open Court Publishing Company, Chicago, Illinois. (Notes renumbered.)

I take as my starting point the "one very simple principle" proclaimed by Mill in *On Liberty*. . . "That principle is, that the sole end for which mankind are warranted, individually or collectively, in interfering with the liberty of action of any of their number, is self-protection. That the only purpose for which power can be rightfully exercised over any member of a civilized community, against his will, is to prevent harm to others. He cannot rightfully be compelled to do or forbear because it will be better for him to do so, because it will make him happier, because, in the opinion of others, to do so would be wise, or even right."[1]

This principle is neither "one" nor "very simple." It is at least two principles; one asserting that self-protection or the prevention of harm to others is sometimes a sufficient warrant and the other claiming that the individual's own good is *never* a sufficient warrant for the exercise of compulsion either by the society as a whole or by its individual members. I assume that no one with the possible exception of extreme pacifists or anarchists questions the correctness of the first half of the principle. This essay is an examination of the negative claim embodied in Mill's principle—the objection to paternalistic interferences with a man's liberty.

I

By paternalism I shall understand roughly the interference with a person's liberty of action justified by reasons referring exclusively to the welfare, good, happiness, needs, interests or values of the person being coerced. One is always well-advised to illustrate one's definitions by examples but it is not easy to find "pure" examples of paternalistic interferences. For almost any piece of legislation is justified by several different kinds of reasons and even if historically a piece of legislation can be shown to have been introduced for purely paternalistic motives, it may be that advocates of the legislation with an anti-paternalistic outlook can find sufficient reasons justifying the legislation without appealing to the reasons which were originally adduced to support it. Thus, for example, it may be that the original legislation requiring motorcyclists to wear safety helmets was introduced for purely paternalistic reasons. But the Rhode Island Supreme Court recently upheld such legislation on the grounds that it was "not persuaded that the legislature is powerless to prohibit individuals from pursuing a course of conduct which could conceivably result in their becoming public charges," thus clearly introducing reasons of a quite different kind. Now I regard this decision as being based on reasoning of a very dubious nature but it illustrates the kind of problem one has in finding examples. The following is a list of the kinds of interferences I have in mind as being paternalistic.

II

1. Laws requiring motorcyclists to wear safety helmets when operating their machines.

2. Laws forbidding persons from swimming at a public beach when lifeguards are not on duty.

3. Laws making suicide a criminal offense.

4. Laws making it illegal for women and children to work at certain types of jobs.

5. Laws regulating certain kinds of sexual conduct, e.g. homosexuality among consenting adults in private.

6. Laws regulating the use of certain drugs which may have harmful consequences to the user but do not lead to anti-social conduct.

7. Laws requiring a license to engage in certain professions with those not receiving a license subject to fine or jail sentence if they do engage in the practice.

8. Laws compelling people to spend a specified fraction of their income on the purchase of retirement annuities. (Social Security)

9. Laws forbidding various forms of gambling (often justified on the grounds that the poor are more likely to throw away their money on such activities than the rich who can afford to).

10. Laws regulating the maximum rates of interest for loans.

11. Laws against duelling.

In addition to laws which attach criminal or civil penalties to certain kinds of action there are laws, rules, regulations, decrees, which make it either difficult or impossible for people to carry out their plans and which are also justified on paternalistic grounds. Examples of this are:

1. Laws regulating the types of contracts which will be upheld as valid by the courts, e.g. (an example of Mill's to which I shall return) no man may make a valid contract for perpetual involuntary servitude.

2. Not allowing as a defense to a charge of murder or assault the consent of the victim.

3. Requiring members of certain religious sects to have compulsory blood transfusions. This is made possible by not allowing the patient to have recourse to civil suits for assault and battery and by means of injunctions.

4. Civil commitment procedures when these are specifically justified on the basis of preventing the person being committed from harming himself.

(The D.C. Hospitalization of the Mentally Ill Act provides for involuntary hospitalization of a person who "is mentally ill, and because of that illness, is likely to injure *himself* or others if allowed to remain at liberty." The term injure in this context applies to unintentional as well as intentional injuries.)

5. Putting fluorides in the community water supply.

All of my examples are of existing restrictions on the liberty of individuals. Obviously one can think of interferences which have not yet been imposed. Thus one might ban the sale of cigarettes, or require that people wear safety-belts in automobiles (as opposed to merely having them installed) enforcing this by not allowing motorists to sue for injuries even when caused by other drivers if the motorist was not wearing a seat-belt at the time of the accident. . . .

III

Bearing these examples in mind let me return to a characterization of paternalism. I said earlier that I meant by the term, roughly, interference with a person's liberty for his own good. But as some of the examples show the class of persons whose good is invoked is not always identical with the class of persons whose freedom is restricted. Thus in the case of professional licensing it is the practitioner who is directly interfered with and it is the would-be patient whose interests are presumably being served. Not allowing the consent of the victim to be a defense to certain types of crime primarily affects the would-be aggressor but it is the interests of the willing victim that we are trying to protect. Sometimes a person may fall into both classes as would be the case if we banned the manufacture and sale of cigarettes and a given manufacturer happened to be a smoker as well.

Thus we may first divide paternalistic interferences into "pure" and "impure" cases. In "pure" paternalism the class of persons whose freedom is restricted is identical with the class of persons whose benefit is intended to be promoted by such restrictions. Examples: the making of suicide a crime, requiring passengers in automobiles to wear seat-belts, requiring a Christian Scientist to receive a blood transfusion. In the case of "impure" paternalism in trying to protect the welfare of a class of persons we find that the only way to do so will involve restricting the freedom of other persons besides those who are benefitted. Now it might be thought that there are no cases of "impure" paternalism since any such case could always be justified on non-paternalistic grounds, i.e. in terms of preventing harm to others. Thus we might ban cigarette manufacturers from continuing to manufacture their product on the grounds that we are preventing them from causing illness to others in the same way that we prevent other manufacturers from releasing pollutants into the atmosphere, thereby causing danger to the members of the community. The difference is, however, that in the former but not the latter case the harm is of such a nature that it could be avoided by those individuals affected if they so chose. The incurring of the harm requires, so to speak, the active co-operation of the victim. It would be mistaken theoretically and hypocritical in practice to assert that our interference in such cases is just like our interferences in standard cases of protecting others from harm. At the very least someone interfered with in this way can reply that no one is complaining about his activities. It may be that impure paternalism requires arguments or reasons of a stronger kind in order to be justified since there are persons who are losing a portion of their liberty and they do not even have the solace of having it be done "in their own interest." Of course in some sense, if paternalistic justifications are ever correct then we are protecting others, we are preventing some from injuring others, but it is important to see the differences between this and the standard case.

Paternalism then will always involve limitations on the liberty of some individuals in their own interest but it may also extend to interferences with the liberty of parties whose interests are not in question.

IV

Finally, by way of some more preliminary analysis, I want to distinguish paternalistic interferences with liberty from a related type with which it is often confused. Consider, for example, legislation which forbids employees to work more than, say, 40 hours per week. It is sometimes argued that such legislation is paternalistic for if employees desired such a restriction on their hours of work they could agree among themselves to impose it voluntarily. But because they do not the society imposes its own conception of their best interests upon them by the use of coercion. Hence this is paternalism.

Now it may be that some legislation of this nature is, in fact, paternalistically motivated. I am not denying that. All I want to point out is that there is another possible way of justifying such measures which is not paternalistic in nature. It is not paternalistic because as Mill puts it in a similar context such measures are "required not to overrule the judgment of individuals respecting their own interest but to give effect to that judgment they being unable to give effect to it except by concert, which concert again cannot be effectual unless it receives validity and sanction from the law."[2]

The line of reasoning here is a familiar one first found in Hobbes and developed with great sophistication by contemporary economists in the last decade or so. There are restrictions which are in the interests of a class of persons taken collectively but are such that the immediate interest of each individual is furthered by his violating the rule when others adhere to it. In such cases the individuals involved may need the use of compulsion to give effect to their collective judgment of their own interest by guaranteeing each individual compliance by the others. In these cases compulsion is not used to achieve some benefit which is not recognized to be a benefit by those concerned, but rather because it is the only feasible means of achieving some benefit which is recognized as such by all concerned. This way of viewing matters provides us with another characterization of paternalism in general. Paternalism might be thought of as the use of coercion to achieve a good which is not recognized as such by those persons for whom the good is intended. Again while this formulation captures the heart of the matter—it is surely what Mill is objecting to in *On Liberty*—the matter is not always quite like that. For example when we force-motorcyclists to wear helmets we are trying to promote a good—the protection of the person from injury—which is surely recognized by most of the individuals concerned. It is not that a cyclist doesn't value his bodily integrity; rather, as a supporter of such legislation would put it, he either places, perhaps irrationally, another value or good (freedom from wearing a helmet) above that of physical well-being or, perhaps, while recognizing the danger in the abstract, he either does not fully appreciate it or he underestimates the likelihood of its occurring. But now we are approaching the question of possible justifications of paternalistic measures and the rest of this essay will be devoted to that question.

V

I shall begin for dialectical purposes by discussing Mill's objections to paternalism and then go on to discuss more positive proposals.

An initial feature that strikes one is the absolute nature of Mill's prohibitions against paternalism. It is so unlike the carefully qualified admonitions of Mill and his fellow Utilitarians on other moral issues. He speaks of self-protection as the *sole* end warranting coercion, of the individual's own goals as *never* being a sufficient warrant.... The structure of Mill's argument is as follows:

1. Since restraint is an evil the burden of proof is on those who propose such restraint.

2. Since the conduct which is being considered is purely self-regarding, the normal appeal to the protection of the interests of others is not available.

3. Therefore we have to consider whether reasons involving reference to the individual's own good, happiness, welfare, or interests are sufficient to overcome the burden of justification.

4. We either cannot advance the interests of the individual by compulsion, or the attempt to do so involves evil which outweighs the good done.

5. Hence the promotion of the individual's own interests does not provide a sufficient warrant for the use of compulsion.

Clearly the operative premise here is 4 and it is bolstered by claims about the status of the individual as judge and appraiser of his welfare, interests, needs, etc.

With respect to his own feelings and circumstances, the most ordinary man or woman has means of knowledge immeasurably surpassing those that can be possessed by any one else.[3]

He is the man most interested in his own well-being: the interest which any other person, except in cases of strong personal attachment can have in it, is trifling, compared to that which he himself has.[4]

These claims are used to support the following generalizations concerning the utility of compulsion for paternalistic purposes.

The interferences of society to overrule his judgment and purposes in what only regards himself must be grounded in general presumptions; which may be altogether wrong; and even if right are as likely as not to be misapplied to individual cases.[5]

But the strongest of all the arguments against the interference of the public with purely personal conduct is that when it does interfere, the odds are that it interferes wrongly and in the wrong place.[6]

All errors which the individual is likely to commit against advice and warning are far outweighed by the evil of allowing others to constrain him to what they deem his good.[7]

Performing the utilitarian calculation by balancing the advantages and disadvantages we find that:

Mankind are greater gainers by suffering each other to live as seems good to themselves, than by compelling each other to live as seems good to the rest.[8]

From which follows the operative premise 4.

This is clearly the main channel of Mill's thought and it is one which has been subjected to vigorous attack from the moment it appeared—most often by fellow Utilitarians. The link that they have usually seized on is, as Fitzjames Stephen put it, the absence of proof that the "mass of adults are so well acquainted with their own interests and so much disposed to pursue them that no compulsion or restraint put upon them by any others for the purpose of promoting their interest can really promote them."[9]

Now it is interesting to note that Mill himself was aware of some of the limitations on the doctrine that the individual is the best judge of his own interests. In his discussion of government intervention in general (even where the intervention does not interfere with liberty but provides alternative institutions to those of the market) after making claims which are parallel to those just discussed, e.g.

People understand their own business and their own interests better, and care for them more, than the government does, or can be expected to do.[10]

He goes on to an intelligent discussion of the "very large and conspicuous exceptions" to the maxim that:

Most persons take a juster and more intelligent view of their own interest, and of the means of promoting it than can either be prescribed to them by a general enactment of the legislature, or pointed out in the particular case by a public functionary.[11]

Thus there are things

of which the utility does not consist in ministering to inclinations, nor in serving the daily uses of life, and the want of which is least felt where the need is greatest. This is peculiarly true of those things which are chiefly useful as tending to raise the character of human beings. The uncultivated

cannot be competent judges of cultivation. Those who most need to be made wiser and better, usually desire it least, and, if they desired it, would be incapable of finding the way to it by their own lights.

. . . A second exception to the doctrine that individuals are the best judges of their own interest, is when an individual attempts to decide irrevocably now what will be best for his interest at some future and distant time. The presumption in favor of individual judgment is only legitimate, where the judgment is grounded on actual, and especially on present, personal experience; not where it is formed antecedently to experience, and not suffered to be reversed even after experience has condemned it.[12]

The upshot of these exceptions is that Mill does not declare that there should never be government interference with the economy but rather that

. . . in every instance, the burden of making out a strong case should be thrown not on those who resist but on those who recommend government interference. Letting alone, in short, should be the general practice: every departure from it, unless required by some great good, is a certain evil.[13]

In short, we get a presumption not an absolute prohibition. The question is why doesn't the argument against paternalism go the same way?

I suggest that the answer lies in seeing that in addition to a purely utilitarian argument Mill uses another as well. . . . A consistent Utilitarian can only argue against paternalism on the grounds that it (as a matter of fact) does not maximize the good. It is always a contingent question that may be refuted by the evidence. But there is also a non-contingent argument which runs through *On Liberty.* When Mill states that "there is a part of the life of every person who has come to years of discretion, within which the individuality of that person ought to rein uncontrolled either by any other person or by the public collectively" he is saying something about what it means to be a person, an autonomous agent. It is because coercing a person for his own good denies this status as an independent entity that Mill objects to it so strongly and in such absolute terms. To be able to choose is a good that is independent of the wisdom of what is chosen. A man's "mode" of laying out his existence is the best, not because it is the best in itself, but because it is his own mode.[14]

It is the privilege and proper condition of a human being, arrived at the maturity of his faculties, to use and interpret experience in his own way.[15]

As further evidence of this line of reasoning in Mill consider the one exception to his prohibition against paternalism.

In this and most civilised countries, for example, an engagement by which a person should sell himself, or allow himself to be sold, as a slave, would be null and void; neither enforced by law nor by opinion. The ground for thus limiting his power of voluntarily disposing of his own lot in life, is apparent, and is very clearly seen in this extreme case. The reason for not interfering, unless for the sake of others, with a person's voluntary acts, is consideration for his liberty. His voluntary choice is evidence that what he so chooses is desirable, or at least endurable, to him, and his good is on the whole best provided for by allowing him to take his own means of pursuing it. But by selling himself for a slave, he abdicates his liberty; he foregoes any future use of it beyond that single act.

He therefore defeats, in his own case, the very purpose which is the justification of allowing him to dispose of himself. He is no longer free; but is thenceforth in a position which has no longer the presumption in its favour, that would be afforded by his voluntarily remaining in it. The principle of freedom cannot require that he should be free not to be free. It is not freedom to be allowed to alienate his freedom.[16]

Now leaving aside the fudging on the meaning of freedom in the last line it is clear that part of this argument is incorrect. While it is true that *future* choices of the slave are not reasons for thinking that what he chooses then is desirable for him, what is at issue is limiting his immediate choice; and since this choice is made freely, the individual may be correct in thinking that his interests are best provided for by entering such a contract. But the main consideration for not allowing such a contract is the need to preserve the liberty of the person to make future choices. This gives us a principle—a very narrow one, by which to justify some paternalistic interferences. Paternalism is justified only to preserve a wider range of freedom for the individual in question. How far this principle could be extended, whether it can justify all the cases in which we are inclined upon reflection to think paternalistic measures justified remains to be discussed. What I

have tried to show so far is that there are two strains of argument in Mill—one a straight-forward Utilitarian mode of reasoning and one which relies not on the goods which free choice leads to but on the absolute value of the choice itself. The first cannot establish any absolute prohibition but at most a presumption and indeed a fairly weak one given some fairly plausible assumptions about human psychology; the second while a stronger line of argument seems to me to allow on its own grounds a wider range of paternalism than might be suspected. I turn now to a consideration of these matters.

VI

We might begin looking for principles governing the acceptable use of paternalistic power in cases where it is generally agreed that it is legitimate. Even Mill intends his principles to be applicable only to mature individuals, not those in what he calls "non-age." What is it that justifies us in interfering with children? The fact that they lack some of the emotional and cognitive capacities required in order to make fully rational decisions. It is an empirical question to just what extent children have an adequate conception of their own present and future interests but there is not much doubt that there are many deficiencies. For example it is very difficult for a child to defer gratification for any considerable period of time. Given these deficiencies and given the very real and permanent dangers that may befall the child it becomes not only permissible but even a duty of the parent to restrict the child's freedom in various ways. There is however an important moral limitation on the exercise of such parental power which is provided by the notion of the child eventually coming to see the correctness of his parent's interventions. Parental paternalism may be thought of as a wager by the parent on the child's subsequent recognition of the wisdom of the restrictions. There is an emphasis on what could be called future-oriented consent—on what the child will come to welcome, rather than on what he does welcome.

The essence of this idea has been incorporated by idealist philosophers into various types of "real-will" theory as applied to fully adult persons. Extensions of paternalism are argued for by claiming that in various respects, chronologically mature individuals share the same deficiencies in knowledge, capacity to think rationally, and the ability to carry out decisions that children possess. Hence in interfering with such people we are in effect doing what they would do if they were fully rational. Hence we are not really opposing their will, hence we are not really interfering with their freedom. The dangers of this move has been sufficiently exposed by Berlin in his "Two Concepts of Liberty." I see no gain in theoretical clarity nor in practical advantage in trying to pass over the real nature of the interferences with liberty that we impose on others. Still the basic notion of consent is important and seems to me the only acceptable way of trying to delimit an area of justified paternalism.

Let me start by considering a case where the consent is not hypothetical in nature. Under certain conditions it is rational for an individual to agree that others should force him to act in ways which, at the time of action, the individual may not see as desirable. If, for example, a man knows that he is subject to breaking his resolves when temptation is present, he may ask a friend to refuse to entertain his requests at some later stage.

A classical example is given in the Odyssey when Odysseus commands his men to tie him to the mast and refuse all future orders to be set free because he knows the power of the Sirens to enchant men with their songs. Here we are on relatively sound ground in later refusing Odysseus' request to be set free. He may even claim to have changed his mind but since it is just such changes that he wishes to guard against we are entitled to ignore them.

A process analogous to this may take place on a social rather than individual basis. An electorate may mandate its representatives to pass legislation which when it comes time to "pay the price" may be unpalatable. I may believe that a tax increase is necessary to halt inflation though I may resent the lower pay check each month. However in both this case and that of Odysseus the measure to be enforced is specifically requested by the party involved and at some point in time there is genuine consent and agreement on the part of those persons whose liberty is infringed. Such is not the case for the paternalistic measures we have been speaking about. What must be involved here is not consent to specific measures but rather consent to a system of government run by elected representatives, with an understanding that they may act to safeguard our interests in certain limited ways.

I suggest that since we are all aware of our irrational propensities, deficiencies in cognitive and emotional capacities and avoidable and unavoidable ignorance it is rational and prudent for us to in effect take out "social insurance policies." We may argue for and against proposed paternalistic measures in terms

of what fully rational individuals would accept as forms of protection. Now, clearly since the initial agreement is not about specific measures we are dealing with a more-or-less blank check and therefore there have to be carefully defined limits. What I am looking for are certain kinds of conditions which make it plausible to suppose that rational men could reach agreement to limit their liberty even when other men's interests are not affected.

Of course as in any kind of agreement schema there are great difficulties in deciding what rational individuals would or would not accept. Particularly in sensitive areas of personal liberty, there is always a danger of the dispute over agreement and rationality being a disguised version of evaluative and normative disagreement.

Let me suggest types of situations in which it seems plausible to suppose that fully rational individuals would agree to having paternalistic restrictions imposed upon them. It is reasonable to suppose that there are "goods" such as health which any person would want to have in order to pursue his own good—no matter how that good is conceived. This is an argument that is used in connection with compulsory education for children but it seems to me that it can be extended to other goods which have this character. Then one could agree that the attainment of such goods should be promoted even when not recognized to be such, at the moment, by the individuals concerned.

An immediate difficulty that arises stems from the fact that men are always faced with competing goods and that there may be reasons why even a value such as health—or indeed life—may be overridden by competing values. Thus the problem with the Christian Scientist and blood transfusions. It may be more important for him to reject "impure substances" than to go on living. The difficult problem that must be faced is whether one can give sense to the notion of a person irrationally attaching weights to competing values.

Consider a person who knows the statistical data on the probability of being injured when not wearing seat-belts in an automobile and knows the types and gravity of the various injuries. He also insists that the inconvenience attached to fastening the belt every time he gets in and out of the car outweighs for him the possible risks to himself. I am inclined in this case to think that such a weighing is irrational. Given his life plans which we are assuming are those of the average person, his interests and commitments already undertaken, I think it is safe to predict that we can find inconsistencies in his calculations at some point. I am assuming that this is not a man who for some conscious or unconscious reasons is trying to injure himself nor is he a man who just likes to "live dangerously." I am assuming that he is like us in all the relevant respects but just puts an enormously high negative value on inconvenience—one which does not seem comprehensible or reasonable.

It is always possible, of course to assimilate this person to creatures like myself. I, also, neglect to fasten my seat-belt and I concede such behavior is not rational but not because I weigh the inconvenience differently from those who fasten the belts. It is just that having made (roughly) the same calculation as everybody else I ignore it in my actions. [Note: a much better case of weakness of the will than those usually given in ethics texts.] A plausible explanation for this deplorable habit is that although I know in some intellectual sense what the probabilities and risks are I do not fully appreciate them in an emotionally genuine manner.

We have two distinct types of situation in which a man acts in a non-rational fashion. In one case he attaches incorrect weights to some of his values; in the other he neglects to act in accordance with his actual preferences and desires. Clearly there is a stronger and more persuasive argument for paternalism in the latter situation. Here we are really not—by assumption—imposing a good on another person. But why may we not extend our interference to what we might call evaluative delusions? After all in the case of cognitive delusions we are prepared, often, to act against the expressed will of the person involved. If a man believes that when he jumps out the window he will float upwards—Robert Nozick's example—would not we detain him, forcibly if necessary? The reply will be that this man doesn't wish to be injured and if we could convince him that he is mistaken as to the consequences of his action he would not wish to perform the action. But part of what is involved in claiming that a man who doesn't fasten his seat-belts is attaching an irrational weight to the inconvenience of fastening them is that if he were to be involved in an accident and severely injured he would look back and admit that the inconvenience wasn't as bad as all that. So there is a sense in which if I could convince him of the consequences of his action he also would not wish to continue his present course of action. Now the notion of consequences being used here is covering a lot of ground. In one case it's being used to indicate what will or can happen as a result of a course of action and

in the other it's making a prediction about the future evaluation of the consequences—in the first sense—of a course of action. And whatever the difference between facts and values—whether it be hard and fast or soft and slow—we are genuinely more reluctant to consent to interferences where evaluative differences are the issue. Let me now consider another factor which comes into play in some of these situations which may make an important difference in our willingness to consent to paternalistic restrictions.

Some of the decisions we make are of such a character that they produce changes which are in one or another way irreversible. Situations are created in which it is difficult or impossible to return to anything like the initial stage at which the decision was made. In particular some of these changes will make it impossible to continue to make reasoned choices in the future. I am thinking specifically of decisions which involve taking drugs that are physically or psychologically addictive and those which are destructive of one's mental and physical capacities.

I suggest we think of the imposition of paternalistic interferences in situations of this kind as being a kind of insurance policy which we take out against making decisions which are far-reaching, potentially dangerous and irreversible....

A second class of cases concerns decisions which are made under extreme psychological and sociological pressures. I am not thinking here of the making of the decision as being something one is pressured into—e.g. a good reason for making duelling illegal is that unless this is done many people might have to manifest their courage and integrity in ways in which they would rather not do so—but rather of decisions such as that to commit suicide which are usually made at a point where the individual is not thinking clearly and calmly about the nature of his decision. In addition, of course, this comes under the previous heading of all-too-irrevocable decision. Now there are practical steps which a society could take if it wanted to decrease the possibility of suicide—for example not paying social security benefits to the survivors or as religious institutions do, not allowing such persons to be buried with the same status as natural deaths. I think we may count these as interferences with the liberty of persons to attempt suicide and the question is whether they are justifiable.

Using my argument schema the question is whether rational individuals would consent to such limitations. I see no reason for them to consent to an absolute prohibition but I do think it is reasonable for them to agree to some kind of enforced waiting period. Since we are all aware of the possibility of temporary states, such as great fear or depression, that are inimical to the making of well-informed and rational decisions, it would be prudent for all of us if, there were some kind of institutional arrangement whereby we were restrained from making a decision which is (all too) irreversible. What this would be like in practice is difficult to envisage and it may be that if no practical arrangements were feasible then we would have to conclude that there should be no restriction at all on this kind of action. But we might have a "cooling off" period, in much the same way that we now require couples who file for divorce to go through a waiting period. Or, more far-fetched, we might imagine a Suicide Board composed of a psychologist and another member picked by the applicant. The Board would be required to meet and talk with the person proposing to take his life, though its approval would not be required.

A third class of decisions—these classes are not supposed to be disjoint—involves dangers which are either not sufficiently understood or appreciated correctly by the persons involved. Let me illustrate, using the example of cigarette smoking, a number of possible cases.

1. A man may not know the facts—e.g. smoking between 1 and 2 packs a day shortens life expectancy 6.2 years, the costs and pain of the illness caused by smoking, etc.

2. A man may know the facts, wish to stop smoking, but not have the requisite willpower.

3. A man may know the facts but not have them play the correct role in his calculation because, say, he discounts the danger psychologically because it is remote in time and/or inflates the attractiveness of other consequences of his decision which he regards as beneficial.

In case 1 what is called for is education, the posting of warnings, etc. In case 2 there is no theoretical problem. We are not imposing a good on someone who rejects it. We are simply using coercion to enable people to carry out their own goals. (Note: There obviously is a difficulty in that only a subclass of the individuals affected wish to be prevented from doing what they are doing.) In case 3 there is a sense in which we are imposing a good on someone since given his current appraisal of the facts he doesn't wish to be restricted. But in another sense we are not imposing a good since what is being claimed—and what must be shown or at least argued for—is that an accurate accounting on his part would lead him to reject his current course of action. Now we all know that such cases exist, that we are prone to disregard dangers that are only possibilities, that immediate pleasures are often magnified and distorted.

If in addition the dangers are severe and far-reaching we could agree to allowing the state a certain degree of power to intervene in such situations. The difficulty is in specifying in advance, even vaguely, the class of cases in which intervention will be legitimate.

A related difficulty is that of drawing a line so that it is not the case that all ultra-hazardous activities are ruled out, e.g. mountain-climbing, bullfighting, sports-car racing, etc. There are some risks—even very great ones—which a person is entitled to take with his life.

A good deal depends on the nature of the deprivation—e.g. does it prevent the person from engaging in the activity completely or merely limit his participation—and how important to the nature of the activity is the absence of restriction when this is weighed against the role that the activity plays in the life of the person. In the case of automobile seat-belts, for example, the restriction is trivial in nature, interferes not at all with the use or enjoyment of the activity, and does, I am assuming, considerably reduce a high risk of serious injury. Whereas, for example, making mountain climbing illegal prevents completely a person engaging in an activity which may play an important role in his life and his conception of the person he is.

In general the easiest cases to handle are those which can be argued about in the terms which Mill thought to be so important—a concern not just for the happiness or welfare, in some broad sense, of the individual but rather a concern for the autonomy and freedom of the person. I suggest that we would be most likely to consent to paternalism in those instances in which it preserves and enhances for the individual his ability to rationally consider and carry out his own decisions.

I have suggested in this essay a number of types of situations in which it seems plausible that rational men would agree to granting the legislative powers of a society the right to impose restrictions on what Mill calls "self-regarding" conduct. However, rational men knowing something about the resources of ignorance, ill-will and stupidity available to the lawmakers of a society—a good case in point is the history of drug legislation in the United States—will be concerned to limit such intervention to [a] minimum. I suggest in closing two principles designed to achieve this end.

In all cases of paternalistic legislation there must be a heavy and clear burden of proof placed on the authorities to demonstrate the exact nature of the harmful effects (or beneficial consequences) to be avoided (or achieved) and the probability of their occurrence. The burden of proof here is twofold—what lawyers distinguish as the burden of going forward and the burden of persuasion. That the authorities have the burden of going forward means that it is up to them to raise the question and bring forward evidence of the evils to be avoided. Unlike the case of new drugs where the manufacturer must produce some evidence that the drug has been tested and found not harmful, no citizen has to show with respect to self-regarding conduct that it is not harmful or promotes his best interests. In addition the nature and cogency of the evidence for the harmfulness of the course of action must be set at a high level. To paraphrase a formulation of the burden of proof for criminal proceedings—better 10 men ruin themselves than one man be unjustly deprived of liberty.

Finally I suggest a principle of the least restrictive alternative. If there is an alternative way of accomplishing the desired end without restricting liberty then although it may involve great expense, inconvenience, etc. the society must adopt it.

Notes

1. J.S. Mill, *Utilitarianism* and *On Liberty* (Fontana Library Edition, ed. by Mary Warnock, London, 1962), p. 135. All further quotes from Mill are from this edition unless otherwise noted.
2. J.S. Mill, *Principles of Political Economy* (New York P. F. Collier and Sons, 1900), p. 442.
3. *Mill, Utilitarianism* and *On Liberty*, p. 214.
4. *Ibid.*, p. 206.
5. *Ibid.*, p. 207.
6 *Ibid.*, p. 214.
7. *Ibid.*, p, 207.
8. *Ibid.*, p. 138.
9. J.F. Stephen, *Liberty, Equality, Fraternity* (New York; Henry Holt & Co., n.d.), p. 24.
10. *Ibid.*, p. 33.
11. Mill, *Principles*, II, 458.
12. *Ibid.*, II, 459.
13. *Ibid.*, II, 451.
14. Mill, *Utilitarianism* and *On Liberty*, p. 197.
15. *Ibid.*, p. 186.
16. *Ibid.*, pp. 235–236.

Confronting Death: Who Chooses, Who Controls? A Dialogue

Dax Cowart and Robert Burt

Dax Cowart and Robert Burt agree that the principle of autonomy gives competent patients the right to refuse or discontinue medical treatment. Burt suggests, however, that the physician should stop treatment only after a time during which the physician explores the patient's reasons for refusing it and perhaps even argues with him to get him to set aside any preconceptions that may be influencing his decision.

Cowart does not reject Burt's general views, but he is inclined to see the need for physicians to accept patients' decisions relatively quickly. Mentioning his own experiences, Cowart stresses that severe pain permits little delay and that patients should not be forced to endure what they do not wish to endure. That they may later be glad to be alive does not justify violating their autonomy and forcing treatment on them. For Cowart, respecting autonomy means recognizing that a patient is free to make wrong choices, as well as right ones.

Background Note: For background, see Case Presentation: Donald (Dax) Cowart Rejects Treatment—And Is Ignored.

From Dax Cowart and Robert Burt, "Confronting Death: Who Chooses, Who Controls? A Dialogue Between Dax Cowart and Robert Burt," *Hastings Center Report*, Vol. 28, no. 1, (1998): 14–17. Copyright © 1998 Hastings Center Report. Reproduced by permission of the publisher.

Robert Burt: Let me start at a place where I think we agree. Before 1974, the dominant attitude of physicians toward patients was by and large intensely disrespectful of patients' autonomy. The basic posture was paternalistic. Physicians knew what was best for patients, and the patient's job was just to go along. Dax himself has been a critically important actor and symbol in identifying the wrongdoing in that attitude, and raising into high social visibility the proposition that autonomy is a vitally important value; patients are the central actors here and physicians must attend to them in a respectful and careful way. On that point we agree.

The place at which I get troubled or confused is what exactly follows if we embrace this important norm of autonomy. Start with a simple version of two alternatives, perhaps extreme alternatives, to try and sharpen what the issues are. One version of autonomy says: well, it's the physician's job, like it's anybody's job who needs to respect autonomy, to say to a patient, "What do you want?"; the patient says "I want A, B, C," or "I don't want A, B, and C," and then it's just the physician's job to implement that. That is a possible interpretation of the law and way of proceeding.

I find that interpretation of the law, however, to be quite unsatisfactory. It is not only permissible, but important—I would even say essential—that a somewhat different step be taken by a physician (or anyone dealing with a patient). "What do you want?" Dax says, "I don't want treatment." At that point I think it is not only permissible but imperative that whoever hears that respond not with "OK, great, let's go ahead," but instead with, "Well, why exactly do you want that? Why have you come to that conclusion? I want to explore that with you." Now imagine the next step. Dax says, "None of your business." I think it is then both permissible and essential for the doctor to say, "No, no, it is my business, and not because I'm a doctor but because I am another human being who is necessarily involved in your life. We define one another in important kinds of ways, and while, of course, I can't define you, we have to negotiate together what our shared meanings are about, what it is that you want me to do or not to do." It is correct not only for me to say, "Why do you want to do that?" but also permissible for me to argue with you if I disagree, and to argue strenuously with you on a variety of grounds.

Now come the end of the day, yes, it's your life, it's not my life. But the question is, When have we reached the end of the day? When may we terminate this conversation so that I believe that the choice that you're making is as considerate a choice as I think it is morally obligatory for you to make? I know that this can become a kind of trick, and it shouldn't be that this is only the first step in a conversation.

Why do I think it's not just important but imperative that anybody hearing such a request on Dax's part explore it with him and even quarrel with him? I think we define one another for one another. We are not isolated creatures, popped into this world, who chart ourselves only by what's in our head. We are intensely social creatures. Dax himself has become more than just an individual, he has become a symbol and independent force that shapes our way of thinking about ourselves when we imagine ourselves to be patients. We are mutually shaped by our expectation in lots of ways.

There is one way I want to particularize that in Dax's case. All of us, as members of a society, have attitudes toward people with disabilities. Those of us who are able-bodied or, as they say correctly among disability advocates, those of us who are temporarily able-bodied, often spend an enormous amount of energy denying the fact that our able-bodied status is, in fact, temporary. It is for many, many of us an unattractive, if not to say frightening, possibility to think of ourselves as significantly disabled. Many people in this society, for lots of different reasons, have stereotypical views of disabled people and what their possibilities are. You correct me if I misstep here, Dax, but just on the face of the matter, it seems to me that until your accident you were a member of the able-bodied community, and a very able-bodied member at that, for whom your physical prowess was a matter of great importance and pride to you. Suddenly and deeply beyond your control, in a way that can happen frighteningly to any of us, you found yourself pushed over this divide between the able-bodied and the not-able-bodied. But you inevitably brought with you attitudes that were shaped at a time when you were comfortably, happily, proudly a member of the able-bodied community.

Now it seems to me that having been pushed over that divide in physical terms, there still was a question, at least, about your attitudinal concerns, your attitudinal shift.

Let me read one passage from this initial conversation that Dax had with Dr. White.[1] Dr. White said to Dax, "From the very beginnings according to what you've told me, and what's been written in your hospital record, you had very strong feelings that you didn't want the doctors to go on with your treatment, that you wanted them to leave you alone and not attempt to sustain your life. How do you feel about that at this point?" Dax said in response, "At this point I feel much the same way. If I felt that I could be rehabilitated to where I could walk and do other things normally, I might have a different feeling about it. I don't know. But being blind itself is one big factor that influences my thinking on the matter. I know that there's no way that I want to go on as a blind and a cripple."

Now human communication is a chancy and somewhat crude thing. I only have your words. Dr. White only had Dax's words. Reading those words and putting myself imaginatively in the shoes of your physician, or your lawyer asked to represent you, I have a whole series of questions. How realistic was your perception at that point, just a few months after your accident? How realistic was it of the full range of capacities that could be held out to you, even if you were permanently blind, and even if you were permanently unable to walk (which it turns out, of course, you were not)? How much contact had you had with people with significant disabilities of these sorts? How much were you devaluing your own capacity, thinking that in fact you would be able to do nothing more than your mother's observation in the subsequent videotape interview. She said that you said at one point, "You know, all I'm going to be able do is to sit on a street corner and sell pencils." Well, of course we see today that you are very active and don't sell pencils. But this is a very common fear of able-bodied people who have had no substantial contact with people with disabilities.

So I would ask myself first of all, how realistic is someone like Dax's sense of the real possibilities open for him? But then second of all, how can I as a helper, someone who wants to be useful and helpful to him, communicate in a way that is fully understandable and believable what the real range of options are to him, disabled, that he, formerly able-bodied and now still able-bodied in his image of himself, is not able to see. What do you do? There are many possibilities. You bring people to talk, you discuss, you challenge. All this takes time. It's not something that you can just say to Dax, "Well, how realistic are you? Let's have a brief discussion." In the kind of immensely difficult, immensely traumatic situation in which he found himself, in the midst of his treatment and with the physical pain that he was feeling, and with the psychological pain of his losses including the loss of his father in the same accident, this is not a conversation that can take place in ten minutes or one day. Over how much time and with what kind of constraints?

Dax Cowart: Now I know how it feels to be killed. It makes it more difficult to take the opposing position, but being the good lawyer that I am I will do my best (audience laughter).

The right to control your own body is a right you're born with, not something that you have to ask anyone else for, not the government, not your treating physician, not your next-of-kin. No one has the right to amputate your arms or your legs without your consent. No one has the right to remove your internal organs without your consent. No one has the right to force other kinds of medical treatment upon you without your consent. There is no legitimate law, there is no legitimate authority, there is no legitimate power anywhere on the face of this earth that can take the right away from a mentally competent human being and give it to a state, to a federal government, or to any other person.

A number of quotations constitute a brief overview of what others have said throughout history and also give insight into my own feelings. In *A Connecticut Yankee in King Arthur's Court*, the leading character and one of his companions come across a whole family which has almost died of smallpox. The mother appears to be the only one still alive. Later on they discover she has a fifteen-year-old daughter up in a sleeping loft who is in a near-comatose state and almost dead. So they rushed the young girl down and began administering aid to her. I'll pick up the quotation there. "I snatched my liquor flask from my knapsack, but the woman forbade me and said: 'No, she does not suffer; it is better so. It might bring her back to life. None that be so good and kind as ye are would do her that cruel hurt. Thou go on thy way, and be merciful friends that will not hinder.'"

I was asking my own physicians to be merciful friends who go on their way and do not hinder. But they would not listen. In the first part of this century, Justice Louis Brandeis wrote in one of his Supreme Court opinions: "The makers of our Constitution sought to protect Americans, and their beliefs, their thoughts, their emotions, and their sensations. They conferred as against the government the right to be left alone, the most comprehensive of rights and the right most valued by civilized man."

Warren Burger, who later became chief justice, referred to Justice Brandeis: "Nothing suggests that Justice Brandeis thought an individual possessed these rights only as to sensible beliefs, valid thoughts, reasonable emotions or well-founded sensations. I suggest that he intended to include a great many foolish, unreasonable and even absurd ideas that do not conform, such as refusing medical treatment even at great risk."

Justice Burger did not want to encourage foolish, unreasonable, or absurd conduct, but he did recognize the importance that the individual has in making his or her own decision. He understood that what some of us might think of as foolish, unreasonable, or absurd can also be something that is very precious and dear to someone else.

The English poet John Keats, almost 200 years ago, wrote simply, "Until we are sick, we understand not." That is so true—until we are the ones who are feeling the pain, until we are the ones who are on the sick bed, we cannot fully appreciate what the other person is going through. And even having been there myself today I cannot fully appreciate what someone who has been badly burned is going through on the burn ward. Our mind mercifully blocks out much of that pain.

When I was in the second grade, a popular joke concerned a mother who severely reprimanded her young son for coming home late from school. He said, "Mom, now that I'm a Boy Scout, I stopped to do my good deed for the day and helped this little old granny lady cross the street." She said, "Young man, it sure doesn't take an hour to help one little old granny lady cross the street." He said, "Well, it sure did this one, 'cause she didn't want to go." I was like that little old granny lady; I didn't want to go. And even today there are many patients who are being forced to endure things that they do not wish to endure, while being taken places that they don't even want to go.

John Stuart Mill, the English philosopher, in his essay *On Liberty*, came down on the side of the right to self-determination by dividing acts into those that are self-regarding and those that are other-regarding in nature. Mill concluded that when the act is self-regarding in nature, the individual should be left to make his or her own decisions. That is precisely my view. In a medical context, I am saying that before a physician is allowed to pick up a saw and saw off a patient's fingers or pick up a scalpel and cut out a patient's eyes, we must make sure that the physician has first obtained that patient's informed consent. I always like to stick the word "voluntary" in there—informed and voluntary consent—because consent that is obtained through coercion or by telling half-truths or withholding the full measure of risk and benefit is not truly consent. Medical providers need to understand that patients do not lose their constitutional rights simply because they find

themselves behind a hospital wall. They have the same constitutional rights that the rest of us have, that we expect and enjoy outside hospital walls.

Fortunately today we have many protections that we did not have when I was in the hospital in 1973 and 1974. We have legally enforceable advance directives such as durable power of attorney and other health care proxies. Studies, though, have shown that even when these advance directives are part of the patient's hospital records, over half the time they are ignored by the patient's physician.

When I was in the hospital there were many reasons I wanted to refuse treatment, but one was overriding—the pain. The pain was so excruciating, it was so far beyond any pain that I ever knew was possible, that I simply could not endure it. I was very naive. I had always thought in that day and age, 1973, that a doctor would not let his or her patient undergo that kind of pain; they would be given whatever was needed to control it. Then I found out that was not true. I found out later that much more could have been done for my pain.

There were other important issues, too. One, though it was a distant second, was what Dr. Burt mentioned, my quality of life. I just did not feel that living my life blind, disfigured, with my fingers amputated and at that time not even able to walk, would be worthwhile. With that quality of life it did not seem that I would ever want to live. I have freely admitted for many years now that I was wrong about that.

I want to clarify this, though. Freedom, true freedom, not only gives us the right to make the correct choices; it also has to give us the right sometimes to make the wrong choices. In my case, however, it was a moot point whether I was wrong as far as my quality of life went, because that was a secondary issue. The immediate issue, the urgent issue, was that my pain was not being taken care of. That was why I wanted to die.

Today I'm happy; in fact I even feel that I'm happier than most people. I'm more active physically than I thought I ever would be. I've taken karate for a couple of years, I've climbed a 50-foot utility pole with the assistance of a belay line on the ropes course. I do other mental things, like write poetry and practice law. That is not to say, though, that the doctors were right. To say that would reflect a mentality that says, all's well that ends well, or the ends justify the means—whatever means necessary to achieve the results are okay to use. That totally ignores the pain that I had to go through. I check myself on this very often, several times a year, since I do speak so much. I ask if the same thing were to happen today under identical circumstance, would I still want the freedom? Knowing what I know now, would I still want the freedom to refuse treatment and die? And the answer is always yes, a resounding yes. If I think about having to go through that kind of pain again, I know that it's not something I would want. Another individual may well make a different decision. That's the beauty of freedom; that's his or her choice to do so. . . .

Acknowledgments

Quotation from "Dax's Case" used with permission of Choice in Dying, 1035 30th Street, N.W., Washington, D.C. 2007.

Note

1. From the transcript made of the initial videotape and published as an appendix to Robert Burt, *Taking Care of Stangers: The Rule of Law in Doctor–Patient Relations* (New York: The Free Press, 1979), pp. 174–80.

Section 2: Truth Telling and Deception

On Telling Patients the Truth

Mack Lipkin

Mack Lipkin provides a defense of the paternatlistic practice of withholding information from patients. Lipkin claims it is a practical impossibility to tell patients "the whole truth." They usually simply do not possess enough information about how their bodies work to understand the nature of their disease, and their understanding of the terms used by a physician is likely to be quite different from the meanings intended. Besides, some patients do not wish to be told the truth about their illness. Whether it is a matter of telling the truth or of deceiving patients by giving them placebos, the crucial question, according to Lipkin, is "whether the deception was intended to benefit the patient or the doctor."

Should a doctor always tell his patients the truth? In recent years there has been an extraordinary increase in public discussion of the ethical problems involved in this question. But little has been heard from physicians themselves. I believe that gaps in understanding the complex interactions between doctors and patients have led many laymen astray in this debate.

It is easy to make an attractive case for always telling patients the truth. But as L.J. Henderson, the great Harvard physiologist-philosopher of decades ago, commented:

> To speak of telling the truth, the whole truth and nothing but the truth to a patient is absurd. Like absurdity in mathematics, it is absurd simply because it is impossible. . . . The notion that the truth, the whole truth, and nothing but the truth can be conveyed to the patient is a good specimen of that class of fallacies called by Whitehead "the

Mack Lipkin, From "On Telling Patients the Truth", *Newsweek*, June 4th, (1979): 13. Copyright © 1979 Newsweek Inc. Reproduced by permission.

> fallacy of misplaced concreteness." It results from neglecting factors that cannot be excluded from the concrete situation and that are of an order of magnitude and relevancy that make it imperative to consider them. Of course, another fallacy is also often involved, the belief that diagnosis and prognosis are more certain than they are. But that is another question.

Words, especially medical terms, inevitably carry different implications for different people. When these words are said in the presence of anxiety-laden illness, there is a strong tendency to hear selectively and with emphases not intended by the doctor. Thus, what the doctor means to convey is obscured.

Indeed, thoughtful physicians know that transmittal of accurate information to patients is often impossible. Patients rarely know how the body functions in health and disease, but instead have inaccurate ideas of what is going on; this hampers the attempts to "tell the truth".

Take cancer, for example. Patients seldom know that while some cancers are rapidly fatal, others never amount to much; some have a cure rate of 99 percent, others less than 1 percent; a cancer may grow rapidly for months and then stop growing for years; may remain localized for years or spread all over the body almost from the beginning; some can be arrested for long periods of time, others not. Thus, one patient thinks of cancer as curable, the next thinks it means certain death.

How many patients understand that "heart trouble" may refer to literally hundreds of different abnormalities ranging in severity from the trivial to the instantly fatal? How many know that the term "arthritis" may refer to dozens of different types of joint involvement? "Arthritis" may raise a vision of the appalling disease that made Aunt Eulalee a helpless invalid until her death years later; the next patient remembers Grandpa grumbling about the damned arthritis as he got up from his chair. Unfortunately but understandably, most people's ideas about the implications of medical terms are based on what they have heard about a few cases.

The news of serious illness drives some patients to irrational and destructive behavior; others handle it sensibly. A distinguished philosopher forestalled my telling him about his cancer by saying, "I want to know the truth. The only thing I couldn't take and wouldn't want to know about is cancer." For two years he had watched his mother die slowly of a painful form of cancer. Several of my physician patients have indicated they would not want to know if they had a fatal illness.

Most patients should be told "the truth" to the extent that they can comprehend it. Indeed, most doctors, like most other people, are uncomfortable with lies. Good physicians, aware that some may be badly damaged by being told more than they want or need to know, can usually ascertain the patient's preference and needs.

Discussions about lying often center about the use of placebos. In medical usage, a "placebo" is a treatment that has no specific physical or chemical action on the condition being treated, but is given to affect symptoms by a psychologic mechanism, rather than a purely physical one. Ethicists believe that placebos necessarily involve a partial or complete deception by the doctor, since the patient is allowed to believe that the treatment has a specific effect. They seem unaware that placebos, far from

being inert (except in the rigid pharmacological sense), are among the most powerful agents known to medicine.

Placebos are a form of suggestion, which is a direct or indirect presentation of an idea, followed by an uncritical, i.e., not thought-out, acceptance. Those who have studied suggestion or looked at medical history know its almost unbelievable potency; it is involved to a greater or lesser extent in the treatment of every conscious patient. It can induce or remove almost any kind of feeling or thought. It can strengthen the weak or paralyze the strong; transform sleeping, feeding, or sexual patterns; remove or induce a vast array of symptoms; mimic or abolish the effect of very powerful drugs. It can alter the function of most organs. It can cause illness or a great sense of well-being. It can kill. In fact, doctors often add a measure of suggestion when they prescribe even potent medications for those who also need psychologic support. Like all potent agents, its proper use requires judgment based on experience and skill.

Communication between physician and the apprehensive and often confused patient is delicate and uncertain. Honesty should be evaluated not only in terms of a slavish devotion to language often misinterpreted by the patient, but also in terms of intent. *The crucial question is whether the deception was intended to benefit the patient or the doctor.*

Physicians, like most people, hope to see good results and are disappointed when patients do poorly. Their reputations and their livelihood depend on doing effective work; purely selfish reasons would dictate they do their best for their patients. Most important, all good physicians have a deep sense of responsibility toward those who have entrusted their welfare to them.

As I have explained, it is usually a practical impossibility to tell patients "the whole truth." Moreover, often enough, the ethics of the situation, the true moral responsibility, may demand that the naked facts not be revealed. The now popular complaint that doctors are too authoritarian is misguided more often than not. Some patients who insist on exercising their right to know may be doing themselves a disservice.

Judgment is often difficult and uncertain. Simplistic assertions about telling the truth may not be helpful to patients or physicians in times of trouble.

The End of Therapeutic Privilege?

Nicole Sirotin and Bernard Lo

Sirotin and Lo endorse new AMA guidelines that narrow a physician's "therapeutic privilege" to withhold medical information from a patient to prevent potential harm. They maintain, however, that physicians need additional guidance in specific cases and present two cases to illustrate their claim. In one case, cancer is unexpectedly discovered, and in the other, a patient's HIV status is revealed by an mistakenly ordered test.

The authors suggest that, to deal with disclosure in difficult cases, physicians would find it useful to organize their approach around a series of questions: Whether to disclose information? Who should disclose it? Where and where to disclose it? What to say to the patient? These practical questions should allow physicians to "build on the trust and communication" that are basic to the doctor–patient relationship.

Truth-telling and good communication are essential components of a trusting (and trustworthy) doctor–patient relationship. The AMA guidelines, "Withholding Information From Patients: Rethinking the Propriety of 'Therapeutic Privilege'," provide clear and thoughtful justification for disclosing health information to patients. These new AMA guidelines sharply narrow "therapeutic privilege," defined as the practice of withholding information from patients when disclosure is deemed to be medically contraindicated or to avoid potential physical or psychological harm to the patient. If MDs withhold health information from patients, they need to provide a convincing justification. This is a stark change from the historical practice that a physician's duty included the beneficent withholding of information for the sake of the patient. The presumption now in the AMA guidelines is "to offer all patients the opportunity to receive relevant medical information." Medical information should never be permanently withheld from a patient, although there are situations when postponement or a step-wise approach to disclosure may be more appropriate. In addition, the guidelines suggest that patient-physician communication can be enhanced by asking patients how much information they would like and how it should be delivered. This approach allows the physician to respect the wishes of the patient concerning

withholding information. Although the recommendations are clear, physicians still need more specific guidance. What harm or "medical contraindication" would justify withholding information? To date, most discussions have concerned withholding the diagnosis of cancer from a patient from a cultural background where such diagnoses are not usually disclosed.[1] The following two cases illustrate additional dilemmas regarding disclosure and suggest how to resolve the practical issues that physicians face when implementing the AMA guidelines. Physicians may find it useful to organize their approach around a series of questions (see table 1): Whether to disclose? Who should disclose? When to disclose? Where to disclose? What to say to the patient?

The Patients

Case 1

Ms E. is a 67-year-old African-American woman brought in by ambulance to the emergency department (ED) at a busy public hospital after a bus accident. She was found to have a dislocated shoulder, which was reduced. Because the patient also reported vague abdominal pain, a CT [computed tomography] scan of the abdomen and pelvis was obtained. The scan revealed no evidence of trauma, but diffuse masses consistent with metastatic disease were seen.

Ms E. was terrified, and repeated, "I'm in pain, I'm in pain." She had trouble answering questions because of her distress. The ED staff became frustrated and felt she needed to cooperate more with the history taking.

After receiving opioids for pain, Ms E. remained agitated. She was given promethazine. She then became drowsy and slightly confused.

Because Ms E. was brought into the ED as a trauma patient, she was placed in one of the trauma bays, which had bright lights, deafening noise, and many people coming in and out. She repeatedly asked for her belongings and stated that she did not feel secure. A physician who was involved with her care from the beginning decided to tell Ms E. the results of the CT scan. Asking further information about Ms E.'s medical history, the doctor learned that Ms E. had been diagnosed with breast cancer 10 years ago. The physician started by saying,"I have something to tell you about your CT scan. There is no sign of injury from the accident, but I am afraid there were multiple spots seen on the scan. I think this might be cancer". Ms E. was appropriately stunned by this information. She stated that she would stay to have this further evaluated.

A few hours later, after the physician who told her this information finished her shift, Ms E. left the emergency room against medical advice.

Case 2

Mr. G. is a 35-year-old man who was admitted to the ICU [intensive care unit] with respiratory failure requiring ventilator support after an overdose as a suicide attempt. An HIV viral load was mistakenly ordered and the result was consistent with active HIV infection. Mr. G was critically ill and was not improving on broad-spectrum antibiotics. No microbial information was available and, due to the HIV + test, he was presumed to be immunocompromised. A bronchoscopy was performed and revealed an infection with *Pneumocystis carinii* pneumonia. The patient was treated appropriately, but was difficult to wean off the ventilator. The patient was extremely anxious and spent many days awake, intubated, and repeatedly failed spontaneous breathing trials. An HIV test was offered and declined by the patient. Attempts to find a surrogate decision maker were unsuccessful. Due to Mr. G.'s extreme anxiety, the team decided to wait until he was extubated and less anxious to disclose his HIV status. After the patient was extubated, the team told the patient the HIV test was inappropriately ordered and disclosed the results. The patient then told the team that his former partner had just died of an AIDS-related illness and that his grief and fear of his own HIV status both contributed to his suicide attempt.

Disclose or Not?

The reasons for offering to disclose information to patients are summarized in table 2.

Most patients want to know their diagnosis, even if it is unfavorable.[2] They need full disclosure of their diagnosis or condition to move forward with decision making and planning for the future. In addition, once a piece of information is withheld, more deception is often required to keep it from the patient. For example, if a child would like to keep the diagnosis of cancer from an ailing parent, healthcare workers need to provide the patient another explanation of illness. In reality, to keep a diagnosis from a patient is often impossible. Many members of the healthcare team will be directly involved with the patient but will not be aware of the decision to withhold information.

TABLE 1. CONSIDERATIONS FOR DISCLOSING INFORMATION AND STRATEGIES FOR PHYSICIANS TO ADDRESS THEM

Considerations for Disclosure	Strategies for Physicians
Who discloses the information	Physician with most long-standing, trusting relationship with patient should disclose the information
Where to disclose	Create a private, quiet setting for disclosure
	Delay complete disclosure until optimal setting is obtained
When to disclose	Assess patient's ability to cope with information
	Address barriers to understanding and coping
What to say to the patient	Determine patient's readiness for information
	Fit pace of disclosure to patient
	Use simple, unambiguous language
	Provide empathy and support

TABLE 2. CONSIDERATIONS FOR WHETHER TO WITHHOLD INFORMATION

Reasons to disclose information

 Most patient want to know

 Patient's need for information for decision making

 Deception requires more deception

 Might be impossible to keep the information from the patient

Reasons for withholding information

 Prevent harm

 Not culturally appropriate

 Patient does not want to be told

Source: B. Lo, Resolving Ethical Dilemmas: A Guide for Clinicians, 3rd ed. (Philadelphia: Lippincott Williams & Wilkins, 2005), 45–56.

These cases suggest the type of harms that might justify withholding information from patients, at least partially or temporarily. In these cases, disclosure might lead directly to serious, immediate harm to the patient. In case 2, the patient's suicide attempt suggests severe mental illness and a danger that disclosure of an incurable illness might lead the patient to harm himself or others. Furthermore, anxiety was making extubation more difficult. Under these circumstances, disclosure may be postponed until the patient is extubated and further psychiatric assessment can be obtained. In case 1, the patient's anxiety, pain, and mistrust of her surroundings was exacerbated by the commotion in the emergency department. While the patient was not known to have a serious psychiatric condition, the physicians appropriately considered how to optimize the timing and setting of disclosing her serious medical condition. In other cases, a patient may specifically state that he or she does not want to know the medical information. The physician must be confident that the patient has the capacity to make that decision and is not being influenced by family or friends.

These principles are detailed in the AMA guidelines and elsewhere,[3] but we will discuss more practical issues and offer strategies for resolving difficult scenarios. The physician must evaluate the reasons to withhold or disclose information. Once the decision has been made to tell the patient the information, a framework for approaching disclosure includes deciding who will tell the patient, when, in what setting and what will be said during the disclosure (see table 1).

Using our cases, we will highlight practical strategies that clinicians can use when they are confronted with difficult scenarios involving disclosing information.

Who Should Disclose?

Ideally the patient's primary care provider or a physician with a long-standing relationship with the patient should disclose a serious diagnosis to the patient. If that is not possible, as in the case with Ms E., the team member who discusses the diagnosis should be the one who is most available to spend time with the patient, answer all of her questions, and provide support. When a patient from an ethnic minority group mistrusts the medical system, involving a healthcare worker from a similar cultural background can be helpful. If a nurse has the best relationship with the patient, he or she should be present when a physician discloses the CT results. If the patient is going to be admitted to the hospital, the in-patient team, who will develop a relationship with the patient, is better suited than the ER staff to disclose an incidentally found, serious diagnosis. In the case of Mr. G. most ICUs use a team-based approach in which different people care for patients on different days, rather than one primary individual. In this case also, the person with the most trusting relationship with the patient should disclose information to the patient.

When to Disclose?

The timing of disclosure is crucial. The physician should consider the patient's readiness to absorb information, in addition to what is happening around the patient at the time of disclosure. It may be desirable to defer disclosure until reversible barriers to good communication have been overcome. In the case of Ms E., specific issues that should be addressed include pain, the central nervous system side-effects of medications, and anxiety. In the case of Mr. G., his suicide attempt and his anxiety at being on a ventilator were pertinent concerns. Disclosure of his HIV status was postponed until he was extubated and psychiatric consultation was obtained.

Where to Disclose?

Neither the ER nor the ICU is an ideal place for a private, sensitive conversation. Yet simple measures can help create a calm, confidential environment. These include closing doors or curtains, turning off alarms, and obtaining comfortable seating that allows level eye contact with the patient. Pagers should be turned to silent or given to a colleague. Ancillary staff should be informed that there is going to be an important discussion and should be asked to avoid unnecessary interruption.

What to Say to the Patient?

As physicians, the words we choose to use can help patients understand and cope with bad news.[4] In the case of Mr. G., the physicians could have started by evaluating Mr. G.'s own assessment of his situation: "Mr. G., what is your understanding of your condition?" This open-ended question should elicit the patient's fears regarding HIV infection. This information would help the team disclose his HIV test results. Next, the physician can ascertain the patient's readiness to hear the information with a warning that bad news is coming: "Ms E., I am afraid I have some bad news. Do you feel like talking now?" This could be followed with a step-wise approach to disclosure based on how much information Ms E. wanted to hear at that time. Telling Ms E. that something serious was seen on her CT scan, that needs further medical attention, impacts the seriousness of the condition without overwhelming her with information.

In the case of Mr. G., it was essential to admit that the test was sent in error. "A test was sent by mistake that gives us important information about your health, We apologize for sending for this test without your knowledge. Now that we have the results, we would like to discuss them with you. Would you like to do that now?" Ideally, ascertaining the patient's preferences regarding information happens before a test is ordered, but this approach can be used for incidental findings, tests sent in error, or other situations in which discussions before the test are impossible.

When partial disclosure is chosen, a plan must then be put in place for full disclosure. At that later time, it is best to use simple, unambiguous, lay terms such as, "I'm sorry that the CT scan shows some bad news. I'm afraid you might have cancer." Keeping the information simple and concise will allow the patient to absorb what she or he can. The physician should then pause, allow the patient to react, and then address the patient's immediate concerns. As in all sensitive interactions, it is important to show empathy and support, and to reassure the patient that she or he will receive the best care possible.

How Should Special Issues Be Addressed?

Our two cases raise unusual concerns that deserve additional comment. If a patient leaves the hospital against medical advice after hearing of a serious diagnosis, as occurred with Ms E., steps should be taken to attempt to keep her in care. The ER can make a follow-up telephone call or send a letter to the patient or to the patient's primary physician. The case of Mr. G. was complicated because the HIV antibody test was sent by mistake. The error should be disclosed as such to the patient.[5] However, there are strong reasons to obtain HIV testing for a critically ill patient who is not improving and who may have an opportunistic infection that would require a radical change in treatment.[6] When the patient is unable to make a decision, a surrogate decision maker should be sought to give surrogate consent. If no surrogate can be identified, as in the case of Mr. G., it may be medically and ethically appropriate to obtain an HIV test without consent. If this occurs, the physicians need to explain reasons for obtaining the test when the patient recovers sufficiently to understand.

Conclusion

The AMA guidelines provide physicians with a solid framework with which to think through difficult situations of withholding information from patients. Our two cases add to this framework by posing a series of practical questions for clinicians who are disclosing information to patients. These questions shift the focus from whether to disclose information to *how to do so* in ways that minimize harms and maximize benefits to patients. By addressing these questions, physicians can continue to build on the trust and communication that is at the heart of any doctor–patient relationship.

Acknowledgments

Nicole Sirotin is supported by the Health Resources and Services Administration.

Bernard Lo is supported by the Greenwall Foundation.

Notes

1. D.B. Gordon and E. Paci, "Disclosure Practices and Cultural Narratives: Understanding Concealment and Silence around Cancer in Tuscany, Italy," *Social Science & Medicine* 46 (1997): 1433–52; A. Surbone, "Truth Telling to the Patient," *Journal of the American Medical Association* 268 (1992): 61–2.

2. L.J. Blackhall et al., "Ethnicity and Attitudes toward Patient Autonomy," *Journal of the American Medical Association* 274 (1995): 820–5.

3. B. Lo, *Resolving Ethical Dilemmas: A Guide for Clinicians*, 3rd ed. (Philadelphia, Pa.: Lippincott, Williams & Wilkins, 2005), 45–56.

4. R. Buckman, *How to Break Bad News: A Guide for Health Care Professionals* (Baltimore: Johns Hopkins University Press, 1992), 2; L. Fallowfield, "Giving Sad and Bad News," *Lancet* 341 (1993): 476–8; J.T. Ptacek and T.L. Eberhardt, "Breaking Bad News: A Review of the Literature," *Journal of the American Medical Association* 276 (1996): 496–502.

5. T.H. Gallagher and W. Levinson, "Disclosing Harmful Medical Errors to Patients: A Time for Professional Action," *Archives of Internal Medicine* 165 (2005): 1819–24.

6. L. Huang et al., "Intensive Care of Patients with HIV Infection," *New England Journal of Medicine* 355 (2006): 173–81.

Section 3: Confidentiality

Confidentiality in Medicine—A Decrepit Concept

Mark Siegler

Mark Siegler calls attention to the impossibility of preserving the confidentiality traditionally associated with the physician–patient relationship. In the modern hospital, a great many people have legitimate access to a patient's chart and so to all medical, social, and financial information the patient has provided. Yet the loss of confidentiality is a threat to good medical care. Confidentiality protects a patient at a time of vulnerability and promotes the trust that is necessary for effective diagnosis and treatment. Siegler concludes by suggesting some possible solutions for preserving confidentiality while meeting the needs of others to know certain things about the patient.

Medical confidentiality, as it has traditionally been understood by patients and doctors, no longer exists. This ancient medical principle, which has been included in every physician's oath and code of ethics since Hippocratic times, has become old, worn-out, and useless; it is a decrepit concept. Efforts to preserve it appear doomed to failure and often give rise to more problems than solutions. Psychiatrists have tacitly acknowledged the impossibility of ensuring the confidentiality of medical records by choosing to establish a separate, more secret record. The following case illustrates how the confidentiality principle is compromised systematically in the course of routine medical care.

A patient of mine with mild chronic obstructive pulmonary disease was transferred from the surgical intensive-care unit to a surgical nursing floor two days after an elective cholecystectonomy. On the day of transfer, the patient saw a respiratory therapist writing in his medical chart (the therapist was recording the results of an arterial blood gas analysis) and became concerned about the confidentiality of his hospital records. The patient threatened to leave the hospital prematurely unless I could guarantee that the confidentiality of his hospital record would be respected.

Supported by a grant (OSS-8018097) from the National Science Foundation and by the National Endowment for the Humanities. The views expressed are those of the author and do not necessarily reflect those of the National Science Foundation or the National Endowment for the Humanities. Mark Siegler. From "Confidentiality in Medicine- A Decrepit Concept," *New England Journal of Medicine*, Vol. 307, no. 24. (1982):1518–521. Copyright © 1982 MASSACHUSETTS MEDICAL SOCIETY. All rights reserved. Reproduced by permission.

The patient's complaint prompted me to enumerate the number of persons who had both access to his hospital record and a reason to examine it. I was amazed to learn that at least 25 and possibly as many as 100 health professionals and administrative personnel at our university hospital had access to the patient's record and that all of them had a legitimate need, indeed a professional responsibility, to open and use that chart. These persons included 6 attending physicians (the primary physician, the surgeon, the pulmonary consultant and others); 12 house officers (medical, surgical, intensive-care unit, and "covering" house staff); 20 nursing personnel (on three shifts); 6 respiratory therapists; 3 nutritionists; 2 clinical pharmacists; 15 students (from medicine, nursing, respiratory therapy, and clinical pharmacy); 4 unit secretaries; 4 hospital financial officers; and 4 chart reviewers (utilization review, quality assurance review, tissue review, and insurance auditor). It is of interest that this patient's problem was straightforward, and he therefore did not require many other technical and support services that the modern hospital provides. For example, he did not need multiple consultants and fellows, such specialized procedures as dialysis, or social workers, chaplains, physical therapists, occupational therapists, and the like.

Upon completing my survey I reported to the patient that I estimated that at least 75 health professionals and hospital personnel had access to his medical record. I suggested to the patient that these people were all involved in providing or supporting his health-care services. They were, I assured him, working for him. Despite my reassurances the patient was obviously distressed and retorted,"I always believed that medical confidentiality was part of a doctor's code of ethics. Perhaps you should tell me just what you people mean by 'confidentiality'!"

Two Aspects of Medical Confidentiality

Confidentiality and Third-Party Interests

Previous discussions of medical confidentiality usually have focused on the tension between a physician's responsibility to keep information divulged by patients secret and a physician's legal and moral duty, on occasion, to reveal such confidences to third parties, such as families, employers, public health authorities, or police authorities. In all these instances, the central question relates to the stringency of the physician's obligation to maintain patient confidentiality when the health, well-being, and safety of identifiable others or of society in general would be threatened by a failure to reveal information about the patient. The tension in such cases is between the good of the patient and the good of others.

Confidentiality and the Patient's Interest

As the example above illustrates, further challenges to confidentiality arise because the patient's personal interest in maintaining confidentiality comes into conflict with his personal interest in receiving the best possible health care. Modern high-technology health care is available principally in hospitals (often, teaching hospitals), requires many trained and specialized workers (a "health-care team"), and is very costly. The existence of such teams means that information that previously had been held in confidence by an individual physician will now necessarily be disseminated to many members of the team. Furthermore, since health-care teams are expensive and few patients can afford to pay such costs directly, it becomes essential to grant access to the patient's medical record to persons who are responsible for obtaining third-party payment. These persons include chart reviewers, financial officers, insurance auditors, and quality-of-care assessors. Finally, as medicine expands from a narrow, disease-based model to a model that encompasses psychological, social, and economic problems, not only will the size of the health-care team and medical costs increase, but more sensitive information (such as one's personal habits and financial condition) will now be included in the medical record and will no longer be confidential.

The point I wish to establish is that hospital medicine, the rise of health-care teams, the existence of third-party insurance programs, and the expanding limits of medicine all appear to be responses to the wishes of people for better and more comprehensive medical care. But each of these developments necessarily modifies our traditional understanding of medical confidentiality.

The Role of Confidentiality in Medicine

Confidentiality serves a dual purpose in medicine. In the first place, it acknowledges respect for the patient's sense of individuality and privacy. The patient's most personal physical and psychological secrets are kept confidential in order to decrease a sense of shame and vulnerability. Secondly, confidentiality is important in improving the patient's health care—a basic goal of medicine. The promise of confidentiality permits people to trust (i.e., have confidence) that information revealed to a physician in the course of a medical encounter will not be disseminated further. In this way patients are encouraged to communicate honestly and forthrightly with their doctors. This bond of trust between patient and doctor is vitally important both in the diagnostic process (which relies on an accurate history) and subsequently in the treatment phase, which often depends as much on the patient's trust in the physician as it does on medications and surgery. These two important functions of confidentiality are as important now as they were in the past. They will not be supplanted entirely either by improvements in medical technology or by recent changes in relations between some patients and doctors toward a rights-based, consumerist model.

Possible Solutions to the Confidentiality Problem

First of all, in all nonbureaucratic, noninstitutional medical encounters—that is, in the millions of doctor–patient encounters that take place in physicians' offices, where more privacy can be preserved—meticulous care should be taken to guarantee that patients' medical and personal information will be kept confidential.

Secondly, in such settings as hospitals or large-scale group practices, where many persons have opportunities to examine the medical record, we should aim to provide access only to those who have "a need to know." This could be accomplished through such administrative changes as dividing the entire record into several sections—for example, a medical and financial section—and permitting only health professionals access to the medical information.

The approach favored by many psychiatrists—that of keeping a psychiatric record separate from the general medical record—is an understandable strategy but one that is not entirely satisfactory and that should not be generalized. The keeping of separate psychiatric records implies that psychiatry and medicine are different undertakings and thus drives deeper the wedge between them and between physical and psychological illness. Furthermore, it is often vitally important for internists or surgeons to know that a patient is being seen by a psychiatrist or is taking a particular medication. When separate records are kept, this information may not be available. Finally, if generalized, the practice of keeping a separate psychiatric record could lead to the unacceptable consequence of having a separate record for each type of medical problem.

Patients should be informed about what is meant by "medical confidentiality." We should establish the distinction between information about the patient that generally will be kept confidential regardless of the interest of third parties and information that will be exchanged among members of the health-care team in order to provide care for the patient. Patients should be made aware of the large number of persons in the modern hospital who require access to the medical record in order to serve the patient's medical and financial interests.

Finally, at some point most patients should have an opportunity to review their medical record and to make informed choices about whether their entire record is to be available to everyone or whether certain portions of the record are privileged and should be accessible only to their principal physician or to others designated explicitly by the patient. This approach would rely on traditional informed-consent procedural standards and might permit the patient to balance the personal value of medical confidentiality against the personal value of high-technology, team health care. There is no reason that the same procedure should not be used with psychiatric records instead of the arbitrary system now employed, in which everything related to psychiatry is kept secret.

Afterthought: Confidentiality and Indiscretion

There is one additional aspect of confidentiality that is rarely included in discussions of the subject. I am referring here to the wanton, often inadvertent, but avoidable exchanges of confidential information that occur frequently in hospital rooms, elevators, cafeterias, doctors' offices, and at cocktail parties. Of course, as more people have access to medical information about the patient the potential for this irresponsible abuse of confidentiality increases geometrically.

Such mundane breaches of confidentiality are probably of greater concern to most patients than the broader issue of whether their medical records may be entered into a computerized data bank or whether a respiratory therapist is reviewing the results of an arterial blood gas determination. Somehow, privacy is violated and a sense of shame is heightened when intimate secrets are revealed to people one knows or is close to—friends, neighbors, acquaintances, or hospital roommates—rather than when they are disclosed to an anonymous bureaucrat sitting at a computer terminal in a distant city or to a health professional who is acting in an official capacity.

I suspect that the principles of medical confidentiality, particularly those reflected in most medical codes of ethics, were designed principally to prevent just this sort of embarrassing personal indiscretion rather than to maintain (for social, political, or economic reasons) the absolute secrecy of doctor–patient communications. In this regard, it is worth noting that Percival's Code of Medical Ethics (1803) includes the following admonition: "Patients should be interrogated concerning their complaint in a tone of voice which cannot be overheard" [Leake, C. D., ed., *Percival's Medical Ethics*, Baltimore: Williams and Wilkins, 1927]. We in the medical profession frequently neglect these simple courtesies.

Conclusion

The principle of medical confidentiality described in medical codes of ethics and still believed in by patients no longer exists. In this respect, it is a decrepit concept. Rather than perpetuate the myth of confidentiality and invest energy vainly to preserve it, the public and the profession would be better served if they devoted their attention to determining which aspects of the original principle of confidentiality are worth retaining. Efforts could then be directed to salvaging those.

Decision in the *Tarasoff* Case

Supreme Court of California

This ruling of the California Supreme Court has been of particular concern to psychiatrists and psychotherapists. The court ruled that therapists at the student health center of the University of California, Berkeley, were negligent in their duty to warn Tatiana Tarasoff that Prosenjit Poddar, one of their patients, had threatened her life. Although the therapists reported the threat to the police, Tarasoff herself was not warned, and she was murdered by Poddar.

The ruling and dissenting opinions in this case address the issue of balancing the state's interest in protecting its citizens from injury against the interest of patients and therapists in preserving confidentiality. Does a therapist have a duty to warn at all? Should a patient be informed that not everything he tells his therapist will be held in confidence? Is a therapist obliged to seek a court order committing a patient involuntarily to an institution if the patient poses a threat the therapist deems to be seriously motivated?

In the majority opinion, Justice Matthew Tobriner argues that a therapist whose patient poses a serious danger to someone has a legal obligation to use "reasonable care" to protect the intended victim. This may involve warning the person, but if it is reasonable to believe that a warning is not enough, then the therapist has a duty to seek to have the patient involuntarily institutionalized.

In the dissenting opinion, Justice William Clark argues that the law should not interfere with the confidentiality between therapist and patient for three reasons: (1) Without the guarantee of confidentiality, those needing treatment may not seek it; (2) violence may increase, because those needing treatment were deterred from getting it; and (3) therapists, to protect their interest, will seek more involuntary commitments, thus violating the rights of their patients and undermining the trust needed for effective treatment.

Poddar was convicted of second-degree murder. The conviction was overturned on appeal, on the grounds that the jury had not been properly instructed. The state decided against a second trial, and Poddar was released on the condition that he return to India. Although Poddar escaped punishment for his actions, the issues of confidentiality raised by the case have yet to be satisfactorily resolved.

Justice Matthew O. Tobriner; Majority Opinion

On October 27, 1969, Prosenjit Poddar killed Tatiana Tarasoff. Plaintiffs, Tatiana's parents, allege that two months earlier Poddar confided his intention to kill Tatiana to Dr. Lawrence Moore, a psychologist employed

From California Supreme Court, Tarasoff v. Regents of the University of California, 131 *California Reporter*, 14 (July 1, 1976).

by the Cowell Memorial Hospital at the University of California at Berkeley. They allege that on Moore's request, the campus police briefly detained Poddar, but released him when he appeared rational. They further claim that Dr. Harvey Powelson, Moore's superior, then directed that no further action be taken to detain Poddar. No one warned plaintiffs of Tatiana's peril....

We shall explain that defendant therapists cannot escape liability merely because Tatiana herself was not their patient. When a therapist determines, or pursuant to the standards of his profession should determine, that his patient presents a serious danger of violence to another, he incurs an obligation to use reasonable care to protect the intended victim against such danger. The discharge of this duty may require the therapist to take one or more of various steps, depending upon the nature of the case. Thus it may call for him to warn the intended victim or others likely to apprise the victim of the danger, to notify the police, or to take whatever other steps are reasonably necessary under the circumstances. . . .

1. Plaintiff's Complaints

. . . Plaintiffs' first cause of action, entitled "Failure to Detain a Dangerous Patient," alleges that on August 20, 1969, Poddar was a voluntary outpatient receiving therapy at Cowell Memorial Hospital. Poddar informed Moore, his therapist, that he was going to kill an unnamed girl, readily identifiable as Tatiana, when she returned home from spending the summer in Brazil. Moore, with the concurrence of Dr. Gold, who had initially examined Poddar, and Dr. Yandell, assistant to the director of the department of psychiatry, decided that Poddar should be committed for observation in a mental hospital. Moore orally notified Officers Atkinson and Teel of the campus police that he would request commitment. He then sent a letter to Police Chief William Beall requesting the assistance of the police department in securing Poddar's confinement.

Officers Atkinson, Brownrigg, and Halleran took Poddar into custody, but, satisfied that Poddar was rational, released him on his promise to stay away from Tatiana. Powelson, director of the department of psychiatry at Cowell Memorial Hospital, then asked the police to return Moore's letter, directed that all copies of the letter and notes that Moore had taken as therapist be destroyed, and "ordered no action to place Prosenjit Poddar in 72-hour treatment and evaluation facility."

Plaintiffs' second cause of action, entitled "Failure to Warn on a Dangerous Patient," incorporates the allegations of the first cause of action, but adds the assertion that defendants negligently permitted Poddar to be released from police custody without "notifying the parents of Tatiana Tarasoff that their daughter was in grave danger from Prosenjit Poddar." Poddar persuaded Tatiana's brother to share an apartment with him near Tatiana's residence; shortly after her return from Brazil, Poddar went to her residence and killed her. . . .

2. Plaintiffs Can State a Cause of Action Against Defendant Therapists for Negligent Failure to Protect Tatiana

The second cause of action can be amended to allege 'that Tatiana's death proximately resulted from defendants' negligent failure to warn Tatiana or others likely to apprise her of her danger. Plaintiffs contend that as amended, such allegations of negligence and proximate causation, with resulting damages, establish a cause of action. Defendants, however, contend that in the circumstances of the present case they owed no duty of care to Tatiana or her parents and that, in the absence of such duty, they were free to act in careless disregard of Tatiana's life and safety.

. . . In analyzing this issue, we bear in mind that legal duties are not discoverable facts of nature, but merely conclusory expressions that, in cases of a particular type, liability should be imposed for damage done. As stated in *Dillon* v. *Legg* (1968): . . . "The assertion that liability must . . . be denied because defendant bears no 'duty' to plaintiff begs the essential question—whether the plaintiff's interests are entitled to legal protection against the defendant's conduct. . . . [Duty] is not sacrosanct in itself, but only an expression of the sum total of those considerations of policy which lead the law to say that the particular plaintiff is entitled to protection." . . .

In the landmark case of *Rowland* v. *Christian* (1968), . . . Justice Peters recognized that liability should be imposed "for an injury occasioned to another by his want of ordinary care or skill" as expressed in section 1714 of the Civil Code. Thus, Justice Peters, quoting from *Heaven* v. *Pender* (1883) . . . stated: " 'whenever one person is by circumstances placed in such a position with regard to another . . . that if he did not use ordinary care and skill in his own conduct . . . he would cause danger of injury to the person or property of the other, a duty arises to use ordinary care and skill to avoid such danger.' "

. . . We depart from "this fundamental principle" only upon the "balancing of a number of considerations"; major ones "are the foreseeability of harm to the plaintiff, the degree of certainty that the plaintiff suffered injury, the closeness of the connection between the defendant's conduct and the injury suffered, the moral blame attached to the defendant's conduct, the policy of preventing future harm, the extent of the burden to the defendant and consequences to the community of imposing a duty to exercise care with resulting liability for breach, and the availability, cost and prevalence of insurance for the risk involved."

The most important of these considerations in establishing duty is foreseeability. As a general principle, a "defendant owes a duty of care to all persons who are foreseeably endangered by his conduct, with respect to all risks which make the conduct unreasonably dangerous." As we shall explain, however, when the avoidance of foreseeable harm requires a defendant to control the conduct of another person, or to warn of such conduct, the common law has traditionally imposed liability only if the defendant bears some special relationship to the dangerous person or to the potential victim. Since the relationship between a therapist and his patient satisfies this requirement, we need not here decide whether foreseeability alone is sufficient to create a duty to exercise reasonable care to protect a potential victim of another's conduct. . . .

Although plaintiffs' pleadings assert no special relation between Tatiana and defendant therapists, they establish as between Poddar and defendant therapists the special relation that arises between a patient and his doctor or psychotherapist. Such a relationship may support affirmative duties for the benefit of third persons. Thus, for example, a hospital must exercise reasonable care to control the behavior of a patient which may endanger other persons. A doctor must also warn a patient if the patient's condition or medication renders certain conduct, such as driving a car, dangerous to others.

. . . Although the California decisions that recognize this duty have involved cases in which the defendant stood in a special relationship *both* to the victim and to the person whose conduct created the danger, we do not think that the duty should logically be constricted to such situations. Decisions of other jurisdictions hold that the single relationship of a doctor to his patient is sufficient to support the duty to exercise reasonable care to protect others against dangers emanating from the patient's illness. The courts hold that a doctor is liable to persons infected by his patient if he negligently fails to diagnose a contagious disease, . . . or, having diagnosed the illness, fails to warn members of the patient's family.

Since it involved a dangerous mental patient, the decision in *Merchants Nat. Bank Tust Co. of Fargo* v. *United States* . . . comes closer to the issue. The Veterans Administration arranged for the patient to work on a local farm, but did not inform the farmer of the man's background. The farmer consequently permitted the patient to come and go freely during nonworking hours; the patient borrowed a car, drove to his wife's residence and killed her. Notwithstanding the lack of any "special relationship" between the Veterans Administration and the wife, the court found the Veterans Administration liable for the wrongful death of the wife.

In their summary of the relevant rulings Fleming and Maximov conclude that the "case law should dispel any notion that to impose on the therapists a duty to take precautions for the safety of persons threatened by a patient, where due care so requires, is in any way opposed to contemporary ground rules on the duty relationship. On the contrary, there now seems to be sufficient authority to support the conclusion that by entering into a doctor–patient relationship the therapist becomes sufficiently involved to assume some responsibility for the safety, not only of the patient himself, but also of any third person whom the doctor knows to be threatened by the patient." . . .

Defendants contend, however, that imposition of a duty to exercise reasonable care to protect third persons is unworkable because therapists cannot accurately predict whether or not a patient will resort to violence. In support of this argument amicus representing the American Psychiatric Association and other professional societies cites numerous articles which indicate that therapists, in the present state of the art, are unable reliably to predict violent acts; their forecasts, amicus claims, tend consistently to overpredict violence, and indeed are more often wrong than right. . . .

We recognize the difficulty that a therapist encounters in attempting to forecast whether a patient presents a serious danger of violence. Obviously we do not require that the therapist, in making that determination, render a perfect performance; the therapist need only exercise "that reasonable degree of skill, knowledge, and care ordinarily possessed and exercised by members of [that professional specialty] under similar circumstances." Within the broad range of reasonable practice and treatment in which professional opinion and judgment may differ, the therapist is free to exercise his or her own best judgment without liability; proof, aided by hindsight, that he or she judged wrongly is insufficient to establish negligence.

In the instant case, however, the pleadings do not raise any question as to failure of defendant therapists to predict that Poddar presented a serious danger of violence. On the contrary, the present complaints allege that defendant therapists did in fact predict that Poddar would kill, but were negligent in failing to warn.

. . . Amicus contends, however, that even when a therapist does in fact predict that a patient poses a serious danger of violence to others, the therapist should be absolved of any responsibility for failing to act to protect the potential victim. In our view, however, once a therapist does in fact determine, or under applicable professional standards reasonably should have determined, that a patient poses a serious danger of violence to others, he bears a duty to exercise reasonable care to protect the foreseeable victim of that danger. While the discharge of this duty of due care will necessarily vary with the facts of each case, in each instance the adequacy of the therapist's conduct must be measured against the traditional negligence standard of the rendition of reasonable care under the circumstances.... As explained in Fleming and Maximov, *The Patient or His Victim: The Therapist's Dilemma* (1974): "... the ultimate question of resolving the tension between the conflicting interests of patient and potential victim is one of social polity, not professional expertise.... In sum, the therapist owes a legal duty not only to his patient, but also to his patient's would-be victim and is subject in both respects to scrutiny by judge and jury."...

The risk that unnecessary warnings may be given is a reasonable price to pay for the lives of possible victims that may be saved. We would hesitate to hold that the therapist who is aware that his patient expects to attempt to assassinate the President of the United States would not be obligated to warn the authorities because the therapist cannot predict with accuracy that his patient will commit the crime.

Defendants further argue that free and open communication is essential to psychotherapy; ... that "Unless a patient ... is assured that ... information [revealed by him] can and will be held in utmost confidence, he will be reluctant to make the full disclosure upon which diagnosis and treatment ... depends."... The giving of a warning, defendants contend, constitutes a breach of trust which entails the revelation of confidential communications.

... We recognize the public interest in supporting effective treatment of mental illness and in protecting the rights of patients to privacy, ... and the consequent public importance of safeguarding the confidential character of psychotherapeutic communication. Against this interest, however, we must weigh the public interest in safety from violent assault....

We realize that the open and confidential character of psychotherapeutic dialogue encourages patients to express threats of violence, few of which are ever executed. Certainly a therapist should not be encouraged routinely to reveal such threats; such disclosures could seriously disrupt the patient's relationship with his therapist and with the persons threatened. To the contrary, the therapist's obligations to his patient require that he not disclose a confidence unless such disclosure is necessary to avert danger to others, and even then that he do so discreetly, and in a fashion that would preserve the privacy of his patient to the fullest extent compatible with the prevention of the threatened danger.

The revelation of a communication under the above circumstances is not a breach of trust or a violation of professional ethics; as stated in the Principles of Medical Ethics of the American Medical Association (1957), section 9: "A physician may not reveal the confidence entrusted to him in the course of medical attendance ... *unless he is required to do so by law or unless it becomes necessary in order to protect the welfare of the individual or of the community.*" (Emphasis added.) We conclude that the public policy favoring protection of the confidential character of patient–psychotherapist communications must yield to the extent to which disclosure is essential to avert danger to others. The protective privilege ends where the public peril begins....

For the foregoing reasons, we find that plaintiffs' complaints can be amended to state a cause of action against defendants Moore, Powelson, Gold, and Yandell and against the Regents as their employer, for breach of a duty to exercise reasonable care to protect Tatiana.

Justice William P. Clark, Dissenting Opinion

Until today's majority opinion, both legal and medical authorities have agreed that confidentiality is essential to effectively treat the mentally ill, and that imposing a duty on doctors to disclose patient threats to potential victims would greatly impair treatment. Further, recognizing that effective treatment and society's safety are necessarily intertwined, the Legislature has already decided effective and confidential treatment is preferred over imposition of a duty to warn.

The issue whether effective treatment for the mentally ill should be sacrificed to a system of warnings is, in my opinion, properly one for the Legislature, and we are bound by its judgment. Moreover, even in the absence of clear legislative direction, we must reach the same conclusion because imposing the majority's new duty is certain to result in a net increase in violence....

Overwhelming policy considerations weigh against imposing a duty on psychotherapists to warn a potential victim against harm. While offering virtually no benefit to society, such a duty will frustrate psychiatric treatment, invade fundamental patient rights and increase violence....

Assurance of confidentiality is important for three reasons.

Deterrence from Treatment

First, without substantial assurance of confidentiality, those requiring treatment will be deterred from seeking assistance. It remains an unfortunate fad in our society that people seeking psychiatric guidance tend to become stigmatized. Apprehension of such stigma—apparently increased by the propensity of people considering treatment to see themselves in the worst possible light—creates a well-recognized reluctance to seek aid. This reluctance is alleviated by the psychiatrist's assurance of confidentiality.

Full Disclosure

Second, the guarantee of confidentiality is essential in eliciting the full disclosure necessary for effective treatment. The psychiatric patient approaches treatment with conscious and unconscious inhibitions against revealing his innermost thoughts. "Every person, however well-motivated, has to overcome resistance to therapeutic exploration. These resistances seek support from every possible source and the possibility of disclosure would easily be employed in the service of resistance."... Until a patient can trust his psychiatrist not to violate their confidential relationship, "the unconscious psychological control mechanism of repression will prevent the recall of past experiences."...

Successful Treatment

Third, even if the patient fully discloses his thoughts, assurance that the confidential relationship will not be breached is necessary to maintain his trust in his psychiatrist—the very means by which treatment is effected. "[T]he essence of much psychotherapy is the contribution of trust in the external world and ultimately in the self, modelled upon the trusting relationship established during therapy."... Patients will be helped only if they can form a trusting relationship with the psychiatrist.... All authorities appear to agree that if the trust relationship cannot be developed because of collusive communication between the psychiatrist and others, treatment will be frustrated.

Given the importance of confidentiality to the practice of psychiatry, it becomes clear the duty to warn imposed by the majority will cripple the use and effectiveness of psychiatry. Many people, potentially violent—yet susceptible to treatment—will be deterred from seeking it; those seeking it will be inhibited from making revelations necessary to effective treatment; and, forcing the psychiatrist to violate the patient's trust will destroy the interpersonal relationship by which treatment is effected.

Violence and Civil Commitment

By imposing a duty to warn, the majority contributes to the danger to society of violence by the mentally ill and greatly increases the risk of civil commitment—the total deprivation of liberty—of those who should not be confined. The impairment of treatment and risk of improper commitment resulting from the new duty to warn will not be limited to a few patients but will extend to a large number of the mentally ill. Although under existing psychiatric procedures only a relatively few receiving treatment will ever present a risk of violence, the number making threats is huge, and it is the latter group—not just the former—whose treatment will be impaired and whose risk of commitment will be increased.

Both the legal and psychiatric communities recognize that the process of determining potential violence in a patient is far from exact, being fraught with complexity and uncertainty. In fact precision has not even been attained in predicting who of those having already committed violent acts will again become violent, a task recognized to be of much simpler proportions. . . .

This predictive uncertainty means that the number of disclosures will necessarily be large. As noted above, psychiatric patients are encouraged to discuss all thoughts of violence, and they often express such thoughts. However, unlike this court, the psychiatrist does not enjoy the benefit of overwhelming hindsight in seeing which few, if any, of his patients will ultimately become violent. Now, confronted by the majority's new duty, the psychiatrist must instantaneously calculate potential violence from each patient on each visit. The difficulties researchers have encountered in accurately predicting violence will be heightened for the practicing psychiatrist dealing for brief periods in his office with heretofore nonviolent patients. And, given the decision not to warn or commit must always be made at the psychiatrist's civil peril, one can expect most doubts will be resolved in favor of the psychiatrist protecting himself.

Neither alternative open to the psychiatrist seeking to protect himself is in the public interest. The warning itself is an impairment of the psychiatrist's ability to treat, depriving many patients of adequate treatment. It is to be expected that after disclosing their threats, a significant number of patients, who would not become violent if treated according to existing practices, will engage in violent conduct as a result of unsuccessful treatment. In short, the majority's duty to warn will not only impair treatment of many who would never become violent but worse, will result in a net increase in violence.

The second alternative open to the psychiatrist is to commit his patient rather than to warn. Even in the absence of threat of civil liability, the doubts of psychiatrists as to the seriousness of patient threats have led psychiatrists to overcommit to mental institutions. This overcommitment has been authoritatively documented in both legal and psychiatric studies. This practice is so prevalent that it has been estimated that "as many as twenty harmless persons are incarcerated for every one who will commit a violent act." . . .

Given the incentive to commit created by the majority's duty, this already serious situation will be worsened, contrary to Chief Justice Wright's admonition "that liberty is no less precious because forfeited in a civil proceeding than when taken as a consequence of a criminal conviction."

Section 4: Children and Consent

Parental Refusals of Medical Treatment: The Harm Principle as Threshold for State Intervention

Douglas S. Diekema

Douglas Diekema argues that the "best interest" standard is not adequate for making decisions about the welfare of a child when state intervention is required because of parental failure to see to a child's welfare. Nor does the best-interest standard reflect the standard used in practice. The harm principle, Diekema claims, "provides a more appropriate standard for court intervention." He offers eight criteria for deciding when the state should intervene on behalf of a child and presents a series of cases illustrating the use of the criteria. (For a discussion of the harm principle, see p. 903.)

Introduction

It is well established in American law that a patient must give informed consent before a physician may administer treatment. The U.S. Supreme Court recognized the right to refuse unwanted medical treatment as early as 1891 in Union Pacific Railway Company v. Botsford: "no right is held more sacred, or is more carefully guarded, by the common law, than the right of every individual to the possession and control of his own person, free from all restraint or interference of others."[1] The Supreme Court has reaffirmed this notion on several occasions, most recently in Cruzan v. Director, Missouri Department of Health: "a competent person has a constitutionally protected liberty interest

Douglas S. Diekema, From "Parental Refusals of Medical Treatment: The Harm Principle as Threshold for State Intervention," *Theoretical Medicine*, Vol. 25, (2004): 243–253, 255–258. Copyright © 2004 Springer-Verlag. Reproduced by permission.

in refusing unwanted medical treatment."[2] The failure to obtain informed consent constitutes a battery under the law, for which a physician might be either criminally or civilly liable. This right to refuse treatment and grant informed consent does not disappear for individuals who are incompetent. Rather the right is one that must be exercised for them.

Under U.S. law, minors are generally considered incompetent to provide legally binding consent regarding their health care, parents or guardians are generally empowered to make those decisions on their behalf, and the law has respected those decisions except where they place the child's health, well-being, or life in jeopardy. There are several good reasons for this presumption to respect parental autonomy and family privacy. First, because most parents care about their children, they will usually be better situated than others to understand the unique needs of their children, desire what's best for their children, and make decisions that are beneficial to their children. Second, the interests of family members may sometimes conflict, and some family members may be subject to harms as a consequence of certain decisions. Parents are often better situated than others outside of the family to weigh the competing interests of family members in making a final decision. Third, parents should be permitted to raise their children according to their own chosen standards and values and to transmit those to their children. Finally, in order for family relationships to flourish, the family must have sufficient space and freedom from intrusion by others. Without some decision-making autonomy, families would not flourish, and the important function served by families in society would suffer. For all of these reasons, U.S. law (and most ethical analysis) begins with the assumption that parents are the persons best suited and most inclined to act in the best interests of their children, and that in most cases they will do so. In most situations, parents are given wide latitude in terms of the decisions they make on behalf of their children.

Parental authority is not absolute, however, and when a parent acts contrary to the best interest of a child, the state may intervene. The doctrine of *parens patriae* holds that the state may act as "surrogate parent" when necessary to protect the life and health of those who cannot take care of themselves, including children. According to the Supreme Court in Prince v. Massachusetts," . . . neither rights of religion nor rights of parenthood are beyond limitation. Acting to guard the general interest in youth's well being, the state as *parens patriae* may restrict the parent's control by requiring school attendance, regulating or prohibiting the child's labor, and in many other ways."[3] Child abuse laws are recognition that parental rights are not absolute. If a parent refuses to provide necessary care to a child, the state can assume temporary custody for the purpose of authorizing medical care under the claim of medical neglect. The "best interest" standard has become the judicial and ethical standard used to determine when state interference is justified. In the remainder of this paper, I will argue that the best interest standard provides insufficient guidance for decision-making regarding children and does not reflect the actual standard used by medical providers and courts. Rather, I will suggest that the "harm principle" provides a more appropriate threshold for state intervention than the "best interest" standard. Finally, I will suggest a series of criteria that can be used in deciding whether the state should intervene in a parent's decision to refuse medical care on behalf of a child.

Threshold for Intervention: Best Interests

Several judicial standards have evolved in an effort to determine the proper course of action for individuals who are judged incompetent to make medical decisions for themselves. In general, a proxy decision-maker is to make decisions that most faithfully reflect the patient's wishes or, if those wishes cannot be known, the best interest of the patient. . . .

Brock and Buchanan define best interest as "acting so as to promote maximally the good of the individual."[4] Beauchamp and Childress define the best interest standard as one in which ". . . a surrogate decision maker must determine the highest net benefit among the available options, assigning different weights to interests the patient has in each option and discounting or subtracting inherent risks or costs."[5] In both cases, the standard requires the surrogate to act so as to always make the decision most favorable to the child.

However, for a number of reasons, the best interest standard proves difficult to apply and may provide little meaningful guidance in practice. First, it may be difficult to precisely define the "best interest" of a child, and controversy may surround that determination. The best interest standard is most easily applied in situations where a child's life is jeopardized and where death can be averted with easy, safe, and effective treatments. Thus, little controversy exists regarding the use of blood transfusions for children in life-threatening situations. However, in situations involving less serious threats to a child's health, as in the case of cleft lip and palate repair, it may be more difficult to determine whether parental refusal of permission violates the standard.

Second, the notion of "best interest" is inherently a question of values, and most parents believe they are making a decision in the best interest of their child. Parents who are Jehovah's Witnesses, for example, may truly believe that they are making a decision in the best interest of their child when they refuse to consent to a blood transfusion. Loss of salvation is not, after all, a trivial consequence of acting on the physician's recommendation. Most medical and legal assessments of these cases, however, ignore the theological consequences in making a best interest determination. Appealing to a best interest standard does not help the courts decide whose conception of the child's best interest should prevail. Ultimately, these are not objective "best interest" cases, but involve assessments of which values should carry the most weight. They pit the state's determination of "best interest" against that of the parents.

Third, the nature of interests is frequently complex. Although medical considerations are important, a child's interests will also be affected by emotional and physical accompaniments of the chosen course. Best interests all too frequently may be reduced to objective medical interests alone. In discussing chemotherapy for a child with leukemia, for example, medical professionals frequently focus on the fact that therapy will increase the child's chance of survival while underestimating the negative aspects of cancer treatment. Some parents may place greater weight on the risks, side effects, discomforts, and disruptions that the child may endure in being treated, perhaps making the judgment that the increased chance of survival does not justify those burdens. Determining how these multiple factors ought to be weighed is no simple matter.

Finally, it is not clear that the best interest of the child should always be the sole or primary consideration in treatment decisions. There are few situations in which society actually requires parents to always act in a way that is optimal for their children. In seeking to optimize family welfare, parental decisions may commonly subjugate the interests of individual children, and while the state can certainly intervene when parents endanger their children, it is not justified in intervening simply because parental decisions may compromise the interests of a child in favor of those of the family. For example, few would argue that a college education would not be in the best interest of most children. Yet we do not require parents to provide their children with a college education. Nor do we require parents to send their children to the best elementary schools. Murray argues that while avoiding harm is important, parents are not obliged to elevate avoiding harm to children above all other goods. Parents are not required to go to all lengths to avoid every conceivable harm: we do not require or expect parents to barricade children in their yards to avoid contact with neighborhood dogs, bullies, or runaway cars. . . .

In reality, few parents can attain the ideal represented by a best interest standard, since the interests of one child will at times conflict with the interests of others within (and outside of) the family in ways that require parents to balance the importance of the competing interests, at times subjugating the interests of one or more children. Conceptually, isolating a child

from the familial context would simply suppress other legitimate interests. . . .

In many discussions of the best interest standard, an effort is made to identify a threshold other than best interest below which state intervention would be justified. Kopelman argues: "A morally and socially defensible policy presupposes a justifiable threshold of adequate parenting." She further states "The best-interests standard . . . does not require us to act in accord with what is literally best for a child, ignoring all other considerations, or even to presuppose that there is always one best solution shaping duties or guiding actions. Rather, it requires us to focus on the child, and select wisely from among alternatives, while taking into account how our lives are woven together[6] . . .

The real question is not so much about identifying which medical alternative represents the best interest of the child, but rather about identifying a harm threshold below which parental decisions will not be tolerated. Referring to a best interest standard merely confuses the matter. I would suggest that the Harm Principle represents the proper legal and ethical basis for state intervention in these cases, and that the Harm principle is consistent with the threshold level suggested by most commentators and applied by most courts.

The Harm Principle and State Action

The government's authority in the health arena arises primarily from its constitutionally sanctioned "police power" to protect the public's health, welfare, and safety. The ethical basis for the exercise of these police powers lies in what has become known as the "harm principle." In *On Liberty* John Stuart Mill argued that "The only purpose for which power can rightfully be exercised over any member of a civilized community, against his will, is to prevent harm to others. His own good, either physical or moral, is not a sufficient warrant."[7] In his work to establish a group of "liberty-limiting principles" that enunciate types of considerations that are always morally relevant reasons to support state action, Joel Feinberg has further refined the principle by arguing that to be justified, restriction of an individual's freedom must be effective at preventing the harm in question and no option that would be less intrusive to individual liberty would be equally effective at preventing the harm: "It is always a good reason in support of penal legislation that it would be effective in preventing (eliminating, reducing) harm to persons other than the actor (the one prohibited from acting) *and* there is no other means that is equally effective at no greater cost to other values."[8] . . .

Having identified the harm principle as a basis for state action, the next step is to further define the harm threshold by identifying the level of harm to be tolerated in parental decisions. It seems clear that not all harms should trigger state intervention. As we discussed earlier, parents should be given some leeway in making decisions for their children, even when those decisions may pose some small degree of risk to the child. Parents will from time to time have to make decisions that "harm" one child in order to benefit the family or meet the needs of another child. . . .

For the medical professional facing a parent refusing to consent to a suggested course of treatment, the proper question is not, "Is this intervention in the child's best interest?" but rather "Does the decision made by the parents significantly increase the likelihood of serious harm as compared to other options?" Parental decisions that do not significantly increase the likelihood of serious harm as compared to other options should be tolerated.

Justifying State Intervention: Eight Conditions

Having identified a reasonable justification for state intervention in the harm principle and further refined the tolerable harm threshold for parental decisions as an increased likelihood of serious harm as compared to other options, we must still deal with several procedural issues. Building on Feinberg's discussion of the harm principle,[9] I would propose that the following eight conditions must be met before considering the use of state intervention to require medical treatment of children over parental objections:

1. By refusing to consent are the parents placing their child at significant risk of serious harm?

2. Is the harm imminent, requiring immediate action to prevent it?

3. Is the intervention that has been refused necessary to prevent the serious harm?

4. Is the intervention that has been refused of proven efficacy, and therefore, likely to prevent the harm?

5. Does the intervention that has been refused by the parents not also place the child at significant risk of serious harm, and do its projected benefits outweigh its projected burdens significantly more favorably than the option chosen by the parents?

6. Would any other option prevent serious harm to the child in a way that is less intrusive to parental autonomy and more acceptable to the parents?

7. Can the state intervention be generalized to all other similar situations?

8. Would most parents agree that the state intervention was reasonable?

[The author's discussion of these principles has been omitted.]

The Harm Principle Applied

The final section of this article will attempt to apply the eight requirements of the harm principle to some of the common cases encountered in pediatric practice. Legal precedent seems most clear for cases that involve medical treatments that are proven to be efficacious, pose little medical risk, and offer significant benefit by preventing the harm of death. Two common examples include parents of the Jehovah's Witness faith who refuse to consent to a blood transfusion for a child and parents of the Christian Science faith who refuse to provide insulin to a child with diabetes. There is consistent agreement among medical professionals and the courts that state intervention is justified in these cases. These cases satisfy the eight conditions of the harm principle rather easily. In both situations, withholding treatment (blood or insulin) represents a significant risk of serious harm (i.e., death). Treatment is necessary to prevent harm befalling the child, and treatment is of proven efficacy. Treatment provides great benefit (prevention of death), imparts minimal risk of harm, and represents proportionately greater benefit than harm to the child. State intervention is justified in all similar cases, and is not restricted solely to those cases in which the parents refuse treatment on religious grounds. For example, if a parent refused because of their concern about the potential for tainted blood being introduced into their child, state intervention would still be sought (because the potential for harm to the child does not differ). Finally, the decision to intervene in these situations can be defended in the public forum and will most likely be overwhelmingly supported. Those six criteria support state intervention in these paradigmatic cases. The remaining two criteria serve to modify state action by requiring the need for action to be imminent and the consideration of alternatives that might be acceptable to the parents. In the case of blood transfusion, some situations would demand immediate action, others might allow time for a consideration of bloodless treatment alternatives or a more extended discussion involving church elders that might result in an agreement regarding treatment. In both cases, if an alternative acceptable to the parents that will also prevent harm to the child can be identified, it should be pursued first.

What of parental decisions that expose a child to serious harms, but do not place a child at risk of death? A child with cancer suffering intensely from pain because his parents will not allow the use of pain medication for fear that it will kill their child suffers a serious and immediate harm. The child's pain is easily and safely treatable with medications that have been studied extensively and proven efficacious. Those medications provide a benefit that far exceeds any risk. In this case non-pharmacologic methods of pain control (like hypnosis) may be more acceptable to the parents and should be pursued, but if narcotics prove necessary to achieve adequate pain relief, they should not be withheld, and state intervention is justified to assure that the child receives adequate relief from pain.

What of those situations in which a parent refuses a therapeutic intervention that poses greater potential risk to a child than either a blood transfusion, insulin, or pain medication? Colin Newmark was a young boy with Burkitt's Lymphoma from the State of Delaware in the U.S. whose parents (Christian Scientists) refused to consent to a regimen of chemotherapy that would provide Colin with less than a 40% chance of survival. Delaware's Division of Child Protective Services intervened and wanted to authorize treatment over the objection of the parents. The Delaware Supreme Court rendered the opinion that the parents' decision ought to be respected. In so doing, they distinguished Colin's case from others like those above by pointing to the low likelihood of success (less than 40%) and the high level of risk and burden entailed in the treatment being offered.[10]

Looking at the Newmark case from the perspective of the harm principle, the first question we ask is whether the decision to refuse chemotherapy placed Colin at significant risk of serious harm. The answer would appear to be yes. By refusing treatment, Colin's chance of death (a serious harm) goes from 60% to 100%, a significant increase in risk. Was the harm imminent? While treatment did not need to be started

within the hour, a delay of more than a few days would place Colin at greater risk, further reducing the chance of successful therapy. Nonetheless, it did leave some time to try to resolve the situation through negotiation. Was treatment necessary to prevent the harm and was it likely to do so? In this case, the only proven treatment available was that offered by Colin's physicians: chemotherapy. It was the only treatment likely to treat Colin's tumor, and therefore necessary to prevent the harm of death. But did this treatment regimen offer Colin significant net benefit over his parent's choice of no treatment or did it simply replace one serious harm with another? This is where the Delaware Supreme Court could not justify state interference with the decision of Colin's parents. The Court argued that when a treatment offered only a 40% chance of survival and was itself ". . . extremely risky, toxic and dangerously life-threatening . . . ," the treatment did not provide a great enough net benefit to justify the harm of interfering with parental decision-making and autonomy."[11] One could disagree with the court's assessment regarding this calculation, but for purposes of our discussion, it is sufficient to point out that the harm principle adequately focuses on the proper concern in this case: harm to the child. The court also properly focused on harm to Colin, not the religious motivation of his parents. Had the court decided to interfere with parental choice, the remaining elements of the harm principle would apply, including using the least restrictive means of preventing harm to the child. If any less toxic but similarly efficacious regimen were available that was more acceptable to the parents, it should have been offered. Furthermore, Colin should have been allowed to remain in the custody of his parents as long as they did not interfere with his treatment. Ultimately, however, this case illustrates that we should be reluctant to override parental wishes when therapy itself poses grave risks or limited likelihood of success.

A final example concerns parents who refuse to immunize their children with recommended childhood vaccines. Parents may refuse to immunize their children for a variety of reasons including religious proscriptions, naturopathic preferences and beliefs, or a rational calculation that remaining unvaccinated would be better for their children. This decision goes contrary to the very strong recommendations of most physicians and most pediatric organizations. Many physicians believe strongly that parental decisions to refuse immunization are contrary to the best interest of a child, and a few would argue that state intervention is justified on that basis. Most who feel this way appeal to the best interest standard.

But parents may also use the best interest standard in refusing immunization of behalf of their children. While most mandatory vaccines are effective and safe, a small possibility of adverse reactions exists. For example, a parent might reasonably conclude that refusing the measles vaccine is in the best interests of a child living in a community with a high immunization rate. In such a community, the prevalence of measles is sufficiently low that an unimmunized child would be unlikely to contract measles and therefore, could be safely spared any possible risks associated with the vaccine. In fact, it has been argued that "any successful immunization programme will inevitably create a situation, as the disease becomes rare, where the individual parent's choice is at odds with society's needs."[12]

Under what conditions would the harm principle support state intervention to vaccinate a child for the child's own sake? In cases where the parental decision to refuse immunization places a child at significant risk of serious harm, state agencies may be obligated to intervene and provide the necessary immunization over the parents' objections. But in a well-immunized community, these situations will be rare indeed. A child lacking tetanus immunity who has sustained a deep and contaminated puncture wound might provide one example. Epidemic conditions might provide another. In both situations, state intervention for the child's sake can only be justified if the case can be made that the child is placed at significant risk of serious harm by remaining unimmunized. Routine childhood vaccinations have been proven effective at preventing disease and have a very low risk of serious side effects. But to justify their use against parental wishes, the need to vaccinate must be imminent, and must be necessary to prevent the harm. If the parents prefer an option that prevents the harm without vaccination (like quarantine) serious consideration must be given to that alternative. Even in the event of an epidemic or contact with an infectious agent that justifies immunization, it must be pointed out that only the immunization necessary to prevent the imminent harm can be justified. If the child has a deep contaminated wound that requires tetanus vaccine to prevent serious harm, the state is

not justified administering the chicken pox vaccine at the same time. With a few notable exceptions, the harm principle rarely provides sufficient justification for interference with parental decisions regarding immunization.

Conclusion

While there are good reasons for granting parents significant freedom in making health care decisions for their children, there are certain decisions that are sufficiently harmful that they ought not be allowed. The best interest standard has long been used to identify the threshold at which the state is justified in interfering with parental decision-making. In practice, however, parents cannot and should not always be expected to make decisions that are in the child's best interest. Using such a standard disallows other important considerations that might conflict with the child's best interest. The harm principle provides a foundation for interfering with parental freedom that more accurately describes an appropriate standard for interfering with parents who refuse to consent to medical treatment on behalf of a child. State intervention is justified not when a parental refusal is contrary to a child's best interest, but when the parental refusal places the child at significant risk of serious preventable harm.

Notes

1. *Union Pacific Railway Company v. Botsford*, US 141:250 (1891).
2. *Cruzon v. Director, Missouri Department of Health*, US 497:261 (1990).
3. *Prince v. Massachusettss*, U.S. 321:158 (1944).
4. Allen E. Buchanan and Dan W. Brock, *Deciding for Others: The Ethics of Surrogate Decision-Makers* (New York: Cambridge University Press, 1990), p. 88.
5. Tom L. Beauchamp and James F. Childress, *Principles & Biomedical Ethics*, 5th edition (New York: Oxford University Press, 2001), p. 102.
6. Loretta M. Kopelman, "The Best-Interests Standard as Threshold, Ideal, and Standard of Reasonableness," *The Journal of Medicine and Philosophy* 22 (1997): 276, 279.
7. John Stuart Mill, "On Liberty," in John Stuart Mill, *On Liberty and Utilitarianism* (New York: Bantam Books, 1993), p. 12.
8. Joel Feinberg, *Harm to Others: The Moral Limits of the Criminal Law* (New York: Oxford University Press, 1984), p. 26.
9. Ibid.
10. *Newmark v. Williams*, Del Super Ct 588: A. 2d 1108 (1991).
11. *Ibid.*
12. Ray Anderson and Robert May, "The Logic of Vaccination," *Nato Scientist* 96 (1982): 415.

Do Parents Have the Right to Refuse Standard Treatment for Their Child with Favorable-Prognosis Cancer?

Jeffrey D. Hord, Waqas Rehman, Patricia Hannon, Lisa Anderson-Shaw, Mary Lou Schmidt

Jeffrey Hord and his collaborators present the case of a seven-year-old boy with a form of leukemia that responds well to standard treatment and has an 85% chance of long-term survival. The boy's leukemia went into remission after the first round of chemotherapy, but his parents decided to discontinue the chemotherapy in favor of a holistic treatment that would not damage his immune system. The hospital went to court seeking an order to continue the child's chemotherapy, but the judge ruled in favor of the patents' right to make medical decisions for their child.

The authors outline the ethical principles of autonomy, beneficence, non-maleficence, and justice as they relate to the case. They emphasize the difficulty of finding a threshold of therapeutic success at which treatment should be given to children contrary to the wishes of their parents. The pediatric oncologist must, in their view, act as an advocate for the child and fight to see that the child is given the best chance for a cure.

Introduction

A 7-year-old boy presenting with bone pain and fever was found to have standard-risk pre-B-cell precursor acute lymphoblastic leukemia (ALL). Parental written consent was obtained to begin a standard 3.5-year chemotherapy treatment regimen with an estimated 85% chance of long-term survival. Induction chemotherapy was successful in producing remission; however, after 3 months of chemotherapy, the parents opposed continuation of the standard treatment, citing concerns that chemotherapy would damage their son's immune system and cause other long-term problems.[1,2]

As a replacement for standard treatment, the parents elected to pursue alternative holistic approaches including nutritional supplements, dietary changes, and stress reduction techniques. The parents transferred the care of their child to a licensed family medicine physician who was board certified in holistic medicine. The new physician agreed to monitor the

Waqas Rehman, Patricia Hannon, Lisa Anderson-Shaw, Mary Lou Schmidt, Jeffrey D. Hord, From "Do Parents Have the Right to Refuse Standard Treatment for Their Child with Favorable-Prognosis Cancer?", *Journal of Clinical Oncology*, Vol. 24, no. 34 (2006): 5454–5456. Copyright © 2006 by the American Society of Clinical Oncology. Reproduced by permission.

patient's blood counts to monitor the leukemia, and if the patient's blood counts suggested relapse, he would refer him back to a pediatric oncologist.[1-3]

The Department of Job and Family Services in the patient's county of residence was notified, and a hearing was held in the county Court of Common Pleas (family court division) to determine whether the parents were guilty of neglect and whether standard therapy should be mandated. The pediatric oncologist involved with this case testified that he believed that stopping standard therapy at this point would almost certainly result in a return of the leukemia. Furthermore, he testified that the child's likelihood of being cured would be significantly less on relapse. The court dismissed the case stating that the parents' "concerns about long-term effects of chemotherapy" did not qualify as neglect. Furthermore, the court recognized that the patient was under the care of a licensed physician and refused to judge the relative merits of the two different treatment options recommended by two different physicians licensed to practice medicine in the state.[1]

After the hearing, the holistic physician was reported to the State Medical Board to determine whether he had "departed from or failed to conform to minimal standards of care." After an investigation, the Secretary and Supervising Member of the State Medical Board determined that formal disciplinary charges were not warranted. Approximately 4 months after the court's decision, the patient experienced a recurrence of acute leukemia.[4]

Discussion

Over the past several decades, the traditional approach of physician-directed decision making has decreased, whereas shared decision making, which strives to include the wishes of the patient and family, has increased. Although there is substantial literature dealing with declining or withdrawing treatment in adults with life-threatening illnesses, there is considerably less discussion of parents refusing or discontinuing therapy on behalf of their minor children with malignancies. Because cure rates for many childhood malignancies are more than 50% with standard therapy regimens, withholding treatment can be a difficult ethical dilemma for the treatment providers. The American Academy of Pediatrics[5] and the International Society of Pediatric Oncology[6] assert that physicians are obliged to seek legal recourse when parental refusal places a child at clear and substantial risk. Many have assumed that a court will automatically order that the child be treated, but such an assumption is incorrect, as is illustrated by this case.[7]

Each year in the United States, approximately 14,000 children are diagnosed with cancer, with ALL representing nearly one third of all these cancers. According to the National Cancer Institute's Surveillance, Epidemiology, and End Results program, the 5-year survival rate for children diagnosed with all forms of cancer between 1986 and 1993 was 72%, whereas the 5-year survival rate for ALL for the same period was 79%.[8] Standard treatment for ALL consists of multiagent chemotherapy, although the specific agents, dose-intensity, and duration of therapy vary based on a variety of prognostic factors. ALL therapy requires an exhaustive commitment by the parents or caretakers for several years because these caretakers give chemotherapy at home by mouth or by injection; observe the patient for signs of infection, anemia, or bleeding; and bring the patient for frequent doctor visits and hospitalizations.

Within the framework of informed consent for treatment, physicians are obligated to provide the pediatric patient and family information pertaining to the diagnosis, prognosis, range of medical therapy available, and the risks and benefits of treatment or nontreatment. In addition, it is the physician's responsibility to the patient to establish the course of treatment that will provide the best opportunity for long-term survival. When dealing with patients with poor prognosis, limiting medical therapy is reasonable, ethical, and morally defensible because the burdens of therapy may outweigh the benefits, and parents must consider quality of life.[9] Conversely, when standard therapy offers a high likelihood of long-term survival and a reasonable quality of life, it is difficult for the managing physician to understand withholding such therapy. Current laws provide parents with wide discretionary authority in raising their children.[10] These laws, however, are balanced with child abuse and neglect laws to ensure that a parent's decision regarding treatment is in the best interest of the child. In addition to these legal aspects, ethical issues are intimately woven within the context of each clinical case.

The biomedical ethical principles of respect for autonomy (allowing free choice by the patient, perhaps exercised through a surrogate), beneficence (providing benefit to the patient), nonmaleficence (doing no harm to the patient), and justice (the obligation to distribute benefits and burdens proportionally) all weigh heavily on the providers' decision about how to respond when parents refuse standard therapy for their child with a favorable-prognosis malignancy.[11]

In cases involving children, respect for autonomy is not seen in the same manner as in adults because young children often are not felt to have decisional capacity, which is prerequisite for autonomy. As children mature and enter the teen years, they usually develop capacity, and their input related to health care is often sought, acknowledged, and respected by their parents as well as their health care providers. However, unless the child has been declared emancipated by a court of law (i.e., deemed to possess competence), it is the parent or guardian who theoretically exercises autonomy on behalf of their child. In such cases, proxy decisions should strive to be a "reasonable presumption of the child's wishes" even though such wishes may not be known.[12]

Beneficence and nonmaleficence are both somewhat murky principles as they relate to many cancer treatments and regimens. To reap the ultimate benefits from the intended therapy, harm must often result, as seen by various side effects of chemotherapy. In addition to the physical harms that a child may experience from the treatments, there are emotional harms that may be experienced not only by the child undergoing treatment, but also by family members. The emotional roller coaster that cancer patients and their loved ones experience may seem like a benefit if treatment is successful and cure is attained, or it may seem like harm if treatment ultimately fails.

Finally, the principle of justice is of interest. Cancer among children is not distributed with fairness or with equality. To those families affected by a child with cancer, it is seen as a cruel, unjust, and random assault. Justice appears, then, not in relationship to the disease, but rather to the treatment options. For many cancers, there are approved and effective standard treatments. Receiving a standard treatment for a specific cancer might be perceived as a right by those individuals afflicted with that specific cancer. "A holder of a valid claim based in justice has a right, and therefore is due something."[11]

When parents wish to withhold or discontinue standard proven treatment in a child with cancer that has a likelihood of long-term cure, referral to the local child protection agency is indicated because a parent's inability to provide adequate care for a child is a criminal offense.[10] The difficulty lies in defining a threshold of therapeutic success where treatment should be initiated against the wishes of the parent or guardian. This problem has been challenging for the legal system to resolve. Courts will order treatment over parental objections for conditions that are immediately life threatening, such as antibiotics for bacterial meningitis or insulin injections for diabetes mellitus; however, when the disease does not cause imminent harm but there are significant risks involved with the treatment, the decision of the court is less predictable (S. Weitzman, personal communication, December, 2002; S. Dubansky, personal communication, December, 2002).[13–15] Oncologists must also deal with the fact that their patients will require treatment for extended periods of time, and a significant portion of the therapy involves the home administration of oral medications.[16]

Five cases similar to the one presented here were found in the legal and ethics literature, from court transcripts, and from personal communication with treating oncologists. In all these court cases, the parents declined or withdrew standard treatment for their children with favorable-prognosis cancer. In two of the six cases, courts upheld the parents' wishes to withhold standard therapy. Factors considered in making these rulings included prognosis, therapeutic risks/complications, the parents' beliefs (religious/holistic), and whether the alternative therapy was under the direction of a licensed physician. To date, courts have generally defined adequate care as that care given by a licensed physician. The courts have almost never chosen one medical approach over another as long as both were directed by licensed physicians.[16] The health care providers involved in such cases have had the option to report a licensed physician to a regulatory board if he or she was operating outside the minimum standard of care.

Recent studies indicate an increased use of complementary or alternative medicine in pediatric oncology patients, with 47% of patients using at least one alternative treatment, such as vitamin therapy, herbal remedies, or dietary regimens.[17] For those families who lack faith in the possibility of cure from conventional medical treatment, the increased availability of alternative and complementary medicines may make them more likely to refuse standard well-tested therapies.

Physicians should also be aware that their actions may be perceived differently by different populations. Although the opinion of the pediatric oncology community is strongly in favor of following standard proven therapies, the general public may not be as supportive and may be swayed by the manner in which the case is presented in the media. In the case presented here, a local television station posted an internet-based survey, and 83% of the 395 responders supported the parents' "right to choose the kind of treatment for their kids."[18] Furthermore, the vast majority of published editorials and letters to the editor regarding the present case, printed in local newspapers, strongly opposed the Department of Job and Family Services' decision to pursue standard treatment for the child in opposition of the parents' views (15 opposed compared with two in favor).[19–23]

In summary, pediatric oncologists should be prepared for the many implications brought by a case such as this, in which parents refuse standard treatment for their child with cancer who has a favorable prognosis. As the probability of encountering a similar situation increases, so does the need to fully understand the relevant laws and ethical principles that apply. In dealing with the issues presented here, the oncologist must act as an advocate fighting to ensure that the child is given the best chance of cure while trying to balance the harms that may occur. In addition, the oncologist should consider reporting any physician to the state medical board who may have failed to meet the minimal standards of care.

References

1. In re *Maxin*, Case No. JU 124198 (Court of Common Pleas, Stark County, OH, 2002)

2. Gross A: Boy's cancer regimen up to court. *Akron Beacon Journal* November 15, 2002: A1

3. Gross A: Boy's care allowed. *Akron Beacon Journal* November 19, 2002: A1

4. Spector H: Little Noah now uses chemo. *Plain Dealer* May 30, 2003: A1

5. American Academy of Pediatrics, Committee on Bioethics: Informed consent, parental permission, and assent in pediatric practice. Pediatrics 95: 314–317, 1995[Abstract/Free Full Text]

6. The International Confederation of Childhood Cancer Parent Organisations. SIOP Working Committee on Psychosocial Issues in Pediatric Oncology. Guidelines for refusal, non-compliance, and abandonment of treatment in children and adolescents with cancer. http://www.icccpo.org/articles/psychosocial/guidelines_refusal.html

7. Field MJ, Behrman RE: When Children Die: Improving Palliative and End-of-Life Care for Children and Their Families. Washington, DC, National Academies Press, 2003

8. Ries LAG, Eisner MP, Kosary CL, et al.: (eds) SEER Cancer Statistics Review, 1973–1998. Bethesda, MD, National Cancer Institute, 2001

9. Freyer DR: Children with cancer: Special considerations in the discontinuation of life-sustaining treatment. J Med Pediatr Oncol 20: 136–142, 1992[CrossRef]

10. Holder AR: Parents, courts and decision making. J Pediatr 103: 515–521, 1983[CrossRef][Medline]

11. Beauchamp T, Childress J: Principles of Biomedical Ethics (ed 5). New York, NY, Oxford University Press, 2001

12. McCormick RA: Proxy consent in the experimentation situation. Perspect Biol Med 18: 11–13, 1974

13. In re *Custody of a Minor*, 379 NE2d 1053 (MA 1978)

14. In re *Hofbauer*, 395 NE2d 1109 (NY App. 1979)

15. In re *Wilimann*, 493 NE2d 1380 (OH App. 1986)

16. Holder AR: Childhood malignancies and decision making. Yale J Biol Med 65: 99–104, 1992[Medline]

17. McCurdy EA, Spangler JG, Wofford MM, et al: Religiosity is associated with the use of complementary medical therapies by pediatric oncology patients. J Pediatr Hematol Oncol 25: 125–129, 2003[CrossRef][Medline]

18. News Channel 5, Cleveland, OH: Judge: Stopping son's chemo not neglect. http://www.newsnet5.com/news/1792069/detail.html

19. *The Plain Deafer*, Letters to the Editor, Liveline, November 30, 2002. Cleveland, OH. http://www.cleveland.com/livelines/index/ssf7/livelines/more/112902.html

20. Letters to the Editor. Wednesday forum. *Akron Beacon Journal* November 27, 2002: B3.

21. *The Canton Repository*. Editorial: Local case may redefine neglect. November 15, 2002. http://www.cantonrep.com/index.php?ID=71682&Category=3&fromSearch=yes&subCategoryID=0

22. "Complications in Care", editorial. Akron Beacon Journal, Section B, page 2, November 19, 2002. Akron, OH.

23. Editorial: A rainbow for Noah. *Plain Dealer* November 20, 2002.

24. To the Editor: Liveline: Should Stark County officials appeal a judge's ruling that the parents of a 7-year-old boy with leukemia are permitted to have him treated by nontraditional methods rather than chemotherapy? http://www.cleveland.com/livelines/index.ssf?/livelines/more/112902.html

The Dilemma of Jehovah's Witness Children Who Need Blood to Survive

Anita Catlin

Catlin presents the case of a child given a blood transfusion even though his parents, both Jehovah's Witnesses, refused to consent to the procedure and tried to prevent it. The parents believed, on biblical grounds, that blood transfusions are forbidden and that, as punishment for violating God's commandment, their child would be separated from them for all eternity. Catlin explores the ethical and legal issues relevant to the decisions of both medical staff and parents when the question of transfusion arises for a child whose parents are Jehovah's Witnesses.

She argues that, although the blood transfusion was judged by a physician as medically necessary to serve the best interest of the child, the possibility of effective alternative treatments not requiring the use of blood products should have been explored. This is the approach that should be taken in all similar cases, the author holds, and the exploration of treatment alternatives could be facilitated by a knowledgeable ethics consultant.

Anita Catlin, From "The Dilemma of Jehovah's Witness Children Who Need Blood to Survive," *HEC Forum*, Vol. 8, (1996): 195–207. Copyright © 1996 by Springer-Verlag. Reproduced by permission.

The Story

In 1993, at a major medical center in the Midwest, parents were handcuffed and removed from their son's bedside and their child was taken into custody by the attending physician. What was the crime that these parents committed, resulting in the father's incarceration and the child being made a ward of the state for the following year? The case was a refusal by Jehovah's Witnesses parents to allow blood transfusion to their six-year-old child. The child was in a sickle cell crisis, with a stroke in progress, hemiplegia, and a hemoglobin so low that death was imminent. This essay examines the case as it progressed, the norms and values involved, the positions of the attending doctors and nurses, and the legal actions that took place, and makes recommendations for nursing and ethics committee considerations for the future.

Persons who practice the Jehovah's Witnesses faith accept medical and surgical treatment. However, they are deeply religious people who believe that blood transfusion is forbidden for them. This prohibition is construed from the following biblical passages: "Only flesh with its soul—its blood—you must not eat" (Genesis 9:3–4); "Abstain from . . . fornication and from what is strangled and from blood" (Acts 15:19–21). "You must not eat the blood of any sort of flesh, because the soul of every sort of flesh is its blood. I will set my face against that person who eats blood. . . . Anyone eating it will be cut off (Leviticus 17:10, 13–14). Jehovah's Witnesses interpret these passages as forbidding the transfusion of whole blood, packed red blood cells, plasma, white blood cells, and platelets. Jehovah's Witnesses are allowed to decide for themselves, as a matter of conscience, whether or not to accept albumin, immune globulins, cryoprecipitate, and organ transplants[1]. Non-blood plasma expanders such as saline solution, Ringer's lactate, and hetastarch are acceptable[2]. When a Jehovah's Witness patient receives blood, this constitutes a grave sin. By disobeying God and being "cut off," they are denied life through resurrection. If a person's life is extended by a transfusion, it may become meaningless and lack spiritual purpose because the hope of everlasting life may be forfeited[1].

In sickle cell anemia, the red blood cells become damaged and are unable to deliver oxygen. The standard treatment for this condition is hydration, oxygenation, blood replacement and exchange transfusion. When parents of the little boy presented to the emergency room, they said, "We want you to treat and save

our child, but you may not administer blood to him." When the child was admitted to the pediatric intensive care unit and found to be in critical condition, the parents were told, "There is no option, your child needs to have blood. If you wish to call in a specialist who treats Jehovah's Witnesses without blood, or wish to transfer him elsewhere, we will support that. If you would like to call your church elders to provide support or advice, you may do that. It will take two hours to type and cross match the blood. At the end of two hours, if alternative arrangements have not been made, we will transfuse your child."

Two hours passed. Phone calls were made but no transfer or alternative care was found. The parents held the child in their arms, lay across his bed, and said "you may not transfuse our child." Attempts to gain their cooperation failed. The hospital legal department advised the physician to proceed with the transfusion. Two hospital security guards physically removed the parents from the child's room. When the father would not cooperate with the separation from his child, he was handcuffed, taken into custody and remanded to the local jail facility. The mother was allowed to remain on the ward, but continued to protest. The blood was administered and the child's life was saved.

Goals of Medicine and Conflicting Principles

Healthcare personnel are trained to be true to the virtue of helping others. Their mission is to achieve the goals of medicine, which include: promoting health; preventing disease; relieving symptoms, pain, and suffering; curing disease; preventing untimely death; improving functional status; counseling patients and families; and avoiding harm to the patient[3]. In this case, giving blood met every goal of medicine, and withholding blood constituted doing harm and causing the untimely death of a child. The organizational mission of a pediatrics unit supports the ethical principle of beneficence.

A case like this, however, brings out competing principles. Non-maleficence is the ethical principle which urges us to refrain from actions that would cause harm. For the healthcare team, the parents' refusal to allow the child to receive blood is seen as serious harm. For the parents, disobeying a religious commandment and having the child's soul in jeopardy was considered serious harm. Quintero, writing in *Pediatric Nursing*, pointed out that "what is right in the eyes of Jehovah's Witness parents is the need to ensure a life for their child after death, even if this means an early end to the child's life on earth"[4]. The dilemma of the case is the harm of the child's death lying in balance with the harm of not honoring the parents' beliefs.

Ethical Principles Regarding Children

Social historian M. Steinfels[5] traced how thinking about children has changed over time. Historically, parents' desires and authority dominated and children had no interests apart from their parents'. Then there was a period when parents had duties to raise a child to fulfill a religiously, socially, or professionally agreed upon role, which did not necessarily represent the direct self-interests of the parents or the child. And presently, the child has individual interests and needs that must be given consideration apart from those of the parents and others who purport to define children's interests.

The principle of non-maleficence becomes more complex when the interests of children are involved. Attorney J. Goldstein reviewed the case law regarding parents and children:

"[1] To be an *adult* is to be a risk taker, independent, and with capacity and authority to decide and to do what is best for oneself.

"[2] To be an *adult who is a parent* is to be presumed by law to have the capacity, authority, and responsibility to determine and to do what is good for one's children.

"[3] The law is designed to assure for each child an opportunity to meet and master the developmental crises on the way to adulthood—to that critical age when he or she is presumed by the state to be qualified to determine what is best for oneself.

"[4] It is the function of the law to protect family privacy as a means of safeguarding parental autonomy in child rearing. At the same time the law attempts to safeguard each child's entitlement to autonomous parents who care and who feel responsible and who can be held accountable for continually meeting the child's . . . needs"[5].

Goldstein wrote that there can be state supervention of parental autonomy in health care matters only if three conditions are met: a) the medical profession is in agreement about the treatment, b) the expected outcome of the treatment is what society agrees to be right for any child (one which would give a chance for a normal healthy life or a life worth living), and c) the expected

outcome of denial of that treatment would mean death for the child[5]. Here the definition of society for those who would override parental autonomy is the "mainstream" society, which unfortunately is not inclusive of an individual religious group's dissenting opinion.

Jonsen, Siegler, and Winslade maintain that freedom of religion is highly valued and is protected by the U.S. Constitution, but that this freedom does not extend to making decisions about children[3]. Parents are granted wide discretion about the values they believe their children's lives should embody, but parental discretion is limited in medical care when certain beliefs would disadvantage the child's health. This opinion was upheld in a 1978 Court decision in which Jehovah's Witnesses were told that it was not unconstitutional for the State to insist on blood transfusion for children in appropriate cases[6].

Ruth Macklin notes that the invasion of family privacy must be weighed against a lifetime of health, well being, or bodily integrity for the child on whose behalf the state seeks to intervene. The potential harm to the family must be weighed against the potential harm to the child. Macklin states that it is possible to accord a great deal of respect to family autonomy and integrity, and "at the same time recognize that close and loving family units are not destroyed by an occasional outside intervention aimed at serving the best interest of a child"[5]. Macklin's opinion, however, appears to downplay the potential for psychological harm that forcing a transfusion could cause.

What Did the Key Players Think?

The pediatrician in charge of the pediatric intensive care unit, Dr. B., recalled the case matter-of-factly, reciting the medical facts in a clinical manner. It was the agreement of consults from medicine, neurology, and hematology that this child would die if blood was not given. The parents, due to religious teachings, would not consent. Dr. B. stated that there was no alternative treatment and no other options available. When questioned about the use of hyperbaric oxygen and hypothermia to treat the anemia, as described by Akingbola et al.[7], he stated that these cooling methods could not be used with sickle cell patients, as cooling increases the sickling. If the child was to live, he would have to be given transfused blood over parental objection.

Dr. B. recounted the call made to the legal affairs officer on duty that day. The legal opinion was given that [1] the emergency was reasonable and correct, [2] giving blood to Jehovah's Witness children over parental objection was well established in the courts, and [3] that Dr. B. himself must take personal, immediate, legal custody of the child. Dr. B. indicated that he was apprehensive about this responsibility, and that he was on the phone once every hour with the legal affairs attorney. He was advised by the attorney that the child could not be transferred and must be immediately treated, as he, Dr. B., was now the guardian of the child.

Both Dr. B. and the clinical nurse specialist described the pain of the moment. They recounted the tears shed by nurses who had to assist security guards to pull the parents off the child's bed when the parents were trying physically to prevent the transfusion. When asked what their ethical thinking was at the time, both mentioned the principle of the child's best interest. Perhaps they were recalling the ruling of the Supreme Court *in Prince v. Commonwealth of Massachusetts*, which states: "Parents may make martyrs of themselves, but it does not follow that they are free, in identical circumstances, to make martyrs of their children. . ."[8]. When questioned about the sanctity of the commandment the parents were trying to uphold, or the seriousness of the harm of violating this commandment, both Dr. B. and Nurse C. could not reply. Protecting the child from death was the job that was to be done, and to them no argument existed that held greater moral weight.

When Dr. B. was later called to court to testify in the parental custody hearing, the judge stated that there was no need even to evaluate the case, that the correct legal actions had been taken. In fact, custody, was not immediately returned to the parents, as the child would need on-going transfusion in the years ahead, and the judge wished to prevent further such occurrences. . . .

What Can the Literature Add?

Many physicians have written in opposition to treating children against their parents' wishes. In 1976, surgeons Gardner *et al.* posed the following question: "Who would benefit if the [adult] patient's corporal malady is cured but the spiritual life with God, as he sees it, is compromised, which leads to a life that is meaningless and perhaps worse than death itself[9]. . . .

Richard Spence, in *Critical Care Medicine*, wrote: "Physicians must understand the severe consequences of transfusion to the Jehovah's Witness. The action is not considered by the church to be a minor infraction, punishable by a simple reprimand. The Jehovah's Witness may suffer excommunication from the church, which means forfeiture of a chance for eternal life and severance of the individual's relationship with God. Although

it may be difficult for the physician to accept this position, especially in a situation in which transfusion can be lifesaving, he/she must contrast saving a life with the potential loss of everlasting life and redemption, as understood by the Jehovah's Witness"[10].

Writing in the *Journal of the American Medical Association*, Dixon and Smalley state: Witness parents ask that therapies be used that are not religiously prohibited. This accords with the medical tenet of treating the "whole person," not overlooking the possible lasting psychosocial damage of an invasive procedure that violates a family's fundamental beliefs"[11].

A number of legal actions in the United States and Canada have allowed parents to refuse blood and seek alternative therapies for their children. In the case of *In Re: E.G., a Minor*[12], physicians went to court to insist that a 17-year-old girl be treated with blood for her leukemia. The court upheld her right to refuse blood. The Illinois Appellate Court ruled in 1989, and upheld the ruling in 1990, that teenage children could decide whether or not to receive blood, and that parents were not neglectful when they did not allow blood transfusion for their children. In *Re Children's Aid Society of Metropolitan Toronto versus F.R.*[13] Witness parents were allowed to refuse transfusion for their four-year-old child who was bleeding after a tonsillectomy.

At times, children themselves were asked what they wished to do. In Fox, a 13-year-old child injured in a car accident refused blood[14]. In Robb, a 16-year-old with leukemia refused blood[15]. In Akingbola et al., a 12-year-old with renal failure refused blood[7]. In each of these cases, the physicians were supportive of the child's view and did not insist on overruling. In each case, other treatment modalities were found and were successful. The children's long term prognoses without transfusion were not certain. Dr. Mary Scully, attending physician of the child with leukemia has observed:

> *I was convinced that overall he did have very strong spiritual beliefs and that he was very anxious to maintain his personal integrity. . . . I was concerned what damage would be done to him and his psyche and his relationship with his family if that was disturbed . . . going against his will would seriously jeopardize his chances of recovery*[15].

A contrasting view can be found in the *Journal of Christian Nursing*. Here Rita Swan, a mother whose own child died because of parental religious convictions, wrote adamantly about how wrong she was, and how wrong the state was in not overruling her wishes. "Other children have inherent rights to appropriate medical care and their parents have a duty to provide them," Swan states, but "religious immunity laws are perpetrating crimes against children, the nursing profession and society"[16]. [Swan has been active in supporting legislative changes to repeal religious exemption laws from the child abuse statutes in the U.S.]

May describes the recent attempts by the American Academy of Pediatrics to remove these religious exemptions from the child abuse statute laws. Hawaii, South Dakota, and Massachusetts have already done so[17]. May also notes that in a pluralistic society like America's, which was founded on the basis of religious freedom, it is hard to reconcile the imposition of the dominant society's values upon a religious group's values. I agree with May and find painful the idea that one group can say that another groups' deeply held beliefs are wrong and should not be followed.

What Could an Ethics Consultant Have Done?

In this case, the staff was very clear that there was to be no mediating, arbitrating, or negotiating, and they had obtained their own legal opinion. An ethics consultation was not requested at the time. But there are other roles that the ethics consultant could assist with, such as educating, problem solving, providing family advocacy, and helping to support the providers.

Education includes making sure that the most up-to-date medical care was available. Ethics consultants must keep up-to-date on the literature regarding controversial issues. Strokes in sickle cell children are frequent (6–9%) and at an increased risk in the 5 to 10 year old age group[18]. A Jehovah's Witness child with stroke was likely to appear again in a hospital treating large numbers of sickle cell children. There are many recent studies which describe how to handle severe anemia in the Jehovah's Witness patient, but in this case, the physician stated that no alternative treatment would work. . . .

The consultant could also supply the clinicians with the 24-hour Jehovah's Witness hospital assistance phone line located in Brookline, Massachusetts. There is on file a data bank of 21,000 U.S. physicians who are trained in the care of patients without transfusion, and multiple hospitals that have special Bloodless Medicine and Surgery programs. The ethics consultant could suggest a physician-to-physician referral using this data bank, rather than relying on parents to find someone to care for their child in an emergency situation, as was done in this case. . . .

Providing advocacy for the family is the third of the ethics consultant's roles. In this case, the family is in great need of support. An ethics consultation early in the case may have been able to prevent the physical nature of the confrontation. In future cases, parents must be comforted in a much more pro-active way. A quiet place, such as the hospital chapel, should be found for prayer with their minister and friends. The nurse ethicist can advocate by "bridging, negotiating, and mediating between these two systems, (acting as) a middle man—a culture broker"[19]. A psychiatric nurse liaison could be called on the unit. The ethicist could say to the family "You are *not* consenting, you are *not* responsible, this is *not* voluntary, and your God knows that"—and this might help. I believe that under no circumstances should anyone be allowed to try convincing the parents to give up their beliefs. What nurses can do is assist parents with the guilt and pain they will feel[4]. . . .

Summary

Medical researchers must continue to develop and test non-blood oxygen-transport products. Resources provided by the Jehovah's Witness Hospital Assistance Line must be consulted. Sickle cell researchers must continue to test non-blood treatment. Information about non-blood treatments must be disbursed. Ways to enhance parental comfort as the laws further and further support children's best interest must be provided. Information regarding cultural diversity must be disseminated. Hospitals and healthcare agencies that have not done so must institute the use of ethics consulting or ethics committees. Nurse ethicists must continue development of the role of educating staff; mediation, arbitration and negotiation; problem solving; obtaining legal opinion; providing patient, family, or staff advocacy; and helping to reduce suffering on the part of the providers. Difficult ethical decisions should continue to be debated.

Were the staff at X Med Center correct in overriding parental wishes and breaking tenets of their faith? In the doctor's, nurse's, lawyer's, and judge's view they were. The child, now eight years old, is alive and well. The stroke resolved, and imminent death averted. The parents' and child's views are not presently available. Whether the family is suffering from the child's loss of his relationship with God, or are secretly relieved in their hearts that they are not, like Rita Swan, mourning their dead son, is unknown. What is known, is that this was a difficult case for all involved, and that such cases will continue to present themselves in the future.

References

1. Rosam E. Personal communication with Hospital Information Services, Watchtower, Jehovah's Witnesses Organization. 1995; 25 Columbia Heights, Brooklyn, NY.

2. Thurkauf GC. Understanding the beliefs of the Jehovah's Witnesses. *Focus on Critical Care.* 1989; 16(3): 199–204.

3. Jonsen AJ, Siegler M, Winslade W. *Clinical Ethics.* New York, NY: Mcgraw-Hill; 1992.

4. Quintero C. Blood administration in pediatric Jehovah's Witnesses. *Pediatric Nursing.* 1993; 19(1): 46–48.

5. Gaylin W, Macklin R (eds.). *Who speaks for the child? The problems of proxy consent.* New York, NY: Plenum Press; 1992; 186–188.

6. *Jehovah's Witnesses versus King County Hospital*, 1967. Federal Supplement 278, 309 U.S. 598, 278 F. Supp. 488, 1967, 488–508.

7. Akingbola OA, Custer JR, Bunchman TE, Sedman AB. Management of severe anemia without transfusion in a pediatric Jehovah's Witness patient. *Critical Care Medicine.* 1994; 22(3): 524–28.

8. *Prince vs. Commonwealth of Massachusetts.* Jan. 31, 1944. 321 U.S. 804, 64 S. Ct. 784, sec. 64, 438.

9. Gardner B, Bivona J, Alfonso A, Herbsman H. Major surgery in Jehovah's Witnesses. *New York State Journal of Medicine.* 1976; 76: 765–66.

10. Spence RK. Management of severe anemia without transfusion in a pediatric Jehovah's Witness patient (letter to the editor). *Critical Care Medicine.* 1995; 23(2): 416–17.

11. Dixon JL, Smalley MG. Jehovah's Witnesses: The surgical/ethical challenge. *Journal of American Medical Association.* 1981; 246(21): 2471–72.

12. North Eastern Reporter, 549, 2nd Series, 1990. *In Re: E.G., a Minor*, Supreme Court of Illinois, No. 66089, pp. 322–31.

13. *Children's Aid Society of Metropolitan Toronto v. F.R.*, Ontario Province Court, Family Division, 1988.

14. Fox V. Caught between religion and medicine. *AORN Journal* 1990; 52(1): 131–46.

15. Robb N. Ruling on Jehovah's Witness teen in New Brunswick may have "settled the law" for MDs. *Canadian Medical Association Journal.* 1994; 151(5): 625–8.

16. Swan R. The law should protect all children. *Journal of Christian Nursing.* Spring 1987; 40.

17. May L. Challenging medical authority: The refusal of treatment by Christian Scientists. *Hastings Center Report*, 1995; 25(1): 15–21.

18. Ohene-Frempong K. Stroke in sickle cell disease: Demographic, clinical and therapeutic considerations. *Seminars in Hematology.* 1991; 28(3): 213–9.

19. Jezewski MA. Culture brokering as a model for advocacy. *Nursing and Health Care.* 1993; 14(2): 78–85.

Reply to Anita Catlin

Eugene Rosam

Rosam, in his reply to Catlin, points out that Jehovah's Witness parents do not believe that children should be allowed to die and are not against medical treatment for their children. The parents seek medical treatment for their children, just not treatment that involves blood transfusion. Also, Rosam claims, we must recognize that a transfusion has the potential to cause medical harm, not just medical benefit. Thus, giving a child blood, contrary to Catlin, does not necessarily "meet every goal of medicine."

Some laws and recent court decisions, Rosam points out, do not require that a child receive the "best" treatment, but only a treatment that is "adequate" or "reasonable." Thus, if a treatment does not involve the use of blood, even if some do not consider it the best treatment, there are no grounds for interfering with parental decision making. Like Catlin, Rosam thinks it is unacceptable to try to convince Jehovah's Witness parents to give up their beliefs.

We have read with interest the well researched article by Anita Catlin. We agree with her that the case she mentions is one that would pose a dilemma for the healthcare community as it indeed does for Jehovah's Witnesses themselves. Of all the conditions in adults

Eugene Rosam, From "Reply to Anita Catlin," *HEC Forum*, Vol. 8, (1996): 208–211. Copyright © 1996 by Springer-Verlag. Reproduced by permission.

and children that we find most difficult to deal with, and admittedly have few answers for, a sickle cell crisis, with a stroke in progress, is indeed a challenge. The case presents multiple problems.

We, too, like the author, would never recommend that the child be allowed to die. What we would ask is that the doctor do everything he can to save the life of the child *without* using a blood transfusion. The situation with Jehovah's Witnesses is not one of parents refusing all medical treatment, but simply differing with the doctor as to what *kind* of treatment is preferred. We often see both child and adult cases described in such a way as to indicate that when blood transfusion was administered the life was saved. One has to ask what the eventual outcome of these "saved" lives will be? What will be the quality of life in the years ahead? Could this child suffer from the potential adverse effects of blood transfusion, such as iron overload, hepatitis or other viral transmission? Thus, we cannot agree with the author that giving blood "meets every goal of medicine." Is blood the only thing that saves lives? In the majority of our cases there are new medical modalities that "save lives," such as erythropoietin, desmopressin, hemodilution, or the use of a blood salvage device. If one is going honestly to say that withholding blood constitutes doing harm, then one would have also to honestly admit that giving blood can also do harm. If there is a risk both ways, who should decide for the child which risk is to be taken?

Although the doctor said that nothing else would do but blood (granting that was his sincere judgment), another doctor may have felt differently. At least, we have often found this to be the case in many other situations where a controversy arose over whether blood should be given. In fact, in a growing number of cases, judges are now asking doctors to try the non-blood alternatives preferred by the parents first, and then give blood if the alternatives fail. These children are going home healthy and in good condition without blood transfusions.

It is unfortunate that the writer in *Pediatric Nursing* claimed that "what is right in the eyes of Jehovah's Witness parents is the need to insure life for their child after death, even if this means an early end to the child's life on earth." This puts the emphasis on the negative. The parents want the child to live, or they would not have brought it to the hospital and put it in the care of a doctor. They simply asked for alternative treatment. True, in this case there may not have been effective alternatives, but the statement in *Pediatric Nursing* is not correct. We do not wish to make martyrs of our children and we are not exercising a right to die.

Some articles that deal with this subject refer to what is called "the best interests standard." We find that the most relevant statutes do not mandate what is "best" for a child in need of medical care, but what is "adequate" or "reasonable." Thus, if non-blood care provides what is adequate or reasonable, then there is no basis to interfere with parental decision making in this regard.

On this point, the New York Court of Appeals said *In re Hofbauer*[1]: "The most significant factor in determining whether a child is being deprived of adequate medical care . . . is whether the parents have provided an acceptable course of medical treatment . . . in light of all the surrounding circumstances. This inquiry cannot be posed in terms of whether the parent has made a 'right' or 'wrong' decision, for the present state of the practice of medicine, despite its vast advances, very seldom permits such definitive conclusions. Nor can a court assume the role of surrogate parent and establish as the objective criteria with which to evaluate a parent's decision its own judgement as to the exact method or degree of medical treatment which should be provided, for such standard is fraught with subjectivity."

Also pertinent is what was observed in *Guides to the Judge in Medical Orders Affecting Children*:

> *Although an emergency may exist from the physician's point of view, the person may not in fact be in* extremis. *This does not imply that doctors do not testify in good faith as to a person's likelihood of surviving a crisis without undergoing a particular procedure. It means, rather, that medical knowledge is not sufficiently advanced to enable a physician to predict with reasonable certainty that his patient will live or die or will suffer a permanent physical impairment or deformity. Doctors tend to urge the imposition of a treatment when, in their expert opinion, death or permanent physical impairment is more likely to occur if the treatment is not given than if it is. However, it is the duty of the court to determine the seriousness of the emergency in a particular case, to press the testifying physician on the imminent likelihood of death or impairment, the chance of survival or of alleviation of prolonged agonizing pain if the proposed treatment is given, and the danger of the treatment itself*[2].

There are many lawyers who are convinced that doctors and hospitals do not have official standing under the *parens patriae* provision of the law. That is for the State to exercise, not the hospital or doctor. If the State appoints a doctor as guardian, we would accept that. But we believe that if the court had time to hear the parents, *ex parte* orders for transfusion could be avoided.

No reasonable person would want to support a religious belief that is interpreted as bringing death to children. But there is a lot of interpretation involved in supporting such a position. For example, there have been harmful effects resulting from circumcisions performed for religious reasons. Are we to curb that practice? Is it an invasion of the child's right for its parents to insist upon this surgical procedure for male children without the knowledge and consent of the infant? Should we have to wait until the child is of a legal age to see what he would like to do about circumcision?

We are not suggesting that these situations are simple ones to handle. But we are convinced that there is a greater need for more communication with the Hospital Liaison Committees for Jehovah's Witnesses in a sincere effort to avoid blood transfusions where this is humanly possible. We agree with the idea that an ethics consultation early in the case can make a difference. It was this type of dialogue that has been missing in our cases for decades. *Ex parte* orders were issued without any possibility for the parents to have their rights recognized where possible. Working with the Liaison Committee and with ethics consultation will take care of the greater number of cases, leaving only the unusual and rare medical problems to be worked out on a case-by-case basis. Some time ago it was thought that one would never get remissions in cases of leukemia without using blood

transfusions to combat the anemia created by the chemotherapy, but there has been some success at this at M.D. Anderson Cancer Center (Houston, Texas).

I agree with the author of this article who contends that under no circumstances should anyone be allowed to try convincing the parents to give up their beliefs. This effort is frequently made. Though many do not appreciate the fact, what we often encounter is people who want to impose their religious beliefs on others, while asking parents not to impose their religious beliefs on their own children! Does it end up as a matter of whose religious beliefs are imposed upon the child? At least this illustrates how some get off track in reflecting on these matters. We would like to see these cases dealt with in an objective fashion, working out what can be done within the realm of good medicine, and to look after these children without blood transfusions wherever possible.

References

1. *In re Hofbauer*, 1979, 47 N.Y. 2d 648,393 N.E. 2d 1009, 1014, 419 N.Y.S. 2d, 940–941.
2. National Council on Crime and Delinquency, *Guides to the Judge in Medical Orders Affecting Children*, Crime and Delinquency, 1968, 109, 116.

DECISION SCENARIOS

The questions following each decision scenario are intended to prompt reflection and discussion. In deciding how to answer them, you should consider the information in the Briefing Session; the ethical theories and principles presented in Part V, "Foundations of Bioethics," and the arguments and criticisms offered in the relevant readings in this chapter.

DECISION SCENARIO **1**

HPV Vaccination Required?

"Your daughter is age 13 and the state requires that she be vaccinated against HPV before she is allowed to register for school," said Mavis Buckley, the principal of Beaumont School. "I know you are new to the state, but I'm sure you can find a doctor or Simka."

"I don't want my daughter vaccinated," Bryan Mendez said. "She is not sexually active, and even if she were, I wouldn't want her vaccinated."

"Why is that?" Ms. Buckley asked. "Don't you want your daughter protected against cervical cancer?"

"Nobody knows enough about the effects of the vaccine for me to feel confident that it's not going

to harm her." Mendez scowled at Buckley. "When she's old enough, I'll make sure she understands she needs to get a Pap smear regularly. That's all she needs, really, to keep herself safe from cervical cancer."

1. How strong a case can be made for requiring that schoolgirls ages 12 and upward be required to be vaccinated against HIV?

2. How well grounded are Mendez's objections?

3. Can the case be made that the developer of the HPV vaccine oversold its importance and usefulness for financial reasons?

DECISION SCENARIO **2**

When Prayer Is Not Enough

"You'll feel better soon," Marylyn Tauber told her 8-year-old son Madison. "God doesn't let bad things happen to people who believe in Him with all their heart, all their mind, and all their strength."

Madison said nothing, but from his bed, he looked up at her with eyes that were dull. His lips were dry and cracked, and his face a dusky red. He didn't seem to understand her. She put a hand on Madison's cheek. He was burning with fever, and she wondered if it would be all right for her to put a cool washcloth on his forehead.

Madison had been ill for three days. He had come home from school with a flushed face and a sore throat. She thought it was just another one of those summer colds he was always getting. But he'd gotten worse, not better. And his temperature was 102°F the last time she had taken it. She had given him ice and tried to get him to drink some Coke, but he hadn't wanted anything since.

"I've been praying for you night and day," Marylyn said. She tried to sound cheerful so she could lift Madison's spirits. "I know God loves little boys, and he is going to heal you before long."

She had to keep believing that, because she couldn't face the possibility that Madison might die. He might, of course, if that were God's will. But she wasn't sure she was a good enough person to accept God's will without complaint. She was frightened, but she knew she had to do the right thing. She couldn't take him to a doctor without admitting that everything she believed was false.

1. We can assume that Marylyn loves Madison and wants to do what is best for him. She believes that prayer, not seeking medical help, is the best thing for Madison. Should parents always be the ones to decide what is in the best interest of their child?

2. If Madison dies, should Marylyn be charged with a crime?

3. The state places some limits on the expression of religious beliefs. We do not, for example, permit human or animal sacrifices. Should we require parents to seek medical assistance for their child when the child becomes ill, even if this means violating their religious beliefs?

DECISION SCENARIO **3**

Protecting against Disease

First-time parents Bob and Susan Slocombe (as we will call them) were distressed when their 14-month-old son Cooper seemed to undergo a sudden change in character.

Cooper had been a burbling, happy baby who caught the eyes of his parents, then gurgled and smiled while kicking his feet in the air. Then, in what seemed to the Slocombes almost overnight, Cooper stopped making eye contact and smiling. He cried when they picked him up, as if they were causing him pain, and when he was startled by a noise, he began to cry uncontrollably.

The Slocombes initially thought that Cooper was only going through a new phase of development—babies were always changing. But by the time Cooper was 18 months old, they realized that he was never going to change back to being anything like the baby he had been before. In fact, Cooper seemed to have become more withdrawn and unresponsive. The babbling noises they used to think were his way of talking

went away and were replaced by fretting and crying, and he stopped playing peek-a-boo, which once had made him laugh and kick his feet. The fun the Slocombes had once enjoyed with their baby turned into a nightmare of exhaustion, frustration, depression, and worry.

Cooper's pediatrician had been vague, but generally reassuring, when they first expressed concern about Cooper. Dr. Cynthia Nathan was finally concerned enough herself to run some tests. She asked them dozens of detailed questions about how Cooper behaved with them, responded to others, reacted to noises and smells, what upset him, and what soothed him. She then took a detailed history of both families, asking if anyone on either side had suffered from learning or language difficulties, neurological problems, or an illness like schizophrenia. Her interest was piqued when she discovered that Bob's brother and two of his cousins had been diagnosed with learning disabilities.

Dr. Nathan then tested Cooper's blood for the presence of lead, but as she had predicted, the test was negative. She sent a cheek swab from Cooper to a genetics lab to be tested for chromosomal abnormalities, but it, too, didn't turn up anything unusual. She had tested Cooper's hearing in her office, but she asked the Slocombes to take him to a pediatric otologist for a more thorough assessment than she could do in the office. The otologist assured them that Cooper's hearing was normal.

Almost a month passed before the Slocombes got a call from Dr. Nathan's office asking them to make an appointment to see her. The hopes they had that Cooper's problems were not serious were destroyed the moment they heard Dr. Nathan's diagnosis. "Cooper has autism," she told them. "It's too early to say how severe it will be, but you need to prepare yourselves to meet whatever problems may arise."

"Could it have been caused by one of the vaccinations he's had?" Bob asked. "My chiropractor said that some of those vaccines, especially the ones for measles, are dangerous for kids."

"I've heard that, too," Susan said. "I read someplace that they're the reason autism is increasing."

"I wish I'd listened to my chiropractor." Bob sounded sad. "He told me I shouldn't get Cooper vaccinated, that he'd be all right without his shots."

1. What evidence, if any, is there to support the belief that autism may be the result of childhood vaccinations?

2. What evidence, if any, is there to support the claim that autism is on the increase? Discuss the difference between an increase in number of diagnosed cases and an increase in the number of actual cases.

3. What might account for the increase in diagnosed cases?

4. Is there a social duty for parents to have their children vaccinated against infectious diseases like pertussis (whooping cough), mumps, measles, and rubella?

5. Should childhood vaccinations be required by law, or should parents be able to opt out on behalf of their children?

DECISION SCENARIO 4

Weight Cops

"I'm referring you to the Bariatrics Clinic," Dr. Himmer said. He glanced at Carla Tolar, then quickly bent his head to write something in her record. "They're very helpful."

"The what clinic?" Carla Tolar asked. She was sorry she had insisted on taking her shoes off before she was weighed, because now she was struggling to get them on. She couldn't bend over far enough to use a finger to slip on the heel, and she was twisting her right foot, trying to work it into the shoe. She was only halfway paying attention to Dr. Himmer.

"It specializes in weight loss." He still avoided looking at her. "It's federally financed, so it's not going to cost you anything."

"I told you I can lose weight on my own." Carla pressed her lips together.

"You've been saying that for two years." Dr. Himmer finally looked up. He gave her an artificial smile. "But now you are more than 150 pounds over your proper weight, and it's out of my hands. I'm required by law to refer you to the Bariatrics Clinic."

"Oh, my God," Carla said. "I never heard that. What if I don't go?" She straightened up in the chair, forgetting about her shoe. "I don't want to go. I won't go."

"You don't have a choice, really," Dr. Himmer said. "It's sort of like if you have a car, you've got to get a license for it. It's for your protection and for society's. If you don't go to the clinic, you become subject to fines."

"And if I don't pay?" Carla was stunned.

"I think you can be sent to jail," Dr. Himmer said. "Just the way you can be for driving without a license."

1. Should the government establish weight-loss clinics to assist people in losing weight?

2. If such clinics are established, to what extent should the government require those who are overweight to participate in weight-control programs? (Fines are possible, but so, too, are rewards like tax credits or cash bonuses.)

3. Is Dr. Himmer's driver's license analogy a good one? Can overweight people damage society to such an extent that the government is justified in requiring them to make an effort to control their weight?

4. If considerations of autonomy are sufficient to bar society from using the powers of government to require adults to participate in weight-loss programs, would it be legitimate for society to require children to take steps to control their weight?

DECISION SCENARIO 5

Baby vs. Mom

Angela Carter was diagnosed as having bone cancer when she was 13 years old. Over the following years, she received a variety of treatments and underwent surgery several times. In one operation, her leg was amputated. By the time she was 27, the cancer had been in remission for three years, and she became pregnant. Twenty-five weeks into the pregnancy, she went for a routine checkup, and her physician discovered a large tumor in a lung. She was told she might have only days to live. She was admitted to George Washington Hospital, and five days later her condition worsened.

Despite the objections of Angela, her family, and even her physician, the hospital decided to attempt to save the developing child. The hospital went to court, and at a hearing staff physicians stated that, despite the feet that the fetus was only twenty-six weeks old, there was a fifty to sixty percent percent chance that it would survive if a cesarean section was performed. Furthermore, they estimated that there was less than a twenty percent chance that the child would be disabled. The physicians also testified that the surgery would increase the chances of Angela Carter's death.

The hospital obtained a court order, which was immediately appealed. Because the case demanded a quick resolution, the three judges on the appeals court consulted by telephone. The whole process, hearing and appeal, took less than six hours. During this time, the hospital had ordered Angela prepared for surgery.

The appeals court let the lower court ruling stand, and Angela underwent the court-ordered surgery. The child, a girl, lived for only two hours. Angela lived for two days. The surgery was listed as a contributing cause of her death.

1. On what grounds might one object to the court-ordered surgery?

2. Is there any reason to view this case as different from ones involving drug abuse by a pregnant woman? That is, are the issues the same in both kinds of cases?

3. Suppose Angela Carter had been further along in her pregnancy so that the chance of her child's survival was virtually certain and that she refused to have a cesarean birth. Would it be right to force her to have a cesarean delivery against her will?

4. Consider the claim that although a woman has a right to seek an abortion, if she decides to carry the fetus to term, then it has a right to have her promote its best interest. Is this position consistent?

DECISION SCENARIO 6

Pregnancy and Autonomy— in Conflict?

For five years, the hospital of the Medical University of South Carolina followed a controversial policy with respect to pregnant women. Pregnant women admitted to the hospital were asked to sign a consent form agreeing to drug testing if their physicians decided they needed it. Those who tested positive for cocaine were turned in to local police and were arrested, unless they agreed to take part in a drug rehabilitation program. Forty-two women were turned in. Some agreed to drug treatment, while others were charged with distributing drugs to minors—their fetuses. (These charges were later dropped.)

Critics of the policy claimed that it focused on poor, black women, who form a large proportion of the hospital's patient population. Furthermore, the policy violated the confidentiality of the physician–patient relationship and the woman's right to privacy.

In September 1994, responding to pressure from the federal government, the hospital agreed to change its policy. Had the hospital not complied with federal demands, it stood to lose $18 million of federal research money.

1. What is the gravest danger in adopting a policy like the hospital's?

2. Under what conditions, if any, would the hospital's policy be justified?

3. Is there a policy that the hospital might pursue that would prevent prenatal harm while also avoiding violating the autonomy of the pregnant woman and preserving the confidentiality of the physician–patient relationship?

Some Truth Better Than the Whole Truth?

Multiple sclerosis (MS) is a chronic, progressive neurological disease with symptoms that include loss of coordination, blurred vision, speech difficulties, and severe fatigue. It is most frequent among young adults. A recent study at Albert Einstein Medical College revealed that MS patients typically had a very hard time getting an explicit diagnosis and explanation from their physicians. Yet the physicians surveyed reported overwhelmingly that they always or usually tell patients the diagnosis.

The researchers learned that a variety of factors account for this discrepancy. Physicians find many reasons for delay: The patient may be under twenty years old, emotionally unstable, or apparently incapable of understanding the diagnosis. Also, the patient may not ask specifically, a relative may ask that the patient not be told, or the patient may be medically unsophisticated or in the midst of an emotional crisis. Most important, there is no cure or wholly effective therapy for MS, and emotional stress seems to aggravate its symptoms. Thus, telling a patient that she or he has a progressive, incurable disease may do no good and may do harm.

Instead of being told they have MS, patients are sometimes told that they have "a chronic virus infection," "neuritis," or "inflammation of the nervous system." This sometimes leads patients to consult several physicians and to undergo expensive and unnecessary diagnostic tests in the attempt to get a diagnosis.

1. Are the physicians who claim they believe in telling MS patients the diagnosis but then don't do so necessarily being hypocritical?

2. What sorts of arguments or considerations might be offered in their defense?

3. In what sort of cases would it be justifiable to withhold a diagnosis from a patient?

4. If there is a chance that knowing the diagnosis will make the symptoms of an MS patient worse and if there is no wholly effective therapy for MS, why is it not the duty of a physician to withhold the diagnosis? After all, "Do no harm" is perhaps the most important of the Hippocratic maxims.

When Does "No" Mean No?

"I don't want to be treated," Alice Nuvo said. "According to the statistics you gave me, even with the best treatment I've got no more than a 5% chance of surviving for another year."

"Pancreatic cancer is a bad customer," Dr. Cervando Lupe said. "I wish the numbers were better."

"So why should I suffer the pain and nausea of chemotherapy and then radiation if I'm going to die anyway?" Alice snorted in contempt. "It's absurd. I'd rather spend the remaining time with my husband and two daughters, then die in peace, instead of puking up my guts in some hospital."

"We can use drugs to control the nausea from the chemotherapy," Dr. Lupe said. "And we don't know that the statistics apply to you. They apply to a whole group of people, and I never tell a patient that *she* has a 5% chance."

"Just give me something to control the pain and let me go home," Alice said. "I don't want to talk about it anymore."

1. Should Dr. Lupe argue with Alice and try to persuade her to undergo treatment?

2. If Dr. Lupe thinks Alice is making the wrong decision, how far should he go to try to persuade her to accept the treatment?

3. What method should be used for getting patients to give their informed consent to treatment?

4. Is it possible to justify forcing treatment on someone who refuses it?

DECISION SCENARIO 9

Vampire Confession

"Sometimes I think that what I really want to do is to kill people and drink their blood."

Dr. Allen Wolfe looked at the young man in the chair across from him. The face was round and soft and innocent looking, like that of a large baby. But the body had the powerful shoulders of a college wrestler. There was no doubt that Hal Crane had the strength to carry out his fantasies.

"Any people in particular?" Dr. Wolfe asked.

"Women. Girls about my age. Maybe in their early 20s."

"But no one you're personally acquainted with."

"That's right. Just girls I see walking down the street or getting off a bus. I have a tremendous urge to stick a knife into their stomachs and feel the blood come out on my hands."

"But you've never done anything like that?"

Crane shook his head. "No, but I'm afraid I might."

Dr. Wolfe considered Crane a paranoid schizophrenic with compulsive tendencies, someone who might possibly act out his fantasies. He was a potentially dangerous person.

"Would you be willing to take my advice and put yourself in a hospital under my care for a while?"

"I don't want to do that," Crane said. "I don't want to be locked up like an animal."

"But you don't really want to hurt other people, do you?"

"I guess not," Crane said. "I haven't done anything yet."

"But you might," Dr. Wolfe said. "I'm afraid you might let yourself go and kill someone."

Crane smiled. "That's just the chance the world will have to take, isn't it?"

1. Suppose that you are Dr. Wolfe. To take the legal steps necessary to have Crane committed against his will requires that you violate his confidentiality. What justification might you offer for doing this?

2. As a physician, how would you justify acting to protect others while going against the wishes of your patient?

3. Should a physician be required by law to act to protect the welfare of others?

4. How does this case compare to the *Tarasoff* case?

DECISION SCENARIO 10

Whose Decision Is It?

In October 1993, 15-year-old Benito Agrela stopped taking FK506, a toxic drug that suppresses the immune response. Agrela was taking the drug to prevent the rejection of his second liver transplant.

In June, the Florida Department of Health learned that he was no longer taking his medicine and forcibly removed him from his parents' home. Agrela was confined to the transplant floor of a Miami hospital for four days, but he refused to give blood or to cooperate in any examination other than a basic physical. Agrela had been born with an enlarged liver, and at the age of 8 he had his first transplant. After a few years, the donor organ failed, and a second transplant was necessary. However, Agrela did not have an easy time with the result. The drug's side effects left him feeling weak and constantly ill, and finally he decided that he did not want to continue to take the medication. He wanted only to die in peace.

Judge Arthur Birken of Broward County Circuit Court ruled that Agrela could stop taking his medication and return to his family's home to live out the remainder of his life. Judge Birken reached his decision after a long visit with Agrela and listening to four hours of testimony from his physicians.

"I should have the right to make my own decisions," Agrela said as he left the hospital after the judge's ruling. "I know the consequences, I know the problems."

Benito Agrela died shortly before 5 on Saturday, August 21. "He went in a very good way," his sister said. "He didn't complain of any pain."

1. Benito Agrela was only 15 years old. Should a minor ever be allowed to decide whether to reject a lifesaving therapy?

2. What criteria might be helpful in deciding whether a minor is capable of giving informed consent?

Chapter **2**

Research Ethics and Informed Consent

CHAPTER CONTENTS

CASES AND CONTEXTS

SOCIAL CONTEXT
Face Transplants: The Dream of Looking Ordinary

Connie Culp's husband shot her in the face with a shotgun. The blast destroyed her nose, teeth, cheeks, one eye, and much of her mouth and upper jaw. Lead pellets and bone splinters lacerated her face, turning it into mangled flesh. Culp lived, but she was horribly disfigured. Even after surgeons performed thirty operations, Culp's face, noseless and puckered with scars, seemed more alien than human. She couldn't eat in the normal fashion and could breathe only through an opening in her trachea. When she went out in public, people turned their heads and called her ugly names. Children ran away.

Connie Culp was shot in 2004 and thought her disfigurement was permanent. On December 10, 2008, however, in a twenty-three-hour operation, Dr. Maria Sieminow and her surgical team at the Cleveland Clinic replaced eighty percent of Culp's face with the face of a deceased donor. This made Culp the first person in the United States, and the fourth person in the world, to receive a face transplant.

By the end of 2009, seven procedures had been performed, and two patients had died. Thus, although the procedure has not been wholly successful, many surgeons believe it is sufficiently promising to justify continuing to offer it as a treatment option to a limited number of appropriate patients—ones like Connie Culp. The hope is that additional research and surgical experience will establish face transplants as a standard treatment for those suffering from significant facial disfigurement due to trauma, birth impairments, or disease.

Surgeons are not yet prepared to endorse face transplants as anything more than an experimental procedure worth pursuing. Even so, this represents a triumph over the bad publicity provoked by the first face transplant. The case raised many of the issues about informed consent and potential risks and benefits that continue to hold for subsequent cases.

Isabelle Dinoire: First Face Transplant

Isabelle Dinoire was a thirty-eight-year-old, divorced, unemployed mother of two living in the town of Valenciennes in northern France. On a Sunday evening in May 2005, Dinoire had an argument with her seventeen-year-old daughter. The daughter, angry, left the house to spend the night with her grandmother. After this point, many facts become hazy and disputed.

In the initial version of events released by one of Dinoire's doctors, Jean-Michel Dubernard, she was upset and wanted to calm herself. To achieve this, she took a couple of pills to help her sleep and went to bed. But this account contradicted an earlier one by Dinoire's daughter, who said her mother tried to commit suicide by taking an overdose of sleeping pills. Dinoire eventually confirmed her daughter's version of what happened, but she said that her reason for trying to kill herself was a "secret." Dubernard, however, continued to insist that his patient had made no effort to commit suicide.

According to Dubernard, after Dinoire took the sleeping drug, she woke up sometime during the night and got out of bed. Walking through the dark house, she stumbled over the large dog she had recently adopted. The dog, startled, then attacked her. But once again, Dinoire's daughter told a different story. According to her, after taking the drug, Dinoire fell to the floor unconscious, and the dog tried to rouse her by clawing at her face.

No matter which version is correct, the result was the same. The dog ripped off Dinoire's lips and tore the flesh off her nose and chin. How she was discovered has not been made public, but she eventually was rushed to the local hospital, bleeding and in great pain.

The dog, justly or not, was later killed by the authorities.

A short time after Dinoire was stabilized medically and her injuries treated, she was examined by Dr. Bernard Devauchelle, Chairman of the Department of Maxillofacial Surgery at Amiens University Hospital. Because of Dinoire's seriously disfiguring wounds but general good health, he decided that she was an excellent candidate for a partial face transplant. It would have to be done without great delay, however, because once scar tissue was fully formed, a transplant would become extremely difficult. Scar tissue lacks blood vessels and so would have to be cut away even to start the transplant. Also, the muscles in her face and jaw might become permanently contracted and incapable of functioning. Eating and speaking in any normal sense would become impossible. Devauchelle listed her as an urgent case with *Agence de la biomédecine*, the French organization responsible for acquiring and distributing transplant organs.

Dinoire's Transplant

Isabelle Dinoire, some seven months later, became the first person to receive a face transplant, albeit a partial one. Yet surgeons and bioethicists in France, Britain, the United States, and elsewhere had been discussing the possibility of and the issues associated with such a transplant for some time. Some transplant programs, including the one at the Cleveland Clinic, were on the verge of finding a suitable candidate for the novel procedure.

France's national ethics committee had ruled that a face transplant should not be performed as an emergency procedure. Under those conditions, the committee decided, the notion of informed consent was an "illusion," even if the patient asked for the transplant and was provided with the relevant information, and even if a donor graft were available. In the absence of experience with face transplants, "The surgeon cannot make any promises regarding the results of his restorative efforts, which are always doubtful. Authentic consent, therefore, will never exist." The committee did approve partial face transplants, assuming the local hospital ethics committee also approved, but warned that such a transplant would be "high-risk experimentation."

In July of 2005, Dr. Dubernard, a noted transplant surgeon and a member of parliament, was asked by Dr. Devauchelle to consult on the case. In August, Dr. Dubernard visited the hospital and examined Isabelle Dinoire. "The moment she removed her mask, which she always wore, I had no more hesitation about doing a transplant," he later said.

Dr. Benoit Lengele, a Belgian plastic and reconstructive surgeon, was also called into the case by Dr. Devauchelle. Dr. Lengele assessed Dinoire's condition and reached the conclusion that at least three or four operations would be needed to reconstruct her face by using bone, cartridge, and skin taken from other parts of her body. The result, he thought, was not likely to be successful either functionally or aesthetically. She was having difficulty eating and talking, because so much of her face was missing, but he was not sure that her problems could be adequately corrected by reconstructive surgery.

Dr. Devauchelle and Dr. Dubernard discussed the possibility of a partial face transplant with Dinoire. They told her that the chance that a transplant would be successful was about thirty-three percent and the chance that it would be rejected was the same. Most important, there was also a thirty-three percent chance that she might die from the surgery, from an infection, or as a result of the immunosuppressive drugs she would have to take to control the tissue rejection.

Dinoire agreed to the transplant at once, even though the doctors reminded her that the procedure was highly experimental and had never been done before. "We got her permission several times," Dubernard later told a reporter, and Dinoire understood the risks she would be taking. He also said that he had secured all the permission required for the transplant from the French national ethics committee

and the hospital ethics committee. Dinoire, he said, had asked only that the name of the hospital, as well as her name, be withheld from the public.

On Sunday, November 27, a surgical team headed by Devauchelle operated on Dinoire at Amiens University Hospital. He grafted onto her damaged and disfigured face a large segment of a donor face that included the nose, lips, chin, and the lower cheeks.

The face graft was taken from a suicide victim, a woman declared brain dead in Lille, a city some eighty-five miles north of Amiens. French law permits "presumed consent" in removing organs for transplant, thus making it unnecessary to secure the permission of relatives. Even so, because of the special nature of a facial transplant, the surgeons asked the donor's family for consent before removing the tissue. A team of clinical psychologists provided support to the family on the Saturday before the transplant surgery.

On Saturday night, a surgical team headed by Dr. Devauchelle arrived in Lille to remove the donor face. Meanwhile, in Amiens, Dr. Dubernard and a second surgical team were preparing Isabelle Dinoire for the transplant. This involved cutting away the scar tissue that had already formed in just a few months and identifying the nerves, muscles, and blood vessels that would have to be connected to the donor graft for the transplant to be viable.

Dr. Devauchelle's team finished its work around five in the morning on Sunday, then rushed the face graft to Amiens. It was preserved in a saline solution chilled to thirtynine degrees Fahrenheit. Once tissue has been removed from its blood supply, cells begin to die. Although keeping a graft cold slows the process, the more quickly its blood supply is reestablished, the more likely it is that the transplant will be successful.

Devauchelle's team of eight surgeons began using established microsurgical techniques to attach the graft to the remaining portion of Dinoire's face. The techniques are tedious and demanding, requiring, as Dr. Dubernard later said, sewing together the ends of nerves and muscles no larger than "the fibers hanging from a string bean." If vessels are not connected properly, blood clots may form and the tissue may die, and if muscles are not sewn together correctly, the patient not only will lack facial expressions, but may not be able to speak, drink, or chew.

By nine Sunday morning, four hours after the face graft had been removed from the donor in Lille, its blood supply was reestablished. Surgery could then continue at a slower, more deliberate pace. Eventually, the top layers of muscle, then the layers of the skin, were stitched into place. The surgeons implanted a piece of donor tissue under Dinoire's arm so that it, rather than her face, could be used as a source of biopsies to assess how well her body was accepting the graft of foreign tissue. The operation took a total of fifteen hours of meticulous work, with most of the surgery being performed within the narrow field of an operating microscope. When the operation was over, the nurses applauded.

Dinoire, after she returned to consciousness Sunday evening, wrote "Merci" on the paper she had been given to help her communicate. By Friday morning, her doctors reported, she was eating, drinking, and speaking clearly, although she still lacked sensation and muscle control in the transplanted segment. The scar running around the edges of the segment was thin, and the skin tones of the donor and recipient were an almost perfect match. From the beginning, Dinoire showed signs of accepting her new appearance. "This is my face," she said on Thursday, studying it in a mirror. Because underlying muscles and bone account for much of facial appearance, Dinoire's face looked neither like her donor's nor like her original face.

In addition to treating her with immunosuppressive drugs, Dinoire's doctors injected her with bone marrow taken from the donor. The idea behind the treatment was that the marrow would turn her into a chimera—that

is, her body would acquire a mixture of cell types. This, in turn, might lead her immune system to recognize the cells from the face graft as "self," instead of attacking it as a foreign body. If it attacked the graft the drugs might not be able to prevent the face graft from being rejected.

Critical Reactions

On December 1, Dr. Dubernard held a press conference and announced that surgical teams headed by him and Dr. Devauchelle had performed the world's first partial face transplant. The procedure, he reported, had been a success and the patient was recovering well.

Dubernard's announcement was met with an immediate barrage of criticisms and questions from the transplant community. The most common criticism was that Dubernard's group had rushed the transplant. They ought to have attempted standard reconstructive surgery first. Now Isabelle Dinoire would be exposed to all the hazards of a transplant. She would have to take immunosuppressive drugs for the rest of her life, and this would increase her risk of cancer and potentially lethal infections. Also, the face graft might still be rejected at any time, maybe even years down the road. These are risks that might be too great for the treatment of a nonfatal condition. Saving someone's life by giving him a new liver is one thing, but giving someone a new face to improve her appearance . . . can this be worth the risks?

Also, critics charged, Dubernard's group had selected the wrong sort of patient for a transplant. If Dinoire had attempted to kill herself, she might very well lack the psychological strength to cope with the stresses and uncertainties associated with an experimental surgical procedure. Furthermore, people who are emotionally unstable do not do well in keeping to the rigid drug regimen that a transplant patient must follow to prevent rejection. Finally, the first person to receive a face transplant, even a partial one, could be expected to become the subject of intense public interest, and someone like Isabelle Dinoire might lack the psychological strength to cope with the demands of the media and the curiosity of the public.

Critics also charged that even the quality of the informed consent Dinoire gave to become a face transplant patient might be regarded as questionable. Does someone despairing enough to attempt suicide who has also had her face destroyed possess the rational capacity to make a free and informed decision about a new procedure that holds the promise of restoring her appearance? Isn't she more likely to be impulsive and to have unrealistic expectations of the outcome of the surgery?

Transplant professionals directed some of their harshest criticism at the decision by the French surgeons to inject Dinoire with the blood-producing bone-marrow stem cells taken from the deceased donor. This is a treatment that is not standard in organ transplantation, and, although the technique has been used before, the results have been mixed. "They should not be doing two experiments on one patient," said Dr. Maria Siemionow, the surgeon who later operated on Connie Culp. "Ethics aside, it will make it difficult to get clean answers—if [the transplant] works, why does it work, and if it goes wrong, was it the transplant or the stem cells?" This view was also expressed by the French surgeon Dr. Laurent Lantieri, who reviewed Isabelle Dinoire's medical records, although he was not involved with the transplant team.

Dr. Siemionow's group at the Cleveland Clinic was among those who had developed an experimental protocol for doing a full face transplant. Researchers had also framed protocols at Duke University, the University of California–San Francisco, and several other medical centers in the United States and Europe. Criticisms from people at some of these institutions suggested a dissatisfaction with Dubernard's approach to the Dinoire case.

The most common criticisms were that neither he nor Dr. Devauchelle was engaged in face-transplant research and so did not go through the review of the scientific, medical, and ethical issues performed by others. They acted in an impulsive way and, by doing so, acquired immediate celebrity.

Dr. Dubernard had already attracted worldwide attention in 1998 when he performed the first hand transplant. The recipient, Clint Hallum, was a man with a criminal record who fabricated part of his past when he offered himself as a candidate. Hallum failed to adhere to the regimen of immunosuppressive drugs, and his body eventually rejected the transplant. The hand was amputated in 2001.

Critics of Dubernard speculated that, in proceeding with the face transplant, he might be trying to establish for himself and Devauchelle another high-profile surgical first. Some even wondered whether he had not, as a member of the French parliament, used his political influence to get approval for the face graft from the ethics committee.

Isabelle Dinoire's motives also became clouded by public revelations. She told a French newspaper a week after the transplant that she had been upset by the media coverage. "I need to live through these moments quietly," she said. Yet her attitude toward publicity was soon challenged when the *London Times* revealed that she had signed contracts that would allow her to make tens of thousands of dollars from the sale of photographs of herself and the release of a film.

The French magazine *Paris Match* is reported to have paid about $120,000 for the right to publish photographs of her, and even before the surgery, Dinoire signed a contract with the British director Michael Hughes to make a documentary film of her story. According to the agreement, she will collect all profits from the film, after Hughes has recovered his expenses and the company that distributes his films recouped its costs.

Some have raised the question of whether the possibility of profiting financially from her story was discussed with Isabelle Dinoire before she consented to the transplant. If it was, this would be a prima facie violation of any ethically legitimate informed consent procedure. The possibility of making a substantial amount of money might serve as an inducement for an unemployed single mother to risk her life. Her consent would thus not be freely given.

Establishing the Procedure

Criticisms of the surgeons responsible for the Dinoire transplant did not end face-transplant research. In April 2006, Dr. Guo Shuzhong at China's Xijing Hospital carried out a partial face transplant on Li Guoxing, a thirty-two-year-old farmer from a remote village in China's Yunnan province. While out hunting eighteen months earlier, Li had been attacked by a bear, and about half his face was destroyed. The donor tissue used in the transplant was taken from a twenty-five-year-old man killed in a traffic accident.

Li was the second face-transplant recipient, but the first to die. He survived three episodes of tissue rejection, then decided to treat himself with traditional medicines, rather than immunosuppressive drugs. He died in July 2006, perhaps from liver damage caused by the herbal medicines.

The third face-transplant recipient was another French patient. His name has not been made public, but we know that he was a twenty-nine-year-old man suffering from neurofibromatosis, a genetic disease in which tumors grow on nerve sheaths. His face was covered with numerous bulbous tumors, some the size of ping-pong balls. Tumors around his mouth made it hard for him to eat, and those near his eyes blocked his vision. His face was so disfigured that in public people shied away from him, considering him to be (he reported) a "monster."

In January 2007, his surgeon, Dr. Laurent Lantieri of Henri Mondor Hospital in Paris, replaced most of the patient's face with a graft from a recently deceased man. Lantieri not only changed the patient's appearance, but also used microsurgical techniques to connect facial muscles and nerves, allowing the man to talk, eat, and smile. The patient was delighted by the result, reporting that he could once again move through a crowd without attracting notice.

Dr. Lantieri had criticized the surgeons in the Isabelle Dinoire case for their selection of her as a patient and for injecting her with bone marrow from the face donor. Even so, Lantieri is a strong proponent of face transplants, but only when the surgery is done in accordance with research standards he considers acceptable.

It was Lantieri who performed what is considered to be the first full face transplant. In April 2009, Lantieri operated on a severely burned thirty-year-old man and replaced the upper half of his face: scalp, forehead, ears, nose, and upper and lower eyelids. This was the first time that eyelids were successfully transplanted. The man's hands had also been destroyed in the fire, and in a separate operation by another surgeon, the patient received a double hand transplant.

Surgeons had been working toward full face transplants, and with this operation, Lantieri came close enough to declare the goal achieved. Now that the possibility has been realized, "you transplant according to the patient's needs," whether it is part of the face or the whole face, Lantieri said at a news conference about the case.

Lantieri's patient died on June 8, 2009. His body had not rejected the transplant, but the graft became infected. While undergoing surgery to remove some of the infected tissue, he died of a heart attack. Lantieri praised the young man's courage and reasserted his view that the man "was so badly maimed and disfigured that he could only be treated by transplant surgery."

A Legitimate Option

Despite the death of Lantieri's patient, we may now have reached the point where surgeons should consider face transplants an option for people who are severely disfigured.

Injuries like those suffered by Isabelle Dinoire, Li Guoxing, Connie Culp, and Lantieri's unnamed patient are unusual among civilians, but they occur frequently in military conflicts. Department of Defense (DOD) figures show that more than 16,000 Americans have suffered serious combat injuries in the wars in Iraq and Afghanistan. Improvised explosive devices, rocket-propelled grenades, and rapid-fire assault rifles have produced a wide range of devastating wounds. The DOD figures don't reveal how many of the injured have suffered severe facial trauma, but it is reasonable to assume that, as in past wars, they number in the thousands.

Reconstructive surgery is outstanding at treating most facial trauma. Yet when the damage is severe and extensive, satisfying results aren't possible. Even if problems affecting eating and talking are solved, the patient is left with a face so scarred and distorted as to look hardly human. As Connie Culp's experience indicates, this causes psychological pain to patients and to those who love them. For military casualties, the reward for bravery and sacrifice is often a life of sorrow, disappointment, and depression.

The time may have come for surgeons to offer military personnel with damaged faces the option of a face transplant. Lantieri and others have demonstrated that the procedure can produce excellent results. Although face transplants must still be considered experimental, additional surgical experience may soon move them into the category of a standard treatment.

Face transplants have a serious downside. For the rest of their lives, recipients must take immunosuppressive drugs and live with the possibility of their bodies rejecting the new face. Also, whereas no one dies from a disfigured face, a transplant recipient may (like Lantieri's patient) die from an infection.

Thus, a transplant may not be the option chosen by those with even the most serious facial damage. Some might prefer to live with the face they have, but others may be prepared to take serious risks, if offered the prospect of looking ordinary. For them, a transplant might hold the promise of finding a job, falling in love, and starting a family—possibilities they may have believed their disfigurement closed off forever. What is true of those injured in war is also true for civilians who suffer severe facial trauma or disfigurement from disease.

Donations

Surgical and medical problems are not the only ones that must be solved before face transplants can become a standard therapy. We have mechanisms in place to procure solid organs such as hearts, kidneys, and livers for transplant, but we have no mechanism for procuring faces.

It may be difficult to establish one, given the nature of the graft. People have no direct experience of (say) the liver of a loved one, but the face is of primary importance to them. Thus, even those willing to donate the organs of a family member may be reluctant to donate the face. A face graft doesn't look exactly like the face of the donor, but this may not be enough to overcome a family's hesitation. Because an appropriate face graft must come from someone with the same blood type and skin tone, it may be difficult to find enough donors.

Also, donated kidneys, hearts, and livers can extend the lives of transplant recipients. Face transplants, by contrast, are not lifesaving surgery. It may be difficult to convince a broad public that it is inappropriate to compare a face transplant to a cosmetic procedure like a face-lift. Candidates for face transplants are people who suffer from severe facial deformity, not merely ones who want to enhance their normal appearance.

Yet as face transplants become more common and more successful, it may be that people come to understand the wish of those who are horribly disfigured merely to look ordinary. If that time comes, people may become as willing to donate their faces after they are dead as they are now to donate their hearts.

Abigail Alliance v. FDA: Do Terminally Ill People Have a Right to Take Experimental Drugs?

Abigail Burroughs was nineteen years old in 1999, the year she was diagnosed with squamous cell cancer of the head and neck. She was treated with chemotherapy and radiation at Johns Hopkins Hospital in Baltimore, but the cancer was not driven into remission.

A cytological study of the cells of her tumor conducted at Hopkins showed an excess of epidermal growth factor reception (EGFR) on the surfaces of the cell membranes. Two drugs were then being tested against EGFR: genfiitinib and centuxinab. Abigail's oncologist thought she might benefit from being treated with one of these drugs, but neither had been approved for use by the FDA. The only way for Abigail to receive either drug was to qualify as a participant in a clinical trial in which they were being used.

Unfortunately, Abigail didn't meet the inclusion criteria that would have allowed her to become a participant in the genfiitinib clinical trial. Nor could she qualify for the centuxinab trial, because admission to it was restricted to patients with colon cancer. Abigail's oncologist was as frustrated and as helpless as she was.

Abigail eventually met the criteria required to be included in a clinical trial of a third drug (erlotinib). By then, however, she was too sick for the drug to help her. Abigail died from her disease on June 9, 2001.

Abigail Alliance

Shortly before Abigail died, she had given a TV interview in which she expressed her frustration at not being able to gain access to a drug her doctor thought might help her. She and her family had petitioned the FDA and talked to members of Congress in an effort to get FDA policy changed. "This is not just about me," she told the interviewer. "I'm trying to help so many others."

Frank Burroughs, Abigail's father, remembered her words, and according to his account, ten hours after she died he realized he needed to continue the fight Abigail had been involved in. Burroughs founded the Abigail Alliance for Better Access to Developmental Drugs in November 2001. The Alliance's aim was to change FDA policies to give terminally ill people easier access to investigational drugs that might benefit them.

Ordinarily, investigational drugs are available only to patients enrolled in clinical trials in which the drugs are being tested. (Even these patients may not get the investigational drug; depending on how the trial is designed, they may receive the standard drug or even a placebo.) In 1990, the FDA approved a "compassionate use" policy that makes it possible for a patient to be treated with a drug under development if these conditions are met: (1) the drug is already being tested in a clinical trial; (2) no comparable alternative treatment is available; (3) the drug's developer has applied for FDA approval; (4) available evidence suggests that the drug may be effective for the intended use and that it is not likely to pose a significant risk of harm to the patient.

The Alliance claimed that the FDA had made its requirements for compassionate use so stringent that few patients could qualify for access to investigational drugs. As a result, drug developers manufactured only enough of an investigational drug to meet the needs of researchers giving them to patients in clinical trials. The restricted supply of drugs thus made it almost impossible for patients who were not in a clinical trial to get the drugs.

Lawsuit and Appeal

The Alliance was joined by the Washington Legal Foundation in petitioning the FDA to make more investigational drugs available under its compassionate-use policy. Before the FDA responded to the petition, the petitioners filed suit in the Washington, DC, Federal District Court. The suit claimed that the FDA violated terminally ill patients' constitutional right to privacy (self-defense), as well as their right to due process. (Under the due process clause of the Fifth Amendment, no citizen can be deprived of life, liberty, or property without due process of the law.)

In August 2002, the U.S. District Court dismissed the suit. The decision held, in effect, that terminally ill patients have no constitutionally based right to gain access to investigational drugs. The Alliance and the Foundation appealed the ruling to the U.S. Court of Appeals of the District of Columbia.

The appeal was heard by a three-judge panel, and on May 2, 2006, the panel, in a 2–1 decision, overturned the decision of the District Court. (Versions of the majority and the dissenting opinion are given in the readings.) This was not the end of the matter, however: the full Appeals Court, instead of just the three-person panel, reconsidered the case and ruled against the appeal in an 8–2 decision. In upholding the original decision, the Appeals Court decided, in effect, that terminally ill patients have no right to gain access to investigational drugs. The Alliance appealed the decision to the Supreme Court, but the Court declined to hear the case. This meant that Abigail Alliance had exhausted all possible legal remedies.

FDA Eases—but Does Not End—Restrictions

In 2006, the FDA revised its regulations to make it somewhat easier for patients to receive treatment with investigational drugs under its "compassionate use" and "expanded access" policies. Patients must have serious or immediately life-threatening diseases or conditions, lack other therapeutic options, and have a chance of benefiting from the drug. Also, the drug must be available in sufficient supply, the

drug's manufacturer must agree to supply the drug, and the patient must also have a way to pay for the costs involved in being treated with the drug. (These can be expensive if frequent monitoring of the patient is involved.)

Defenders of FDA policies point out that if patients were allowed access to unproven drugs, it would be very difficult to get enough patients enrolled in clinical trials to determine whether the drugs are effective. Indeed, one study shows that clinical trials of drugs available outside the trial take much longer to complete (forty-eight months) than drugs available only in the trial (twenty-six weeks). Also, even though patients hope otherwise, less than ten percent of drugs tested in clinical trials are approved as safe and effective by the FDA.

Those committed to giving people who are desperate even a slim chance to save their lives are not persuaded by the statistics or by the FDA's new, more relaxed policies. They will not be satisfied until terminally ill patients have the legal right to be treated with the drugs their doctors think might be beneficial. The debate over access to experimental drugs is not likely to go away.

SOCIAL CONTEXT
Prisoners as Test Subjects?

In a 1966 interview, Dr. Albert Klingman, professor of dermatology at the University of Pennsylvania, recalled his impression of Holmesburg State Prison in Philadelphia on his first visit. He looked around at the prisoners, many of them shirtless, and "All I saw before me were acres of skin. It was like a farmer seeing a fertile field for the first time."

Klingman went on to conduct a large number and variety of clinical trials at Holmesburg, using prisoners as research subjects. He was not, however, the only scientist to see the prison as a field of potential participants. Allen M. Hornblum's 1998 book *Acres of Skin: Human Experiments at Holmesburg Prison* documents hundreds of cases of human research carried out at the prison from 1951 to 1974. The University of Pennsylvania established a research clinic and laboratory at the prison, and it was

under its auspices that many investigations were carried out. University scientists carried out research supported by contracts from more than thirty private companies (e.g., Johnson & Johnson and Dow Chemical), as well as from the United States Army and thirty federal agencies, including the Central Intelligence Agency.

Numerous clinical trails were carried out to determine the safety and effectiveness of dermatological products. Thus, prisoners were recruited to test skin creams, shampoos, moisturizers, deodorants, and foot powders. (Dr. Klingman's Holmesburg research established the effectiveness of Retin-A in treating acne.) Trials were not limited to skin products, and prisoners were also enrolled to test toothpaste, eyedrops, and liquid diets. Although most of tests were carried out to develop products with commercial value, clinical trials of experimental drugs were also conducted at Holmesburg. Over the years, thirty-three drug companies employed prisoners as subjects in testing more than three hundred drugs.

Although some substances studied at Holmesburg were relatively benign, others posed a serious risk to the safety of the human subjects. Thus, more than seventy prisoners were exposed to dioxin, a major component of Agent Orange, a defoliant used during the Vietnam War and suspected of causing cancers and neurological disorders. Other prisoners were exposed to potentially harmful doses of radioactive materials and to chemicals that left some with lifelong problems. Edward Anthony, an inmate in 1962, was one of the many who were permanently harmed by serving as a research subject. He told reporter Jan Urbina in a 2006 interview that "When they put the chemicals on me, my hands swelled up like eight-ounce boxing gloves, and they've never gone back to normal."

One of several Army projects involved administering various doses of seven powerful psychotropic (mind-altering) drugs like LSD to 320 subjects. The aim of the research, carried out during the Cold War, was to find the minimum dose of a drug that would be effective in disabling half the population receiving it. Thus, if the drug were added to a water supply, those drinking the water, whether members of a military unit or inhabitants of a city, could be effectively immobilized. Psychotropic drugs are highly dangerous, with the potential to cause death or trigger a psychosis. It is almost certain that some inmates who served as test subjects for these drugs were irreversibly harmed.

Informed Consent?

Researchers recruited prisoners to participate in the Holmesburg experiments, and no one was forced to participate. In this sense, the prisoners were all volunteers. Hornblum and others familiar with the circumstances under which recruiting took place, however, doubt whether the conditions required for legitimate

informed consent were satisfied. Prisoners were not supplied with information in a form they could understand and deliberate about in making a decision, and their autonomy was compromised by their being prisoners and by the offer of inducements that encouraged them to disregard their self-interest.

First, many prisoners at Holmesburg either couldn't read or read poorly, making it unlikely that they were able to understand the risk of becoming a subject in a clinical investigation. Such prisoners had to depend on explanations provided by the researchers conducting the investigation, and the researchers can't be assumed to have provided unbiased information. Thus, it is doubtful that a prisoner's signature on an informed-consent document indicated that he had an adequate understanding of the nature of the clinical trial and the risk he might run as a participant.

Second, prisoners at Holmesburg, like those elsewhere, lived in a routine and boring environment, one characterized by a lack of even small luxuries and by an ever-present threat of violence. Thus, participating in a clinical trial not only offered prisoners welcome distraction from boredom, but often gave them a chance to spend time in the more comfortable and safer environment of a study clinic. While there, they would be fed better food, have more of a chance to socialize, and receive frequent personal attention from the researchers. Prisoners, then, were likely to view even such small rewards as inducements to take risks they otherwise wouldn't agree to take. Thus, their autonomy was compromised, and their consent was not genuine.

Third, Holmesburg inmates were given the chance to earn, by prison standards, a significant amount of money. Inmates ordinarily worked in the prison's industries, making shoes and clothes or doing carpentry or laundry. For such work, they were paid fifteen to twenty-five cents a day. By contrast, an inmate volunteering to be a research subject might earn as much as $300 to $400 a month. Inmates who started out volunteering for relatively safe trials paying $50 or $75 a month sometimes worked toward earning more money by volunteering for research that increased their risks. Thus, in the circumstance of prison life, the potential to earn a substantial sum of money served as an inducement to become a research subject. The individual's autonomy was, once more, compromised and his consent rendered invalid.

Informed consent at Holmesburg seemed more a formal ritual than a genuine process for protecting autonomy and showing respect for persons. It is doubtful that the great majority of inmates who agreed to become subjects in clinical trials gave their informed consent in a legitimate sense.

Other Prisons

Research of the sort conducted at Holmesburg also took place at other prisons throughout the country. During the 1950s, Hornblum points out, in state prisons in Oregon and Washington, the testicles of 130 prisoners were exposed to radiation in an experiment to determine its effects on reproductive tissue. In 1963, prisoners in Ohio and Illinois were injected with blood from leukemia patients to determine whether the disease could be transmitted.

During the Second World War, prisons were sites of considerable research activity. Most able-bodied men were in the armed forces, and an unprecedented number of women had entered the workforce. Prisoners could prove that they were patriotic by becoming "guinea pigs" in one of the many research projects conducted under military auspices. Some experiments required exposure to extreme temperatures to test survival clothing, while others involved skingrafting, nutritional deficiencies, inducing dysentery, and attempts to find a substitute for human blood for use in transfusions.

Hornblum cites the case of one prison trial in which filtered beef blood was injected into 64 inmate volunteers as part of a transfusion study. The experiment was ended when twenty people sickened from an immune reaction. Eight of those who fell ill developed high fever, rashes, and joint pain, and one of them died.

The best-known prison experiment during the war years was the study of malaria conducted in 1944 at Illinois State Penitentiary in Statesville. University of Chicago researchers, working under a contract with the U.S. Army, infected five hundred healthy volunteers with malaria. (An early volunteer was Nathan Leopold, who had been convicted, along with Richard Loeb, of killing fourteen-year-old Bobby Franks in Chicago in 1924.) The study was conducted to discover the effectiveness of various drugs in preventing the relapse rate of those already infected with malaria. (Results weren't published until 1946, the year after the war ended.) Because United States and Allied forces were fighting in malaria-plagued regions of the world, finding effective treatments was crucial to the war efforts. Participants in the study were rewarded by being credited with time served for good behavior, making early release possible in some cases.

When the war ended, with prison experimentation an established practice, prisons in almost every state became places where pharmaceutical companies could find the subjects needed to conduct Phase I clinical trials of experimental drugs. Phase I trials are conducted to discover a new drug's side effects and establish a safe dose. Phase I trials are required by the FDA as part of the drug-approval process, but a Phase I trial does not have a therapeutic aim. Because of this, it has always been difficult to enroll an adequate number of people as test subjects. Prisons offered a solution to the problem. As one researcher observed in 1973, "Phase I is very big in prisons. FDA prefers Phase I to be an in-patient basis— the only place available for large-scale toxicity studies is prison. The FDA estimates that, until the early 1970s, about ninety percent of new drugs were first tested on prison inmates.

An experiment conducted by Robert E. Hodges in 1970 is typical of the nontherapeutic research carried out with prison inmates at the time. By withholding ascorbic acid from the diet of his research subjects, Hodges experimentally induced scurvy in five inmates from Iowa State Prison. The five developed hemorrhages under the skin, swollen joints, bleeding gums, severe joint pain, weight gain followed by swelling of the legs, hair loss, dental caries, shortness of breath, scaly skin, and depression. Hodges' results did no more than confirm what was already known about the lack of ascorbic acid in the diet. For volunteering, inmates earned a dollar a day during the course of the experiment. All the inmates suffered, but there was also doubt about whether the youngest of the five would ever recover fully from the induced disease.

New Regulations

In 1972, information about the *Tuskegee Study of Untreated Syphilis in the Negro Male* became public. (See Chapter 11, *"The Tuskegee Syphilis Study,"* for details.) Revelations about the deception, exploitation, and harm caused to individuals in this federally sponsored study produced a public and political furor that led to the demand that regulations governing research involving human subjects be strengthened so that something like the Tuskegee experiment could never happen again.

Institutional Review Boards (IRBs) were established to review human research projects, and rules to protect confidentiality and enable informed consent were introduced. The general protections extended to prison inmates, but in 1978 a set of regulations that applied specifically to federally funded research involving prisoners was introduced.

A major aim of the regulations was to protect the autonomy of prisoners by preventing them from being coerced into becoming research subjects. IRBs were instructed to consider the following before approving a research proposal:

1. Compensation must not be coercive. Even the opportunity to live in greater comfort or receive better food may be coercive in a prison environment.

2. Risks of participating in the research should be acceptable to potential subjects who are not prisoners.

3. Prisoners who decide against participation must not suffer such consequences as being denied parole or privileges to which they would otherwise be entitled.

4. Participants, after the end of the research, must be provided with medical care needed for any condition associated with the research.

In 2001, two more regulations were added:

5. At least one IRB member must be a prisoner or a prisoner representative.

6. A majority of the nonprisoner IRB members must not have any other association with the prison.

The FDA also recognized prisoners as constituting a "vulnerable population," putting them in the same category as children and the mentally ill. This means that IRB oversight of the research in which prisoners are involved is required to be especially vigilant.

The new federal regulations essentially ruled out the participation of prisoners in Phase I (for safety and side effects) and Phase II (for effectiveness) clinical trials of experimental drugs. The "acres of skin" viewed with excitement for so long by Albert Klingman and other researchers became forbidden fields.

The new, more stringent rules made it extremely difficult for new drugs to be tested by using prisoners in the ways required to gain FDA approval. More and more often, pharmaceutical companies began to test the safety and effectiveness of potentially useful drugs in European, Asian, and African countries. The rules for protecting human subjects are less strict in a number of other countries, and "offshore" testing has become a common practice.

Change Current Restrictions?

In 2006, the National Institute of Medicine was commissioned by the Office for Human Research Protections (OHRP), a division of the federal Department of Health and Human Services, to review the ethical considerations in research involving prisoners. OHRP asked for the study to help it decide whether it needed to revise regulations protecting prisoners as research subjects.

The Institute's report made five recommendations to expand the protections accorded prisoners, while also permitting prisoners to gain potential benefits from research.

1. *Expand the definition of "prisoner."* Almost seven million people are under "adult correction supervision," but only two million are in prisons. Nearly five million are on parole or probation, and they don't satisfy the narrow definition of "prisoner" in current regulations. They remain a vulnerable population, though, and the old definition should be expanded.

2. *Ensure universal ethical protection.* Federal regulations now apply only to prisoners participating in research funded by DHHS, the CIA, and the Social Security Administration. All research, including that funded by military and private corporations, should be regulated by the same set of ethical standards.

3. *Shift from Category to Risk–Benefit.* Instead of determining what category of research is acceptable for prisoners, decide on the basis of whether a proposed research project offers potential benefits to prisoners that outweigh the risks. Thus, testing cosmetics would be excluded, but testing an HIV vaccine might not, because HIV infections are frequent in prison population. Prisoners could be helped by such a vaccine.

   Even if regulations were shifted to consider potential risk–benefit outcomes, Phase 1 and Phase 2 clinical trials of a drug would not be permitted. The trials are needed to test the "safety and effectiveness" of the drug. Not knowing these facts about the drug would make it impossible to determine whether the benefit of giving the drug to a volunteer would exceed the risk. Phase 3 trials (which use a drug shown to have therapeutic benefits) are allowable, but only when the ratio of prisoners to nonprisoners in the study doesn't exceed fifty percent.

   This last restriction minimizes the possibility of using prisoners because they are convenient and accessible. The benefits considered in making decisions about whether research ought to be allowed must be benefits that accrue to the prisoners themselves, not to some other group or to society. For behavioral or epidemiological studies, however, if the risks are very low (e.g., filling out a questionnaire) and the knowledge obtained may benefit prisoners as a class (e.g., prevent the spread of disease), the study may be conducted.

4. *Make responsibility collaborative.* To the extent feasible, all aspects of a research project (design, planning, and implementation) should include the participation of the stakeholders—prisoners, corrections officers, medical staff, and administrators.

5. *Provide systematic oversight.* The OHRP should monitor the conduct of the research throughout the study. Also, the OHRP model for ethical research should be extended so that it covers privately funded research, as well as research funded by all federal and state agencies. This is not the case now, but giving OHRP an oversight role in all human research would afford the participants more protection than they now have.

Critics of the Institute of Medicine's recommendations express the fear that if they are accepted, an increasing number of prisoners may be recruited as research subjects. This holds the threat that prisoners may once more become exploited. Too much need exists for research subjects and too much money is at stake, critics say, for a maginalized and unsympathetic population to count on the rigorous enforcement of even the most stringent regulations. Deals will be made, shortcuts taken, and people exploited.

CASE PRESENTATION
Jesse Gelsinger: the First Gene-Therapy Death

When Jesse Gelsinger was three months short of his third birthday, he was watching cartoons on TV when he fell asleep. Except it was a sleep from which his parents were unable to rouse him. Panicked, they rushed him to a local hospital.

When Jesse was examined, he responded to stimuli but didn't awaken. The physicians classified him as being in a level-one coma. Laboratory tests showed he had a high level of ammonia in his blood, but it was only after several days and additional blood assays that Jesse's physicians arrived at a diagnosis of ornithine transcarbamylase deficiency—OTC.

OTC is a rare genetic disorder in which the enzyme ornithine transcarbamylase, one of the five involved in the urea cycle, is either missing or in short supply. The enzymes in the cycle break down the ammonia that is a by-product of protein metabolism.

A deficiency of OTC means the body cannot get rid of the ammonia, and it gradually accumulates in the blood. When the ammonia reaches a crucial level, it causes coma, brain damage, and eventually death. The disease results from a mutation on the X chromosome; thus females are carriers of the gene, which they pass on to their sons. The disorder occurs in one of every 40,000 births. Infants with the mutation usually become comatose and die within seventy-two hours of birth. Half die within a month of birth, and half of those who remain die before age five.

Although OTC is a genetic disease, no one else in Jesse's immediate family or ancestry had ever been diagnosed with the disease. His disease was probably the result of a spontaneous mutation. He was a genetic mosaic, which meant his body contained a mixture of normal and mutated cells. For this reason, Jesse had a comparatively mild form of OTC. His body produced enough of the enzyme that he could remain in stable health if he stuck to a low-protein diet and took his medications. These included substances, like sodium benzoate, that chemically bind to ammonia and make it easier for the body to excrete it.

At age ten, after an episode of consuming too much protein, Jesse once again fell into a coma and was hospitalized. But five days later, he was back home with no apparent neurological damage. During his teens, Jesse's condition was monitored by semiannual visits to a metabolic clinic in his hometown of Tucson, Arizona.

In 1998, Jesse, now seventeen, and his father, Paul Gelsinger, heard from Dr. Randy Heidenreich, a doctor at the clinic, about a clinical trial at the University of Pennsylvania. Researchers at the Institute for Human Gene Therapy, Heidenreich told the Gelsingers, were trying to use gene therapy to supply the gene for OTC. Their success would not be a cure for the disease, but it would be a treatment that might be able to bring babies out of comas and prevent their having brain damage.

The Gelsingers were interested, but Jesse was still a year short of being old enough to participate. In April 1999, during another visit to the clinic, they again talked to Dr. Heidenreich about the trial, and Paul mentioned that the family would be taking a trip to New Jersey in June. They would be able to make a side trip to Philadelphia and talk to the investigators.

Dr. Heidenreich contacted an investigator at the Institute and mentioned the Gelsingers' interest in the research, and Paul received a letter from him in April. Jesse would be interviewed and tested at the university hospital on June 22 to determine whether he met the criteria for becoming a research participant.

A bioethicist at the university, Arthur Caplan, had advised the researchers that it would be morally wrong to use infants born with OTC as participants in the gene-therapy trial. Because they could not be expected to live, Caplan reasoned, their parents would be desperate to find a way to save their child's life. Hence, driven by desperation, their consent would not be free. The appropriate participants would be women who were carriers of the gene or men in stable health with only a mild form of the disease. Jesse would celebrate his eighteenth birthday the day the family flew to the East Coast, and his age would then make him eligible to become a participant.

On June 22, 1999, Jesse and Paul Gelsinger met with Dr. Steven Raper for forty-five minutes to review the consent forms and discuss the procedure for which Jesse might volunteer if he qualified. Dr. Raper, a surgeon, would be the one performing the gene-therapy procedure.

According to Paul Gelsinger's recollections, Raper explained that Jesse would be sedated and two catheters inserted: one in the artery leading to his liver, the second in the vein leaving it. A weakened strain of adenovirus (the virus causing colds), genetically modified to include the OTC gene, would be injected into the hepatic artery. Blood would then be taken from the vein to monitor whether the viral particles were being taken up by the liver cells.

To reduce the risk of a blood clot's breaking loose from the infusion site, Jesse would have to remain in bed for eight hours after the procedure. Most likely, he would soon develop flu-like symptoms lasting for a few days. He might develop hepatitis, an inflammation of the liver. The consent form mentioned that if hepatitis progressed, Jesse might need a liver transplant. The consent form also mentioned that death was a possible outcome.

Paul Gelsinger saw this as such a remote possibility that he was more concerned about the needle biopsy of the liver to be performed a week after the procedure. The risk of death from the biopsy was given as one in 10,000. Paul urged Jesse to read the consent document carefully and to make sure he understood it. Paul thought the odds looked very good.

Dr. Raper explained that Jesse couldn't expect to derive any personal medical benefit from participating in the clinical trial. Even if the genes became incorporated into his cells and produced OTC, the effect would only be transitory. His immune system would attack the viral particles and destroy them within a month to six weeks.

Jesse, at the end of the information session, agreed to undergo tests to determine how well the OTC he produced got rid of ammonia in his blood—a measure of OTC efficiency. Samples of his blood were taken; then he drank a small amount of radioactively tagged ammonia. Later,

samples of his blood and urine were taken to see how much of the ingested ammonia had been eliminated. The results showed his body's efficiency was only six percent of a normal performance.

A month later, the Gelsingers received a letter from Dr. Mark Bratshaw, the pediatrician at the Institute who proposed the clinical trial. Bratshaw confirmed the six percent efficiency figure from additional test results and expressed his wish to have Jesse take part in the study. A week later, Bratshaw called Jesse and talked to him. Jesse had already expressed to his father a wish to participate, but he told Bratshaw to talk to his father.

Bratshaw told Paul about the results of their animal studies. The treatment had worked well in mice, preventing the death of those given a lethal injection of ammonia. Also, the most recent patient treated had shown a fifty percent increase in her ability to excrete ammonia. Paul Gelsinger later recalled saying, "Wow! This really works. So, with Jesse at six percent efficiency, you may be able to show exactly how well this works."

Bratshaw said their real hope was to find a treatment for newborns lacking any OTC efficiency and with little chance of survival. Also, another twenty-five liver disorders could potentially be treated with the same gene-therapy technique. The promise, then, was that hundreds of thousands, if not millions, of lives might be saved. Bratshaw and Paul never talked about the dangers to Jesse of becoming a subject in the clinical trial.

Paul discussed participation with Jesse. They both agreed that it was the right thing to do. Jesse would be helping babies stay alive, and perhaps in the long run, he might even be helping himself.

Approval

The clinical trial was supported by a National Institutes of Health grant awarded to Dr. James Wilson, the head of the Institute, and Mark Bratshaw. Their protocol had been reviewed by the federal Recombinant-DNA Advisory Committee (RAC) and the FDA . The animal studies Bratshaw had mentioned to Paul included twenty studies on mice to show the efficacy of the proposed technique. Wilson and his group had also conducted studies on monkeys and baboons to demonstrate the safety of the procedure.

Three of the treated monkeys had died of severe liver inflammation and a blood-clotting disorder when they had been given a stronger strain of adenovirus at a dose twenty times that proposed in the human trial. Both of the scientists assigned by the RAC to review the proposal thought the trial was too dangerous to include stable, asymptomatic volunteers. But Wilson and Bratshaw, employing Caplan's argument, convinced the panel that using subjects capable of giving consent was morally preferable to using OTC newborns.

The initial protocol called for the modified viruses to be injected into the right lobe of the liver. The thinking was that if the treatment caused damage, the right lobe could be removed and the left lobe spared. But the RAC objected to injecting the viruses into the liver and the investigators agreed to change the protocol. The decision was later reversed by the FDA, on the grounds that wherever the viruses were injected, they would end up in the liver. The RAC was in the process of being reorganized and, in effect, taken out of the approval loop for proposals; it never received notice of the change. The investigators continued to operate under the modified protocol.

Protocol

The study was a Phase I clinical trial. According to its protocol, eighteen patients were to receive an infusion of the genetically modified adenovirus. The aim of the study was to determine "the maximum tolerated dose." The investigators wanted to determine the point at which the transferred gene would be producing OTC in the maximum amount compatible with side effects that could be tolerated.

The eighteen patients were divided into six groups of three. Each successive group was to receive a slightly higher dose than the preceding one. The idea behind this common procedure is to protect the safety of the study participants. By increasing doses slightly, the hope is to spot the potential for serious side effects in time to avoid causing harm to the participants.

Preparation

On Thursday, September 9, Jesse Gelsinger, carrying one suitcase of clothes and another of videos, caught a plane for Philadelphia. He checked into the hospital alone. His father, a self-employed handyman, stayed in Tucson to work. Paul planned to arrive on the 18th to be present for what he considered the most dangerous part of the trial—the liver biopsy.

"You're my hero," Paul told Jesse. He looked him in the eye, and then gave him a big hug.

The level of ammonia in Jesse's blood was tested on Friday and Sunday. Sunday night he called his father, worried. His ammonia level was high, and his doctors had put him on IV medication to lower it. Paul reassured his son, reminding him that the doctors at the Institute knew more about OTC than anybody else in the world.

Tragedy

On the morning of Monday, September 13, Gelsinger became the eighteenth patient treated. He was transported from his room to the hospital's interventional radiology suite, where a catheter was snaked through an artery in his groin to the hepatic artery. A second catheter was placed in the vein exiting the liver.

Dr. Raper then slowly injected thirty milliliters of the genetically altered virus into Jesse's hepatic artery. This was the highest dose given to any participant. Patient 17, however, had received the same-size dose from a different lot of the virus and had done well. The procedure was completed around noon, and Jesse was returned to his room.

That evening Gelsinger, as expected, began to develop flu-like symptoms. He was feeling ill and feverish when he talked to his father and his stepmother, Mickie, that evening. "I love you, Dad," Jesse told his father. They all said what turned out to be their last goodbyes.

During the night, Jesse's fever soared to 104.5 degrees. A nurse called Dr. Raper at home, and when he arrived at the hospital around 6:15 that morning, the whites of Jesse's eyes had a yellowish tinge. This was a sign of jaundice, not something the doctors had encountered with the other trial participants. Laboratory findings revealed that Jesse's bilirubin, the product of red blood cell destruction, was four times the normal level.

Raper called Dr. Bratshaw, who was in Washington, to tell him their patient had taken a serious turn. Bratshaw said he would catch the train and arrive in Philadelphia in two hours. Raper also called Paul Gelsinger to explain the situation.

The jaundice was worrying to Jesse's physicians. Either his liver was not functioning adequately or his blood was not clotting properly and his red blood cells were breaking down faster than his liver could process them. Such a breakdown was life threatening for someone with OTC, because the destroyed cells released protein the body would have to metabolize. Jesse was showing the same problem as the monkeys that had been given the stronger strain of the virus.

Tuesday afternoon Paul received a call from Dr. Bratshaw. Jesse's blood-ammonia level had soared to 250 micromoles per deciliter, with 35 being a normal measure. He had slipped into a coma and was on dialysis to try to clear the ammonia from his blood. Paul said he would catch a plane and be at the hospital the next morning.

By the time Paul arrived at eight o'clock on Wednesday and met Bratshaw and Raper, Jesse had additional problems. Dialysis had brought his ammonia level down to 70 from its peak of 393, but he was definitely having a blood-clotting problem. Also, although placed on a ventilator, he continued to breathe for himself, causing hyperventilation. This increased the pH of his blood, which increased the level of ammonia circulating to his brain. Paul gave his permission for the doctors to give Jesse medications that would paralyze his breathing muscles and allow the machine to take over completely.

By Wednesday afternoon, Jesse's breathing was under control. His blood pH had fallen back to normal, and the clotting disorder was improving. Bratshaw returned to Washington. Paul began to relax, and at 5:30 he went out to dinner with his brother and his wife. But he returned to the hospital to find that Jesse had been moved to a different intensive care ward, and as he watched the monitors, he saw that the oxygen content of Jesse's blood was dropping. A nurse asked him to wait outside.

At 10:30 that evening, a doctor told Paul that Jesse's lungs were failing. Even by putting him on pure oxygen, they were unable to get an adequate amount of oxygen into his blood. The doctors had also talked with a liver transplant team and learned that Jesse was not a good candidate for a transplant.

Raper, very worried, discussed Jesse's problems with Bratshaw and Wilson, and the three of them decided to put Jesse on extracorporeal membrane oxygenation— ECMO. The machine would remove carbon dioxide from Jesse's blood and supply it with the needed oxygen. The procedure was far from standard, however. Only half of the 1000 people placed on ECMO had lived, but Paul was informed that Jesse had only a ten percent chance of surviving without ECMO.

"If we could just buy his lungs a day or two," Raper later told a reporter, "maybe he would go ahead and heal up."

Jesse was not hooked up to the ECMO unit until five o'clock Thursday morning. Bratshaw attempted to return from Washington, but he was trapped in an Amtrak train

outside Baltimore. Hurricane Floyd was headed toward the East Coast; Jesse's stepmother arrived from Tucson just before the airport closed.

The ECMO appeared to be working. But Paul was told that Jesse's lungs were so severely damaged that, if he survived, it would take a long time for him to recover.

When Paul finally saw his son at mid-morning, Jesse was still comatose and bloated beyond recognition. Only the tattoo on his right calf and a scar on his elbow assured Paul that the person in the bed was Jesse.

That evening, unable to sleep, Paul walked the half-mile from his hotel to the hospital to check on Jesse. His son was no better, and Paul noticed that the urine-collecting bag attached to Jesse's bed contained blood. He realized that this meant Jesse's kidneys were shutting down. "He was sliding into multiple-organ-system failure," Raper later recalled.

The next morning, Friday, September 17, Raper and Bratshaw met with Paul and Mickie to give them the bad news that Paul had already predicted. Jesse had suffered irreversible brain damage, and the doctors wanted Paul's permission to turn off the ventilator. At Paul's request, he and Mickie were left alone for a few minutes. He then told the doctors he wanted to bring in his family and have a brief service for Jesse.

Paul and Mickie, seven of Paul's fifteen siblings and their spouses, and about ten staff members crowded into Jesse's room. Paul leaned over Jesse, then turned and told the crowd, "Jesse was a hero." The chaplain said a prayer; then Paul gave a signal. Someone flipped one switch to turn off the ventilator, and flipped a second to turn off the ECMO unit.

Dr. Raper watched the heart monitor. When the line went flat, he put his stethoscope against Jesse's chest. At 2:30 P.M. Raper officially pronounced him dead. "Goodbye, Jesse," he said. "We'll figure this out."

Gathering Storm

Dr. James Wilson, the head of the Institute, immediately reported Jesse's death to the FDA. Paul Gelsinger, sad as he was, didn't blame Jesse's physicians for what had happened. Indeed, he supported them in the face of an initial round of criticism. "These guys didn't do anything wrong," he told reporters.

Then journalists began to bring to light information that raised questions about whether Jesse and his father had been adequately informed about the risks of the trial that claimed Jesse's life. Also, it raised questions about a conflict of interest that might have led researchers to minimize the risks. The FDA initiated an investigation, and the University of Pennsylvania conducted an internal inquiry.

Paul Gelsinger decided to attend the December 1999 RAC that discussed his son's death. He learned for the first time at that meeting, according to his account, that gene therapy had never been shown to work in humans. He had been misled, not necessarily deliberately, by the researcher's accounts of success in animals. As Paul listened to criticisms of the clinical trial, his faith in the researchers waned and was replaced by anger and a feeling of betrayal.

Other information fed his anger. When a month earlier he had asked James Wilson, "What is your financial position in this?" Wilson's reply, as Paul recalled, was that he was an unpaid consultant to the biotech company, Genovo, that was partially funding the Institute. Then later Paul learned that both Wilson and the University of Pennsylvania were major stockholders in Genovo and that Wilson had sold his thirty percent share of the company for $13.5 million.

Wilson and the university, as Paul saw it, had good reason to recruit volunteers for the clinical trial and produce positive results. Thus, they might not have been as careful as they should have been, in warning the Gelsingers about the risks of the study. Also, the bioethicist approving the trial was someone who held an appointment in the department headed by Wilson. This, in effect, made Wilson his superior and thus automatically raised a question about the independence of his judgment.

A year and a day after Jesse's death, the Gelsinger family filed a wrongful-death lawsuit against the people conducting the clinical trial and the University of Pennsylvania. The university settled the suit out of court. The terms of the settlement were not disclosed.

FDA Findings

An investigation by the FDA resulted in a report to Wilson and the University of Pennsylvania pointing to two flaws in the way the clinical trial was conducted. First, the investigators failed to follow their protocol and failed to report liver toxicity in four patients treated prior to Gelsinger. Second, the investigators failed to acknowledge the death of two rhesus monkeys injected with a high level of a similar vector.

Wilson's response was that he had sent the FDA the liver-toxicity information prior to the final approval of the protocol, although his report had been late. Further, the two monkeys that died were part of another study that used a different, stronger virus. In effect, then, Wilson was claiming that he and his colleagues had done nothing wrong and the FDA criticisms were unjustified.

Critics point out, apart from the question of how legitimate the criticisms were, that the FDA itself does not have enough power to oversee clinical trials properly. Most important, it is prohibited by law from distributing some so-called adverse-event reports. Difficulties encountered by patients in the fifty or so gene-therapy trials are often not made public, or even shared with investigators conducting similar trials, because drug-company sponsors regard information about adverse events as proprietary. This, critics say, puts participants in the position of having to take risks that they know nothing about. The law seems to favor protecting the investments of the pharmaceutical industry more than protecting human subjects.

Outcome

What caused the death of Jesse Gelsinger? Even after the autopsy, the answer isn't clear. The most suggestive finding was that Jesse had abnormal cells in his bone marrow. This may have been a preexisting condition, and it may account for why his immune system reacted in such an unpredicted way to the viral injection. He apparently died from an immunological response.

The FDA, after Jesse's death, shut down all gene-therapy operations temporarily for review. The University of Pennsylvania, after its internal review, restricted the role of the Institute for Human Gene Therapy to conducting basic biological research. Unable to carry out clinical trials, the Institute was de facto put out of business. A year or so later, it ceased to exist.

Because of Jesse's death, the Office for the Protection of Human Research Subjects committed itself to a major effort to educate researchers in the requirements for protecting participants in clinical trials and to stress the importance of Institutional Review Boards in seeing to the safety of participants. Even so, adverse-event reporting is still prohibited by law when it can be deemed to constitute proprietary information. Critics continue to see this as incompatible with the idea behind informed consent.

The Cold-War Radiation Experiments

Amelia Jackson was a cook at Pogue's department store in Cincinnati in 1966, when she was diagnosed with colon cancer. In October, she was treated with 100 rads of full-body radiation—the equivalent of 7500 chest X-rays. Until the treatment, Ms. Jackson was strong and still working, but after the treatment, she bled and vomited for days and was never again able to care for herself.

Ms. Jackson was treated as part of a program operated by the University of Cincinnati and supported in part by funds from the Pentagon. She was one of several cancer patients in a research program in which people were subjected to radiation in massive doses to determine its biological effects.

The aim of the study, according to researchers, was to develop more effective cancer treatments. However, the military was interested in determining how much radiation military personnel could be subjected to before becoming disoriented and unable to function effectively.

A Patchwork of Radiation Experiments

The Cincinnati project was only one of a patchwork of human experiments involving radiation that were carried out with funding from a variety of military and civilian agencies of the U.S. government over a period of at least thirty years. The experiments took place at government laboratories and university hospitals and research centers. Some experiments involved exposing patients to high-energy beams of radiation, while others involved injecting them with such dangerous radioactive substances as plutonium.

The experiments started toward the end of World War II. They were prompted by both scientific curiosity and the practical and military need to know more about the damaging effects of radiation on people. The advent of the Cold War between the United States and the Soviet Union and the real possibility that the political conflict would lead to nuclear war gave a sense of urgency to the research. Little was known about the harmful effects of radiation, and researchers believed their experiments not only would contribute to understandings but would provide the basis for more effective medical therapies.

In the late 1940s, Vanderbilt University exposed about eight hundred pregnant women to radiation to determine its effects on fetal development. A follow-up study of the children born to the women showed a higher-than-average rate of cancer.

At the Oak Ridge National Laboratory in Tennessee, patients with leukemia and other forms of cancer were exposed to extremely high levels of radiation from isotopes of cesium and cobalt. Almost two hundred patients, including a six-year-old boy, were subjected to such treatment, until the experiment was ended in 1974 by the Atomic Energy Commission, on the grounds of lack of patient benefit.

From 1963 to 1971, experiments were conducted at Oregon State Prison in which the testicles of sixty-seven inmates were exposed to X-rays to determine the effects of radiation on sperm production. Prisoners signed consent statements that mentioned some of the risks of the radiation. However, the possibility that the radiation might cause cancer was not mentioned. A similar experiment was conducted on sixty-four inmates at Washington State Prison.

At Columbia University and Montefiore Hospital in New York, during the late 1950s, twelve terminally ill cancer patients were injected with concentrations of radioactive calcium and strontium-85 to measure the rate at which the substances are absorbed by various types of tissues.

At a state residential school in Waltham, Massachusetts, from 1946 to 1956, nineteen mentally retarded teenaged boys were fed radioactive iron and calcium in their breakfast oatmeal. The aim of the research was to provide information about nutrition and metabolism. In the consent form mailed to parents of the boys, no mention was made of radiation.

The Experiments Become Public

The radiation experiments became public only in 1993, when reporters for the *Albuquerque Tribune* tracked down five of the eighteen patients who had been subjects in an experiment conducted from 1945 to 1957 in which patients were injected with plutonium. The work was done at the University of Rochester, Oak Ridge Laboratory, the University of Chicago, and the University of California, San Francisco Hospital. Apparently, some of the patients did not receive information about their treatment and were injected with radioactive materials without first giving consent.

Relying on the Freedom of Information Act, Eileen Welsome, a reporter for the newspaper, attempted to get documents from the Department of Energy concerning the radiation research, including ones containing the names of subjects. However, she was able to secure little information, and Tara O'Toole, the Assistant Secretary of Energy for Environment, Safety, and Health at the time, expressed reservations about releasing documents containing the names of research subjects. "Does the public's right to know include releasing names?" O'Toole asked. "It is not clear to me that it is part of the ethical obligation of the Government."

Did Participants Give Their Informed Consent?

Secretary of Energy Hazel R. O'Leary soon committed her department to a full investigation of the radiation experiments. A major focus of the inquiry was on whether patients were fully informed about the risks of the treatments they received and whether they gave meaningful consent to them.

In a number of cases, the government discovered, the experimental subjects were not informed of the risks they faced and did not consent to participate in the research. Patients were sometimes misled about the character of the treatments, and in some cases even the signatures on consent forms were forged. Ms. Jackson's granddaughter claims that although her grandmother was illiterate, she could sign her name, and the signature on the form used by the University of Cincinnati was not hers. The same claim is made by other relatives of subjects in the study.

In one known instance, a researcher found the radiation experiments to be morally suspect and warned his colleagues against pursuing them. C. E. Newton at the Hanford nuclear weapons plant wrote in an internal memorandum about the work done with prisoners at Washington State Prison: "The experiments do not appear to have been in compliance with the criminal codes of the state of Washington, and there is some question as to whether they were conducted in compliance with Federal laws."

Similarly, in a 1950 memorandum, Joseph G. Hamilton, a radiation biologist, warned his supervisors that the experiments "might have a little of the Buchenwald touch." Hamilton warned that the Atomic Energy Commission would be "subject to considerable criticism."

Some observers claim that work carried out twenty or thirty years ago cannot be judged by the same ethical standards as we would use today. Robert Loeb, speaking for Strong Memorial Hospital, where some of the studies were carried out, put the point this way: "In the 1940s, what was typical in research involving human subjects was for physicians to tell the patients that they would be involved in a study and not always give full details. That is not the standard today. Many of these studies would be impossible to conduct today."

By contrast, Dr. David S. Egilman, who has investigated instances of research with human subjects conducted by the military and the Atomic Energy Commission, claims there is adequate evidence to conclude that the researchers and their supporting agencies knew they were conducting immoral experiments. "They called the work, in effect, Nazi-like," he says. "The argument we hear is that these experiments were ethical at the time they were done. It's simply not true."

The initial question about the use of human subjects in radiation experiments conducted under the auspices of what is now the Department of Energy was expanded to include those conducted by several federal agencies. It seems as if at least 1000 people were exposed to varying levels of radiation in a variety of experiments conducted over a number of years at various locations. Some observers believe the actual figures are much higher.

The President's Advisory Committee on Human Radiation Experiments reviewed records from the Energy Department, Defense Department, Central Intelligence Agency, NASA, and federal health agencies in an attempt to locate research projects involving radiation and identify the people who were their experimental subjects. After eighteen months of investigation, the committee reported in 1995 that many of the government-sponsored experiments had been illegal and that their survivors ought to be compensated.

Compensation

In November 1996, the federal government agreed to pay $4.8 million as compensation for injecting twelve people with plutonium or uranium. At the time of the settlement, only one of the twelve was still alive, and the $400,000 award was paid to the families of the other participants. In 1998, the Quaker Oats Company and M.I.T. agreed to pay $1.85 million to the more than one hundred men who, as boys, had been fed the radioactive oatmeal at the Fernald School and other study sites.

A large number of claims from other experiments involving radiation and consent were filed against the federal government, universities, and hospitals. Advocates for those whose rights may have been violated charge the government with failing to make an effort to find the names of the people who were participants in the various radiation experiments. This would be a difficult and time-consuming process, because often names and addresses were not made a part of the experimental records.

The National Archives has placed all the hundreds of thousands of pages of records acquired by the Presidential Commission in files available to the public, and instead of the government notifying people that they may have a legal claim for compensation, individuals must come forward on their own initiative.

New Regulations

In 1997, President Clinton endorsed a stringent set of policies governing all human research receiving federal support. Under the new rules, explicit informed consent is required, the sponsor of the experiment must be identified to the subject, the subject must be told whether the experiment is classified, and permanent records of the experiment and the subjects must be kept. Further, an external review must be conducted before the experiment can proceed. The hope was that the new rules would put an end to secret experiments in which human subjects are subjected to radioactive, chemical, or other dangerous substances without their knowledge or consent.

With respect to the radiation experiments, Representative David Mann of Ohio summed up the views of most citizens: "I believe we have no choice but to conclude that the radiation experiments were simply wrong and that the Government owes a huge apology to the victims, their families, and the nation."

The Willowbrook Hepatitis Experiments

The Willowbrook State School in Staten Island, New York, is an institution devoted to housing and caring for mentally retarded children. In 1956, a research group led by Saul Krugman and Joan P. Giles of the New York University School of Medicine initiated a long-range study of viral hepatitis at Willowbrook. The children confined there were made experimental subjects of the study.

Hepatitis, a disease affecting the liver, is now known to be caused by one of two (possibly more) viruses. Although the viruses are distinct, the results they produce are the same. The liver becomes inflamed and increases in size as the invading viruses replicate themselves. Also, part of the tissue of the liver may be destroyed and the liver's normal functions impaired. Often the flow of bile through the ducts is blocked, and bilirubin (the major pigment in bile) is forced into the blood and urine. This produces the symptom of yellowish or jaundiced skin.

The disease is generally relatively mild, although permanent liver damage can be produced. The symptoms are ordinarily flu-like—mild fever, tiredness, and inability to keep food down. The viruses causing the disease are transmitted orally through contact with the feces and bodily secretions of infected people.

Krugman and Giles were interested in determining the natural history of viral hepatitis—the mode of infection and the course of the disease over time. They also wanted to test the effectiveness of gamma globulin as an agent for inoculating against hepatitis. (Gamma globulin is a protein complex extracted from the blood serum that contains antigen—substances that trigger the production of specific antibodies to counter infectious agents.)

Endemic Hepatitis

Krugman and Giles considered Willowbrook to be a good choice for investigation because viral hepatitis occurred more or less constantly in the institution. In the jargon of medicine, the disease was endemic. That this was so was recognized in 1949, and it continued to be so as the number of children in the school increased to more than 5000 in 1960. Krugman and Giles claimed that "under the chronic circumstances of multiple and repeated exposure . . . most newly admitted children became in-

fected within the first six to twelve months of residence in the institution."

Over a fourteen-year period, Krugman and Giles collected more than 25,000 serum specimens from more than seven hundred patients. Samples were taken before exposure, during the incubation period of the virus, and for periods after the infection. In an effort to get the kind of precise data they considered most useful, Krugman and Giles decided to deliberately infect some of the incoming children with the strain of the hepatitis virus prevalent at Willowbrook.

Justifying Deliberate Infection

They justified their decision in the following way: It was inevitable that susceptible children would become infected in the institution. Hepatitis was especially mild in the three- to ten-year age group at Willowbrook. These studies would be carried out in a special unit with optimum isolation facilities to protect the children from other infectious diseases, such as shigellosis (dysentery caused by a bacillus) and parasitic and respiratory infections, which are prevalent in the institution.

Most important, Krugman and Giles claimed that being an experimental subject was in the best medical interest of the child, for not only would the child receive special care, but infection with the milder form of hepatitis would provide protection against the more virulent and damaging forms. As they say, "It should be emphasized that the artificial induction of hepatitis implies a 'therapeutic' effect because of the immunity which is conferred."

Consent

Krugman and Giles obtained what they considered to be adequate consent from the parents of the children used as subjects. Where they were unable to obtain consent, they did not include the child in the experiment. In the earlier phases of the study, parents were provided with relevant information either by letter or orally, and written consent was secured from them. In the later phases, a group procedure was used:

First, a psychiatric social worker discusses the project with the parents during a preliminary interview.

Those who are interested are invited to attend a group session at the institution to discuss the project in greater detail. These sessions are conducted by the staff responsible for the program, including the physician, supervising nurses, staff attendants, and psychiatric social workers . . . . Parents in groups of six to eight are given a tour of the facilities. The purposes, potential benefits, and potential hazards of the program are discussed with them, and they are encouraged to ask questions. Thus, all parents can hear the response to questions posed by the more articulate members of the group. After leaving this briefing session parents have an opportunity to talk with their private physicians who may call the unit for more information. Approximately two weeks after each visit, the psychiatric social worker contacts the parents for their decision. If the decision is in the affirmative, the consent is signed but parents are informed that signed consent may be withdrawn any time before the beginning of the program. It has been clear that the group method has enabled us to obtain more thorough informed consent. Children who are wards of the state or children without parents have never been included in our studies.

Krugman and Giles point out that their studies were reviewed and approved by the New York State Department of Mental Hygiene, the New York State Department of Mental Health, the Armed Forces Epidemiological Board, and the human-experimentation committees of the New York University School of Medicine and the Willowbrook School. They also stress that, although they were under no obligation to do so, they chose to meet the World Medical Association's Draft Code on Human Experimentation.

Ethical Concerns

The value of the research conducted by Krugman and Giles has been recognized as significant in furthering a scientific understanding of viral hepatitis and methods for treating it. Yet serious moral doubts have been raised about the nature and conduct of the experiments. In particular, many have questioned the use of retarded children as experimental subjects, some claiming children should never be experimental subjects in investigations that are not directly therapeutic. Others have raised questions about the ways in which consent was obtained from the parents of the children, suggesting that parents were implicitly blackmailed into giving their consent

CASE PRESENTATION

Echoes of Willowbrook or Tuskegee? Experimenting with Children

In April 1998, the National Bioethics Advisory Committee was asked to investigate three experiments conducted from 1993 to 1996 at the New York State Psychiatric Institute.

The subjects of the experiment were almost one hundred boys ranging in age from six to eleven. All were from New York City, and many were black or Hispanic. The boys were chosen as subjects because their older brothers had been legally charged with some form of delinquency.

Researchers identified the potential subjects by combing through court records and by interviewing the mothers of the boys charged with crimes. The ones chosen for the experiment were considered by the researchers to be boys who had experienced "adverse rearing practices." The mothers of the boys selected were asked to take their children to the Psychiatric Institute to take part in the experiment. Mothers bringing in their boys were given a $125 cash payment.

The research subjects were given a small intravenously administered dose of the drug fenfluramine, and their blood was then assayed for a change in the level of neurotransmitters. The aim of the experiment was to test the hypothesis that violent behavior can be predicted by the use of neurochemical markers. The boys were given only a single dose of the drug.

In two of the three studies conducted at the Psychiatric Institute, the sixty-six boys who served as subjects were between seven and eleven and had been diagnosed as having attention deficit hyperactivity disorder. They were taken off their medication for a time before the fenfluramine was administered.

Fenfluramine has now been withdrawn from medical practice by the Federal Drug Administration. In combination with another drug ("fen–phen"), it was used to treat obesity until it was discovered that in some people it caused damage to the heart valves. Experts on the use of fenfluramine consider it unlikely that the boys in the experiments suffered any harm from the drug. They were given only a single small dose, whereas those with heart damage used the drug in larger doses over a period of months.

Even so, critics of the experiments charge that the boys were exposed to a substantial risk in experiments in which they had no chance of receiving any benefit. The experiments were for the sake of science, not for their own sake. Further, the drug is not free of such side effects as nausea, headache, dizziness, anxiety, and irritability. The children, then, suffered to some extent without gaining any advantage.

While the critics have not mentioned the role played by the boys' mothers, we might ask whether they can be said to have acted in the best interest of their children. Some of the women may have been induced to ignore their child's interest by the $125 payment. Thus, the payment itself raises the question of whether the consent of the mothers to their children's participation was legitimate. If their income was low, the prospect of receiving money may have tainted the quality of their consent.

"What value does the President's apology for Tuskegee have when there are no safeguards to prevent such abuses now?" asked Vera Sharay, director of Citizens for Responsible Care in Psychiatry and Research. "These racist and morally offensive studies put minority children at the risk of harm in order to prove that they are generally predisposed to violence in the future," she charged. "It demonstrates that psychiatric research is out of control."

A spokesperson for Mount Sinai Hospital, which participated in the studies, refused to reveal how many of the subjects were black or Hispanic. He commented only that the subjects chosen reflected "the ethnically diverse population of the catchment area."

Dr. John Oldham, director of the New York Psychiatric Institute, said during an interview that such studies are crucial to acquiring an understanding of the biological basis of behavior. "Is there a correlation between certain biological markers and conduct disorders or antisocial behaviors?" he asked. "This study was an effort to look at this with a relatively simple method using fenfluramine."

CASE PRESENTATION
The Use of Morally Tainted Sources: The Pernkopf Anatomy

In November 1996, Howard A. Israel and William E. Seidelman wrote a letter to *JAMA*, the *Journal of the American Medical Association*, asking that the University of Vienna attempt to determine the source of the cadavers used as subjects of the illustrations in the multivolume book known as the *Pernkopf Anatomy*. Rumors surrounding the book's author and artists had long suggested that some of the cadavers employed in the dissections might have been victims of the Nazis.

Eduard Pernkopf, the book's author, was a member of the Nazi party, and, although never charged with war crimes, he spent three years in an Allied prison camp. He returned afterward to his academic position at the University of Vienna and worked on his atlas of anatomy until he died in 1955. The four main artists illustrating the anatomy were also Nazi party members, and one of them sometimes incorporated into his signature a swastika and the lightning bolts of the SS. These have been airbrushed out in contemporary printings of the book.

Pernkopf began his work in 1933, well before the beginning of the war, but he died in 1955; the book was completed by others and published in 1960. The American edition has dropped Pernkopf's text, but it uses the original illustrations, which some anatomists consider to be masterpieces of medical paintings. The atlas is admired for its accuracy and is widely used by anatomists and others in medical schools.

After investigating the charge that cadavers from concentration camps or the bodies of Nazi opponents from the district prison were used as subjects, the anatomist David P. Williams concluded that either was possible but couldn't be proved one way or the other. Because of this doubt about the source of the cadavers, uncertainty about the moral legitimacy of using the atlas continues to be debated.

Anatomist E. W. April expressed the opinion of one faction. The atlas is "a phenomenal book," he told reporter Nicholas Wade, "very complete and thorough and authoritative, and you can't detract from that regardless of the fact that [Pernkopf] might not have been a good person or belonged to the wrong party."

The opposite view is expressed by Howard Israel, the coauthor of the letter to *JAMA*. "I have looked at a lot of anatomy textbooks, and these [volumes] are terrific in terms of the quality of pictures," he told Wade. "But that doesn't mean it's right to use them."

What if the source of the cadavers was known? What if they turned out to be the bodies of victims of the Holocaust? Would it be wrong to use an anatomy text based on the dissection of the victims? This is one aspect of the general question of whether it is morally acceptable to use scientific data or any other sort of information that has been obtained in an immoral way. In the view of some, we have a moral duty to avoid tainted data, because to use it is in an indirect way of benefit from the wrongdoing that produced it. Others, however, believe that using the data is a way of rescuing something worthwhile from something that was wrong. As such, it is a way of honoring those who suffered a terrible injustice by making sure their sacrifice is not wasted.

CASE PRESENTATION
Stopping the Detrozole Trial: A Case of "Ethical Overkill"?

Tamoxifen is one of the new drugs helping to transform breast cancer from an acute, fatal disease into one that is chronic and treatable. Tamoxifen blocks the uptake of estrogen, a hormone some tumors need to grow, and it is remarkably effective in treating post-menopausal women. Tamoxifen stops producing any benefit after five years, however. Thus, whether women continue to take the drug or not, they all have the same two to four percent chance of having a recurrence of their disease.

The need for a drug to reduce or even eliminate this chance was obvious as soon as researchers realized the limits of tamoxifen's effectiveness. The pharmaceutical manufacturer Novartis decided that its drug letrozole (marketed as Femera) was a good candidate for following tamoxifen. Letrozole was already approved by the FDA for cancer treatment, but it had never been studied as a treatment for breast cancer specifically.

Novartis initiated a clinical trial of letrozole in 2001, and researchers enrolled more than 5000 women at medical centers in the United States, Canada, and Europe. The investigator's plan was to recruit women treated with tamoxifen whose breast cancer was in remission, then randomly assign them (with their consent) to one of two groups. One group would be treated with letrozole, the other with a placebo. The use of a placebo was justified, because, after tamoxifen stopped being effective, no drug was known that would reduce the risk of a recurrence of the disease. Physicians would examine the women regularly, keep records on their medical condition, and then, at the end of five years, assess the effectiveness of letrozole.

But in November 2003, less than halfway into the study, Novartis called a halt to the clinical trial. The study's Data and Safety Monitoring Committee had reviewed the accumulating treatment data and discovered that letrozole was so much more effective than the placebo in reducing the recurrence of breast cancer that, the investigators decided, it would not be ethical to continue the study. Statistics showed that women taking letrozole were only half as likely to develop breast cancer again as women taking the placebo.

More precisely, 2.4 years after receiving the last tamoxifen treatment, 132 women taking the placebo either had a recurrence of their disease or developed cancer in their other breast. By contrast, this happened to only seventy-five women taking letrozole. This amounted to almost half the number of cases—forty-three percent—expected on the basis of previous data. Letrozole clearly worked.

The investigators viewed taking letrozole as offering women with breast cancer such a large advantage that it would be unfair to deny it to women taking a placebo. This was fair in the beginning, because the situation was one of clinical equipoise—so far as anyone knew, the placebo was just as good a treatment as the letrozole—but now the data had shifted the balance.

The investigators also thought it would be wrong to keep quiet about what they had learned about letrozole and allow the study to continue for another 2.5 years. Because letrozole already had FDA approval, women with breast cancer who had completed their course of tamoxifen could then take letrozole and improve their chances of avoiding a recurrence of their cancer. Some ten thousand women would immediately have a chance to benefit from the drug.

The decision by Novartis and the investigators to stop the trial of letrozole halfway through met with sharp criticism. An editorial in the *New York Times* asked whether scientists weren't engaging in "ethical overkill" in stopping the trial to bring immediate benefit to eligible women. A patient advocacy group, the National Breast Cancer Coalition, condemned ending the study prematurely. Both the editorial and the advocacy group pointed to the questions left unanswered by the uncompleted trial—whether letrozole (in addition to preventing the recurrence of breast cancer) prolonged lives, how likely and how severe were the cardiovascular problems and the osteoporosis already known to be associated with it, and how long letrozole remains effective.

"There seems little doubt that a trial must be terminated if it is harming the participants," the *Times* editorial said. "But it is much less clear that trials should be halted to spread the presumed benefits before the full data are at hand."

So far as the critics are concerned, some may wonder whether there is a relevant moral difference between withholding a treatment that evidence suggests reduces the likelihood of the recurrence of a potentially fatal disease and administering a treatment likely to cause harm. Breast cancer does not always cause the death of patients with the disease, so it is true that reducing the chance of its recurrence is not equivalent to preventing death. Even so, preventing a potentially fatal disease may be a compelling reason for not waiting to see whether a drug that cuts in half the recurrence of breast cancer also reduces deaths.

The case can be made that the data accumulating from patients treated with letrozole compared with patients treated with a placebo reached the point that the situation could no longer be described as one of therapeutic equipoise. Letrozole, it became clear, was better at preventing a recurrence of breast cancer than a placebo. At that point, the investigators could no longer justify treating half the participants with a placebo. While it would be useful to know whether letrozole extends lives and to learn the frequency and seriousness of its side effects, this is not knowledge that can be purchased at the expense of the study's participants. Thus, Novartis and the investigators were right to stop the clinical trial when they did. Indeed, had they continued, they might legitimately be charged with exploiting the women in the placebo group, as well as with depriving other women with breast cancer access to an apparently effective drug.

CASE PRESENTATION
Baby Fae

On October 14, 1984, a baby was born in a community hospital in southern California with a malformation known as hypoplastic left-heart syndrome. In such a condition, the mitral valve or aorta on the left side of the heart is underdeveloped, and essentially only the right side of the heart functions properly. Some 300 to 2000 infants a year are born with this defect, and most die from it within a few weeks.

The infant, who became known to the public as Baby Fae, was taken to the Loma Linda University Hospital Center. There, on October 26, a surgical team headed by Dr. Leonard Bailey performed a heart transplant; Baby Fae became the first human infant to receive a baboon heart. She died twenty days later.

Baby Fae was not the first human to receive a so-called xenograft, or cross-species transplant. In early 1964, a sixty-eight-year-old deaf man, Boyd Rush, was transplanted with a chimpanzee heart at the University of Mississippi Medical Center. The heart failed after only an hour, and the patient died. Before Baby Fae, three other cross-species transplants had also ended in a quick death.

Moral Questions

In the case of Baby Fae, questions about the moral correctness and scientific legitimacy of the transplant were raised immediately. Hospital officials revealed that no effort had been made to find a human donor before implanting the baboon heart, and this led some critics to wonder if research interests were not being given priority over the welfare of the patient. Others questioned whether the parents were adequately informed about alternative corrective surgery, the Norwood procedure, available from surgeons in Boston and Philadelphia.

Other observers wondered whether the nature of the surgery and its limited value had been properly explained to the parents. Also, some critics raised objections to sacrificing a healthy young animal as part of an experiment not likely to bring any lasting benefit to Baby Fae.

Scientific critics charged that not enough is known about crossing the species barrier to warrant the use of transplant organs at this time. The previous record of failures, with no major advances in understanding, did not make the prospect of another such transplant reasonable. Furthermore, critics said, chimpanzees and gorillas are genetically more similar to humans than baboons, so the choice of a baboon heart was not a wise one. The only advantage of baboons is that they are easier to breed in captivity. Also, other critics claimed Dr. Bailey was merely engaged in "wishful thinking" in believing that Baby Fae's immune system would not produce a severe rejection response because of its immaturity.

Postmortem

An autopsy on Baby Fae showed that her death was caused by the incompatibility of her blood with that of the baboon heart. Baby Fae's blood was type O, the baboon's type AB. This resulted in the formation of blood clots and the destruction of kidney function. The heart showed mild signs of rejection.

In an address before a medical conference after Baby Fae's death, Dr. Bailey commented on some of the criticisms. He is reported to have said that it was "an oversight on our part not to search for a human donor from the start." Dr. Bailey also told the conference that he and his team believed that the difference in blood types between Baby Fae and the baboon would be less important than other factors and that the immunosuppressive drugs used to prevent rejection would also solve the problem of blood incompatibility. "We came to regret those assumptions," Dr. Bailey said. The failure to match blood types was "a tactical error that came back to haunt us."

On other occasions, Dr. Bailey reiterated his view that, because infant donors are extremely scarce, animal-to-human transplants offer a realistic hope for the future. Before the Baby Fae operation, Dr. Bailey had transplanted organs in more than 150 animals. None of his results were in published papers, however, and he performed all his work on local grants. He indicated that he would use the information obtained from Baby Fae to conduct additional animal experiments before attempting another such transplant.

NIH Report

In March of 1985, the National Institutes of Health released a report of a committee that made a site visit to Loma Linda to review the Baby Fae matter. The committee found that the informed-consent process was generally satisfactory, in that "the parents were given an appropriate and thorough explanation of the alternatives available, the risks and benefits of the procedure and the experimental nature of the transplant." Moreover, consent was obtained in an "atmosphere which allowed the parents an opportunity to carefully consider, without coercion or undue influence, whether to give permission for the transplant."

The committee also pointed out certain flaws in the consent document. First, it "did not include the possibility of searching for a human heart or performing a human heart transplant." Second, the expected benefits of the procedure "appeared to be overstated," because the consent document "stated that 'long-term survival' is an expected possibility with no further explanation." Finally, the document did not explain "whether compensation and medical treatment were available if injury occurred."

The committee did not question the legitimacy of the cross-species transplant. Moreover, it made no mention of the Norwood procedure, except to say that it had been explained to the mother at the community hospital at the birth of the infant. (The consent document described the procedure as a generally unsuccessful "temporizing operation.")

Although the committee was generally critical of Loma Linda's Institutional Review Board in "evaluating the entire informed-consent process," it reached the conclusion that "the parents of Baby Fae understood the alternatives available as well as the risks and reasonably expected benefits of the transplant."

Officials at Loma Linda University Medical Center promised that, before performing another such transplant, they would first seek a human infant heart donor.

BRIEFING SESSION

In 1947, an international tribunal meeting in Nuremberg convicted fifteen German physicians of "war crimes and crimes against humanity." The physicians were charged with taking part in "medical experiments without the subjects' consent." But the language of the charge fails to indicate the cruel and barbaric nature of the experiments. Here are just some of them:

- At the Ravensbrueck concentration camp, experiments were conducted to test the therapeutic powers of the drug sulfanilamide. Cuts were deliberately made on the bodies of people; then the wounds were infected with bacteria. The infection was worsened by forcing wood shavings and ground glass into the cuts. Then sulfanilamide and other drugs were tested for their effectiveness in combating the infection.

- At the Dachau concentration camp, healthy inmates were injected with extracts from the mucous glands of mosquitos to produce malaria. Various drugs were then used to determine their relative effectiveness.

- At Buchenwald, numerous healthy people were deliberately infected with the spotted-fever virus merely for the purpose of keeping the virus alive. Over ninety percent of those infected died as a result.

- Also at Buchenwald, various kinds of poisons were secretly administered to a number of inmates to test their efficacy. Either the inmates died or they were killed at once so that autopsies could be performed. Some experimental subjects were shot with poisoned bullets.

- At Dachau, to help the German Air Force, investigations were made into the limits of human endurance and existence at high altitudes. People were placed in sealed chambers, then subjected to very high and very low atmospheric pressures. As the indictment puts it, "Many victims died as a result of these experiments and others suffered grave injury, torture, and ill-treatment."

Seven of the physicians convicted were hanged, and the other eight received long prison terms. From the trial there emerged the Nuremberg Code, a statement of the principles that should be followed in conducting medical research with human subjects.

Despite the moral horrors that were revealed at Nuremberg, few people doubt the need for medical research involving human subjects. The extent to which contemporary medicine has become effective in the treatment of disease and illness is due almost entirely to the fact that it has become scientific medicine. This means that contemporary medicine must conduct inquiries in which data are gathered to test hypotheses and general theories related to disease processes and their treatment. Investigations involving nonhuman organisms are essential, but the ultimate tests of the effectiveness of medical treatments and their side effects must involve human beings as research subjects. Human physiology and psychology are sufficiently different to make animal studies alone inadequate.

The German physicians tried at Nuremberg were charged with conducting experiments without the consent of their subjects. The notion that consent must be given before a person becomes a research subject is still considered the basic requirement that must be met for an experiment to be morally legitimate. Moreover, it is not merely consent—saying yes—but informed consent that is demanded. The basic idea is simply that a person decides to participate in research after he or she has been provided with background information relevant to making the decision.

This same notion of informed consent is also considered a requirement that must be satisfied before a person can legitimately be subjected to medical treatment. Thus, people are asked to agree to submit themselves to such ordinary medical procedures as blood transfusion or to more extraordinary ones such as surgical operations or radiation therapy.

The underlying idea of informed consent in both research and treatment is that people have a right to control what is done to their bodies. The notion of informed consent is thus a recognition of an individual's autonomy—of the right to make decisions governing one's own life. This right is recognized both in practice and in the laws of our society. (Quite often, malpractice suits turn on the issue of whether a patient's informed consent was valid.)

In the abstract, informed consent seems a clear and straightforward notion. After all, we all have an intuitive grasp of what it is to make a decision after we have been supplied with information. Yet, in practice, informed consent has proved to be a slippery and troublesome concept. We will identify later some of the moral and practical difficulties that make the application of the concept difficult and controversial.

Our focus will be on informed consent in the context of research involving human subjects. But most of the issues that arise here also arise in connection with giving and securing informed consent for the application of medical therapies. (They also arise in special forms in abortion and euthanasia.) In effect, then, we will be considering the entire topic.

Before discussing the details of informed consent, it's useful to have an idea of what takes place in a typical clinical trial. Clinical trials account for the great majority of all medical research involving human subjects.

CLINICAL TRIAL PHASES

Testing a new drug, surgical procedure, or other therapy takes place in the sequence of phases that follows. Animal testing, when appropriate, is done before human studies begin, although additional testing may be done in parallel with human studies.

Phase I: Investigators test the therapy in a small number of people (10–80) to evaluate its safety, identify its side effects, and (if a drug) determine the range of a safe dose. Testing the effectiveness of the therapy is not the aim of the trial.

Phase II: Investigators test the treatment in a larger group of people (100–300) to determine whether the therapy is effective and to further test its safety. Both effectiveness and safety are usually measured statistically.

Phase III: Investigators test the therapy in a significantly larger number of people (1000–3000) to confirm its effectiveness, monitor its side effects, and compare it with accepted therapies. Investigators also collect data that may be relevant to improving the therapy or increasing its safety.

Phase IV: Investigators collect data about the therapy's effects after the therapy has become established as a standard treatment. The aim is to refine the use of the therapy and improve its safety.

Clinical Trials

The United States spends almost $100 billion per year on medical research, and a large proportion of the money goes to fund clinical trials. A clinical trial is a form of research in which the effectiveness and side effects of a treatment are tested by administering it to human subjects. The treatment may be a drug, surgical procedure, special diet, medical device, or even a form of behavior, such as getting out of bed or listening to music. The most common clinical trials are ones in which the effectiveness of a new drug is tested, so let's sketch just what this involves.

Traditions of medical research and regulations of the U.S. Food and Drug Administration more or less guarantee that the development of new drugs follows a set procedure. The procedure consists of two major parts: preclinical and clinical testing. When investigators think that a particular chemical compound might be useful in treating a particular disorder, they conduct animal experiments to determine how toxic it is. They use these tests to estimate the drug's therapeutic index (the ratio of a dose producing toxic effects to a dose producing desired effects). The effects of the substance on particular organs and tissues, as well as on the whole animal, are also studied. In addition, the investigators make an effort to determine the drug's potential side effects and hazards. (Does it produce liver or kidney damage? Is it carcinogenic? Does it cause heart arrhythmias?) If a drug shows promise in animal testing and its side effects are acceptable, it is then tested in humans in randomized clinical trials.

Clinical testing of the substance occurs in three phases. In Phase I, healthy human volunteers are used to determine whether the drug can be tolerated and whether its side effects are acceptable. If it causes serious "adverse events" (e.g., severe headaches, rashes, anemia, or a suppressed immune response), it may be too dangerous to give to people. The aim of a Phase I trial is to answer questions about safety and effectiveness, not to determine whether the drug is effective.

In a Phase II trial, the drug is administered to a limited number of patients who might be expected to benefit from it. If the drug produces desirable results, and causes no serious side effects, then Phase III studies are initiated.

In Phase III, the drug is administered to a larger number of patients by (typically) a larger number of clinical investigators. Such multicenter trials usually take place at teaching hospitals or in large public institutions. Often, they are sponsored by the drug's manufacturer. Successful results achieved in this phase ordinarily lead to the licensing of the drug for general use. If this happens, a Phase IV study may be conducted to gather more data about the drug and determine whether it is more effective—or perhaps more dangerous—for certain types of patients.

In the clinical part of testing, careful procedures are followed to attempt to exclude bias in the results. Investigators want their tests to be successful and patients want to get well, and either or both of these factors may influence test results. Investigators may perceive a patient as "improved" because they want or expect him to be. What is more, medications themselves may produce a "placebo effect." That is, when patients are given inactive substances (placebos), they nevertheless may show improvement. Their hopes and expectations may affect how their bodies respond and how they feel. (In a pain-relief study, patients responded better to a placebo they were told cost $2.50 than to one said to cost ten cents.)

To rule out these kinds of influences, a common procedure followed in drug testing is the "double-blind" (or "doubles masked") test design. In the classic version of this design, a certain number of patients are given the drug being tested and the remainder of the test group is given placebos. Patients are assigned to the treatment group or the placebo group in a random fashion (e.g., by the flip of a coin). Neither the investigators nor the patients are allowed to know who is receiving the drug and who is not—both are kept "blind." (A variant of the double-blind trial is a trial with "three arms": part of the test group gets placebos all of the time, part gets them only some of the time, and part gets genuine medication all of the time.)

Placebos may be no more than sugar pills. Yet, frequently, substances are prepared to produce side effects like those of the drug being tested. If, for example, the drug causes drowsiness, a placebo will be used that produces drowsiness. In this way, investigators will not be able to learn, on the basis of irrelevant observations, which patients are being given placebos.

In recent decades, clinical trials involving placebos are most often designed so that a patient is never given only a placebo to treat a serious medical problem. Rather, patients in one group are given a placebo *plus* a drug established as effective, while those in another group are given the established drug *plus* an experimental drug. The established drug represents the "standard of care," and the aim of the trial is to determine whether the new drug is more effective than the old. In this design, no patient is denied the standard of care—that is, the best available treatment.

In 2008, the FDA dropped the requirement that clinical trials compare a new drug with one recognized as the most effective one currently available. This allows pharmaceutical companies to conduct trials in which a new drug is tested against a placebo. Critics have charged that, by dropping the old requirement, the FDA is failing to provide the most effective protection for patients who volunteer to participate in studies.

The double-blind test design is employed in many kinds of clinical investigations, not just in drug testing. Thus, the testing of new vaccines and even surgeries often follows the same form. A major variation is the "single-blind" design, in which those who must evaluate the results of some treatment are kept ignorant of which patients have received it.

Randomized clinical trials are typically referred to as constituting the "gold standard" of medical research. Thus, a treatment or drug that has not gone through the process of such a trial is often regarded with suspicion or considered unproven. Some critics consider this view too extreme and point to cases in which experience over a long time has shown a treatment to be effective.

Clinical trials may also fail to establish a treatment as effective for a whole population if those who participated as subjects failed to represent the population. Thus, the subjects in a clinical trial for prostate cancer were predominately men in their fifties; a treatment shown to be effective might not be effective for men in their sixties. Similarly, if 90% of the participants were white, the results may not apply to Asians or African-Americans. Clinical trials—even ones that are well designed—don't always produce trustworthy results, unless they include very large and diverse groups of participants.

The "Informed" Part of Informed Consent

Consent, at first sight, is no more than agreement. A person consents when he or she says "yes" when asked to become a research subject. But legitimate or valid consent cannot be merely saying yes. If people are to be treated as autonomous agents, they must have the opportunity to decide whether they wish to become participants in research.

Deciding, whatever else it may be, is a process in which we reason about an issue at hand. We consider such matters as the risks of our participation, its possible advantages to ourselves and others, the risks and advantages of other alternatives that are offered to us, and our own values. In short, valid consent requires that we deliberate before we decide.

But genuine deliberation requires both information and understanding. These two requirements are the source of difficulties and controversies. After all, medical research and treatment are highly technical enterprises. They are based on complicated scientific theories that are expressed in a special vocabulary and involve unfamiliar concepts.

For this reason, some physicians and investigators have argued that it is virtually useless to provide patients with relevant scientific information about research and treatment. Patients without the proper scientific background, they argue, simply don't know what to make of the information. Not only do patients find it puzzling, but they find it frightening. Thus, some have suggested, informed consent is at worst a pointless charade and at best a polite fiction. The patient's interest is best served by allowing a physician to make the decision.

This obviously paternalistic point of view (see Chapter 1) implies, in effect, that all patients are incompetent to decide their best interest and that physicians must assume the responsibility of acting for them.

An obvious objection to this view is its assumption that, because patients lack a medical background, they cannot be given information in a form they can understand that is at least adequate to allow them to decide how they are to be treated. Thus, proponents of this view confuse difficulty of communication with impossibility of communication. While it is true that it is often hard to explain technical medical matters to a layperson, this hardly makes it legitimate to conclude that people should turn over their right to determine what is done to them to physicians. Rather, it imposes on physicians and researchers the obligation to find a way to explain medical matters to their patients.

The information provided to patients must be usable. That is, patients must understand enough about the proposed research and treatment to deliberate and reach a decision. From the standpoint of the researcher the problem here is to determine when the patient has an adequate understanding to make informed consent valid. Patients, being people, do not like to appear stupid and say they don't understand an explanation. Also, they may believe they understand an explanation when, as a matter of fact, they don't.

Until recently, little effort was made to deal with the problem of determining when a patient understands the information provided and is competent to assess it. In the last few years, researchers have investigated situations in which individuals have been asked to consent to become research subjects. Drawing upon these data, some writers have attempted to formulate criteria for assessing competency for giving informed consent. The problem is not one that even now admits of an ideal solution, but, with additional empirical investigation and philosophical analysis, the situation may improve even more.

The "Consent" Part of Informed Consent

We have talked so far as though the issue of gaining the legitimate agreement of someone to be a research subject or patient involved only providing information to an ordinary person in ordinary circumstances and then allowing the person to decide. But the matter is more complicated than this, because often either the person or the circumstances possess special features. These features can call into question the very possibility of valid consent.

It's generally agreed that, in order to be valid, consent must be voluntary. The person must of his or her "own free will" agree to become a research subject. This means that the person must be capable of acting voluntarily. That is, the person must be competent.

This is an obvious and sensible requirement accepted by all. But the difficulty lies in specifying just what it means to be competent. One answer is that a person is competent if he or she is capable of acting rationally. Because we have some idea of what it is to act rationally, this is a movement in the direction of an answer.

The problem with it, however, is that people sometimes decide to act for the sake of moral (or religious) principles in ways that may not seem reasonable. For example, someone may volunteer to be a subject in a potentially hazardous experiment because she believes the experiment holds out the promise of helping countless others. In terms of self-interest alone, such an action would not be reasonable.

Vulnerable Populations

Even in the best of circumstances, it is not always easy to determine who is competent to consent and who is not. Yet researchers and ethicists must also face the issue of how children, the mentally retarded, prisoners, and those suffering from psychiatric illnesses are to be considered with respect to consent. Should no one in any of these vulnerable populations be considered capable of giving consent? If so, then is it ever legitimate to secure the consent from some third party—from a parent or guardian—in some cases?

One possibility is simply to rule out all research that involves such people as subjects.

FDA REGULATIONS

1906   Pure Food and Drug Act: Makes it illegal to sell adulterated or mislabeled medicines.

1938   Food, Drug, and Cosmetics Act (FDCA): Requires the FDA to test drugs for safety.

The FDCA was prompted by deaths and illnesses caused by a pharmaceutical company's distribution of an elixir of acetaminophen that used diethylene glycol, an ingredient in antifreeze, as the flavoring syrup.

1962   Kefauver–Harris Amendment to the FDCA: Requires pharmaceutical companies to present data to the FDA demonstrating the effectiveness of a drug and gives the FDA the power to regulate clinical trials.

The amendment was prompted by the 1960 refusal of Frances Kelsey, an FDA physician–pharmacologist, to approve the drug Thalidomide on the basis of the safety data submitted by the manufacturer. Thalidomide had been approved in forty-two European countries as an antinausea agent and sedative and prescribed widely to pregnant women to treat morning sickness. The drug turned out to produce severe arm and leg deformities, gum anomalies, and undeveloped ear canals in children born to women who had taken the drug. The United States was spared the epidemic.

1987   FDA "compassionate use" and "expanded access" program: Allows doctors to provide drugs that have completed Phase II clinical trials to patients who are too debilitated to participate in clinical trials or too far away from a center conducting a trial.

Prompted by AIDS activists who argued that people with AIDS not in clinical trials should not be denied access to potentially useful drugs. At the time, no effective treatment for AIDS was available.

But this has the undesirable consequence of severely hampering efforts to gain the knowledge that might be of use either to the people themselves or to others with similar medical problems. Later we will consider some of the special problems that arise with children and other vulnerable groups as research subjects.

The circumstances in which research is done can also call into question the voluntariness of consent. This is particularly so with prisons, nursing homes, and mental hospitals. These are all what the sociologist Erving Goffman called "total institutions," for within then, all aspects of a person's life are connected with the social structure. People have a definite place and particular social roles in the structure. Moreover, there are social forces at work that both pressure and encourage an inmate to do what is expected of him or her.

Later in this chapter, we will discuss some of the special problems that arise in research with prisoners. Here we need only point out that gaining voluntary consent from inmates in institutions may not be possible, even in principle. If it is possible, it's necessary to specify the kinds of safeguards that must be followed to free them from the pressures resulting from the very fact that they are inmates. Those who suffer from psychiatric illnesses may be considered just as capable intellectually of giving consent, but here too safeguards to protect them from the pressures of the institution need to be specified.

In recent years, researchers have expanded the testing of new drugs and drug regimens into developing countries. The citizens of these countries are typically less well educated and less scientifically sophisticated than their counterparts in industrialized nations. They may also be more likely to trust that what they are asked to do by some medical authority will be in their best interest. Hence, securing informed consent from them that is valid presents particular difficulties.

It's important to keep in mind that ordinary patients in hospitals may also be subject to pressures that call into question the voluntariness of the consent that they give. Patients are psychologically predisposed to act in ways that please physicians. Not only do physicians possess a social role that makes them figures of authority, but an ill person feels very dependent on those who may possess the power to make her well. Thus, she will be inclined to go along with any suggestion or recommendation made by a physician.

The ordinary patient, like the inmate in an institution, needs protection from the social and psychological pressures that are exerted by circumstances. Otherwise, the voluntariness of consent will be compromised, and the patient cannot act as a free and autonomous agent.

Medical Research and Medical Therapy

Medical therapy aims at relieving the suffering of people and restoring them to health. It attempts to cure diseases, correct disorders, and bring about normal bodily functioning. Its focus is on the individual patient, and his or her welfare is its primary concern.

Medical research, by contrast, is a scientific enterprise. Its aim is to acquire a better understanding of the biochemical and physiological processes involved in human functioning. It is concerned with the effectiveness of therapies in ending disease processes and restoring functioning. But this concern is not for the patient as an individual. Rather it's directed toward establishing theories. The hope, of course, is that this theoretical understanding can be used as a basis for treating individuals. But helping a particular patient get well is not a goal of medical research.

The related but distinct aims of medical research and medical therapy are a source of conflict in human experimentation. It's not unusual for a physician to be acting both as a researcher and as a therapist. This means that although she must be concerned with the welfare of her patient, her aims must also include

acquiring data that are important to her research project. It is possible, then, that she may quite unconsciously encourage her patients to volunteer to be research subjects, provide them with inadequate information on which to base their decisions, or minimize the risks they are likely to be subject to.

The patient, for his part, may be reluctant to question his physician to acquire more information or to help him understand his role and risks in research. Also, as mentioned previously, the patient may feel pressured into volunteering for research, just because he wants to do what his physician expects of him.

Medical research is a large-scale operation in this country and affects a great many people. It has been estimated that 400,000–800,000 people a year are patients in research programs investigating the effectiveness of drugs and other therapies. Since 1980, the number of clinical studies has increased more than thirty percent, from about 3500 to 5000. Informed consent is more than an abstract moral issue.

The aims of therapy and the aims of research may also cause moral difficulties for the physician that go beyond the question of consent. This is particularly so in certain kinds of research. Let's look at some of the ethical issues more specifically.

Investigators and Financial Conflict

Paul Gelsinger's eighteen-year-old son Jesse died in a clinical trial of gene therapy. Although devastated by his loss, Paul was initially prepared to support the work of James Wilson, the project's principal investigator at the University of Pennsylvania. Then he learned that Wilson and the university were major stockholders in Genovo, the biotech company sponsoring the research, and that Wilson had sold his thirty percent share of the company for $13.5 million. Gelsinger not only stopped defending Wilson; he sued him and the university. (See the Classic Case Presentation for more details.)

Private industry now supports academic research to the tune of about $1.5 *billion* a year. One study showed that 2.8 percent of researchers in the biomedical sciences received at least some funding from private sponsors. Such sponsors are mainly pharmaceutical, medical-device, and biotech companies that expect to profit from patents based on the research.

It is not unusual, as was the case with James Wilson, for an investigator to have a financial stake in the research. The stake may be slight, or when the investigator is a major shareholder in the company sponsoring the research, it may be significant. In 2006, forty-one universities reported to the National Institutes of Health that 165 researchers had a potential financial conflict of interest with the NIH-funded research.

These figures probably represent only a small fraction of the cases in which conflicts of interest are present.

Other studies have shown that one-fifth to one-third of all doctors providing patient care in clinical trials have financial ties to drug or device makers. Some were paid to be speakers (at fees ranging from $250 to $20,000 a year), while thirty-two percent of them held positions on the company's advisory committee or board of directors.

An investigator who stands to earn a considerable sum of money from the success of the clinical trial he is conducting has a clear conflict of interest. He may (even quite unconsciously) minimize the risks of participating when seeking the consent of a volunteer. Or he may be inclined to delay reporting adverse events associated with the trial to a regulatory agency or institutional review board (IRB), to avoid having the agency or IRB halt the study. He may also be prone to overestimating the value of the treatment or device being tested.

Federal agencies and the IRBs of most institutions now require investigators to reveal whether they have a financial stake in the outcome of the research. Yet having such a stake does not automatically disqualify an investigator from conducting the research, and

IRBs work to accommodate the interest of the investigator.

A 2009 study by the Department of Health and Human Services found that ninety percent of universities relied completely on researchers themselves to decide whether the money they earned as consultants constituted a potential conflict of interest with respect to their work on projects sponsored by federal funds. Also, almost half of the universities didn't require researchers to disclose the amount of money they were paid. Yet in the absence of such information, it is hard to determine the extent of an investigator's personal stake in the outcome of the research.

Institutions at which research is funded privately, rather than by federal grants, may not require an investigator to inform potential participants that the investigator has a financial interest in the research. Further, even when investigators are required to reveal a potential conflict of interest, if they fail to do so, the consequences may consist only of a notice of violation or a scolding letter. Universities do not see it as in their interest to press researchers to avoid conflicts of interest. Even if a university is not in line to make money from particular research projects, if it puts too many restrictions on its leading investigators, the investigators may take jobs elsewhere or leave the university to start their own companies.

Because more and more investigators are acquiring a financial stake in the results of their research, we need to develop national regulations for avoiding financial conflicts of interest and effective mechanisms for enforcing the regulations. It may not be a good idea to forbid researchers to profit financially from the success of their research, but it does raise questions we must address.

Placebos and Research

As we saw earlier in the description of a typical drug experiment, placebos are often considered essential to determine the true effectiveness of the drug being tested. In practice, this means that, during all or some of the time they are being "treated," patients who are also subjects in a research program will not be receiving genuine medication. They are not, then, receiving the best available treatment for their specific condition.

This is one of the risks that a patient needs to know about before consenting to become a research subject. After all, most people become patients in order to be cured, if possible, of their ailments, not to further science or anything of the kind. The physician-as-therapist will continue to provide medical care to a patient, for under double-blind conditions the physician does not know who is being given placebos and who is not. But the physician-as-researcher will know that a certain number of people will be receiving medication that cannot be expected to help their condition. Thus, the aims of the physician who is also a researcher come into conflict.

This conflict is particularly severe in cases in which it is reasonable to believe (on the basis of animal experimentation, in vitro research, and so on) that an effective disease preventative exists, yet, to satisfy scientific rigor, tests of its effectiveness involve the giving of placebos.

This was the case with the development of a polio vaccine by Thomas Weller, John F. Enders, and Frederick C. Robbins in 1960. The initial phase of the clinical testing involved injecting 30,000 children with a substance known to be useless in the prevention of polio—a placebo injection. It was realized, statistically, that some of those children would get the disease and die from it.

Since Weller, Enders, and Robbins believed they had an effective vaccine, they can hardly be regarded as acting in the best interest of these children. As physicians they were not acting to protect the interest and well-being of the children. They did, of course, succeed in proving the safety and effectiveness of the polio vaccine. The moral question is whether they were justified in failing to provide 30,000

children with a vaccine they believed to be effective, even though it had not been tested on a wide scale with humans. That is, did they correctly resolve the conflict between their roles as researchers and their roles as physicians?

Placebos also present physician-researchers with another conflict. As we noticed in the earlier discussion, placebos are not always just "sugar pills." They often contain active ingredients that produce in patients effects that resemble those caused by the medication being tested—nervousness, vomiting, loss of appetite, and so on. This means that a patient receiving a placebo is sometimes not only failing to receive any medication for his illness, but also receiving a medication that may do him some harm. Thus, the physician committed to care for the patient and to relieve his suffering is at odds with the researcher who may be harming the patient. Do the aims of scientific research and its potential benefits to others justify treating patients in this fashion? Here is another moral question that the physician must face in particular and we must face in general.

We should not leave the topic of the use of placebos without the reminder of what was mentioned earlier—that it is possible to make use of an experimental design in research that does not require giving placebos to a control group. An investigator can compare the results of two treatment forms: a standard treatment whose effectiveness is known and a new treatment with a possible but not proven effectiveness. This is not as scientifically satisfactory as the other approach, because the researcher must do without a control group that has received no genuine treatment. But it does provide a way out of the dilemma of both providing medical care and conducting research.

This way of proceeding has associated with it another moral issue. If a clinical trial of a drug is scheduled to last for a long period of time (perhaps years) but accumulating-statistical results indicate that the drug is more effective in the treatment or prevention of a disease than the established one it is being compared with, should the trial be stopped so that all the patients in the study can gain the benefits of the test drug? Or does the informed consent of the participants warrant continuing the trial until the therapeutic value of the test drug is fully established?

The view generally accepted now is that if the evidence strongly indicates that a treatment being tested is more effective than the standard one, researchers have an obligation to discontinue the trial and offer the new treatment to those who were not receiving it.

Therapeutic and Nontherapeutic Research

We have mentioned the conflict that faces the physician who is also an investigator. But the patient who has to decide whether to consent to become a research subject is faced with a similar conflict.

Some research holds out the possibility of a direct and immediate advantage to those patients who agree to become subjects. For example, a new drug may, on the basis of limited trials, promise to be more effective in treating an illness than drugs in standard use.

Or a new surgical procedure may turn out to give better results than one that would ordinarily be used. By agreeing to participate in research involving such a drug or procedure, a patient may have a chance of gaining something more beneficial than he or she would gain otherwise.

Yet the majority of medical research projects do not offer any direct therapeutic advantages to patients who consent to be subjects. The research may eventually benefit many patients, but seldom does it bring more than usual therapeutic benefits to research participants. Ordinarily, the most that participants can expect to gain are the advantages of having the attention of physicians who are experts on their illness and receiving close observation and supervision from researchers.

Some patients don't get even this much advantage. Pharmaceutical companies may

pay physicians in private practice to conduct a study of a drug they manufacture in order to get the physician to prescribe the drug more often. Typically, in such research projects the study is not well designed, the number of participants is too small to be statistically meaningful, and the results are never published. The physician gets paid and the company gets its drug prescribed more often, but the patient is not likely to benefit. Indeed, the patient may not even get the drug that is best for her.

All these are matters an investigator ought to present to the patient as information that is relevant to the decision the patient must make. The patient must then decide whether he or she is willing to become a participant, even if there are risks involved and no special therapeutic advantages to be gained. It is in making this decision that one's moral beliefs can play a role. Some people volunteer to become research subjects without hope of reward because they believe that their action may eventually be of help to others. (See the Jesse Gelsinger Case Study on page 123.)

* * *

In the sections that follow, we will examine some problems of clinical research when special groups are its focus.

Offshore Research

In recent years, researchers have expanded the testing of new drugs and drug regimens into other countries. A 2009 study by Seth Glickman and Charles Cairns showed that, during the decade 1995–2005, almost half of Phase III clinical trials sponsored by drug companies were carried out somewhere other than the United States. The countries favored were often Eastern Europe and Russia, but studies were also conducted in Malaysia and India.

Several reasons lie behind the increase in offshore drug testing. First, in the United States it is difficult to get subjects to volunteer for clinical trials. Only half the trials sponsored by the National Cancer Institute enrolled the number of participants needed to produce statistically significant results. Second, the United States has stringent requirements to protect human subjects, and these requirements slow the testing process. The result is that drugs both take longer to test and are more expensive to test in the United States than in many other countries.

The cost of a clinical trial conducted in a major medical center in India is $1,500–$2000. By contrast, a trial conducted in the United States at a second-tier institution costs $15,000–$20,000. Testing a drug in a clinical trial is a major part of the expense of drug development. Given that the cost for developing a drug in the United States averages $800–$900 million, the incentive for drug companies to turn to overseas test sites is understandable.

However, significant ethical questions arise about offshore testing. In poorer countries, even a small amount of money can serve as an inducement for people to ignore their best interest and become a participant. The citizens of such countries are also likely to have a low level of education and scientific sophistication. They may not understand what the clinical trial of a drug requires of them and what the risks are. They may put their trust in the researcher, even though the researcher has a conflict of interest.

The countries where companies decide to conduct drug tests are not likely to have strong regulations to protect test subjects. Hence, the primary question that arises with respect to every offshore clinical trial is whether the conditions for legitimate informed consent have been satisfied. Furthermore, participants in trials may not be monitored as carefully as they are in the United States. Even very serious adverse events (e.g., kidney damage) affecting some participants may not be caught and the trial ended before others are harmed. If serious adverse events are detected, they might be ignored so that the trial can continue as planned. Participants are thus put at greater risk than they would be in a United States trial.

Such considerations are relevant to the decision that must be made by federal agencies and professional organizations in the United States about accepting the results of clinical trial conducted elsewhere. If the research was carried out in an impoverished country that lacks strong and enforced regulations to protect human subjects, should United States scientific and medical institutions accept the results without raising ethical questions about how they were obtained? If the trial doesn't satisfy regulations comparable to those of the United States, should the results be rejected as morally tainted?

This might mean that a potentially lifesaving drug shown to be effective in a trial wouldn't be available to patients who need it. A new trial would have to be conducted. Not only would that add to the cost of developing the drug, but it might be months or even years before patients could be treated with it. Many patients could die while the second trial is being conducted.

Accepting the results of an offshore drug trial without questioning whether the autonomy and safety of participants were protected also has a cost associated with it. Patients in the United States could benefit immediately from a drug proved effective in the trial, but the benefit might come as a result of exploiting the poor and ignorant in some other country. In such a case, the cost of the benefit would be a moral one.

Research Involving Children

One of the most controversial areas of all medical research has been that involving children as subjects. The Willowbrook project discussed in a Case Presentation earlier in the chapter is just one among many investigations that have drawn severe criticism and, quite often, court action.

Why Study Children at All?   The obvious question is, why should children ever be made research subjects? Children clearly lack the physical, psychological, and intellectual maturity of adults. It does not seem that they are as capable as adults of giving informed consent, because they can hardly be expected to grasp the nature of research and the possible risks to themselves.

Furthermore, because children have not yet developed their capacities, it seems wrong to subject them to risks that might alter the course of their lives for the worse. They are in a position or relative dependency, relying upon adults to provide the conditions for their existence and development. It seems almost a betrayal of trust to allow children to be subjected to treatment that is of potential harm to them.

Such considerations help explain why we typically regard research involving children with deep suspicion. It is easy to imagine children being exploited and their lives blighted by callous researchers. Some writers have been sufficiently concerned by the possibility of dangers and abuses that they have advocated an end to all research with children as subjects.

But there is another side to the coin. Biologically, children are not just small adults. Their bodies are developing, growing systems. Not only are there anatomical differences; there are also differences in metabolism and biochemistry. For example, some drugs are absorbed and metabolized more quickly in children than in adults, whereas other drugs continue to be active for a longer time. Often, some drugs produce different effects when administered to children.

Also, precisely because the bodies of children are still developing, their nutritional needs are different. Findings based on adult subjects cannot simply be extrapolated to children, any more than results based on animal studies can be extrapolated to human beings.

Further, children are prone to certain kinds of diseases (measles or mumps, for example) that either are less common in adults or occur in different forms. It is important to know the kinds of therapies that are most successful in the treatment of children afflicted with them.

Children also have problems that are not seen in adults, because with such problems they do not survive unless they are treated effectively. Various heart anomalies, for example, must be corrected to keep children alive. Thus, the development of new surgical techniques must necessarily involve children.

Finally, even familiar surgical procedures cannot be employed in a straightforward way with children. Their developing organ systems are sufficiently different that special pediatric techniques must often be devised.

For many medical purposes, children must be thought of almost as if they were wholly different organisms. Their special biological features set them apart and mark them as subjects requiring special study. To gain the kind of knowledge and understanding required for effective medical treatment of children, it is often impossible to limit research solely to adults.

Excluding Children. Failing to conduct research on children raises its own set of ethical issues. If children are excluded from investigations, then the development of pediatric medicine will be severely hindered. In general, this would mean that children would receive medical therapies that are less effective than might be possible. Also, since it is known that children differ significantly from adults in drug reactions, it seems wrong to subject children to the risks of drugs and drug dosages that have been tested only on adults.

Research involving children can also be necessary to avoid causing long-term harm to numerous people. The use of pure oxygen in the environments of prematurely born babies in the early 1940s resulted in hundreds of cases of blindness and impaired vision. It was not until a controlled study was done that retinal damage was traced to the effects of the oxygen. Had the research not been allowed, the chances are very good that the practice would have continued and thousands more infants would have been blinded.

Ethical Issues. Yet, even if we agree that not all research involving children should be forbidden, we still have to face up to the issues that such research generates. Without attempting to be complete, we can mention the following three issues as among the more prominent:

Who Is a Child? Who is to be considered a child? For infants and children in elementary school, this question is not a difficult one. But what about people in their teens? Then the line becomes hard to draw. Indeed, perhaps it is not possible to draw a line at all without being arbitrary.

The concern behind the question is with the acquisition of autonomy—of self-direction and responsibility. It is obvious on the basis of ordinary experience that people develop at different rates, and some people at sixteen are more capable of taking charge of their own lives than others are at twenty. Some teenagers are more capable of understanding the nature and hazards of a research project than are many people who are much older.

This suggests that many people who are legally children may be quite capable of giving their informed consent. Of course, many others probably are not, so that decisions about capability would have to rest on an assessment of the individual. Where medical procedures that have a purely therapeutic aim are concerned, an individual who is capable of deciding whether it is in his or her best interest should probably be the one to decide. The issue may be somewhat different when the aim is not therapy. In such cases, a better policy might be to set a lower limit on the age at which consent can be given, and those below that limit should not be permitted to consent to participate in research. The problem is, of course, what should that limit be?

Parental Consent. Can anyone else consent on behalf of a child? Parents or guardians have a duty to act for the sake of the welfare of a child under their care. In effect, they have a duty to substitute their judgment for that of the child. We generally agree to this because most often we consider the judgment of an adult more mature and informed than a child's. And because the responsibility for care rests with the adult, we customarily recognize that the adult has a right to decide. It is almost as though the adult's autonomy is being shared with the

child—almost as though the child were an extension of the adult.

Society and its courts have recognized limits on the power of adults to decide for children. When it seems that the adult is acting in an irresponsible or unreasonable manner, society steps in to act as a protector of the child's right to be cared for. Thus, courts have ordered that lifesaving procedures or blood transfusions be performed on children even when their parents or guardians have decided against it. The criterion used in such judgments is "the best interest of the child."

What sort of limits should govern a parent's or guardian's decision to allow a child to become a research subject? Is it reasonable to believe that if a parent would allow herself to be the subject of research, then it is also right for her to consent to her child's becoming a subject? Or should something more be required before consent for a child's participation can be considered legitimate?

Therapeutic Benefits. Should children be allowed to be subjects of research that does not offer them a chance of direct therapeutic benefits? Perhaps the "something more" that parents or guardians ought to require before consenting on behalf of a child is the genuine possibility that the research will bring the child direct benefits. This would be in accordance with a parent's duty to seek the welfare of the child. It is also a way of recognizing that the parent's autonomy is not identical with that of the child: one may have the right to take a risk oneself without having the right to impose the risk on someone else.

This seems like a reasonable limitation, and it has been advocated by some writers. Yet there are difficulties with the position. Some research that is virtually free from risk (coordination tests, for example) might be stopped because of its lack of a "direct therapeutic value."

More important, however, much research promising immense long-term benefits would have to be halted. Research frequently involves the withholding of accepted therapies without any guarantee that what is used in their place will be as effective. Sometimes the withholding of accepted treatment is beneficial. Thus, as it turned out, in the research on the incidence of blindness in premature infants in the 1940s, premature infants who were not kept in a pure oxygen environment were better off than those who received ordinary treatment.

But no one could know this in advance, and such research as this is, at best, ambiguous as to the promise of direct therapy. Sheer ignorance imposes restrictions. Yet if the experiment had not been done, the standard treatment would have continued with its ordinary course of (statistically) disastrous results. Here, at least, there was the possibility of better results from the experimental treatment.

But in research that involves the substitution of placebos for medications or vaccines that are acknowledged to be effective, it is known in advance that some children will not receive medical care considered to be the best. A child who is a subject in such research is then put in a situation in which he or she is subjected to a definite hazard. The limitation on consent that we are considering would rule out such research. But the consequence of doing this would be to restrict the development of new and potentially more effective medications and treatment techniques. That is, future generations of children would be deprived of at least some possible medical advances.

These, then, are some of the issues that we have to face in arriving at a view of the role of children in research. Perhaps the greatest threat to children, however, has to do with social organization. Children, like prisoners, are often grouped together in institutions (schools, orphanages, detention centers, and so on) and are attractive targets for clinical investigators because they inhabit a limited and relatively controlled environment, can be made to follow orders, and do not ask too many questions that have to be answered. It is a misimpression to see researchers in such situations as "victimizing" children, but at the same time, careful

controls are needed to see that research involving children is legitimate and carried out in a morally satisfactory way.

Guidelines. In response to some of these difficulties, the Department of Health and Human Services has issued guidelines designed specifically to protect children as research subjects. First, for children to become participants, permission must be obtained from parents or guardian and children must give their "assent." Second, an Institutional Review Board is assigned the responsibility of considering the "ages, maturity, and psychological states" of the children and determining whether they are capable of assenting. (A failure to object cannot be construed as assent.)

Third, children who are wards of the state or of an institution can become participants only if the research relates to their status as wards or takes place in circumstances in which the majority of subjects are not wards. Each child must also be supplied with an "advocate" to represent her or his interest.

Research Involving Prisoners

Prisoners are in some respects social outcasts. They have been found guilty of breaking the laws of society and, as a consequence, are removed from it. Stigmatized and isolated, prisoners in the relatively recent past were sometimes thought of as less than human. It seemed only reasonable that such depraved and corrupt creatures should be used as the subjects of experiments that might bring benefits to the members of the society that they wronged. Indeed, it seemed not only reasonable, but fitting.

Accordingly, in the early part of the twentieth century, tropical medicine expert Richard P. Strong obtained permission from the governor of the Philippines to inoculate a number of condemned criminals with plague bacillus. The prisoners were not asked for their consent, but they were rewarded by being provided with cigarettes and cigars.

Episodes of this sort were relatively common during the late nineteenth and early twentieth centuries. But as theories about the nature of crime and criminals changed, it became standard practice to use only volunteers and to secure the consent of the prisoners themselves.

In the 1940s, for example, the University of Chicago infected more than four hundred prisoners with malaria in an attempt to discover new drugs to treat and prevent the disease. A committee set up by the governor of Illinois recommended that potential volunteers be informed of the risks, be permitted to refuse without fear of such reprisals as withdrawal of privileges, and be protected from unnecessary suffering. The committee suggested also that volunteering to be a subject in a medical experiment is a form of good conduct that should be taken into account in deciding whether a prisoner should be paroled or have his sentence reduced.

But the committee also called attention to a problem of great moral significance. They pointed out that, if a prisoner's motive for volunteering is the wish to contribute to human welfare, then a reduction in his sentence would be a reward. But if his motive is to obtain a reduction in sentence, then the possibility of obtaining one is really a form of duress. In this case, the prisoner cannot be regarded as making a free decision. The issue of duress, or "undue influence," as it is called in law, is central to the question of deciding whether and under what conditions valid informed consent can be obtained for research involving prisoners. Some ethicists have argued that, to avoid undue influence, prisoners should never be promised any substantial advantages for volunteering to be research subjects. If they volunteer, they should do so for primarily moral or humane reasons.

Others have claimed that becoming research subjects offers prisoners personal advantages that they should not be denied. For example, participation in a research project frees them from the boredom of prison life, gives them an opportunity to increase their feelings of self-worth, and allows them to exercise their autonomy as moral agents. It has been argued, in fact, that prisoners have a right to participate in research if the opportunity is offered to them and they wish to do so. To forbid the use of prisoners as research subjects is thus to deny to them, without adequate grounds, a right that all human beings possess. As a denial of their basic autonomy—of their right to take risks and control their own bodies—not allowing them to be subjects might constitute a form of cruel and unusual punishment.

By contrast, it can also be argued that prisoners do not deserve to be allowed to exercise such autonomy. Because they have been sentenced for crimes, they should be deprived of the right to volunteer to be research subjects: that right belongs to free citizens. Being deprived of the right to act autonomously is part of their punishment. This is basically the position taken by the House of Delegates of the American Medical Association. The delegates passed a resolution in 1952 expressing disapproval of the use as research subjects of people convicted of "murder, rape, arson, kidnapping, treason, and other heinous crimes."

A more worrisome consideration is the question of whether prisoners can be sufficiently free of undue influence or duress to make their consent legitimate. As we mentioned earlier, prisons are total institutions and the institutional framework itself puts pressures on people to do what is desired or expected of them. There need not be, then, either promises of rewards (such as reduced sentences) or overt threats (such as withdrawal of ordinary privileges) for coercion to be present. That people may volunteer to relieve boredom is itself an indication that they may be acting under duress. That "good conduct" is a factor in deciding whether to grant parole may function as another source of pressure.

The problem presented by prisoners is fundamentally the same as that presented by inmates in other institutions, such as nursing homes and mental hospitals. In these cases, once it has been determined that potential subjects are mentally competent to give consent, then it must also be decided whether the institutional arrangements allow the consent to be "free and voluntary."

To protect prisoners from exploitation, the FDA instituted stringent regulations governing research conducted in prisons. The regulations constituted such barriers that most academic investigators and pharmaceutical companies essentially stopped using prisoners as research subjects. In 2006, the National Institute of Medicine issued a report that aimed to protect prisoners as research subjects, while also making it easier for prisoners to participate in research that might benefit them. Critics of the report charged that the prison environment alone makes it impossible for inmates to act autonomously and provide informed consent. (See "Social Context: Prisoners as Test Subjects?" at the end of this Briefing Session.)

Research Involving the Poor

In the eighteenth century, Princess Caroline of England requested the use of six "charity children" as subjects in the smallpox vaccination experiments she was directing. Then, and well into the twentieth century, charity cases, like prisoners, were regarded by some medical researchers as prime research subjects.

A horrible example of medical research involving the poor is the Tuskegee Syphilis Study that was conducted under the auspices of the U.S. Department of Public Health (USPH). From 1932 to 1970, a number of black males suffering from the later stages of syphilis were examined at regular intervals to determine the course their disease was taking. The men in the study were poor and uneducated and believed that they were receiving proper medical care from the state and local public health clinics.

As a matter of fact, they were given either no treatment or inadequate treatment, and at least forty of them died as a result of factors connected with their disease. Their consent was never obtained, and the nature of the study, its risks, and the alternatives open to them were never explained.

It was known when the study began that those with untreated syphilis have a higher death rate than those whose condition is treated, and although the study was started before the advent of penicillin (which is highly effective against syphilis), other drugs were available but were not used in ways to produce the best results. When penicillin became generally available, it still was not used.

The Tuskegee Study clearly violated the Nuremberg Code, but it was not stopped even after the War Crimes trials. It was reviewed in 1969 by a USPH ad hoc committee, and it was decided that the study should be phased out in 1970. The reasons for ending the experiment were not moral ones. Rather, it was believed nothing much of scientific value was to be gained by continuing the work. In 1973, a United States Public Health Department Ad Hoc Advisory Panel, which had been established as a result of public and congressional pressure to review the Tuskegee Study, presented its final report. It condemned the study both on moral grounds and because of its lack of worth and rigor. (See the Case Presentation "Bad Blood, Bad Faith" in Chapter 4 for more details.)

No one today argues that disadvantaged people ought to be made subjects of research simply because of their social or economic status. The "back wards" in hospitals whose poor patients once served as a source of research subjects have mostly disappeared as a result of such programs as Medicare and Medicaid. Each person is now entitled to his or her own physician and is not under the general care of the state or of a private charity.

Yet many research projects continue to be based in large public or municipal hospitals. And such hospitals have a higher percentage of disadvantaged people as patients than do private institutions. For this reason, such people are still more likely to become research subjects than are the educated and wealthy. If society continues to accept this state of affairs, special precautions must be taken to see to it that those who volunteer to become research subjects are genuinely informed and free in their decisions.

Research Involving the Terminally Ill

People who have been diagnosed with a terminal illness characteristically experience overwhelming feelings of despair. Within a few days or weeks, some are able to acknowledge and accept the situation, but others are driven to desperation by the imminent prospect of their death.

When they learn that conventional therapies offer little hope of prolonging their lives, they vow to fight their disease by other means. They look for hope in a situation that seems hopeless, and with the encouragement of family and friends, they seek new therapies.

Some turn to quack medicine or suspect remedies, but others seek out clinical trials of new drugs for their diseases. They seek acceptance into trials from the hospitals and medical centers where they are being conducted.

Critics of the policy of accepting terminally ill patients into clinical trials base their objections on the vulnerability of patients. Most often, critics charge, such patients are not sufficiently aware of what they are getting into, nor are they aware of how little personal payoff they may reasonably expect to receive from an experimental therapy.

To be enrolled in a drug trial, patients must satisfy the study's research protocol. They must meet diagnostic criteria for having a particular disease, or their disease must be at a certain stage in its natural history. Or perhaps the patients must not have received certain treatments, such as radiation, or must not have been taking a particular drug for several weeks. Perhaps the patients must not have signs of liver damage or kidney disease. Some of the criteria may require that patients be tested. The testing may involve only drawing blood for analysis, but it may also require submitting to painful and potentially harmful surgical procedures to biopsy tissue.

A patient who qualifies for admission to a study may still have a difficult time ahead. If the study is at an institution that is hundreds, even thousands, of miles away, the patient must either move nearer or travel to the institution regularly. In either case, much expense and inconvenience may be involved.

Critics also charge that patients may have unreasonable expectations about the effectiveness of experimental therapies. Patients may believe, for example, that a drug has at least some record of success, but in fact the therapeutic benefits of the drug may be uncertain at best. Indeed, in the initial stage of drug testing with human subjects, Phase I trials, the aim is not to determine the therapeutic effectiveness of the drug, but to determine such matters as its toxicity, rate of metabolism, or most effective mode of administration.

The chance that a drug under investigation will actually prolong the life of a patient in the final stages of a terminal illness is small. One study reviewed the results of forty-two preliminary reports on drugs used to treat colon cancer and thirty-three on drugs used to treat non-small-cell lung cancer, but only one drug was found to have therapeutic effects.

Furthermore, critics charge, patients may not realize the extent to which an experimental drug may turn out to cause unpleasant, painful, or harmful side effects. Patients may suffer nausea, vomiting, chills, fevers, neurological damage, or lowered immunological functioning.

Such effects may not even be known to the investigators, so they cannot inform patients about them at the time consent is sought. The last weeks or months of terminally ill patients may thus be spent more painfully than if they had simply waited for death, and in fact, patients may even shorten their lives by becoming subjects in a study.

As a sort of final disappointment, critics point out, the study that a dying patient was counting on to give her a last chance at lengthening her life might drop her as a subject. The aim of a clinical trial of a new drug, for example, is to discover such medically important characteristics of the drug as its side effects, what constitutes an effective dosage, and whether the drug has therapeutic benefits. Patients in the study are sources of data, and if a patient who is receiving no therapeutic benefit from a drug turns out to be of no value to the study, she may be dropped from it. Dying patients may be hit particularly hard by such a rejection.

In the view of critics, the desperation of terminally ill patients makes them too vulnerable to be able to give meaningful consent to participate in experimental trials. Even if they are fairly informed that a drug trial will offer them only a remote possibility of prolonging their lives, they are under such pressure from their illness that, in a sense, they are not free to consent. Patients and their families may be so frightened and emotionally distraught that they hear only what they want to hear about an experimental therapy. They may be unable to grasp the fact that the therapy probably will not benefit them and may even harm them.

Opponents of enrolling terminally ill patients in clinical investigations charge that the patients are often treated as though they are only a research resource, a pool from which subjects can be selected for whatever testing needs to be done. That people are dying does not mean that it is justifiable to exploit them, and the only way to avoid this is to exclude them as eligible candidates for research subjects.

While no one advocates the exploitation of terminally ill people, most observers believe it is morally legitimate to include them in clinical trials. The patients themselves may have something to gain. The very act of trying a new drug might make some patients feel better, even if it is only a placebo effect. Also, patients and their families can feel that they are genuinely doing everything possible to improve the patient's health. Moreover, the drug might be of some therapeutic benefit to the patient, even

if the chance of its prolonging the patient's life is remote.

Furthermore, defenders of the policy hold, allowing dying patients to participate in research is to recognize their status as autonomous persons, while to exclude them as candidates for research subjects is to deny them that status.

Finally, defenders claim, in connection with their status as moral agents, dying patients deserve to be given a chance to do something for others. In fact, when dying patients are recruited or seek to enroll in a study, instead of stressing the possible therapeutic benefit they might secure, the experimenter should emphasize the contribution that patients' participation might make to helping others in the future.

To put this last point in perspective, consider the responses of twenty-seven cancer patients enrolled in a Phase I clinical trial who were interviewed by Mark Siegler and his colleagues at the University of Chicago. Eighty-five percent of the patients said they had agreed to participate because they hoped for therapeutic benefits, eleven percent enrolled at the suggestion of their physicians, and four percent did so at the urging of their families. No one reported enrolling out of a desire to help others.

Research Involving Fetuses

In 1975, legal charges were brought against several physicians in Boston. They had injected antibiotics into living fetuses that were scheduled to be aborted. The aim of the research was to determine by autopsy, after the death of the fetuses, how much of the drug got into the fetal tissues.

Such information is considered to be of prime importance because it increases our knowledge of how to provide medical treatment for a fetus still developing in its mother's womb. It also helps to determine ways in which drugs taken by a pregnant woman may affect a fetus and so points the way toward improved prenatal care.

Other kinds of research involving the fetus also promise to provide important knowledge. Effective vaccines for preventing viral diseases, techniques for treating children with defective immune-system reactions, and hormonal measurements that indicate the status of the developing fetus are just some of the potential advances that are partially dependent on fetal research.

But a number of moral questions arise in connection with such research. Even assuming that a pregnant woman consents to allow the fetus she is carrying to be injected with drugs prior to abortion, is such research ethical? Does the fact that the fetus is going to be aborted alter the moral situation in any way? For example, prior to abortion, should the fetus be treated with the same respect and concern for its well-being as a fetus that is not scheduled for abortion?

After the fetus is aborted, if it is viable—if it can live separated from the mother—then we seem to be under an obligation to protect its life. But what if a prenatal experiment threatens its viability? The expectation in abortion is that the fetus will not be viable, but this is not in fact always the case. Does this mean that it is wrong to do anything before abortion to threaten the life of the fetus or reduce its chance for life, even though we do not expect it to live?

These are difficult questions to answer without first settling the question of whether the fetus is to be considered a person. (See the discussion of this issue in the Briefing Session in Chapter 9.) If the fetus is a person, then it is entitled to the same moral considerations that we extend to other persons. If we decide to take its life, if abortion is considered to be at least sometimes legitimate, then we must be prepared to offer justification. Similarly, if we are to perform experiments on a fetus, even one expected to die, then we must also be prepared to offer justification. Whether the importance of the research is adequate justification is a matter that currently remains to be settled.

If the fetus is not a person, then the question of fetal experimentation becomes less important

morally. Because, however, the fetus may be regarded as a potential person, we may still believe it is necessary to treat it with consideration and respect. The burden of justification may be somewhat less weighty, but it may still be there.

Let us assume that the fetus is aborted and is apparently not viable. Typically, before such a fetus dies, its heart beats and its lungs function. Is it morally permissible to conduct research on the fetus before its death? The knowledge that can be gained, particularly of lung functions, can be used to help save the lives of premature infants, and the fetus is virtually certain of dying, whether or not it is made a subject of research.

After the death of a fetus that is either deliberately or spontaneously aborted, are there any moral restraints on what is done with the remains? It is possible to culture fetal tissues and use them for research purposes.

These tissues might, in fact, be commercially grown and distributed by biological supply companies in the way that a variety of animal tissues are now dealt with. Exactly when a fetus can be considered to be dead so that its tissues and organs are available for experimentation, even assuming that one approves of their use in this manner, is itself an unsettled question.

Scientists have long been concerned about federal guidelines and state laws regulating fetal research. Most investigators feel that they are forced to operate under such rigid restrictions that research is slowed and, in some instances, even prohibited. Everyone agrees, however, that fetal research involves important moral and social issues. (See Chapter 9 for more detail.)

Fetal research has to be considered a part of human research. Not only are some fetuses born alive even when deliberately aborted, but all possess certain human characteristics and potentialities. But who should give approval to what is done with the fetus? Who should be responsible for consent?

To some it seems peculiar to say that a woman who has decided to have an abortion is also the one who should consent to research involving the aborted fetus. It can be argued that in deciding to have an abortion she has renounced all interest and responsibility with respect to the fetus. Yet, if the fetus does live, we would consider her, at least in part, legally and morally responsible for seeing to its continued well-being.

But if the woman (or the parents) is the one who must give consent for fetal experimentation, are there limits to what she can consent to on behalf of the fetus?

With this question, we are back where we began. It is obvious that fetal research raises both moral and social issues. We need to decide, then, what is right as a matter of personal conduct and what is right as a matter of social policy. At the moment, issues in each of these areas remain highly controversial.

Research Involving Animals

The seventeenth-century philosopher René Descartes doubted whether animals experience pain. They may act as if they are in pain, but perhaps they are only complicated pieces of clockwork designed to act that way. Humans feel pain, but then, unlike animals, humans have a "soul" that gives them the capacity to reason, be self-conscious, and experience emotions. The *bodies* of humans are pieces of machinery, but the *mental states* that occur within the bodies are not.

If the view of animals represented by Descartes and others in the mechanistic tradition he initiated is correct, we need to have no moral concern about the use of animals in research. Animals of whatever species have the status of any other piece of delicate and often expensive lab equipment. They may be used in any way for any purpose.

Here are some of the ways in which animals are being or have been used in biomedical research:

- A standard test for determining the toxicity of drugs or chemicals is the "lethal dose-50" (LD-50) test. The LD-50 is the amount of a substance that, when administered to a group of experimental animals, will kill fifty percent of them.

- The Draize test, once widely used in the cosmetics industry, involves dripping a chemical substance into the lidless eyes of rabbits to determine its potential to cause eye damage.

- The effects of cigarette smoking were investigated by a series of experiments using beagles with tubes inserted into holes cut into their tracheas so that, when breathing, they were forced to inhale cigarette smoke. The dogs were then "sacrificed" and autopsied to look for significant changes in cells and tissues.

- Surgical procedures are both developed and acquired by using animals as experimental subjects. Surgical residents spend much time in "dog labs" learning to perform standard surgical procedures on live dogs. Limbs may be deliberately broken and organs damaged or destroyed to test the usefulness of surgical repair techniques.

- A traditional medical-school demonstration consisted in exsanguinating (bleeding to death) a dog to illustrate the circulation of the blood. High school and college biology courses sometimes require that students destroy the brains of frogs with long needles (pithing) and then dissect the frogs to learn about physiological processes.

- Chimpanzees and other primates have served as experimental subjects for the study of the induction and treatment of infectious diseases. Perfectly healthy chimps and monkeys have been inoculated with viruses resembling the AIDS virus; then the course of the resulting diseases is studied.

A list of the ways in which animals are used would include virtually all basic biomedical research. The discovery of an "animal model" of a disease typically signals a significant advancement in research. It means that the disease can be studied in ways it cannot be in humans. The assumption is that animals can be subjected to experimental conditions and treatments that humans cannot be subjected to without violating basic moral principles.

Is the assumption that we have no moral obligation toward animals warranted? Certainly the crude "animal machine" view of Descartes has been rejected, and no one is prepared to argue that no nonhuman animal can experience pain.

Exactly which animals have the capacity for suffering is a matter of dispute. Mammals undoubtedly do, and vertebrates in general seem to experience pain, but what about insects, worms, lobsters, and clams? Is the identification of endorphins, naturally occurring substances associated with pain relief in humans, adequate grounds for saying that an organism that produces endorphins must experience pain?

Once it is acknowledged that at least some animals can suffer, most philosophers agree that we have some moral responsibility with respect to them. At the least, some (like W. D. Ross) say that, since we have a prima facie duty not to cause unnecessary suffering, we should not inflict needless pain on animals.

This does not necessarily mean that biomedical research should discontinue the use of animals. Strictly construed, it means only that the animals should be treated in a humane way. For example, surgical techniques should be practiced only on dogs that have been anesthetized. Understood in this way, the principle raises no objection to humanely conducted animal research, even if its purpose is relatively trivial.

Philosophers like Kant and most of those in the natural law tradition would deny that we have any duties to animals at all. The only proper objects of duty are rational agents; unless we are prepared to argue that animals are rational, we have to refuse them the status of moral persons. We might treat animals humanely because we are magnanimous, but they are not in a position to lay claims against us. Animals have no rights.

Some contemporary philosophers (Tom Regan, in particular) have argued that, although animals are not rational agents, they have preferences. This gives them an autonomy that makes them "moral patients." Like humans, animals possess the right to respectful treatment, and this entails that they not be treated only as a means to some other end. They are ends in themselves, and this intrinsic worth makes it wrong to use them as subjects in research, even when alternatives to animal research are not available.

Contrary to Regan, a number of philosophers have taken a utilitarian approach to the issue of animal experimentation. Some (like Peter Singer) have argued that, although animals cannot be said to have rights, they have interests. If we recognize that the interests of humans are deserving of consideration, then so, too, are the interests of nonhuman animals. Hence, we can recognize that animals have inherent worth without assigning them rights, but this does not mean that we must treat them exactly as we treat humans.

Most people, whether utilitarians or not, argue that at least some forms of animal experimentation can be justified by the benefits produced. After all, they point out, the understanding of biological processes we have acquired since the time of Aristotle has been heavily dependent on animal experimentation. This understanding has given us insights into the causes and processes of diseases, and, most important, it has put us in a position to invent and test new therapies and modes of prevention.

Without animal experimentation, the identification of the role played by insulin, the development of the polio vaccine, and the perfection of hundreds of major surgical techniques surely would not have been possible. The list could be extended to include virtually every accomplishment of medicine and surgery. Countless millions of human lives have been saved by using the knowledge and understanding gained from animal studies.

Animals, too, have benefited from the theoretical and practical knowledge of research. An understanding of nutritional needs has led to healthier domestic animals, and an understanding of environmental needs has produced a movement to protect and preserve many kinds of wild animals. At the conceptual and scientific levels, veterinary medicine is not really distinct from human medicine. The same sorts of surgical procedures, medicines, and vaccines that benefit the human population also benefit many other species.

However, even from a broadly utilitarian perspective, accepting the general principle that the results justify the practice does not mean that every experiment with animals is warranted. Some experiments might be trivial, unnecessary, or poorly designed. Others might hold no promise of yielding the kind or amount of knowledge sufficient to justify causing the animal subjects to suffer pain and death.

Furthermore, the utilitarian approach supports (as does a rights view like Regan's) looking for an alternative to animal experimentation. If good results can be obtained, for example, by conducting experiments with cell cultures (in vitro), rather than with whole organisms (in vivo), then in vitro experiments are to be preferred. However, if alternatives to animal testing are not available and if the benefits secured promise to outweigh the cost, animal testing may be morally legitimate.

The utilitarian justification faces what some writers see as a major difficulty. It is one posed by the fact that animals like chimpanzees and even dogs and pigs can be shown to possess mental abilities superior to those of humans suffering from severe brain damage and retardation. If experiments on mammals are justifiable by appealing to the benefits, then why aren't experiments on humans with serious mental impairments equally justified? Indeed, shouldn't we experiment on a human in a chronic vegetative state, rather than on a healthy and alert dog?

The use made of animals in biomedical research is a significant issue, but it is no more than one aspect of the general philosophical question about the status of animals. Do animals have rights? If so, what grounds can be offered for them? Do animals have a right to coexist with humans? Do animals have a right to be free? Is it wrong to eat animals or use products made from their remains? These questions and many others like them are now being given the most careful scrutiny they have received since the nineteenth century. How they are answered will do much to shape the character both of medical research and of our society.

Women and Medical Research

Critics have charged that medical research has traditionally failed to include women as experimental subjects, even when women might also stand to benefit from the results. Most strikingly, a study showing the effectiveness of small doses of aspirin in reducing the risk of heart attack included 2201 subjects—all male. The relevance of the study to women is in doubt, but the need to include women in such studies is clear from the fact that, although more men than women die of heart disease, after women reach menopause the difference in mortality rates between genders becomes much smaller.

Until recently, studies of the therapeutic effectiveness of drugs characteristically included only males. Although the effects of many drugs are the same for women as for men, this is not always true. Hormonal differences may alter drug reactions, so conclusions based on the reactions of men may be misleading when applied to women.

In the view of critics, the traditionally male-dominated research establishment has been responsible for perpetuating an unacceptable state of affairs. To change the situation so that both women and men are included in studies adds to their costs. By introducing gender as a variable, a study must include more subjects in order to get the degree of statistical reliability that could be achieved with fewer subjects of the same gender. However, such studies have the additional value of yielding results known to be applicable to women.

That this issue is a matter of social fairness is obvious, but its connection with informed consent is less direct. As we mentioned in connection with prisoners, not allowing someone to consent may be viewed as treating that person as having less worth than someone who is allowed to consent. From this perspective, then, women have traditionally been denied the opportunity to be full persons in the moral sense. They have not been able to exercise their autonomy in ways permitted to men. Of course, they have also not been permitted to gain benefits that might be associated with the research projects from which they have been excluded. (For more details on women and medical research, see Chapter 4, "Race, Gender, and Medicine.")

Summary

There are other areas of medical experimentation that present special forms of moral problems. We have not discussed, for example, research involving military personnel or college and university students. Moreover, we mentioned only a few of the special difficulties presented by the mentally retarded, psychiatric patients, and old people confined to institutions.

We have, however, raised such a multiplicity of questions about consent and human research that it is perhaps worthwhile to attempt to restate some of the basic issues in a general form.

Basic Issues Three issues are particularly noteworthy:

1. Who is competent to consent? (Are children? Are mental patients? If a person is not competent, who—if anyone—should have the power to consent for him or

her?) Given that animals have no power to consent, is research involving them legitimate?

2. When is consent voluntary? (Is any institutionalized person in a position to offer free consent? How can even hospitalized patients be made free of pressures to consent?)

3. When are information and understanding adequate for genuine decision making? (Can complicated medical information ever be adequately explained to laypeople? Should we attempt to devise tests for understanding?)

Standards Although we have concentrated on the matter of consent in research, there are other morally relevant matters connected with research that we have not discussed. These often relate to research standards. Among them are the following:

1. Is the research of sufficient scientific and medical worth to justify the human risk involved? Research that involves trivial aims or that is unnecessary (when, for example, it merely serves to confirm what is already well established) cannot be used to justify causing any threat to human well-being.

2. Can the knowledge sought be obtained without human clinical research? Can it be obtained without animal experimentation?

3. Have animal (and other) studies been done to minimize as far as is possible the risk to human subjects? A great deal can be learned about the effects of drugs, for example, by using "animal models," and the knowledge gained can be used to minimize the hazards in human trials. (Ethical issues involving animals in research may also be called into question.)

4. Does the design of the research meet accepted scientific standards? Sloppy research that is scientifically worthless means that people have been subjected to

risks for no legitimate purpose and that animals have been harmed or sacrificed needlessly.

5. Do the investigators have the proper medical or scientific background to conduct the research effectively?

6. Is the research designed to minimize the risks and suffering of the participants? As we noted earlier, it is sometimes possible to test new drugs without using placebos. Thus, people in need of medication are not forced to be without treatment for their condition.

7. Have the aims and the design of the research and the qualifications of the investigators been reviewed by a group or committee that is competent to judge them? Such "peer review" is intended to ensure that only research that is worthwhile and that meets accepted scientific standards is conducted. And although such review groups can fail to do their job properly, as they apparently did in the Tuskegee Syphilis Study, they are still necessary instruments of control.

Most writers on experimentation would agree that these are among the questions that must be answered satisfactorily before research involving human subjects is morally acceptable. Obviously, however, a patient who is asked to give his or her consent is in no position to judge whether the research project meets the standards implied by these questions. For this reason, it is important that there be social policies and practices governing research. Everyone should be confident that a research project is, in general, a legitimate one before having to decide whether to volunteer to become a participant.

Special problems are involved in seeing to it that these questions are properly answered. It is enough for our purposes, however, merely to notice that the character of the research and the manner in which it is to be performed are factors that are relevant to determining the moral legitimacy of experimentation involving human subjects.

Ethical Theories: Medical Research and Informed Consent

We have raised too many issues in too many areas of experimentation to discuss how each of several ethical theories might apply to them all. We must limit ourselves to considering a few suggestions about the general issues of human experimentation and informed consent.

Utilitarianism

Utilitarianism's principle of utility tells us, in effect, to choose those actions which will produce the greatest amount of benefit. Utilitarianism must approve human research in general, since there are cases in which the sacrifices of a few bring great benefits to many. We might, for example, design our social policies to make it worthwhile for people to volunteer for experiments with the view that, if people are paid to take risks and are compensated for their suffering or for any damage done to them during the course of a research project, then the society as a whole might benefit.

The principle of utility also tells us to design experiments to minimize suffering and the chance of harm. Further, it forbids us to do research of an unnecessary or trivial kind—research that is not worth its cost in either human or economic resources.

As to the matter of informed consent, utilitarianism does not seem to require it. If more social good is to be gained by making people research subjects without securing their agreement, then this is morally legitimate. It is not, of course, necessarily the best procedure to follow. A system of rewards to induce volunteers might be more likely to lead to an increase in general happiness. Furthermore, the principle of utility suggests that the best research subjects would be "less valuable" members of the society, such as the mentally retarded, the habitual criminal, or the dying. This, again, is not a necessary consequence of utilitarianism, although it is a possible one. If the recognition of rights and dignity would produce a better society in general, then a utilitarian would also say that they must be taken into account in experimentation with human beings.

For utilitarianism, that individual is competent to give consent who can balance benefits and risks and decide what course of action is best for him or her. Thus, if informed consent is taken to be a requirement supported by the principle of utility, those who are mentally ill or retarded or senile have to be excluded from the class of potential experimental subjects. Furthermore, investigators must provide enough relevant information to allow competent people to make a meaningful decision about what is likely to serve their own interests the most.

Kant

For Kant, an individual capable of giving consent is one who is rational and autonomous. Kant's principles would thus also rule out as research subjects people who are not able to understand experimental procedures, aims, risks, and benefits. People may volunteer for clinical trials if they expect them to be of therapeutic benefit to themselves, or they may act out of duty and volunteer, thus discharging their imperfect obligation to advance knowledge or to improve human life.

Yet, for Kant, there are limits to the risks that one should take. We have a duty to preserve our lives, so no one should agree to become a subject in an experiment in which the likelihood of death is great. In addition, no one should subject himself to research in which there is considerable risk that his capacity for rational thought and autonomy will be destroyed. Indeed, Kant's principles appear to require us to regard as morally illegitimate those experiments which seriously threaten the lives or rationality of their subjects. Not only should we not subject ourselves to them, but we should not subject others to them.

Kant's principles also rule out as potential research participants those who are not in a position to act voluntarily, that is, those who cannot exercise their autonomy. This makes it important to determine, from a Kantian point of view, whether children and institutionalized people (including prisoners) can be regarded as free agents capable of moral choice. Also, as in the case of abortion, the status of the fetus must be determined. If the fetus is not a person, then fetal experimentation presents no particular moral problems. But if the fetus is a person, then we must accord it a moral status and act for its sake and not for the sake of knowledge or for others.

Kant's view of people as autonomous rational beings requires that informed consent be obtained for both medical treatment and research. We cannot be forced to accept treatment for "our own good," nor can we be turned into research subjects for "the good of others." We must always be treated as ends and never as means only. To be treated in this way requires that others never deliberately deceive us, no matter how good their intentions. In short, we have a right to be told what we are getting into so that we can decide whether we want to go through with it or not.

Ross

Ross's theory imposes on researchers prima facie duties to patients that are similar to Kant's requirements. The nature of people as autonomous moral agents requires that their informed consent be obtained. Researchers ought not to deceive their subjects, and protocols should be designed in ways in which suffering and the risk of injury or death are minimized.

These are all prima facie duties, of course, and it is possible to imagine situations in which other duties might take precedence over them.

In general, however, Ross, like Kant, tells us that human research cannot be based on what is useful; it must be based on what is right. Ross's principles, like Kant's, do not tell us, however, how we are to deal with such special problems as research involving children or prisoners.

Natural Law

The principle of double effect and the principle of totality, which are based on the natural law theory of morality, have specific applications to experimentation. (See Part V, "Foundations of Bioethics.") Because we hold our bodies in trust, we are responsible for assessing the degree of risk to which we might be put if we agree to become research subjects. Thus, others have an obligation to supply us with the information that we need in order to make our decision. If we decide to give our consent, it must be given freely and not be the consequence of deception or coercion.

If available evidence shows that a sick person may gain benefits from participating in a research project, then the research is justified. But if the evidence shows that the benefits may be slight or if the chance of serious injury or death is relatively great, then the research is not justified.

In general, the likelihood of a person's benefiting from becoming a participant must exceed the danger of the person's suffering greater losses. The four requirements that govern the application of the principle of double effect determine what is and what is not an allowable experiment. (See Part V, "Foundations of Bioethics," for a discussion of these requirements.)

People can volunteer for experiments from which they expect no direct benefits. The good they seek in doing so is not their own good but the good of others. But there are limits to what they can subject themselves to. A dying patient, for example, cannot be made the subject of a useless or trivial experiment. The probable value of the knowledge to be gained must balance the risk and suffering the patient is subjected to, and there must be no likelihood that the experiment will seriously injure or kill the patient.

These same restrictions also apply to experiments involving healthy people. The principle of totality forbids a healthy person to submit to an experiment that involves the probability of serious injury, impaired health, mutilation, or death.

The status of the fetus is clear in the Roman Catholic version of the natural law theory: the fetus is a person. As such, the fetus is entitled to the same dignity and respect we accord to other persons. Experiments that involve doing it injury or lessening its chances of life are morally prohibited. But not all fetal research is ruled out. That which may be of therapeutic benefit or which does not directly threaten the fetus's well-being is allowable. Furthermore, research involving fetal tissue or remains is permissible, if it is done for a serious and valuable purpose.

Rawls

From Rawls's point of view, the difficulty with utilitarianism with respect to human experimentation is that the principle of utility would permit the exploitation of some groups (the dying, prisoners, the retarded) for the sake of others. By contrast, Rawls's principles of justice would forbid all research that involves violating a liberty to which a person is entitled by virtue of being a member of society.

As a result, all experiments that make use of coercion or deception are ruled out. And since a person has a right to decide what risks she is willing to subject herself to, voluntary informed consent is required of all subjects. Society might, as in utilitarianism, decide to reward those who volunteer to become research subjects. As long as this is a possibility open to all, it is not objectionable.

It would never be right, according to Rawls, to take advantage of those in the society who are least well off to benefit those who are better off. Inequalities must be arranged so that they bring benefits (ideally) to everyone or, at least, to those who are most disadvantaged. Research involving direct therapeutic benefits is clearly acceptable (assuming informed consent), but research that takes advantage of the sick, the poor, the retarded, or the institutionalized and does not benefit them is unacceptable. The status of the fetus—whether or not it is a person in the moral senses—is an issue that has to be resolved before we know how to apply Rawls's principles to fetal research.

We have been able to provide only the briefest sketch of some of the ways in which our moral theories might apply to the issues in human experimentation. The remarks are not meant to be anything more than suggestive.

A satisfactory moral theory of human experimentation requires working out the application of principles to problems in detail, as well as resolving such issues as the status of children and fetuses and the capability of institutionalized people to act freely.

In the Case Presentations and Social Contexts presented earlier in the chapter, the issues we have discussed can be recognized as pressing problems requiring decisions about particular situations and general policies.

READINGS

Section 1:   Consent and Experimentation

The Willowbrook Letters: Criticism and Defense

Stephen Goldby, Saul Krugman, M. H. Pappworth, and Geoffrey Edsall

"The Willowbrook Letters," by Stephen Goldby, Saul Krugman, M. H. Pappworth, and Geoffrey Edsall, concern the moral legitimacy of the study of viral hepatitis that was conducted at the Willowbrook School by Krugman and his associates. (See the Case Presentation for more detail.) Goldby charges that the study was "quite unjustifiable" because it was morally wrong to infect children when no benefit to them could result. Krugman defends himself by claiming that his results demonstrated a "therapeutic effect" for the children involved, as well as for others. He presents four reasons for holding that the infecting of the children was justified.

Pappworth claims that Krugman's defense is presented only after the fact, whereas an experiment is ethical or not in its inception. Moreover, he asserts, consent was obtained through the use of coercion. Parents who wished to put their children in the institution were told there was room only in the "hepatitis unit."

In the final letter, Edsall defends the Krugman study. The experiments, he asserts, involved no greater risk to the children involved than they would have run in any case. What is more, the results obtained were of general benefit.

SIR.—You have referred to the work of Krugman and his colleagues at the Willowbrook State School in three editorials. In the first article the work was cited as a

Stephen Goldby, Saul Krugman, M.H. Pappworth, and Geoffrey Edsall, From "The Willowbrook Letters: Criticism and Defense." *The Lancet*, April 10, May 8, June 5, and July 10, 1971. Copyright © 1971 Elsevier Properties S.A. Reprinted by permission.

notable study of hepatitis and a model for this type of investigation. No comment was made on the rightness of attempting to infect mentally retarded children with hepatitis for experimental purposes, in an institution where the disease was already endemic.

The second editorial again did not remark on the ethics of the study, but the third sounded a note of doubt as to the justification for extending these experiments.

The reason given was that some children might have been made more susceptible to serious hepatitis as the result of the administration of previously heated ictero-genic material.

I believe that not only this last experiment, but the whole of Krugman's study, is quite unjustifiable, whatever the aims, and however academically or therapeutically important are the results. I am amazed that the work was published and that it has been actively supported editorially by the *Journal of the American Medical Association* and by Ingelfinger in the 1967–68 *Year Book of Medicine*. To my knowledge only the *British Journal of Hospital Medicine* has clearly stated the ethical position on these experiments and shown that it was indefensible to give potentially dangerous infected material to children, particularly those who were mentally retarded, with or without parental consent, when no benefit to the child could conceivably result.

Krugman and Giles have continued to publish the results of their study, and in a recent paper go to some length to describe their method of obtaining parental consent and list a number of influential medical boards and committees that have approved the study. They point out again that, in their opinion, their work conforms to the World Medical Association Draft Code of Ethics on Human Experimentation. They also say that hepatitis is still highly endemic in the school.

This attempted defense is irrelevant to the central issue. Is it right to perform an experiment on a normal or mentally retarded child when no benefit can result to that individual? I think that the answer is no, and that the question of parental consent is irrelevant. In my view the studies of Krugman serve only to show that there is a serious loophole in the Draft Code, which under General Principles and Definitions puts the onus of consent for experimentation on children on the parent or guardian. It is this section that is quoted by Krugman. I would class his work as "experiments conducted solely for the acquisition of knowledge," under which heading the code states that "persons retained in mental hospital[s] or hospitals for mental defectives should not be used for human experiment." Krugman may believe that his experiments were for the benefit of his patients, meaning the individual patients used in the study. If this is his belief he has a difficult case to defend. The duty of a pediatrician in a situation such as exists at Willowbrook State School is to attempt to improve that situation, not to turn it to his advantage for experimental purposes, however lofty the aims.

Every new reference to the work of Krugman and Giles adds to its apparent ethical respectability and

in my view such references should stop, or at least be heavily qualified. The editorial attitude of *The Lancet* to the work should be reviewed and openly stated. The issue is too important to be ignored.

If Krugman and Giles are keen to continue their experiments I suggest that they invite the parents of the children involved to participate. I wonder what the response would be.

Stephen Goldby

SIR.—Dr. Stephen Goldby's critical comments about our Willowbrook studies and our motives for conducting them were published without extending us the courtesy of replying in the same issue of *The Lancet*. Your acceptance of his criticisms without benefit of our response implies a blackout of all comment related to our studies. This decision is unfortunate because our recent studies on active and passive immunization for the prevention of viral hepatitis, type B, have clearly demonstrated a "therapeutic effect" for the children involved. These studies have provided us with the first indication and hope that it may be possible to control hepatitis in this institution. If this aim can be achieved, it will benefit not only the children, but also their families and the employees who care for them in the school. It is unnecessary to point out the additional benefit to the worldwide populations which have been plagued by an insoluble hepatitis problem for many generations.

Dr. Joan Giles and I have been actively engaged in studies aimed to solve two infectious-disease problems in the Willowbrook State School—measles and viral hepatitis. These studies were investigated in this institution because they represented major health problems for the 5000 or more mentally retarded children who were residents. Uninformed critics have assumed or implied that we came to Willowbrook to "conduct experiments on mentally retarded children."

The results of our Willowbrook studies with the experimental live attenuated measles vaccine developed by Enders and his colleagues are well documented in the medical literature. As early as 1960 we demonstrated the protective effect of this vaccine during the course of an epidemic. Prior to licensure of the vaccine in 1963 epidemics occurred at two-year intervals in this institution. During the 1960 epidemic there were more than 600 cases of measles and 60 deaths. In the wake of our ongoing measles vaccine programme, measles has been eradicated as a disease in the Willowbrook State School. We have not had a single case of measles since 1963. In this regard the children at the Willowbrook State School have been more fortunate than unimmunized children in Oxford, England, [and] other areas in Great Britain, as well as certain groups of children in the United States and other parts of the world.

The background of our hepatitis studies at Willowbrook has been described in detail in various publications. Viral hepatitis is so prevalent that newly admitted susceptible children become infected within 6 to 12 months after entry in the institution. These children are a source of infection for the personnel who care for them and for their families if they visit with them. We were convinced that the solution of the hepatitis problem in this institution was dependent on the acquisition of new knowledge leading to the development of an effective immunizing agent. The achievements with smallpox, diphtheria, poliomyelitis, and more recently measles represent dramatic illustrations of this approach.

It is well known that viral hepatitis in children is milder and more benign than the same disease in adults. Experience has revealed that hepatitis in institutionalized, mentally retarded children is also mild, in contrast with measles, which is a more severe disease when it occurs in institutional epidemics involving the mentally retarded. Our proposal to expose a small number of newly admitted children to the Willowbrook strains of hepatitis virus was justified in our opinion for the following reasons: (1) they were bound to be exposed to the same strains under the natural conditions existing in the institution; (2) they would be admitted to a special, well-equipped, and well-staffed unit where they would be isolated from exposure to other infectious diseases which were prevalent in the institution—namely, shigellosis, parasitic infections, and respiratory infections—thus, their exposure in the hepatitis unit would be associated with less risk than the type of institutional exposure where multiple infections could occur; (3) they were likely to have a subclinical infection followed by immunity to the particular hepatitis virus; and (4) only children with parents who gave informed consent would be included.

The statement by Dr. Goldby accusing us of conducting experiments exclusively for the acquisition of knowledge with no benefit for the children cannot be supported by the true facts.

Saul Krugman

Sɪʀ.—The experiments at Willowbrook raise two important issues: What constitutes valid consent and do ends justify means? English law definitely forbids experimentation on children, even if both parents consent, unless done specifically in the interests of each individual child. Perhaps in the U.S.A. the law is not so clear-cut.

According to Beecher, the parents of the children at Willowbrook were informed that, because of overcrowding, the institution was to be closed; but only a week or two later they were told that there would be vacancies in the "hepatitis unit" for children whose parents allowed them to form part of the hepatitis research study. Such consent, ethically if not legally, is invalid because of its element of coercion, some parents being desperately anxious to institutionalize their mentally defective children. Moreover, obtaining consent after talking to parents in groups, as described by Krugman, is extremely unsatisfactory because even a single enthusiast can sway the diffident who do not wish to appear churlish in front of their fellow citizens.

Do ends justify the means? Krugman maintains that any newly admitted children would inevitably have contracted infective hepatitis, which was rife in the hospital. But this ignores the statement by the head of the State Department of Mental Hygiene that during the major part of the 15 years these experiments have been conducted, a gamma-globulin inoculation programme had already resulted in over an 80 percent reduction of that disease in that hospital. Krugman and Pasamanick claim that subsequent therapeutic effects justify these experiments. This attitude is frequently adopted by experimenters and enthusiastic medical writers who wish us to forget completely how results are obtained but instead enjoy any benefits that may accrue. Immunization was not the purpose of these Willowbrook experiments but merely a by-product that incidentally proved beneficial to the victims. Any experiment is ethical or not at its inception, and does not become so because it achieved some measure of success in extending the frontiers of medicine. I particularly object strongly to the views of Willey," . . . risk being assumed by the subjects of the experimentation balanced against the potential benefit to the subjects *and* [Willey's italics] to society in general." I believe that experimental physicians never have the right to select martyrs for society. Every human being has the right to be treated with decency, and that right must always supersede every consideration of what may benefit mankind, what may advance medical science, what may contribute to public welfare. No doctor is ever justified in placing society or science first and his obligation to patients second. Any claim to act for the good of society should be regarded with distaste because it may be merely a highflown expression to cloak outrageous acts.

M.H. Pappworth

Sɪʀ.—I am astonished at the unquestioning way in which *The Lancet* has accepted the intemperate position taken by Dr. Stephen Goldby concerning the experimental studies of Krugman and Giles on hepatitis at the Willowbrook State School. These investigators have repeatedly explained for over a decade that natural hepatitis infection occurs sooner or later in virtually 100% of the patients admitted to Willowbrook, and that it is better for the patient to have a known, timed, controlled infection than an untimed, uncontrolled one. Moreover, the wisdom and human justification of these studies have been repeatedly and carefully examined and verified by a number of very distinguished, able individuals who are respected leaders in the making of such decisions.

The real issue is: Is it not proper and ethical to carry out experiments in children, which would apparently incur no greater risk than the children were likely to run by nature, in which the children generally receive better medical care when artificially infected than if they had been naturally infected, and in which the parents as well as the physician feel that a significant contribution to the future well-being of similar children is likely to result from the studies? It is true, to be sure, that the W.M.A. code says,"Children in institutions and not under the care of relatives should not be the subjects of human experiments." But this unqualified *obiter dictum* may represent merely the well-known inability of committees to think a problem through. However, it has been thought through by Sir Austin Bradford Hill, who has pointed out the unfortunate effects for these very children that would have resulted, were such a code to have been applied over the years.

Geoffrey Edsall

Judgment on Willowbrook

Paul Ramsey

Paul Ramsey reviews the justifications offered for the Willowbrook experiments presented by Krugman. Ramsey observes that there is nothing about hepatitis which requires that research be conducted on children, that no justification except the needs of the experiment is given for withholding gamma globulin from the subjects, and that nothing is said about attempting to control the low-grade epidemic by other means. Furthermore, Ramsey questions the morality of consent secured from the parents of the children. His basic recommendation is that the use of captive populations of children ought to be made legally impossible.

In 1958 and 1959 the *New England Journal of Medicine* reported a series of experiments performed upon patients and new admittees to the Willowbrook State School, a home for retarded children in Staten Island, New York.[1] These experiments were described as"an attempt to control the high prevalence of infectious hepatitis in an institution for mentally defective patients."The experiments were said to be justified because, under conditions of an existing uncontrolled outbreak of hepatitis in the institution,"knowledge obtained from a series of suitable studies could well lead to its control."In actuality, the experiments were designed to duplicate and confirm the efficacy of gamma globulin in immunization against hepatitis,

to develop and improve or improve upon that inoculum, and to learn more about infectious hepatitis in general.

The experiments were justified—doubtless, after a great deal of soul searching—for the following reasons: there was a smoldering epidemic throughout the institution and"it was apparent that most of the patients at Willowbrook were naturally exposed to hepatitis virus"; infectious hepatitis is a much milder disease in children; the strain at Willowbrook was especially mild; only the strain or strains of the virus already disseminated at Willowbrook were used; and only those small and incompetent patients whose parents gave consent were used.

The patient population at Willowbrook was 4478, growing at a rate of one patient a day over a three-year span, or from 10 to 15 new admissions per week. In the first trial the existing population was divided into two groups: one group served as uninoculated controls, and the other group was inoculated with 0.01 ml of gamma globulin per pound of body weight. Then for a second trial new admittees and those left uninoculated before were again divided: one group served as uninoculated controls and the other was inoculated with 0.06 ml of gamma globulin per pound of body weight. This proved that Stokes et al. had correctly demonstrated that the larger amount would give significant immunity for up to seven or eight months.[2]

Serious ethical questions may be raised about the trials so far described. No mention is made of any attempt to enlist the adult personnel of the institution, numbering nearly 1000 including nearly 600 attendants on ward duty, and new additions to the staff, in these studies whose excusing reason was that almost everyone was "naturally" exposed to the Willowbrook virus. Nothing requires that major research into the natural history of hepatitis be first undertaken in children. Experiments have been carried out in the military and with prisoners as subjects. There have been fatalities from the experiments; but surely in all these cases the consent of the volunteers was as valid or better than the proxy consent of these children's "representatives." There would have been no question of the understanding consent that might have been given by the adult personnel at Willowbrook, if significant benefits were expected from studying that virus.

Second, nothing is said that would warrant withholding an inoculation of some degree of known efficacy from part of the population, or for withholding in the first trial less than the full amount of gamma globulin that had served to immunize in previous tests, except the need to test, confirm, and improve the inoculum. That, of course, was a desirable goal; but it does not seem possible to warrant withholding gamma globulin for the reason that is often said to justify controlled trials, namely, that one procedure is *as likely* to succeed as the other.

Third, nothing is said about attempts to control or defeat the low-grade epidemic at Willowbrook by more ordinary, if more costly and less experimental, procedures. Nor is anything said about admitting no more patients until this goal had been accomplished. This was not a massive urban hospital whose teeming population would have to be turned out into the streets, with resulting dangers to themselves and to public health, in order to sanitize the place. Instead, between 200 and 250 patients were housed in each of 18 buildings over approximately 400 acres in a semi-rural setting of fields, woods, and well-kept, spacious

lawns. Clearly it would have been possible to secure other accommodation[s] for new admissions away from the infection, while eradicating the infection at Willowbrook building by building. This might have cost money, and it would certainly have required astute detective work to discover the source of the infection. The doctors determined that the new patients likely were not carrying the infection upon admission, and that it did not arise from the procedures and routine inoculations given to them at the time of admission. Why not go further in the search for the source of the epidemic? If this had been an orphanage for normal children or a floor of private patients, instead of a school for mentally defective children, one wonders whether the doctors would so readily have accepted the hepatitis as a "natural" occurrence and even as an opportunity for study.

The next step was to attempt to induce "passive–active immunity" by feeding the virus to patients already protected by gamma globulin. In this attempt to improve the inoculum, permission was obtained from the parents of children from 5 to 10 years of age newly admitted to Willowbrook, who were then isolated from contact with the rest of the institution. All were inoculated with gamma globulin and then divided into two groups: one served as controls while the other group of new patients were fed the Willowbrook virus, obtained from feces, in doses having 50 percent infectivity, i.e., in concentrations estimated to produce hepatitis with jaundice in half the subjects tested. Then twice the 50 percent infectivity was tried. This proved, among other things, that hepatitis has an "alimentary-tract phase" in which it can be transmitted from one person to another while still "inapparent" in the first person. This, doubtless, is exceedingly important information in learning how to control epidemics of infectious hepatitis. The second of the two articles mentioned above describes studies of the incubation period of the virus and of whether pooled serum remained infectious when aged and frozen. Still the small, mentally defective patients who were deliberately fed infectious hepatitis are described as having suffered mildly in most cases: "The liver became enlarged in the majority, occasionally a week or two before the onset of jaundice. Vomiting and anorexia usually lasted only a few days. Most of the children gained weight during the course of hepatitis."

That mild description of what happened to the children who were fed hepatitis (and who continued to be introduced into the unaltered environment of Willowbrook) is itself alarming since it is now definitely known that cirrhosis of the liver results from infectious hepatitis more frequently than from excessive consumption of alcohol! Now, or in 1958 and 1959, no one knows what may be other serious consequences of contracting infectious hepatitis. Understanding human volunteers were then and are now needed in the study of this disease, although a South American monkey has now successfully been given a form of hepatitis, and can henceforth serve as our ally in its conquest. But not children who cannot consent knowingly. If Peace Corps workers are regularly given gamma globulin before going abroad as a guard against their contracting hepatitis, and are inoculated at intervals thereafter, it seems that this is the least we should do for mentally defective children before they "go abroad" to Willowbrook or other institutions set up for their care.

Discussions pro and con of the Willowbrook experiments that have come to my attention serve only to reinforce the ethical objections that can be raised against what was done simply from a careful analysis of the original articles reporting the research design and findings. In an address at the 1968 Ross Conference on Pediatric Research, Dr. Saul Krugman raised the question, Should vaccine trials be carried out in adult volunteers before subjecting children to similar tests?[3] He answered this question in the negative. The reason adduced was simply that "a vaccine trial may be a more hazardous procedure for adults than for children." Medical researchers, of course, are required to minimize the hazards, but not by moving from consenting to unconsenting subjects. This apology clearly shows that adults and children have become interchangeable in face of the overriding importance of obtaining the research goal. This means that the special moral claims of children for care and protection are forgotten, and especially the claims of children who are most weak and vulnerable. (Krugman's reference to the measles vaccine trials is not to the point.)

The *Medical Tribune* explains that the 16-bed isolation unit set up at Willowbrook served "to protect the study subjects from Willowbrook's other endemic diseases—such as shigellosis, measles, rubella and respiratory and parasitic infections—while exposing them to hepatitis."[4] This presumably compensated for the infection they were given. It is not convincingly shown that the children could by no means, however costly, have been protected from the epidemic of hepatitis. The statement that Willowbrook "had endemic infectious hepatitis and a sufficiently open population so that the disease could never be quieted by exhausting the supply of susceptibles" is at best enigmatic.

Oddly, physicians defending the propriety of the Willowbrook hepatitis project soon began talking like poorly instructed "natural lawyers"! Dr. Louis Lasagna and Dr. Geoffrey Edsall, for example, find these experiments unobjectionable—both, for the reason stated by Edsall: "the children would apparently incur no greater risk than they were likely to run by nature." In any case, Edsall's example of parents consenting with a son 17 years of age for him to go to war, and society's agreements with minors that they can drive cars and hurt themselves were entirely beside the point. Dr. David D. Rutstein adheres to a stricter standard in regard to research on infectious hepatitis: "It is not ethical to use human subjects for the growth of a virus for any purpose."[5]

The latter sweeping verdict may depend on knowledge of the effects of viruses on chromosomal difficulties, mongolism, etc., that was not available to the Willowbrook group when their researches were begun thirteen years ago. If so, this is a telling point against appeal to "no discernible risks" as the sole standard applicable to the use of children in medical experimentation. That would lend support to the proposition that we always know that there are unknown and undiscerned risks in the case of an invasion of the fortress of the body—which then can be consented to by an adult in behalf of a child only if it is in the child's behalf medically.

When asked what she told the parents of the subject children at Willowbrook, Dr. Joan Giles replied, "I explain that there is no vaccine against infectious hepatitis. . . . I also tell them that we can modify the disease with gamma globulin but we can't provide lasting immunity without letting them get the disease."[6] Obviously vaccines giving "lasting immunity" are not the only kinds of vaccine to be used in caring for patients.

Doubtless the studies at Willowbrook resulted in improvement in the vaccine, to the benefit of present and future patients. In September 1966, "a routine program of GG [gamma globulin] administration to every new patient at Willowbrook" was begun. This cut the incidence of icteric hepatitis 80 to 85 percent. Then follows a significant statement in the *Medical Tribune* article: "A similar reduction in the icteric form of the disease has been accomplished among the employees, who began getting routine GG earlier in the study."[7] Not only did the research team (so far as these reports show) fail to consider and adopt the alternative that new admittees to the staff be asked to become volunteers for an investigation that might improve the vaccine against the strain of infectious hepatitis to which they as well as the children were exposed. Instead, the staff was routinely protected earlier than the inmates were! And, as we have seen, there was evidence from the beginning that gamma globulin provided at least some protection. A "modification" of the disease was still an inoculum; even if this provided no lasting immunization and had to be repeated. It is axiomatic to medical ethics that a known remedy or protection—even if not perfect or even if the best exact administration of it has not been proved—should not be withheld from individual patients. It seems to a layman that from the beginning various trials at immunization of all new admittees might have been made, and controlled observation made of their different degrees of effectiveness against "nature" at Willowbrook. This would doubtless have been a longer way round, namely, the "anecdotal" method of investigative treatment that comes off second best in comparison with controlled trials. Yet this seems to be the alternative dictated by our received medical ethics, and the only one expressive of minimal care of the primary patients themselves.

Finally, except for one episode, the obtaining of parental consent (on the premise that this is ethically valid) seems to have been very well handled. Wards of the state were not used, though by law the administrator at Willowbrook could have signed consent for them. Only new admittees whose parents were available were entered by proxy consent into the project. Explanation was made to groups of these parents, and they were given time to think about it and consult with their own family physicians. Then late in 1964 Willowbrook was closed to all new admissions because of overcrowding. What then happened can most impartially be described in the words of an article defending the Willowbrook project on medical and ethical grounds:

> Parents who applied for their children to get in were sent a form letter over Dr. Hammond's signature saying that there was no space for new admissions and that their name was being put on a waiting list.
>
> But the hepatitis program, occupying its own space in the institution, continued to admit new patients as each new study group began. "Where do you find new admissions except by canvassing the people who have applied for admission?" Dr. Hammond asked.
>
> So a new batch of form letters went out saying that there were a few vacancies in the hepatitis research

> unit if the parents cared to consider volunteering their child for that. In some instances the second form letter apparently was received as closely as a week after the first letter arrived.[8]

Granting—as I do not—the validity of parental consent to research upon children not in their behalf medically, what sort of consent was that? Surely, the duress upon these parents with children so defective as to require institutionalization was far greater than the duress on prisoners given tobacco or paid or promised parole for their cooperation! I grant that the timing of these events was inadvertent. Since, however, ethics is a matter of criticizing institutions and not only of exculpating or making culprits of individual men, the inadvertence does not matter. This is the strongest possible argument for saying that even if parents have the right to consent to submit the children who are directly and continuously in their care to nonbeneficial medical experimentation, this should not be the rule of practice governing institutions set up for their care.

Such use of captive populations of children for purely experimental purposes ought to be made legally impossible. My view is that this should be stopped by legal acknowledgement of the moral invalidity of parental or legal proxy consent for the child to procedures having no relation to a child's own diagnosis or treatment. If this is not done, canons of loyalty require that the rule of practice (by law, or otherwise) be that children in institutions and not directly under the care of parents or relatives should *never* be used in medical investigations having present pain or discomfort and unknown present and future risks to them, and promising future possible benefits only for others.

Notes

1. Robert Ward, Saul Krugman, Joan P. Giles, A. Milton Jacobs, and Oscar Bodansky, "Infectious Hepatitis: Studies of Its Natural History and Prevention," *New England Journal of Medicine* 258, no. 9 (February 27, 1958): 407–16; Saul Krugman, Robert Ward, Joan P. Giles, Oscar Bodansky, and A. Milton Jacobs, 'Infectious Hepatitis: Detection of the Virus during the Incubation Period and in Clinically Inapparent Infection," *New England Journal of Medicine* 261, no. 15 (October 8, 1959): 725–34. The following account and unannotated quotations are taken from these articles.

2. J. Stokes, Jr., et al., "Infectious Hepatitis: Length of Protection by Immune Serum Globulin (Gamma Globulin) during Epidemics," *Journal of the American Medical Association* 147 (1951): 714–19. Since the half-life of gamma globulin is three weeks, no one knows exactly why it immunizes for so long a period. The "highly significant protection against hepatitis obtained by the use of gamma globulin," however, had been confirmed as early as 1945 (see Edward B. Grossman, Sloan G. Stewart,

and Joseph Stokes, "Post-Transfusion Hepatitis in Battle Casualties," *Journal of the American Medical Association* 129, no. 15 [December 8, 1945]: 991–94). The inoculation *withheld* in the Willowbrook experiments had, therefore, proved valuable.

3. Saul Krugman, "Reflections on Pediatric Clinical Investigations," in *Problems of Drug Evaluation in Infants and Children*, Report of the Fifty-eighth Ross Conference on Pediatric Research, Dorado Beach, Puerto Rico, May 5–7, 1968 (Columbus: Ross Laboratories), pp. 41–42.

4. "Studies with Children Backed on Medical Ethical Grounds," *Medical Tribune and Medical News* 8, no. 19 (February 20, 1967):1,23.

5. *Daedalus*, Spring 1969, pp. 471–72, 529. See also pp. 458, 470–72. Since it is the proper business of an ethicist to uphold the proposition that only retrogression in civility can result from bad moral reasoning and the use of inept examples, however innocent, it is fair to point out

the startling comparison between Edsall's "argument" and the statement of Dr. Karl Brandt, plenipotentiary in charge of all medical activities in the Nazi Reich': "Do you think that one can obtain any worthwhile, fundamental results without a definite toll of lives? The same goes for technological development. You cannot build a great bridge, a gigantic building–you cannot establish a speed record without deaths!" (quoted by Leo Alexander, "War Crimes: Their Social-Psychological Aspects," *American Journal of Psychiatry* 105, no. 3 [September 1948]: 172). Casualties to progress, or injuries accepted in setting speed limits, are morally quite different from death or maiming or even only risks, or unknown risks, directly and deliberately imposed upon an unconsenting human being.

6. *Medical Tribune*, February 20, 1967, p. 23.

7. *Ibid.*

8. *Ibid.*

Principles of the Nuremberg Code

1. The voluntary consent of the human subject is absolutely essential.

   This means that the person involved should have legal capacity to give consent; should be so situated as to be able to exercise free power of choice, without the intervention of any element of force, fraud, deceit, duress, over-reaching, or other ulterior form of constraint or coercion; and should have sufficient knowledge and comprehension of the elements of the subject matter involved as to enable him to make an understanding and enlightened decision. This latter element requires that before the acceptance of an affirmative decision by the experimental subject there should be made known to him the nature, duration, and purpose of the experiment; the method and means by which it is to be conducted; all inconveniences and hazards reasonably to be expected; and the effects upon his health or person which may possibly come from his participation in the experiment.

   The duty and responsibility for ascertaining the quality of the consent rests upon each individual who initiates, directs or engages in the experiment. It is a personal duty and responsibility which may not be delegated to another with impunity.

2. The experiment should be such as to yield fruitful results for the good of society, unprocurable by other methods or means of study, and not random and unnecessary in nature.

3. The experiment should be so designed and based on the results of animal experimentation and a knowledge of the natural history of the disease or other problem under study that the anticipated results will justify the performance of the experiment.

4. The experiment should be so conducted as to avoid all unnecessary physical and mental suffering and injury.

5. No experiment should be conducted where there is an *a priori* reason to believe that death or disabling injury will occur; except, perhaps, in those experiments where the experimental physicians also serve as subjects.

6. The degree of risk to be taken should never exceed that determined by the humanitarian importance of the problem to be solved by the experiment.

7. Proper preparations should be made and adequate facilities provided to protect the experimental subject against even remote possibilities of injury, disability, or death.

8. The experiment should be conducted only by scientifically qualified persons. The highest degree of skill and care should be required through all stages of the experiment of those who conduct or engage in the experiment.

From "Permissible Medical Experiments," Trials of War Criminals Before the Nuremberg Military Tribunals Under Control Council Law No. 0: Nuremberg, October 1946-April 1949 (Washington D.C.: Government Printing Office, n.d., vol. 2), 181–182.

9. During the course of the experiment the human subject should be at liberty to bring the experiment to an end if he has reached the physical or mental state where continuation of the experiment seems to him to be impossible.

10. During the course of the experiment the scientist in charge must be prepared to terminate the experiment at any stage, if he has probable cause to believe, in the exercise of the good faith, superior skill and careful judgment required of him that a continuation of the experiment is likely to result in injury, disability, or death to the experimental subject.

Belmont Report

National Commission for the Protection of Human Subjects

The 1974 National Research Act mandated that every institution receiving federal funding and conducting research involving human subjects establish an institutional review board (IRB) to oversee such research. The Act was prompted by public revelations about the United States Public Health Service–sponsored Tuskegee syphilis study (see Chapter 4) in which investigators enrolled patients without their consent and treated them in ways that were condemned at the 1947 Nuremberg trials of Nazi physicians and researchers.

The 1974 act also established the National Commission for the Protection of Human Subjects of Biomedical and Behavioral Research and charged it with identifying the ethical principles basic to human research and formulating guidelines to guarantee that they are followed in its conduct. The Commission met for four days of discussion at the Smithsonian Institution's Belmont Conference Center; and its deliberations were published as the *Belmont Report* in the *Federal Register* in 1979. The report was accepted by the Secretary of what is now the Department of Health and Human Services as the department's policy statement on the use of human research subjects.

The *Belmont Report* is not a set of regulations, but a framework for identifying, discussing, and settling ethical matters, while leaving open the possibility that reasonable people may sometimes differ irreconcilably. The report distinguishes medical practice from research (see the Briefing Session in this chapter for a discussion) and identifies three principles as most relevant for evaluating the ethical legitimacy of research involving human subjects. The principles, which in our society are generally accepted as so uncontroversial as not to require argument, are respect for persons, beneficence, and justice.

Belmont Report From The National Commission for the Protection of Human Subjects of Biomedical and Behavioral Research, The Belmont Report: Ethical Principles and Guidelines for the Protection of Human Subjects of Research (April 18, 1979), http://ohsr.od.nih.gov/guidelines/belmont.html. Notes omitted.

Ethical Principles and Guidelines for Research Involving Human Subjects

A. Boundaries Between Practice and Research

It is important to distinguish between biomedical and behavioral research, on the one hand, and the practice of accepted therapy on the other, in order to know what activities ought to undergo review for the protection of human subjects of research. The distinction between research and practice is blurred partly because both often occur together (as in research designed to evaluate a therapy) and partly because notable departures from standard practice are often called "experimental" when the terms "experimental" and "research" are not carefully defined.

For the most part, the term "practice" refers to interventions that are designed solely to enhance the well-being of an individual patient or client and that have a reasonable expectation of success. The purpose of medical or behavioral practice is to provide diagnosis, preventive treatment or therapy to particular individuals. By contrast, the term "research" designates an activity designed to test an hypothesis, permit conclusions to be drawn, and thereby to develop or contribute to generalizable knowledge (expressed, for example, in theories, principles, and statements of relationships). Research is usually described in a formal protocol that sets forth an objective and a set of procedures designed to reach that objective.

When a clinician departs in a significant way from standard or accepted practice, the innovation does not, in and of itself, constitute research. The fact that a procedure is "experimental," in the sense of new, untested or different, does not automatically place it in the category of research. Radically new procedures of this description should, however, be made the object of formal research at an early stage in order to determine whether they are safe and effective. Thus, it is the responsibility of medical practice committees, for example, to insist that a major innovation be incorporated into a formal research project.

Research and practice may be carried on together when research is designed to evaluate the safety and efficacy of a therapy. This need not cause any confusion regarding whether or not the activity requires review; the general rule is that if there is any element of research in an activity, that activity should undergo review for the protection of human subjects.

B. Basic Ethical Principles

The expression "basic ethical principles" refers to those general judgments that serve as a basic justification for the many particular ethical prescriptions and evaluations of human actions. Three basic principles, among those generally accepted in our cultural tradition, are particularly relevant to the ethics of research involving human subjects: the principles of respect of persons, beneficence and justices.

1. Respect for Persons. Respect for persons incorporates at least two ethical convictions: first, that individuals should be treated as autonomous agents, and second, that persons with diminished autonomy are entitled to protection. The principle of respect for persons thus divides into two separate moral requirements: the requirement to acknowledge autonomy and the requirement to protect those with diminished autonomy.

An autonomous person is an individual capable of deliberation about personal goals and of acting under the direction of such deliberation. To respect autonomy is to give weight to autonomous persons' considered opinions and choices while refraining from obstructing their actions unless they are clearly detrimental to others. To show lack of respect for an autonomous agent is to repudiate that person's considered judgments, to deny an individual the freedom to act on those considered judgments, or to withhold information necessary to make a considered judgment, when there are no compelling reasons to do so.

However, not every human being is capable of self-determination. The capacity for self-determination matures during an individual's life, and some individuals lose this capacity wholly or in part because of illness, mental disability, or circumstances that severely restrict liberty. Respect for the immature and the incapacitated may require protecting them as they mature or while they are incapacitated.

Some persons are in need of extensive protection, even to the point of excluding them from activities which may harm them; other persons require little protection beyond making sure they undertake activities freely and with awareness of possible adverse consequence. The extent of protection afforded should depend upon the risk of harm and the likelihood of benefit. The judgment that any individual lacks autonomy should be periodically reevaluated and will vary in different situations.

In most cases of research involving human subjects, respect for persons demands that subjects enter into the research voluntarily and with adequate information. In some situations, however, application of the principle is not obvious. The involvement of prisoners as subjects of research provides an instructive example. On the one hand, it would seem that the principle of respect for persons requires that prisoners not be deprived of the opportunity to volunteer for research. On the other hand, under prison conditions they may be subtly coerced or unduly influenced to engage in research activities for which they would not otherwise volunteer. Respect for persons would then dictate that prisoners be protected. Whether to allow prisoners to "volunteer" or to "protect" them presents a dilemma. Respecting persons, in most hard cases, is often a matter of balancing competing claims urged by the principle of respect itself.

2. Beneficence.

Persons are treated in an ethical manner not only by respecting their decisions and protecting them from harm, but also by making efforts to secure their well-being. Such treatment falls under the principle of beneficence. The term "beneficence" is often understood to cover acts of kindness or charity that go beyond strict obligation. In this document, beneficence is understood in a stronger sense, as an obligation. Two general rules have been formulated as complementary expressions of beneficent actions in this sense: (1) do not harm and (2) maximize possible benefits and minimize possible harms.

The Hippocratic maxim "do no harm" has long been a fundamental principle of medical ethics. Claude Bernard extended it to the realm of research, saying that one should not injure one person regardless of the benefits that might come to others. However, even avoiding harm requires learning what is harmful; and, in the process of obtaining this information, persons may be exposed to risk of harm. Further, the Hippocratic Oath requires physicians to benefit their patients "according to their best judgment." Learning what will in fact benefit may require exposing persons to risk. The problem posed by these imperatives is to decide when it is justifiable to seek certain benefits despite the risks involved, and when the benefits should be foregone because of the risks.

The obligations of beneficence affect both individual investigators and society at large, because they extend both to particular research projects and to the entire enterprise of research. In the case of particular projects, investigators and members of their institutions are obliged to give forethought to the maximization of benefits and the reduction of risk that might occur from the research investigation. In the case of scientific research in general, members of the larger society are obliged to recognize the longer term benefits and risks that may result from the improvement of knowledge and from the development of novel medical, psychotherapeutic, and social procedures.

The principle of beneficence often occupies a well-defined justifying role in many areas of research involving human subjects. An example is found in research involving children. Effective ways of treating childhood diseases and fostering healthy development are benefits that serve to justify research involving children–even when individual research subjects are not direct beneficiaries. Research also makes it possible to avoid the harm that may result from the application of previously accepted routine practices that on closer investigation turn out to be dangerous. But the role of the principle of beneficence is not always so unambiguous. A difficult ethical problem remains, for example, about research that presents more than minimal risk without immediate prospect of direct benefit to the children involved. Some have argued that such research is inadmissible, while others have pointed out that this limit would rule out much research promising great benefit to children in the future. Here again, as with all hard cases, the different claims covered by the principle of beneficence may come into conflict and force difficult choices.

3. Justice.

Who ought to receive the benefits of research and bear its burdens? This is a question of justice, in the sense of "fairness in distribution" or "what is deserved." An injustice occurs when some benefit to which a person is entitled is denied without good reason or when some burden is imposed unduly. Another way of conceiving the principle of justice is that equals ought to be treated equally. However, this statement requires explication. Who is equal and who is unequal? What considerations justify departure from equal distribution? Almost all commentators allow that distinctions based on experience, age, deprivation, competence, merit and position do sometimes constitute criteria justifying differential treatment for certain purposes. It is necessary, then, to explain in what respects people should be treated equally. There are several widely accepted formulations of just ways to distribute burdens and benefits. Each formulation mentions some relevant property on the basis of which burdens and benefits should be distributed. These formulations are

(1) to each person an equal share, (2) to each person according to individual need, (3) to each person according to individual effort, (4) to each person according to societal contribution, and (5) to each person according to merit.

Questions of justice have long been associated with social practice[s] such as punishment, taxation and political representation. Until recently these questions have not generally been associated with scientific research. However, they are foreshadowed even in the earliest reflections on the ethics of research involving human subjects. For example, during the 19th and early 20th centuries the burdens of serving as research subjects fell largely upon poor ward patients, while the benefits of improved medical care flowed primarily to private patients. Subsequently, the exploitation of unwilling prisoners as research subjects in Nazi concentration camps was condemned as a particularly flagrant injustice. In this country, in the 1940's, the Tuskegee syphilis study used disadvantaged, rural black men to study the untreated course of a disease that is by no means confined to that population. These subjects were deprived of demonstrably effective treatment in order not to interrupt the project, long after such treatment became generally available.

Against this historical background, it can be seen how conceptions of justice are relevant to research involving human subjects. For example, the selection of research subjects needs to be scrutinized in order to determine whether some classes (e.g., welfare patients, particular racial and ethnic minorities, or persons confined to institutions) are being systematically selected simply because of their easy availability, their compromised position, or their manipulability, rather than for reasons directly related to the problem being studied. Finally, whenever research supported by public funds leads to the development of therapeutic devices and procedures, justice demands both that these not provide advantages only to those who can afford them and that such research should not unduly involve persons from groups unlikely to be among the beneficiaries of subsequent applications of the research.

Philosophical Reflections on Experimenting with Human Subjects

Hans Jonas

Hans Jonas argues that if we justify experiments by considering them a right of society, then we are exposing individuals to dangers for the general good. This, for Jonas, is inherently wrong, and no individual should be forced to surrender himself or herself to a social goal.

Any risk that is taken must be voluntary; but obtaining informed consent, Jonas claims, is not sufficient to justify the experimental use of human beings. Two other conditions must be met: first, subjects must be recruited from those who are most knowledgeable about the circumstances of research and who are intellectually most capable of grasping its purposes and procedures; second, the experiment must be undertaken for an adequate cause. Jonas cautions us that the progress which may come from research is not necessarily worth our efforts or approval, and he reminds us that there are moral values which we ought not to lose in the pursuit of science.

Reprinted by permission of *Daedalus, Journal of the American Academy of Arts and Sciences,* Spring 1969, Boston, Mass. This essay is included, on pp. 105–131, in a 1980 reedition of Jonas's *Philosophical Essays: from Current Creed to Technological Man,* published by the University of Chicago Press. Notes omitted.

Experimenting with human subjects is going on in many fields of scientific and technological progress. It is designed to replace the overall instruction by natural, occasional experience with the selective information from artificial, systematic experiment which physical science has found so effective in dealing with inanimate nature. Of the new experimentation with man, medical is surely the most legitimate; psychological, the most dubious; biological (still to come), the most dangerous. I have chosen here to deal with the first only, where the case *for* it is strongest and the task of adjudicating conflicting claims hardest. . . .

The Melioristic Goal, Medical Research, and Individual Duty

Nowhere is the melioristic goal [of working toward improvement] more inherent than in medicine. To the physician, it is not gratuitous. He is committed to curing and thus to improving the power to cure. Gratuitous we called it (outside disaster conditions) as a *social* goal, but noble at the same time. Both the nobility and the gratuitousness must influence the manner in which self-sacrifice for it is elicited, and even its free offer accepted. Freedom is certainly the first condition to be observed here. The surrender of one's body to medical experimentation is entirely outside the enforceable "social contract."

Or can it be construed to fall within its terms—namely, as repayment for benefits from past experimentation that I have enjoyed myself? But I am indebted for these benefits not to society, but to the past "martyrs" to whom society is indebted itself, and society has no right to call in my personal debt by way of adding new to its own. Moreover, gratitude is not an enforceable social obligation; it anyway does not mean that I must emulate the deed. Most of all, if it was wrong to exact such sacrifice in the first place, it does not become right to exact it again with the plea of the profit it has brought me. If, however, it was not exacted, but entirely free, as it ought to have been, then it should remain so, and its precedence must not be used as a social pressure on others for doing the same under the sign of duty. . . .

The "Conscription" of Consent

The mere issuing of the appeal, the calling for volunteers, with the moral and social pressures it inevitably generates, amounts even under the most meticulous rules of consent to a sort of *conscripting*. And some soliciting is necessarily involved. . . . And this is why "consent," surely a nonnegotiable minimum requirement, is

not the full answer to the problem. Granting then that soliciting and therefore some degree of conscripting are part of the situation, who may conscript and who may be conscripted? Or less harshly expressed: Who should issue appeals and to whom?

The naturally qualified issuer of the appeal is the research scientist himself, collectively the main carrier of the impulse and the only one with the technical competence to judge. But his being very much an interested party (with vested interests, indeed, not purely in the public good, but in the scientific enterprise as such, in "his" project, and even in his career) makes him also suspect. The ineradicable dialectic of this situation—a delicate incompatibility problem—calls for particular controls by the research community and by public authority that we need not discuss. They can mitigate, but not eliminate the problem. We have to live with the ambiguity, the treacherous impurity of everything human.

Self-Recruitment of the Community

To whom should the appeal be addressed? The natural issuer of the call is also the first natural addressee: the physician-researcher himself and the scientific confraternity at large. With such a coincidence—indeed, the noble tradition with which the whole business of human experimentation started—almost all of the associated legal, ethical, and metaphysical problems vanish. If it is full, autonomous identification of the subject with the purpose that is required for the dignifying of his serving as a subject—here it is; if strongest motivation—here it is; if fullest understanding—here it is; if freest decision—here it is; if greatest integration with the person's total, chosen pursuit—here it is. With the fact of self-solicitation the issue of consent in all its insoluble equivocality is bypassed per se. Not even the condition that the particular purpose be truly important and the project reasonably promising, which must hold in any solicitation of others, need be satisfied here. By himself, the scientist is free to obey his obsession, to play his hunch, to wager on chance, to follow the lure of ambition. It is all part of the "divine madness" that somehow animates the ceaseless pressing against frontiers. For the rest of society, which has a deep-seated disposition to look with reverence and awe upon the guardians of the mysteries of life, the profession assumes with this proof of its devotion the role of a self-chosen, consecrated fraternity, not unlike the monastic orders of the past, and this would come nearest to the actual, religious origins of the art of healing. . . .

"Identification" as the Principle of Recruitment in General

If the properties we adduced as the particular qualifications of the members of the scientific fraternity itself are taken as general criteria of selection, then one should look for additional subjects where a maximum of identification, understanding, and spontaneity can be expected—that is, among the most highly motivated, the most highly educated, and the least "captive" members of the community. From this naturally scarce resource, a descending order of permissibility leads to greater abundance and ease of supply, whose use should become proportionately more hesitant as the exculpating criteria are relaxed. An inversion of normal "market" behavior is demanded here—namely, to accept the lowest quotation last (and excused only by the greatest pressure of need); to pay the highest price first.

The ruling principle in our considerations is that the "wrong" of reification can only be made "right" by such authentic identification with the cause that it is the subject's as well as the researcher's cause—whereby his role in its service is not just permitted by him, but *willed*. That sovereign will of his which embraces the end as his own restores his personhood to the otherwise depersonalizing context. To be valid it must be autonomous and informed. The latter condition can, outside the research community, only be fulfilled by degrees; but the higher the degree of understanding regarding the purpose and the technique, the more valid becomes the endorsement of the will. A margin of mere trust inevitably remains. Ultimately, the appeal for volunteers should seek this free and generous endorsement, the appropriation of the research purpose into the person's own scheme of ends. Thus, the appeal is in truth addressed to the one, mysterious, and sacred source of any such, generosity of the will— "devotion," whose forms and objects of commitment are various and may invest different motivations in different individuals. The following, for instance, may be responsive to the "call" we are discussing: compassion with human sufferings, zeal for humanity, reverence for the Golden Rule, enthusiasm for progress, homage to the cause of knowledge, even longing for sacrificial justification (do not call that "masochism," please). On all these, I say, it is defensible and right to draw when the research objective is worthy enough; and it is a prime duty of the research community (especially in view of what we

called the "margin of trust") to see that this sacred source is never abused for frivolous ends. For a less than adequate cause, not even the freest, unsolicited offer should be accepted.

The Rule of the "Descending Order" and Its Counterutility Sense

We have laid down what must seem to be a forbidding rule to the number-hungry research industry. Having faith in the transcendent potential of man, I do not fear that the "source" will ever foil a society that does not destroy it—and only such a one is worthy of the blessings of progress. But "elitistic" the rule is (as is the enterprise of progress itself), and elites are by nature small. The combined attribute of motivation and information, plus the absence of external pressures, tends to be socially so circumscribed that strict adherence to the rule might numerically starve the research process. This is why I spoke of a descending order of permissibility which is itself permissive, but where the realization that it is a *descending* order is not without pragmatic import. Departing from the august norm, the appeal must need shift from idealism to docility, from high-mindedness to compliance, from judgment to trust. Consent spreads over the whole spectrum. I will not go into the casuistics of this penumbral area. I merely indicate the principle of the order of preference: The poorer in knowledge, motivation, and freedom of decision (and that alas, means the more readily available in terms of numbers and possible manipulation), the more sparingly and indeed reluctantly should the reservoir be used, and the more compelling must therefore become the countervailing justification.

Let us note that this is the opposite of a social utility standard, the reverse of the order by "availability and expandability": The most valuable and scarcest, the least expendable dements of the social organism, are to be the first candidates for risk and sacrifice. It is the standard of *noblesse oblige*, and with all its counterutility and seeming "wastefulness," we feel a rightness about it and perhaps even a higher "utility," for the soul of the community lives by this spirit. It is also the opposite of what the day-to-day interests of research clamor for, and for the scientific community to honor it will mean that it will have to fight a strong temptation to go by routine to the readiest sources of supply—the suggestible, the ignorant, the dependent, the "captive" in various senses. I do not believe that heightened resistance here must cripple research, which cannot be permitted; but it may indeed slow it down by the smaller numbers fed into experimentation in consequence. This price—a possibly slower rate of progress—may have to be paid for the preservation of the most precious capital of higher communal life.

Experimentation on Patients

So far we have been speaking on the tacit assumption that the subjects of experimentation are recruited from among the healthy. To the question "Who is conscriptable?" the spontaneous answer is: Least and last of all the sick—the most available of all as they are under treatment and observation anyway. That the afflicted should not be called upon to bear additional burden and risk, that they are society's special trust and the physician's trust in particular—these are elementary responses of our moral sense. Yet the very destination of medical research, the conquest of disease, requires at the crucial stage trial and verification on precisely the sufferers from the disease, and their total exemption would defeat the purpose itself. In acknowledging this inescapable necessity, we enter the most sensitive area of the whole complex, the one most keenly felt and most searchingly discussed by the practitioners themselves. No wonder, it touches the heart of the doctor–patient relation, putting its most solemn obligations to the test. There is nothing new in what I have to say about the ethics of the doctor–patient relation, but for the purpose of confronting it with the issue of experimentation some of the oldest verities must be recalled.

The Fundamental Privilege of the Sick

In the course of treatment, the physician is obligated to the patient and to no one else. He is not the agent of society, nor of the interests of medical science, nor of the patient's family, nor of his co-sufferers, nor of future sufferers from the same disease. The patient alone counts when he is under the physician's care. By the simple law of bilateral contract (analogous, for example, to the relation of lawyer to client and its "conflict of interest" rule), the physician is bound not to let any other interest interfere with that of the patient in being cured. But manifestly more sublime norms than contractual ones are involved. We may speak of a sacred trust; strictly by its terms, the doctor is, as it were, alone with his patient and God.

There is one normal exception to this—that is, to the doctor's not being the agent of society vis-à-vis the patient, but the trustee of his interests alone: the quarantining of the contagious sick. This is plainly not for the patient's interest, but for that of others threatened by him. (In vaccination, we have a combination of both: protection of the individual and others.) But preventing the patient from causing harm to others is not the same as exploiting him for the advantage of others. And there is, of course, the abnormal exception of collective catastrophe, the analogue to a state of war. The physician who desperately battles a raging epidemic is under a unique dispensation that suspends in a nonspecifiable way some of the structures of normal practice, including possibly those against experimental liberties with his patients. No rules can be devised for the waiving of rules in extremities. And as with the famous shipwreck examples of ethical theory, the less said about it the better. But what is allowable there and may later be passed over in forgiving silence cannot serve as a precedent. We are concerned with non-extreme, non-emergency conditions where the voice of principle can be heard and claims can be adjudicated free from duress. We have conceded that there are such claims, and that if there is to be medical advance at all, not even the superlative privilege of the suffering and the sick can be kept wholly intact from the intrusion of its needs. About this least palatable, most disquieting part of our subject I have to offer only groping, inconclusive remarks.

The Principle of "Identification" Applied to Patients

On the whole, the same principles would seem to hold here as are found to hold with "normal subjects": motivation, identification, understanding on the part of the subject. But it is clear that these conditions are peculiarly difficult to satisfy with regard to a patient. His physical state, psychic preoccupation, dependent relation to the doctor, the submissive attitude induced by treatment—everything connected with his condition and situation makes the sick person inherently less of a sovereign person than the healthy one. Spontaneity of self-offering was almost to be ruled out; consent is marred by lower resistance or captive circumstance, and so on. In fact, all the factors that make the patient, as a category, particularly accessible and welcome for experimentation at the same time compromise the quality of the responding affirmation that must morally redeem the making use of them. This, in addition to the primacy of the physician's duty, puts a heightened onus on the physician-researcher to limit his undue power to the most important and defensible research objectives and, of course, to keep persuasion at a minimum.

Still, with all the disabilities noted, there is scope among patients for observing the rule of the "descending order of permissibility" that we have laid down for normal subjects, in vexing inversion of the utility order of quantitative abundance and qualitative "expendability." By the principle of this order, those patients who most identify with and are cognizant of the cause of research—members of the medical profession (who after all are sometimes patients themselves)—come first; the highly motivated and educated, also least dependent, among the lay patients come next; and so on down the line. An added consideration here is seriousness of condition, which again operates in inverse proportion. Here the profession must fight the tempting sophistry that the hopeless case is expendable (because in prospect already expended) and therefore especially usable; and generally the attitude that the poorer the chances of the patient the more justifiable his recruitment for experimentation (other than for his own benefit). The opposite is true.

Nondisclosure as a Borderline Case

Then there is the case where ignorance of the subject, sometimes even of the experimenter, is of the essence of the experiment (the "double-blind"–control group–placebo syndrome). It is said to be a necessary element of the scientific process. Whatever may be said about its ethics in regard to normal subjects, especially volunteers, it is an outright betrayal of trust in regard to the patient who believes that he is receiving treatment. Only supreme importance of the objective can exonerate it, without making it less of a transgression. The patient is definitely wronged even when not harmed. And ethics apart, the practice of such deception holds the danger of undermining the faith in the *bona fides* of treatment, the beneficial intent of the physician—the very basis of the doctor–patient relationship. In every respect it follows that concealed experiment on patients—that is, experiment under the guise of treatment—should be the rarest exception, at best, if it cannot be wholly avoided.

This has still the merit of a borderline problem. The same is not true of the other case of necessary ignorance of the subject—that of the unconscious patient. Drafting him for nontherapeutic experiments is simply and unqualifiedly impermissible; progress or not he must never be used, on the inflexible principle that utter helplessness demands utter protection.

When preparing this paper, I filled pages with a casuistic of this harrowing field, but then scrapped most of it, realizing my dilettante status. The shadings are endless, and only the physician-researcher can discern them properly as the cases arise. Into his lap the decision is thrown. The philosophical rule, once it has admitted into itself the idea of a sliding scale, cannot really specify its own application. It can only impress on the practitioner a general maxim or attitude for the exercise of his judgment and conscience in the concrete occasions of his work. In our case, I am afraid, it means making life more difficult for him.

It will also be noted that, somewhat at variance with the emphasis in the literature, I have not dwelt on the element of "risk" and very little on that of "consent." Discussion of the first is beyond the layman's competence; the emphasis on the second has been lessened because of its equivocal character. It is a truism to say that one should strive to minimize the risk and to maximize the consent. The more demanding concept of "identification," which I have used, includes "consent" in its maximal or authentic form, and the assumption of risk is its privilege.

No Experiments on Patients Unrelated to Their Own Disease

Although my ponderings have, on the whole, yielded points of view rather than definite prescriptions, premises rather than conclusions, they have led me to a few unequivocal yeses and nos. The first is the emphatic rule that patients should be experimented upon, if at all, *only* with reference to *their disease*. Never should there be added to the gratuitousness of the experiment as such the gratuitousness of service to an unrelated cause. This follows simply from what we have found to be the only excuse for infracting the special exemption of the sick at all—namely, that the scientific war on disease cannot accomplish its goal without drawing the sufferers from disease into the investigative process. If under this excuse they become subjects of experiment, they do so *because*, and only because, of *their* disease.

This is the fundamental and self-sufficient consideration. That the patient cannot possibly benefit from the unrelated experiment therapeutically, while he might from experiment related to his condition, is also true, but lies beyond the problem area of pure experiment. I am in any case discussing nontherapeutic experimentation only, where *ex hypothesi* the patient does not benefit. Experiment as part of therapy—that is, directed toward helping the subject himself—is a different matter altogether and raises its own problems but hardly philosophical ones. As long as a doctor can say, even if only in his own thought: "There is no known cure for your condition (or: You have responded to none); but there is promise in a new treatment still under investigation, not quite tested yet as to effectiveness and safety; you will be taking a chance, but all things considered, I judge it in your best interest to let me try it on you"—as long as he can speak thus, he speaks as the patient's physician and may err, but does not transform the patient into a subject of experimentation. Introduction of an untried therapy into the treatment where the tried ones have failed is not "experimentation on the patient."

Generally, and almost needless to say, with all the rules of the book, there is something "experimental" (because tentative) about every individual treatment, beginning with the diagnosis itself and he would be a poor doctor who would not learn from every case for the benefit of future cases, and a poor member of the profession who would not make any new insights gained from his treatments available to the profession at large. Thus, knowledge may be advanced in the treatment of any patient, and the interest of the medical art and all sufferers from the same affliction as well as the patient himself may be served if something happens to be learned from his case. But his gain to knowledge and future therapy is incidental to the *bona fide* service to the present patient. He has the right to expect that the doctor does nothing to him just in order to learn.

In that case, the doctor's imaginary speech would run, for instance, like this: "There is nothing more I can do for you. But you can do something for me. Speaking no longer as your physician but on behalf of medical science, we could learn a great deal about future cases of this kind if you would permit me to perform certain experiments on you. It is understood that you yourself would not benefit from any knowledge we might gain; but future patients would." This statement would express the purely experimental situation, assumedly here with the subject's concurrence

and with all cards on the table. In Alexander Bicker's words: "It is a different situation when the doctor is no longer trying to make [the patient] well, but is trying to find out how to make others well in the future."

But even in the second case, that of the nontherapeutic experiment where the patient does not benefit, at least the patient's own disease is enlisted in the cause of fighting that disease, even if only in others. It is yet another thing to say or think: "Since you are here—in the hospital with its facilities—anyway, under our care and observation anyway, away from your job (or, perhaps, doomed) anyway, we wish to profit from your being available for some other research of great interest we are presently engaged in." From the standpoint of merely medical ethics, which has only to consider risk, consent, and the worth of the objective, there may be no cardinal difference between this case and the last one. I hope that the medical reader will not think I am making too fine a point when I say that from the standpoint of the subject and his dignity there is a cardinal difference that crosses the line between the permissible and the impermissible, and this by the same principle of "Identification" I have been invoking all along. Whatever the rights and wrongs of any experimentation on any patient—in the one case, at least that residue of identification is left him that it is his own affliction by which he can contribute to the conquest of that affliction, his own kind of suffering which he helps to alleviate in others; and so in a sense it is his own cause. It is totally indefensible to rob the unfortunate of this intimacy with the purpose and make his misfortune a convenience for the furtherance of alien concerns.

Conclusion

. . . I wish only to say in conclusion that if some of the practical implications of my reasonings are felt to work out toward a slower rate of progress, this should not cause too great dismay. Let us not forget that progress is an optional goal, not an unconditional commitment and that its tempo in particular, compulsive as it may become, has nothing sacred about it. Let us also remember, that a slower progress in the conquest of disease would not threaten society, grievous as it is to those who have to deplore that their particular disease be not yet conquered, but that society would indeed be threatened by the erosion of those moral values whose loss, possibly caused by too ruthless a pursuit of scientific progress, would make its most dazzling triumphs not worth having. Let us finally remember that it cannot be the aim of progress to abolish the lot of mortality. Of some ill or other, each of us will die. Our mortal condition is upon us with its harshness but also its wisdom—because without it there would not be the eternally renewed promise of the freshness, immediacy, and eagerness of youth; nor would there be for any of us the incentive to number our days and make them count. With all our striving to wrest from our mortality what we can, we should bear its burden with patience and dignity.

Section 2:   The Ethics of Randomized Clinical Trials

How to Resolve an Ethical Dilemma Concerning Randomized Clinical Trials

Don Marquis

Don Marquis addresses the dilemma a physician faces when she believes that one of the two treatments in a clinical trial is better for her patient. Should she advise the patient to choose the treatment she thinks best or let him enter the trial and have to accept the randomly assigned treatment? If she keeps quiet she won't be giving the patient the benefit of her judgment but if she doesn't advise him, she will hinder the clinical trial.

Marquis rejects two attempts at resolving the dilemma. The equipoise notion holds that she doesn't really know which treatment is better, because she's lacking the best evidence, but it wrongly assumes that only such evidence can support a view. The second approach holds that because the professional community has not decided which treatment is best, she need not express her view about the matter. Marquis finds this unpersuasive: we expect the best advice from our physician, just as we do our attorney.

Resolving the dilemma requires that we take informed consent seriously. The physician explains her views to the patient, informs the patient of the alternatives (explaining also that in the clinical trial the patient may not get the experimental treatment), then allows the patient to make the decision.

An apparent ethical dilemma arises when physicians consider enrolling their patients in randomized clinical trials. Suppose that a randomized clinical trial comparing two treatments is in progress, and a physician has an opinion about which treatment is better. The physician has a duty to promote the patient's best medical interests and therefore seems to be obliged to advise the patient to receive the treatment that the physician prefers. This duty creates a barrier to the enrollment of patients in randomized clinical trials.[1-10] Two strategies are often used to resolve the dilemma in favor of enrolling patients in clinical trials.

The "Either You Know Which Is Better or You Don't" Strategy

According to one strategy, physicians should not recommend the treatment over another if they do not really know which one is better, and they do not

Don Marquis, From "How to Resolve an Ethical Dilemma Concerning Randomized Clinical Trials," *New England Journal of Medicine*, Vol 341 (August 26,1999), pp. 691–693. Copyright © 1999 Massachusetts Medical Society. All rights reserved. Reprinted with permission.

really know which treatment is better in the absence of data from randomized clinical trials.[11] Data from uncontrolled studies are often influenced by the desire on both the investigator's part and the patient's part to obtain positive results.[12] Journal editors are more likely to publish reports of studies with positive results than reports of studies with negative results.[13] A treatment recommendation based on weaker evidence than that obtained from a randomized clinical trial is like a recommendation based on a mere hunch or an idiosyncratic preference.[14] Thus, according to this argument, in the absence of data from a randomized clinical trial, evidence that provides an adequate basis for recommending a treatment rarely exists, and the enrollment dilemma is based on a mistake.

This strategy for resolving the dilemma is simplistic. It assumes that evidence available to physicians can be only one of two kinds: gold standard evidence or worthless prejudice. But clinical judgments may be based on evidence of intermediate quality, including physicians' experience with their own patients, their conversations with colleagues concerning their colleagues' experience, their evaluation of the results of nonrandomized studies reported in the literature, their judgment about the mechanism of action of one or both treatments, or their view of the natural history of a given disease. Evidence need not be conclusive to be valuable; it need not be definitive to be suggestive. Because all good physicians allow evidence of intermediate quality to influence their professional judgment when a relevant randomized clinical trial is not being conducted, it is unreasonable to claim that such evidence has no worth when a relevant randomized clinical trial is being conducted. Therefore, the "either you know which is better or you don't" strategy for dealing with the enrollment dilemma is not persuasive.

Adopting a Less Strict Therapeutic Obligation

The dilemma about enrolling patients in randomized clinical trials is generated by the claim that a physician has a strict therapeutic obligation to inform the patients of the physician's treatment preference, even when the preference is based on evidence that is not of the highest quality. The dilemma could be resolved if the physician's therapeutic obligation were less strict. This strategy was developed by Freedman.[14,15] He argued that the standard for determining whether a physician has engaged in medical malpractice or

committed some other violation punishable by a professional disciplinary body is the standard of good practice as determined by a consensus of the medical community. There is no consensus about which of two treatments being compared in a randomized clinical trial is superior. (Otherwise, why conduct the trial?) Therefore, enrolling a patient in the trial does not violate the physician's therapeutic obligation to the patient regardless of the physician's treatment preference. In addition, a patient who consults a physician with a preference for treatment A could have consulted a physician who preferred treatment B. Therefore, enrolling a patient in a randomized clinical trial in order to be randomly assigned (perhaps) to treatment B does not make such a patient worse off than he or she would otherwise have been.

Despite these points, compelling arguments for the stricter interpretation of therapeutic obligation remain. In the first place, consider what physicians expect when they seek professional advice from their malpractice attorneys, their tax advisors, or for that matter, their own physicians. Surely they expect–and believe they have a right to expect—not merely minimally competent advice, but the best professional judgments of the professionals they have chosen to consult. In the second place, patients choose physicians in order to obtain medical advice that is, in the judgment of those physicians, the best available. If physicians do not provide such advice, then they tacitly deceive their patients, unless they disclose to their patients that they are not bound by this strict therapeutic obligation. Physicians should adopt the strict therapeutic obligation.

A Resolution

The clash between a strict therapeutic obligation and a less strict one is only apparent. On the one hand, the less strict therapeutic obligation is supported by the argument that it is morally permissible to offer to enroll a patient in a randomized, clinical trial. On the other hand, the strict therapeutic obligation is supported by the arguments concerning treatment recommendations. Recommending is different from offering to enroll. A recognition of this difference provides the basis for a solution to the dilemma.

Suppose that a randomized clinical trial is being conducted to compare treatments A and B and that a physician prefers A and informs the patient of this preference. All physicians have an obligation to obtain their patients' informed consent to treatment.

A physician has respected this right only if he or she explains to the patient the risks and benefits of reasonable alternatives to the recommended treatment and offers the patient an opportunity to choose an alternative, if that is feasible. Either treatment B or enrollment in the trial comparing A and B is a reasonable alternative to treatment A, because presumably, A is not known to be superior to B: Indeed, there is some evidence that enrollment in a randomized clinical trial is a superior therapeutic alternative when a trial is available.[16] Respect for a patient's value is a central purpose of informed consent. A particular patient may place a greater value on participation in a study that will contribute to medical progress and to the well-being of patients in the future than on the unproved advantages of following the physician's recommendation. Therefore, a physician can both recommend a treatment and ask whether the patient is willing to enroll in the randomized clinical trial.

This resolution is based on the recognition that there can be evidence of the superiority of a treatment that falls short of the gold standard for evidence but is better than worthless. It also takes into account the good arguments for the view that physicians have a strict obligation to recommend the best treatment on the basis of their professional judgment, even when the recommendation is based on evidence that falls short of the gold standard. Nevertheless, because all physicians have an obligation to take informed consent seriously, because respect for informed consent entails offering a patient the reasonable alternatives to the recommended treatment, and because enrollment in an appropriate randomized clinical trial is often a reasonable therapeutic option, one could argue that offering a patient the opportunity to be enrolled in a clinical trial is not only morally permissible but, in many cases, also morally obligatory, if a relevant trial is being conducted and if enrollment in it is feasible. Taking informed consent seriously resolves the dilemma about whether to enroll patients in randomized clinical trials.

Is this analysis clinically realistic? Some may argue that if clinicians inform their patients that they prefer treatment A, then few of their patients will consent to participate in a trial comparing A with B. Furthermore, many clinicians may be unwilling to invest the time necessary to explain the option of enrollment in a trial, particularly if it seems unlikely that a patient, knowing the physician's preference for one of the treatments, will choose to participate in the trial.

On the other hand, in recent years the public has been exposed to a barrage of medical information and misinformation. Explaining to patients the difference between solid scientific evidence of the merits of a treatment and weaker evidence of its merits is worthwhile, whether or not a relevant randomized clinical trial is being conducted. When a relevant trial is being conducted, offering the patient enrollment in the trial should not impose on the physician a large, additional burden of explanation. Physicians can promote enrollment by explaining that their preference is based only on limited evidence, which may or may not be reliable. They can also explain that data from randomized clinical trials have often shown that the initial studies of new treatments were overly optimistic.[17]

In addition, using this informed-consent strategy to resolve the enrollment dilemma may not be morally optional. My analysis is based on two important obligations of physicians. The first is the strict obligation to commend the treatment that is, in the physician's professional judgment, the best choice for the patient. The second is the obligation to obtain the patient's informed consent to the recommended treatment. The duty of obtaining informed consent implies that the physician is obligated to offer the patient the opportunity to enroll in a clinical trial when one is available, even if the physician has a treatment preference. The physician owes this duty to the individual patient, not simply to future patients who may benefit from advances in medical knowledge. Thus, the informed-consent strategy for resolving [the] dilemma about enrolling patients in randomized clinical trials leads to the conclusion that physicians have a greater duty to offer their patients enrollment in trials than has previously been realized. A strict, thoroughly defensible, therapeutic obligation need not interfere with the conduct of randomized clinical trials.

I am indebted to Erin Fitz-Gerald, Nina Ainslie, Stephen Williamson, Sarah Taylor, Jerry Menikoff, Don Hatton, and Ron Stephens for their criticisms.

References

1. Chalmers T. C. The ethics of randomization as a decision-making technique and the problem of informed consent Report of the 14th conference of cardiovascular training grant program directors, June 3–4, 1967. Bethesda, Md.: National Heart Institute, 1967; 87–93.
2. Shaw L. W, Chalmers TG Ethics in cooperative clinical trials. *Ann N Y Acad Sci* 1970; 169:487–95.
3. Kolata G. B. Clinical trials: methods and ethics are debated. *Science* 1977; 198:1127–31.

4. Wilder D. Ethical considerations in randomized clinical trials. *Semin Oncol* 1981; 8:437–41.

5. Schafer A. The ethics of the randomized clinical trial, *N Engl J Med* 1982; 307:719–24.

6. Marquis D. Leaving therapy to chance. *Hastings Cent Rep* 1983; 13:40–7.

7. Gifford R. The conflict between randomized clinical trials and the therapeutic obligation. *J Med Philos* 1936; 11:347–66.

8. Hellman S, Hellman D. S. Of mice but not men: problems of the randomized clinical trial. *N Engl J Med* 1991; 324:1585–9.

9. Gifford R. Community equipoise and the ethics of randomized clinical trials. *Bioethics* 1995; 9:127–48.

10. Markman M. Ethical difficulties with randomized clinical trials involving cancer patients: examples from the field of gynecologic oncology. *J Clin Ethics* 1992; 3:193–5.

11. Spodick D. H. Ethics of the randomized clinical trial. *N Engl J Med* 1983; 308:343.

12. Passamani E. Clinical trials—are they ethical? *N Engl J Med* 1991; 324:1589–92.

13. Altman L. Negative results; a positive viewpoint. *New York Times.* April 29,1986:B6.

14. Freedman B. Equipoise and the ethics of clinical research. *N Engl J Med* 1987; 317:141–5.

15. *Idem.* A response to a purported ethical difficulty with randomized clinical trials involving cancer patients. *J. Clin Ethics* 1992; 3:231–4.

16. Davis S, Wright PW, Schulman S. F., et al. Participants in prospective, randomized clinical trials for resected non-small cell lung cancer have improved survival compared with nonparticipants in such trials. *Cancer* 1985; 56:1710–8.

17. Sacks H, Chalmers T. C. Smith H]r. Randomized versus historical controls for clinical trials. *Am J Med* 1982; 72:233–40.

Clinical Trials: Are They Ethical?

Eugene Passamani

Eugene Passamani argues that randomized clinical trials (RCTs) are the most reliable means of evaluating new therapies. Without RCTs, chance and bias may affect our conclusions.

Passamani rejects the argument that the physician–patient relationship demands that physicians recommend the "best" therapy for patients, no matter how poor the data on which the recommendation is based. He acknowledges that RCTs pose ethical problems for physician-researchers but believes the difficulties can be overcome by employing three procedural safeguards.

First, all participants must give their informed consent. They must be told about the goals of the research and its potential benefits and risks. Moreover, they must be informed about alternatives to their participation, and they must be permitted to withdraw from the trial at any time they choose. Second, for an RCT to be legitimate, a state of clinical *equipoise* must exist. Competent physicians must be genuinely uncertain about which of the alternative therapies in the trial is superior and content to allow their patients to be treated with any of them. Finally the clinical trial must be designed as a critical test of the therapeutic alternatives. Properly carried out Passamani holds, RCTs protect physicians and patients from therapies that are ineffective or toxic.

[A Type I error consists in deciding that therapy A is better than therapy B when, in fact both are of equal worth (i.e., a true null hypothesis is rejected). A Type II error consists in deciding that the treatments are equally good when A is actually better than B (i.e., a false null hypothesis is accepted).—Ronald Munson.]

Eugene Passamani, From "Clinical Trials: Are They Ethical?", *New England Journal of Medicine*, Vol. 324, no. 22 (1991), pp. 1589-1591. © 1991 Massachusetts Medical Society. All rights reserved. Reprinted by permission.

Biomedical research leads to better understanding of biology and ultimately to improved health. Physicians have for millenniums attempted to understand disease, to use this knowledge to cure or palliate, and to relieve attendant suffering. Improving strategies for prevention and treatment remains an ethical imperative for medicine. Until very recently, progress depended largely on a process of carefully observing groups of patients given a new and promising therapy; outcome was then compared with that previously observed in groups undergoing a standard treatment. Outcome in a series of case patients as compared with that in nonrandomized controls can be used to assess the treatment of disorders in which therapeutic effects are dramatic and the pathophysiologic features are relatively uncomplicated, such as vitamin deficiency or some infectious diseases. Observational methods are not very useful, however, in the detection of small treatment effects in disorders in which there is substantial variability in expected outcome and imperfect knowledge of complicated pathophysiologic features (many vascular disorders and most cancers, for example). The effect of a treatment cannot easily be extracted from variations in disease severity and the effects of concomitant treatments. Clinical trials have thus become a preferred means of evaluating an ever increasing flow of innovative diagnostic and therapeutic maneuvers. The randomized, double-blind clinical trial is a powerful technique because of the efficiency and credibility associated with treatment comparisons involving randomized concurrent controls.

The modern era of randomized trials began in the early 1950s with the evaluation of streptomycin in patients with tuberculosis.[1] Since that time trial techniques and methods have continuously been refined.[2] In addition, the ethical aspects of these experiments in patients have been actively discussed.[3–7]

In what follows I argue that randomized trials are in fact the most scientifically sound and ethically correct means of evaluating new therapies. There is potential conflict between the roles of physician and physician-scientist, and for this reason society has created mechanisms to ensure that the interests of individual patients are served should they elect to participate in a clinical trial.[6]

Clinical Research

The history of medicine is richly endowed with therapies that were widely used and then shown to be ineffective or frankly toxic. Relatively recent examples of such therapeutic maneuvers include gastric freezing for peptic ulcer disease, radiation therapy for acne, MER-29 (triparanol) for cholesterol reduction, and thalidomide for sedation in pregnant women. The 19th century was even more gruesome, with purging and bloodletting. The reasons for this march of folly are many and include, perhaps most importantly, the lack of complete understanding of human biology and pathophysiology, the use of observational methods coupled with the failure to appreciate substantial variability between patients in their response to illness and to therapy, and the shared desire of physicians and their patients for cure or palliation.

Chance or bias can result in the selection of patients for innovative treatment who are either the least diseased or the most severely affected. Depending on the case mix, a treatment that has no effect can appear to be effective or toxic when historical controls are used. With the improvement in diagnostic accuracy and the understanding of disease that has occurred with the passage of time, today's patients are identified earlier in the natural history of their disease. Recently selected case series therefore often have patients who are less ill and an outcome that is considerably better than that of past case series, even without changes in treatment.

Randomization tends to produce treatment and control groups that are evenly balanced in both known and unrecognized prognostic factors, which permits a more accurate estimate of treatment effect in groups of patients assigned to experimental and standard therapies. A number of independent randomized trials with congruent results are powerful evidence indeed.

A physician's daily practice includes an array of preventive, diagnostic, and therapeutic maneuvers, some of which have been established by a plausible biologic mechanism and substantial evidence from randomized clinical trials (e.g., the use of beta-blockers, thrombolytic therapy, and aspirin in patients with myocardial infarction).[8] It is unlikely that our distant descendants in medicine will discover that we late 20th-century physicians were wrong in these matters. However, new therapeutic maneuvers that have not undergone rigorous assessment may well turn out to be ineffective or toxic. Every therapy adopted by common consent on the basis of observational studies and plausible mechanism, but without the benefit of randomized studies, may be categorized by future physicians as useless or worse.

Physicians are aware of the fragility of the evidence supporting many common therapies, and this is why properly performed randomized clinical trials have profound effects on medical practice. The scientific importance of randomized, controlled trials is in safeguarding current and future patients from our therapeutic passions. Most physicians recognize this fact.

Like any human activity, experimentation involving patients can be performed in an unethical and even criminal fashion. Nazi war crimes led to substantial efforts to curb abuse, beginning with the Nuremberg Code and the Helsinki Declaration and culminating in the promulgation of clearly articulated regulations in the United States and elsewhere.[1-6] There are abuses more subtle than those of the Gestapo and the SS. Involving patients in experiments that are poorly conceived and poorly executed is unethical. Patients who participate in such research may incur risk without the hope of contributing to a body of knowledge that will benefit them or others in the future. The regulations governing human experimentation are very important, as is continuing discussion and debate to improve the scientific and ethical aspects of this effort.

Several general features must be part of property designed trials. The first is informed consent, which involves explicitly informing a potential participant of the goals of the research, its potential benefits and risks, the alternatives to participating, and the right to withdraw from the trial at any time. Whether informed consent is required in all trials has been debated.[5] I believe that patients must always be aware that they are part of an experiment. Second, a state of clinical equipoise must exist. Clinical equipoise means that on the basis of the available data, a community of competent physicians would be content to have their patients pursue any of the treatment strategies being tested in a randomized trial, since none of them have been clearly established as preferable.[7] The chief purpose of a data-monitoring committee is to stop the trial if the accumulating data destroy the state of clinical equipoise—that is, indicate efficacy or suggest toxicity. Finally, the trial must be designed as a critical test of the therapeutic alternatives being assessed. The question must be clearly articulated, with carefully defined measures of outcome; with realistic estimates of sample size, including probable event rates in the control group and a postulated and plausible reduction in the event rates in the treatment group; with Type I and II errors specified; and

with subgroup hypotheses clearly stated if appropriate. The trial must have a good chance of settling an open question.[2]

Ethical Dimensions of Properly Constituted Trials

Experimentation in the clinic by means of randomized, controlled clinical trials has been periodically attacked as violating the covenant between doctor and patient.[10-12] Critics have charged that physicians engaged in clinical trials sacrifice the interests of the patient they ask to participate to the good of all similarly affected patients in the future. The argument is that physicians have a personal obligation to use their best judgment and recommend the "best" therapy, no matter how tentative or inconclusive the data on which that judgment is based. Physicians must play their hunches. According to this argument, randomized clinical trials may be useful in seeking the truth, but carefully designed, legitimate trials are unethical and perhaps even criminal because they prevent individual physicians from playing their hunches about individual patients. Therefore, it is argued, physicians should not participate in such trials.

It is surely unethical for physicians to engage knowingly in an activity that will result in inferior therapy for their patients. It is also important that the community of physicians be clear in distinguishing between established therapies and those that are promising but unproved. It is this gulf between proved therapies and possibly effective therapies (all the rest) that defines the ethical and unethical uses of randomized clinical trials. Proved therapies involve a consensus of the competent medical community that the data in hand justify using a treatment in a given disorder. It is this consensus that defines an ethical boundary. The physician-investigator who asks a patient to participate in a randomized, controlled trial represents this competent medical community in asserting that the community is unpersuaded by existing data that an innovative treatment is superior to standard therapy. Arguments that a physician who believes that such a treatment *might be* useful commits an unethical act by randomizing patients are simply wrong. Given the history of promising but discarded therapies, hunches about potential effectiveness are not the ideal currency of the patient–doctor interchange.

Lest readers conclude that modem hunches are more accurate than older ones, I have selected an example from the current cardiovascular literature that reveals the problems inherent in relying on hunches to the occlusion of carefully done experiments.

The Cardiac Arrhythmia Suppression Trial

Sudden death occurs in approximately 300,000 persons in the United States each year and is thus a problem worthy of our best efforts. In the vast majority of cases the mechanism is ventricular fibrillation superimposed on a scarred or ischemic myocardium. It had been observed that the ventricular extrasystoles seen on the ambulatory electrocardiographic recordings of survivors of myocardial infarction were independently and reproducibly associated with an increased incidence of subsequent mortality.[13,14] It had been established that a variety of antiarrhythmic drugs can suppress ventricular extrasystoles. Accordingly, physicians had the hunch that suppressing ventricular extrasystoles in the survivors of myocardial infarction would reduce the incidence of ventricular fibrillation and sudden death.

The Cardiac Arrhythmia Suppression Thai (CAST) investigators decided to test this hypothesis in a randomized, controlled trial. They sought survivors of myocardial infarction who had frequent extrasystoles on electrocardiographic recordings. The trial design included a run-in period during which one of three active drugs was administered and its effect on extrasystoles noted. Those in whom arrhythmias were suppressed were randomly assigned to active drug or placebo. The trial had to be stopped prematurely because of an unacceptable incidence of sudden death in the treatment group.[15] During an average follow-up of 10 months, 56 of 730 patients (7.7 percent) assigned to active drug and 22 of 725 patient (3.0 percent) assigned to placebo died. Clinical equipoise was destroyed by this striking effect. It is quite unlikely that observational (nonrandomized) methods would have detected this presumably toxic effect.

The CAST trial was a major advance in the treatment of patients with coronary disease and ventricular arrhythmia. It clearly revealed that the hunches of many physicians were incorrect. The trial's results are applicable not only to future patients with coronary disease and ventricular arrhythmia but also to the patients who participated in the study. By randomizing, investigators ensured that half the participants received the better therapy—in this case placebo—and, contrary to intuition, most of them ultimately received the better therapy after the trial ended prematurely and drugs were withdrawn.

To summarize, randomized clinical trials are an important element in the spectrum of biomedical research. Not all questions can or should be addressed by this technique; feasibility, cost, and the relative importance of the issues to be addressed are weighed by investigators before they elect to proceed. Properly carried out, with informed consent, clinical equipoise, and a design adequate to answer the question posed, randomized clinical trials protect physicians and their patients from therapies that are ineffective or toxic. Physicians and their patients must be clear about the vast gulf separating promising and proved therapies. The only reliable way to make this distinction in the face of incomplete information about pathophysiology and treatment mechanism[s] is to experiment, and this will increasingly involve randomized trials. The alternative—a retreat to older methods—is unacceptable.

Physicians regularly apply therapies tested in groups of patients to an individual patient. The likelihood of success in an individual patient depends on the degree of certainty evident in the group and the scientific strength of the methods used. We owe patients involved in the assessment of new therapies the best that science and ethics can deliver. Today, for most unproved treatments, that is a properly performed randomized clinical trial.

Notes

1. Streptomycin in Tuberculosis Trials Committee, Medical Research Council. Streptomycin treatment of pulmonary tuberculosis: a Medical Research Council investigation. *BMJ* 1948; 2:769–82.

2. Friedman LM, Furberg CD, DeMets DL. *Fundamentals of clinical trials*. Boston: John Wright/PSG, 1981.

3. Beecher HK. Ethics and clinical research. *N Engl J Med* 1966; 274:1354–60.

4. Appendix II (The Nuremberg Code). In; Beauchamp TL, Childress JF. *Principles of biomedical ethics*. New York: Oxford University Press, 1979; 287–9.

5. Appendix II (The World Medical Association Declaration of Helsinki). In: Beauchamp TL, Childress JF. *Principles of biomedical ethics*. New York: Oxford University Press, 1979; 289–93.

6. The National Commission for the Protection of Human Subjects of Biomedical and Behavioral Research. The Belmont report: ethical principles and guidelines for the protection of human subjects of research. Washington, D.C.: Government Printing Office, 1978. (DHEW publication no. (05) 78-0012.)

7. Freedman B. Equipoise and the ethics of clinical research. *N Engl J Med* 1987; 317:141–5.

8. Yusuf S, Wittes J, Friedman L. Overview of results of randomized clinical trials in heart disease. L Treatments following myocardial infarction. *JAMA* 1988; 260:2088–93.

9. Brahams D. Randomized trials and informed consent. *Lancet* 1988; 1033–4.

10. Burkhardt R, Kienle G. Controlled clinical trials and medical ethics. *Lancet* 1978; 2:1356–9.

11. Marquis D. Leaving therapy to chance. *Hastings Cent Rep* 1983; 13(4):40–7.

12. Gifford F. The conflict between randomized clinical trials and the therapeutic obligation. *J Med Philos* 1986; 1:347–66.

13. Ruberman W, Weinblatt E, Goldberg JD, Frank CW, Shapiro S. Ventricular premature beats and mortality after myocardial infarction. *N Engl J Med* 1977; 297:750–7.

14. Lown B. Sudden cardiac death: the major challenge confronting contemporary cardiology. *Am J Cardiol* 1979; 43:313–28.

15. The Cardiac Arrhythmia Suppression Trial (CAST) investigators. Preliminary report: effect of encainide and flecainide on mortality in a randomized trial of arrhythmia suppression after myocardial infarction. *N Engl J Med* 1989; 321:406–12.

How Necessary Are Randomized Controlled Trials?

Robert Northcott

Robert Northcott argues that although randomized controlled trials (RCTs) are usually considered the "gold standard" for testing a new treatment, they are not always the preferred way. Historical studies, which assess the effectiveness of treatments on the basis of data drawn from experiences using them, are sometimes preferable to RCTs in showing that new treatments are superior to standard ones.

Northcott uses the case of extracorporeal membranous oxygenation (ECMO) to argue that when the treatment was introduced, it was so successful in saving the lives of newborns with underdeveloped lungs that no RCT was needed to prove its superiority to conventional treatment. The belief that an RCT was required, Northcott claims, led to deaths that were not only tragic, but unnecessary.

Historically, newborns with a form of respiratory failure called persistent pulmonary hypertension (PPHS) faced a mortality rate of more than 80 percent. The main symptom is immaturity of the lungs, leading to poor oxygenation of the blood. Doctors seek desperately to keep the baby alive until the lungs mature. But recently it happened that suffering babies faced these terrible odds . . . when, all along, a new treatment that had recorded an 80 percent *survival* rate was available but left unused. In particular, this occurred during several trials of the treatment known as extracorporeal membranous oxygenation (ECMO).

Developed in the late 1970s, ECMO in effect takes over the function of the lungs by withdrawing blood and oxygenating and then reheating it artificially, before finally returning it to the baby. Nevertheless, despite immensely promising initial results, the researchers behind ECMO felt that, in order to prove their therapy, they needed to conduct a randomized controlled trial (RCT) of it. Otherwise, they worried,

the treatment would never gain general acceptance (Bartlett et al., 1982). Is this how it should be? Are RCTs really the unique "gold standard" that should always trump other kinds of evidence? The stakes are high. Of course, no one in this story *wanted* newborn babies to die unnecessarily. The dispute, rather, was a sincere one about how best to prove ECMO's effectiveness.

As is well known, RCTs work roughly as follows: they randomly divide a trial sample into two groups, one of which (the "treatment group") receives the new treatment and the other of which (the "control group") receives only a placebo or the old treatment. Outcomes in the two groups are then compared. If the first group does better this is strong evidence in favor of the new treatment, because randomization is designed to ensure that the only relevant difference between the two groups—and hence the only possible explanation for the different outcomes—is the different treatments received.

A common worry is that asking patients to participate in RCTs can be unethical, because often we have reason to believe that a new treatment is rather promising, in which case those in the control group are thereby being denied what is probably better care. Newborn babies being denied ECMO is an especially striking example. Are such unlucky patients being put at risk unjustifiably? The most powerful reply is that RCTs are the only way to establish secure knowledge of therapeutic effectiveness, so, in the long run, it would be ethically disastrous to stymie medical progress by stopping them. Besides, advocates claim, until an RCT is carried out, we cannot know for sure whether a new treatment actually *is* better.

Reconciling these two positions is often a nuanced matter. The vital underlying issue is the extent to which, in the absence of RCT evidence, a physician is entitled to judge one treatment more effective than another. That is, matters turn on something more properly located in philosophy of science than in bioethics—namely, to what extent *are* RCTs the indispensable best method for judging a treatment's effectiveness?

Are RCTs Special?

When it comes to establishing whether a particular treatment causes better outcomes, there is plenty of common ground. Everyone agrees that the ideal situation is to compare the effects of a treatment with the effects of the alternative, *all else equal*. The problem, of course, is that usually many things affect an outcome besides the treatment itself: the patient's age, general health, and sex; how early the condition has been diagnosed; and so on. The key is to balance treatment and control groups with respect to "confounders"— that is, with respect these other, potentially muddying factors.

Across the sciences, many methods exist for doing this besides RCTs. Perhaps the most famous is the simple controlled experiment with no randomization element. Another is the historical or observational study. These studies use data that do not come from experiments. As a result, those data must be selected with extra care so as to make due allowance for potential confounders and thus avoid being distorted. In the context of medicine, it is these historical studies that are especially controversial. In the past, they were often conducted poorly. Common problems included inconsistent diagnostic procedures and interpretations, uneven rates of hospitalization across groups, and difficulty in "blinding" data collection. For example, if patients in the past were diagnosed less quickly, then

superior outcomes today might reflect simply earlier diagnosis rather than anything special about new treatments. Overall, historical studies had a tendency to overestimate treatment effects (Chalmers et al., 1983). Compared with this shortcoming, the rigor of testing for new treatments today is rightly lauded, and RCTs are central to that. It is this record that has motivated many to insist on RCTs—and only RCTs—as the gold standard.

However, recent work in philosophy of science casts doubt upon such an insistence. No one defends poorly conducted historical studies, let alone reliance on individual physicians' personal hunches. And no one denies that well run RCTs are often the most effective method—sometimes, indeed, perhaps the only available one. However, it is now argued, RCTs are not *always* best. First, techniques for running historical studies have improved enormously; great strides have been made in research design and in techniques for causal inference from statistics. Indeed, more recent analyses suggest that historical studies now perform equally as well as RCTs and perhaps even *better* (Benson and Hartz 2000; Concato et al., 2000). Much turns out to depend on the specifics of each case: sometimes one method may be the superior choice, sometimes another. This is especially true when one also takes into account "external" considerations such as cost, timing, or convenience.

Moreover, plenty of other sciences have prospered without RCTs. Even within medicine, some of our most reliable and important knowledge has come from historical studies, formal and informal. Examples include most surgical techniques, that smoking causes cancer, and that aspirin relieves headaches.

Problems to be avoided

There are several well-known difficulties that efficiently conducted RCTs have proved effective at guarding against:

* Doctors might select only the most medically promising patients for the treatment group, a strategy that risks distorting the results. Or they might interpret a patient's symptoms differently, depending on which group the patient is in. Avoiding these risks is the motivation for blinding a trial from *physicians*.

* If patients know that they are in the treatment group rather than the control group, this knowledge can affect how they self-report their outcomes, a consideration that is often relevant—for instance,

with regard to psychiatric conditions. Avoiding this risk is the motivation for blinding a trial from *patients*.

※ Generally, treatment and control groups can be imbalanced with respect to confounders both known and unknown. A *randomized* allocation seeks to head off this problem (more on the issue of randomization shortly).

However, it is helpful also to be aware of several other difficulties that can lead even an RCT astray. Examples include the following:

※ The patients recruited for a trial might be unrepresentative of the general population. For example, if a drug is especially effective only in one ethnic group, but that ethnic group is underrepresented in the trial, then this efficacy might well be missed. Observational studies are often *more* careful about matching the tested population with the wider eventual target population.

※ Not all patients who sign up for a trial persevere with it. If the dropouts are unrepresentative and are omitted from the final results, the trial can be skewed. For example, imagine testing a safe-sex program among sex workers: some of the subjects in the safe-sex treatment group will drop out rather than lose income. Those who drop out will likely not be typical, thus distorting the results. Again, such programs can often be assessed much better by using historical control groups rather than RCTs.

※ A treatment might have positive effects on one subgroup but negative effects on another. A trial's overall results might then simply reflect the net balance between these two subgroups, missing the individual effects.

※ A treatment might be based on mistaken units of analysis. For example, often an education program should allocate whole schools to treatment and control groups, not just classes or individuals. As a result, the effective sample size is the number of schools, which is a much smaller number than the number of classes or individuals. But analyses of such trial results might misstate or ignore this fact.

※ A treatment might produce false negatives, meaning that the effectiveness of the treatment is missed, perhaps because of small numbers or insensitive outcome measures.

※ There may be problems with blinding and the use of a suitable placebo, meaning that bias is not controlled effectively.

Of course, well-designed RCTs try their best to counter these difficulties—and poorly conducted historical studies will also be vulnerable to many of them. The point is only that conducting an RCT is no guarantee—they, too, can go wrong.

Some of these difficulties are especially likely to crop up when social policy or public health interventions are assessed. As a result, in these domains observational studies are often not only more feasible than RCTs but actually give more accurate results, too. It might be difficult to set up a useful RCT for a food policy program, for instance. But if we put weight only on RCTs, observational studies will inevitably be downgraded. As a result, the food program might be denied funding, even though it potentially has more of an impact on public health than most drug trials put together. That is, an overemphasis on RCTs over all other methods risks unhealthily distorting which science is funded in the first place (Grossman & Mackenzie, 2005).

ECMO Again

Historical studies, like RCTs, need to avoid the various problems just listed. But sometimes they will prove preferable to RCTs. ECMO is a good example, for in that case there was good reason to trust the historical data. For instance, all newborns with PPHS were treated without exception, there was no ambiguity regarding the interpretation or reporting of outcomes, and there was no known muddying confounder, such as speed of diagnosis, correlated with the split of the historical sample between ECMO and conventional treatments. In sum, was not the established 80 percent mortality rate for conventional treatment already a rigorous enough control group? And was not the 20 percent mortality rate of the babies treated with ECMO already a rigorous enough treatment group? Moreover, the improvement in outcomes reported for ECMO was so huge that any confounding effect would have to have been correspondingly huge to nullify it.

The only element missing from the ECMO data was randomization. Yet this single omission was taken to be reason enough to demand a "proper" (i.e., randomized) trial. As we shall see, such an insistence was highly questionable. As it turned out, the complex procedure eventually adopted for ECMO's RCT, carried out in the early 1980s, resulted in 11 patients being assigned the ECMO treatment, who all survived, and one assigned the conventional treatment, who died (Bartlett et al., 1985). Yet, despite this 100 percent 11-for-11 survival rate for ECMO, as opposed remember, to historical survival rates of only 20 percent, critics still insisted that the evidence was insufficient to prove ECMO's efficacy, because only one baby had been assigned the conventional treatment.

Therefore, another RCT was carried out in the late 1980s. Nine babies received ECMO; all nine survived. Ten received conventional treatment; only six survived. At that stage, prespecified criteria deemed the evidence sufficiently conclusive for the trial to be halted. A further 20 babies who arrived at trial centers suffering from PPHS were all assigned ECMO; 19 of those survived (O'Rourke et al., 1989).

Finally, even after this second RCT, some statisticians objected that the sample sizes were still too small for definitive conclusions. Amazingly, a *third* trial was begun in the UK. The result? It had to be stopped early because of too many deaths in the control group.

Is Randomization Really Necessary?

The only virtue missing from the original ECMO data, recall, was randomization. But is randomization really so necessary? The case for it is well known. In particular, while we can arrange "by hand" for a treatment and control group to be equally balanced with respect to known possible confounders, such as age and health, we obviously cannot balance by hand with respect to *unknown* confounders, precisely because they are unknown. If we allocate randomly, however, it automatically ensures that there will be no systematic bias with respect to *any* confounder at all, known or unknown.

However—return to that word "systematic." True enough, in the long run over many distributions, allocating patients randomly will ensure no systematic bias. But any *one* allocation might certainly turn out to be very biased indeed. For example, suppose that age is important and that we randomly allocate 20 patients, 10 young and 10 old. Quite possibly, just by chance, we may end up with a treatment group of, say, eight young and two old, and a control group the other way round. (Such imbalances are especially likely with smaller sample sizes and when there are many known confounds all needing to be balanced.) In such circumstances, the usual remedy is to rerandomize to get a better balance, a procedure known as baseline rebalancing. Once we arrive at an allocation that is deemed sufficiently balanced with respect to all known factors, a trial may go ahead.

But if the only factors that are skewed are unknown ones, then we will have no way of recognizing the need for baseline rebalancing. In other words, in any *particular* case, randomization provides no guarantee at all that we actually are balanced with respect to unknown factors, even though this is supposedly its unique advantage.

Compare balancing by hand instead. Known factors can obviously be allocated evenly that way; there is no need for randomization. With respect to unknown factors, meanwhile, there is no reason to expect a hand allocation to be any less balanced than a random one. If these unknown factors are correlated with any known ones, then the best we can do is balance with respect to the latter—and that is exactly what's done anyway.[1] The conclusion is that randomization in itself adds nothing (Worrall, 2002, 2007).[2] It might be objected that, be that as it may, in any case randomization does no harm either, assuming that any baseline rebalancing is performed thoroughly. But the real point is that the perception that randomization is necessary leads to the unjustified shunning of other forms of evidence. That was why, for instance, the dramatically heightened survival rates associated with the ECMO treatment were not thought decisive—even though there was no strong reason to think them the result of any of various known confounders. Only an unreasonable prejudice in favor of randomization for its own sake can explain why the existing ECMO evidence wasn't deemed sufficient.

To what extent, then, are RCTs necessary? Many times, they will indeed be the best evidence. But not always—other times, historical or observational trials may be equally or even more persuasive. Or, as with ECMO, the historical data should already be considered sufficient. Overall, there is no one-size-fits-all answer. Decisions must be made case by case. Whether it is indeed unethical to recruit participants for an RCT can therefore also only be assessed case by case.

References

Bartlett, R.H., A.F. Andrews, J.M. Toomasian, N.J. Haiduc, and A.B. Gazzaniga (1982). "Extracorporeal Membrane Oxygenation for Newborn Respiratory Failure: 45 Cases," *Surgery* 92:425–433.

[1] A large sample size is a red herring here. True, a large sample makes it more likely that a random assignment will be evenly balanced with respect to unknown factors—but equally, it makes it more likely that a by-hand assignment will be, too.

[2] True, randomization can also help ensure the blinding of trials from physicians, something agreed by everyone to be desirable. But there are plenty of other ways to ensure such blinding.

Bartlett, R.H., D.W. Roloff, R.G. Cornell, A.F. Andrews, P.W. Dillon, and J.B. Zwischenberger (1985). "Extracorporeal Circulation in Neonatal Respiratory Failure: A Prospective Randomized Study," *Pediatrics* 76: 479–487.

Benson, K. and A J. Hartz (2000). "A Comparison of Observational Studies and Randomized, Controlled Trial," *New England Journal of Medicine* 342: 1878–1886.

Chalmers, T.C., P. Celano, H.S. Sacks, and H. Smith (1983). "Bias in Treatment Assignment in Controlled Clinical Trials," *New England Journal of Medicine* 309: 1358–1361.

Concato, J., N. Shah, and R.I. Horwitz (2000). "Randomized Controlled Trials, Observational Studies, and the Hierarchy of Research Design," *New England Journal of Medicine* 342: 1887–1892.

Grossman, J., and F.J. Mackenzie (2005). "The Randomized Controlled Trial: Gold Standard, or Merely Standard?" *Perspectives in Biology and Medicine* 48: 516–534.

O'Rourke, P.P., R.K. Crone, J.P. Vacanti, J.H. Ware, C.W. Lillehei, R.B. Parad, and M.F Epstein (1989). "Extracorporeal Membrane Oxygenation and Conventional Medical Therapy in Neonates with Persistent Pulmonary Hypertension of the New Born: A Prospective Randomized Study," *Pediatrics* 84: 957–963.

Worrall, J. (2002). "*What* Evidence in Evidence-Based Medicine?" *Philosophy of Science* 169: S316–S330.

Worrall, J. (2007). "Why There's No Cause to Randomize," *British Journal for the Philosophy of Science* 58: 451–488.

Section 3: Access to Experimental Drugs

Abigail Alliance v. FDA Majority Opinion: Patients Have a Right to Have Access to Experimental Drugs

Judith W. Rogers

Circuit Judge Rogers argues that terminally ill adult patients should have access to investigational drugs if (a) they have no better treatment options and (b) the drugs have completed Phase I trials and been found safe enough for additional human testing. She bases her argument, among others, on two claims: first, there has been no long-standing tradition in the U.S of government concern with the effectiveness of drugs. Second, the right to access lifesaving drugs can be inferred from the *Cruzan* decision, in which the Supreme Court found a right to refuse lifesaving treatment. (For the Cruzan case, see pp. 591–593.)

The Abigail Alliance for Better Access to Developmental Drugs seeks to enjoin the Food and Drug Administration from continuing to enforce a policy barring the sale of new drugs that the FDA has determined, after Phase I trials on human beings, are sufficiently safe for expanded human testing. . . . More specifically,

United States Court of Appeals for the District of Columbia Circuit, No. 04-5350 (Decided May 2, 2006). *Abigail Alliance for Better Access to Developmental Drugs and Washington Legal Foundation*, Appellants v. Andrew C. von Eeschenbach, M.D. in His Official Capacity as Acting Commissioner, Food and Drug Adminstration and Michael O. Leavitt, in his Official Capacity as Secretary of the U.S. Department of Health and Human Services, Appellees. Appeal from the United States District Court for the District of Columbia (No. 03cv01601). Headings added by editor.

the Alliance seeks access to potentially life-saving post-Phase I investigational new drugs on behalf of mentally competent, terminally ill adult patients who have no alternative government approved treatment options. . . .

The Alliance contends that the FDA's policy violates the substantive due process rights to privacy, liberty, and life of its terminally ill members. The complaint presents the question of whether the Due Process Clause protects the right of terminally ill patients to decide, without FDA interference, whether to assume the risks of using potentially life-saving investigational new drugs that the FDA has yet to approve for commercial marketing but that the FDA has determined, after Phase I clinical human trials, are safe enough for further testing on a substantial number of human beings. . . .

Government Permits Liberty

We find, upon examining "our Nation's history, legal traditions, and practices," that the government has not blocked access to new drugs throughout the greater part of our Nation's history. Only in recent years has the government injected itself into consideration of the effectiveness of new drugs. [Moreover], Supreme Court precedent on liberty indicates that the right claimed by the Alliance can be inferred from the Court's conclusion in *Cruzan v. Director, Missouri Department of Health* that an individual has a due process right to refuse life-sustaining medical treatment. . . . Here, the claim implicates a similar right—the right to access potentially life-sustaining medication where there are no alternative government-approved treatment options. In both instances, the key is the patient's right to make the decision about her life free from government interference. . . .

[T]he Supreme Court has employed two distinct approaches when faced with a claim to a fundamental right. In some cases, the Court has discerned the existence of fundamental rights by probing what "personal dignity and autonomy" demand. . . . In other cases, the Court has derived fundamental rights by reference to the Nation's history and legal tradition. . . . Because we conclude, upon applying the seemingly more restrictive analysis of *Glucksberg* [which held that there is no right to physician-assisted suicide], that the claimed right warrants protection under the Due Process Clause, we need not decide whether the line of cases construing the concept of "personal dignity and autonomy" would also lend protection to the claimed right. . . .

Alliance Claim

The Alliance claims neither an unfettered right of access to all new or investigational new drugs nor a right to receive treatment from the government or at government expense. The Alliance's claim also does not challenge the Controlled Substances Act or the government's authority to regulate substances deemed harmful to public health, safety, and welfare. Rather, the Alliance contends that the fundamental due process rights to privacy, liberty, and life include the right of terminally ill patients, acting on a doctor's advice, to obtain potentially lifesaving medication when no alternative treatment approved by the government is available. Recognizing that the effectiveness and side effects of the investigational new drugs may still be in question after the Phase I trials have been completed, the Alliance asks only that the decision to assume these known or unknown risks be left to the terminally ill patient and not to the FDA. . . .

Roots of Control Over Body

A right of control over one's body has deep roots in the common law. The venerable commentator on the common law William Blackstone wrote that the right to "personal security" includes "a person's legal and uninterrupted enjoyment of his life, his limbs, his body, [and] his health," as well as "the preservation of a man's health from such practices as may prejudice or annoy it." This right included the right to self-defense and the right to self-preservation. "For whatever is done by a man, to save either life or member, is looked upon as done upon the highest necessity and compulsion." As recognized throughout Anglo-American history and law, when a person is faced with death, necessity often warrants extraordinary measures not otherwise justified. . . . Barring a terminally ill patient from the use of a potentially lifesaving treatment impinges on this right of self-preservation. Such a bar also puts the FDA in the position of interfering with efforts that could save a terminally ill patient's life. Although the common law imposes no general duty to rescue or to preserve a life, it does create liability for interfering with such efforts. . . . .

Control Over Drugs

In contrast to these ancient principles, regulation of access to new drugs has a history in this country that is of recent origin. . . . For over half of our Nation's history, . . . a person could obtain access to any new drug without any government interference whatsoever. Even after enactment of the FDCA [Food, Drug, and Cosmetic Act] in 1938, Congress imposed no limitation on the commercial marketing of new drugs based upon the drugs' effectiveness. Rather, at that time, the FDA could only interrupt the sale of new drugs based on its determination that a new drug was unsafe. Government regulation of drugs premised on concern over a new drug's efficacy, as opposed to its safety, is of recent origin. And even today, a patient may use a drug for unapproved purposes even where the drug may be unsafe or ineffective for the off-label purpose. . . . Therefore, it cannot be said that government control of access to potentially lifesaving medication "is now firmly ingrained in our understanding of the appropriate role of government," so as to overturn the long-standing tradition of the right of self-preservation.

The Alliance's . . . claimed right is implied by the Court's conclusion in *Cruzan* that due process protects a person's right to refuse life-sustaining treatment. . . . Chief Justice Rehnquist noted in examining the origins of the doctrine of informed consent that the Court had observed early on that "[n]o right is held more sacred, or is more carefully guarded, by the common law, than the right of every individual to the possession and control of his own person, free from all restraint or interference of others, unless by clear and unquestionable authority of law." The Court reasoned that "[t]he logical corollary of the doctrine of informed consent is that the patient generally possesses the right not to consent, that is, to refuse treatment." The Court turned to the language of the Fourteenth Amendment and its precedent to determine whether "the United States Constitution grants what is in common parlance referred to as a 'right to die.'" Without qualification, the Court stated: "It cannot be disputed that the Due Process Clause protects an interest in life as well as an interest in refusing life-sustaining medical treatment."

A similar analysis leads to the conclusion that the Due Process Clause protects the liberty interest claimed by the Alliance for its terminally ill members. . . . The text of the Due Process Clause refers to protecting "liberty" and "life." Although there is no similarly clear textual basis for a "right to die" or [to refuse] life-sustaining medical treatment, the Supreme Court in *Cruzan* recognized, in light of the common law and constitutionally protected liberty interests based on the inviolability of one's body, that an individual has a due process right to make an informed decision to engage in conduct, by withdrawing treatment, that will cause one's death. The logical corollary is that an individual must also be free to decide for herself whether to assume any known or unknown risks of taking a medication that might prolong her life. . . . Much as the guardians of the comatose patient in *Cruzan* did, the Alliance seeks to have the government step aside by changing its policy so the individual right of self-determination is not violated. The Alliance claims that there is a protected right of terminally ill patients to choose to use potentially lifesaving investigational new drugs that have successfully cleared Phase I. If there is a protected liberty interest in self-determination that includes a right to refuse life-sustaining treatment, even though this will hasten death, then the same liberty interest must include the complementary right of access to potentially life-sustaining medication, in the light of the explicit protection accorded "life." . . . .

Ruling

Accordingly, we hold . . . that where there are no alternative government-approved treatment options, a terminally ill, mentally competent adult patient's informed access to potentially lifesaving investigational new drugs determined by the FDA after Phase I trials to be sufficiently safe for expanded human trials warrants protection under the Due Process Clause.

Abigail Alliance v. FDA Dissenting Opinion: Patients Have No Right to Experimental Drugs

Thomas B. Griffith

Circuit Judge Griffith argues that Rogers' opinion is based on a series of faulty inferences: (1) that government has not always regulated drugs does not imply a recognition of a constitutional right to be free of such regulation; (2) the traditions of the necessity defense and the prohibition of forced medication do not imply a right of access to medication; (3) that a drug has completed Phase I testing does not imply that it has a medical benefit and a minimal risk. In fact, the government has

United States Court of Appeals for the District of Columbia Circuit, No. 04-5350 (Decided May 2, 2006). *Abigail Alliance for Better Access to Developmental Drugs and Washington Legal Foundation*, Appellants v. Andrew C. von Eeschenbach, M.D. in His Official Capacity as Acting Commissioner, Food and Drug Adminstration and Michael O. Leavitt, in his Official Capacity as Secretary of the U.S. Department of Health and Human Services, Appellees. Appeal from the United States District Court for the District of Columbia (No. 03cv01601). Headings added by editor.

regulated drugs for a long time through the executive and legislative bodies. To ignore this and give the judicial branch the role of deciding which drugs are safe and beneficial enough for use would burden the courts with a task both practically and logically impossible to carry out. Griffith concludes by agreeing with the lower court decision that even terminally ill patients have no right to get access to drugs that are still in the testing stage.

Inferential Basis of Claimed Right

. . . The majority creates a fundamental right by making a series of inferences. . . . From the fact that the Government has not always regulated drugs, the majority infers a constitutional right to be free from such regulation. From the common law defense of necessity and the tradition prohibiting battery and forced medication, the majority infers a fundamental right of access to medication. From the fact that drugs in the first phase of FDA testing have undergone some testing, the majority infers that those drugs will probably have a medical benefit with sufficiently minimal risk. But there is no evidence in this Nation's history and traditions of a right to access experimental drugs. Balancing the risks and benefits found at the forefront of uncertain science and medicine has been, for good reason, the historical province of the democratic branches. Because I can find no basis in the Constitution or judicial precedents to remove that function from the elected branches, I respectfully dissent.

Safety and Post-Phase-I Testing

. . . In the Alliance's view, the Due Process Clause of the Constitution guarantees terminally ill patients a fundamental "right of access to drugs that have cleared Phase I trials" because those drugs are "safe enough to be tested in humans" and "simply ha[ve] not yet met FDA's standards." Based upon that argument, the majority creates a fundamental right and concludes that, under the Constitution, "a terminally ill, mentally competent adult patient's informed access to potentially lifesaving investigational new drugs determined by the FDA after Phase I trials to be sufficiently safe for expanded human trials warrants protection under the Due Process Clause." . . .

The Alliance's proposed new constitutional right would exempt terminally ill patients from much of the legislative and regulatory approval process created by Congress and the FDA for new experimental drugs. . . . Testing a new drug for safety and effectiveness in treating humans generally requires three or sometimes four phases. . . . The majority and I differ in our understanding of the importance of the testing that occurs after Phase I. The majority implies that the FDA is primarily concerned with effectiveness after Phase I and that the right argued for by the Alliance would only override FDA regulation for effectiveness. Contrary to the majority's suggestion, all phases of the FDA's testing process for new drugs involve testing for safety. . . .

Thus, at issue today is whether terminally ill patients have a fundamental right to procure and use an experimental drug before the FDA and the scientific community have evaluated its scientific and medical risks and corresponding benefits as called for in the FDCA [Food, Drug, and Cosmetics Act] and its accompanying regulations. . . .

The Doctrine of Necessity

[T]he Supreme Court's guidance in *Oakland* indicates that the common law doctrine of necessity is not deeply rooted in this Nation's history and traditions. In *Oakland*, a group of patients seeking access to marijuana for medicinal purposes argued that "because necessity was a defense at common law, medical necessity should be read into the Controlled Substances Act." . . . [T]he Court noted that . . . "under any conception of legal necessity, one principle is clear: The defense cannot succeed when the legislature itself has made a determination of values." The structure of the FDCA does just that: Congress has prohibited general access to experimental drugs, . . . and has prescribed in detail how experimental drugs may be studied and used by the scientific and medical communities. . . . Given the Supreme Court's conclusion that the common law defense of necessity remains controversial and cannot override a value judgment already determined by the legislature, I cannot see how the majority's proposed right is supported by the common law doctrine of necessity. . . .

Ordered Liberty

The majority never provides evidence . . . that the Alliance's *asserted* right is deeply rooted and implicit in ordered liberty. Instead, the majority infers its new right from several broad principles. . . . The majority concludes that these principles are deeply rooted based upon a passage from Blackstone describing an individual's interest in being free from battery at common law, and a provision . . . discussing when one person will be liable under the common law for preventing aid from reaching another. The majority infers from these principles a liberty interest in procuring and using experimental drugs. But *Glucksberg* [which held that there is no right to physician-assisted suicide] does not authorize courts to create substantive due process rights by inference. These principles are precisely the type of "abstract concepts of personal autonomy" that do not constitute evidence of a fundamental right. . . .

History of Government Drug Regulation

The remainder of the majority's analysis sets out to prove an unremarkable proposition: the federal government has only regulated drugs for approximately 100 years. From the lack of federal regulation prior to 1906, the majority infers a constitutional right to be free from regulation. It is not difficult to see the sweeping claims of fundamental rights that such an analysis would support. Because Congress did not significantly regulate marijuana until relatively late in the constitutional day, there must be a tradition of protecting marijuana use. Because Congress did not regulate narcotics until 1866 when it heavily taxed opium, a drug created long before our Nation's founding, it must be that individuals have a right to acquire and use narcotics free from regulation. But this is not the law. . . .

The history of drug regulation in this country does not evidence a tradition of protecting a right of access to drugs; instead, it evidences government responding to new risks as they are presented. . . . The majority's historical analysis of the FDCA demonstrates that Congress has expressed a keen interest in regulating drugs as science has progressed. Congress has responded to evolving medical technology with evolving regulation. But, unlike the majority, I do not see how the decision by Congress to regulate an area of concern in the early part of the twentieth century

demonstrates a fundamental right to be free from regulation today.

Tradition of Prohibiting Battery

Nor does the majority's analogy to *Cruzan* . . . . and [to] forced medication at common law explain why there is a fundamental, deeply rooted right to "self-preservation" protecting a "terminally ill, mentally competent adult patient's informed access to potentially life-saving investigational new drugs determined by the FDA after Phase I trials to be sufficiently safe for expanded human trials." The Court's assumption that there is a right to refuse lifesaving treatment in some circumstances was predicated upon "the common-law rule that forced medication was a battery and the long legal tradition protecting the decision to refuse unwanted medical treatment." But a tradition protecting individual *freedom* from life-saving, but forced, medical treatment does not evidence a constitutional tradition of providing affirmative *access* to a potentially harmful, and even fatal, commercial good.

In light of *Cruzan's* discussion of the "right of a *competent* individual to refuse medical treatment," the majority attempts to limit its new right to a patient who is "mentally competent" and has "informed access" to experimental drugs. The majority never explains what mental competence, in this context, would require. As the FDA noted in response to the Alliance's proposal, "with so little data available, it is hard to understand how a patient could be truly informed about the risks—or potential benefits—associated with the drug." By injecting patients into an early stage of the FDA's process for testing experimental drugs, the majority's approach allows terminally ill patients to take experimental drugs unknowingly—that is, without anyone having knowledge of potential risks and benefits. I fail to see how such a right is supported by *Cruzan. Cruzan* rejected an argument that an incompetent person has a right to withdraw treatment absent intent expressed while competent. Under the majority's decision, terminally ill patients seem to have a right to make an uninformed and involuntary choice. . . .

Vexing Questions

The majority's new right to procure and use experimental drugs raises a number of vexing questions. . . . If a terminally ill patient has such a right, are patients with serious medical conditions entitled to the benefit of the same logic and corresponding access? If an indigent cannot afford potentially life-saving treatment, would the Constitution mandate access to such care under the right recognized by the majority? Can a patient access any drug (i.e., marijuana for medicinal purposes), if she believes, in consultation with a physician, it is potentially life-saving? Would the majority's right guarantee access to federally-funded stem cell research and treatment? Perhaps most significantly, what potential must a treatment have in order for the Constitution to mandate access? . . .

Because the majority does not answer this last question, the District Court faces an impossible task on remand. The majority concludes that the District Court must "determine whether the FDA's policy barring access to post-Phase I investigational new drugs by terminally ill patients is narrowly tailored to serve a compelling governmental interest." Under the majority's approach on the face of it, the District Court must examine every drug undergoing FDA testing and every drug that may ever undergo FDA testing. . . . [T]he unknown risks and benefits of these experimental drugs will make nearly impossible a judicial examination of whether some level of access short of a prohibition would be more narrowly tailored to protect the majority's constitutional right of access.

Moreover, the level of benefit a patient will have to show, in order to demonstrate that under the majority's right a drug is potentially lifesaving, remains an enigma. Whatever the majority means by "potentially," its use of that term suggests that some drugs will not demonstrate enough potential benefit, while simultaneously presenting extraordinary risks. Considering the potential benefits of an experimental drug in light of its risks will require the District Court to step into the role of the FDA. . . .

Conclusion

Because the Alliance has failed to present objective evidence establishing a deeply rooted right to procure and use experimental drugs, I would apply rational basis review to its due process challenge. . . . For the terminally ill, as for anyone else, a drug is unsafe if its potential for inflicting death or physical injury is not offset by the possibility of therapeutic benefit. Although terminally ill patients desperately need curative treatments, their death can certainly be hastened by the use of a toxic drug. Prior to distribution of a drug outside of controlled studies, the Government has a rational basis for ensuring that there is a scientifically and medically acceptable level of knowledge about the risks and benefits of such a drug. I would affirm the decision of the District Court [barring access to experimental drugs].

Section 4: Animal Experimentation

Animal Experimentation

Peter Singer

Peter Singer argues that the vast majority of animal experiments cannot be justified. They exact an extraordinary cost in animal suffering, while producing little or no knowledge—and whatever knowledge they do produce can usually be obtained in other ways.

Singer provides multiple examples of painful, pointless experiments leading to the death of animal subjects. He argues that our willingness to tolerate such experiments can be explained only by our "speciesism"—the notion that the interests of nonhuman animals

From *Animal Liberation*, 2d ed., by Peter Singer (Random House/New York Review of Books, New York, 1990), pp. 31–33, 40, 45–46, 48, 61–63, 65, 90–92. (Notes and references omitted.)

need not be considered. Speciesism, Singer holds, is analogous to racism and is just as indefensible.

Singer argues that the fundamental issue in determining how we may treat animals is whether they suffer and that the pains of animals and humans deserve equal consideration. Many animals are more intelligent than severely retarded or infant humans, so that if lack of intelligence would justify painful animal experiments, it would also justify the same experiments on retarded and infant humans. Because it is immoral to subject humans to such experiments, we have good reason to believe it is also wrong to subject animals to them.

Singer holds that researchers should be required to demonstrate that the benefits of their research will outweigh the suffering of the animals involved. He recommends that ethics committees, with members representing the welfare of animals, be established to oversee experiments.

There has been opposition to experimenting on animals for a long time. This opposition has made little[1] headway because experimenters, backed by commercial firms that profit by supplying laboratory animals and equipment, have been able to convince legislators and the public that opposition comes from uninformed fanatics who consider the interests of animals more important than the interests of human beings. But to be opposed to what is going on now it is not necessary to insist that all animal experiments stop immediately. All we need to say is that experiments serving no direct, and urgent purpose should stop immediately, and in the remaining fields of research, we should, whenever possible, seek to replace experiments that involve animals with alternative methods that do not. . . .

Professor [Harry] Harlow, who worked at the Primate Research Center in Madison, Wisconsin, was for many years editor of a leading psychology journal, and until his death a few years ago was held in high esteem by his colleagues in psychological research. His work has been cited approvingly in many basic textbooks of psychology, read by millions of students taking introductory psychology courses over the last twenty years. The line of research he began has been continued after his death by his associates and former students.

In a 1965 paper, Harlow describes his work as follows:

For the past ten years we have studied the effects of partial social isolation by raising monkeys from birth onwards in bare wire cages. . . . These monkeys suffer total maternal deprivation. . . . More recently we have initiated a series of studies on the effects of total social isolation by rearing monkeys from a few hours after birth until 3, 6,

or 12 months of age in [a] stainless steel chamber. During the prescribed sentence in this apparatus the monkey has no contact with any animal, human or sub-human.

These studies, Harlow continues, found that

sufficiently severe and enduring early isolation reduces these animals to a social–emotional level in which the primary social responsiveness is fear.

In another article Harlow and his former student and associate Stephen Suomi described how they were trying to induce psychopathology in infant monkeys by a technique that appeared not to be working. They were then visited by John Bowlby, a British psychiatrist. According to Harlow's account, Bowlby listened to the story of their troubles and then toured the Wisconsin laboratory. After he had seen the monkeys individually housed in bare wire cages he asked, "Why are you trying to produce psychopathology in monkeys? You already have more psychopathological monkeys in the laboratory than have ever been seen on the face of the earth."

Bowlby, incidentally, was a leading researcher on the consequences of maternal deprivation, but his research was conducted with children, primarily war orphans, refugees, and institutionalized children. As far back as 1951, before Harlow even began his research on nonhuman primates, Bowlby concluded:

The evidence has been reviewed. It is submitted that evidence is now such that it leaves no room for doubt regarding the general proposition that the prolonged deprivation of the young child of maternal care may have grave and far-reaching effects on his character and so on the whole of his future life.

This did not deter Harlow and his colleagues from devising and carrying out their monkey experiments.

In the same article in which they tell of Bowlby's visit, Harlow and Suomi describe how they had the "fascinating idea" of inducing depression by "allowing baby monkeys to attach to cloth surrogate mothers who could become monsters":

The first of these monsters was a cloth monkey mother who, upon schedule or demand, would eject high-pressure compressed air. It would blow the animal's skin practically off its body. What did the baby monkey do? It simply clung tighter and tighter to the mother, because a frightened infant clings to its mother at all costs. We did not achieve any psychopathology.

However, we did not give up. We built another surrogate monster mother that would rock so violently that the baby's head and teeth would rattle. All the baby did was cling tighter and tighter to the surrogate. The third monster we built had an embedded wire frame within its body which would spring forward and eject the infant from its ventral surface. The infant would subsequently pick itself off the floor, wait for the frame to return into the cloth body, and then cling again to the surrogate. Finally, we built our porcupine mother. On command, this mother would eject sharp brass spikes over all of the ventral surface of its body. Although the infants were distressed by these pointed rebuffs, they simply waited until the spikes receded and then returned and clung to the mother.

These results, the experimenters remark, were not so surprising, since the only recourse of an injured child is to cling to its mother. . . .

Harlow is now dead, but his students and admirers have spread across the United States and continue to perform experiments in a similar vein. . . .

Since Harlow began his maternal deprivation experiments some thirty years ago, over 250 such experiments have been conducted in the United States. These experiments subjected over seven thousand animals to procedures that induced distress, despair, anxiety, general psychological devastation, and death. . . .

An equally sad tale of futility is that of experiments designed to produce what is known as "learned helplessness"—supposedly a model of depression in human beings. In 1953 R. Solomon, L. Kamin, and L. Wynne, experimenters at Harvard University, placed forty dogs in a device called a "shuttlebox," which consists of a box divided into two compartments, separated by a barrier. Initially the barrier was set at the height of the dog's back. Hundreds of intense electric shocks were delivered to the dogs' feet through a grid floor. At first the dogs could escape the shock if they learned to jump the barrier into the other compartment. In an attempt to "discourage" one dog from jumping, the experimenters forced the dog to jump one hundred times onto a grid floor in the other compartment that also delivered a shock to the dog's feet. They said that as the dog jumped he gave a "sharp anticipatory yip which turned into a yelp when he landed on the electrified grid." They then blocked the passage between the compartments with a piece of plate glass and tested the dog again. The dog "jumped forward and smashed his head against the glass." The dogs began by showing symptoms such as defecation, urination, yelping and shrieking, trembling, attacking the apparatus, and so on; but after ten or twelve days of trials dogs who were prevented from escaping shock ceased to resist. The experimenters reported themselves "impressed" by this, and concluded that a combination of the plate glass barrier and foot shock was "very effective" in eliminating jumping by dogs.

This study showed that it was possible to induce a state of hopelessness and despair by repeated administration of severe inescapable shock. Such "learned helplessness" studies were further refined in the 1960s. One prominent experimenter was Martin Seligman of the University of Pennsylvania. He electrically shocked dogs through a steel grid with such intensity and persistence that the dogs stopped trying to escape and "learned" to be helpless. In one study, written with colleagues Steven Maier and James Geer, Seligman describes his work as follows:

When a normal, naive dog receives escape/ avoidance training in a shuttlebox, the following behavior typically occurs: at the onset of electric shock the dog runs frantically about, defecating, urinating, and howling until it scrambles over the barrier and so escapes from shock. On the next trial the dog, running and howling, crosses the barrier more quickly, and so on, until efficient avoidance emerges.

Seligman altered this pattern by strapping dogs in harnesses and giving them shocks from which they had no means of escape. When the dogs were then placed in the original shuttlebox situation from which escape was possible, he found that

> *such a dog reacts initially to shock in the shuttlebox in the same manner as the naive dog. However in dramatic contrast to the naive dog it soon stops running and remains silent until shock terminates. The dog does not cross the barrier and escape from shock. Rather it seems to "give up" and passively "accept" the shock. On succeeding trials the dog continues to fail to make escape movements and thus takes 50 seconds of severe, pulsating shock on each trial. . . . A dog previously exposed to inescapable shock . . . may take unlimited shock without escaping or avoiding at all. . . .*

Electric shock has also been used to produce aggressive behavior in animals. In one study at the University of Iowa, Richard Viken and John Khutson divided 160 rats into groups and "trained" them in a stainless steel cage with an electrified floor. Pairs of rats were given electric shocks until they learned to fight by striking out at the other rat while facing each other in an upright position or by biting. It took an average of thirty training trials before the rats learned to do this immediately on the first shock. The researchers then placed the shock-trained rats in the cage of untrained rats and recorded their behavior. After one day, all the rats were killed, shaved, and examined for wounds. The experimenters concluded that their "results were not useful in understanding the offensive or defensive nature of the shock-induced response. . . . "

When experiments can be brought under the heading "medical" we are inclined to think that any suffering they involve must be justifiable because the research is contributing to the alleviation of suffering. But . . . the testing of therapeutic drugs is less likely to be motivated by the desire for maximum good to all than by the desire for maximum profit. The broad label "medical research" can also be used to cover research that is motivated by a general intellectual curiosity. Such curiosity may be acceptable as part of a basic search for knowledge when it involves no suffering, but should not be tolerated if it causes pain. Very often, too, basic medical research has been going on for decades and much of it, in the long run, turns out to have been quite pointless. As an illustration, consider the following series of experiments stretching back nearly a century, on the effects of heat on animals:

In 1880 H.C. Wood placed a number of animals in boxes with glass lids and placed the boxes on a brick pavement on a hot day. He used rabbits, pigeons, and cats. His observations on a rabbit are typical. At a temperature of 109.5 degrees Fahrenheit the rabbit jumps and "kicks hind legs with great fury." The rabbit then has a convulsive attack. At 112 degrees Fahrenheit the animal lies on its side slobbering. At 120 degrees Fahrenheit it is gasping and squealing weakly. Soon after it dies.

In 1881 a report appeared in *The Lancet* on dogs and rabbits whose temperatures had been raised to 113 degrees Fahrenheit. It was found that death could be prevented by cool air currents, and the results were said to indicate "the importance of keeping down the temperature in those cases in which it exhibits a tendency to rise to [an] extreme height."

In 1927 W.W. Hall and E.G. Wakefield of the U.S. Naval Medical School placed ten dogs in a hot humid chamber to produce experimental heatstroke. The animals first showed restlessness, breathing difficulties, swelling and congestion of the eyes, and thirst. Some had convulsions. Some died early in the experiment. Those who did not had severe diarrhea and died after removal from the chamber.

In 1954 at Yale University School of Medicine, M Lennox, W. Sibley, and H Zimmerman placed thirty-two kittens in a "radiant-heating" chamber. The kittens were "subjected to a total of 49 heating periods. . . . Struggling was common, particularly as the temperature rose." Convulsions occurred on nine occasions: "Repeated convulsions were the rule." As many as thirty convulsions occurred in rapid sequence. Five kittens died during convulsions, and six without convulsions. The other kittens were killed by the experimenters for autopsies. The experimenters reported: "The findings in artificially induced fever in kittens conform to the clinical and EEG findings in human beings and previous clinical findings in kittens. . . . "

In 1969 S. Michaelson, a veterinarian at the University of Rochester, exposed dogs and rabbits to heat-producing microwaves until their temperatures reached the critical level of 107 degrees Fahrenheit or greater. He observed that dogs start panting shortly after microwave exposure begins. Most "display increased activity varying from restlessness to extreme agitation." Near the point of death, weakness and prostration occur. In the case of rabbits "within 5 minutes, desperate attempts are made to escape the cage," and the rabbits die within forty minutes. Michaelson concluded that an increase in heat from microwaves produces damage "indistinguishable from fever in general. . . . "

In 1984 experimenters working for the Federal Aviation Administration, stating that "animals occasionally die from heat stress encountered during shipping in the nation's transportation systems," subjected ten beagles to experimental heat. The dogs were isolated in chambers, fitted with muzzles, and exposed to 95 degrees Fahrenheit combined with high humidity. They were given no food or water, and were kept in these conditions for twenty-four hours. The behavior of the dogs was observed; it included "deliberate agitated activity such as pawing at the crate walls, continuous circling, tossing of the head to shed the muzzle, rubbing the muzzle back and forth on the floor of the crate, and aggressive acts on the sensor guards." Some of the dogs died in the chambers. When the survivors were removed, some vomited blood, and all were weak and exhausted. The experimenters refer to "subsequent experiments on more than 100 beagles. . . . "

Here we have cited a series of experiments going back into the nineteenth century—and I have had space sufficient to include only a fraction of the published literature. The experiments obviously caused great suffering; and the major finding seems to be the advice that heatstroke victims should be cooled. . . . Similar series of experiments are to be found in many other fields of medicine. In the New York City offices of United Action for Animals there are filing cabinets full of photocopies of experiments reported in the journals. Each thick file contains reports on numerous experiments, often fifty or more, and the labels on the files tell their own story: "Acceleration," "Aggression," "Asphyxiation," "Blinding," "Burning," "Centrifuge," "Compression," "Concussion," "Crowding," "Crushing," "Decompression," "Drug Tests," "Experimental Neurosis," "Freezing," "Heating," "Hemorrhage," "Hindleg Beating," "Immobilization," "Isolation," "Multiple Injuries," "Prey Killing," "Protein Deprivation," "Punishment," "Radiation," "Starvation," "Shock," "Spinal Cord Injuries," "Stress," "Thirst," and many more. While some of the experiments may have led to advances in medical knowledge, the value of this knowledge is often questionable, and in some cases the knowledge might have been gained in other ways. Many of the experiments appear to be trivial or misconceived, and some of them were not even designed to yield important-benefits. . . .

When are experiments on animals justifiable? Upon learning of the nature of many of the experiments carried out, some people react by saying that all experiments on animals should be prohibited immediately. But if we make our demands as absolute as this, the experimenters have a ready reply: Would we be prepared to let thousands of humans die if they could be saved by a single experiment on a single animal?

This question is, of course, purely hypothetical. There has never been and never could be a single experiment that saved thousands of lives. The way to reply to this hypothetical question is to pose another. Would the experimenters be prepared to carry out their experiment on a human orphan under six months old if that were the only way to save thousands of lives?

If the experimenters would not be prepared to use a human infant then their readiness to use non-human animals reveals an unjustifiable form of discrimination on the basis of species, since adult apes, monkeys, dogs, cats, rats, arid other animals are more aware of what is happening to them, more self-directing, and, so far as we can tell, at least as sensitive to pain as a human infant. (I have specified that the human infant be an orphan, to avoid the complications of the feeling of parents. Specifying the case in this way is, if anything, overgenerous to those defending the use of nonhuman animals in experiments, since mammals intended for experimental use are usually separated from their mothers at an early age, when the separation causes distress for both mother and young.)

So far as we know, human infants possess no morally relevant characteristic to a higher degree than adult nonhuman animals, unless we are to count the infants' potential as a characteristic that makes it wrong to experiment on them. Whether this characteristic should count is controversial—if we count it, we shall have to condemn abortion along with experiments on infants, since the potential of the infant and the fetus is the same. To avoid the complexities of this issue, however, we can alter our original question a little and assume that the infant is one with irreversible brain damage so severe as to rule out any mental development beyond the level of a six-month-old infant. There are, unfortunately, many such human beings, locked away in special wards throughout the country, some of them long since abandoned by their parents and other relatives, and, sadly, sometimes unloved by anyone else. Despite their mental deficiencies, the anatomy and physiology of these infants are in nearly all respects identical with those of normal humans. If, therefore, we were to force-feed them with large quantities of floor polish or drip concentrated solutions of cosmetics into their eyes, we would have a much more reliable indication of the safety of these products for humans than we now get by attempting to extrapolate the results of tests on a variety of other species. The LD50 tests, the Draize eye tests, the radiation experiments, the heatstroke experiments, and many others could have told us more about human reactions to the experimental situation if they had been carried out on severely brain-damaged humans instead of dogs or rabbits.

So whenever experimenters claim that their experiments are important enough to justify the use of animals, we should ask them whether they would be prepared to use a brain-damaged human being at a similar mental level to the animals they are planning to use. I cannot imagine that anyone would seriously propose carrying out the experiments described in this chapter on brain-damaged human beings. Occasionally it has become known that medical experiments have been performed on human beings without their consent; one case did concern institutionalized intellectually disabled children, who were given hepatitis. When such harmful experiments on human beings become known, they usually lead to an outcry against the experimenters, and rightly so. They are, very often, a further example of the arrogance of the research worker who justifies everything on the grounds of increasing knowledge. But if the experimenter claims that the experiment is important enough to justify inflicting suffering on animals, why is it not important enough to justify inflicting suffering on humans at the same mental level? What difference is there between the two? Only that one is a member of our species and the other is not? But to appeal to that difference is to reveal a bias no more defensible than racism or any other form of arbitrary discrimination.

The analogy between speciesism and racism applies in practice as well as in theory in the area of experimentation. Blatant speciesism leads to painful experiments on other species, defended on the grounds of their contribution to knowledge and possible usefulness for our species. Blatant racism has led to painful experiments on other races, defended on the grounds of their contribution to knowledge and possible usefulness for the experimenting race. Under the Nazi regime in Germany, nearly two hundred doctors, some of them eminent in the world of medicine, took part in experiments on Jews and Russian and Polish prisoners. Thousands of other physicians knew of these experiments, some of which were the subject of lectures at medical academies. Yet the records show that the doctors sat through verbal reports by doctors on how horrible injuries were inflicted on these "lesser races," and then proceeded to discuss the medical lessons to be learned from them, without anyone making even a mild protest about the nature of the experiments. The parallels between this attitude and that of experimenters today toward animals are striking. Then, as now, subjects were frozen, heated, and put in decompression chambers. Then, as now, these events were written up in dispassionate scientific jargon. The following paragraph is taken from a report by a Nazi scientist of an experiment on a human being, placed in a decompression chamber:

> *After five minutes spasms appeared; between the sixth and tenth minute respiration increased in frequency, the TP [test person] losing consciousness. From the eleventh to the thirtieth minute respiration slowed down to three inhalations per minute, only to cease entirely at the end of that period. . . . About half an hour after breathing ceased, an autopsy was begun.*

Decompression chamber experimentation did not stop with the defeat of the Nazis. It shifted to nonhuman animals. At the University of Newcastle on Tyne, in England, for instance, scientists used pigs. The pigs were subjected to up to eighty-one periods of decompression over a period of nine months. All suffered attacks of decompression sickness, and some died from these attacks. The example illustrates only too well what the great Jewish writer Isaac Bashevis Singer has written: "In their behavior towards creatures, all men [are] Nazis. . . . "

We have still not answered the question of when an experiment might be justifiable. It will not do to say "Never!" Putting morality in such black-and-white terms is appealing, because it eliminates the need to think about particular cases; but in extreme circumstances, such absolutist answers always break down. Torturing a human being is almost always wrong, but it is not absolutely wrong. If torture were the only way in which we could discover the location of a nuclear bomb hidden in a New York City basement and timed to go off within the hour, then torture would be justifiable. Similarly, if a single experiment could cure a disease like leukemia, that experiment would be justifiable. But in actual life the benefits are always more remote, and more often than not they are non-existent. So how do we decide when an experiment is justifiable?

We have seen that experimenters reveal a bias in favor of their own species whenever they carry out experiments on nonhumans for purposes that they would not think justified them in using human beings, even brain-damaged ones. This principle gives us a guide toward an answer to our question. Since a speciesist bias, like a racist bias, is unjustifiable, an experiment cannot be justified unless the experiment is so important that the use of a brain-damaged human would also be justifiable.

This is not an absolutist principle. I do not believe that it could never be justifiable to experiment on a brain-damaged human. If it really were possible to save several lives by an experiment that would take just one life, and there were no other way those lives could be saved, it would be right to do the experiment. But this would be an extremely rare case. Certainly none of the experiments described in this chapter could pass this test. Admittedly, as with any dividing line, there would be a gray area where it was difficult to decide if an experiment could be justified. But we need not get distracted by such considerations now. As this chapter has shown, we are in the midst of an emergency in which appalling suffering is being inflicted on millions of animals for purposes that on any impartial view are obviously inadequate to justify the suffering. When we have ceased to carry out all those experiments, then there will be time enough to discuss what to do about the remaining ones which are claimed to be essential to save lives or prevent greater suffering. . . .

In the United States, where experimenters can do virtually as they please with animals, one way of making progress might be to ask those who use this argument to defend the need for animal experiment whether they would be prepared to accept the verdict of an ethics committee that, like those in many other countries, includes animal welfare representatives and is entitled to weigh the costs to the animals against the possible benefits of the research. If the answer is no, the defense of animal experimentation by reference to the need to cure major diseases has been proved to be simply a deceitful distraction that serves to mislead the public about what the experimenters want: permission to do whatever they like with animals. For otherwise why would the experimenter not be prepared to leave the decision on

carrying out the experiment to an ethics committee, which would surely be as keen to see major diseases ended as the rest of the community? If the answer is yes, the experimenter should be asked to sign a statement asking for the creation of such an ethics committee.

Suppose that we were able to go beyond minimal reforms of the sort that already exist in the more enlightened nations. Suppose we could reach a point at which the interests of animals really were given equal consideration with the similar interests of human beings. That would mean the end of the vast industry of animal experimentation as we know it today. Around the world, cages would empty and laboratories would close down. It should not be thought, though, that medical research would grind to a halt or that a flood of untested products would come onto the market. So far as new products are concerned it is true, as I have already said, that we would have to make do with fewer of them, using ingredients already known to be safe. That does not seem to be any great loss. But for testing really essential products, as well as for other kinds of research, alternative methods not requiring animals can and would be found. . . .

The defenders of animal experimentation are fond of telling us that animal experimentation has greatly increased our life expectancy. In the midst of the debate over reform of the British law on animal experimentation, for example, the Association of the British Pharmaceutical Industry ran a full-page advertisement in the *Guardian* under the headline "They say life begins at forty. Not so long ago, that's about when it ended." The advertisement went on to say that it is now considered to be a tragedy if a man dies in his forties, whereas in the nineteenth century it was commonplace to attend the funeral of a man in his forties, for the average life expectancy was only forty-two. The advertisement stated that "it is thanks largely to the breakthroughs that have been made through research which requires animals that most of us are able to live into our seventies."

Such claims are simply false. In fact, this particular advertisement was so blatantly misleading that a specialist in community medicine, Dr. David St. George, wrote to *The Lancet* saying "the advertisement is good teaching material, since it illustrates two major errors in the interpretation of statistics." He also referred to Thomas McKeown's influential book *The Role of Medicine*, published in 1976, which set off a debate about the relative contributions of social and environmental changes, as compared with medical intervention, in improvements in mortality since the mid-nineteenth century; and he added:

> This debate has been resolved, and it is now widely accepted that medical interventions had only a marginal effect on population mortality and mainly at a very late stage, after death rates had already fallen strikingly.

J. B. and S. M. McKinley reached a similar conclusion in a study of the decline of ten major infectious diseases in the United States. They showed that in every case except poliomyelitis the death rate had already fallen dramatically (presumably because of improved sanitation and diet) before any new form of medical treatment was introduced. Concentrating on the 40 percent fall in crude mortality in the United States between 1910 and 1984, they estimated "conservatively" that

> perhaps 3.5 percent of the fall in the overall death rate can be explained through medical interventions for the major infectious diseases. Indeed, given that it is precisely for these diseases that medicine claims most success in lowering mortality, 3.5 percent probably represents a reasonable upper-limit estimate of the total

> contribution of medical measures to the decline in infectious disease mortality in the United States.

Remember that this 3.5 percent is a figure for all medical intervention. The contribution of animal experimentation itself can be, at most, only a fraction of this tiny contribution to the decline in mortality. . . .

Finally, it is important to realize that the major health problems of the world largely continue to exist, not because we do not know how to prevent disease and keep people healthy, but because no one is putting enough effort and money into doing what we already know how to do. The diseases that ravage Asia, Africa, Latin America, and the pockets of poverty in the industrialized West are diseases that, by and large, we know how to cure. They have been eliminated in communities that have adequate nutrition, sanitation, and health care. It has been estimated that 250,000 children die each week around the world, and that one quarter of these deaths are by dehydration caused by diarrhea. A simple treatment, already known and needing no animal experimentation, could prevent the deaths of these children. Those who are genuinely concerned about improving health care would probably make a more effective contribution to human health if they left the laboratories and saw to it that our existing stock of medical knowledge reached those who need it most.

The Case for the Use of Animals in Biomedical Research

Carl Cohen

Carl Cohen rejects arguments by those who favor severely curbing or eliminating animal experimentation, then defends the position that we have a strong duty to conduct such experiments to alleviate human suffering and extend human lives.

Animals have no rights, Cohen claims. To have a right is to have a moral claim against others. This means having the capacity to recognize conflicts between one's self-interest and what is right and being able to restrain one's self-interest when appropriate. Animals lack these capacities. Hence, they are not the sort of beings who can possess rights, and lacking rights, their interests may be sacrificed for the welfare of others.

Cohen rejects Peter Singer's argument that the pleasures and pains of animals deserve consideration equal to those of humans in calculating the overall benefits of animal experiments, because holding otherwise is "speciesism." Singer's analogy with racism and sexism does not hold, Cohen claims, because animals lack autonomy and membership in the moral community. Indeed, speciesism is "essential to right conduct," because those who fail to make the relevant distinctions between humans and nonhumans will fail to recognize their moral duties.

In his conclusion, Cohen claims that a proper analysis of animal experimentation shows "that contrary to Singer; instead of having a duty to decrease the use of animal experimentation, we have a duty to increase it."

Using animals as research subjects in medical investigations is widely condemned on two grounds: first, because it wrongly violates the *rights* of animals,[1] and second, because it wrongly imposes on sentient creatures much avoidable *suffering*.[2] Neither of these arguments is sound. The first relies on a mistaken understanding of rights; the second relies on a mistaken calculation of consequences. Both deserve definitive dismissal.

Why Animals Have No Rights

A right, properly understood, is a claim, or potential claim, that one party may exercise against another. The target against whom such a claim may be registered can be a single person, a group, a community, or (perhaps) all humankind. The content of rights claims also varies greatly: repayment of loans, nondiscrimination by employers, noninterference by the state, and so on. To comprehend any genuine right fully, therefore, we must know *who* holds the right, *against whom* it is, held, and *to what* it is a right.

Alternative sources of rights add complexity. Some rights are grounded in constitution and law (e.g., the right of an accused to trial by jury); some rights are moral but give no legal claims (e.g., my right to your keeping the promise you gave me); and some rights (e.g., against theft or assault) are rooted both in morals and in law.

The differing targets, contents, and sources of rights, and their inevitable conflict, together weave a tangled web. Notwithstanding all such complications, this much is clear about rights in general: they are in every case claims, or potential claims, within a community of moral agents. Rights arise, and can be intelligibly defended, only among beings who actually do, or can, make moral claims against one another. Whatever else rights may be, therefore, they are necessarily human; their possessors are persons, human beings.

The attributes of human beings from which this moral capability arises have been described variously by philosophers, both ancient and modern: the inner consciousness of a free will (Saint Augustine[3]); the grasp, by human reason, of the binding character of moral law (Saint Thomas[4]); the self-conscious participation of human beings in an objective ethical order (Hegel[5]); human membership in an organic moral community (Bradley[6]); the development of the human self through the consciousness of other moral selves (Mead[7]); and the underivative, intuitive cognition of the rightness of an action (Prichard[8]). Most influential has been Immanuel Kant's emphasis on the universal human possession of a uniquely moral will and the autonomy its use entails.[9] Humans confront choices that are purely moral; humans—but certainly not dogs or mice—lay down moral laws, for others and for themselves. Human beings are self-legislative, morally *autonomous*.

Animals (that is, nonhuman animals, the ordinary sense of that word) lack this capacity for free moral judgment. They are not beings of a kind capable of exercising or responding to moral claims. Animals therefore have no rights, and they can have none. This is the core of the argument about the alleged rights of animals. The holders of rights must have the capacity to comprehend rules of duty, governing all including themselves. In applying such rules, the holders of rights must recognize possible conflicts between what is in their own interest and what is just. Only in a community of beings capable of self-restricting moral judgments can the concept of a right be correctly invoked.

Humans have such moral capacities. They are in this sense self-legislative, are members of communities governed by moral rules, and do possess rights. Animals do not have such moral capacities. They are not morally self-legislative, cannot possibly be members of a truly moral community, and therefore cannot possess rights. In conducting research on animal subjects, therefore, we do not violate their rights, because they have none to violate.

To animate life, even in its simplest forms, we give a certain natural reverence. But the possession of rights presupposes a moral status not attained by the vast majority of living things. We must not infer, therefore, that a live being has, simply in being alive, a "right" to its life. The assertion that all animals, only because they are alive and have interests, also possess the "right to life"[10] is an abuse of that phrase, and wholly without warrant.

It does not follow from this, however, that we are morally free to do anything we please to animals. Certainly not. In our dealings with animals, as in our dealings with other human beings, we have obligations that do not arise from claims against us based on rights. Rights entail obligations, but many of the things one ought to do are in no way tied to another's entitlement. Rights and obligations are not reciprocals of one another, and it is a serious mistake to suppose that they are.

Illustrations are helpful. Obligations may arise from internal commitments made: physicians have obligations to their patients not grounded merely in their patients' rights. Teachers have such obligations to their students, shepherds to their dogs, and cowboys to their horses. Obligations may arise from differences of status: adults owe special care when playing with young children, and children owe special care when playing with young pets. Obligations may arise from special relationships: the payment of my son's college tuition is something to which he may have no right, although it may be my obligation to bear the burden if I reasonably can; my dog has no right to daily exercise and veterinary care, but I do have the obligation to provide these things for her. Obligations may arise from particular acts or circumstances: one may be obliged to another for a special kindness done, or obliged to put an animal out of its misery in view of its condition—although neither the human benefactor nor the dying animal may have had a claim of right.

Plainly, the grounds of our obligations to humans and to animals are manifold and cannot be formulated simply. Some hold that there is a general obligation to do no gratuitous harm to sentient creatures (the principle of nonmaleficence); some hold that there is general obligation to do good to sentient creatures when that is reasonably within one's power (the principle of beneficence). In our dealings with animals, few will deny that we are at least obliged to act humanely—that is, to treat them with the decency and concern that we owe,

as sensitive human beings, to other sentient creatures. To treat animals humanely, however, is not to treat them as humans or as the holders of rights.

A common objection, which deserves a response, may be paraphrased as follows:

> *If having rights requires being able to make moral claims, to grasp and apply moral laws, then many humans—the brain-damaged, the comatose, the senile—who plainly lack those capacities must be without rights. But that is absurd. This proves [the critic concludes] that rights do not depend on the presence of moral capacities.[1,10]*

This objection fails; it mistakenly treats an essential feature of humanity as though it were a screen for sorting humans. The capacity for moral judgment that distinguishes humans from animals is not a test to be administered to human beings one by one. Persons who are unable, because of some disability, to perform the full moral functions natural to human beings are certainly not for that reason ejected from the moral community. The issue is one of kind. Humans are of such a kind that they may be the subject of experiments only with their voluntary consent. The choices they make freely must be respected. Animals are of such a kind that it is impossible for them, in principle, to give or withhold voluntary consent or to make a moral choice. What humans retain when disabled, animals have never had.

A second objection, also often made, may be paraphrased as follows:

> *Capacities will not succeed in distinguishing humans from the other animals. Animals also reason; animals also communicate with one another; animals also care passionately for their young; animals also exhibit desires and preferences.[11,12] Features of moral relevance— rationality, interdependence, and love—are not exhibited uniquely by human beings. Therefore [this critic concludes] there can be no solid moral distinction between humans and other animals.[10]*

This criticism misses the central point. It is not the ability to communicate or to reason, or dependence on one another, or care for the young, or the exhibition of preference, or any such behavior that marks the critical divide. Analogies between human families and those of monkeys, or between human communities and those of wolves, and the like, are entirely beside the point. Patterns of conduct are not at issue. Animals do indeed exhibit remarkable behavior at times. Conditioning, fear, instinct, and intelligence all contribute to species survival. Membership in a community of moral agents nevertheless remains impossible for them. Actors subject to moral judgment must be capable of grasping the generality of an ethical premise in a practical syllogism. Humans act immorally often enough, but only they—never wolves or monkeys—can discern, by applying some moral rule to the facts of a case, that a given act ought or ought not to be performed. The moral restraints imposed by humans on themselves are thus highly abstract and are often in conflict with the self-interest of the agent. Communal behavior among animals, even when most intelligent and most endearing, does not approach autonomous morality in this fundamental sense.

Genuinely moral acts have an internal as well as an external dimension. Thus, in law, an act can be criminal only when the guilty deed, the actus reus, is done with a guilty mind, mens rea. No animal can ever commit a crime; bringing animals to criminal trial is the mark of primitive ignorance. The claims of moral right are similarly inapplicable to them. Does a lion have a right to eat a baby zebra? Does a baby zebra have a right not to be eaten? Such questions, mistakenly invoking the concept of right where it does not belong do not make good sense. Those who condemn biomedical research because it violates "animal rights" commit the same blunder.

In Defense of "Speciesism"

Abandoning reliance on animal rights, some critics resort instead to animal sentience—their feelings of pain and distress. We ought to desist from the imposition of pain insofar as we can. Since all or nearly all experimentation on animals does impose pain and could be readily forgone, say these critics, it should be stopped. The ends sought may be worthy, but those ends do not justify imposing agonies on humans, and by animals the agonies are felt no less. The laboratory use of animals (these critics conclude) must therefore be ended—or at least very sharply curtailed.

Argument of this variety is essentially utilitarian, often expressly so[13]; it is based on the calculation of the net product, in pains and pleasures, resulting from experiments on animals. Jeremy Bentham, comparing horses and dogs with other sentient creatures, is thus commonly quoted: "The question is not, Can they reason? nor Can they talk? but, Can they suffer?"[14]

Animals certainly can suffer and surely ought not to be made to suffer needlessly. But in inferring, from these uncontroversial premises, that biomedical research causing animals distress is largely (or wholly) wrong; the critic commits two serious errors.

The first error is the assumption, often explicitly defended, that all sentient animals have equal moral standing. Between a dog and a human being, according to this view, there is no moral difference; hence the pains suffered by dogs must be weighed no differently from the pains suffered by humans. To deny such equality, according to this critic, is to give unjust preference to one species over another; it is "speciesism." The most influential statement of this moral equality of species was made by Peter Singer:

> *The racist violates the principle of equality by giving greater weight to the interests of members of his own race when there is a clash between their interests and the interests of those of another race. The sexist violates the principle of equality by favoring the interests of his own sex. Similarly the speciesist allows the interests of his own species to override the greater interests of members of other species. The pattern is identical in each case.[2]*

This argument is worse than unsound; it is atrocious. It draws an offensive moral conclusion from a deliberately devised verbal parallelism that is utterly specious. Racism has no rational ground whatever. Differing degrees of respect or concern for humans for no other reason than that they are members of different races is an injustice totally without foundation in the nature of the races themselves. Racists, even if acting on the basis of mistaken factual beliefs, do grave moral wrong precisely because there is no morally relevant distinction among the races. The supposition of such differences has led to outright horror. The same is true of the sexes, neither sex being entitled by right to greater respect or concern than the other. No dispute here.

Between species of animate life, however— between (for example) humans on the one hand and cats or rats on the other—the morally relevant differences are enormous, and almost universally appreciated. Humans engage in moral reflection; humans are morally autonomous; humans are members of moral communities, recognizing just claims against their own interest. Human beings do have rights; theirs is a moral status very different from that of cats or rats.

I am a speciesist. Speciesism is not merely plausible; it is essential for right conduct, because those who will not make the morally relevant distinctions among species are almost certain, in consequence, to misapprehend their true obligations. The analogy between speciesism and racism is insidious. Every sensitive moral judgment requires that the differing natures of the beings to whom obligations are owed be considered. If all forms of animate life—or vertebrate animal life?—must be treated equally, and if therefore in evaluating a research program the pains of a rodent count equally with the pains of a human, we are forced to conclude (1) that neither humans nor rodents possess rights, or (2) that rodents possess all the rights that humans possess. Both alternatives are absurd. Yet one or the other must be swallowed if the moral equality of all species is to be defended.

Humans owe to other humans a degree of moral regard that cannot be owed to animals. Some humans take on the obligation to support and heal others, both humans and animals, as a principal duty in their lives; the fulfillment of that duty may require the sacrifice of many animals. If biomedical investigators abandon the effective pursuit of their professional objectives because they are convinced that they may not do to animals what the service of humans requires, they will fail, objectively, to do their duty. Refusing to recognize the moral differences among species is a sure path to calamity. (The largest animal rights group in the country is People for the Ethical Treatment of Animals; its codirector, Ingrid Newkirk, calls research using animal subjects, "fascism" and "supremacism." "Animal liberationists do not separate out the *human* animal," she says, "so there is no rational basis for saying that a human being has special rights. A rat is a pig is a dog is a boy. They're all mammals."[15])

Those who claim to base their objection to the use of animals in biomedical research on their reckoning of the net pleasures and pains produced make a second error, equally grave. Even if it were true—as it is surely not—that the pains of all animate beings must be counted equally, a cogent utilitarian calculation requires that we weigh all the consequences of the use, and of the nonuse, of animals in laboratory research. Critics relying (however mistakenly) on animal rights may claim to ignore the beneficial results of such research, rights being trump cards to which interest and advantage must give way. But an argument that is explicitly framed in terms of interest and benefit for all over the long run must attend also to the disadvantageous consequences of not using animals in research, and to all the achievements attained and attainable only through their use. The sum of the benefits of their use is utterly beyond quantification. The elimination of horrible disease, the increase of longevity, the avoidance of great pain, the

saving of lives, and the improvement of the quality of lives (for humans and for animals) achieved through research using animals is so incalculably great that the argument of these critics, systematically pursued, establishes not their conclusion but its reverse: to refrain from using animals in biomedical research is, on utilitarian grounds, morally wrong.

When balancing the pleasures and pains resulting from the use of animals in research, we must not fail to place on the scales the terrible pains that would have resulted, would be suffered now, and would long continue had animals not been used. Every disease eliminated, every vaccine developed, every method of pain relief devised, every surgical procedure invented, every prosthetic device implanted—indeed, virtually every modern medical therapy is due, in part or in whole, to experimentation using animals. Nor may we ignore, in the balancing process, the predictable gains in human (and animal) well-being that are probably achievable in the future but that will not be achieved if the decision is made now to desist from such research or to curtail it.

Medical investigators are seldom insensitive to the distress their work may cause animal subjects. Opponents of research using animals are frequently insensitive to the cruelty of the results of the restrictions they would impose.[2] Untold numbers of human beings—real persons, although not now identifiable—would suffer grievously as the consequence of this well-meaning but shortsighted tenderness. If the morally relevant differences between humans and animals are borne in mind, and if all relevant considerations are weighed, the calculation of long-term consequences must give overwhelming support for biomedical research using animals.

Concluding Remarks

Substitution

The humane treatment of animals requires that we desist from experimenting on them if we can accomplish the same result using alternative methods—in vitro experimentation, computer simulation, or others.

Critics of some experiments using animals rightly make this point.

It would be a serious error to suppose, however, that alternative techniques could soon be used in most research now using live animal subjects. No other methods now on the horizon—or perhaps ever to be available—can fully replace the testing of a drug, a procedure, or a vaccine, in live organisms. The flood of new medical possibilities being opened by the successes of recombinant DNA technology will turn to a trickle if testing on live animals is forbidden. When initial trials entail great risks, there may be no forward movement whatever without the use of live animal subjects. In seeking knowledge that may prove critical in later clinical applications, the unavailability of animals for inquiry may spell complete stymie. In the United States, federal regulations require the testing of new drugs and other products on animals, for efficacy and safety, before human beings are exposed to them.[16,17] We would not want it otherwise.

Every advance in medicine—every new drug, new operation, new therapy of any kind—must sooner or later be tried on a living being for the first time. That trial, controlled or uncontrolled, will be an experiment. The subject of that experiment, if it is not an animal, will be a human being. Prohibiting the use of live animals in biomedical research, therefore, or sharply restricting it, must result either in the blockage of much valuable research or in the replacement of animal subjects with human subjects. These are the consequences—unacceptable to most reasonable persons—of not using animals in research.

Reduction

Should we not at least reduce the use of animals in biomedical research? No, we should increase it, to avoid when feasible the use of humans as experimental subjects. Medical investigations putting human subjects at some risk are numerous and greatly varied. The risks run in such experiments are usually unavoidable, and (thanks to earlier experiments on animals) most such risks are minimal or moderate. But some experimental risks are substantial.

When an experimental protocol that entails substantial risk to humans comes before an institutional review board, what response is appropriate? The investigation, we may suppose, is promising and deserves support, so long as its human subjects are protected against unnecessary dangers. May not the investigators be fairly asked, Have you done all that you can to eliminate risk to humans by the extensive testing of that drug that procedure, or that device on animals? To achieve maximal safety for humans we are right to require thorough experimentation on animal subjects before humans are involved.

Opportunities to increase human safety in this way are commonly missed; trials in which risks may be shifted from humans to animals are often not devised, sometimes not even considered. Why? For the investigator, the use of animals as subjects is often more

expensive, in money and time, than the use of human subjects. Access to suitable human subjects is often quick and convenient, whereas access to appropriate animal subjects may be awkward, costly, and burdened with red tape. Physician-investigators have often had more experience working with human beings and know precisely where the needed pool of subjects is to be found and how they may be enlisted. Animals, and the procedures for their use, are often less familiar to these investigators. Moreover, the use of animals in place of humans is now more likely to be the target of zealous protests from without. The upshot is that humans are sometimes subjected to risks that animals could have borne, and should have borne, in their place. To maximize the protection of human subjects, I conclude, the wide and imaginative use of live animal subjects should be encouraged rather than discouraged. This enlargement in the use of animals is our obligation.

Consistency

Finally, inconsistency between the profession and the practice of many who oppose research using animals deserves comment. This frankly *ad hominem* observation aims chiefly to show that a coherent position rejecting the use of animals in medical research imposes costs so high as to be intolerable even to the critics themselves.

One cannot coherently object to the killing of animals in biomedical investigations while continuing to eat them. Anesthetics and thoughtful animal husbandry render the level of actual animal distress in the laboratory generally lower than that in the abattoir. So long as death and discomfort do not substantially differ in the two contexts, the consistent objector must not only refrain from all eating of animals but also protest as vehemently against others eating them as against others experimenting on them. No less vigorously must the critic object to the wearing of animal hides in coats and shoes, to employment in any industrial enterprise that uses animal parts, and to any commercial development that will cause death or distress to animals.

Killing animals to meet human needs for food, clothing and shelter is judged entirely reasonable by most persons. The ubiquity of these uses and the virtual universality of moral support for them confront the opponent of research using animals with an inescapable difficulty. How can the many common uses of animals be judged morally worthy, while their use in scientific investigation is judged unworthy?

The number of animals used in research is but the tiniest fraction of the total used to satisfy assorted human appetites. That these appetites, often base and satisfiable in other ways, morally justify the far larger consumption of animals, whereas the quest for improved human health and understanding cannot justify the far smaller, is wholly implausible. Aside from the numbers of animals involved, the distinction in terms of worthiness of use, drawn with regard to any single animal, is not defensible. A given sheep is surely not more justifiably used to put lamb chops on the supermarket counter than to serve in testing a new contraceptive or a new prosthetic device. The needless killing of animals is wrong; if the common killing of them for our food or convenience is right, the less common but more humane uses of animals in the service of medical science are certainly not less right.

Scrupulous vegetarianism, in matters of food, clothing, shelter, commerce, and recreation, and in all other spheres, is the only fully coherent position the critic may adopt. At great human cost, the lives of fish and crustaceans must also be protected, with equal vigor, if speciesism has been forsworn. A very few consistent critics adopt this position. It is the *reductio ad absurdum* of the rejection of moral distinctions between animals and human beings.

Opposition to the use of animals in research is based on arguments of two different kinds—those relying on the alleged rights of animals and those relying on the consequences for animals. I have argued that arguments of both kinds must fail. We surely do have obligations to animals, but they have, and can have, no rights against us on which research can infringe. In calculating the consequences of animal research, we must weigh all the long-term benefits of the results

achieved—to animals and to humans—and in that calculation we must not assume the moral equality of all animate species.

Notes

1.   Regan T. *The case for animal rights.* Berkeley, Calif.: University of California Press, 1983.

2.   Singer P. *Animal liberation.* New York: Avon Books, 1977.

3.   St. Augustine. *Confessions. Book Seven. 397 A.D.* New York: Pocketbooks, 1957:104–26.

4.   St Thomas Aquinas. *Summa theologica 1273 A.D. Philosophic texts.* New York: Oxford University Press, 1960; 353–66.

5.   Hegel GWF. *Philosophy of right.* 1821. London: Oxford University Press, 1952; 105–10.

6.   Bradley FH. Why should I be moral? 1876. In: Melden AI, ed. *Ethical theories.* New York: Prentice-Hall, 1950; 345–59.

7.   Mead GH. The genesis of the self and social control. 1925. In: Reck AJ, ed. *Selected writing.* Indianapolis: Bobbs-Merrill, 1964; 264–93.

8.   Prichard HA. Does moral philosophy rest on a mistake? 1912. In: Cellars W, Hospers J, eds. *Readings in ethical theory.* New York: Appleton-Century-Crofts, 1952; 149–63.

9.   Kant L. *Fundamental principles of the metaphysic of morals.* 1785. New York: Liberal Arts Press, 1949.

10. Rollin BE. *Animal rights and human morality.* New York: Prometheus Books, 1981.

11. Hoff C. Immoral and moral uses of animals. *N Engl J Med* 1980; 302:115–8.

12. Jamieson D. Killing persons and other beings. In: Miller HB, Williams WH, eds. *Ethics and animals.* Clifton, N.J.: Humana Press, 1983; 135–46.

13. Singer P. Ten years of animal liberation. *New York Review of Books.* 1985; 31:46–52.

14. Bentham J. *Introduction to the principles of morals and legislation.* London: Athlone Press, 1970.

15. McCabe K. Who will live, who will die? *Washingtonian Magazine.* August 1986; 115.

16. U.S. Code of Federal Regulations. Tide 21, Sect 505(i). Food, drug, and cosmetic regulations.

17. United States Code of Federal Regulations. Title 16, Sect. 1500.40–2. Consumer product regulations.

DECISION SCENARIOS

The questions following each decision scenario are intended to prompt reflection and discussion. In deciding how to answer them, you should consider the information in the Briefing Session, the ethical theories and principles presented in Part V, "Foundations of Bioethics," and the arguments and criticisms offered in the relevant readings in this chapter.

DECISION SCENARIO 1

Boyd Rush: The First Animal–Human Transplant

The first human heart was transplanted in 1967 in South Africa by Dr. Christiaan Barnard. However, this was not the first heart transplant on a human being. In

January 1964, Dr. James Hardy of the University of Mississippi transplanted a chimpanzee heart into Boyd Rush.

Boyd Rush was a deaf-mute who was brought to the University of Mississippi Medical Center unconscious and on the verge of dying. A stepsister, the only relative who could be located, signed a consent form permitting, if necessary, "the insertion of a suitable heart transplant." The form made no reference to the sort of heart that might be employed. Mr. Rush lived for two hours after the transplant.

Dr. Hardy justified the use of the chimpanzee heart on the ground that it was impossible to obtain a human heart. Also, he was encouraged to think the transplant might be successful because of the limited success obtained by Dr. Keith Reentsma in transplanting chimpanzee kidneys into a man dying of glomerulonephritis. The kidney recipient lived for two months.

Dr. Leonard Bailey, the surgeon who transplanted the baboon heart into the child known as Baby Fae, expressed his view of Dr. Hardy in an interview: "He's an idol of mine because he followed through and did what he should have done. . . he took a gamble to try to save a human life."

1. Evaluate the quality of the consent that was secured for transplant surgery in this case.

2. Suppose Mr. Rush's stepsister did know that a chimpanzee heart might be used. Should anyone be permitted to give consent to such a transplant on behalf of someone else?

3. If the only way to save Mr. Rush's life was to transplant a chimpanzee heart, was the surgery justified?

4. Suppose the transplant could have been expected to postpone Mr. Rush's death for only a relatively short time. Could the sacrifice of a baboon be justified?

5. Evaluate the criticism that Dr. Hardy was doing no more than performing a medical experiment in which Mr. Rush was the unknowing and unconsenting subject.

DECISION SCENARIO 2

Phase I and Consent

Mrs. Wilkins, "Dr. Blake said, "I want to ask you to participate in what we call a Phase I trial of a new drug called Novamed. The aim of such a trial, is my duty to tell you, isn't to treat your disease, but to help us determine how toxic Novamed is. What we learn may help us figure out how to help other people."

"You mean Novamed won't help me?" Mrs. Wilkins asked.

"I can't say that it won't," Dr. Blake said. "Quite frankly, we just don't know. That possibility is always there, but that's not why you should agree to participate. If you do agree, that is."

"I've been told my disease is terminal," Mrs. Wilkins said. "I'm in the last stage of life right now. So it looks

to me like I don't have anything to lose and, potentially, I've got something to gain. Its a gamble, and I'm ready to take it."

"So long as you know Novamed isn't likely to help you," Dr. Blake said. "I'll get the consent forms, and you can ask me any other questions that occur to you."

1. Should Mrs. Wilkins consent to participate in a Phase I trial be regarded as informed?

2. Is Mrs. Wilkins as an appropriate candidate to participate in a Phase I clinical trial?

3. How should investigators go about getting people to consent legitimately to Phase I trials?

DECISION SCENARIO 3

Stopping Tamoxifen

On April 6, 1998, researchers at the National Cancer Institute announced that the clinical trials of the drug tamoxifen had produced enough statistical data to show that there was a clear difference in the

incidence of breast cancer among women taking the drug, compared with women who were not. Because half of the 13,388 women in the study were receiving a placebo instead of an active drug, the study was stopped before its originally planned date so that all of them could receive the drug's benefits. The trial had lasted six years and was intended to determine whether tamoxifen had a protective effect against breast cancer. "We all felt that question had been answered," said Leslie Ford of the National Cancer Institute.

British researchers were unhappy with the American decision and called the cancellation of the clinical trial premature. "The Americans have unblinded the trial, which means it will be unbalanced, and they will not be able to answer many questions," said Trevor Powles, the head of the pilot study with tamoxifen. "Our emphasis is to try to get long-term data from the trial," said Tony Howell of Christie's Hospital, cochair of the seven-nation British study.

"Unfortunately the Americans will not be able to do that now."

1. Assuming that the data show that women who take the drug are less likely to get breast cancer, would it be morally wrong to continue the study?

2. Suppose Tony Howell is right and that canceling the trial makes it impossible to answer a number of important questions. Would it be wrong to continue the trial? Those who are receiving a placebo are not being given something that will cause them harm. Also, because they gave their consent, they knew they might be receiving a placebo, so why isn't it all right to continue the trial?

DECISION SCENARIO 4

Clinical Testing in Foreign Countries

Cardiologist William O'Neill decided he would have to go to Germany to do a clinical test on a device to clean out clogged arteries. Several years previously, researchers at the Centers for Disease Control planned to test the effectiveness of giving vitamin supplements to pregnant women to prevent spina bifida in their children. The National Institute for Child Health and Development objected to the plan to withhold vitamins from the control group. The researchers found Chinese collaborators who arranged for the clinical studies to be done.

Some clinical researchers believe cases like these are widespread and increasing. More and more often, researchers and drug companies are choosing to test medical devices, therapies, and drugs in foreign countries.

Two reasons are mentioned as responsible for the increase. First, the FDA and other federal agencies require so many levels of approval and so much paper work that efforts to mount clinical trials are discouraged. Second, overzealous advocates of patients' rights have both complicated the approval process and made it difficult to recruit test subjects. Speaking about informed-consent forms to test a new clot-dissolving drug used during a heart attack, one British researcher said, "The American documents were three pages of legalistic junk. That's not the sort of thing you want to push under someone's nose as he's having a heart attack, terrified with chest pain, on morphine. You want to tell him about the trial, but you want to be humane."

Furthermore, critics of testing have made people so suspicious of medical research that they refuse to participate when asked. By contrast, patients in other countries are more trusting and give their consent more readily.

The situation has been encouraged by an FDA decision to accept data from some foreign trials. The aim of the policy change was to make effective drugs more quickly available in the United States, but a consequence has been to encourage researchers to avoid problems at home by going abroad.

1. Do we have an obligation to make sure that clinical trials in other countries involve the free and informed consent of participants? Do we have a prima facie duty to protect research subjects everywhere?

2. Suppose that, in a scientifically well-designed trial, a drug to prevent strokes was found to be highly effective, but we learn that the trial was conducted in a third-world country and that the patients in the study were not aware of their status as experimental subjects. Should we refuse to use the drug until the same studies are repeated with subjects who were informed and consenting participants?

3. Suppose the drug was first tested in the United States with consenting subjects and found effective. Because it is too expensive to use in a third-world country, researchers decide to initiate a clinical trial that will test a cheaper drug against

a placebo in Namibia and Zaire. Is it legitimate to use a placebo in such a situation? Could there be a better alternative?

4. Given the reasons mentioned for shifting testing to foreign countries, should we weaken current laws designed to protect research subjects?

DECISION SCENARIO 5

Genuine Consent?

"You realize," Dr. Thorne said, "that you may not be in the group that receives medication. You may be in the placebo group for at least part of the time."

"Right," Ms. Ross said. "You're just going to give me some medicine."

"And do you understand the aims of the research?"

"You want to help me get better," Ms. Ross suggested hesitantly.

"We hope you get better, of course. But that's not what we're trying to accomplish here. We're trying to find out if this medication will help other people in your condition if we can treat them earlier than we were able to treat you."

"You want to help people," Ms. Ross said.

"That's right. But you do understand that we may not be helping you in this experiment?"

"But you're going to try?"

"Not exactly. I mean, we aren't going to try to harm you. But we aren't necessarily going to be giving you the preferred treatment for your complaint either. Do you know the difference between research and therapy?"

"Research is when you're trying to find something out. You're searching around."

"That's right. And we're asking you to be part of a research effort. As I told you, there are some risks. Besides the possibility of not getting treatment that you need, the drug may produce limited hepatic portal damage. We're not sure how much."

"I think I understand," Ms. Ross said.

"I'm sure you do," said Dr. Thorne. "I understand that you are freely volunteering to participate in this research."

"Yes, sir. Mrs. Woolerd, she told me if I volunteered, I'd get a letter put in my file and I could get early release."

"Mrs. Woolerd told you the review board would take your volunteering into account when they considered whether you should be put on work-release."

"Yes, sir. And I'm awfully anxious to get out of here. I've got two children staying with my aunt, and I need to get out of this place as quick as I can."

"I understand. We can't promise you release, of course. But your participation will look good on your record. Now I have some papers here I want you to sign."

1. Discuss some of the difficulties involved in explaining research procedures to nonexperts and determining whether they are aware of the nature and risks of their participation.

2. What reasons are there for believing that Ms. Ross does not understand what she is volunteering for?

3. Discuss the problems involved in securing free and voluntary consent from a person involuntarily confined to an institution (a prisoner, for example).

4. Is it possible to obtain genuine consent from patients in Phase I cancer trials even if they are not in prison?

DECISION SCENARIO 6

When the Numbers Are Small, Can a Trial Be Ethical?

"The Human Subjects Committee has reviewed your protocol for using MK-47 to treat patients with Napier's syndrome," Dr. Helen Laski announced to Dr. Tom Kline. "We can't approve it, because it would

be unethical to enroll only six patients, as you propose. Such a clinical trial would involve so few patients as to have no statistical significance."

1. Suppose Napier's syndrome (a fictitious disease) is relatively common. Explain how you would support the decision of the Human Subjects Committee.

2. Suppose MK-47 is a drug that anecdotal evidence suggests may be appropriate for treating Napier's syndrome. Would this be grounds for approving the protocol?

3. Suppose Napier's syndrome is a rare disease. What sort of evidence would the committee require Dr. Kline to present to persuade them to approve his protocol?

DECISION SCENARIO 7

Using Nazi Data

During World War II, the Nazis conducted experiments on human beings to test the effects of phosgene gas. In 1988, the Environmental Protection Agency decided to exclude the Nazi data from a study it had commissioned. Those favoring the exclusion held that data obtained by unethical means should never be used. Opponents of this view held that making use of such data is a way of honoring and remembering those who were sacrificed to obtain it.

1. On what grounds can we say that the data obtained by the Nazis were unethical? According to their principles, they were doing nothing wrong.

2. Suppose the data had never been published but were available as research notes. Would this make any difference to the question of whether the data ought to be used?

DECISION SCENARIO 8

Primate Head Trauma

During the two years he had worked for the Bioplus Foundation, Dennis Quade had been in many labs. Before he could renew the funding of a grant, he was required to make an on-site inspection of the facilities and review the work of the investigators. Now he was sitting in a small, chilly conference room about to watch a videotape of a phase of the work done at Carolyn Sing's lab.

Sing herself was sitting at the table with him, and she leaned forward and pushed the play button. "The experimental subjects we used are baboons," she told him. "We think they possess facial and cranial structures sufficiently similar to humans to make them the best animal models." Dennis nodded, then watched the monitor in complete silence. He was appalled by what he saw. An adult animal, apparently limp from anesthesia, was strapped to a stainless-steel table. Its head was fitted into a viselike device, and several clamps were tightened to hold it immobile. The upper-left side of the baboon's head had been shaved and the area painted with a faintly purple antiseptic solution. A dark circle had been drawn in the center of the painted area.

The white-coated arms of an assistant appeared in the tight focus of the picture. The assistant was holding a device that looked like an oversized electric drill.

A long transparent plastic sleeve stuck out from the chuck end of the device, and through it Dennis could see a round, stainless-steel plate. A calibrated dial was visible on the side of the device, but Dennis couldn't read the marks.

"That's an impact hammer," Dr. Sing said. "We thought at first we were going to be able to use one off the shelf, but we had to modify one. That's an item we didn't anticipate in our initial budget."

The assistant centered the plastic tube over the spot marked on the baboon's head and pulled the trigger of the impact hammer. The motion of the steel plate was too swift for Dennis to see, but he saw the results. The animal's body jerked in spasm, and a froth of blood, brain tissue, and bone fragments welled up from the purple spot.

Dennis Quade turned away from the monitor, unable to stand the images any longer.

"Through induced head trauma studies, we have been able to learn an enormous amount," Carolyn Sing said. "Not only do we know more about what happens to brain tissue during the first few minutes after trauma, but we've used that knowledge to develop some new management techniques that may save literally tens of thousands of people from permanent brain damage."

Dennis Quade nodded.

1. On what grounds might someone oppose such experiments? Suppose it is true that brain damage from head trauma may be reduced or eliminated in thousands of people. Would this change the matter?

2. If you knew that the information gained from the study described would prevent your child from suffering from brain damage, should this count in your decision about whether such an experiment is justifiable?

3. Is there any reason to suppose that a human life (of any sort) is worth more than an animal life (of any sort)? On what moral grounds, if any, might one object to using patients in a chronic vegetative state as experimental subjects in the study?

Part II

Controls

Chapter 3

Genetic Control

CHAPTER CONTENTS

CASES AND CONTEXTS

CASE PRESENTATION

Genae Girard and Gene Patents

Genae Girard was only thirty-six years old in 2006, when she was diagnosed with breast cancer. She had been working hard building a veterinary supply business in Austin, Texas, and as with so many others, the cancer caught her off guard. She felt she still had many more things to accomplish in her life, but the breast cancer threatened to destroy all her plans.

Following the advice of her doctor, Girard agreed to a genetic test, and the results showed that she was positive for the BRCA2 gene mutation. That she had the gene made it likely that she would develop cancer in the other breast as well. She needed to have a mastectomy to treat her cancer, and to reduce the chances of developing cancer in the other breast, her doctor recommended that she have a double mastectomy.

The bad news got worse for Girard. She learned that BRCA2 also put her at risk for ovarian cancer. By some estimates, women who carry one of the known BRCA mutations have as high as a sixty percent chance of a developing ovarian cancer by age 65. To improve her chances of remaining alive, she would need to have her ovaries surgically removed.

Girard was unmarried and had no children, and without ovaries, she would never be able to have children of her own. This caused her to wonder, What if the test were wrong? What if she didn't have the BRCA2 mutation? Then maybe she wouldn't have to have the double mastectomy, and she wouldn't have to lose her ovaries. After all, she recalled later, "There is human error, and labs make mistakes." She was being asked to make a decision about her future on the basis of a single laboratory test.

Girard told her doctor that she wanted to have another test, one performed by another lab. That was when she learned—to her surprise—that there was no other test available, because Myriad Genetics owned the patent on the BRCA1 and BRCA2 genes. This gave Myriad the sole right to test for the presence of the mutations. Thus, Girard learned, Myriad was not merely the only game in town, it was the only game legally allowed.

Patenting Life?

When most people learn that it is possible to secure a patent on a gene, they are disbelieving. Common sense seems to suggest that genes have the same status as things in the world like oak trees, granite boulders, and sheet lightning. How could anyone patent such things?

No one can. The patent laws of the United States explicitly rule out patents on natural objects, processes, or laws of nature. Nor is it possible to patent naturally occurring organisms such as the oak tree, grizzly bear, army ant, or *E. coli* bacterium. With the development of molecular biology in the 1960s and recombinant-DNA technology in the 1970s, however, the line between "naturally occurring" organisms and altered or "manufactured" organisms began to blur.

Consider what was done with the bacterium *Pseudomonas* by Ananda Chakrabarty. *Pseudomonas*, which is found in soil the world over, was known to metabolize hydrocarbons, and for decades it was referred to as an "oil-eating" bacterium. The bacterium does its metabolic work very slowly, however, and Chakrabarty, a microbiologist employed by General Electric, conceived the idea of developing a strain of *Pseudomonas* that would be what he called a "superbug."

The new strain would be highly effective in breaking down hydrocarbons, and this would make it valuable in cleaning up oil spills rapidly and cheaply. A superbug would also be valuable financially, if it were possible to secure a patent on it. It could then be licensed, and the patent owners could demand a fee every time the bacterium was employed.

Chakrabarty began experimenting with four strains of *Pseudomonas,* and he soon realized that the bacterial enzymes that break down hydrocarbons aren't produced by genes in the nucleus. Rather, the relevant genes were in the extranuclear DNA in a cell's plasmids. The bacterial strains naturally exchange plasmids, and after much experimental work, Chakrabarty discovered that, following a plasmid transfer, he could use ultraviolet light to induce a host plasmid to incorporate DNA from other plasmids into its genetic material. Thus, after six years' work, he succeeded in creating a new strain of *Pseudomonas*.

Chakrabharty gave the new strain the descriptive name "multiplasmid hydrocarbon-degrading pseudomonas." Tests showed that the new strain would degrade oil ten to one hundred times faster than any of the four naturally occurring strains that he had worked with.

Patent Applied For

Chakrabarty (along with General Electric) applied for a patent on the superbug he had developed. The application was rejected on the ground that the law does not permit living things to be patented. Chakrabarty filed an appeal with the Board of Patent Appeal, but the board allowed the original decision to stand.

Chakrabarty then took the issue to the U.S. Court of Patent Appeals. This time his luck changed, and the appeals court ruled that Chakrabarty had produced a novel microorganism, one that does not appear in nature.

Moreover, the court held, "The fact that microorganisms are alive is without legal significance" with respect to the patent law.

This time it was the Patent Office that appealed. Sidney A Diamond, the Commissioner of Patents, took the case to the U.S. Supreme Court. On June 16, 1980, the Court, in a five to four ruling, upheld the decision of the Court of Patent Appeals.

Patent law states, "Whoever invents or discovers any new and useful process, machine, manufacture, or composition of matter, or any new and useful improvement thereof, may obtain a patent therefore. . . ." The majority of the Supreme Court decided that Chakrabarty's "microorganism constitutes a 'manufacture' or 'composition of matter' within the meaning of the law." This was the legal precedent for the thousands of biotech patents that would follow, but the courts had already upheld patents on products found in the human body.

Human Products

The first U.S. patent for a naturally occurring product was granted to Jokichi Takamine, a Japanese chemist who spent most of his professional life in New York. In 1906, Takamine and his sponsor, the drug company Parke-Davis, applied for a patent on "a blood pressure raising" substance that he had isolated from secretions of the "supradrenal glands" and purified. Parke-Davis gave the substance the trade name Adrenaline.[2] (It was later found to be a combination of epinephrine and norepinephrine.)

The patent was challenged in court by a rival drug company, on the ground that the substance was "a part of nature and not something invented or manufactured." Judge Learned Hand ruled in 1911 that Adrenaline could be patented, and his decision established the legal precedent that patents could be issued on isolated and purified versions of substances found in the human body. Such versions of the substances, Hand reasoned, wouldn't be available without the procedures chemists performed to produce them.

Human insulin, as soon as it was available in a purified form, was patented in 1923. A variety of other biological products, including vaccines, medical tests, and medical treatments, were patented in the decades that followed. Such patents became so common that it was striking news in 1955 (and remains so today) when Jonas Salk, the developer of the first effective polio vaccine, announced that he wouldn't seek a patent on it, because to do so would be as wrong as "to patent the sun."

Human Genes

The steady stream of patents for human and other biological materials became a flood with the increasing success of recombinant-DNA techniques. In 1977, three years before the Chakrabarty decision, the University of California applied for a patent on the genes for the production of human insulin and human grown hormone by genetically modified bacteria. The patents were granted in 1982 and 1987, and in 1985 the Cetus Corporation was granted a patent for the protein interleukin-2, an immune system activator used in the treatment of some cancers.

Patents were also issued for specific antibodies, various human hormones and growth factors, and blood factors used in the treatment of hemophilia, as well as for a variety of genetically engineered viruses. Many of the specialized viruses are vaccines, while others are used to transport genes into cells in gene-therapy experiments. Animals that have been genetically modified to allow the study of human diseases (animal models) have also been patented. (Transgenic organisms that include genes from other species, including humans, are themselves a source of controversy.)

The Human Genome Project decoded major amounts of the human genetic material, and as large numbers of human genes were identified, they were quickly patented. (See "Social Context: The Human Genome Project," in this chapter.) The patents include DNA sequences that encode instructions for making particular proteins or for regulating the way a gene is expressed, but they also encompass variants of normal genes associated with diseases. The BRCA1 and BRCA2 mutations patented by Myriad Genetics fall into this category. So does the HHF gene, a mutation leading to hemochromatosis (a disease in which so much iron accumulates in the blood as to cause organ damage), and the genetic variants that produce hypocholesterolimia (a lipid disorder in which excess cholesterol increases the risk of heart disease and stroke). Patents have also been issued for RNA sequences, such as those which function as switches to turn genes off or on.

The genes mapped and sequenced by the Human Genome Project now number from twenty to twenty-five thousand. Some experts estimate that about twenty percent of these genes, three to five thousand, have been patented. In addition, as many as fifty thousand patents involving genetic material—RNA sequences, transgenic animals, and modified bacteria—may have been issued.

Myriad Flexes Its Patents

The United States is not the only country that allows genes, genetically altered organisms, and products based on genetic material to be patented. Because these patents include tests designed to detect the presence of a gene or a mutation, tests themselves have sparked a great amount of concern and anger.

Holders of gene patents have not, in general, made it expensive for a scientist to get a license to work on a gene or to develop diagnostic tests for it. The most glaring exception has been Myriad Genetics. In 2001, the company sent letters to biological and medical researchers in industrialized countries, informing them that Myriad owned the rights to BRCA1 and BRCA2 and that all testing for the presence of these genes had to be done in a laboratory operated or licensed by Myriad.

Canada refused to recognize the terms of Myriad's patents, and in Europe the patents were challenged in court. The patent claims on BRCA1 were reduced, and a BRCA2 patent was granted to the British Cancer Research Campaign, a research organization that has pledged to offer unrestricted access to scientists.

Myriad, as Genae Girard discovered, has a monopoly on testing for the breast-cancer genes in the United States Critics claim that the $3,000 Myriad charges for a test could be reduced if Myriad allowed them to perform the tests. (The cost of the test in Canada is about $1,000.) Other labs might also be able to perform the tests more quickly, but so long as Myriad asserts its patent rights, hospitals and clinical laboratories don't want to risk a lawsuit. Before Myriad sent its warning letter, some physician-researchers had been testing breast-cancer patients for the mutations, but they stopped.

The cost of the tests can have a personal impact on patients. Genae Girard wanted a second test by another lab before she agreed to have a double mastectomy and her ovaries removed. Lisbeth Ceriani, according to reporter John Schwartz, had a double mastectomy for breast cancer, then wanted to be tested for BRCA1 and BRCA2 to see if she was at risk for ovarian cancer and needed to have her ovaries removed. Myriad refused to accept her insurance, and Ceriani was unable to come up with the cash. Ceriani hesitated to have surgery she might not need, but as the mother of an eight-year-old daughter, she also wanted to know if her child might have inherited gene mutations predisposing her to breast cancer and ovarian cancer.

Con and Pro

Critics of gene patenting point to its negative impact on patients, but they also worry about the consequence it may have on biomedical research. If no one is able to conduct research on the BRCA1 and BRCA2 genes without paying Myriad or at least getting the company's permission, this alone has a chilling effect. Researchers who attempt to understand the still unknown ways in which genetic variants operate to produce disease, but who do not gain Myriad's approval, risk lawsuits for patent infringement.

Indeed, researchers can't even compare a normal stretch of DNA with one containing mutated genes without Myriad's permission. Rather than court legal entanglements, research institutions, universities, and scientists work in areas where patents are not a problem. In the view of a representative of the American Liberties Union, Myriad's patent claims constitute restrictions on the free exchange of ideas and thus violate the First Amendment.

Defenders of gene patents reject these criticisms and argue that, without patent protection, research wouldn't flourish the way it has for the last several decades. Researchers, institutions, and venture capitalists would not invest the talent, time, and money that are necessary to advance genetic research without the promise of a significant financial payoff.

The very purpose of a patent system, they point out, is to encourage innovation and effort by rewarding those who succeed in acquiring potentially useful knowledge. For example, the processes and materials involved in the production of microchips couldn't be patented, the computer industry probably wouldn't have made such great strides forward in such a short time. If we want to see biotech industries flourish in a similar way, we need to recognize the importance of the patent system in providing the promise of incentives. Refusing to recognize the legitimacy of gene patents could have the effect of slowing the development of "personalized medicine," medical practice in which treatments are tailored to fit the genetic profile of individual patients.

Genae Girard's Day in Court

Genae Girard, with the backing of the American Civil Liberties Union and the Association for Molecular Pathology, filed a lawsuit against Myriad Genetics challenging several of its BRCA1 and BRCA2 patent claims. The case was heard by Judge Robert Sweet of the United States District Court of New York, and Judge Sweet issued his ruling on March 29, 2010.

Judge Sweet rejected seven of Myriad's patent claims involving the BRCA1 and BRCA2 genes. Myriad, he decided, had no legitimate patent claim on the DNA sequences related to the two genes or to the methods of analyzing or comparing the sequences to detect the presence or absence of the mutated genes. The Patent Office, he said, should not have granted the patents, because the genes are a "law of nature" and do not therefore qualify, according to the law, as something for which patents can be granted.

Judge Sweet did not deny the importance of the research performed by Myriad leading to the identification of the genes. Even so, the importance of the discoveries does not mean that Myriad can patent them. As Sweet wrote in the decision

The identification of the BRCAI and BRCA2 gene sequences is unquestionably a valuable scientific achievement for which Myriad deserves recognition, but this not the same as concluding that it is something for which they are entitled to a patent.

Although the suit against Myriad had challenged the patents on the ground that they, in effect, restricted the free exchange of ideas and thus violated the First Amendment, Judge Sweet declined to rule on the issue. In his view, the case could be settled within the area of patent law alone.

The ACLU attorney, Chris Hansen, underscored the nature of the ruling: "The human genome, like the structure of blood, air or water, was discovered, not created. There is an endless amount of information on genes that begs for further discovery, and gene patents put up unacceptable barriers to the free exchange of ideas."

Genae Girard declared that the court decision was "a big turning point for all women in the country that may have breast cancer that runs in their family."

Promote or Impede

Myriad Genetics issued no public statement, but knowledgeable observers expect their attorneys to file an appeal. The legal battle over gene patents may take years to resolve, but if higher courts uphold Judge Sweet's ruling, thousands of patents granted to biotech companies may be either invalidated or considerably restricted.

Whether such an outcome would promote or impede the advancement of our understanding of genetics and the development of personalized medicine is a debate that will continue.

Huntington's Disease: Deadly Disease, Personal Dilemmas

Huntington's disease (HD) is a particularly cruel and frightening genetic disorder. It has no effective treatment and is invariably fatal. Furthermore, each child of an affected parent has a fifty percent chance of developing the disease.

The disease typically makes its appearance between the ages of thirty-five and forty-five in men and women who have shown no previous symptoms. The signs of its onset may be quite subtle—a certain clumsiness in performing small tasks, a slight slurring of speech, a few facial twitches. But the disease is progressive. Over time, the small signs develop into massive physical and mental changes. Walking becomes jerky and unsteady, the face contorts into wild grimaces, the hands repeatedly clench and relax, and the whole body writhes with involuntary muscle spasms. The victim eventually loses the power of speech, becomes disoriented, and gives way to irrational emotional outbursts. Before mental deterioration becomes too advanced, HD victims often kill themselves out of sheer hopelessness and despair. Death may occur naturally from fifteen to twenty years after the beginning of the symptoms. Usually, it results from massive infection and malnutrition—as the disease progresses, the victim loses the ability to swallow normally.

In the United States, at any given time, some 30,000 people are diagnosed as having the disease, and as many as 150,000 more may have the gene responsible for it. The incidence of the disease is only one in 10,000, but for the child of someone with the disease, the chances of having it are one in two.

Gene Identified

The gene causing the disease was identified in 1993 after ten years of intensive research carried out in six laboratories in the United States, England, and Wales. Following the leads provided by genetic markers for the disease, the gene was finally located near the tip of chromosome 4. When researchers sequenced the nucleotides making up the gene, they discovered that the mutation was a trinucleotide repeat. In healthy individuals, the nucleotides CAG are repeated eleven to thirty-four times, whereas in individuals with HD, the repetitions typically range from thirty-seven to eighty-six. Some evidence suggests that higher numbers of repetitions are associated with earlier onset.

When the HD gene was identified, it was expected that this would have almost immediate consequences for the development of an effective treatment. This has not turned out to be the case, because the mechanism of the gene's action is not yet understood. Furthermore, the gene was expected to be found functioning only in the brain, but in fact radioactive tagging has shown that the gene operates in virtually every tissue of the body, including the colon, liver, pancreas, and testes. The protein the gene codes for is believed to be toxic to neuronal development, but the protein itself has not yet been isolated. (In 1998, it was discovered that the disease involves the formation of a protein plaque in brain cells that destroys them, but this hasn't yet led to a therapy.)

Before the HD gene was identified or a marker for it discovered, the disease was known to be transmitted from generation to generation in the sort of hereditary pattern indicating that it is caused by a single gene. However, because the disease makes its appearance relatively late in life, an unsuspecting victim may already have passed on the gene to a child before showing any sign of the disease. In the absence of a genetic test to detect the gene, the individual could not know whether he or she was a carrier.

In 1983, a major step toward the development of such a test was announced by James F. Gusella and his group at Massachusetts General Hospital. The team did not locate the gene itself, but discovered a "genetic marker" indicating its presence. They began by studying the DNA taken from members of a large American family with a history of Huntington's disease, then employed recombinant-DNA techniques to attempt to locate DNA segments that might be associated with the HD gene.

The techniques involved using proteins known as restriction enzymes. A particular enzyme, when mixed with a single strand of DNA, cuts the strand at specific locations known as recognition sites. After the DNA strand has been cut up by restriction enzymes, short sections of radioactive, single-stranded DNA are added to serve as probes. The probes bind to particular segments of the DNA. Because the probes are radioactive, the segments to which they are attached can be identified on photographic film. The various fragments of DNA produced by the restriction enzymes and identified by probes form a pattern that is typical of individuals. Thus, if the pattern of someone who does not have the disease is compared with the pattern of a family member who does, the fragments that include the faulty gene can be identified, even when the gene itself is unknown. The pattern serves as a marker for the presence of the gene.

Gusella's group faced the problem of finding a marker consistently inherited by those with Huntington's disease but not by those free of the disease. This meant identifying perhaps as many as eight hundred markers and determining whether one could serve as the marker for the HD gene. Incredibly, the team identified a good candidate on its twelfth try. It was a marker found in all members of the family they were studying. Those with the disease had the same form of the marker, while those free of the disease had some other form.

Gusella and other researchers were supported in their work by the Hereditary Disease Foundation. The organization was founded by Milton Wexler after his wife was diagnosed with Huntington's. Wexler hoped a treatment for the disease could be found that might benefit his daughters, Nancy and Alice, who stood a fifty percent chance of developing the disease. Nancy Wexler soon became an active participant in research activities aimed at discovering a genetic marker.

In collaboration with the Hereditary Disease Foundation, plans were made to test Gusella's candidate marker in a large population. It was known that a large family with a high incidence of HD lived along the shores of Lake Maracaibo in Venezuela. Nancy Wexler led a team to this remote location to collect a family history and to obtain blood and skin samples for analysis. The lake-dwelling family included some 100 people with the disease and 1100 children with the risk of developing it. Analysis of the samples showed that those with the disease also carried the same form of the marker as their American counterparts. Gusella estimated that the odds were one hundred million to one that the marker was linked to the HD gene. Subsequent work by Susan Naylor indicated that the marker was on chromosome 4. When the gene itself was identified in 1993, this turned out to be correct.

Genetic Test Available

Once the location of the gene for Huntington's disease was known, a genetic test for its presence was quickly developed. The availability of the test, however, raises a number of serious ethical and social issues. The basic question people with a family history that puts them at risk for the disease must ask is whether they should have the test.

A study conducted in Wales revealed that more than half of those whose parents or relatives were victims of Huntington's disease would not want to have a test that would tell them whether they had the HD gene, even if such a test were available. Considering that the disease cannot be effectively treated and is invariably fatal, this is not a surprise finding.

Nancy Wexler confided to a reporter that she and her sister had assumed that once a test for determining whether they were carrying the HD gene was available, they would take it. However, when they met with their father to work out the details for a test based on a genetic marker, he suddenly said, "What are we doing here? Are we sure we want to do this?" The sisters, Nancy recalled, "had a visceral understanding that either one of us could get bad news and that it would certainly destroy my father."

But do those who are at risk have obligations to others? Because a test is available, is it fair to a potential marriage partner to marry without finding out whether one is a carrier of the HD gene and informing the potential partner of the result? Perhaps he or she may be willing to take the chance that the offspring of an HD parent will not have the disease. Even so, because of the tremendous burden the disease places on the other spouse, the possibility of being tested for the presence of the gene deserves serious consideration.

The decision about whether to have children can also be affected by the knowledge that one partner is a carrier of the HD gene so that there is a fifty percent chance that any child will also develop the disease. Should a potential carrier of the gene impose on the other partner the risk of having a child who will inherit the gene? Should such a risk be imposed on a potential child? The genetic test can determine whether an individual carries the gene. If he or she does, then the couple has knowledge of the relevant facts that will put them in a position to make a decision about having a child.

Prenatal Testing and Embryo Screening

The test now in use can also be employed in conjunction with amniocentesis to determine whether a developing fetus carries the HD gene. This fact raises problems for potential parents. A child born with the HD gene will inevitably develop the disease but may not do so for three, four, or even five or more decades. Does this mean that an abortion is not justified in the event of a positive test? But if the potential parents aren't prepared to seek an abortion, why should they have wanted the test? Finally, is the fact that the fetus can be expected to develop into an adult who will eventually succumb to the disease reason enough to make an abortion morally obligatory?

A disadvantage of the direct testing of the fetus for the presence of the HD gene is that if the fetus is found to have the gene, then the parent with a family history of the disease will know that she or he also has the gene. To avoid this consequence, a "nondisclosing" prenatal test may be possible. The test employs a gene-probe method to determine how a segment of fetal chromosome 4 compares with segments from grandparents. If the segment

resembles that of a healthy grandparent, the child is not likely to have the HD gene. If it matches that of a grandparent with the disease, the chances are one in two that the child possesses the gene.

This is the same as the risk for a mother or father with one parent who developed the disease. Hence, the potential parent has learned nothing new about his or her own chance of having the gene, and it is this that makes the test nondisclosing. However, if the potential parents do not plan to abort the fetus should they learn that it has a fifty-fifty chance of possessing the HD gene, they have no reason to perform the nondisclosing test.

An alternative to abortion for potential parents who worry about one of them passing on the HD gene to a child is to make use of the techniques of assisted reproduction. Once embryos have been produced by artificial insemination from the parents' donated ova and sperm, the embryos can be tested for the HD gene. Only embryos without the gene can then be transferred to the woman's uterus for development.

Personal Risks

The advent of a standard, inexpensive test for the HD gene raises various other personal and social issues. For example, insurance companies may refuse to provide life insurance to those from families with Huntington's disease, unless they prove that they are not carriers of the gene. (The Genetic Information Nondiscrimination Act—GINA—does not forbid insurers from using genetic information in underwriting life insurance.) Adoption agencies have requested that infants offered for adopting be tested to assure adopting families that the children are not at risk for HD. (Whether such would violate GINA screening has not been tested.) As Nancy Wexler put the point, "In our culture, people assume that knowledge is always good. . . . But our experience with Huntington's has shown that some things may be better left unknown."

Informing someone that he or she carries the gene also has problems associated with it. Such news can be devastating, both to the person and to the person's family. The most recent evidence indicates that the suicide rate among those with HD is ten times the rate of the general population. In a recent survey of 175 medical centers in which a total of 4,527 people tested positive for the HD gene, 5 killed themselves, 21 attempted suicide, and 18 were hospitalized for psychiatric reasons. Thus, the mere act of conveying the information that someone will later develop the signs of a fatal disease can itself constitute a threat to life. Nancy Wexler has refused to disclose publicly whether she has been tested for the HD gene. "I don't want to influence anyone's decision," she says.

Envoi

In the best of worlds, an effective means of preventing the onset of Huntington's disease or treating it effectively would be available. Then the moral, social, and personal issues associated with a genetic test for it would disappear without having to be resolved. Regrettably, that world still lies in the future.

SOCIAL CONTEXT
Testing for Disease Predispositions: Is It Better Not to Know?

The discovery of hundreds of disease-predisposing genes has been accompanied by the development of new genetic tests. Given the increasing sophistication of biotechnology, tests that were complex and expensive have become simple and cheap. By using cells from a cheek swab or a blood sample in an automated process involving biochip arrays of genetic probes, it should be possible to screen simultaneously for the presence of literally hundreds of genes. (For more details, see "Social Context: What Are My Chances? Direct to Consumer Genetic Testing," in this chapter.)

Genetic Disease: Blurred Concept

Researchers are well on the way to identifying an entire catalogue of genes and diseases associated with them, but the concept of a genetic disease is not as clear-cut as it may seem. Rarely is it the case that if a person carries a certain gene, she will invariably develop a certain disease. Although single-gene disorders such as sickle-cell disease, cystic fibrosis, and Huntington's disease have been at the focus of much research, they account for only about two percent of genetic disorders. Most diseases result from a multiplicity of conditions, including the particular form of a gene (many genes have scores, and even hundreds, of mutated versions), the presence or absence of other genes, and the presence or absence of specific environmental factors. Being predisposed to develop a disease raises a number of questions about the value and dangers of genetic testing.

Individual Choice

The ambivalence most people feel about genetic testing is shown by the results of a recent survey. When five hundred people were asked if they would like to take a genetic test that would tell them what diseases they would suffer from later in life, fifty percent said they would want to take it and forty-nine percent said they wouldn't. We all seem torn between seeing the value of knowing and the comfort of not knowing.

Information about a genetic predisposition to a particular disease can be beneficial to people. It can alert them to the need to seek medical surveillance so that they can receive appropriate therapy for the disease, should it develop, at the earliest time. Further, it can make them aware of the need to avoid environmental factors that may trigger the disease. For example, those with the gene for xeroderma pigmentosum are extremely sensitive to ultraviolet radiation, and exposure to it is likely to lead to a form of skin cancer (melanoma) that is usually incurable. However, if those with the gene avoid prolonged exposure to sunlight, they have a good chance of avoiding developing melanoma.

By contrast, in the case of some single-gene diseases like Huntington's, knowing that one is a carrier of the gene opens up no ways of altering the outcome of the disease. No way of preventing the disease is known, and early

A Sample of DNA Tests Currently Available	
Disease	Description
Huntington's disease	Progressive neurological disorder, onset in 40s or 50s
Polycystic kidney disease	Multiple kidney cysts leading to loss of kidney function
Cystic fibrosis	Mucus clogs lungs and pancreas; death in 30s is common
Sickle-cell disease	Hemoglobin defect; anemia, strokes, and heart damage
Alpha-1-antitrypsin deficiency	Can cause hepatitis, cirrhosis, and emphysema
Familial adenomatous polyposis	Colon polyps by age 35, often leading to cancer
Muscular dystrophy	Progressive muscle deterioration
Hemophilia	Blood fails to clot properly
Tay–Sachs disease	Lipid metabolism disorder causing death in first one to four years of life
Retinoblastoma	Cancerous tumor of the eye; most common in childhood
Phenylketonuria	Enzyme deficiency producing mental retardation
Retinitis pigmentosa	Progressive retinal degeneration leading to blindness
Familial breast cancer	five to ten percent of breast cancers
Familial hypercholesterolemia	High levels of cholesterol leading to early heart disease
Spinocerebellar ataxia	Neurological disorder producing lack of muscle control

intervention makes no difference in the course of the illness. Although some might want to know whether they are carriers of the gene in order to make informed decisions about such personal matters as marriage, childbearing, and lifestyle, others might prefer to live their lives without knowing. (See "Case Presentation: Huntington's Disease," in this chapter.)

Equally difficult issues are associated with testing for the genes known to be associated with familial breast cancer. The mutated gene BRCA1, located on chromosome 17, was identified in 1994 as responsible for the susceptibility to breast cancer and ovarian cancer in a group of families with multiple incidence of the diseases.

A "frame-shift mutation" involving an extra nucleotide apparently causes the translation of codons to start in the wrong place, producing a nonsense protein. A second gene, BRCA2, located on chromosome 13, that also causes susceptibility to breast cancer was discovered in 1995. More than two hundred mutations have been identified on the BRCA genes, but one study suggests that it is a mutation in BRCA1 which is most likely to cause cancer in younger women.

Women who carry one of the mutated genes are estimated to have an eighty-five percent chance of developing breast cancer and a sixty percent chance of developing ovarian cancer by age 65. Whether these figures can be generalized to any carrier of the gene is in dispute, because they are based on samples from families with a history of breast cancer. Some suggest that a more realistic figure for breast cancer for a woman with the BRCA mutation is fifty-six percent.

The two mutated genes may explain the majority of hereditary breast cancers. (BRCA1 appears responsible for about 50% and BRCA2 for 30–40 %.) Yet to the surprise of researchers, no evidence suggests that the BRCA1 or BRCA2 gene plays a role in the 90% to 95% of "sporadic" breast cancers—ones not known to be due to inherited susceptibility. (The possibility that mutations in other genes are responsible is under investigation.)

But susceptibility to breast cancer means only that a woman is more likely than average to develop the disease. The extent to which she might control the outcome by altering such factors as diet, alcohol consumption, and exercise isn't known.

The evidence shows that a woman's chances of developing cancer can be significantly reduced by a prophylactic double mastectomy. Even so, cancer can still occur in the remaining tissue. Also, ovarian cancer remains as likely as before, so to lower those odds, a woman at risk must also have her ovaries removed. Should a woman with a strong family history of breast and ovarian cancer be tested for BRCA1 and BRCA2?

The generally accepted view is that this is a question that should be answered by the woman herself. Some women want to know, because they want to have the surgery that may extend their lives. Other women, particularly those who may be looking to find a partner or to have children, may be unwilling to have the surgery. Thus, from this point of view, they may see no practical value in finding out.

Another group of women might value discovering something important about themselves. Even if they don't plan to have surgery, what they learn from the test might influence the way they live their lives. If they test negative for the genes, knowing that they are no more likely than other women to develop breast or ovarian cancer would allow them to go about their lives without the worry that speculation and uncertainty might produce. If they test positive, they are in a position to reconsider the surgery option and have been alerted to the need to make sure that they get regular mammograms and, perhaps, a blood test for ovarian cancer.

Should We Tell the Children?

Researchers attempting to identify a gene predisposing women to breast cancer conducted their work among families with a high incidence of the disease. During the course of their work, they learned which females in the family had to be carriers of the BRCA1 gene and so had an eighty-five percent chance of developing the disease. The question they faced was, Should they inform the women that they or their children were at such risk?

Some researchers decided that they would not volunteer any information and would provide it only to women eighteen or older who asked for it. They refused to divulge any information about children, even when pressed to do so by their parents, because being predisposed to breast cancer is not a condition for which there is a treatment. Also, the researchers reasoned, if a child knew she was predisposed to breast cancer, she might be inclined to think of herself as sick and her breasts as likely to kill her.

Some critics of testing have argued that children should not be included in screening tests, except when there is some direct benefit for them. The acquisition of knowledge is not in itself a justification for testing children, the critics hold, nor is the usefulness of the knowledge in the treatment of others. Genetic tests and the results they yield have the potential to damage or destroy a child's self-esteem, causing emotional harm or altering the way the family views the child. In some instances, upon learning that a child is likely to develop a disease, some families distanced themselves from the child, even to the point of placing the child in a foster home. When the child herself receives no benefit, the threat of such outcomes makes the test unjustifiable.

At least one survey shows, however, that parents often believe that children should be aware of their risks for developing a particular disease. Some sixty-one percent of parents visiting prenatal testing clinics said that they should be permitted to have their children tested for Alzheimer's, and forty-seven percent said that parents should inform the children of the results.

However, another survey of families with members already diagnosed with genetic diseases shows a different result. Survey participants seemed to feel strongly that parents should have their children tested for a disease only when it is a treatable or preventable one. When the disease is neither, as is the case with Alzheimer's, the screening should not be done.

The issue may be complicated in some cases by the discovery that a disease, which is mild or even asymptomatic in a parent may be much worse in an offspring. This was found to be the case with myotonic muscular dystrophy, the most common form of the disease. A segment of DNA on chromosome 19 appears to repeat itself with increasing frequency over generations. Hence, someone who does not have any clinical sign of the disease may pass on the gene to a child, who will develop a devastating form of the disease. It could be argued that if a parent knows that a child is at high risk for developing a life-threatening disease, the parent has a duty to inform the child, although perhaps only after the child has reached a certain level of maturity.

Whether children should be given genetic tests for diseases for which there is no immediate treatment is likely to remain controversial. The views of parents, genetic counselors, and physicians may conflict where certain diseases are concerned. Who should make the decision? How much should the child be told? These are questions likely to become more pressing as the number of tests for disease-associated genes increases.

Protection against Discrimination

Until recently, the main worry associated with our newly acquired abilities to test adults for genes associated with diseases was that the information could be used by employers and insurers to the disadvantage of those who decided to be tested. Thus, genetic testing was seen as opening the way for new forms of discrimination—discrimination based on genetic predisposition.

Indeed, the discrimination became real. Some employers refused to hire people whose genetic profile suggested that they might develop diseases such as breast cancer, ovarian cancer, Huntington's disease, or hypercholesterolemia (and the heart and vascular diseases accompanying it) that might lead to many absences from work or to expensive treatments that would raise a company's health insurance costs. Similarly, insurance companies often turned down for coverage people likely to file claims for costly treatments and medicines. Insurers were also moving in the direction of regarding a genetic predisposition to develop a disease as a "prexisisting condition," something not covered by most health insurance policies.

The Genetic Information Nondiscrimination Act (GINA) was framed to prevent discrimination of the sort just described. The act took effect in November 2009 and is supposed to make it possible for people to keep genetic information about themselves private without suffering a penalty. Employers and insurers can no longer require, for example, that people be tested for specific genetic predispositions, nor can they make use of such information if they find it in someone's medical record. (See "Social Context: GINA," in this chapter.) GINA extends to children as well, so that parents will not be expected to pay higher premiums for a child who tests positive for a genetic disorder.

Not enough time has passed to determine how effective GINA will be in protecting the genetic privacy of individuals. Before a realistic assessment can be made, the regulations and penalties specified in the legislation will need to be tested in court. Most observers agree, however, that GINA is a significant step in the direction of safeguarding personal genetic information.

"Genetic Undesirables"

A part from issues connected with employment and insurance, genetic testing opens up the possibility of identifying a class of people that may become regarded as socially undesirable.

As genetic sophistication and genetic information spread, people can be expected to develop a better understanding of what it means to be genetically predisposed to develop a disease such as ovarian cancer or to be carrying the gene for retinitis pigmentosa or sickle-cell disease. In a society that prizes health, being predisposed to a genetic disease may become a stigma. Genetic carriers of disease-causing genes might be shunned as marriage partners or find it difficult to make their way into positions of social power and influence. Regarded as genetic pariahs, they might come to be outcasts in their own society, stigmatized by their biological inheritance.

The more we learn about our genes and the more individuals learn about their personal genome, people's genetic profile might come to be considered as important as their appearance, income, or personality.

Envoi

The difficulties discussed here are only some of those raised by the new possibilities of testing for the genetic predisposition to diseases. The promise of being able to prevent the occurrence of some disease in many individuals is genuine, but we have yet to make an adequate effort to resolve the social and moral issues that fulfilling the promise presents. Until we deal with them satisfactorily, a powerful technology may remain underutilized. Genetic information may become a case of dangerous knowledge that we shy away from using because of its destructive potential.

SOCIAL CONTEXT
Predictive Genetic Testing: To Test or Not to Test?

The success of genetic testing in predicting that a baby may be born with one of a variety of possible diseases or conditions is considered by many a triumph of contemporary biomedical science. No longer must we acknowledge genetic fate and accept what happens with resignation. Rather, in many cases we have the power to avoid the outcome of having a child with a serious or even fatal disease. Genetic testing is thus a way of dodging a bullet that can destroy hopes and shatter lives.

Don't Test

Not everyone takes such a positive view of predictive genetic testing, however. The optimistic view celebrates the fact that genetic testing can allow parents a certain amount of control over what their child will be like. But critics worry about the use of this power and about its consequences for people born with certain genetic traits or disorders.

First, the critics ask, what condition is sufficiently serious to justify a decision to have an abortion (or, alternatively, avoid implanting an embryo with a certain gene)? Those who accept the legitimacy of abortion for serious reasons may agree that the prospect of having a child with a disease like Tay–Sachs that is untreatable and fatal in early childhood would warrant an abortion.

By contrast, people with the Huntington's gene don't develop the disease until middle age, and the lives of those with cystic fibrosis can be extended into their thirties or even forties. Should these lives be prevented by abortion or embryo selection? Moreover, what about hereditary conditions like some forms of deafness and blindness? Should we even consider these as diseases, much less view them as conditions that justify aborting a fetus carrying the genes responsible for them?

Second, some critics maintain that genetic testing with the aim of aborting fetuses considered in some way "abnormal" is a form of discrimination against people with disabilities. It is, they say, an implicit endorsement of the notion that someone who has Down syndrome or is born blind, deaf, or a dwarf is not the equal of (not as good as) someone who is "normal." Thus, genetic testing can be seen as a socially approved eugenics program that devalues the worth of people with disabilities.

Third, critics worry that diminishing the number of people with conditions such as cystic fibrosis, Down syndrome, muscular dystrophy, and hereditary deafness will have a negative impact on those now living with those conditions. For one, a reduction in the number of affected people will mean that those with the condition will have a smaller community. Thus, they risk becoming even more socially isolated than they are now.

Also, a smaller number of affected people means that the group might lose much of its political influence. Public programs established to move disabled people into the mainstream of school and life will either have their funding cut or become so small that their aims can no longer be achieved. For example, school districts can have a program in special athletics if only three people qualify to participate. Thus, individuals for whom such programs were designed will no longer be able to benefit.

Finally, critics say, a drastic reduction in the number of people born with genetic diseases or conditions would mean that researchers will no longer be motivated to develop new drugs or treatments for the diseases or disabilities people now live with. If cystic fibrosis can be eliminated by early genetic screening and the number of people with the disease falls below some crucial level, researchers aren't likely to devote their careers to improving the lot of a handful of people, because the rewards and support aren't there. Rather, cystic fibrosis will become another "orphan" disease—a disease affecting so few people that it can't command the resources and talent needed to find a better way to treat it. Such an investment is more likely to be made in finding better ways of treating breast cancer or heart disease.

Test

The preceding criticisms do not meet with much sympathy from those who believe that prenatal genetic testing, when combined with abortion and screening embryos before implantation, offers a way to reduce the amount of misery in the world by preventing the birth of children who may suffer from one of a large number of devastating and incurable diseases or may lack some beneficial natural capacity such as sight or hearing.

Advocates of prenatal genetic testing answer the critics' first point by arguing that potential parents are the ones who should decide whether they want to accept the burden of caring for a child with a debilitating disease. Someone with cystic fibrosis may live thirty or even forty years, but this is not likely to happen unless the parents make keeping their child alive their central priority and devote the majority of their time and effort to that task. Typically, such devotion shortchanges other children in the family and requires parents to become martyrs. Some people may want to make this decision, but others may not.

Also, defenders of testing say, some believe it is not morally responsible to have a child with a disease or condition that can significantly shorten his life or seriously affect his prospects in life. Yes, someone with Huntington's disease may live more than forty years, but the final years will be spent in a condition of physical and mental decline. The person will suffer greatly and become a burden to himself or others. Similarly, if we recognize a gene in an embryo that, if implanted in a women's uterus, will lead to the birth of a blind child, why should the woman not ask that an embryo lacking that gene be implanted? Such a limiting condition as blindness will make the child's lot in life harder in general and eliminate many possibilities of both pleasure and accomplishment. A blind child also imposes burdens on the parents, the family, and society. In these cases and in similar ones, defenders of testing say, we can see ourselves as having an obligation to both prevent suffering and protect an individual's range of possibilities.

Defenders of genetic testing are equally unconvinced by the second criticism. In their view, the idea that making a reproductive decision on the grounds that a genetic test predicting a disorder is equivalent to devaluing individuals with the disorder involves two errors. First, the critics assume that an embryo or a fetus has the same moral status as a person. Some people believe this, but it is not an idea accepted by everyone and so cannot be used as a general objection to genetic testing. Second, the critics confuse people with their condition. That we don't want a child to be born blind (for example) does not mean we don't value blind people. We value them because they are *people*, though, not because they are blind. People who are blind lack a capacity (sight) that is of value in coping with the world and in appreciating the things in it. The world would be better, in this respect, if those who are blind could see. Yet to say it would be a better world if there were no blind people is not to devalue the people or wish them out of existence. Rather, it is to wish for everyone to possess the capacity of sight.

Most defenders of prenatal genetic testing reject the idea that deciding not to implant an embryo that will lead to the birth of a child with a serious disease or disability is eugenics. Such a practice can be regarded as negative eugenics in a narrow, technical sense, but it isn't what we usually think of as eugenic. It is not, that is, part of a social policy intended to improve the human race. Typically, the use of prenatal genetic testing is only the attempt by potential parents to have a child as free of diseases and problems as possible. Although people who seek genetic testing in connection with reproduction are often described as attempting to have a "perfect baby," the great majority say they want only a healthy baby.

Defenders of genetic testing reject the third and fourth criticisms as little more than expressions of self-interest. The critics tend to be people with diseases (or family members of such people) that would be decreased in frequency if genetic testing became widely used in making reproductive decisions. Thus, the Cystic Fibrosis Foundation, the main organization of people with the disease and their families, does not promote prenatal testing for the CF gene. By contrast, the American College of Obstetrics and Gynecology recommends it to pregnant women.

The critics, it appears, want to maintain the number of similarly affected people so that they or their family members can receive benefits gained by their political activism. These benefits may be directly personal (medical expenses, educational mainstreaming, etc.) or they may be ones such as improved treatments that benefit everyone with their condition. But, defenders say, this is an approach that is both unimaginative and of doubtful moral legitimacy.

So far as getting benefits is concerned, wouldn't it be better for the critics to advocate for reforms in education and health care that would provide all people in the society with the support they need? Similarly, instead of wanting to increase the number of people born with (say) cystic fibrosis so that the disease would continue to attract research money and talent, wouldn't it be better to advocate a change in the way that medical research takes place? Finding a way to encourage research on "orphan" diseases seems a more reasonable way to approach the problem than trying to make sure that a large number of people are born with cystic fibrosis.

As to moral legitimacy, can we believe that people are doing the right thing in promoting and welcoming the birth of more children with serious diseases to benefit themselves or members of their family? Surely, advocates for people with disabilities should not want to encourage the birth of *more* people with disabilities.

Research Results

Instead of giving answers either favoring or objecting to reproductive genetic testing in a wholesale fashion, people often make more nuanced, case-by-case decisions. A study of the choices of 53,000 women that was published in *Obstetrics and Gynecology* in 2002 (the most recent study of its kind) showed that when prenatally diagnosed conditions would have no impact on the quality of a child's life, the termination rate was only about one percent. However, when the conditions would have a serious negative impact, the rate rose to fifty percent.

When a diagnosis indicated a disability likely to affect cognitive functioning, the women in the study were much more likely to choose to terminate their pregnancy. If a condition was predicted that would require surgery or special medical treatment, the abortion rate was sixteen percent. This rate doubled, though, when the condition was likely to cause some form of mental dysfunction, such as cognitive impairment.

The disposition favoring cognitive abilities found in the 2002 study also seems to hold when decisions are made about Down syndrome. The condition invariably involves, among other traits, mental retardation. While the statistics are not wholly reliable, physicians in reproductive medicine estimate that when prenatal tests show that a fetus will develop Down syndrome, about eighty percent of the women decide to terminate their pregnancy.

The issues connected with prenatal genetic testing, embryo testing, and abortion are complex and vexed. People who advocate one view sometimes find themselves behaving at odds with it when their own circumstances force them to make a decision. When an issue becomes personal, abstract ideological commitments are frequently discarded.

SOCIAL CONTEXT
GINA: Genetic Information Nondiscrimination Act

Judith Berman Carlisle was forty-eight years old and in the process of setting up a therapy practice when she realized that she had a reason to be worried about her health.

The year before, her sister had been diagnosed with ovarian cancer and her aunt had died of the disease. Earlier, her grandmother and another aunt had died of breast cancer. Carlisle knew that she could be tested for the BRCA1 or BRCA2 gene mutations and learn whether she was predisposed to develop breast or ovarian cancer.

She decided against the test, however. She was planning on becoming self-employed, and if she tested positive for either of the genes, she might not be able to get health insurance. Instead, she told reporter Amy Harmon, she decided to tell her doctor about her family history and request surgery to remove her ovaries.

Carlisle suspected that the surgery wouldn't raise a red flag the way genetic information would. She saw an important difference between saying "I have a strong family history predisposing me to breast cancer" and saying "I only have a thirteen percent chance of not getting breast cancer during the time you are insuring me."

Carlisle had the surgery to remove her ovaries; then, after she got health insurance and couldn't be turned down because of a "preexisting condition," she had herself tested for BRCA1 and BRCA2. The test results were negative. She hadn't needed to have her ovaries removed after all, but she hadn't dared to be tested to find that out.

Insurance Driven
Stories like Judith Carlisle's are common in the American health care system. They will

most likely remain common until 2014, which is when health care reforms take effect that forbid insurers to reject applicants for having a preexisting medical condition. Since the beginning of genetic testing, Americans have been extremely cautious about agreeing to tests that can become part of their medical records and perhaps lead to health insurance coverage being denied or even canceled.

The insurance industry has frequently denied that health insurers engage in genetic discrimination. A study conducted by Georgetown University, however, supports the generally accepted view that they do. Researchers, as part of their experiment, provided insurance underwriters with health and genetic information about hypothetical applicants and asked the underwriters to decide which people they would insure. In seven of ninety-two decisions, when genetic tests indicated that an applicant had an increased risk of disease, the underwriters said they would deny coverage, exclude coverage for certain disorders, or charge higher premiums.

In a few notorious instances, employers have attempted to control their insurance costs by denying coverage to employees on the grounds that their genetic makeup constitutes a preexisting condition. Health insurance policies typically do not pay medical costs for conditions that existed before the policy went into effect.

The Burlington Northern Railroad company took this path when it required each employee making an insurance claim for treatment of carpal tunnel syndrome to have blood drawn by a company doctor. The railway then, without telling the employees, had the blood tested to see if a genetic factor predisposing them to carpal tunnel syndrome could be found.

If such a factor were found, the company could then say it was a preexisting condition. The claim would be that carpal tunnel syndrome was, in effect, already present in the employee's genes. Thus, the company wouldn't have to pay the employee's medical costs. The railway was sued by the Equal Employment

Opportunities Commission, and the case was settled out of court in 2002.

Protecting Themselves

To avoid putting themselves in a position that would allow their employer or insurer to use genetic information to their disadvantage, Americans have either avoided finding out such information or tried to acquire it in such a way that it does not become part of their medical record. Consider the following illustrations:

* People who have a parent or sibling with Huntington's disease have a fifty percent chance of also having the gene that causes the disease. HD typically appears between the ages of 35 and 44. It is a progressive neurological disorder that cannot be effectively treated and is invariably fatal. (See "Case Presentation: Huntington's Disease," in this chapter.)

Some who are at risk for the disease may not wish to know whether they are carrying the gene, but others may want to know so that they can better plan their lives. Comparative data suggest, however, that the decision whether to find out about one's HD genetic status has more to do with fears about keeping health insurance than an individual's wishes. In the United States only five percent of those at risk for HD choose to be tested for the HD gene. In Canada, twenty percent of those at risk decide to have the test.

Although it is possible that the fourfold difference can be ascribed to cultural differences, the most likely explanation is that the Canadian health care system does not deny treatment on the basis of a preexisting condition. The U.S. figures may change after health care reforms eliminate having a preexisting condition as a reason to deny health insurance coverage.

* The head of the breast cancer research program at Weil–Cornell Medical Center in New York estimated in 2008 that twenty percent of the patients who chose to be tested for BRCA1 and BRCA2 paid for the tests in cash. This

meant that they would not have to file a claim with their insurer and thus tip off the insurer that they might be predisposed to develop breast and ovarian cancer.

* Thousands of people who worry about whether they have genes known to predispose them to specific diseases don't consult a physician. Rather, they pay private companies such as DNA Direct and deCODE Genetics for genetic testing. The companies promise confidentiality, and thus the test results do not become a part of their clients' medical record. If someone asked his doctor for the tests, the results would become part of his medical chart and available to his insurance company.

Hindering Medicine

Physicians need reliable information about their patients to make accurate diagnoses and prescribe the most effective treatments. When, for whatever reason, a patient withholds relevant information, the physician is hindered in carrying out the tasks essential to taking care of her patient. The case of Katherine Anderson shows how things can go badly wrong for a patient when information is withheld.

Katherine Anderson's parents were told by their doctor that Katherine might have inherited from her father the gene for Factor V Leiden, a disorder in which life threatening blood clots may form. If Katherine tested positive for the gene, the doctor warned, she might find it difficult to get insurance. The Andersons decided not to have her tested.

When Katherine turned sixteen and began having irregular periods, her gynecologist prescribed a birth-control drug to regulate them. She didn't mention to him that she might be positive for the Factor V Leiden gene. The result was life threatening.

The blood in a vein extending from Katherine's abdomen to her knee formed a single long clot. The drug her doctor had prescribed was a hormone, and, in combination with her genetic predisposition, it raised the chance of Katherine's developing blood clots to thirty times the average risk. If Katherine's gynecologist had known that she was prone to developing blood clots, he wouldn't have put her life in jeopardy by prescribing the drug.

Katherine eventually recovered, but her case illustrates what can happen when patients fail to provide their physicians with information relevant to making diagnostic or treatment decisions. If patients are worried that employers or insurers may use genetic information as grounds for firing them or denying them insurance, it makes sense for patients to want to keep that information private. A society with policies that encourage such secrecy, however, is not one in which medicine of the highest order can be practiced.

GINA

The Genetic Information Nondiscrimination Act took effect on November 21, 2009. GINA was designed to address problems like those in the cases discussed in this section and to make it possible for people to keep genetic information about themselves private without suffering a penalty.

The major provisions of GINA and its accompanying regulations are better summarized than described. GINA:

* Prohibits employers from requiring any genetic test as a condition of hiring, firing, promotion, setting compensation, or determining other terms, conditions, or privileges of employment.

* Prohibits employers from requesting or purchasing genetic information about an employee or any member of an employee's family.

* Prohibits insurers from requiring or requesting that an individual take any genetic test.

* Prohibits insurers from using genetic information to determine an individual's eligibility for health insurance or to set the amount

of an individual's premium for either individual or group health care coverage.

* Prohibits both employers and health insurers from disclosing genetic information about an individual.

The "genetic information" that employers and insurers are prohibited from acquiring, using, or revealing encompasses more than the results of genetic tests. It includes, for example, family histories of breast cancer, heart disease, or Huntington's disease. It also includes information about prescribed medications that would allow someone to draw the inference that someone may have a particular genetic disorder.

Accidental Knowledge

GINA acknowledges the possibility that employers may acquire genetic information in an inadvertent or accidental way. For example, an employee who requests a leave of absence under the Family Medical Leave Act may tell an employer that she needs the time to help her mother through breast-cancer surgery. Similarly, an employer may hear gossip that an employee's father died from a heart attack at age 48 or read an obituary which says that an employee's oldest child died at age 20 from cystic fibrosis. Such information about family history might lead an employer to draw conclusions about the genetic risks of the employees.

Even though such information may be acquired accidentally, as distinct from intentionally, GINA forbids employers and insurers from making decisions based on it. What is likely to have to be decided in court in particular cases is whether any genetic information an employer accidentally acquired about an individual played a role in the employer's decision to fire him. Like discrimination on the basis of age, gender, or race, genetic discrimination may be easy to suspect but difficult to prove.

GINA allows employers' group health plans to ask employees to provide their family histories for the purpose of assigning employees

to "wellness" programs designed to reduce employees' risk factors for disorders like heart attacks, high blood pressure, or diabetes. This information must be volunteered by each employee, and the health plan cannot use it as a condition for granting, denying, or limiting insurance coverage.

GINA also does not allow any penalty or reward to be connected to an employee's providing a family history. The no-reward provision seems incompatible with the way many large companies have structured their wellness programs. To encourage participation, some employers award bonuses or extra vacation days to employees who participate regularly or achieve goals like losing weight or lowering blood pressure. No administrative or court decision has yet determined whether such programs violate the provisions of GINA.

What GINA Permits

The framers of GINA were concerned not to place so many restrictions on genetic information to prevent its abuse that it would make its legitimate uses difficult. It is important to notice what GINA does not prohibit:

* A health care professional treating a patient is free to ask the patient or the patient's family members to take a genetic test.

* Health plans and insurers that operate wellness programs are free to notify and discuss with employees the availability and potential usefulness of genetic tests.

* Insurers are free to evaluate an applicant for health insurance on the grounds of the applicant's current health status.

* Genetic data can be collected for the purposes of monitoring toxic conditions in the workplace, auditing employer-sponsored wellness programs, and administering federal and state family leave laws. Data about individuals, however, may not be disclosed to the employer.

* GINA does not cover life, disability, or long-term-care insurance.

Redundant?

Before GINA was passed into law, critics argued that the legislation wasn't necessary, because the Americans with Disabilities Act makes it illegal to use the results of a genetic test to turn down someone for a job or to justify denying someone a promotion. This interpretation of the ADA has yet to be tested in a court, however.

The ADA also does not explicitly bar insurers from regarding a positive test for a disease-associated gene (like one for familial breast cancer) as a preexisting condition and denying health insurance to an applicant on those grounds. GINA eliminates ambiguities and gray areas: neither employers nor health insurers can require individuals to provide them with genetic information, nor can they use such information to make decisions about individuals.

The health care legislation passed in 2010 contains provisions that will not permit health insurers to refuse to insure individuals or to terminate their insurance on the basis of preexisting conditions. These conditions may include being genetically predisposed to the development of diseases like breast and colon cancer and cystic fibrosis. The legislation may eventually make GINA seem unnecessary. However, some of its provisions will not take effect until 2014 or later, and no one is sure how the overall plan will work in practice.

GINA may become redundant, but for the moment it makes clear in a useful way what can and cannot be done with genetic information. Besides, when something as important as individual rights is at stake, it is better that the laws protecting them be redundant than ambiguous or nonexistent.

Retrospect and Prospect

Consider again the cases of Judith Carlisle and Katherine Andersons—people who put themselves at risk so that an insurance company wouldn't be able to deny them health insurance coverage on the basis of their genetic inheritance.

GINA has changed that. No longer need people fear that a genetic test will stand in the way of their getting or keeping their health insurance, getting or keeping a job, or winning a promotion. No longer must people get genetic tests in secret and worry that the result will find its way into their medical records.

All people carry genes that predispose them to diseases and disorders. This means that GINA is a shield against discrimination of a kind that could be exercised against literally anyone.

SOCIAL CONTEXT

What Are My Chances? Direct-to-Consumer Genetic Testing

As soon as Kathy Klowsky (we will call her) turned thirty, she decided it was time to take charge of her health. She planned to improve her diet, lose weight, and get more exercise. But was there something else, she wondered, that she ought to be doing?

Her mom was extremely overweight—fat, really—and her dad had died of colon cancer when he was only fifty-eight. So should she be worried that maybe she inherited genes for obesity and colon cancer? If she were sure she had, she would work particularly hard to stick to her diet. She would also talk to a doctor and see if she should start getting colonoscopies earlier than most people.

So when Kathy read a magazine article about genetic tests you could get without going to a doctor, she was immediately interested. You could read about the services on-line, and all you had to do was wipe the inside of your cheek with a swab and then mail it to the company. Depending on how much you paid, they would tell you how likely you were to develop a number of common diseases. They would also tell you such things as whether you were a "supertaster" and could detect bitter flavors at low concentrations or whether your ear wax was the dry or wet kind. She cared nothing about any of those things, but she did want to know how much at risk she was for obesity and colon cancer.

Genetic-Testing Companies

About thirty genetic-testing companies are in the business of analyzing a client's DNA for a fee. Some companies check for the presence of a few specific genes, such as ones associated with baldness or sickle-cell disease, and others determine paternity or trace genetic ancestry. The major companies, however, sample an individual's entire genome and provide various amounts of information, depending on the level of service requested (and paid for) and the company's policy. The largest genetic-testing companies offering services to consumers are deCODE Genetics, 23andMe, DNA Direct, and Navigenics.

SNPs

The tests performed by all companies involve analyzing hundreds of thousands of segments of DNA known as *single-nucleotide polymorphisms,* or SNPs (pronounced "snips"). SNPs are variations in nucleotides (the adenine, cytosine, guanine, or tyrosine on a DNA strand) that occur at the same location in a genome. In one person's genome, for example, cytosine might occur where most genomes have guanine. Or, possibly, at that location, the nucleotide may be missing or an additional nucleotide may be present.

These substitutions, deletions, and insertions may be harmless human variants that reflect population-related or racial differences. SNPs themselves aren't genes, but they can occur within genes. (They can also occur in nongene segments of DNA.) Thus, they may be found in gene mutations (a variant form of a gene), or they may alter the way a gene is expressed. (The gene fails to make an enzyme, for example.) Some of those expressions may be harmless, but others may prove disastrous.

SNPs function as genetic markers. Whether or not they are responsible for a disease or trait, SNPs have been shown to be associated with diseases like breast cancer, asthma, bipolar disorder, macular degeneration, cluster headaches, Crohn's disease, amyotrophic lateral sclerosis (ALS, Lou Gehrig's disease), diabetes, and colon cancer. SNPs have also been associated with traits like height, eye and hair color, obesity, lactose intolerance, and muscle performance. Also, some SNPs may predict how individuals will respond to chemotherapy drugs, antibiotics, or antidepressants.

SNPs and Risks

If an individual's entire genome were sequenced, the variants in the nucleotides would show up. But such sequencing is still too expensive to be performed as a matter of course. (The aim is to bring the cost down from $5,000 to about $1,000.) An alternative to sequencing is made possible by biochips programmed to detect nucleotide differences at locations along a DNA strand known to vary. The biochip provides, in effect, a catalogue of the variants displayed by an individual's DNA. The SNPs in the catalogue are then compared with those in a database that associates particular SNPs with particular diseases. (The same holds for traits.)

This technique establishes the individual's relative risk of developing particular diseases. Some SNPs may correlate strongly with (say) obesity, but other SNPs may correlate weakly. Thus, someone whose genome includes several weakly correlated SNPs may have an increased risk of obesity, compared with someone whose genome lacks all or most of those SNPs.

Associating SNPs with diseases is not a genetic test in the usual sense that the SNPs indicate the presence of a particular gene. This can happen, though, when a SNP identifies a mutated gene known to be responsible for a disease. Some companies will not test clients for a SNP known to be associated with a high degree of probability of certain diseases. DeCODE, for example, refuses to test for the mutation

ApoE4. This mutation is associated with high cholesterol, and it could be useful for a client to know that he carries the gene. However, as many as ninety-five percent of those who test positive for the gene develop Alzheimer's.

Kathy would be able to find out from XY Genetics and most other companies that her genetic profile indicates that she has a number of genetic "risk factors" which predispose her to heart disease. When the separate risks associated with each SNP are added up, it may be that she has a sixty-five percent chance of developing arteriosclerosis and cardiac problems. She is not doomed by the findings, and she may have learned something that will guide her in changing her behavior in order to avoid having a heart attack.

Inconsistent Results

Suppose Kathy is a cautious person and sends in a cheek swab to PDQGenetics to be tested for a predisposition to developing heart disease. She may be surprised to get back results that are very different from the results she received from XYGenetics.

Inconsistent results are possible because genetic testing companies may use different biochips to sort through personal genomes, so different SNPs are searched for and identified. Perhaps one company will look for more SNPs connected with obesity than another, and the client may learn from the first company that she has more "risk factors" than that showed up on the second analysis.

Also, companies may use different databases to look for an association between SNPs and common diseases. This makes it possible, given a difference in the size of the databases, for a client to appear to be more at risk for a particular disease as a result of one analysis than another.

Finally, even given the same data, different companies may provide different estimates of disease risks because they don't use the same method to calculate risk. XYGenetics may figure a client's risk of colon cancer over a lifetime, while PDQGenetics calculates the risk for the decade between the ages of 40 and 50. The result

of these differences is that a client may be given test results that are so disparate as to be unhelpful, confusing, or misleading.

Clinical laboratories used by hospitals and physicians must be approved by the Centers for Medicare and Medicaid Services. This federal agency certifies that labs have met the standards required by the federal Clinical Laboratory Improvement Amendment, which includes quality-control procedures, proficiency testing by outside experts, and educational qualifications for laboratory personnel. The way the law is written, genetic-testing companies are exempt from these regulations.

In April 2008, a federal advisory committee recommended that new federal rules be introduced to regulate the genetic-testing industry. The California Department of Health sent letters to thirteen companies warning them to stop doing business in California until they could prove that they were compliant with state laws. (California law allows only physicians to order laboratory tests, and the labs must have federal certification.) New York State sent letters to thirty-one companies informing them that a state license was required to solicit DNA samples from state residents.

Partly in response to the threat of being put out of business by federal and state regulation, several major genetic-testing companies (including deCODE, 23andMe, and Navigenics) made a commitment to develop their own industry-wide standards. They pledged to work with the nonprofit educational organization Personalized Medicine Coalition to develop shared guidelines.

Medical Advice?

Companies that offer genetic testing directly to consumers typically deny that they are providing medical advice. They are, in their view, providing people with information about themselves that they want to know.

Critics claim that, whether or not what the genetic information companies provide should be considered medical advice, it can pose risks to clients. Although some companies provide genetic counseling as part of the testing package, not all do. Hence, some clients may not know what to make of the information they are given. They may believe, for example, that they are at a much greater risk for colon cancer or mental illness than they are. The test results may thus provoke needless anxiety. Indeed, a client might become depressed or suicidal if informed that she tested positive for BRCA1.

The results may also keep people from getting the medical attention they need. Companies (unlike deCODE) which inform clients that they are at risk for Alzheimer's or carry a mutation that puts them at risk for breast and ovarian cancer are not equipped to carry out the appropriate medical follow-up. The clients, even those receiving genetic counseling from a company, may think they have done all that needs to be done. This may lead them to avoid going to a doctor and getting a genetic test from a certified clinical laboratory to confirm that they are predisposed to developing the disease indicated by SNP testing. Thus, the clients may fail to become patients and gain the benefit of medical advice and treatment.

Failing Business?

The three major genetic-testing companies that began in the late 1990s—deCODE Genetics, 23andMe, and Navigenics—have recently become struggling enterprises that have had to redefine themselves to remain in business.

The most successful company, 23andMe, has had only 3500 clients, and the other two have had fewer. Navigenics cut its staff, replaced its CEO twice, and expanded its marketing to include services to physicians and corporate wellness programs. deCODE Genetics, which includes research and drug development divisions, went through bankruptcy and was acquired by new owners. The newly organized company markets genetic tests directly to doctors. Although it still has a consumer division, in 2010 the company raised its prices to around $2000 to avoid hurting the tests sold to physicians. This is about twice the costs of personal genome scans sold by 23andMe.

Over-the Counter Sales

On May 9, 2010, Pathway Genomics of San Diego announced that it planned to offer a testing kit that would be sold nationwide for $20–$30 at 7500 Walgreens drugstores. The kit is to be sold in a box labeled "Discover Your DNA," but it will contain nothing more than a saliva-collecting tube and a mailer to send the tube to a Pathway laboratory. The customer must then go to the company website, set up an account, and decide which of the tests offered by Pathway he wants to order. The tests range in costs from $79 to $249 for the full panel. The consumer's information will be protected by a privacy code.

Pathway also operates an on-line testing service, but by making kits available in stores, it thinks it can boost its business. Like the other companies, it will use biochips and DNA probes to test for the presence of genes or markers that are associated with about two dozen particular diseases. The company will also (for a price) test for the likelihood of a bad reaction to certain drugs and estimate the likelihood that the gene for a particular disease (e.g. cystic fibrosis) will be passed on to an offspring. The tests offered are thus open to the same objections: that such tests are unreliable and, because of the lack of understanding of the connection between genes and diseases in most cases, they promise more information than they can deliver.

Only two days after Pathway's announcement, Walgreens issued a statement saying that it would delay selling the test kits. Although similar kits have been sold on-line for years, the Pathway announcement reawakened the interest of the FDA. It is concerned, once again, with the question of whether the tests offered are medical tests. If they are, they must meet FDA requirements and be licensed and regulated. But if the tests are a way for people to acquire information about themselves, the FDA has no authority over them.

Pathway is not likely to have been more successful in attracting customers than the other on-line companies, which may be why it moved to over-the-counter sales. Perhaps the testing companies in general have misjudged the interest people have in their risks for developing common diseases or learning a little about their genetically determined traits. Those who are genetically sophisticated may see the limited value of the tests, while those who are not fail to see the point of them. Whether the kits are bought on-line or in a drugstore, the tests may be viewed by many as little more than an expensive form of entertainment.

GINA

The genetic-testing companies may have had their business undermined by a major piece of legislation. Before the Genetic Information Nondiscrimination Act (GINA) took effect in November 2009, people hesitated to have any genetic test, because it would become part of their medical record. They might lose their job, or their insurer might refuse to cover their medical expenses on the ground that their problem was a preexisting condition. (See "Social Context: GINA," in this chapter.) Hence, anyone wanting to know if she was at risk for a genetic disease would try to get the information from a source that would guarantee privacy.

Genetic-testing companies offered the best possibility of acquiring the information and escaping the social consequences. Most likely, although no one knows for sure, much of the business of 23andMe and the other major and minor testing services came from people worried about the confidentiality of their results. With the passage of GINA, keeping such results private is no longer so important. GINA makes it illegal to discriminate on the basis of genetic data, and this ban extends to employment, promotion, and insurance coverage.

Depending on the way GINA changes the legal environment, people who want to acquire information about their genetic predisposition to diseases may be confident enough to seek it from their doctors. We may not need to worry about regulating the genetic-testing companies, because they will either disappear or transform themselves into organizations that meet the standards of clinical laboratories.

Gene Therapy: Slowly Delivering on the Promise

On September 14, 1990, at the National Institutes of Health in Bethesda, Maryland, a four-year-old girl became the first patient to be treated by gene therapy under an approved protocol. The child, whose parents initially asked that her identity not be made public, lacked the gene for producing adenosine deaminase (ADA), an enzyme required to keep immune cells alive and functioning.

Her life expectancy was low, because, without ADA, she would almost certainly develop cancers and opportunistic infections that cannot be effectively controlled by conventional treatments. The aim of the therapy was to provide her with cells that would boost her immune system by increasing the production of essential antibodies. During the months that followed, she received four injections of altered cells.

The treatment, under the direction of W. French Anderson, R. Michael Blaese, and Kenneth Culver, involved taking blood from the patient, isolating the T-cells, and then growing a massive number of them. These cells were infected with a weakened retrovirus into which a copy of the human gene for ADA had been spliced. The cells were then injected into the patient in a blood transfusion.

The Therapy

The idea behind the therapy was for the ADA gene to migrate to the cellular DNA, switch on, and begin producing ADA. If the cells produced enough of the enzyme, the child's immune system would not be destroyed. Because most T-cells live for only weeks or months, the process had to be repeated at regular intervals.

The girl's parents, from a Cleveland suburb, later revealed their daughter's identity. She is Ashanthi Desilva, and more than a decade later she is alive and doing well. Soon after her treatment, on January 30, 1991, nine-year-old Cynthia Cutshall became the second person to receive gene therapy.

Laboratory tests showed that both children's immune systems were functioning effectively. But the need to replace short-lived T-cells means that Ashanthi and Cynthia had to continue to receive regular injections of altered cells. However, Anderson and his collaborators had always hoped to find a way around this need, and the break came when an NIH group developed a procedure for isolating stem cells from the bone marrow. If enough stem cells could be obtained and genetically altered, then, when injected back into the patient, the cells might produce enough T-cells for an adequately functioning immune system.

In May 1993, Cynthia's stem cells were harvested, exposed to the retrovirus containing the normal ADA gene, and reinjected. She tolerated the procedure with no apparent ill effects, and later that year essentially the same procedure was repeated with Ashanthi. The immune systems of both children continued to function within the normal range.

This may seem to be an unequivocal success for gene therapy, but the value of the experiment in establishing this is difficult to assess. Both subjects continued to be treated with a standard drug regimen, so was it gene therapy or the drugs that saved the lives of the children? Although gene therapy can't be said to have produced a cure for ADA, advocates believe that eventually it will.

Definitive Evidence, Potential Risks

More definitive evidence for the effectiveness of gene therapy comes from results of clinical trials conducted at Paris' Necker Hospital in 2000 by Alain Fischer. Fischer's group treated eleven patients (ten infants and a teenager) with severe combined immunodeficiency disease (SCID), a disorder caused by a defect on the X chromosome. Nine of those treated by using a retrovirus to insert new genes were cured. This is an astounding outcome, considering that most children born with the defect die from the disease by the end of their first year. Bone marrow transplants, the standard treatment, are successful only about seventy-five of the time.

Then, in 2002, a three-year-old boy in the study developed leukemia-like symptoms. The clinical trial was immediately halted. Regulatory agencies in the United States were already particularly inclined to caution because of the death of eighteen-year-old Jesse Gelsinger in 1999 (see the case presentation in Chapter 2), so the adverse event in France once more raised the question of whether gene-therapy trials were so unsafe as to be discontinued. After a period of suspension to permit a safety review, the FDA once again allowed the trials to go forward.

Parkinson's Disease

Parkinson's disease, which affects more than 500,000 people in the United States, is a progressive disorder in which cells in the part of the brain called the substantia nigra die off, resulting in a lack of the neurotransmitter dopamine. This condition leads to symptoms such as hand tremors, impaired balance, and "freezing" in place. As more cells die, the symptoms become progressively worse, and the disease may have a fatal outcome.

In August 2007, the results of a Phase 1 clinical trial conducted by Michael Kaplitt using gene therapy to increase the amount of gamma-aminobutyric acid (GABA) in the brain were published in the *Lancet*. GABA is one of the major inhibitory neurotransmitters in the central nervous system, and in Parkinson's patients it is in short supply. By using a retrovirus to introduce billions of copies of the gene that encodes GABA into brain cells, Kaplitt's group was able to increase the amount of the neurotransmitter present in the brains of the trial's subjects. This resulted in bringing under control the sort of unchecked movements characteristic of the disease.

The trial involved twelve patients, and all of them continued to take their prescribed medications. They also continued to have some of the symptoms of the disease. Even so, over the year the patients were monitored, they showed general improvement in symptoms, such as less difficulty walking, less rigidity, and fewer hand tremors. The researchers claimed a twenty-four percent improvement in patients who were off their medications and a twenty-seven percent improvement in those who were on their medications. Most important for gene therapy, none of the patients showed any side effects from the treatment.

Inherited Retinal Degeneration

Photoreceptors in the retina convert light energy into electrical impulses that travel along the optic nerve to the brain. Retinol, a form of vitamin A that plays key role in the process of converting light into a nerve impulse, is active in the pigmented epithelium—the layer of cells under the photoreceptors. Retinol is kept available by an enzyme (the protein RPE65) that recycles it as it is used by cells,

and when retinol is missing, the photoreceptors can't do their job. The result is a disruption of the visual cycle, and the functional outcome is blindness.

Leber's congenital amaurosis (LCA) is a genetic disorder in which mutations in the gene RPE56 result in a shortage or the complete absence of the enzyme required to recycle retinol. Children born with the mutated gene are not born with normal sight, and what sight they have continues to deteriorate. Over time, photoreceptors deteriorate, and the outcome is significant, if not total, blindness.

In May 2007, a team at Moorfields Eye Hospital in London used a virus to transfer healthy copies of the RPE56 gene into the cells of the pigmented epithelium of seventeen-year-old Robert Johnson. Johnson, diagnosed with LCA, had been steadily losing his sight, but within months of the gene therapy, his vision improved measurably. The same procedure was carried out on eleven other LCA patients, and they, too, showed improvement.

Researchers concluded that younger subjects were most likely to show the greatest amount of improvement. The reason for this is that the gene therapy works only when the photoreceptor cells are intact, and as people with LCA grow older, those cells began to lose their function.

In 2009, an American study reported results similar to the British study. Researchers used viruses to introduce normal copies of REP65 into areas of the pigmented epithelium in which photoreceptor cells seemed most intact. Within two weeks, the five children and seven adults treated began to show significant improvement in their vision. Children improved the most, but the oldest participant, a forty-four-year-old woman who was once housebound, became able to walk outside to meet her children coming home from school.

AIDS Treatment

In 2009, the results of a Phase 2 clinical trial using gene therapy to treat AIDS were characterized by some researchers as a major advance in treating AIDS. A patient's blood stem cells were cultured with OZ1, a genetically altered mouse virus, to get the gene for the so-called hairpin ribozyme incorporated into the DNA of the blood stem cells. The ribozyme chemically slices up RNA, and because HIV depends on RNA for replication, blood cells with altered DNA prevent the virus from reproducing. The idea was for the genetically altered stem cells to populate the bone marrow of the patient and then begin producing blood cells containing the ribosome. When enough altered blood cells are present in an HIV-positive person, the viral load is lowered.

The trial involved seventy-four patients; thirty-eight were transfused with genetically altered blood stem cells, and thirty-six were transfused with an inactive placebo solution. All patients had HIV infections, which were being kept under control by highly active antiretroviral therapy (HAART).

During the one-hundred-week period of the trial, patients receiving altered stem cells had a higher number of CD4 T-cells, which indicated that HIV wasn't killing them off at the same rate as before. During nontreatment intervals, treated patients had higher CD4 counts and a lower HIV load than those patients in the placebo group. Also, when HAART was stopped, those in the treatment group were able to wait longer before starting the drugs again than those in the placebo group.

Enormous Promise

Gene therapy holds enormous promise for those who suffer from a variety of genetic disorders. Experimental clinical protocols for the treatment of a wide range of relatively common diseases such as cystic fibrosis, hemophilia, phenylketonuria, sickle-cell disease, hypercholesterolemia, AIDS, cardiovascular disease, cancer, lupus erythematous, and blood-clotting disorders are either underway or in the planning stage. Following are a few examples.

Sickle-cell disease Sickle-cell disease, affecting about one in four hundred African Americans, is produced by a gene that affects the folding of the two chains making up the hemoglobin molecule. In a proposed treatment, molecular fragments called chimeraplasts will be induced to enter the stem cells in the bone marrow that produce red blood cells.

If a stem cell incorporates the chimeraplast into the nucleus, the cell's own repair system should eliminate the gene for the defective hemoglobin chain and substitute that provided by the chimeraplast. If enough stem cells are altered and function properly, the amount of red blood cells produced should eliminate the heart damage and strokes that can cause early death in those who develop the disease.

Malignant melanoma In one proposed cancer treatment, researchers will make trillions of copies of the gene for the antigen HLA-B7 and then inject them directly into the tumors of those with melanoma. The DNA is expected to enter the cells of the tumor, insert itself in the nuclear DNA, and trigger the production of HLA-B7. The antigen will then extrude from the cell, causing the cell to be attacked by killer T-cells. Two patients were successfully treated by this approach in 2006, demonstrating that gene therapy can be used as a cancer treatment.

Leukemia A genetic abnormality known as the Philadelphia chromosome triggers cancerous changes in stem cells in the bone marrow. The resulting disease is chronic myelogenous leukemia, which affects about 4600 people a year and is responsible for about 1000 deaths a year. The best standard treatment is to inject patients with stem cells from a bone marrow donor. Sometimes, however, a compatible donor can't be located; also, the therapy has a lower level of success in people over fifty-five.

A gene-based therapy is being developed to alter the patient's own stem cells by adding an antisense sequence to the cellular DNA. The sequence is designed to block the formation of the protein leading to cancerous growth, thereby making the cancer cells behave like normal cells. The sequence will also have attached to it a gene making the altered cells more resistant to the chemotherapeutic drug methotrexate. Thus, when a patient receives chemotherapy, the cancerous cells will be killed while the altered ones will survive and reproduce. The altered stem cells should then produce normal red blood cells. The main difficulty, at present, is to get the stem cells to incorporate the new genes.

Hypercholesterolemia Familial hypercholesterolemia is a disease in which an excess production of cholesterol often leads to heart attacks and early death. The gene therapy developed to treat it involves removing part of a patient's liver, culturing the cells that have been collected, and inserting into them a gene that produces the low-density lipoprotein receptor. The receptor plays an important role in removing cholesterol from the blood. The treated cells are then injected into the patient's liver, where they attach themselves to the liver's capillaries and start producing the protein of the receptor.

A clinical trial carried out by James Wilson in 2003–2005 demonstrated that gene therapy could successfully treat the disease. Questions about the safety of the modified virus used in the trial have kept the therapy from being approved.

Collateral blood vessel growth Every year, thirty to forty thousand people in the United States develop almost complete blockage in the arteries of their legs. Shut off from a blood supply, the tissues in the leg develop ulcers that don't heal, and, eventually, when gangrene sets in, the leg must be amputated to save the life of the person. Twenty percent of the patients die in the hospital, and forty percent die within the next year. No drugs are available to increase the blood flow to the legs.

A new treatment under development uses the gene for vascular endothelial growth factor, or vegF, a protein that stimulates the growth of collateral blood vessels. When billions of vegF genes are injected into leg muscle, about five percent of them are incorporated into muscle cells, causing them to start producing the vdgF protein. Because the vessel cells beyond the blockage are deprived of blood, their membranes become altered so as to be more receptive to the vegG molecule. When it attaches to the surface of the cells, the cells begin to produce tiny new blood vessels that grow around the blockage.

While only a few people have been treated with vegF gene therapy, it has shown itself to be effective. Trials are also underway to test the effectiveness of the therapy in heart disease. If vegF can establish collateral circulation in the heart, the need for coronary artery bypass surgery may be reduced or even eliminated. Those too frail or sick to undergo a bypass or even angioplasty might eventually be helped by the new technique.

Cystic fibrosis In April 1993, a twenty-three-year-old man became the first patient to receive human gene therapy for the treatment of cystic fibrosis. An altered form of the adenovirus was used to transport the gene for cystic fibrosis transmembrane conductance regulator into his lungs. The regulator controls the flow of chloride through body cells. Cystic fibrosis patients lack the regulator gene, and as a result, they suffer severe salt imbalances that cause abnormal mucous excretions in the lungs and pancreas.

The therapy was evaluated in 1996. Although the evidence did not demonstrate that it was effective, most investigators think that it ultimately will be. Part of the difficulty is to find a way of getting the gene into the cells of the lungs. If the problems can be solved, gene therapy will offer the 30,000 Americans who suffer from cystic fibrosis a cure for the disease.

Germ-Line Therapy

The gene therapy currently under developments in humans is somatic-cell therapy, wherein modifications take place in the body cells of patients, not in the sex cells. This means that even if the therapy can eliminate the disease produced in an individual who has inherited a defective gene, the therapy will do nothing to alter the probability that a child of that person will inherit the same defective gene. To change this circumstance, germ-line cells would have to be altered. That is, the defective gene in an ovum or sperm cell would have to be replaced.

If this were possible, then certain genetic diseases could be eliminated from families. Germ-line therapy would make it unnecessary to perform somatic-cell therapy for each generation of affected individuals. As appealing as this prospect may be, at present germ-line therapy has many more technical difficulties associated with it than does somatic-cell therapy. No uniformly encouraging results have so far been produced in animal research, and even most forms of somatic-cell therapy in humans remain a distant prospect.

The value of germ-line therapy is also open to question. If the aim is to eliminate heritable diseases from a family, the most direct and effective way to achieve this is to screen embryos and avoid implanting those which carry the flawed gene. This process is currently available at fertility clinics and doesn't involve the risks and uncertainties of tinkering with the DNA of germ cells.

Germ-line therapy, unlike somatic-cell therapy, possesses a potential that has made it the focus of most ethical criticisms. Germ-line therapy holds out the prospect of genetically engineering sex cells to produce offspring with virtually any set of characteristics desired. This possibility has led many critics to warn that "genetic surgery" may be leading us into a sort of "Brave New World" in which we practice eugenics and manufacture our children to order. (See the briefing session in this chapter for a fuller discussion.) However, any dangers posed by germ-line therapy are far from immediate.

Envoi

Somatic-cell therapy continues to be experimental, but some of its forms are likely to become standard therapies within the next decade. Other forms will for some time remain experimental and, as such, will raise the same sorts of moral questions that are typical of any experimental procedure—questions of informed consent, benefit, and risk. As long as viruses and retroviruses must be used to deliver new genes into cells, the risk of serious harm, and even death, will be present. (See "Case Presentation: Jesse Gelsinger: First Gene-Therapy Death," in Chapter 2.) This circumstance has slowed the development of gene therapy more than anyone imagined it would.

Germ-line therapy is not likely ever to be developed as a way to engineer the human future.

SOCIAL CONTEXT
The Human Genome Project: Genes, Diseases, and the Personal Genome

Scientists considered sequencing the human genome so important that they referred to it as the Holy Grail of biology. The Grail, in medieval Christian legend, is the lost cup used by Christ at the Last Supper. Because the Grail delivers salvation to whoever possesses it, finding the Grail was the aim in many tales of valorous quests.

Deciphering the human genome never offered the promise of eternal life, but it offered the benefits of genetic knowledge, including the possibility of understanding genetic diseases and bringing them under control. This has turned out to be harder than those who set out on the quest believed, yet sequencing the genome has brought the goal within sight.

Genome Success

On June 26, 2000, Francis Collins, Director of the National Genome Research Institute, and J. Craig Venter, president of Celera Genetics, announced that, thanks to the joint work of the two groups, the human genome had been sequenced.

This means that the estimated 3.2 billion base pairs making up human DNA have been identified and sequenced; that is, the precise order of the base pairs has been established. Human DNA is now thought to contain about 30,000 genes. Earlier estimates had put this figure around 100,000, so the lower number came as a considerable surprise. Using the comparison by writer Nicholas Wade, if the complete DNA sequence were published in the *New York Times*, it would cover 75,490 pages.

This complete set of genes contained in the forty-six chromosomes is known as the *genome*. Metaphorically, it is the total set of encoded instructions for assembling a human being that is stored in the nucleus of each cell. About seventy-five percent of the genome is thought to be (as geneticists say) junk, consisting of repetitive DNA sequences accumulated during evolution and contributing nothing to human development or functioning. Yet biologists are also quick to say that we don't yet know enough to declare the junk DNA absolutely useless. It may contain sequences that in the future we will realize are crucially important.

Background

In 1985, biologist Robert Sinsheimer began promoting the idea that the entire human genome should be mapped and its genes sequenced. Because the genome was recognized as involving some 3 billion base pairs, the genome project would be on a scale unprecedented in the biological sciences. It would compare with the efforts of physicists to develop the atomic bomb during World War II and with the manned space project in the 1960s.

The size of the genome project made many scientists skeptical about supporting it. Some believed it would drain money away from smaller projects of immediate value in favor of one with only distant and uncertain promise. Also, some feared the genome project would turn out to be too much like the space project, emphasizing the solution to engineering problems more than the advancement of basic science.

Attitudes changed in 1988, when the National Research Council endorsed the genome project and outlined a gradual approach of coordinated research that would protect the interest of the basic sciences. When James Watson (who, along with Francis Crick, worked out the structure of DNA in 1953) agreed to be director of the project, most critics dropped their opposition and many became enthusiastic participants. Watson headed the project with great success until he resigned in 1993, when the position was taken over by Francis S. Collins.

Mapping and sequencing the human genome was expected to take fifteen to twenty years and cost between $3 and $5 billion. In 1989, Congress approved $31 million to initiate the program, but the project eventually came to cost about $200 million per year, and most biological and medical scientists view the money as well and wisely spent. The project was divided among nine different centers at both national laboratories and universities, and hundreds of scientists participated in the research and contributed to the final product.

The project was expected to be completed by 2005, but in response to a challenge by a commercial enterprise to the federal project and eventual cooperation between the two, the project was completed five years ahead of schedule.

Biologist J. Craig Venter, head of Celera Corporation, claimed he would begin sequencing in 1999 and finish in 2001. Venter's group took an approach different from the federal project. Celera sequenced millions of DNA fragments, then used a computer program to piece them together on the basis of their overlaps. Unlike the HEP approach, Celera did not break DNA into fragments and then create a map of each piece's location.

The payoff of the genome project is considered by most biological and medical researchers to be of inestimable worth. The information has already provided us with a better understanding of the patterns and processes of human evolution and clarified our degree of genetic relatedness to other organisms.

The detailed genetic information acquired by sequencing the human genome continues to give us a much-improved understanding of the relationships between certain genes and particular diseases. This information is a crucial step along the path to understanding genetic diseases and devising treatments that will eliminate or control them.

Early Successes

In 1997, a team led by David Schlessinger of the Washington University Medical School completed a high-resolution map of the X chromosome. The 160 million base pairs of the chromosome were mapped, with markers around every 75,000 pairs. Because a number of sex-linked diseases, such as hemophilia, result from a defective gene on the X chromosome, the map made it easier to locate the genes responsible for them. (Females have two copies of the X chromosome. Males have only one; so if it carries a defective gene, they lack a backup gene to prevent the consequences.)

With astonishing rapidity, using human-genome data, researchers identified the genes responsible for a large number of human diseases. A sampling from a list of several thousand gives some idea of the success of researchers in locating actual genes or gene markers for diseases.

Colon cancer. For the familial form of colon cancer, a marker was found on the upper end of chromosome 2 for a "repair" gene that corrects minor errors in cellular DNA. In its mutant form, the gene seems to function by triggering hundreds of thousands of mutations in other genes. One in two hundred people has the gene; sixty-five percent of the carriers are liable to develop cancer. The familial form accounts for about fifteen percent of all colon tumors. (A blood test is expected to be available soon.)

Amyotrophic lateral sclerosis. The familial form of ALS (Lou Gehrig's disease) results from a mutation of a gene on chromosome 21 that encodes the enzyme superoxide dismutase, which plays a role in eliminating free radicals. It is believed that if these radicals aren't controlled, they may damage motor neurons, which will then lead to muscle degeneration. The familial form of the disease accounts for only about ten percent of cases, but those with a family history of the disease can now be screened for the defective gene.

Type II (adult-onset) diabetes. A still unidentified gene on chromosome 7 encodes glucokinase, an enzyme that stimulates the pancreas to produce insulin. At least twenty-three mutated forms of the gene may cause the disease by encoding for a faulty enzyme that apparently fails to trigger insulin production. A screening test for the mutated genes is available.

Alzheimer's disease. The gene ApoE on chromosome 19 encodes a protein that transports cholesterol. People who have both alleles for the form of the protein known as E4 have eight times the risk of developing Alzheimer's; those with one allele have two to three times the risk. The gene could account for as many as half of those with the disease, although the causal role of E4 in producing it is not yet known.

X-linked SCID. Severe combined immunodeficiency diseases (SCID) is caused by a defective gene passed from mothers to sons on the X chromosome. The normal gene encodes part of the receptor of interleukin-2, which serves in the cytokine messenger system that keeps the T-cells of the immune system functioning. Newborns with the mutated gene have few or no T-cells, and even a mild infection is life threatening. The disease occurs in only one in every 100,000 births. (The cells used in the study were from "David," who died in Houston after he was removed from the sterile environment where he had spent almost twelve years of his life and was given a bone marrow transplant. Because of the publicity surrounding him, SCID is known popularly as "the Bubble Boy disease.")

This list can be multiplied to include spinocerebellar ataxia (a degenerative disease linked to a gene on chromosome 6), Huntington's disease (see "Case Presentation: Huntington's Disease" in this chapter), Lorenzo's disease (adrenoleukodystrophy, or ALD, which involves the degeneration of the myelin sheath around nerves), Canavan disease (a rare and fatal brain disorder affecting mostly Ashkenazi Jews and similar to ALD), achondroplastic dwarfism (the gene, FGR3, causes about one-third of the cases of dwarfism), and cystic fibrosis (in which mucus accumulates in the lungs and pancreas; the gene, discovered on chromosome 7, is known to exist in hundreds of mutant forms).

HapMap

The map of the genome is a powerful tool for understanding the role of genes that in the past could only be guessed at or located only by determined research and good luck. Unlike cystic fibrosis or sickle-cell disease, however, most diseases are not the result of a single gene mutation. Breast cancer is caused by a mutated gene, but it also occurs in so-called sporadic ways.

In 2002, an international project was launched to supplement the human genome by assembling a haplotype map—a HapMap. A haplotype is stretch of alleles of different genes that lie closely together on the same chromosome and tend to be inherited together. The idea behind the HapMap was to chart nucleotide differences in haplotypes. These differences could then be linked with particular diseases by comparing the genomes of those with the disease with those who don't have the disease.

Such studies don't compare entire genomes. Rather, they rely on analyzing hundreds of thousands of segments of DNA known as *single-nucleotide polymorphisms*, or SNPs (pronounced "snips"). SNPs are variations in nucleotides (the adenine, cytosine, guanine, or tyrosine on a DNA strand) that occur at the same location in a genome. In one person's genome, for example, cytosine might occur where most genomes have guanine. Alternatively, at that location, the nucleotide may be missing or an additional nucleotide may be present.

These substitutions, deletions, and insertions may be harmless human variants that reflect population-related or racial differences. SNPs themselves aren't genes, but they can occur within genes. Thus, they may be found in a gene mutation (a variant form of a gene), or they may alter the way a gene is expressed. The gene fails to make an enzyme, for example, and the result can be a disease such as Tay–Sachs.

The analysis of SNPs is made possible by biochips programmed to detect nucleotide differences at locations along a DNA. The biochip provides, in effect, a catalogue of the variants displayed by an individual's DNA. The SNPs in the catalogue are then compared with those in a database that associates particular SNPs with particular diseases. The location of the gene containing the SNP variant can then be mapped onto the genome. We should, in principle, be able to eventually have a complete catalogue of all genetic diseases and the genes and mutations responsible for them.

Many researchers have recently concluded that the main assumption behind the HapMap was wrong. It appears not to be true that, as Nicholas Wade put the point, "Mutations causing common diseases are common." Although some 2000 SNPs are found at sites on the human genome that are linked to diseases, the SNPs often occur in nongene segments of DNA—that is, in the so-called junk DNA of the genome. This suggests that the association between a SNP and a disease may often be no more than a statistical artifact. (The SNP may be a genetic marker for a disease, even though it is not causally responsible for it.)

The HapMap approach has turned out to be not completely wrong, but more limited in value than researchers first believed.

Personal Genomes

Researchers now believe that (to quote Nicholas Wade again) "Common diseases are caused by rare mutations." This suggests that the best way to find the gene responsible for a disease is to compare the genome of someone with the disease with the genome of someone who doesn't have it. This approach, unlike the HapMap approach, requires looking at *whole* genomes (about three billion nucleotides each), not just using SNPs as a sample. The genomes must be sequenced—the whole string of nucleotides must be listed in the order in which they occur. Thus, if the entire genome of someone with a disease is compared with that of someone lacking the disease, variants in the nucleotides will show up.

A paradigmatic example of this approach is Richard A. Gibbs's analysis of the genome of James R. Lupski. Gibbs and Lupski are colleagues at Baylor College of Medicine, and Lupski, a medical geneticist, has an inherited neurological disorder called Charcot–Marie–Tooth (CMT) disease.* The disease involves myelin (the insulating sheath around nerves) and leads to a progressive loss of control of the feet, legs, hands, and arms. A single normal copy of the gene involved is enough to prevent a full-blown version of the disease, although those who inherit one normal and one mutated copy may experience mild symptoms. Mutations in any of thirty-nine (known) genes can cause CMT.

Gibbs had already sequenced the genomes of ten healthy people before he asked Lupski to serve as a test case. When Lupski's genome was compared with those of the healthy people, Gibbs found that Lupski had mutations in both copies (alleles) of the gene SH3TC2. Nor did each allele have the same mutation. The one Lupski had inherited from his father was different from the one he inherited from his mother. His mother had one normal gene and one mutated, and his father had one normal and one with a different mutation.

Lupski was one of eight children, and the way the two mutations were distributed from the parents determined whether they were free

---

* The disease is named for its discoverers: Jean-Martin Charcot, Pierre Marie, and Howard Henry Tooth. It has nothing to do with one's teeth.

of CMT, mildly affected, or like Lupski, had a full-blown version of the disease. Two children inherited normal copies of the genes—one from each parent. Two others inherited the mother's mutation and the father's normal copy. Four, including Lupski, inherited each parent's mutated copy and thus developed CMT.

The cost of sequencing Lupski's genome was $50,000. Because of its cost, sequencing the genomes of individuals is primarily a research tool. In 2009, only seven genomes had been sequenced, but by 2010, geneticists Leroy Hood and David Galas planned to try to sequence one hundred genomes a year over the course of several years. They intended to look at multi-generational families, identify disease-causing genes, and trace the way they are inherited. They also planned to search for new mutations in the family lines.

Such research will be impossible unless the costs of sequencing come down. The aim is to bring the cost down from $50,000 to $5,000, then to about $1,000. The way this will be achieved, researchers think, is by getting the automated machines that use microarrays of DNA (biochips) and computer programs to work faster and require fewer people. The pay-off, researchers hope, will be an increasingly more detailed understanding of how genes cause particular diseases. Just as important, being able to sequence someone's genome might allow the development of what is usually known as "personalized medicine."

Not by Genes Alone: Proteins

Being able to locate a gene is a crucial step toward understanding the complex roles of genes, but a knowledge of where genes appear in the human (or individual) genome is incomplete in a crucial way. Such knowledge must be accompanied by an understanding of what proteins the genes encode and what role those proteins play.

Genes do most of their work by producing proteins. The proteins interact with other proteins to regulate human development, cell division, physiological functioning, immunological responses, tissue repair, and so on. An enzyme or hormone that is missing or deficient, for example, is responsible for diseases like Tay–Sachs and diabetes. Indeed, perhaps all diseases can be viewed as involving genetically based responses.

We have identified genes that predispose people to heart disease and breast cancer, and many researchers think it is reasonable to believe that there are scores (if not hundreds) of predisposing genes for many other diseases, ranging from schizophrenia to glaucoma.

We can expect researchers in the future to unravel more connections between proteins and diseases. We can then hope to see new approaches to diagnosing and treating diseases that have often been mysterious and lacking an effective therapy. Instead of a broad diagnostic category like "breast cancer," for example, the disease may be subdivided into many more specific categories, and each may have its own prognosis and its own therapy. Indeed, pharmaceutical companies may be able to design drugs that are specific for individuals and their particular genetic makeup. By tailoring an individual treatment to an individual version of a disease, not only could such designer drugs be more effective, but they could lack some of the worst side effects of drugs aimed at a general population of patients. Thus, if Sonia Henty is treated for breast cancer, she will receive drugs designed to treat her genetically characterized disease, and if the drugs hit their target more specifically, she may not suffer the literally sickening effects of wide-spectrum chemotherapy.

Personalized Medicine

Medicine is already personalized to an extent. Patients allergic to penicillin, for example, are prescribed some other antibiotic. Imagine, though, a form of medicine that is based on an understanding of how your genes are connected with the specific form of a disease that you have and how your particular genetic makeup might determine the treatment you receive. The understanding we have of genes and proteins has already allowed us to move in this direction.

Perhaps the best example of what personalized medicine might look like is the use of trastuzumab (brand name Herceptin®) to treat some types of breast cancer. The gene Her2/neu codes for the protein human epidermal growth factor 2, part of the system that regulates cell growth. All breast tissue contains some Her2, but fifteen to twenty percent of women with breast cancer have a mutation that increases Her2 to a hundred times the usual amount. Tumors identified as Her2 positive tend to be aggressive and to respond poorly to the standard hormone treatment.

Herceptin binds to Her2 receptors on the surface of cells. It kills cancer cells and ends the abnormal cell growth that an overabundance of Her2 produces. Herceptin, taken over a period of years, also keeps the cancer from returning. For some women with breast cancer, the drug can seem almost miraculous in its effects.

Still, Herceptin works only in some fifty percent of women who are Her2 positive. Why that is so is not now known. That the treatment can be so effective suggests that comparing personal genomes of patients would allow researchers to find genetic differences that would account for why some patients respond to the treatment but others don't.

Personalized medicine of the future is likely to feature more targeted therapies. Rather than simply subject every cancer patient to a round of standard chemotherapy, the chemotherapy will be tailored to the genetic predispositions of the patient. A knowledge of those predispositions will come from examining the patient's genome and comparing it with genomes stored in a massive database.

Envoi

When we understand the interplay among genes, proteins, developmental processes, and environmental factors, we will be well on the way to grasping the causes of diseases. Understanding these causes will put us on the road to finding effective measures to prevent them, treat them, or even cure them. Those measures are likely to be designed for the individual on the basis of an analysis of her genome.

That is the new promise of the secular Holy Grail.

SOCIAL CONTEXT
Stem Cells: The End of the Battle?

Research groups headed by John Gearhart of Johns Hopkins University and James Thomson of the University of Wisconsin, Madison, announced in November 1998 that they had succeeded in isolating and culturing human embryonic stem cells.

Embryonic Stem Cells vs. Adult Stem Cells

Embryonic stem cells are undifferentiated cells produced after a fertilized egg has divided several times and developed into a blastocyst. The blastocyst, a hollow ball of cells, contains a little lump called the inner-cell mass consisting of fifteen to twenty embryonic stem cells.

As development proceeds, embryonic stem cells differentiate and become specialized. They turn into so-called *adult* stem cells. These cells go on to produce the approximately 120 different cell types that form tissues and organs such as the blood, brain, bone, and liver. Adult stem cells have been found in the bone marrow and the brain, and some biologists believe that specific adult stem cells are associated with every organ.

Before embryonic stem cells begin to differentiate, they have the potential to become any of the specialized cells. Afterward, their fate is determined, and they do not go back to their previous state. When heart cells divide, for example, they produce only heart cells. Success in cloning mammals demonstrated, however, that the genetic material in a body cell can be made to return to its "default" position, in which each cell retains the genetic information needed to develop into a complete individual—including all the cell types. (As will be discussed later, returning a cell to its "default" position may offer a method for producing embryonic stem cells that does not involve an embryo.)

Original Sources of Stem Cells

Thomson retrieved embryonic stem cells from surplus embryos produced for fertility treatments. (He obtained consent from the egg and sperm donors.) Gearhart used a different method. A group of cells known as *embryonic germ cells* forms the sperm and ova that transmit genetic information to the next generation, and these cells are protected from the process that turns stem cells into specialized components of tissues and organs.

Gearhart retrieved embryonic germ cells from aborted fetuses and cultured them to produce stem cells. Stem cells obtained in this way are apparently no different from the ones obtained directly from blastocysts.

Treatment Dreams

The identification of embryonic stem cells and the ability to culture them are important steps in opening up an amazing new range of possibilities for treating many chronic, debilitating, and life-threatening diseases.

Cultures of embryonic stem cells appear to be what biologists call *immortal* cell lines. That is, the cells can replicate for an indefinite number of generations without dying or accumulating genetic errors. This capacity reduces the need to acquire new stem cells with great frequency. Cell lines can be established to supply the needs of researchers and physicians. If scientists learn how to control the system of chemical messengers and receptors that regulate the development of "blank" embryonic stem cells into specialized brain, heart, liver,

or pancreas cells, it may be possible to repair those organs by injections of stem cells.

This approach may make it possible, for example, to treat Parkinson's disease by injecting stem cells into the substantia nigra in the brain to boost the production of the neurotransmitter dopamine. (The lack of dopamine produces the symptoms of the disease.) Or diabetes might be brought under control by inducing the pancreas to incorporate insulin-producing islet cells developed from stem cells. Or we might be able to produce a potentially limitless amount of red blood cells, sterile and free of viruses, for use in transfusions.

Because embryonic stem cells have the capacity to become cells of any type, it looks as if they could be used to produce whatever sort of cells are needed to treat a particular disease. Damaged spinal nerves that keep people from walking or even moving their bodies might be repaired, and faulty retinas that cause blindness might be replaced with functional ones.

An even more dramatic prospect is that embryonic stem cells might be used to grow body tissues and even whole organs for transplantation. People could be provided with bone or skin grafts, liver segments, lung lobes, or even new kidneys or hearts. The problems caused by the intractable shortage of transplant organs would simply disappear. (See Chapter 8.)

The study of embryonic stem cells may make it possible to understand more about how genes are turned on and off during the process of development. This, in turn, may lead to our ability to control gene expression and eliminate diseases such as cystic fibrosis and muscular dystrophy. We might even be able to treat certain forms of cancer if we can understand how to control the growth of cells.

The problem of the rejection of tissue and organ transplants is now dealt with by using powerful immunosuppressive drugs. Three different strategies are made possible by stem cells:

1. **Stem-Cell Banks.** Good antigen (a collection of proteins on the cell surface) matching, which reduces the severity of

the immune response, might be achieved by maintaining a bank of stem cells. With a wide range of (say) embryonic stem-cell lines to choose from, transplant physicians could select the cells most compatible with the individual.

2. **Suppression of Markers.** A second solution is to find a way to suppress or disguise markers on the surfaces of stem cells so that they don't provoke the immune response. But researchers concerned with preventing the rejection of transplant organs have been trying to accomplish this for a long time and have been thus for unsuccessful.

3. **Cloning (Somatic-Cell Nuclear Transfer).** The third and most elegant solution is to make use of embryonic stem cells acquired from an embryo created by the techniques of cloning. This involves removing the nucleus from a donor egg, then replacing it with the DNA taken from a somatic (body) cell of an individual. The egg will contain only the DNA of the donor. Thus, when the egg develops into an embryo and the stem cells are removed, they will be genetically identical with those of the individual contributing the DNA. The process, technically known as somatic-cell nuclear transfer, is often called *therapeutic cloning*, in contrast to *reproductive cloning*.

Opponents of cloning often reject the use of "therapeutic," because of its positive associations and on the ground that therapeutic benefit has yet to be demonstrated. By contrast, advocates of cloning often prefer to avoid the word "cloning," because of its often negative associations, in favor of "cellular nuclear transfer," or CNT. (For more details on cloning, see "Social Context: Cloning," in Chapter 4.)

Regenerative Medicine

Stem cells have the potential to serve as the foundation for treatments that will allow us to repair or replace most, if not all, of our ailing organs. They hold the promise of a secular miracle. They could provide a way to still the tremors of Parkinson's disease, knit together a severed spinal cord, supply the cells needed to produce the enzyme required to metabolize sugar, replace the cells in a malfunctioning retina, and heal a damaged heart. Stem cells could become treatments for diseases such as Alzheimer's and Huntington's, for which there are no effective therapies. The list goes on and on.

Research using animals has already led to promising results. In 2008, scientists at Novocell announced that they had succeeded in converting mouse embryonic stem cells into insulin-producing cells. When the cells were transplanted into mice that had been made diabetic, the new cells kept their blood sugar within acceptable limits.

Stem cells may offer us the chance to redeem the lives of countless numbers of people from disease and injury. In this respect, they may usher in a new era of medicine. Regenerative medicine, a collection of therapies that produce new tissues and perhaps whole organs, holds out the promise of cures in dozens of cases where no effective treatments now exist.

First Stem-Cell Clinical Trial

In 2001, Hans Keirstead used human embryonic stem cells to produce oligodendrocyte progenitor cells. He injected these cells into rats with partial spinal cord injuries. The cells matured into glial cells, which produce myelin, the material forming the insulating sheath around nerves. The myelin allows impulses to travel from the brain to the motor nerves that operate the muscles.

The injections restored nerve transmission to a limited degree. Rats with injuries older than ten months had a lot of scarring, and the cells failed to help them. Rats with more recent injuries that had rendered them unable to move their rear legs, tails, or trunk muscles recovered substantial movement and function within two months after treatment.

This success prompted the Geron Corporation, which had funded Keirstead's study, to fund additional research, with the aim of testing oligodendrocyte cells in a clinical trial. A treatment reducing the crippling effects of spinal-cord injuries would be of significant medical importance, but it would also be a valuable product. Eventually, partly at the insistence of the FDA, Geron carried out twenty-three studies and spent $45 million to develop the therapy.

(Some observers claim that the Bush administration, not wanting to see embryonic stem-cell therapies develop, pressured the FDA to stall Geron's application for a clinical trial by asking for additional studies. The application was approved only when the Obama administration took office. Geron, however, does not confirm this view.)

Geron secured FDA approval for a Phase 1 clinical trial in January 2009. The trial will eventually enroll eight to ten people with spinal-cord injuries that are recent and severe enough to render them paralyzed from the waist down. The participants must all be volunteers and have no realistic hope of recovering from their injuries. The cells will be injected at the site of the injury during the seven to fourteen days after the injury occurs. The hope is that the growth factors produced by the injected cells will trigger nerve regeneration. The trial will be carried out at as many as seven medical centers, and patients will be closely monitored. During the first year, they will receive regular MRIs, and then they will be followed with regular examinations over a period of fifteen years.

The safety of the trial is of great concern to those who think that embryonic stem cells have the potential to transform medicine. The death of one of the participants could halt the development of all stem-cell–based therapies. Because stem cells have not been extensively studied, the possibility that they might harm a human subject is real.

The cells may cause a lethal form of cancer, for example, or they may provoke a fatal immune response. ("We don't want another Jessie Gelsinger here," the CEO of Geron said, explaining that the company was as certain as it could be that the clinical trial would be safe; see "Case Presentation: Jesse Gelsinger," in Chapter 2.) Because the effects of the therapy on humans are completely unknown, some suggest that the participants should be people with a fatal neurological disease, such as amyotrophic lateral sclerosis, rather than someone with a spinal-cord injury, who may be able to look forward to many decades of life.

The trial employing embryonic stem cells is only Phase 1, so its aim is just to test the safety and side effects of the treatment. Even if the treatment appears safe and effective, it will need to go through Phase 2 and Phase 3 testing. Thus, decades may pass before the treatment becomes available to people with spinal-cord injuries.

Treatments with Adult Stem Cells

The therapeutic promises of embryonic stem cells are, to an extent, paralleled by the promises of adult stem cells. How adult stem cells can be used in treatments is currently being investigated vigorously.

Evidence from animal studies suggests, for example, that heart muscle damaged by a heart attack can be treated effectively by an injection of adult stem cells. These cells produce normal heart cells, forming new tissue to replaced damaged tissue. Amazingly, the stem cells employed come from the bone marrow, where they ordinarily produce blood cells. No adult stem cells have been found in the heart. Apparently, the bone-marrow cells respond to the biochemical environment of the heart, and it reprograms them to produce heart cells.

In January 1999, Swedish scientists identified neural stem cells. These are brain cells that have differentiated to become cavity-lining cells, yet when they divide, their progeny can differentiate into either glial (structural) cells or neurons. When the brain is injured, the cavity-lining cells begin reproducing and the neural stem cells produce glial cells that form scars. If a way could be found to induce the neural stem cells to produce more neurons at the site of the injury, more brain function might be preserved.

Most researchers are not satisfied with the prospect of restricting research to adult stem cells. They point out that we don't yet know enough about embryonic stem cells to determine whether their therapeutic potential could be equaled by using adult stem cells. Only research with embryonic and adult stem cells will answer this question.

Ethical Issues over Acquiring Embryos

The retrieval of embryonic stem cells from human embryos or fetuses raises ethical problems for those who oppose abortion or believe that a fetus or embryo has a special moral status. From this perspective, a fertilized egg (an embryo) has the potential to develop into a human being, and (in a strong version) that entitles it to be treated as a person in the moral sense. Because it is wrong to kill an innocent person, it is thus wrong to destroy a human embryo. (See the discussion in Chapter 5.)

Taking embryonic stem cells from an aborted fetus is also seen as morally wrong by the same critics. Because abortion is viewed as a wrongful act, it is considered morally wrong to benefit from it. Also, as with the use of fetal tissue generally, by giving stem cells an instrumental value (using them to treat a disease, for example), we are tacitly encouraging abortion and endorsing its practice. In addition, by treating the fetus as a product or commodity that we use to suit our needs, we are disrespecting it, given the special status bestowed on the fetus by its potential to develop into a human being.

Some also object to using human eggs to produce embryos. Acquiring eggs has the potential for exploiting women, but more important, the use of eggs to produce embryos for the purpose of research turns the eggs into commodities with an instrumental value. The purpose of the research (acquiring knowledge or developing new treatments) may be laudable, but even so, the eggs are being put to a use that is incompatible with their natural purpose, which is to play a role in reproduction.

Those who do not assign a special status to a fetus or embryo typically do not oppose the use of embryonic stem cells. Rather, their concerns resemble ones associated with cloning and genetic manipulation in general. They oppose reproductive cloning, for example, because they think it cheapens human life. To consider another example, suppose genes could be added to embryonic stem cells to produce individuals with some special trait that could be inherited. In that case, the whole human species might be altered by altering stem cells.

Some critics maintain that to choose such a course of action would be dangerous, because of its unforeseeable biological and social consequences. Others hold that it would be wrong because tampering with the human genome would violate our notion of what it is to be human.

Three Problematic Sources for Embryonic Stem Cells

Most stem-cell opponents object to the ways embryonic stem cells are acquired, rather than to the ways the cells are used. Hence, if it were possible to acquire stem cells without violating moral prohibitions, some critics might drop their opposition. Following are four alternative sources that most critics have found unobjectionable. A fifth source, discussed in the next sections, is sufficiently morally unproblematic to win over the great majority of critics and is still under debate.

1. **Miscarriages.** Those who consider the destruction of an embryo to obtain stem cells immoral, may (but not necessarily) consider it legitimate to obtain stem cells from spontaneously aborted fetuses. If no one did anything to cause the miscarriage, the stem cells cannot be seen as acquired as the result of a morally wrong action.

Practically speaking, however, this way of getting stem cells is difficult, uncertain, and expensive. Also, because a fetus is spontaneously aborted, the stem cells may be abnormal in some way.

2. **Parthenogenesis.** Some who oppose acquiring stem cells from embryos or aborted fetuses would find stem cells produced by a process of parthenogenesis morally acceptable. That is, if an unfertilized human egg could be induced by biochemical means to divide and produce stem cells, the stem cells recovered could be legitimately used. Because the unfertilized egg would lack the genetic information needed for development, even if implanted into a uterus, it would not be a human embryo and thus would have no special moral status.

3. **Blastomeres.** Some might find it acceptable to use stem cells if they could be obtained from fertilized eggs that are not destroyed in the process. In a technique developed in 2006 at Advanced Cell Technology, researchers removed embryonic stem cells from an embryo after only two days of development without destroying it. After two days, a fertilized egg divides into eight cells, or blastomeres. Researchers removed one of the blastomeres and took the stem cells from it. This blastomere was destroyed, but the other seven blastomeres retained the capacity to develop into a normal child if the embryo were implanted into a uterus. There is no reason to believe that a single blastomere, even if implanted, would develop into a child.

The technique is based on a standard procedure of preimplantation genetic testing. One blastomere is removed so that its DNA can be tested for a particular genetic disorder, and if the embryo is found free of the gene connected with the disorder, the embryo (i.e., the other seven blastomeres) is implanted into the uterus of the woman seeking the test. The technique has been used thousands of times during the last two decades, and it has not been associated with abnormal births.

For some people, employing this technique would remove a moral roadblock to the use of stem cells. For most Roman Catholics and social conservatives, however, the technique only compounds the serious moral wrongs of in vitro fertilization and preimplantation genetic screening. In vitro fertilization is wrong, in their view, because it separates procreation from love, may require masturbation to acquire sperm, and turns embryos into a product.

Preimplantation genetic screening, they believe, is also wrong. It involves choosing which embryos to implant and thus allows humans to exercise control over procreation that rightfully belongs only to nature or God. Also, because embryos that are not implanted are discarded, the process involves the destruction of innocent human life. Hence, no matter how reasonable it may seem to some to sidestep the issue of destroying embryos by using a nondestructive method for obtaining stem cells, so many object to other aspects of the method that, if it were perfected, its use would not put an end to the ethical and political debate over stem cells.

These three alternative ways of obtaining embryonic stem cells, which have excited controversy for years, have been superseded by a method that promises to provide embryonic stem cells without provoking serious moral objections.

Cell Conversion: Induced Pluripotent Stem Cells

In 2007, Shinya Yamanaka and Kazutoshi Takahashi of Kyoto University published a paper in which they reported how, after numerous trials, they identified four genes essential to restoring a somatic cell to a pluripotent state. In a process known as cell conversion, they used a retrovirus to insert the four genes into the DNA of mouse skin cells, and the incorporated genes reprogrammed the skin cells into embryonic stem cells. The genes, in effect, restored the cells to their "default" state. (Two groups of American scientists repeated the experiment and confirmed the result.)

The Japanese researchers were not the only ones who succeeded in resetting adult cells to a pluripotent condition. James A. Thompson, one of the researchers who first isolated human embryonic stem cells, working with colleagues at the University of Wisconsin, also identified four genes, two of them different from those identified by Yamanaka and Takahashi, that would reset an adult cell to its default state. Thompson and his colleagues used cells from human foreskins and got the same results as Yamanaka.

Induced pluripotent stem cells, like embryonic stem cells, apparently have the capacity to develop into any of the 120 kinds of cells that form tissues and organs. No one knows, however, whether the induced stem cells will always behave in the body the same way as embryonic stem cells do. Additional studies with converted mouse cells have shown that when they are injected into embryos, they form different types of tissue and developmental layers in ways that are indistinguishable from the actions of embryonic stem cells. It is reasonable to believe that converted human cells would behave in the same way.

Potential Problems

Some difficulties may have to be overcome before many of the promises associated with pluripotent stem cells can be realized. One of the genes used by Yamanaka in his original work, for example, is known to cause cancerous tumors. Yamanaka later showed that he could achieve cell conversion without the gene, but the possibility that pluripotent cells will produce cancer is one of the reasons that using them to treat human diseases remains a problem.

A second major problem is the use of a retrovirus to insert the genes needed for conversion into a cell. Retroviruses themselves are known to induce mutations that can lead to cancer.

Conversion Possibilities

The possibilities of using the cell conversion techniques pioneered by Yamanaka and Thompson are currently being explored at the level of basic science. In August 2008, for example, Harvard researchers reported using transcription factors to convert exocrine cells from a mouse pancreas into insulin-producing beta cells. Transcription factors are proteins that control which genes in a cell are expressed and thus what the cell does. Each type of cell is believed to have a particular set of transcription factors that determine its characteristics, and the identification and use of those factors may make it possible to develop cells of specific types without starting from pluripotent cells.

The mice in the Harvard experiment had been rendered diabetic, but when they were injected with the converted cells, their diabetes was brought under control for as long as the cells lasted. Although the converted cells produced insulin, they did not organize themselves into the characteristic clumps of cells (the islets) in the pancreas. For this reason, the researchers identified the converted cells only as "cells that closely resemble beta cells."

Cells produced by converting the cell of an individual would be genetically compatible with the rest of that person's cells. Thus, they could be used to repair tissues and organs without the risk of provoking a response from the immune system. Until now, the only way scientists could imagine doing this was to acquire stem cells from an embryo created by transferring the nucleus of a somatic cell from the intended recipient into a donor egg. (See the earlier discussion of cloning, or somatic-cell nuclear transfer.)

One of the most exciting prospects is that cells acquired by conversion from someone with a disease like Alzheimer's or Parkinson's would allow researchers to study the ways in which the cells depart from the path of normal development and lead to the disease.

Acceptance by Critics?

The immediate appeal of being able to acquire human embryonic stem cells by converting somatic cells is the possibility that researchers will no longer need to create or destroy human embryos. Thus, the arguments over the moral legitimacy of stem-cell research and treatments based on stem cells should significantly abate, if not wholly disappear.

Obtaining stem cells by conversion, some believe, means that we don't need to worry about the moral status of a blastomere, debate issues connected with using human eggs, or argue about cloning for therapeutic purposes. The status of somatic cells has not been a matter of controversy, so converting them into embryonic stem cells is not likely to generate significant ethical issues. "You should have a solution here that will address the moral objections that have been percolating for years," said Tadeusz Pacholczyk of the National Catholic Bioethics Center.

Yet some observers are not so sure that the debate can be resolved so easily. They point out, first, that if researchers can produce pluripotent cells, then, most likely, with a bit more work, they should be able to convert somatic cells into totipotent cells, ones that have all the capacities of a fertilized egg. Thus, the moral status of such a cell would be the same as that of an embryo. Second, those who think that an embryo has the same status as a person in the moral sense because of its capacity to develop into a person who is born may apply this same line of reasoning to somatic cells. If such cells can be converted and given the capacity to become totipotent, then every cell in the body must be considered the moral equivalent of an embryo—which means that it has the moral status of a person.

From this point of view, the stem-cell debate is not resolved by our new capacity to convert body cells into pluripotent cells. Rather, the debate becomes even more complicated: we must now address the issue raised by the developmental capacities of somatic cells converted into pluripotent cells and, perhaps, into totipotent cells. The dust of serious controversy will not settle until these new issues are resolved. Meanwhile, the old issues will continue to be debated, because scientists still need to answer the question whether stem cells produced by converting somatic cells are exactly the same as the pluripotent cells extracted from an embryo.

The new discoveries may complicate the debate for many. Even so, they still point in the direction of a resolution. Faced with the reality of converted pluripotent cells, those who hold that an embryo is a person may be compelled to rethink their view. They may decide that what they took to be the condition for being a person (having the developmental capacity to become a child) is not as nonarbitrary as they assumed. They may have to look for other criteria, and it is possible that those criteria will exclude embryos from the category of persons in the moral sense.

Laws and Regulations

Only when embryonic stem cells no longer need to be studied will the controversy about them come to an end. Until then, the research must be conducted in an environment of laws and regulations that politics and political pressure make subject to change.

No Federal Funds

The 1995 Dickey–Wicker Amendment prohibits the use of federal funds to create human embryos for research purposes or to support research in which a human embryo is destroyed. (The amendment, which has the status of law, has been attached to appropriation bills that fund the National Institutes of Health.) The research by Thomson and Gearhart leading to the recovery and culturing of stem cells was supported, not by federal grants, but by the Geron Corporation, a small biotechnology company.

When Gearhart and Thomson announced their success, the question of the moral legitimacy of obtaining and using embryonic stem cells quickly became the topic of a national debate.

The National Conference of Catholic Bishops and other social conservative groups and politicians opposed spending federal money on stem-cell research. The opposition included many traditional opponents of abortion. They argued that human embryos have the status of persons, so retrieving their stem cells, and thus killing them, would be morally wrong.

In contrast, many disease-advocacy groups, seeing the possibility of cures by means of stem cells, proposed making stem-cell research eligible for federal funding. Without such funding, they argued, the chances that effective treatments would be found for many diseases would be significantly reduced. Private funding would be inadequate. Also, the United States would fall behind in medical innovation as other countries moved into the research gap that a lack of federal support would produce. Those pressing for going ahead with research included many politicians who ordinarily aligned themselves with social conservatives.

Many people, politicians included, found it hard to object to removing stem cells from embryos created at reproductive clinics and then not used. Ordinarily, such embryos are discarded. If so, then why not retrieve the stem cells and use them to develop treatments for diseases?

Social conservatives—Roman Catholics in particular—did not find this argument persuasive. So far as they were concerned, it was morally wrong to create and destroy embryos for the purpose of assisted reproduction. Hence, destroying them to acquire stem cells would also be wrong. (Even if the stem cells are used to treat disease, it would be wrong: The morally poisoned tree, they argued, bears only poisoned fruit.)

Bush Rules

President George Bush faced this politically vexed situation in 2001, and in August of that year he announced a policy to guide future federal funding of research involving human embryonic stem cells. His decision was to allow research on the (alleged) 64 human embryonic stem-cell lines already established, but not permit federal funds to be used to acquire new stem cells through the destruction of embryos.

The new policy met with a mixed response. It was denounced by the National Conference of Catholic Bishops as "morally unacceptable," while many researchers and patient advocates viewed the policy as placing an unwarranted restriction on research. Scientists were particularly concerned about limiting research to already established cell lines. No one could say in advance, they pointed out, exactly how many genetically different kinds of stem cells would be adequate for treating diseases.

Yet many observers also welcomed the decision as being less restrictive than they had feared. Perhaps the most unfortunate effect of the policy, in the view of patient advocates and researchers, was that it foreclosed the possibility of therapeutic cloning (somatic-cell nuclear transfer). Because the destruction of embryos was not allowed, the earlier mentioned process of acquiring embryonic stem cells genetically identical with one's own cells could not be employed.

Advocates of cloning for therapeutic purposes stressed—and still stress—that they are not advocating reproductive cloning—that is, producing an embryo that will be transferred to a woman's uterus and allowed to develop into a child. Critics of cloning, however, generally oppose its use for any purpose.

Also, the federally approved cell lines have proved to be fewer in number than President Bush initially suggested. Some are apparently contaminated with nonhuman cells, and others are the property of private companies and thus not available to all researchers.

Private and State Funding

In March 2002, the NIH broadened the path for researchers a bit by issuing an interpretation of the federal restrictions on using stem cells. The interpretation holds that scientists can study new stem-cell lines and even create them, so long as the work is not supported by federal money.

This loosening of the Bush restrictions was welcomed by researchers, but they claimed that they were still hampered by the federal policy. Private money for basic research is a scarce commodity, and most progress is made when large amounts of federal grant money is available. Grants drive research, and their absence slows it down.

The restrictions also required a duplication of facilities, equipment, and laboratory supplies. Because federal money cannot be used to create embryos for the purpose of research or for the study of embryonic stem cell lines other than those approved by federal policy, stem-cell research that departs from the guidelines must be carried out without the use of any federal money. Thus, laboratories in universities, and medical schools, and government facilities, nearly all of which are supported to some extent by federal grants, cannot legally engage in research that violates federal guidelines. Some institutes, such as the one at Harvard University, have been established and funded exclusively with private resources. Other universities, like the University of California at San Francisco, used rented space off campus.

Federal regulations do not forbid states from funding stem-cell research. Even though several states attempted to initiate stem-cell research programs, most attempts to substitute state funding for federal funding met with stiff opposition that consigned the proposed programs to legislative limbo.

California remains the exception. In 2004, fifty-nine percent of voters approved Proposition 71, establishing the California Institute for Regenerative Medicine. The Institute, once in operation, is supposed to distribute $3 billion to researchers to develop stem-cell technologies. Quite apart from helping people, however, the Institute is supposed to become such a powerhouse of stem-cell research that it will attract leading scientists and biotech companies to the state and produce a significant amount of money in the form of patent revenues.

For several years after Proposition 71 was approved, the Institute was tied up in court fighting lawsuits filed by those opposed to cloning. These legal entanglements meant that the state was prohibited from pursuing its plan to sell bonds to raise the money needed to fund the Institute. Finally, in May of 2008, Califomia awarded $270 million in grants to build a dozen stem-cell research centers in the state. The universities and institutes receiving the grants pledged to try to raise an additional $560 million of private money.

Obama Rules

In March 2009, President Barack Obama issued an executive order instructing NIH to draft guidelines lifting some of the Bush rules governing stem-cell research. The most important change in the regulations was to make thirteen new human embryonic stem-cell lines eligible for research receiving federal funding. The lines were established by researchers working in privately funded laboratories, and ninety-six more lines are currently under review. (An estimated seven hundred lines have been established with private money.)

The newly approved lines are ones in which stem cells were obtained from embryos created at fertility clinics and then not needed. It remains illegal to use federal money to carry out research on stem cells obtained from human embryos created solely for research purposes. Cloning for therapeutic purposes, the process of somatic-cell nuclear transfer, also remains illegal.

Under the new rules, donors of surplus embryos must be informed that the embryos will be destroyed and that there are other ways of disposing them. Donors must provide written consent, retain the right to change their minds, and receive no payment. For cell lines established before the new regulations, an NIH review panel will decide whether they were produced in an ethically acceptable way and thus are eligible for research supported by federal funding. Critics object to applying standards retroactively that may result in excluding some potentially valuable cell line.

Many researchers and advocates for developing regenerative medicine were disappointed at the comparatively limited changes Obama made in federal policy. During his 2008 campaign, Obama explicitly endorsed the "therapeutic cloning of stem cells." Unless pluripotent stem cells produced by cell conversion turn out to be both equivalent to embryonic stem cells and safe to use in humans, some of the main promises of regenerative medicine can't be achieved without therapeutic cloning.

Critics of stem-cell research were quick to condemn the Obama changes. Because the new rules permit the destruction of discarded embryos, some saw them as a major step toward permitting embryos to be created so they can be "killed" to serve the needs of research.

Envoi

Embryonic stem-cell research is likely to remain a flashpoint of controversy for the immediate future. The production of pluripotent embryonic stem cells by the conversion of somatic cells promises eventually to drain away controversy about the use of such cells, but until research establishes that cells produced by conversion are exactly the same as those acquired from embryos, the conflict will continue. Ironically, the research needed to prove equivalence will require the destruction of embryos, and those who consider the destruction of embryos the moral equivalent of murder will argue for its end.

Furthermore, those who assign the embryo the status of a person will need to face the issues raised by cell conversion. If every cell has the potential to become the equivalent of a pluripotent or totipotent cell, does this mean that every cell in the body must be regarded as the moral equivalent of a person? Most likely, no one wants to endorse such a view. On what grounds, then, can an embryo continue to be assigned a status that is denied to converted somatic cells?

Controversies over stem cells will continue to rage. Even so, for the first time since human embryonic stem cells were identified and isolated in 1998, an end to the stem-cell wars can be imagined.

BRIEFING SESSION

The two great triumphs of nineteenth-century biology were Darwin's formulation of the theory of organic evolution and Mendel's statement of the laws of transmission genetics. One of the twentieth century's outstanding accomplishments was the development of an understanding of the molecular structures and processes involved in genetic inheritance. All three great achievements give rise to moral and social issues of considerable complexity. The theories are abstract, but the problems they generate are concrete and immediate.

Major problems are associated with our increased knowledge of inheritance and genetic change. One class of problems concerns the use we make of the knowledge we possess in dealing with individuals. We know a great deal about the ways genetic diseases are transmitted and the sorts of errors that can occur in human development. We have the means to make reliable predictions about the chances of the occurrence of a disease in a particular case, and we have the medical technology to detect some disorders before birth.

To what extent should we employ this knowledge? One possibility is that we might use it to detect, treat, or prevent genetic disorders. Thus, we might require that everyone submit to screening and counseling before having children. We might require that children be tested either prenatally or immediately after birth. We might recommend or require selective abortions. For some couples, we might require or recommend in vitro fertilization, then the selection of embryos free of a disease-producing gene for implantation. Using some combination of these methods, we might be able to bring many genetic diseases under control (although we could never eliminate them) in the way we have brought contagious diseases under control.

Requiring screening and testing suggests another possibility, one that involves taking a broader view of human genetics. Eliminating genetic disease might simply become part of a much more ambitious plan for deliberately improving the entire species. Shall we attempt to control human evolution by formulating policies and practices designed to alter the genetic composition of the human population? Shall we make use of "gene surgery" and recombinant-DNA technology to shape physical and mental attributes of our species? That is, shall we practice some form of eugenics?

Another class of problems has to do with the wider social and environmental consequences of genetic research and technology. Research in molecular genetics concerned

with recombinant DNA has already revealed to us how the machinery of cells can be beneficially altered. We are able to make bacteria synthesize such important biological products as human insulin, and we are able to alter bacteria to serve as vaccines against diseases. In effect, recombinant-DNA technology produces life-forms that have never existed before. Should biotech industries be allowed to patent such forms in the way that new inventions are patented? Or do even altered organisms belong to us all?

Also, what are we to say about the deliberate release of genetically modified organisms into the environment? Is the threat that such organisms pose greater than the benefits they are likely to produce? We have already witnessed the great damage that can be done by pesticides and chemical pollution. Is there any way we can avoid damage that might be caused by genetically engineered organisms?

In the next three sections, we shall focus attention on the issues raised by the actual and potential use of genetic information. Our topics are these: genetic intervention (screening, counseling, and prenatal diagnosis), eugenics, and genetic research (therapy, technology, and biohazards).

Genetic Intervention: Screening, Counseling, and Diagnosis

Our genes play a major role in making us what we are. Biological programs of genetic information work amazingly well to produce normal, healthy individuals. But sometimes things go wrong, and when they do, the results can be tragic.

Almost 5000 human diseases have been identified as involving genetic factors. Some of the diseases are quite rare, whereas others are relatively common. Some are invariably fatal, whereas others are comparatively minor. Some respond well to treatment, whereas others do not.

The use of genetic information in predicting and diagnosing diseases has significantly increased during the last few decades. New scientific information, new medical techniques, and new social programs have all contributed to this increase.

Three approaches in particular have been adopted by the medical community as means of acquiring and employing genetic information related to diseases: genetic screening, genetic counseling, and prenatal genetic diagnosis. Each approach has been the source of significant ethical and social issues, but before examining the approaches and the problems associated with them, we need to consider the idea of a genetic disease.

Genetic Disease

The concept of a "genetic" disease is far from being clear. Roughly speaking, a genetic disease is a disease in which genes or the ways in which they are expressed are causally responsible for particular biochemical, cellular, or physiological defects. Rather than rely upon such a general definition, it's more useful for understanding genetic diagnosis to consider some of the ways genes play a role in producing diseases.

Gene Defects. The program of information coded into DNA (the genetic material) may in some way be abnormal because of the occurrence of a mutation at some time or other. (That is, a particular gene may have been lost or damaged, or a new gene added.) Consequently, when the DNA code is "read" and its instructions are followed, the child that develops will have impairments.

For example, a number of diseases, like phenylketonuria (PKU), are the result of inborn errors of metabolism. (For an explanation of PKU, see "Genetic Screening" later in the Briefing Session.) The diseases are produced by the lack of a particular enzyme necessary for ordinary metabolic functioning. The genetic coding required for the production of the enzyme is simply not present—the gene for the enzyme is missing.

A missing or defective gene may be due to a new mutation, but more often the condition has been inherited. It has been transmitted to the offspring through the genetic material contributed by the parents. Because defective genes can be passed on in this way, the diseases they produce are themselves described as heritable. (Thus, PKU is a genetically transmissible disease.) The diseases follow regular patterns through generations, and tracing out those patterns has been one of the great accomplishments of modern biology and medicine.

Developmental Defects. The biological development of a human being from a fertilized egg to a newborn child is an immensely complicated process. It involves an interplay between both genetic and environmental factors, and the possibility of errors occurring is quite real.

Mistakes that result as part of the developmental process are ordinarily called "congenital." Such defects are not in the original coding (genes) but result either from genetic damage or from the reading of the code. When either happens, the manufacture and assembly of materials required for normal fetal development are affected.

Radiation, drugs, chemicals, and nutritional deficiencies can all cause changes in an otherwise normal process. Also, biological disease agents, such as certain viruses, may intervene in development. They may alter the machinery of the cells, interfere with the formation of tissues, and defeat the carefully programmed processes that lead to a normal child.

Finally, factors internal to fetal development may also alter the process and lead to defects. The most common form of Down syndrome, for example, is caused by a failure of chromosomes to separate normally. The outcome is a child who has failed to develop properly and displays physical anomalies and some degree of mental retardation.

Defects occurring during the developmental process are not themselves the results of inheritance. Consequently, they cannot be passed on to the next generation.

Genetic Carriers. Some diseases are produced only when an individual inherits two copies of a gene (two alleles) for the disease from the parents. Parents who possess only one copy of the gene generally show none of the disease's symptoms. However, sometimes a parent may have symptoms of the same kind that are associated with the disease, although much less severe.

In the metabolic disease PKU, for example, individuals who have inherited only one allele (i.e., who are heterozygous, rather than homozygous) may show a greater-than-normal level of phenylalanine in their blood. Such people are somewhat deficient in the enzyme required to metabolize this substance, but the level of the substance may not be high enough to cause them any damage. Even so, they are carriers of a gene that, when passed on with another copy of the same gene from the other parent, can cause the disease PKU in their offspring. (As we will see later, this is also true for carriers of the sickle-cell trait.) The individual who receives both alleles for PKU obviously has the disease, but what about the parents? The point at which a condition becomes a disease is often uncertain.

Genetic Predisposition. It's been suggested that every disease involves a genetic component in some way or other. Even when people are exposed to the same new virus, their bodies react differently: some may destroy the virus, while others may become infected. Genetic variations may play a role in these differences. For example, although AIDS researchers noted in the 1980s that some who had been HIV positive for years hadn't developed AIDS, it wasn't until a mutation in the gene called CCR5 was identified that a potential explanation was found. The mutation is present in ten to fifteen percent of whites and appears to be absent in blacks and Asians.

In some cases, genes play a larger role in producing disease than in others. We have good evidence that hypertension, heart disease, various forms of cancer, and differential responses to environmental agents (such as sunlight, molds, and chemical pollutants) run in families, and the genetic makeup of particular individuals may predispose them to specific diseases.

For example, women who carry the BRCA1 gene are more likely to develop breast cancer at an early age than others in the population. Of course, not every woman who carries the gene develops breast cancer. What distinguishes the two groups? Their diet? Possessing other genes? No one knows, and what's true for familial breast cancer is also known to hold for dozens of other diseases.

Even granted the role of genes in producing diseases, it is important to keep in mind that predispositions are not themselves diseases. At best, they can be regarded only as causal conditions that, in conjunction with other conditions (likely to be unknown), can produce disease.

The action of genes in disease processes is even more complicated than described here. Nevertheless, our general categories are adequate to allow us to talk about the use made of information in genetic diagnosis.

Genetic Screening

In 1962, Dr. Robert Guthrie of the State University of New York developed an automated procedure for testing the blood of newborn children for the disease PKU. Although a diagnostic test for PKU had been available since 1934, it was time consuming and labor intensive. The Guthrie test made it practical to diagnose a large number of infants at a relatively low price.

PKU is a serious metabolic disorder. Infants affected are deficient in the enzyme phenylalanine hydroxylase. Because the enzyme is necessary to convert the amino acid phenylalanine into tyrosine as part of the normal metabolic process, a deficiency of the enzyme leads to a high concentration of phenylalanine in the infant's blood. The almost invariable result is severe mental retardation.

If the high level of phenylalanine in an infant's blood is detected very early, the infant can be put on a diet low in that amino acid. Keeping children on the diet until they are around the age of six significantly reduces the severity of the retardation that is otherwise inescapable.

The availability of the Guthrie test and the prospects of saving newborn children from irreparable damage encouraged state legislatures to pass mandatory screening laws. Massachusetts passed the first such law in 1963, and by 1967 similar legislation had been adopted by forty-one states.

The term *genetic screening* is sometimes used to refer to any activity having to do with locating or advising people with genetically connected diseases. We will restrict the term's application here and use it to refer only to public health programs that survey or test target populations with the aim of detecting individuals at risk of disease for genetic reasons.

The Massachusetts PKU law pointed the way to the development of public screening programs. PKU was the first disease tested for, but before long others were added to the list. A number of public health programs now screen particular populations for such conditions as sickle-cell anemia, sickle-cell trait, metabolic disorders, hypothyroidism, and chromosome anomalies. All fifty states now require screening for at least twenty-one of a standard panel of twenty-nine diseases. Some ninety-six percent of the four million babies born in the United States each year are routinely tested. Technological developments make it possible to use a single drop of blood to test for some forty disease conditions in a single analysis. New York state introduced a plan in 2002 to test newborns for all forty.

Although genetic screening is relatively new as a social program, the concept is historically connected with public health measures for the detection and prevention of communicable diseases like tuberculosis and syphilis. (HIV has been added to the list by states and the federal Centers for Disease Control.) If an individual with such a disease is identified, he can receive treatment, but most important, he can be prevented from spreading the disease to other members of the population.

Similarly, it is possible to think of diseases with a genetic basis as resembling contagious diseases. Individuals are affected, and they can pass on the disease. With genetic diseases the potential spread is not horizontal through the population, however, but vertical through the generations.

In terms of this model, public health measures similar to the ones that continue to be effective in the control of contagious diseases

might be used to help bring genetic diseases under control. When screening locates an individual with a genetic disorder, steps can be taken to ensure that she receives appropriate therapy. Furthermore, when carriers of genes that produce diseases are identified, they can be warned about their chances of having children who are genetically impaired. Thus, a limited amount of control over the spread of genetic disease can be exercised, and the suffering of at least some individuals can be reduced or eliminated. Public health experts estimate that about 3000 babies a year are identified as having diseases in which early intervention can save their lives or prevent serious disabilities.

The justification of laws mandating screening programs can be sought in the power and responsibility of government to see to the welfare of its citizens. Here again, the public health measures employed to control contagion might be looked to as a model. This is complicated because state laws vary. Some allow religious exemption, some don't. The general rule is that vaccination is required to go to school, except for medical exemptions. Except in special circumstances, we do not permit the parents of a child to decide on their own whether the child should be vaccinated against measles. We believe that society, operating through its government, has a duty to protect the child. Similarly, some argue that society owes it to the child with PKU to see to it that the condition is discovered as quickly as possible so that treatment can be instituted.

Critics of screening programs haven't been convinced that the contagious-disease model is appropriate in dealing with genetic diseases. Because the way in which genetic diseases are spread is so different, only a very small part of the population can be said to suffer any risk at all. By contrast, an epidemic of smallpox may threaten millions of people. Furthermore, some genetic screening programs don't have follow-up or counseling services attached to them, so often nothing is done that benefits the participants. By being told they are the carriers of a genetic disease, people may be more harmed than helped by the programs.

In general, whether the benefits of screening programs are sufficient to outweigh the liabilities remains a serious question. In particular, are screening programs so worthwhile that they justify the denial of individual choice entailed by required participation? What if

---

Screening Newborns

PKU Metabolic disorder causing seizures and retardation; 1 in 25,000 newborns.

MCAD Enzyme needed to convert fat to energy is missing; causes seizures, respiratory failure, cardiac arrest, and death; 1 in 15,000 newborns.

Congenital hypothyroidism Deficiency of thyroid hormone retards growth and brain development; 1 in 5000 newborns.

Congenital adrenal hyperplasia Defects in the synthesis of the adrenal hormones; can alter sexual development and in severe cases of metabolic disturbance results in death; 1 in 25,000 newborns.

Biotinidase deficiency Results in failure to synthesize biotin (a B vitamin), causing seizures, uncontrolled movements, deafness, and mental retardation; 1 in 75,000 births.

Maple-syrup urine disease (branched-chain ketoaciduria) Inborn metabolic error causing mental retardation and death; 1 in 180,000 births.

Galactosemia Missing enzyme needed to convert galactose sugar into glucose, causing mental retardation, blindness, and death; 1 in 34,000 births.

Homocystinuria Missing enzyme needed to convert galactose sugar into glucose, causing mental retardation, blindness, bone abnormalities, and stroke; 1 in 34,000 births.

Sickle-cell disease Disorder of the red blood cells, causing damage to vital organs resulting in heart attack and stroke, pain, ulceration, and infection; 1 in 400 births among blacks (including African Americans), 1 in 1100 among Hispanics born in the eastern United States.

Source: March of Dimes Foundation to Prevent Birth Defects, 2010

---

parents don't want to know whether their child has the genes responsible for a particular disease? Is it legitimate for a state, in the interest of protecting the child, to require parents to find this out, whether or not they want to know?

These issues and others related to them are easier to appreciate when they are considered in the context of particular kinds of screening programs. We'll discuss briefly two programs that have been both important and controversial.

PKU Screening. Screening for PKU was not only the first mass testing program to be mandated by state laws; it's generally agreed that it has also been the most successful program.

PKU is a relatively rare disease. It accounts for only about 0.8% of mentally retarded people who are institutionalized, and among the infants screened during a year in a state like Massachusetts, only three or four cases of PKU may be discovered. (The incidence is 5.4 per 100,000 infants.) Given this relatively low incidence of the disease, critics have argued that the abrogation of the freedom of choice required by a mandatory program doesn't make the results worthwhile.

This is particularly true, they suggest, because of the difficulties with the testing procedure itself. The level of phenylalanine in the blood may fluctuate so that not all infants with a higher-than-normal level at the time of the test actually have PKU. If they are put on the restricted diet, then they may suffer consequences from the diet that are harmful to their health. Thus, in attempting to protect the health of some infants, a mandatory program may unintentionally injure the health of other infants.

Tests more refined than the Guthrie one are possible. However, their use increases the cost of the screening program considerably, even if they are employed only when the Guthrie test is positive for PKU. From the statistical standpoint of public health, then, the financial cost of preventing a few cases of PKU may be much greater than allowing the cases to remain undetected and untreated.

Furthermore, there are additional hidden social costs. Female infants successfully treated for PKU may grow into adults and have children of their own. Their children run a very high risk of being born with brain damage. The reason for this is not genetic but developmental. The uterine environment of PKU mothers is one high in phenylalanine, and in high concentrations it causes damage to the infant. Thus, one generation may be saved from mental retardation by screening, only to cause mental retardation in the next.

Sickle Cell. Sickle-cell disease is a group of genetic disorders involving the hemoglobin in red blood cells. Because of faulty hemoglobin, the cells assume a characteristic sickle shape and do not transport oxygen as well as normal red cells. They are also fragile and break apart more frequently. The result is anemia and, often, the blocking of blood vessels by fragments of ruptured cells. The pain can be excruciating, and infections in tissues that have broken down because of oxygen deprivation can be life threatening. Stroke and heart disease often cause death in the early thirties.

The disease occurs only in those who have inherited both alleles for the disease from their parents. (That is, the gene for the disease is recessive, and those who are homozygous for the gene are the ones who develop the disease.) Those with only one allele for the disease (that is, those who are heterozygous) are said to have sickle-cell trait. Sickle-cell disease may develop in infancy, or it may manifest itself later in life in painful and debilitating symptoms. Those with sickle-cell trait rarely show any of the more serious clinical symptoms.

In the United States, the disease is most common among African Americans, but it is also found among those of Mediterranean, Caribbean, and Central and South American ancestry. The trait is carried by about seven to nine percent of African Americans (about three million people), and the disease occurs in about 0.3 percent of the population. Many

people with the disease are not severely affected and can live relatively normal lives. However, the disease may also be fatal, and at present there is no cure for it. It can be diagnosed prenatally, however.

In 1970, a relatively inexpensive and accurate test for sickle-cell hemoglobin was developed, making it possible to identify the carriers of sickle-cell trait. This technological development, combined with political pressures generated by rising consciousness among African Americans, led to the passage of various state laws mandating sickle-cell screening. During 1971 and 1972, twelve states enacted sickle-cell legislation.

The results were socially disastrous. Some laws required African Americans who applied for a marriage license to undergo screening. Because the only way to reduce the incidence of the disease was for two carriers to avoid having children (now embryos may be screened before implantation), many African Americans charged that the mandatory screening laws were a manifestation of a plan for genocide.

Medical reports that carriers of sickle-cell trait sometimes suffer from the pain and disability of sickling crises served as a new basis of discrimination. Some employers and insurance companies began to require tests of African American employees, and as a result some job possibilities were closed off to people with sickle-cell trait.

In 1972, Congress passed the National Sickle-Cell Anemia Control Act. In order to qualify for federal grants under the act, states were required to make sickle-cell screening voluntary, provide genetic counseling, and take steps to protect the confidentiality of participants. The most significant impact of the act was to force states to modify their laws to bring them into conformity with the act's requirements. In response, thirty-four states with sickle-cell screening laws now require universal screening.

The National Genetic Diseases Act, passed in 1976 and funded annually since then, provides testing and counseling for the diagnosis and treatment of a number of genetic diseases. The act further strengthens the commitment to voluntary participation and to guarantees of confidentiality.

The lesson learned from the public controversy over the first sickle-cell screening programs is that genetic information can be used in ways that are harmful to the interests of individuals. Furthermore, the information can be used as a basis for systematic discrimination.

In April 1993, an expert panel assembled by the Agency for Health Care and Policy (a part of the Public Health Service) recommended that all newborns, regardless of race, be screened for sickle cell. In making its recommendations, the panel stressed that sickle cell is not uniquely a disease of African Americans or blacks and that the general belief that it is can result in failing to see to it that people of non-African origin receive appropriate treatment.

Furthermore, the panel claimed, targeted screening of high-risk groups is not adequate to identify all infants with sickle-cell disease because it is not always possible to know an individual's racial heritage. Targeted screening, according to one study, may miss as many as twenty percent of cases.

What the panel did not point out was that one advantage of universal screening is that it permits individuals needing treatment to be identified without stigmatizing them just by requiring screening. However, whether having the disease or the trait becomes a social stigma is not a matter that can be resolved by an expert panel. It's something that must be dealt with by law, social policy, and public education.

Genetic Counseling

Much is known about the ways in which a number of genetic diseases are inherited. Those like PKU, sickle cell, and Tay–Sachs follow the laws of Mendelian genetics. Accordingly, given the appropriate information, it is often possible to determine how likely it is that a particular couple will have a child with a certain disease.

Suppose, for example, an African American couple is concerned about the possibility of having a child with sickle-cell disease. Then they will be tested to discover whether either or both of them are carriers of sickle-cell trait.

Sickle-cell disease occurs only when two recessive alleles are present—one inherited from the mother, one from the father. If only one of the parents is a carrier of the trait (is heterozygous), no child will have the disease. If both parents are carriers of the trait, the chances are one out of four that their child will have the disease. (This is determined simply by considering which combinations of the two genes belonging to each parent will produce a combination that is a homozygous recessive. The combination of Ss and Ss will produce ss in only twenty-five percent of the possible cases.)

Such information can be used to explain to potential parents the risks they might run in having children. But, as the case of sickle-cell disease illustrates, it is often very difficult for individuals to know what to do with such information.

Is a twenty-five percent risk of having a child with sickle-cell disease sufficiently high that a couple ought to decide to have no children at all? If the couple is opposed to abortion, the question becomes especially crucial. Answering it is made more difficult by the fact that sickle-cell disease varies greatly in severity. A child with the disease may be virtually normal, or doomed to a short life filled with suffering. No one can say in advance of its birth which possibility is more likely.

If a couple isn't opposed to abortion, is a twenty-five percent risk high enough to warrant a prenatal test? Or perhaps they should avoid the question of abortion by relying on artificial insemination so the embryos could be screened before one is implanted. This would be expensive and probably not be covered by insurance.

It is generally agreed that the question of whether or not to have a child when a serious risk is involved is a decision that must be made by the couple. The counselor may provide information about the risk, and—just as important—the counselor may provide information about medical therapies that are available for a child born with a hereditary disease.

In diseases in which prenatal diagnosis is possible, the option of abortion may be open to potential parents. Here, too, the object of counseling is to see to it that the couple is educated in ways relevant to their needs.

Prenatal Genetic Diagnosis

A variety of new technological developments now make it possible to secure a great amount of information about the developing fetus while it is still in the uterus. Ultrasound, radiography, and fiber optics allow examination of soft-tissue and skeletal development. Anatomical abnormalities can be detected early enough to permit an abortion to be safely performed if that is the decision of the woman carrying the fetus.

Amniocentesis and CVS. Yet the most common methods of prenatal diagnosis are amniocentesis and chorionic villus sampling (CVS), which involve direct cell studies. In amniocentesis, the amnion (the membrane surrounding the fetus) is punctured with a needle and some of the amniotic fluid is removed for study. The procedure cannot be usefully and safely performed until fourteen to sixteen weeks into the pregnancy. Until that time, there is an inadequate amount of fluid. The risk to the woman and to the fetus from the procedure is relatively small, usually less than one percent. (The risk that the procedure will result in a miscarriage is about one in 200.) A recent study shows that if amniocentesis is performed eleven to twelve weeks after conception, there is an increase in foot deformity from 0.1 to 1.3% in the child.

Chorionic villus sampling involves retrieving hairlike villi cells from the developing placenta. The advantage of the test is that it can be employed six to ten weeks after conception. Although the procedure is as safe as amniocentesis, a 1994 study by the Centers for Disease

Control found that infants whose mothers had undergone CVS from 1988 to 1992 had a 0.03% risk of missing or undeveloped fingers or toes. The normal risk is 0.05%. A later study questioned this finding and found reason to believe that the risk of fetal damage is greater than normal.

Amniocentesis came into wide use only in the early 1960s. At first, it was restricted mostly to testing fetuses in cases in which there was a risk of Rh incompatibility. When the mother lacks a group of blood proteins called the Rh (or Rhesus) factor, and the fetus has it, the immune system of the mother may produce antibodies against the fetus. The result for the fetus may be anemia, brain damage, and even death.

It was soon realized that additional information about the fetus could be gained from further analysis of the amniotic fluid and the fetal cells in it. The fluid can be chemically assayed, and the cells can be grown in cultures for study. An examination of the DNA can show whether there are any known abnormalities that are likely to cause serious physical or mental defects. Some metabolic disorders (such as Tay–Sachs disease) can be detected by chemical analysis of the amniotic fluid. However, some of the more common ones, such as PKU and Huntington's or muscular dystrophy, require an analysis of the genetic material. Because only males have a Y chromosome, it's impossible to examine fetal cells without also discovering the gender of the fetus.

Amniocentesis and CVS do have some hazards attached to them. Accordingly, prenatal genetic diagnosis is not at all regarded as a routine procedure to be performed in every pregnancy. There must be some indication that the fetus is at risk from a genetic or developmental disorder. One indication is the age of the mother, Down syndrome is much more likely to occur in fetuses conceived in women over the age of thirty-five. Because the syndrome is produced by a chromosome abnormality, an examination of the chromosomes in the cells of the fetus can reveal the defect.

A relatively new test for Down syndrome employs a blood sample taken from the pregnant woman. The sample is examined for the presence of three fetal proteins. At about sixteen to eighteen weeks of gestation, fetuses with the syndrome are known to produce abnormally small quantities of estriol and alpha fetoprotein and abnormally large amounts of chorionic gonadotropin. The levels of the proteins, plus such factors as the woman's age, can be used to determine the statistical probability of a child with the syndrome.

Genetic screening can also provide an indication of a need to perform amniocentesis. For example, Tay–Sachs disease is a metabolic disorder that occurs ten times as often among Jews originating in central and eastern Europe (the Ashkenazi) as in the general population. (The disease is invariably fatal and follows a sad course. An apparently normal child progressively develops blindness and brain damage, then dies at an early age.) Carriers of the Tay–Sachs gene can be identified by a blood test, and couples who are both carriers of the trait run a twenty-five percent risk of having a child with the disease. In such a case, there would be a good reason to perform amniocentesis.

When Is a Test Justified? Our ability to test for the presence of certain genes can give rise to cases some people find particularly troubling. Suppose, for example, a woman with a family history of breast and ovarian cancer wants to know whether the fetus she is carrying has the BRCA1 gene. If the gene is present, she wants to have an abortion, then get pregnant again.

Chances are good that no clinic or testing center would agree to test the fetus for the BRCA1 gene. After all, its presence only increases the probability that a woman will develop breast and ovarian cancer. Unlike, say, the gene for Huntington's disease, the BRCA1 gene doesn't inevitably produce the disease. Hence, a testing center is likely to reject the woman's request, on the grounds that it's unwilling to support anyone's attempt to get a "perfect baby."

Yet the woman, not the center, is the one who has responsibility for her child. Hence, if she wants to have a child that, so far as can be determined by the tests available, is free from the threat of disease, shouldn't she be allowed to seek that aim? What's wrong about trying to have a baby lacking the gene predisposing her to two forms of cancer?

Another controversy has developed as pregnant women younger than thirty-five with no particular risk factors in their background have increasingly sought prenatal screening. The women argue that even though their risk of having a child with a detectable genetic abnormality is small, the financial and emotional consequences of raising an impaired child are so serious that they should be allowed to take advantage of the technology available to minimize even the slight risk.

Opponents of this view point out that the risk of a miscarriage from a diagnostic procedure is around one in 200 while the risk of a woman below the age of forty having an impaired child is about one in 192. Hence, the chance of losing a normal child to miscarriage is almost as great as the chance of having an impaired child. Further, amniocentesis costs from $1000 to $2500 to perform, and the money spent on such unnecessary screening procedures contributes to the general rise in health care costs.

Such replies aren't convincing to those advocating wider access to prenatal testing. Some see the issue as one of the right of a woman to make choices affecting her body and her life. For some, the distress caused by a miscarriage is much less than that they would experience by having to raise an impaired child, but in any case, women should be the ones to decide what risks and burdens they are willing to bear. Such decisions should not be made unilaterally by physicians, hospitals, and health-policy planners.

Advocates of access to prenatal testing argue that, as far as increasing the cost of health care is concerned, when the costs of raising an impaired child are considered, the money spent on testing is insignificant. It costs about $100,000 to support a Down syndrome child during just the first year of life, and expenditures in the millions may be required to meet the needs of a severely impaired person over a lifetime. In addition, the potential emotional burden of the parents and other family members must be taken into account, even though they can't be assigned a dollar cost.

Some women want the added feeling of control prenatal screening can provide. The test can give them information that will put them in a position to make a decision about abortion, depending on the test results, or will provide them the peace of mind which comes from knowing that their pregnancy is proceeding with only a small likelihood that the developing child will suffer a serious impairment. The general attitude is that the technology to secure relevant information exists and it should be available to anyone who wants to make use of it. It certainly shouldn't be under the complete control of physicians.

Selective Abortion. In most cases in which prenatal diagnosis indicates that the fetus suffers from a genetic disorder or developmental defect, the only means of avoiding the birth of an impaired child is abortion. Because those who go through the tests required to determine the condition of the fetus are concerned with having a child, abortion performed under such circumstances is called *selective*. That is, the woman decides to have an abortion to avoid producing a child with birth impairments, not just to avoid having a child.

Those who oppose abortion in principle (see Chapter 9) also oppose selective abortion. In the view of some, the fact that a child will be born impaired is in no way a justification for terminating the life of the fetus.

Those prepared to endorse abortion at all typically approve of selective abortion as an acceptable way of avoiding suffering. In their view, it's better that the potential person—the fetus—not become an actual person, full of pain, disease, and disability.

The painful decision between having an abortion or giving birth to an impaired child may be avoided by employing ova, sperm, or embryo screening. This means, however, using the techniques developed in assisted reproduction (see Chapter 6), and the costs in time, frustration, and money can be considerable.

In the last few years, another way to avoid abortion has opened up as the techniques of fetal surgery have been employed to correct at least some abnormal physical conditions. Repairs to the heart, the insertion of shunts to drain off excess brain fluids, and the placement of tubes to inflate collapsed lungs are some of the intrauterine surgical procedures now being performed. Some surgeons believe it may be possible to expose the fetus within the uterus, perform surgery, then close up the amnion again. This would allow more extensive surgery for a greater variety of conditions.

The present hope is that as new surgical techniques for the treatment of fetuses are perfected and extended, the need to rely on abortion to avoid the birth of impaired children will decline significantly. Of course, surgery cannot, even in principle, provide a remedy for a large number of hereditary disorders. For example, it can do nothing for a child with Tay–Sachs, sickle cell, cystic fibrosis, muscular dystrophy, or PKU.

Helplessness in this regard is balanced by the hope that in future years pharmaceutical and biochemical therapies will be available to employ in cases involving missing enzymes; or perhaps gene therapy will make it possible to insert the proper gene for manufacturing a needed biochemical into the DNA of the cells of a fetus.

Embryo Selection. Potential parents who learn that they are carriers of genes responsible for lethal or life-threatening diseases may decide to use the techniques of assisted reproduction to avoid having a child affected with the disease.

Their embryos, produced by in vitro fertilization, can be genetically screened, then only those free of the disease-causing genes transferred to the woman's uterus. (See Chapter 6 for a fuller discussion.)

Embryo screening allows couples to avoid the risk their genetic heritage poses for their offspring. Those carrying the Tay–Sachs gene or the gene responsible for cystic fibrosis, for example, can be sure they don't have children with these diseases. It also makes selective abortion unnecessary. (However, some consider destroying embryos, for whatever reason, the moral equivalent of abortion.)

The painful present reality is that, for most children born with genetic diseases or defects, little can be done. Embryo selection and selective abortion are the primary means of avoiding the birth of a child known to be genetically impaired, and only abortion offers the possibility of avoiding the birth of a child discovered to be developmentally impaired.

Ethical Difficulties with Genetic Intervention

Genetic screening, counseling prenatal diagnosis, and embryo selection present bright possibilities for those who believe in the importance of exercising control through rational planning and decision making. They see the prospect of avoiding the birth of children with crippling impairments as one of the triumphs of contemporary medicine.

Furthermore, the additional prospect of wholly eliminating some genetic diseases by counseling and reproductive control holds the promise of an even better future. For example, if people who are carriers of diseases caused by a dominant gene (such as Huntington's) produced no children with the disease, the disease would soon disappear entirely. The gene causing the disease would simply not be passed on to the next generation.

A vision of a world without the misery caused by genetic defects is a motivating factor among those who are strong advocates of programs of genetic intervention. (See the section titled "Eugenics" later in this Briefing Session.) The vision must have its appeal to all who are moved by compassion in the face of suffering. Yet whether or not one shares this vision and is prepared to use it as a basis for social action, serious ethical questions about genetic intervention must be faced.

We've already mentioned some of the issues in connection with particular programs and procedures. We can now add some more general questions to that list. The moral and social issues connected with genetic intervention are woven into a complicated fabric of personal and social considerations, and we can merely sketch the main outline of the pattern.

Is there a right to have children who are likely to be impaired? Suppose a woman is informed, after an alphafetoprotein (AFP) test and amniocentesis, that the child she's carrying will be born with a neural tube defect. Does she have the right to refuse an abortion and have the child anyway?

Those opposed to all abortion on the grounds of natural law would favor the woman's having the child. By contrast, a utilitarian might argue that the decision would be wrong. The amount of suffering the potential child might be expected to undergo outweighs any parental loss. For different reasons, a Kantian might endorse this same point of view. Even if we assume the fetus is a person, a Kantian might argue that we are obliged to prevent its suffering.

Suppose we decide that a woman does have a right to have a child who is almost certain to be impaired. If so, then is society obligated to bear the expense of caring for the child? On the natural law view, the answer is almost certainly yes.

The child, impaired or not, is a person and, as such, is entitled to the support and protection of society. If we agree that the impaired child is a person, he or she is also a disadvantaged person. Thus, an argument based on Rawls' principles of justice would support the view that the child is entitled to social support.

Is society justified in requiring that people submit to genetic screening, counseling, or prenatal diagnosis? Children born with genetic diseases and defects require the expenditure of large amounts of public funds. Mandatory diagnosis need not be coupled with mandatory abortion or abstention from bearing children. (A related question is whether society ought to make available genetic testing to all who wish it, regardless of their ability to pay.)

On utilitarian grounds, it might be argued that society has a legitimate interest in seeing to it that, no matter what people ultimately decide, they should at least have the information about the likelihood that they will produce an impaired child.

If this view is adopted, then a number of specific medically related questions become relevant. For example, who should be screened? It's impractical and unnecessary to screen everyone. For example, why should we screen schoolchildren or prisoners, those who are sterile, or those past the age of childbearing?

This is closely connected with a second question: What should people be screened for? Should everyone be screened for Tay–Sachs disease, even thought it is the Ashkenazi Jewish population that is most at risk? Should everyone be screened for the cystic-fibrosis gene, even though the disease occurs primarily among whites?

Those who accept the contagious-disease model of genetic screening frequently defend it on the utilitarian grounds that screening promotes the general social welfare. However, one might argue that screening can also be justified on deontological grounds. It could be claimed that we owe it to developing fetuses, regarded as persons, to see to it they receive the opportunity for the most effective treatment. For example, it might be said that we have an obligation to provide a PKU child with the immediate therapy required to save him or her from severe mental retardation. The restriction of the autonomy of individuals by requiring screening might be regarded as justified by this obligation. If screening is voluntary, the welfare of the child is made to depend on ignorance and accidental opportunity.

Do physicians have an obligation to inform their patients who are prospective parents about the kinds of genetic tests that are available? A study of one population of women screened for Tay–Sachs disease showed that none had sought testing on the recommendation of her physician.

If the autonomy of the individual is to be preserved, then it seems clear that it is the duty of a physician to inform patients about genetic testing. A physician who disapproves of abortion might be reluctant to inform patients about tests that might encourage them to seek an abortion or embryo screening. Nevertheless, to the extent that abortion is a moral decision, it is a decision properly made by the individual, not by someone acting paternalistically in her behalf.

The duty of a physician to inform patients about the possibility of genetic tests seems quite straightforward. Yet the issue becomes more complicated in light of the next question about truth telling.

Do patients have a right to be informed of all of the results of a genetic test? Ethical theories based on respect for the autonomy of the individual (such as Kant's and Ross') suggest that patients are entitled to know what has been learned from the tests.

But what if the test reveals that the fetus carries the gene for a minor genetically transmissible disease or for increased susceptibility to a serious disease? Should the physician risk the patient's deciding to have an abortion merely because she is committed to the ideal of a "perfect" baby? Or , is such a decision even one for the physician to make?

Furthermore, what about the matter of sex determination? Screening tests can also reveal the gender of the fetus. Are prospective parents entitled to know this information? When an abortion is elective, it is possible for the woman to decide to avoid giving birth to a child of a particular gender. (The same possibility is presented by embryo selection.)

It might be argued on both utilitarian and deontological grounds that the sex of the fetus is information that isn't relevant to the health of the fetus. Accordingly, the physician is under no obligation to reveal the gender. Indeed, the physician may be under an obligation not to reveal the gender to avoid the possibility of its destruction for a trivial reason. But, again, is this really a decision for the physician?

Should public funds be used to pay for genetic tests when an individual is unable to pay? This is a question that holders of various ethical theories may not be prepared to answer in a simple yes-or-no fashion. Those who oppose abortion on natural law grounds might advocate providing funds only for genetic testing and counseling. That is, they might favor providing prospective parents with information they might use to decide whether to refrain from having children. Yet opponents of abortion might be against spending public money on tests that might encourage the use of abortion to prevent the birth of an impaired child.

The views of Rawls and of utilitarianism might support the use of public funds for genetic testing as part of a more general program of providing for health-care needs. Whether genetic testing programs are funded and what the level of funding might be would then depend on judgments about their expected value in comparison with other health-care programs.

A present ethical and social difficulty is caused by the fact that federal funds may be employed to pay for genetic screening and testing, yet federal money cannot legally be used to pay for abortions. Consequently, it's possible for a woman to discover she is carrying a fetus with a serious genetic disease, wish to have an abortion, yet lack the means to pay for it.

Issues about the confidentiality of test results, informed consent, the use of genetic testing to gather epidemiological information, and a variety of other matters might be mentioned here in connection with genetic intervention. Those that have been discussed are sufficient to indicate that the difficulties presented by genetic intervention are at least as numerous as the benefits it promises.

Eugenics

Like other organisms, we are the products of millions of years of evolutionary development. This process has taken place through the operation of natural selection on randomly produced genetic mutations. Individual organisms are successful in an evolutionary sense when they contribute a number of genes to the gene pool of their species proportionately greater than the number contributed by others.

Most often, this means that the evolutionarily successful individuals are those with the largest number of offspring. These are the individuals favored by natural selection. That is, they possess the genes for certain properties that are favored by existing environmental factors. (This favoring of properties is natural selection.) The genes of "favored" individuals will thus occur with greater frequency than the genes of others in the next generation. If the same environmental factors continue to operate, these genes will spread through the entire population.

Thanks to Darwin and the biologists who have come after him, we now have a sound understanding of the evolutionary process and the mechanisms by which it operates. This understanding puts us in a position to intervene in evolution. We no longer have to consider ourselves subject to the blind working of natural selection, and if we wish, we can modify the course of human evolution. As the evolutionary biologist Theodosius Dobzhansky expressed the point: "Evolution need no longer be a destiny imposed from without; it may conceivably be controlled by man, in accordance with his wisdom and values."

Those who advocate eugenics accept exactly this point of view. They favor social policies and practices that, over time, offer the possibility of increasing the number of genes in the human population responsible for producing or improving intelligence, beauty, musical ability, and other traits we value.

The aim of increasing the number of favorable genes in the human population is called *positive eugenics*. By contrast, *negative eugenics* aims at decreasing the number of undesirable or harmful genes. Those who advocate negative eugenics are most interested in eliminating or reducing from the population genes responsible for various kinds of genetic diseases.

Both positive and negative eugenics require instituting some sort of control over human reproduction. Several kinds of policies and procedures have been advocated, and we will discuss a few of the possibilities.

Negative and Positive Eugenics

The discussion of genetic screening, counseling, prenatal genetic diagnosis, and embryo selection makes it unnecessary to repeat here information about the powers we possess for predicting and diagnosing genetic diseases. It is enough to recall that, given information about the genetic makeup and background of potential parents, a large number of genetic diseases can be predicted with a certain degree of probability as likely to occur in a child of such parents. Or the presence of the genes can be determined by genetic analysis of the chromosomes. This is true of such diseases as PKU, sickle-cell disease, hemophilia, Huntington's disease, Tay–Sachs, and muscular dystrophy.

When genetic information isn't adequate for a reliable prediction or direct determination, information about the developing fetus can often be obtained by employing one of several procedures of prenatal diagnosis. Even when information is adequate for a reliable prediction, whether the fetus has a certain disease can be determined by prenatal testing. Thus, in addition to the genetic disorders named previously, prenatal tests can be performed for such developmental defects as neural tube anomalies and Down syndrome. Also, other tests can be performed on ova, sperm, or embryos.

A proponent of negative eugenics might advocate that a screening process for all or some currently detectable genetic diseases or dispositions (or developmental impairments) be required by law. When the probability of the occurrence of a disease is high (whatever figure that might be taken to be), the potential parents might be encouraged to have no children. Indeed, the law might require that such a couple either abstain from having children or rely on embryo selection. The law also might prescribe a penalty for going against the decision of the screening board.

If those carrying the genes for some genetic diseases could be prevented from having children, over time the incidence of the diseases would decrease. In cases when the disease is the result of a dominant gene (as it is in Huntington's disease), the disease would eventually disappear. (It could appear again with new mutations, however.)

When the disease is of the sort that can be detected only after a child is conceived and if the results of a prenatal diagnosis show that the developing fetus has a heritable disease, an abortion might be encouraged. Or a couple identified as at risk might be encouraged to seek artificial insemination and embryo testing and transfer.

Short of a law requiring abortion, a variety of social policies might be adopted to make abortion or embryo selection an attractive option. (For example, the cost of an abortion might be paid for by government funds, or women choosing abortion might be financially rewarded. Or the costs of embryo selection might be paid for under a federal program.) The aborting of a fetus found to have a transmissible genetic disease would not only prevent the birth of an impaired infant, but would also eliminate a potential carrier of the genes responsible for the disease.

Similarly, the sterilization of people identified as having genes responsible for certain kinds of physical or mental impairments would prevent them from passing on these defective genes. In this way, the number of such genes in the population would be proportionately reduced.

Currently, no state or federal laws make it a crime for couples who are genetically a bad risk to have children. Yet a tendency toward more genetic regulation may be developing. Screening newborns for certain genetic diseases that respond well to early treatment is an established practice. Also, genetic testing programs are frequently offered in communities to encourage people to seek information about particular diseases.

At present, genetic testing (for adults) and counseling are voluntary. They aim at providing information and then leave reproductive decisions up to the individuals concerned. Most often, they are directed toward the immediate goal of decreasing the number of children suffering from birth defects and genetic diseases. Yet genetic testing and counseling might also be viewed as a part of negative eugenics. To the extent that they discourage the birth of children carrying deleterious genes, they also discourage the spread of those genes in the human population.

Obviously, genetic testing and genetic counseling programs might also be used to promote positive eugenics. Individuals possessing genes for traits society values might be encouraged to have large numbers of children. In this way, genes for those traits would increase in relative frequency in the population.

No programs of positive eugenics currently operate in the United States. It is easy to imagine, however, how a variety of social and economic incentives (such as government bonuses) might be introduced as part of a plan to promote the spread of certain genes by rewarding favored groups of people for having children.

Use of Desirable Germ Cells

Developments in reproductive technology have opened up possibilities once considered so remote as to be the stuff of science fiction.

Artificial insemination by the use of frozen sperm is already commonplace. So, too, is the use of donor eggs and embryos. While some of the embryos may be donated by couples who don't need or want them, some are produced in infertility clinics by combining sperm from commercial sperm banks with donor ova. The developing embryos can be divided into several genetically identical embryos, and before long it may be possible to clone a human being from a single body cell.

Those wishing to have a child now have the option of selecting donor eggs or sperm from individuals with traits considered desirable. Alternatively, they may select a frozen embryo on the basis of descriptions of the gamete contributors. They may also turn to physicians who may offer them embryos they've created from sperm and eggs obtained from people who have what they judge to be outstanding traits.

We have available to us right now the means to practice both negative and positive eugenics at the level of both the individual and the society. If we wished, we could encourage groups of individuals to avoid having their own biological children and, instead, make use of the "superior" sperm, ova, and embryos currently offered at sperm banks and infertility centers. In this way, we could increase the number of genes for desirable traits in the population. (See Chapter 6.)

Ethical Difficulties with Eugenics

Critics have been quick to point out that the proposals mentioned suffer from serious drawbacks. First, negative eugenics isn't likely to make much of a change in the species as a whole. Most hereditary diseases are genetically recessive and so occur only when both parents possess the same defective gene. Even though a particular couple might be counseled (or required) not to have children, the gene will still be widespread in the population among people we would consider wholly normal. For a similar reason, sterilization and even embryo selection would have few long-range effects.

Also, the uncomfortable fact is that geneticists have estimated that, on the average, everyone carries recessive genes for five genetic defects or diseases. Genetic counseling and the use of the techniques of assisted reproduction may help individuals, but negative eugenics doesn't promise much for the population as a whole.

Positive eugenics can promise little more. It's difficult to imagine that we would all agree on what traits we'd like to see increased in the human species. But even if we could, it's not clear that we'd be able to increase them in any simple way.

For one thing, we have little understanding of the genetic basis of traits such as "intelligence," "honesty," "musical ability," "beauty" and so on. It's clear, however, that there isn't just a single gene for them, and the chances are that they are the result of a complicated interplay between genetic endowment and social and environmental factors. Consequently, the task of increasing their frequency is quite different from that of say, increasing the frequency of shorthorn cattle. Furthermore, desirable traits may be accompanied by less desirable ones, and we may not be able to increase the first without also increasing the second.

Quite apart from biological objections, eugenics also raises questions of a moral kind. Have we indeed become the "business manager of evolution," as Julian Huxley once claimed? If so, do we have a responsibility to future generations to improve the human race? Would this responsibility justify requiring genetic screening and testing? Would it justify establishing a program of positive eugenics? Affirmative answers to these questions may generate conflicts with notions of individual dignity and self-determination.

Of the ethical theories we have discussed, it seems likely that only utilitarianism might be construed as favoring a program of positive eugenics. The possibility of increasing the frequency of desirable traits in the human species might, in terms of the principle of utility,

justify placing restrictions on reproduction. Yet the goal of an improved society or human race might be regarded as too distant and uncertain to warrant the imposition of restrictions that would increase current human unhappiness.

As far as negative eugenics is concerned, the principle of utility could be appealed to in order to justify social policies that would discourage or prohibit parents who are carriers of the genes for serious diseases from having children. The aim here need not be the remote one of improving the human population but the more immediate one of preventing the increase in sorrow and pain that would be caused by an impaired child.

Natural law doctrines of Roman Catholicism forbid abortion, sterilization, and embryo selection. Thus, these means of practicing negative eugenics are ruled out. Also, the natural law view that reproduction is a natural function of sexual intercourse seems, at least prima facie, to rule out negative eugenics as a deliberate policy altogether. It could be argued, however, that voluntary abstinence from sexual intercourse or some other acceptable form of birth control would be a legitimate means of practicing negative eugenics.

Ross' prima facie duty of causing no harm might be invoked to justify negative eugenics. If there is good reason to believe a child is going to suffer from a genetic disease, we may have a duty to prevent the child from being born. Similarly, Rawls' theory might permit a policy that would require the practice of some form of negative eugenics for the benefit of its immediate effects of preventing suffering and sparing all the cost of supporting those with genetic diseases.

It is difficult to determine what sort of answer to the question of negative eugenics might be offered in terms of Kant's ethical principles. Laws regulating conception or forced abortion or sterilization might be considered to violate the dignity and autonomy of individuals. Yet moral agents as rational decision makers require information on which to base their decisions.

Thus, programs of genetic screening and counseling might be considered to be legitimate.

Genetic Research, Therapy, and Technology

By replacing natural selection with artificial selection that is directly under our control, we can, over time, alter the genetic composition of populations of organisms. This has been done for thousands of years by animal and plant breeders, and our improved understanding of genetics allows us to do it today with more effectiveness and certainty of results. Yet such alterations take a long time. Molecular genetics holds out the possibility of immediate changes. Bacteria continue to be the major organisms of research, but genetic technology is already being applied to plants and animals. The same technology is now on the verge of being applied to humans.

Recombinant DNA

The information required for genetic inheritance is coded in the two intertwined strands of DNA (deoxyribonucleic acid) found in plant and animal cells—the double helix. The strands are made up of four kinds of chemical units called nucleotides, and the genetic message is determined by the particular sequence of nucleotides. Three nucleotides in sequence form a triplet codon. Each codon directs the synthesis of a particular amino acid and determines the place it will occupy in making up a protein molecule. Since virtually all properties of organisms (enzymes, organs, eye color, and so on) depend on proteins, the processes directed by DNA are fundamental.

Alterations in the nucleotide sequence in DNA occur naturally as mutations—random changes introduced as "copying errors" when DNA replicates (reproduces) itself. These alterations result in changes in the properties of organisms, because the properties are under the control of DNA. Much research in current molecular genetics is directed toward bringing about desired changes by deliberately manipulating the nucleotide sequences in DNA. The major steps toward this goal have involved the development of techniques for recombining DNA from different sources.

The recombinant process begins by taking proteins known as restriction enzymes from bacteria and mixing them with DNA that has been removed from cells. These enzymes cut open the DNA strands at particular nucleotide locations. DNA nucleotide sequences from another source can then be added, and certain of these will attach to the cut ends. Thus, DNA from distinct sources can be recombined to form a single molecule.

This recombinant DNA can then be made to enter a host cell. The organism most widely employed is the one-celled bacterium *E. coli* that inhabits the human intestine by the billions. In addition to the DNA in its nucleus, *E. coli* has small circular strands of DNA known as *plasmids*. The plasmid DNA can be recombined with DNA from an outside source and returned to the cell. When the plasmid replicates, it will make copies of both the original nucleotides and the added segments. Thus, a strain of bacteria can be produced that will make limitless numbers of copies of the foreign DNA.

The obvious question is, What benefits might recombinant-DNA technology produce? From the standpoint of theory, it might lead to a better understanding of the molecular processes involved in such diseases as cancer, diabetes, and hemophilia. Or it might provide more effective treatment for metabolic diseases like PKU and Tay–Sachs.

From the practical standpoint, recombinant-DNA technology has already led to the development of new breeds of plants able to utilize nitrogen from the air and requiring little or no fertilizer. Specially engineered bacteria might be used to clean up the environment by breaking down currently nonbiodegradable compounds like DDT. Other bacteria might convert petroleum into other useful chemical compounds, including plastics.

The most immediate benefit of recombinant-DNA technology is the use of bacteria modified into chemical factories that produce biological materials of medical importance. A glance at a few of the many recent research developments gives an appreciation of the powerful potential of genetic technology:

* Hypopituitary dwarfism is a condition caused by a deficiency in growth hormone. The hormone itself consists of molecules too large and structurally complex to synthesize in the laboratory, but as early as 1979 researchers employed recombinant-DNA technology to induce bacteria to produce the hormone. It's now available in quantities large enough to be used as a therapy.

* Modified bacteria now produce human insulin in quantities large enough to meet the need of diabetics, some of whom are allergic to swine or bovine insulin.

* Genetically engineered bacteria have been used to produce a vaccine against hepatitis B and against a strain of genital herpes. The clotting factor employed in the treatment of hemophilia has been similarly produced.

* Genetically engineered flu vaccines grown in moth cells may replace some of those currently grown in fertilized chicken eggs, reducing production time from six to nine months to two to three.

* In 1985, the Cetus Corporation was awarded the first patent for an altered form of the protein interleukin-2. Il-2 activates the immune system and is used in the treatment of some cancers. It occurs naturally but in very small amounts; thus, it wasn't possible to use it therapeutically until it was produced in quantity by genetically altered bacteria.

* Researchers have inserted human genes into plants and induced the plants to produce large quantities of medically significant proteins. Antibodies, serum albumin, enkephalins, hormones, and growth factors are among those currently produced.

* Substances occurring in the human body in minute amounts that can be important as drugs when widely available are now being produced in large quantities by genetic engineering. For example, tissue plasminogen activator (TPA), which is produced in blood vessels, dissolves blood clots and is a useful drug in the treatment of heart attacks. Also, blood factor-VIII, a clotting agent, may improve the lives and health of hemophiliacs by reducing their chances of viral infection from donated blood.

* In 1997, researchers genetically engineered mice to serve as an animal model for sickle-cell disease by inserting into the mice human genes for the defective hemoglobin that causes the disease. Having animal models may speed up the testing of new drugs and suggest approaches for an effective treatment.

* Researchers have inserted into mouse embryos human DNA equivalent to an entire chromosome and discovered that the DNA is passed on to the next mouse generation. Such research promises to lead to an understanding of the ways in which genes work normally and in disease processes. Further, animals containing segments of human DNA might be induced to produce medically useful products. (See the Case Presentation "Hello, Dolly," in Chapter 6.)

Gene Therapy

The rapid advancement in genetic knowledge during the last few years has led to the use of recombinant-DNA techniques in experimental medical therapies. Therapy in which a missing or nonfunctioning gene is inserted into a patient's cells is already being employed. So is the use of altered cells to induce the formation of new blood vessels to treat unhealing leg ulcers and, perhaps soon, coronary artery blockages. (See the Case Presentation "Gene Therapy," in this chapter, for more details.)

The ability to alter the basic machinery of life to correct its malfunctioning is surely the most powerful form of therapy imaginable. The immediate prospects for gene therapy involve the relatively modest, but very dramatic, task of splicing into the DNA of body cells a gene that controls the production of a specific substance. Diseases such as PKU that are caused by the absence of an enzyme might then be corrected by inducing the patient's cells to manufacture that enzyme. Some genetic diseases involve dozens or even hundreds of genes, and often the mechanism by which the genes produce the disease is not understood. Consequently, it is likely to be a long while before most genetic diseases can be treated by gene therapy. Even so, the effective treatment of single-gene disorders is a most promising possibility.

Few special moral or social issues are raised by the use of gene therapy as long as the cells modified are somatic (body) cells. The issues change significantly with the prospect of modifying human germ-line (sex) cells. Somatic-cell changes cannot be inherited, but germ-line cell changes can be. This possibility holds out the benign prospect of eliminating forever a number of genetic diseases. However, we need not wait for germ-line therapy to accomplish this. Embryo testing and selection before implantation, a technology already in common use, would be a simpler way to achieve the same goal.

While germ-line therapy may have no medical use, it points toward a frightening prospect. It offers us a way of "engineering" human beings by tinkering with the sex cells to produce people who meet our predetermined specification. Because we will discuss this possibility later in the chapter, it's relevant to note here only that the technology required to alter human sex cells doesn't exist at present.

Biohazards

The issues connected with gene therapy, testing, and screening may be overshadowed in significance by questions concerning dangers inherent in the development of genetic technology and the release of its products into the environment.

The question of whether recombinant-DNA research ought to be halted is no longer a serious social issue. However, this hasn't always been so. In 1974, a group of scientists active in such research issued a report recommending that scientists be asked to suspend work voluntarily on recombinant experiments involving tumor viruses, increased drug resistance in harmful bacteria, and increased toxicity in bacteria. The discussion that ensued resulted in the formulation of guidelines by the National Institutes of Health to regulate research.

The major concern initially was that recombinant techniques might be employed to produce essentially new organisms that would threaten human health. Suppose that the nucleotide sequence for manufacturing a lethal toxin were combined with the DNA of *E. coli*. Then this usually harmless inhabitant of the intestine might be transformed into a deadly organism that would threaten the existence of the entire human population. (In recent years we've seen how deadly naturally occurring mutant forms of *E. coli* can be when they appear in the food supply.)

Or to take another scenario, perhaps a nucleotide sequence that transforms normal cells into cancerous ones might trigger an epidemic of cancer. Without a thorough knowledge of the molecular mechanisms involved, little could be done to halt the outbreak. Indeed it isn't even clear what would happen if one of the engineered insulin-producing strains of bacteria escaped from the lab and spread through the human population.

These and similar dangers prompted some critics to call for an end to all genetic-engineering research. However, almost two decades of recombinant-DNA research have passed without the occurrence of any biological catastrophes. Most observers regard this as sufficient proof of the essential safety of the research. Yet, in the view of others, the fact that no catastrophes have yet occurred must not be allowed to give us a false sense of security. Almost no one advocates that the research be abandoned, but several molecular geneticists have argued that the very fact that we still do not know enough to estimate the risks involved with a high degree of certainty is a good reason for continuing to control it severely.

Quite apart from the possible hazards associated with genetic engineering, many people continue to be uneasy about the direction of research. A number of biotechnological possibilities are on the horizon, some of which might have far-reaching consequences. As we discussed earlier, gene surgery offers more possibilities than just medical therapy. If undesirable DNA segments can be sliced out of the genetic code and replaced with others, this would permit the "engineering" of human beings to an extent and degree of precision never before imagined.

The eugenic dream of producing people to match an ideal model would be a reality. What would happen then to such traditional and moral values as autonomy, diversity, and the inherent worth of the individual?

The same techniques employed to manufacture the ideal person might also be used to design others to fit special needs. It's not difficult to imagine using genetic surgery to engineer a subhuman race to serve as a slave class for the society. The scenarios of cautionary science fiction might be acted out in our own future.

Further, the technique of asexual reproduction known as cloning might be employed to produce individuals who are exact genetic copies of someone whose DNA has been engineered to suit our needs or ideals. While human cloning is not yet a practical reality, a giant step toward it was taken in 1997 when Ian Wilmut and his colleagues at the Roslin Institute in Scotland cloned a sheep. (See Case Presentation: "Hello, Dolly," in Chapter 6.)

We might use reproductive technology in combination with genetic engineering to have several children who are copies of ourselves. If the embryos were stored, some of these might be born years apart.

Consider one last possibility. Virtually new organisms might be produced by splicing together DNA from two or more sources. Thus, the world might be faced with creatures of an unknown and unpredictable nature that are not the product of the natural processes of evolution.

It's little wonder that molecular biologists have become concerned about the nature and direction of their research. As Robert Sinsheimer says, "Biologists have become, without wanting it, custodians of great and terrible power." Such power in the hands of a tyrannical government could be used with irresistible effectiveness to control its subjects. Societies might create a race of semihuman slaves or armies of genetically engineered soldiers. The possibilities are both fantastic and unlimited.

Ethical Difficulties with Genetic Research, Therapy, and Technology

The risks involved in gene therapy are not unique ones. In most respects, they exactly parallel those involved in any new medical treatment. Accordingly, it seems reasonable to believe that the same standards of safety and the same consideration for the welfare of the patient that are relevant to the use of other forms of therapy should be regarded as relevant to gene therapy.

The principles of Kant and Ross suggest that the autonomy of the individual must be respected and preserved. The individual ought not to be viewed as an experimental case for testing a procedure that may later prove helpful. If the person is adequately informed and competent to consent, and if no alternative therapy is likely to be effective, it would be morally legitimate for the patient to be given the opportunity to benefit from the therapy. However, if the hazards are great or completely unknown, it's doubtful whether the patient would be justified in risking his or her life.

By contrast, on utilitarian principles, if the outcome of gene therapy can be reasonably expected to produce more benefit than harm, its use might be considered justifiable. If we assume that a person is likely to die anyway, that in itself might be enough to warrant the use of the therapy. In addition, since each case treated is likely to contribute to increased understanding and to benefit others, this tends to support the use of gene therapy, even in cases in which it is of doubtful help to the individual. (See the Case Presentation "Gene Therapy," in this chapter, for a fuller discussion.)

Genetic research and its associated technology present issues much greater in scope than those raised by gene therapy. They are issues that require us to decide what sort of society we want to live in.

Very few responsible people currently believe we should call a halt to research in molecular genetics and forgo the increase in power and understanding that it has already brought. However, the possibilities of genetic engineering include ones that are frightening and threatening, ones that could wholly alter our society and destroy some of our most cherished values. These are the possibilities that require us to make decisions about whether or to what extent we want to see them realized.

The natural law view of ethics would not, in general, support any policy of restricting scientific inquiry in the area of molecular genetics. For, on this view, there is a natural inclination (and hence a natural duty) to seek knowledge. Yet certain types of experiments and gene engineering would be ruled out. Those which aim at altering human beings or creating new species from mixed DNA are most likely to be considered to violate the natural order. On the Roman Catholic view, such a violation of nature would run counter to God's plan and purpose and so be immoral.

The principle of utility might be invoked to justify limiting, directing, or even ending research in molecular genetics. If research or its results are likely to bring about more harm than benefit, regulation would be called for. Yet if the promise of relieving misery or increasing well-being is great, then some risk that we might also acquire dangerous knowledge in the process might be acceptable.

On the utilitarian view, knowledge may be recognized as a good, but it's only one good among others. Possessing the knowledge to alter human beings in accordance with a eugenic ideal or to create new species means we have to make a decision about whether doing so would result in an overall benefit. That judgment will then be reflected in our social policies and practices.

Such an analysis also seems to be consistent with Rawls' principles. For Rawls, there is no absolute right to seek knowledge, nor is there any obligation to employ knowledge that is available. Restrictions might well be imposed on scientific research and on the technological possibilities it presents if the good of society seems to demand it.

READINGS

Section 1: Dilemmas of Genetic Choice

The Morality of Screening for Disability

Jeff McMahan

Jeff McMahan reviews four common objections to prenatal or preimplantation screening for disabilities: screening is discriminatory, has harmful consequences for disabled people, expresses a hurtful view of disabled people, and reduces human diversity. If these objections are sufficient to show that screening is wrong, McMahan argues, they also imply that it is permissible to cause oneself to have a disabled child.

Indeed, those who accept the objections to screening and claim that being disabled is no worse than being nondisabled seem committed to accepting that it is permissible to deliberately cause a disability prenatally, even for a trivial reason. If we find this view unacceptable, McMahan claims, then we must find the objections to prenatal screening for disability wrong.

My topic is the morality of using screening technologies to enable potential parents to avoid having a disabled child. The relevant techniques include preconception genetic and non-genetic testing of potential parents, preimplantation genetic diagnosis (PGD), and prenatal screening with the option of abortion. Many people use these techniques and are grateful to have them. Others, however, object to their use, even when abortion is not an issue. The most common objections can be grouped into four basic types.

First, the opponents of screening and selection urge that these practices are perniciously discriminatory, in that their aim is to rid the world of people of a certain type, people who have increasingly come to share a sense of collective identity and solidarity. Some might even argue that for society to endorse and support screening for disability is analogous to promoting efforts to prevent the births of people of a particular racial group.

Second, the practices of screening and selection are not just detrimental to the disabled as a group but may also be harmful to individual disabled people in

Jeff McMahan, From "The Morality of Screening for Disability," *Ethics, Law and Moral Philosophy of Reproductive Biomedicine*, Vol. 1, No. 1, (2005): 129–132. Copyright © 2005 Elsevier Inc. All Rights Reserved. Reprinted by permission.

various ways. They may, for example, reinforce or seem to legitimize forms of discrimination against existing disabled people. And, if effective, they also reduce the *number* of disabled people, thereby making each disabled person a bit more unusual and a bit more isolated. The reduction in numbers may, in addition, diminish the visibility and political power of disabled people generally.

Third, it is often held that a reduction in the number of disabled people would have an adverse effect on human diversity. To eliminate the disabled would be to eliminate a type of human being who makes a unique contribution to the world. For the disabled themselves, and indeed their mere presence among the rest of us, teach valuable lessons about respect for difference, about the nobility of achievement in the face of grave obstacles, and even about the value of life and what makes a life worth living.

Fourth, it is often held that practices of screening and selection express a view of disabled people that is hurtful to existing disabled people. Efforts to prevent disabled people from existing are said to express such views as that disabled people ought not to exist, that it is bad if disabled people exist, or at least worse than if normal people exist, that disabled people are not worth the burdens they impose on their parents and on the wider society, and so on. Screening and selection, in other words, seem to say to existing disabled people: The rest of us are trying to prevent the existence of other people like you.

One can respond to these objections to screening and selection, as some of the speakers at this conference have done, by appealing to rights of individual liberty. One could grant that the practices are objectionable for the reasons given but argue that those reasons are overridden by rights to reproductive freedom and by the benefits to those who are able to exercise those rights. But I want to advance a reason for scepticism about the force of the objections themselves.

The objections do of course express serious and legitimate concerns, concerns that must be addressed in appropriate ways. But I will argue that they're insufficiently strong to show that screening and selection are wrong or should be prohibited. For if they were taken to show that, they would also have implications beyond the practices of screening and selection. They would also imply the permissibility of certain types of action that most people believe are impermissible.

Consider this hypothetical example: Suppose there is a drug that has a complex set of effects. It is an aphrodisiac that enhances a woman's pleasure during sexual intercourse. But it also increases fertility by inducing ovulation. If ovulation has recently occurred naturally, this drug causes the destruction of the egg that is present in one of the fallopian tubes but also causes a new and different egg to be released from the ovaries. In addition, however, it has a very high probability of damaging the new egg in a way that will cause any child conceived through the fertilization of that egg to be disabled. The disability caused by the drug is, let us suppose, one that many potential parents seek to avoid through screening. But it is also, like virtually all disabilities, not so bad as to make life not worth living. Suppose that a woman takes this drug primarily to increase her pleasure but also with the thought that it may increase the probability of conception—for she wants to have a child. She is aware that the drug is likely to cause her to have a disabled child but she is eager for pleasure and reflects that it might be rather nice to have a child who might be more dependent than children usually are. Although she does not know it, she has in fact just ovulated naturally so the drug destroys and replaces the egg that was already present but also damages the new egg, thereby causing the child she conceives to be disabled.

Note that because the drug causes the woman's ovaries to release a new egg, the disabled child she conceives is a different individual from the child she would have had if she hadn't taken the drug.

Many people think that this woman's action is morally wrong. It is wrong to cause the existence of a disabled child rather than a child without a disability, just for the sake of one's own sexual pleasure. There are, of course, some who think that rights to reproductive freedom make it permissible to choose to have a disabled child just as they also make it permissible to try to avoid having a disabled child. But most of us do not share that view. Most of us think that if it would be wrong to cause an already born child to become disabled, and if it would be wrong to cause a future child to be disabled through the infliction of prenatal injury, it should also be wrong to cause a disabled child to exist rather than a child without a disability.

There are of course differences. Whether they are morally significant and if so to what extent are matters to which I will return shortly. For the moment, the important point to notice is that if the arguments I cited earlier show that screening and selection are wrong, they should also show that the action of the woman who takes the aphrodisiac is permissible. This is because if it is morally *mandatory* to *allow* oneself to have a disabled child rather than to try, through screening, to have a child who would not be disabled, then it must be at least *permissible* to *cause* oneself to have a disabled rather than a non-disabled child.

Let me try to explain this in greater detail. If it is wrong for the woman to take the aphrodisiac, that must be because there is a moral objection to voluntarily having a disabled child—an objection that's strong enough to make it wrong to cause oneself, by otherwise permissible means, to have a disabled rather than a non-disabled child. But if there is such an objection, it must surely be strong enough to make it at least permissible for people to try, by morally acceptable means, to avoid having a disabled child and to have a non-disabled child instead, and to make it impermissible for others to prevent them from making this attempt.

Yet the critics of screening believe not only that it is wrong for people to try to avoid having a disabled child and to have a non-disabled child instead, but even that it is permissible for others to prevent them from having a non-disabled rather than a disabled child. It would be inconsistent for these critics to condemn the woman in this example for causing herself to have a disabled rather than a non-disabled child and to condemn those who try to cause themselves *not* to have a disabled rather than a non-disabled child.

The crucial premise here is that if it would be morally objectionable to try to *prevent* a certain outcome, and permissible to deprive people of the means of preventing that outcome, then it ought to be permissible to *cause* that outcome, provided one does so by otherwise permissible means.

Note also that if we were to assert publicly that it would be wrong for this woman to do what would cause her to have a disabled child rather than a non-disabled child, or if we were to attempt to prevent her from taking the drug—for example, by making the drug illegal on the ground that it causes "birth defects"—our action would be vulnerable to the same objections that opponents of screening and selection urge against those practices.

If, for example, we were publicly to state the reasons why it would be objectionable for the woman to take the drug—that the disabled child's life might be likely to contain more hardship and less good than the life of a non-disabled child, that provision for the disabled child's special needs would involve greater social costs, and so on—the evaluations of disability and of disabled people that might be thought to be implicit in these claims could be deeply hurtful to existing disabled people, and if we were to prevent this woman and others from being able to take the drug, this would reduce the number of disabled people relative to the number there would otherwise have been, thereby threatening the collective identity and political power of existing disabled people.

In short, the arguments of the opponents of screening seem to imply not only that it would be permissible for the woman to take the aphrodisiac, thereby causing herself to have a disabled child, but also that it would be wrong even to voice objections to her action.

Some opponents of screening and selection may be willing to accept these implications. They might argue that there are relevant differences between causing oneself to have a disabled child rather than a different non-disabled child and causing an existing individual to be disabled. For example, in the latter case but not the former, there is a victim, someone for whom one's act is worse. So there are objections to causing an existing individual to be disabled that do not apply to merely causing a disabled person to exist, and to assert these objections merely expresses the view that it can be worse to be disabled than not to be, which seems

unobjectionable, since it does not imply any view of disabled people themselves. Screening and selection, by contrast, are held to express a pernicious and degrading view of disabled people.

Thus, opponents of screening and selection typically think that they can draw the line between action by a woman that may cause her to conceive a child who will be disabled and, for example, action taken by a pregnant woman that injures her fetus, causing it to be disabled when it otherwise would not have been. But in fact many people, especially among the disabled themselves, contend that it is no worse to be disabled than not to be. They claim that disabilities are "neutral" traits. So, for example, Harriet McBryde Johnson (2003), a disabled lawyer, emphatically repudiates the "unexamined assumption that disabled people are inherently 'worse off,' that we 'suffer,' that we have lesser 'prospects of a happy life.'"

The view that it is not bad to be disabled, apart from any ill effects caused by social discrimination, would be very difficult to sustain if it implied that to cause a person to become disabled would not harm that person, or that it is irrational to be averse to becoming disabled. But in fact those who claim that it is not bad in itself to *be* disabled can accept without inconsistency that it can be bad to *become* disabled. They can appeal to the *transition costs*. It is bad to become disabled because this can involve loss and discontinuity, requiring that one abandon certain goals and projects and adapt to the pursuit of different ones instead. It is these effects that make it rational to fear becoming disabled and they are a major part of the explanation of why it is wrong to cause someone to become disabled. The other major part is that the causation of disability involves a violation of the victim's autonomy.

But notice that these considerations do not count against causing disability through prenatal injury. For congenital disability does not have transition costs, and fetuses are not autonomous.

It seems, therefore, that opponents of screening and selection who also claim that it is not worse to be disabled have no basis for objecting to the infliction of prenatal injury that causes congenital disability. Moreover, to object to the infliction of disabling prenatal injury or to enact measures to prevent it would seem to express a negative view of disability and perhaps of the disabled themselves. At a minimum, it expresses the view that it is bad to be disabled, or at least worse than not to be disabled. And, if effective, efforts to prevent disabling prenatal injury would have other effects comparable to those of prohibiting or restricting screening for disability and selection, such as reducing the number of disabled people who would be born, thereby also threatening the sense of collective identity and solidarity among the disabled as well as diminishing their visibility and political power. Finally, prevention of prenatal injury would also threaten human diversity. It would deprive those who would have had contact with the person if he had been disabled of the unique benefits that disabled people offer to others.

So for those opponents of selection who also hold that it is not a harm or misfortune to be disabled, it seems that there are not only no reasons to object to the infliction of disabling prenatal injury but even positive reasons not to object to it and not to try to prevent it.

Suppose there were an aphrodisiac that would greatly enhance a woman's pleasure during sex but would, if taken during pregnancy, injure the fetus in a way that would cause it to be congenitally severely disabled. Those who oppose screening and selection for the reasons I cited earlier and who also hold that it is not bad in itself to be disabled are logically committed by their own arguments to accept that it would be permissible for a pregnant woman to take this aphrodisiac just to increase her own pleasure, and they are further committed to accept that it would be wrong to try to prevent the woman from taking the aphrodisiac or even to criticize her for doing so.

If we think that these conclusions are mistaken, which they surely are, we must reject some part of the case against screening and selection.

I will conclude by briefly suggesting a more positive way of addressing the concerns of those who oppose screening and selection. My sense is that the chief worry of those opposed to screening and selection has to do with the expressive effects of these practices. The worry is, as I noted earlier, that these practices give social expression to a negative view of disabled people, thereby reinforcing other forms of discrimination against them.

But notice that it is usually only people who have not had a disabled child who are averse to doing so. Those people who actually have a disabled child tend

overwhelmingly to be glad that they had the particular child they had. If any child they might have had would have been disabled, they tend to prefer having had their actual disabled child to having had no child at all. If they could have had a non-disabled child but it would have been a different child, they tend to prefer their actual disabled child. Of course, what they would usually most prefer is that their actual child had not been disabled. But it is almost invariably the case that any action that would have enabled them to avoid having a disabled child would have caused them to have a different child. When the parents appreciate this fact, they cease to wish that anything had been different in the past, and focus their hopes on the possibility of a cure.

In short, most people who currently have or have had a disabled child in the past do not regret having done so. They are, instead, glad to have had their actual child and frequently testify to the special joy and illumination afforded by being bound to a disabled child. This very different evaluation of having a disabled child by those who actually have experience of it is no less rational and no less authoritative than the evaluation that many people make prospectively that it would be bad or worse to have a disabled child.

We could therefore try to offset any negative expressive effects of screening and selection by giving public expression to these different and equally valid evaluations. I do not have any suggestions for how we might do this. That's a matter for specialists in public policy, not philosophers. But the crucial point is that it would be morally and strategically better for disabled people and their advocates to focus their efforts on positive proposals of this sort rather than to stigmatize and to seek to restrict or suppress practices such as screening and selection. By crusading against screening and selection, they risk making themselves appear to the wider public as fanatics bent on imposing harmful restrictions on others. That would certainly not serve the cause of obtaining justice for the disabled.

Reference

Johnson HM. 2003. Unspeakable conversations. *New York Times Magazine* 16 February 2003, p. 79.

Genetic Dilemmas and the Child's Right to an Open Future

Dena S. Davis

Dena Davis asks whether genetic counselors must assist couples who wish to have a child who will be deaf or an achondroplastic dwarf. Taking deafness as an example, she argues that although counselors are professionally committed to an ethic of patient autonomy, they may reject such a request, on the ground that it would limit the future autonomy of any child that might be born.

Davis compares the situation with one in which Jehovah's Witnesses refuse to consent to a lifesaving blood transfusion for their child and one in which Amish parents remove their children from school after the eighth grade. While courts have allowed the second, Davis sees both as unjustifiably denying children an "open future."

Whether or not deafness is considered a disability in a culture, being born deaf significantly restricts the choices open to a child. Thus, if it is chosen before birth by the child's parents, it must be considered a harm. For this reason, genetic counselors should not help parents produce deaf children.

The profession of genetic counseling is strongly characterized by a respect for patient autonomy that is greater than in almost any other area of medicine. When moral challenges arise in the clinical practice of genetics, they tend to be understood as conflicts between the obligation to respect patient autonomy and other ethical norms, such as doing good and avoiding harm. Thus, a typical counseling dilemma exists when a person who has been tested and found to be carrying the gene for Tay–Sachs disease refuses to share that information with siblings and other relatives despite the clear benefits to them of having that knowledge, or when a family member declines to participate in a testing protocol necessary to help another member discover his or her genetic status.

This way of looking at moral issues in genetic counseling often leaves both the counselors and commentators frustrated, for two reasons. First, by elevating respect for patient autonomy above all other values, it may be difficult to give proper weight to other factors, such as human suffering. Second, by privileging patient autonomy and by defining the patient as the person or couple who has come for counseling, there seems no "space" in which to give proper attention to the moral

Dena S. Davis, From "Genetic Dilemmas and the Child's Right to an Open Future," *Hastings Center Report*, Vol. 27, no. 2 (1997): 7–15. Copyright © 1997 Hasting Center Report. Reprinted by permission.

claims of the future child who is the endpoint of many counseling interactions.

These difficulties have been highlighted of late by the surfacing of a new kind of genetic counseling request: parents with certain disabilities who seek help in trying to assure that they will have a child who shares their disability. The two reported instances are in families affected by achondroplasia (dwarfism) and by hereditary deafness. This essay will focus on deafness.

Such requests are understandably troubling to genetic counselors. Deeply committed to the principle of giving clients value-free information with which to make their own choices, most counselors nonetheless make certain assumptions about health and disability—for example, that it is preferable to be a hearing person rather than a deaf person. Thus, counselors typically talk of the "risk" of having a child with a particular genetic condition. Counselors may have learned (sometimes with great difficulty) to respect clients' decisions not to find out if their fetus has a certain condition or not to abort a fetus which carries a genetic disability. But to respect a parental value system that not only favors what most of us consider to be a disability, but actively expresses that preference by attempting to have a child with the condition, is "the ultimate test of nondirective counseling."[1]

To describe the challenge primarily as one that pits beneficence (concern for the child's quality of life) against autonomy (concern for the parents' right to decide about these matters) makes for obvious difficulties. These are two very different values, and comparing and weighing them invites the proverbial analogy of "apples and oranges." After all, the perennial critique of a principle-based ethics is that it offers few suggestions for ranking principles when duties conflict. Further, beneficence and respect for autonomy are values that will always exist in some tension within genetic counseling. For all the reasons I list below, counselors are committed to the primacy of patient autonomy and therefore to nondirective counseling. But surely, most or all of them are drawn to the field because they want to help people avoid or at least mitigate suffering.

Faced with the ethical challenge of parents who wish to ensure children who have a disability, I suggest a different way to look at this problem. Thinking this problem through in the way I suggest will shed light on some related topics in genetics as well, such as sex selection. I propose that, rather than conceiving this as a conflict between autonomy and beneficence, we re-cast it as a conflict between parental autonomy and the child's future autonomy: what Joel Feinberg has called "the child's right to an open future."

New Challenges

The Code of Ethics of the National Society of Genetic Counselors states that its members strive to:

- Respect their clients' beliefs, cultural traditions, inclinations, circumstances, and feelings.
- Enable their clients to make informed independent decisions, free of coercion, by providing or illuminating the necessary facts and clarifying the alternatives and anticipated consequences.[2]

Considering the uncertain and stochastic nature of genetic counseling, and especially in light of the difficulty physicians experience in sharing uncertainty with patients, it is remarkable that medical geneticists have hewed so strongly to an ethic of patient autonomy. This phenomenon can be explained by at least five factors: the desire to disassociate themselves as strongly as possible from the discredited eugenics movement;[3] an equally strong desire to avoid the label of "abortionist," a realistic fear if counselors are perceived as advocates for abortion of genetically damaged fetuses;[4] the fact that few treatments are available for genetic diseases; an awareness of the intensely private nature of reproductive decisions; and the fact that genetic decisions can have major

consequences for entire families.[5] As one counselor was quoted, "I am not going to be taking that baby home—they will."[6]

The commitment to patient autonomy faces new challenges with the advances arising from the Human Genome Project. The example of hereditary deafness is reported by Walter E. Nance, who writes:

It turns out that some deaf couples feel threatened by the prospect of having a hearing child and would actually prefer to have a deaf child. The knowledge that we will soon acquire [due to the Human Genome Project] will, of course, provide us with the technology that could be used to assist such couples in achieving their goals. This, in turn, could lead to the ultimate test of nondirective counseling. Does adherence to the concept of nondirective counseling actually require that we assist such a couple in terminating a pregnancy with a hearing child or is this nonsense?[7]

Several issues must be unpacked here. First, I question Nance's depiction of deaf parents as feeling "threatened" by the prospect of a hearing child. From Nance's own depiction of the deaf people he encounters, it is at least as likely that deaf parents feel that a deaf child would fit into their family better, especially if the parents themselves are "deaf of deaf" or if they already have one or more deaf children. Or perhaps the parents feel that Deafness (I use the capital "D," as Deaf people do, to signify Deafness as a culture) is an asset—tough at times but worthwhile in the end—like belonging to a racial or religious minority.

Second, I want to avoid the issue of abortion by discussing the issue of "deliberately producing a deaf child" as distinct from the question of achieving that end by aborting a hearing fetus. The latter topic is important, but it falls outside the purview of this paper. I will focus on the scenario where a deaf child is produced without recourse to abortion. We can imagine a situation in the near future where eggs or sperm can be scrutinized for the relevant trait before fertilization, or the present situation in which preimplantation genetic diagnosis after in vitro fertilization allows specialists to examine the genetic makeup of the very early embryo before it is implanted.

Imagine a Deaf couple approaching a genetic counselor. The couple's goals are to learn more about the cause(s) of their own Deafness, and, if possible, to maximize the chance that any pregnancy they embark upon will result in a Deaf child. Let us suppose that the couple falls into the 50% of clients whose Deafness has a genetic origin.[8] The genetic counselor who adheres strictly to the tenets of client autonomy will respond by helping the couple to explore the ways in which they can achieve their goal: a Deaf baby. But as Nance's depiction of this scenario suggests, the counselor may well feel extremely uneasy about her role here. It is one thing to support a couple's decision to take their chances and "let Nature take its course," but to treat as a goal what is commonly considered to be a risk may be more pressure than the value-neutral ethos can bear. What is needed is a principled argument against such assistance. This refusal need not rise to a legal prohibition, but could become part of the ethical norms and standard of care for the counseling profession.[9]

The path I see out of this dilemma relies on two steps. First, we remind ourselves why client autonomy is such a powerful norm in genetic counseling. Clients come to genetic counselors with questions that are simultaneously of the greatest magnitude and of the greatest intimacy. Clients not only have the right to bring their own values to bear on these questions, but in the end they must do so because they—and their children—will live with the consequences. As the President's Commission said in its 1983 report on Screening and Counseling for Genetic Conditions:

> The silence of the law on many areas of individual choice reflects the value this country places on pluralism. Nowhere is the need for freedom to pursue divergent conceptions of the good more deeply felt than in decisions concerning reproduction. It would be a cruel irony, therefore, if technological advances undertaken in the name of providing information to expand the range of individual choices resulted in unanticipated social pressures to pursue a particular course of action. Someone who feels compelled to undergo screening or to make particular reproductive choices at the urging of health care professionals or others or as a result of implicit social pressure is deprived of the choice-enhancing benefits of the new advances. The Commission recommends that those who counsel patients and those who educate the public about genetics should not only emphasize the importance of preserving choice but also do their utmost to safeguard the choices of those they serve.[10]

Now let us take this value of respect for autonomy and put it on both sides of the dilemma. Why is it morally problematic to seek to produce a child who is deaf? Being deaf does not cause one physical pain or shorten one's life span, two obvious conditions which it would be prima facie immoral to produce in another person. Deaf people might (or might not) be less happy on average than hearing people, but that is arguably a function of societal prejudice. The primary argument against deliberately seeking to produce deaf children is that it violates the child's own autonomy and narrows the scope of her choices when she grows up; in other words, it violates her right to an "open future."

The Child's Right to an Open Future

Joel Feinberg begins his discussion of children's rights by noticing that rights can ordinarily be divided into four kinds. First, there are rights that adults and children have in common (the right not to be killed, for example). Then, there are rights that are generally possessed only by children (or by "childlike" adults). These "dependency-rights," as Feinberg calls them, derive from the child's dependence on others for such basics as food, shelter, and protection. Third, there are rights that can only be exercised by adults (or at least by children approaching adulthood), for example, the free exercise of religion. Finally, there are rights that Feinberg calls "rights-in-trust," rights which are to be "saved for the child until he is an adult." These rights can be violated by adults now, in ways that cut off the possibility that the child, when it achieves adulthood, can exercise them. A striking example is the right to reproduce. A young child cannot physically exercise that right, and a teenager might lack the legal and moral grounds on which to assert such a right. But clearly the child, when he or she attains adulthood, will have that right, and therefore the child now has the right not to be sterilized, so that the child may exercise that right in the future. Rights in this category include a long list: virtually all the important rights we believe adults have, but which must be protected now to be exercised later. Grouped together, they constitute what Feinberg calls "the child's right to an open future."[11]

Feinberg illustrates this concept with two examples. The first is that of the Jehovah's Witness child who needs a blood transfusion to save his life but whose parents object on religious grounds. In this case, the parents' right to act upon their religious beliefs and to raise their family within the religion of their choice conflicts with the child's right to live to adulthood and to make his own life-or-death decisions. As the Supreme Court said in another (and less defensible) case involving Jehovah's Witnesses:

Parents may be free to become martyrs themselves. But it does not follow that they are free in identical circumstances to make martyrs of their children before they have reached the age of full and legal discretion when they can make that decision for themselves.[12]

The second example is more controversial. In 1972, in a famous Supreme Court case, a group of Old Order Amish argued that they should be exempt from Wisconsin's requirement that all children attend school until they are either sixteen years old or graduate from high school.[13] The Amish didn't have to send their children to public school, of course; they were free to create a private school of their own liking. But they framed the issue in the starkest manner: to send their children to any school, past eighth grade, would be antithetical to their religion and their way of life, and might even result in the death of their culture.

The case was framed as a freedom of religion claim on the one hand, and the state's right to insist on an educated citizenry on the other. And within that frame, the Amish won. First, they were able to persuade the Court that sending their children to school after eighth grade would potentially destroy their community, because it

takes them away from their community, physically and emotionally, during the crucial and formative adolescent period. During this period, the children must acquire Amish attitudes favoring manual work and self-reliance and the specific skills needed to perform the adult role of an Amish farmer or housewife. In the Amish belief higher learning tends to develop values they reject as influences that alienate man from God. (p. 211)

Second, the Amish argued that the state's concerns—that children be prepared to participate in the political and economic life of the state—did not apply in this case. The Court listened favorably to expert witnesses who explained that the Amish system of home-based vocational training—learning from your parent—worked well for that community, that the community itself was prosperous, and that few Amish were likely to end up unemployed. The Court said:

the value of all education must be assessed in terms of its capacity to prepare the child for life. . . .
It is one thing to say that compulsory education for a year or two beyond the eighth grade may be necessary when its goal is the preparation of the child for life in modern society as the majority live, but it is quite another if the goal of education can

be viewed as the preparation of the child for life in the separated agrarian community that is the keystone of the Amish faith. (p. 222)

What only a few justices saw was that the children themselves were largely ignored in this argument. The Amish wanted to preserve their way of life. The state of Wisconsin wanted to make sure that its citizens could vote wisely and make a living. No justice squarely faced the question of whether the liberal democratic state owes all its citizens, especially children, a right to a basic education that can serve as a building block if the child decides later in life that she wishes to become an astronaut, a playwright, or perhaps to join the army. As we constantly hear from politicians and educators, without a high school diploma one's future is virtually closed. By denying them a high school education or its equivalent, parents are virtually ensuring that their children will remain housewives and agricultural laborers. Even if the children agree, is that a choice parents ought to be allowed to make for them?

From my perspective, the case was decided wrongly. If Wisconsin had good reasons for settling on high school graduation or age sixteen as the legal minimum to which children are entitled, then I think that the Amish children were entitled to that minimum as well, despite their parents' objections. In deciding the issue primarily on grounds that the Amish were not likely to create problems for the state if allowed to keep their children out of school, the Court reflected a rather minimalist form of liberalism. In fact, the abiding interest of this case for many political philosophers lies in the deep conflict it highlights between two different concepts of liberalism: commitment to autonomy and commitment to diversity. William Galston, for example, argues that:

A standard liberal view (or hope) is that these two principles go together and complement one another: the exercise of autonomy yields diversity, while the fact of diversity protects and nourishes autonomy. By contrast, my . . . view is that these principles do not always, perhaps even do not usually, cohere; that in practice, they point in quite different directions in currently disputed areas such as education. . . . Specifically: the decision to throw state power behind the promotion of individual autonomy can weaken or undermine individuals and groups that do not and cannot organize their affairs in accordance with that principle without undermining the deepest sources of their identity.[14]

Galston claims that "properly understood, liberalism is about the protection of diversity, not the valorization of choice . . . To place an ideal of autonomous choice . . . at the core of liberalism is in fact to narrow the range of possibilities available within liberal societies" (p. 523).

One can see this conflict quite sharply if one returns to the work of John Stuart Mill. On the one hand, there is probably no philosopher who gives more weight to the value of individual choice than does Mill. In *On Liberty*, he claims that the very measure of a human being is the extent to which he makes life choices for himself, free of societal pressure:

> *The human faculties of perception, judgment, discriminative feeling, mental activity, and even moral preference, are exercised only in making a choice. He who does anything because it is the custom makes no choice.*[15]

Mill would abhor a situation like that of the Amish communities in *Yoder*, which unabashedly want to give their children as few choices as possible. But, on the other hand, it is clear from both common sense and from Mill's own statements that in order for people to have choices about the pattern of their lives (and to be inspired to create new patterns) there must be more than one type of community available to them. To quote Mill again, "There is no reason that all human existence should be constructed on some one or some small number of patterns" (p. 64). As we look at the last three centuries of American history, we see what an important role different community "patterns" have played, from the Shakers to the Mormons to Bronson Alcott's Fruitlands to the communal experiments of the 1960s. If those patterns are to exhibit the full range of human endeavor and experiment, they must include communities that are distinctly antiliberal. Not only does the panoply of widely different communities enrich our culture, but it also provides a welcome for those who do not fit into the mainstream. As Mill says, "A man cannot get a coat or pair of shoes to fit him unless they are either made to his measure, or he has a whole warehouseful to choose from: and is it easier to fit him with a life than with a coat[?]" (p. 64). Some of us are geniuses who make our lives to "fit our measure," others are happy enough to fit into the mainstream, but for others, the availability of a "warehouseful" of choices increases the possibility of finding a good fit. And for some, a good fit means an authoritarian community based on tradition, where one is freed from the necessity of choice. Thus Galston is correct in pointing to the paradox: if the goal of a liberal democracy is to actively promote something like the greatest number of choices for the greatest number of individuals, this seems to entail hostility toward narrow-choice communities like the Amish. But if the Amish, because of that hostility, fail to flourish, there will be fewer choices available to all.

The compromise I promote is that a liberal state must tolerate even those communities most unsympathetic to the liberal value of individual choice. However, this tolerance must exist within a limiting context, which is the right of individuals to choose which communities they wish to join and to leave if they have a mind to. Even Galston begins with the presumption that society must "defend . . . the liberty not to be coerced into, or trapped within, ways of life. Accordingly, the state must safeguard the ability of individuals to shift allegiances and cross boundaries."[16] Thus, I argue that the autonomy of the individual is ethically prior to the autonomy of the group. Both deals have powerful claims on us, but when group rights would extinguish the abilities of the individuals within them to make their own life choices, then the liberal state must support the individual against the group. This is especially crucial when the individual at issue is a child, who is particularly vulnerable to adult coercion and therefore has particular claims on our protection.

Unfortunately, it is precisely where children are concerned that groups are understandably most jealous of their prerogatives to guide and make decisions. The Amish are an example of a group guarding its ability to shape the lives of its children; Deaf parents wishing to ensure Deaf children are an example of families pursuing the same goals. Of course, groups and families ought to—in fact, they must—strive to shape the values and lives of the children in their care; not to do so leads to social and individual pathology. But when that shaping takes the form of a radically narrow range of choices available to the child when she grows up, when it impinges substantially on the child's right to an open future, then liberalism requires us to intervene to support the child's future ability to make her own choices about which of the many diverse visions of life she wishes to embrace.

But I concede one problem with this point of view. As a liberal who believes that the state should not dictate notions of "the good life," Feinberg believes that the state must be neutral about the goals of education, skewing the question neither in favor of Amish lifestyle nor in favor of the "modern," technological life most Americans accept. The goal of education is to allow the child to make up its own mind from the widest array of options; the best education is the one which gives the child the most open future. A neutral decision would assume only that education should equip the child with the knowledge and skills that will help him choose whichever sort of life best fits his native endowment and matured disposition. It should send him out into the adult world with as many open opportunities as possible, thus maximizing his chances for self-fulfillment.[17]

The problem here is that an education which gave a child this array of choices would quite possibly make it impossible for her to choose to remain Old Order Amish. Her "native endowment and matured disposition" might now have taken her away from the kind of personality and habits that would make Amish life pleasant. Even if she envies the peace, warmth, and security that a life of tradition offers, she may find it impossible to turn her back on "the world," and return to her lost innocence. To quote the Amish, she may have failed irreversibly to "acquire Amish attitudes" during "the crucial and formative adolescent period." This problem raises two issues. First, those of us who would make arguments based on the child's right to an open future need to be clear and appropriately humble about what we are offering. Insisting on a child's right to a high school education may open a future wider than she otherwise could have dreamed, but it also may foreclose one possible future: as a contented member of the Amish community. Second, if the Amish are correct in saying that taking their children out of school at grade eight is crucial for the child's development into a member of the Amish community, then there is no "impartial" stance for the state to take. The state may well be impartial about whether the "better life" is to be found within or without the Amish community, but it cannot act in an impartial fashion. Both forcing the parents to send their children to school or exempting them from the requirement has likely consequences for the child's continued existence within the community when she grows up and is able to make a choice. Feinberg seeks to avoid this second problem by claiming that the neutral state would act to

> let all influences . . . work equally on the child, to open up all possibilities to him, without itself influencing him toward one or another of these. In that way, it can be hoped that the chief determining factor in the grown child's choice of a vocation and life-style will be his own governing values, talents, and propensities. (pp. 134–35)

The problem with this is that, as I understand the Amish way of life, being Amish is precisely not to make one's life choices on the basis of one's own "talents and propensities," but to subordinate those individual leanings to the traditions of the group. If one discovers within oneself a strong passion and talent for jazz dancing, one ought to suppress it, not nurture it.

Is Creating a Deaf Child a Moral Harm?

Now, as we return to the example of the couple who wish to ensure that they bear only deaf children, we have to confront two distinctly different issues. The first is, in what sense is it ever possible to do harm by giving birth to a child who would otherwise not have been born at all? The second is whether being deaf rather than hearing is in fact a harm.

The first issue has been well rehearsed elsewhere.[18] The problem is, how can it be said that one has harmed a child by bringing it into the world with a disability, when the only other choice was for the child not to have existed at all? In the case of a child whose life is arguably not worth living, one can say that life itself is a cruelty to the child. But when a child is born in less than ideal circumstances, or is partially disabled in ways that do not entail tremendous suffering, there seems no way to argue that the child herself has been harmed. This may appear to entail the conclusion, counter to our common moral sense, that therefore no harm has been done. "A wrong action must be bad for someone, but [a] choice to create [a] child with its handicap is bad for no one."[19]

All commentators agree that there is no purely logical way out of what Dan Brock calls the "wrongful handicap" conundrum (p. 272). However, most commentators also agree that one can still support a moral critique of the parents' decision. Bonnie Steinbock and Ron McClamrock argue for a principle of "parental responsibility" by which being a good parent entails refraining from bringing a child into the world when one cannot give it "even a decent chance at a good life."[20] Brock, following Parfit, distinguishes same person from same number choices. In same person choices, the same person exists in each of the alternative courses of action the agent chooses, but the person may exist more or less harmed. In same number choices, "the choice affects who, which child, will exist."[21] Brock claims that moral harms can exist in both instances, despite the fact that in same number choices the moral harm cannot be tied to a specific person. Brock generates the following principle:

> *Individuals are morally required not to let any possible child . . . for whose welfare they are responsible experience serious suffering or limited opportunity if they can act so that, without imposing substantial burdens or costs on themselves or others, any alternative possible child . . . for whose welfare they would be responsible will not experience serious suffering or limited opportunity.* (pp. 272–73)

While agreeing with Brock, Steinbock, and others, I locate the moral harm differently, at least with respect to disabled persons wishing to reproduce themselves in the form of a disabled child. Deliberately creating a child who will be forced irreversibly into the parents' notion of "the good life" violates the Kantian principle of treating each person as an end in herself and never as a means only. All parenthood exists as a balance between fulfillment of parental hopes and values and the individual flowering of the actual child in his or her own direction. The decision to have a child is never made for the sake of the child—for no child then exists. We choose to have children for myriad reasons, but before the child is conceived those reasons can only be self-regarding. The child is a means to our ends: a certain land of joy and pride, continuing the family name, fulfilling religious or societal expectations, and so on. But morally the child is first and foremost an end in herself. Good parenthood requires a balance between having a child for our own sakes and being open to the moral reality that the child will exist for her own sake, with her own talents and weaknesses, propensities and interests, and with her own life to make. Parental practices that close exits virtually forever are insufficiently attentive to the child as end in herself. By closing off the child's right to an open future, they define the child as an entity who exists to fulfill parental hopes and dreams, not her own.

Having evaded the snares of the wrongful handicap conundrum, we must tackle the second problem: is being deaf a harm? At first glance, this might appear as a silly question. Ethically, we would certainly include destroying someone's hearing under the rubric of "harm"; legally, one could undoubtedly receive compensation if one were rendered deaf through someone else's negligence. Many Deaf people, however, have recently been claiming that Deafness is better understood as a cultural identity than as a disability. Particularly in

the wake of the Deaf President Now revolution at Gallaudet University in 1988, Deaf people have been asserting their claims not merely to equal access (through increased technology) but also to equal respect as a cultural minority. As one (hearing) reporter noted:

> *So strong is the feeling of cultural solidarity that many deaf parents cheer on discovering that their baby is deaf. Pondering such a scene, a hearing person can experience a kind of vertigo. The surprise is not simply the unfamiliarity of the views; it is that, as in a surrealist painting, jarring notions are presented as if they were commonplace.[22]*

From this perspective, the use of cochlear implants to enable deaf children to hear, or the abortion of deaf fetuses, is characterized as "genocide."[23] Deaf pride advocates point out that as Deaf people they lack the ability to hear, but they also have many positive gains: a cohesive community, a rich cultural heritage built around the various residential schools, a growing body of drama, poetry, and other artistic traditions, and, of course, what makes all this possible, American Sign Language.[24] Roslyn Rosen, the president of the National Association of the Deaf, is Deaf, the daughter of Deaf parents, and the mother of Deaf children. "I'm happy with who I am," she says, "and I don't want to be 'fixed.' Would an Italian-American rather be a WASP? In our society everyone agrees that whites have an easier time than blacks. But do you think a black person would undergo operations to become white?"[25]

On the other side of the argument is evidence that deafness is a very serious disability. Deaf people have incomes thirty to forty percent below the national average.[26] The state of education for the deaf is unacceptable by anyone's standards; the typical deaf student graduates from high school unable to read a newspaper.[27]

However, one could also point to the lower incomes and inadequate state of education among some racial and ethnic minorities in our country, a situation we do not (or at least ought not) try to ameliorate by eradicating minorities. Deaf advocates often cite the work of Nora Ellen Grace, whose oral history of Martha's Vineyard, *Everyone Here Spoke Sign Language*, tells a fascinating story. For over two hundred years, ending in the middle of the twentieth century, the Vineyard experienced a degree of hereditary deafness exponentially higher than that of the mainland. Although the number of deaf people was low in noncomparative terms (one in 155), the result was a community in which deaf people participated fully in the political and social life of the island, had an economic prosperity on par with their neighbors, and communicated easily with the hearing population, for "everyone here spoke sign language." So endemic was sign language for the general population of the island that hearing islanders often exploited its unique properties even in the absence of deaf people. Old-timers told Groce stories of spouses communicating through sign language when they were outdoors and did not want to raise their voices against the wind. Or men might turn away and finish a "dirty" joke in sign when a woman walked into the general store. At church, deaf parishioners gave their testimony in sign.

As one Deaf activist said, in a comment that could have been directly related to the Vineyard experience, "When Gorbachev visited the U.S., he used an interpreter to talk to the President. Was Gorbachev disabled?"[28] Further, one might argue that, since it is impossible to eradicate deafness completely even if that were a worthy goal, the cause of deaf equality is better served when parents who are proud to be Deaf deliberately have Deaf children who augment and strengthen the existing population. Many of the problems that deaf people experience are the result of being born, without advance warning, to hearing parents. When there is no reason to anticipate the birth of a deaf child, it is often months or years before the child is correctly diagnosed. Meanwhile, she is growing up in a world devoid of language, unable even to communicate with her parents. When the diagnosis is made, her parents first must deal with the emotional shock, and then sort through the plethora of conflicting advice on how best to raise and educate their child. Most probably, they have never met anyone who is deaf. If they choose the route recommended by most Deaf activists and raise their child with sign language, it will take the parents years to learn the language. Meanwhile, their child has missed out on the crucial development of language at the developmentally appropriate time, a lack that is associated with poor reading skills and other problems later (p. 43).

Further, even the most accepting of hearing parents often feel locked in conflict with the Deaf community over who knows what is best for their child. If Deafness truly is a culture rather than a disability, then raising a deaf child is somewhat like white parents trying to raise a black child in contemporary America (with a background chorus of black activists telling them that they can't possibly make a good job of it!). Residential schools, for example, which can be part of the family culture for a Deaf couple, can be seen by hearing parents as Dickensian nightmares or, worse, as a "cultlike" experience in which their children will be lost to them forever.

By contrast, deaf children born to Deaf parents learn language (sign) at the same age as hearing children. They are welcomed into their families and inculcated into Deaf culture in the same way as any other children. Perhaps for these reasons, by all accounts the Deaf of Deaf are the acknowledged leaders of the Deaf Pride movement, and the academic crème de la crème. In evaluating the choice parents make who deliberately ensure that they have Deaf children, we must remember that the statistics and descriptions of deaf life in America are largely reflective of the experience of deaf children born to hearing parents, who make up the vast majority of deaf people today.

But if Deafness is a culture rather than a disability, it is an exceedingly narrow one. One factor that does not seem clear is the extent to which children raised with American Sign Language as their first language ever will be completely comfortable with the written word. (Sign language itself has no written analogue and has a completely different grammatical structure from English.) At present, the conflicted and politicized state of education for the deaf, along with the many hours spent (some would say "wasted") on attempting to teach deaf children oral skills, makes it impossible to know what is to blame for the dismal reading and writing skills of the average deaf person. Some deaf children who are raised with sign language from birth do become skilled readers. But there is reason to question whether a deaf child may have very limited access to the wealth of literature, drama, and poetry that liberals would like to consider every child's birthright.

Although Deaf activists rightly show how many occupations are open to them with only minor technological adjustments, the range of occupations will always be inherently limited. It is not likely that the world will become as Martha's Vineyard, where everyone knew sign. A prelingually deafened person not only cannot hear, but in most instances cannot speak well enough to be understood. This narrow choice of vocation is not only a harm in its own sake but also is likely to continue to lead to lower standards of living. (Certainly one reason why the Vineyard deaf were as prosperous as their neighbors was that farming and fishing were just about the only occupations available.)

Either Way, a Moral Harm

If deafness is considered a disability, one that substantially narrows a child's career, marriage, and cultural options in the future, then deliberately creating a deaf child counts as a moral harm. If Deafness is considered a culture, as Deaf activists would have us agree, then deliberately creating a Deaf child who will have only very limited options to move outside of that culture, also counts as a moral harm. A decision, made before a child is even born, that confines her forever to a narrow group of people and a limited choice of careers, so violates the child's right to an open future that no genetic counseling team should acquiesce in it. The very value of autonomy that grounds the ethics of genetic counseling should preclude assisting parents in a project that so dramatically narrows the autonomy of the child to be.

Coda

Although I rest my case at this point, I want to sketch out some further ramifications of my argument. Are there other, less obvious, ways in which genetic knowledge and manipulation can interfere with the child's right to an open future?

The notion of the child's right to an open future can help in confronting the question of whether to test children for adult-onset genetic diseases, for example Huntington disease.[29] It is well known that the vast majority of adults at risk for Huntington disease choose not to be tested. However, it is not uncommon for parents to request that their children be tested; their goals may be to set their minds at rest, to plan for the future, and so on. On one account, parental authority to make medical decisions suggests that clinicians should accede to these requests (after proper counseling about possible risks). A better account, in my opinion, protects the child's right to an open future by preserving into adulthood his own choice to decide whether his life is better lived with that knowledge or without.[30]

Finally, a provocative argument can be made that sex selection can be deleterious to the child's right to an open future. I am ignoring here all the more obvious arguments against sex selection, even when accomplished without abortion. Rather, I suspect that parents who choose the sex of their offspring are more likely to have gender-specific expectations for those children, expectations that subtly limit the child's own individual flowering. The more we are able to control our children's characteristics (and the more time,

energy, and money we invest in the outcome), the more invested we will become in our hopes and dreams for them. It is easy to sympathize with some of the reasons why parents might want to ensure a girl or boy. People who already have one or two children of one sex can hardly be faulted for wanting to "balance" their families by having one of each. And yet, this ought to be discouraged. If I spent a great deal of time and energy to get a boy in the hope of having a football player in the family, I think I would be less likely to accept it with good grace if the boy hated sports and spent all his spare time at the piano. If I insisted on having a girl because I believed that as a grandparent I would be more likely to have close contact with the children of a daughter than of a son, I think I would find it much harder to raise a girl who saw motherhood as a choice rather than as a foregone conclusion. Parents whose preferences are compelling enough for them to take active steps to control the outcome, must, logically, be committed to certain strong gender-role expectations. If they want a girl that badly, whether they are hoping for a Miss America or the next Catherine McKinnon, they are likely to make it difficult for the actual child to resist their expectations and to follow her own bent.

Acknowledgments

The author is grateful to the Cleveland-Marshall Fund for financial support while writing this article, and to Samuel Gorovitz, Eric Juengst, Thomas H. Murray, Lisa Parker, and Matthew Silliman for their comments on earlier drafts.

References

1. Walter E. Nance, "Parables," in *Prescribing Our Future: Ethical Challenges in Genetic Counseling*, ed. Dianne M. Bartels, Bonnie S. LeRoy, and Arthur L. Caplan (New York Aldine De Gruyter, 1993), p. 92.

2. National Society of Genetic Counselors, Code of Ethics, reprinted in *Prescribing Our Future*, pp. 169–71.

3. James R. Sorenson, "Genetic Counseling: Values That Have Mattered," *Prescribing Our Future*, p. 11; Arthur L. Caplan, "The Ethics of Genetic Counseling," *Prescribing Our Future*, p. 161.

4. Charles Bosk, "Workplace Ideology," *Prescribing Our Future*, pp. 27–28.

5. Dianne M Barteis, "Preface," *Prescribing Our Future*, pp. ix–xiii.

6. Barbara Katz Rothman, *The Tentative Pregnancy: Prenatal Diagnosis and the Future of Motherhood* (New York: Viking Press, 1986), p. 41.

7. Nance, "Parables," p. 92.

8. D. Lindhout, P. G. Frets, and M. C. Niermeijer, "Approaches to Genetic Counseling," *Annals of the New York Academy of Sciences* 630 (1991): 223–29, at 224.

9. Jeffrey R. Botkin, "Fetal Privacy and Confidentiality," *Hasting Center Report* 25, no. 3 (1995): 32–39.

10. President's Commission for the Study of Ethical Problems in Biomedical and Behavioral Research, *Screening and Counseling for Genetic Conditions: A Report on the Ethical, Social, and Legal Implications of Genetic Screening, Counseling, and Education Programs* (Washington, D.C: Government Printing Office, 1983), p. 56.

11. Joel Feinberg, "The Child's Right to an Open Future," in *Whose Child? Children's Rights, Parental Authority, and State Power*, ed. William Aiken and Hugh LaFollette (Totowa, N.J.: Littlefield, Adams & Co., 1980), pp. 124–53.

12. *Prince v. Massachusetts*, 321 U.S. 158 (1944), at 170.

13. *Wisconsin v. Yoder*, 406 U.S. 205 (1972).

14. William Gals ton, "Two Concepts of Liberalism," *Ethics* 105, no. 3 (1995): 516–34, at 521.

15. John Stuart Mill, *On Liberty* (New York W.W. Norton, 1975), p. 55.

16. Galston, "Two Concepts of Liberalism," p. 522.

17. Feinberg, "The Child's Right" pp. 134–35.

18. Cynthia Cohen, "'Give Me Children or I Shall Die!' New Reproductive Technologies and Harm to Children," *Hastings Center Report* 26, no. 2 (1996): 19–29.

19. Dan Brock, "The Non-Identity Problem and Genetic Harms," *Bioethics* 9, no. 3/4 (1995): 269–75, at 271.

20. Bonnie Steinbock and Ron McClamrock, "When Is Birth Unfair to the Child?" *Hastings Center Report* 24, no. 6 (1994): 15–21, at p. 17.

21. Brock, "The Non-Identity Problem," p. 272.

22. Edward Dohick "Deafness as Culture," *The Atlantic Monthly* 272/3 (1993): 37–53.

23. Amy Elizabeth Biusky, "Making Decisions for Deaf Children Regarding Cochlear Implants: The Legal Ramifications of Recognizing Deafness as a Culture Rather than a Disability," *Wisconsin Law Review* (1995); 235–70.

24. John B. Christiansen, "Sociological Implications of Hearing Loss," *Annals of the New York Academy of Science* 630 (1991): 230–35.

25. Dolnick, "Deafness as Culture," p. 38.

26. Nora Ellen Grace, *Everyone Here Spoke Sign Language: Hereditary Deafness on Martha's Vineyard* (Cambridge: Harvard University Press, 1985), p. 85.

27. Andrew Solomon, "Defiantly Deaf," *New York Times Magazine*, 28 August 1994: 40–45 et passim.

28. Dolnick, "Deafness as Culture," p. 43.

29. I am grateful to Thomas H. Murray and Ronald M. Green for bringing this topic to my attention.

30. "The Genetic Testing of Children," *Journal of Medical Genetics* 31 (1994): 785–97.

Section 2:   Genetic Selection: A New Eugenics?

Procreative Beneficence: Why We Should Select the Best Children

Julian Savulescu

Julian Savulescu argues that if tests for nondisease genes become available, we have a moral obligation to use them in making decisions about reproduction. Because disease-causing genes reduce the well-being of a person, what he calls the "principle of Procreative Benevolence" directs us to select against them. It isn't the disease itself we are selecting against Savulescu claims, but its impact on a life. But nondisease genes can also have an impact. Intelligence, for example, can also affect well-being. Thus, genetic information about qualities relevant to it should be used to select the embryo or fetus, with the aim of producing a life of the greatest well-being.

Procreative Beneficence, Savulescu holds, must be balanced against Procreative Autonomy. Even so, doctors should try to persuade potential parents to seek out and use genetic information that will let them select for the greatest possible well-being in the life to be created.

Julian Savulescu, From "Procreative Beneficence: Why We Should Select the Best Children," *Bioethics*, Vol. 15 (Oct. 2001): 414–426. Copyright © 2001 Wiley-Blackwell Ltd. Reprinted by permission.

Introduction

Imagine you are having in vitro fertilization (IVF) and you produce four embryos. One is to be implanted. You are told that there is a genetic test for predisposition to scoring well on IQ tests (let's call this intelligence). If an embryo has gene subtypes (alleles) A, B there is a greater than 50% chance it will score more than 140 if given an ordinary education and upbringing. If it has subtypes C, D there is a much lower chance it will score over 140. Would you test the four embryos for these gene subtypes and use this information in selecting which embryo to implant?

Many people believe intelligence is a purely social construct and so it is unlikely to have a significant genetic cause. Others believe there are different sorts of intelligence, such as verbal intelligence, mathematical intelligence, musical ability and no such thing as general intelligence. Time will tell. There are several genetic research programs currently in place which seek to elucidate the genetic contribution to intelligence. This paper pertains to any results of this research even if it only describes a weak probabilistic relation between genes and intelligence, or a particular kind of intelligence.

Many people believe that research into the genetic contribution to intelligence should not be performed, and that if genetic tests which predict intelligence, or a range of intelligence, are ever developed, they should not be employed in reproductive decision-making. I will argue that we have a moral obligation to test for genetic contribution to non-disease states such as intelligence and to use this information in reproductive decision-making.

Imagine now you are invited to play the Wheel of Fortune. A giant wheel exists with marks on it from 0–$1,000,000, in $100 increments. The wheel is spun in a secret room. It stops randomly on an amount. That amount is put into Box A. The wheel is spun again. The amount which comes up is put into Box B. You can choose Box A or B. You are also told that, in addition to the sum already put in the boxes, if you choose B, a [die] will be thrown and you will lose $100 if it comes up 6.

Which box should you choose?

The rational answer is Box A. Choosing genes for non-disease states is like playing the Wheel of Fortune. You should use all the available information and choose the option most likely to bring about the best outcome.

Procreative Beneficence: The Moral Obligation to Have the Best Children

I will argue for a principle which I call Procreative Beneficence:

> *couples (or single reproducers) should select the child, of the possible children they could have, who is expected to have the best life, or at least as good a life as the others, based on the relevant, available information.*

I will argue that Procreative Beneficence implies couples should employ genetic tests for non-disease traits in selecting which child to bring into existence and that we should allow selection for non-disease genes in some cases even if this maintains or increases social inequality.

By "should" in "should choose," I mean "have good reason to." I will understand morality to require us to do what we have most reason to do. In the absence of some other reason for action, a person who has good reason to have the best child is morally required to have the best child.

Consider the following three situations involving normative judgements.

1. "You are 31. You will be at a higher risk of infertility and having a child with an abnormality if you delay child-bearing. But that has to be balanced against taking time out of your career now. That's only something you can weigh up."

2. "You should stop smoking."

3. "You must inform your partner that you are HIV positive or practise safe sex."

The "should" in "should choose the best child" is that present in the second example. It implies that persuasion is justified, but not coercion, which would be justified in the third case. Yet the situation is different from the more morally neutral (1).

Definitions

A disease gene is a gene which causes a genetic disorder (e.g. cystic fibrosis) or predisposes to the development of disease (e.g. the genetic contribution to cancer or dementia). A non-disease gene is a gene which causes or predisposes to some physical or psychological state of the person which is not itself a disease state, e.g. height, intelligence, character (not in the subnormal range).

Selection

It is currently possible to select from a range of possible children we could have. This is most frequently done by employing fetal selection through prenatal testing and termination of pregnancy. Selection of embryos is now possible by employing in vitro fertilization and preimplantation genetic diagnosis (PGD). There are currently no genetic tests available for non-disease states except sex. However, if such tests become available in the future, both PGD and prenatal testing could be used to select offspring on the basis of non-disease genes. Selection of sex by PGD is now undertaken in Sydney, Australia.[1] PGD will also lower the threshold for couples to engage in selection since it has fewer psychological sequelae than prenatal testing and abortion.

In the future, it may be possible to select gametes according to their genetic characteristics. This is currently possible for sex, where methods have been developed to sort X and Y bearing sperm.[2]

Behavioural Genetics

Behavioural Genetics is a branch of genetics which seeks to understand the contribution of genes to complex behaviour. The scope of behavioural genetics is illustrated in Table 1.

An Argument for Procreative Beneficence

Consider the *Simple Case of Selection for Disease Genes.* A couple is having IVF in an attempt to have a child. It produces two embryos. A battery of tests for common diseases is performed. Embryo A has no abnormalities on the tests performed. Embryo B has no abnormalities on the tests performed except its genetic profile reveals it has a predisposition to developing asthma. Which embryo should be implanted?

Embryo B has nothing to be said in its favour over A and something against it. Embryo A should (on pain of irrationality) be implanted. This is like choosing Box A in the Wheel of Fortune analogy.

Why shouldn't we select the embryo with a predisposition to asthma? What is relevant about asthma is that it reduces quality of life. Attacks cause severe breathlessness and in extreme cases, death. Steroids may be required to treat it. These are among the most dangerous drugs which exist if taken long term. Asthma can be lifelong and require lifelong drug treatment. Ultimately it can leave the sufferer wheel chair bound with chronic obstructive airways disease. The

TABLE 1: BEHAVIOURAL GENETICS
Aggression and criminal behaviour
Alcoholism
Anxiety and Anxiety disorders
Attention Deficit Hyperactivity Disorder (ADHD)
Antisocial personality disorder
Bipolar disorder
Homosexuality
Maternal behaviour
Memory and intelligence
Neuroticism
Novelty seeking
Schizophrenia
Substance addiction

morally relevant property of "asthma" is that it is a state which reduces the well-being a person experiences.

Partitian Defence of Voluntary Procreative Beneficence in the Simple Case

The following example, after Parfit,[3] supports Procreative Beneficence. A woman has rubella. If she conceives now, she will have a blind and deaf child. If she waits three months, she will conceive another different but healthy child. She should choose to wait until her rubella is passed.

Or consider the Nuclear Accident. A poor country does not have enough power to provide power to its citizens during an extremely cold winter. The government decides to open an old and unsafe nuclear reactor. Ample light and heating are then available. Citizens stay up later, and enjoy their lives much more. Several months later, the nuclear reactor melts down and large amounts of radiation are released into the environment. The only effect is that a large number of children are subsequently born with predispositions to early childhood malignancy.

The supply of heating and light has changed the lifestyle of this population. As a result of this change in lifestyle, people have conceived children at different times than they would have if there had been no heat or light, and their parents went to bed earlier. Thus, the children born after the nuclear accident would not have existed if the government had not switched to nuclear power. They have not been harmed by the switch to nuclear power and the subsequent accident (unless their lives are so bad they are worse than death). If we object to the Nuclear Accident (which most of us would), then we must appeal to some form of harmless wrong-doing. That is, we must claim that a wrong was done, but no one was harmed. We must appeal to something like the Principle of Procreative Beneficence.

An Objection to Procreative Beneficence in the Simple Case

The following objection to Procreative Beneficence is common.

> "If you choose Embryo A (without a predisposition to asthma), you could be discarding someone like Mozart or an Olympic swimmer. So there is no good Reason to select A."

It is true that by choosing A, you could be discarding a person like Mozart. But it is equally true that if you choose B, you could be discarding someone like Mozart without asthma. A and B are equally likely (on the information available) to be someone like Mozart (and B is more likely to have asthma).

Other Principles of Reproductive Decision-Making Applied to the Simple Case

The principle of Procreative Beneficence supports selecting the embryo without the genetic predisposition to asthma. That seems intuitively correct. How do other principles of reproductive decision-making apply to this example?

1. *Procreative Autonomy:* This principle claims that couples should be free to decide when and how to procreate, and what kind of children to have.[4] If this were the only decision-guiding principle, it would imply couples might have reason to choose the embryo with a predisposition to asthma, if for some reason they wanted that.

2. *Principle of Non-Directive Counselling:* According to this principle, doctors and genetic counselors should only provide information about risk and options available to reduce that risk.[5] They should not give advice or other direction. Thus, if a couple wanted to transfer Embryo B, and they knew that it would have a predisposition to asthma, nothing more is to be said according to Non-Directive Counselling.

3. *The "Best Interests of the Child" Principle:* Legislation in Australia and the United Kingdom related to reproduction gives great weight to consideration of the best interests of the child. For example, the Victorian Infertility Treatment Act 1995 states *"the welfare and interests of any person born or to be born as a result of a treatment procedure are paramount."*[6] This principle is irrelevant to this choice. This couple could choose the embryo with the predisposition to asthma and still be doing everything possible in the interests of *that* child.

None of the alternative principles give appropriate direction in the Simple Case.

Moving from Disease Genes to Non-Disease Genes: What Is the "Best Life"?

It is not asthma (or disease) which is important, but its impact on a life in ways that matter which is important. People often trade length of life for non-health related well-being. Non-disease genes may prevent us from leading the best life.

By "best life," I will understand the life with the most well-being. There are various theories of well-being: hedonistic, desire-fulfilment, objective list theories.[7] According to hedonistic theories, what matters is the quality of our experiences, for example, that we experience pleasure. According to desire-fulfilment theories, what matters is the degree to which our desires are satisfied. According to objective list theories, certain activities are good for people, such as achieving worthwhile things with your life, having dignity having children and raising them, gaining knowledge of the world, developing one's talents, appreciating beautiful things, and so on.

On any of these theories, some non-disease genes will affect the likelihood that we will lead the best life. Imagine there is a gene which contributes significantly to a violent, explosive, uncontrollable temper, and that state causes people significant suffering. Violent outbursts lead a person to come in conflict with the law and fall out of important social relations. The loss of independence, dignity and important social relations are bad on any of the three accounts.

Buchanan et al. argue that what is important in a liberal democracy is providing people with general purpose means, i.e. those useful to any plan of life.[8] In this way we can allow people to form and act on their own conception of the good life. Examples of general purpose means are the ability to hear and see. But similarly the ability to concentrate, to engage with and be empathetic towards other human beings may be all purpose means. To the degree that genes contribute to these, we have reason to select those genes.

Consider another example. Memory (M) is the ability to remember important things when you want to. Imagine there is some genetic contribution to M: Six alleles (genes) contribute to M. IVF produces four embryos. Should we test for M profiles?

Does M relate to well-being? Having to go to the supermarket twice because you forgot the baby formula prevents you doing more worthwhile things. Failing to remember can have disastrous consequences. Indeed, forgetting the compass on a long bush walk can be fatal. There is, then, a positive obligation to test for M and select the embryo (other things being equal) with the best M profile.

Does being intelligent mean one is more likely to have a better life? At a folk intuitive level, it seems plausible that intelligence would promote well-being on any plausible account of well-being. On a hedonistic account, the capacity to imagine alternative pleasures and remember the salient features of past experiences is important in choosing the best life. On a desire-fulfilment theory, intelligence is important to choosing means which will best satisfy one's ends. On an objective list account, intelligence would be important to gaining knowledge of the world, and developing rich social relations. Newson has reviewed the empirical literature relating intelligence to quality of life. Her synthesis of the empirical literature is that "intelligence has a high instrumental value for persons in giving them a large amount of complexity with which to approach their everyday lives, and that it equips them with a tool which can lead to the provision of many other personal and social goods."[9]

Socrates, in Plato's Philebus, concludes that the best life is a mixture of wisdom and pleasure. Wisdom includes thought intelligence, knowledge and memory.[10] Intelligence is clearly a part of Plato's conception of the good life:

> without the power of calculation you could not even calculate that you will get enjoyment in the future; your life would be that not of a man, but of a sea-lung or one of those marine creatures whose bodies are confined by a shell.[11]

Choice of Means of Selecting

This argument extends in principle to selection of fetuses using prenatal testing and termination of affected pregnancy. However, selection by abortion

has greater psychological harms than selection by PGD and these need to be considered. Gametic selection, if it is ever possible, will have the lower psychological cost.

Objections to the Principle of Procreative Beneficence Applied to Non-Disease Genes

1. Harm to the Child. One common objection to genetic selection for non-disease traits is that it results in harm to the child. There are various versions of this objection, which include the harm which arises from excessive and overbearing parental expectations, using the child as a means, and not treating it as an end, and closing off possible future options on the basis of the information provided (failing to respect the child's "right to an open future").

There are a number of responses. Firstly, in some cases, it is possible to deny that the harms will be significant. Parents come to love the child whom they have (even a child with a serious disability). Moreover, some have argued that counselling can reduce excessive expectations.[12]

Secondly, we can accept some risk of a child experiencing some state of reduced well-being in cases of selection. One variant of the harm to child objection is: "If you select embryo A, it might still get asthma, or worse, cancer, or have a much worse life than B, and you would be responsible." Yet selection is immune to this objection (in a way which genetic manipulation is not).

Imagine you select Embryo A and it develops cancer (or severe asthma) in later life. You have not harmed A unless A's life is not worth living (hardly plausible) because A would not have existed if you had acted otherwise. A is not made worse off than A would otherwise have been, since without the selection, A would not have existed. Thus we can accept the possibility of a bad outcome, but not the probability of a very bad outcome. (Clearly, Procreative Beneficence demands that we not choose a child with a low predisposition to asthma but who is likely to have a high predisposition to cancer.)

This is different from genetic manipulation. Imagine you perform gene therapy to correct a predisposition to asthma and you cause a mutation which results in cancer later in life. You have harmed A: A is worse off in virtue of the genetic manipulation than A would have been if the manipulation had not been performed (assuming cancer is worse than asthma).

There is, then, an important distinction between:

* interventions which are genetic manipulations of a single gamete, embryo or fetus

* selection procedures (e.g. sex selection) which select from among a range of different gametes, embryos and fetuses.

2. Inequality. One objection to Procreative Beneficence is that it will maintain or increase inequality. For example, it is often argued that selection for sex, intelligence, favourable physical or psychological traits, etc. all contribute to inequality in society, and this is a reason not to attempt to select the best.

In the case of selection against disease genes, similar claims are made. For example, one version of the *Disability Discrimination Claim* maintains that prenatal testing for disabilities such as Down syndrome results in discrimination against those with those disabilities both by:

* the statement it makes about the worth of such lives

* the reduction in the numbers of people with this condition.

Even if the Disability Discrimination Claim were true, it would be a drastic step in favour of equality to inflict a higher risk of having a child with a disability on a couple (who do not want a child with a disability) to promote social equality.

Consider a hypothetical rubella epidemic. A rubella epidemic hits an isolated population. Embryos produced prior to the epidemic are not at an elevated risk of any abnormality but those produced during the epidemic are at an increased risk of deafness and blindness. Doctors should encourage women to use embryos which they have produced prior to the epidemic in preference to ones produced during the epidemic. The reason is that it is bad that blind and deaf children are born when sighted and hearing children could have been born in their place.

This does not necessarily imply that the lives of those who now live with disability are less deserving of respect and are less valuable. To attempt to prevent accidents which cause paraplegia is not to say that paraplegics are less deserving of respect. It is important to distinguish between disability and persons with disability. Selection reduces the former, but is silent on the value of the latter. There are better ways to make statements about the equality of people with disability (e.g., we could direct savings from selection against embryos/fetuses with genetic abnormalities to improving well-being of existing people with disabilities).

These arguments extend to selection for non-disease genes. It is not disease which is important but its impact on well-being. In so far as a non-disease gene such as a gene for intelligence impacts on a person's well-being, parents have a reason to select for it, even if inequality results.

This claim can have counter-intuitive implications. Imagine in a country women are severely discriminated against. They are abandoned as children, refused paid employment and serve as slaves to men. Procreative Beneficence implies that couples should test for sex, and should choose males as they are expected to have better lives in this society, even if this reinforces the discrimination against women.

There are several responses. Firstly, it is unlikely selection on a scale that contributes to inequality would promote well-being. Imagine that 50% of the population choose to select boys. This would result in three boys to every one girl. The life of a male in such a society would be intolerable.

Secondly, it is social institutional reform, not interference in reproduction, which should be promoted. What is wrong in such a society is the treatment of women, which should be addressed separately to reproductive decision-making. Reproduction should not become an instrument of social change, at least not mediated or motivated at a social level.

This also illustrates why Procreative Beneficence is different from eugenics. Eugenics is selective breeding to produce a better *population*. A *public interest* justification for interfering in reproduction is different from, Procreative Beneficence which aims at producing the best child, of the possible children, a couple could have. That is an essentially private enterprise. It was the eugenics movement itself which sought to influence reproduction, through involuntary sterilisation, to promote social goods.

Thirdly, consider the case of blackmail. A company says it will only develop an encouraging drug for cystic fibrosis (CF) if there are more than 100,000 people with CF. This would require stopping carrier testing for CF. Should the government stop carrier testing?

If there are other ways to fund this research (e.g., government funding), this should have priority. In virtually all cases of social inequality, there are other avenues to correct inequality than encouraging or forcing people to have children with disabilities or lives of restricted genetic opportunity.

Limits on Procreative Beneficence: Personal Concern for Equality or Self Interest

Consider the following cases. David and Dianne are dwarfs. They wish to use IVF and PGD to select a child with dwarfism because their house is set up for dwarfs. Sam and Susie live in a society where discrimination against women is prevalent. They wish to have a girl to reduce this discrimination. These choices would not harm the child produced if selection is employed. Yet they conflict with the Principle of Procreative Beneficence.

We have here an irresolvable conflict of principles:

* personal commitment to equality, personal interests and Procreative Autonomy

* Procreative Beneficence.

Just as there are no simple answers to what should be done (from the perspective of ethics) when respect for personal autonomy conflicts with other principles such as beneficence or distributive justice, so too there are no simple answers to conflict between Procreative Autonomy and Procreative Beneficence.

For the purposes of public policy, there should be a presumption in favour of liberty in liberal democracies. So, ultimately, we should allow couples to make their own decisions about which child to have. Yet this does not imply that there are no normative principles to guide those choices. Procreative Beneficence is a valid principle, albeit one which must be balanced against others.

The implication of this is that those with disabilities should be allowed to select a child with disability, if they have a good reason. But the best option is that we correct discrimination in other ways, by correcting discriminatory social institutions. In this way, we can achieve both equality and a population whose members are living the best lives possible.

Conclusions

With respect to non-disease genes, we should provide:

* information (through PGD and prenatal testing)

* free choice of which child to have

* non-coercive advice as to which child will be expected to enter life with the best opportunity of having the best life.

Selection for non-disease genes which significantly impact on well-being is *morally required* (Procreative Beneficence). "Morally required" implies moral persuasion but not coercion is justified.

If, in the end, couples wish to select a child who will have a lower chance of having the best life, they should be free to make such a choice. That should not prevent doctors from attempting to persuade

them to have the best child they can. In some cases, persuasion will not be justified. If self-interest or concern to promote equality motivate a choice to select less than the best, then there may be no overall reason to attempt to dissuade a couple. But in cases in which couples do not want to use or obtain available information about genes which will affect well-being, and their desires are based on irrational fears (e.g., about interfering with nature or playing God), then doctors should try to persuade them to access and use such information in their reproductive decision-making.

Notes

1. J. Savulescu. Sex Selection—the case for. *Medical Journal of Australia 1999*; 171:373–5.

2. E.F. Fugger, S.H. Black, K. Keyvanfar, J.D. Schulman. Births of normal daughters after Microsoft sperm separation and intrauterine insemination, in-vitro fertilization, or intracytoplasmic sperm injection. *Hum Reprod* 1998; 13:2367–70.

3. D. Parfit. 1976. Rights, Interests and Possible People, in *Moral Problems in Medicine*, S. Gorovitz, et al., eds. Englewood Cliffs. Prentice Hall; D. Parfit 1984. *Reasons and Persons*. Oxford. Clarendon Press: Part IV.

4. R. Dworkin. 1993. *Life's Dominion: An Argument about Abortion and Euthanasia*. London. Harper Collins; J. Harris. Goodbye Dolly? The ethics of human cloning. *Journal of Medical Ethics* 1997; 23:353–60; J. Harris. 1998. Rights and Reproductive Choice, in *The Future of Reproduction*, J. Harris and S. Holm, eds. Oxford. Clarendon Press; J A. Robertson. 1994. *Children of Choice: Freedom, and the New Reproductive Technologies*. Princeton. Princeton University Press; C Strong. 1997. *Ethics in reproductive and perinatal medicine*. New Haven. Yale University Press.

5. J.A.F. Roberts. 1959. *An introduction to human genetics*. Oxford. OUP.

6. The *Human Fertilization and Embryology Act of 1990* in England requires that account be taken of the welfare of any child who will be born by assisted reproduction before issuing a license for assistance (S.13(5)).

7. Parfit, *op. cit.*, Appendix I., pp. 493–502; Griffin. 1986. *Well-Being*. Oxford. Clarendon Press.

8. A. Buchanan, D.W. Brock, N. Daniels, D. Wikler. 2000. *From Chance to Choice*. Cambridge. CUP: 167. Buchanan and colleagues argue in a parallel way for the permissibility of genetic manipulation (enhancement) to allow children to live the best life possible (Chapter Five). They do not consider selection in this context.

9. A. Newson. The value of intelligence and its implications for genetic research. *Fifth World Congress of Bioethics*. Imperial College, London, 21–24 September 2000.

10. *Philebus* 21 C1–12. A.E. Taylor's translation. 1972. Folkstone. Dawsons of Pall Mall: 21 D 11–3. E 1–3.

11. *Philebus* 21 C1–12.

12. J. Robertson. Preconception Sex Selection. *American Journal of Bioethics* 1:1 (Winter 2001).

Section 3:   Genetics and Abortion

Fetal Privacy and Confidentiality

Jeffrey R. Botkin

Botkin argues for placing legal and ethical limits on prenatal testing. A woman's right to get information about her fetus, he claims, is not derived from the right to privacy, which justifies her decision to have an abortion. Rather, it is derived from the doctrine of informed consent. When she seeks prenatal care, she is entitled to receive information not only about herself, but about the health of her fetus.

Even so, as with other sorts of communication between a doctor and a patient, the information the doctor should disclose is subject to rational limits. These limits include protecting the fetus's right to privacy, a right that must be balanced against the potential harm the birth of the fetus poses for the parents. Prenatal testing is justified, Botkin concludes, when the harm the fetus poses is similar in magnitude to the birth of an unwanted child.

. . . In this article, I develop an argument for legal and ethical limitations on the application of prenatal testing and screening technology. The issues of choice in this context are substantially different from the issues in the classic abortion debate. Different rights and interests are involved in prenatal screening and selective abortion, and a different framework must be maintained to debate the moral issues in this context. I will suggest that for some medical conditions, respect for the privacy and confidentiality of the fetus outweigh parental rights to information about the fetus. Preliminary definitions for what constitute "serious defects" and "minor conditions" will be developed.

At the outset, I emphasize that the limitations under discussion for prenatal technology are both legal and ethical in nature. The argument is for a "standard of care" for prenatal services. As such, if practitioners perform below such a standard, meaning that they provide insufficient information, they are at risk for legal sanctions, such as malpractice claims. However, if practitioners provide much more information than the standard outlines, then they are at risk for condemnation on ethical, but not legal grounds. Our medical system is a relatively open market in which services are rarely

prohibited, at least for those who can pay for them. A relevant example is the moratorium on cystic fibrosis (CF) carrier screening in the general population that was advocated by both the American Society of Human Genetics and a National Institutes of Health workshop shortly after the identification of the gene.[1] Health care providers and technology vendors generally honored this moratorium without any significant discussion of legal prohibitions on CF screening. Further, the practical difficulties of prohibiting some approaches to prenatal testing and abortion while permitting others would be substantial. Therefore, the argument to follow does not suggest that prenatal testing for, say, sex selection should be prohibited by law, but rather that it should be made clear that the use of certain technologies is not the standard of practice for the profession, and, further, that their use is contrary to the ethical norms of the profession. This will permit some parents and physicians to proceed with testing against prevailing standards, although we can hope that the force of clearly articulated and generally accepted ethical norms will make such decisions rare.

Justifications for Abortion

It is important to distinguish between the two general justifications for abortion. In the first, the woman chooses to terminate the pregnancy because she does not want to bear a child. In the second, the woman chooses abortion because she does not want to bear this particular child. If the morality of abortion hinges on balancing relevant interests of the fetus and the mother, then this distinction becomes crucial in delineating the moral obligations of physicians to women in the context of prenatal testing and screening. It is important to emphasize that I will not address the issue of whether selective abortion can be a benefit to the fetus. The focus is whether a hereditary or congenital condition poses a sufficient burden to the family to justify prenatal diagnosis. If, in selected cases, it can be argued convincingly that selective abortion is a net benefit to the fetus, this will not change the conclusions developed here since abortion in these cases will also be justified by the burden to the family.

The Roe v. Wade decision remains the foundation of abortion rights in the U.S., so it is useful to return to the specific arguments of the case. The decision developed a complex scheme to balance the state's interest in fetal life with a woman's constitutional right to privacy. The opinion noted specifically that the right to privacy was not absolute and was subject to limitation for the protection of "health, medical standards, and prenatal life." In the balance with the state's interest in potential life was the mother's right to privacy. The right in this context was supported by the gravity of the consequences for the pregnant woman should the abortion option not be available:

Maternity, or additional offspring, may force upon the woman a distressful life and future. Psychological harm may be imminent. Mental and physical health may be taxed by child care. There is also the distress, for all concerned, associated with the unwanted child, and there is the problem of bringing a child into a family already unable, psychologically and otherwise, to care for it.[2]

In the case of an unwanted pregnancy, the prevailing social standard after Roe is that the mother's interest in avoiding the burdens of pregnancy and motherhood outweighs the interest in life or potential life for the fetus.

Two points are important here. First, the right of privacy protecting the abortion decision is not absolute, and is explicitly justified by the burdens of an unwanted pregnancy and motherhood. Second, the right of privacy entitles a woman to pursue an abortion without substantial interference from the state. States may erect some barriers to obtaining the procedure, such as waiting periods and parental notification for minors, but to a large extent a woman is free to have an abortion for any reason that she believes is sufficient. The right of privacy is the right to be left alone

to make and enact this decision. But privacy rights do not provide good leverage for obtaining help from others in carrying out an abortion decision. The right to be left alone to enact personal decisions does not entail a corresponding obligation for others to assist. The obligation for others is simply not to erect unreasonable obstacles. This framework has been the justification for not providing federal funding for nontherapeutic abortions through the Medicaid program or federal block grants.[3] Similarly, individual physicians or hospitals need not provide abortions, and a large number have chosen not to do so. Thus costs and limited access to services may create substantial barriers to women seeking an abortion, and while this may be poor public policy, it is not an infringement on the right of privacy for women.

Genetic information about the fetus can be considered in the same context. Failure to give specific information about the fetus to the prospective parents cannot be considered an infringement on their right to privacy in making an abortion decision. The only information required to fulfill a privacy right is simply the information that the woman is pregnant. From the recognition of the pregnancy on, it is the woman's right to decide if she wishes to remain pregnant. This right remains intact whether or not the parents are provided any information about the fetus.

So the "right to choose" under a privacy doctrine does not require that prenatal diagnostic information be provided. But rights to privacy are not the only rights held by women with respect to their bodies. Pregnancy is considered a medical condition that is attended to by physicians. In the course of prenatal care, women expect to be provided information about their own health and the health of the fetus. One reason that information about the fetus is desired by some women is to make a decision about a pregnancy termination. But there is also a strong desire just to know whether everything is okay. Many women who state they would not consider a pregnancy termination are still interested in obtaining prenatal information about their fetus.[4]

A right to prenatal information about the fetus is becoming increasingly well established in tort law through "wrongful birth" claims. Under a wrongful birth claim, parents may bring suit against a physician if the physician failed to warn prospective parents of an increased risk of bearing a child with congenital impairments. The parents claim they were denied the opportunity to detect the abnormality prenatally and terminate the pregnancy. The most common clinical circumstance leading to a wrongful birth claim is a woman of "advanced maternal age" who is not warned of an increased risk of an infant with Trisomy 21, and subsequently gives birth to an affected child. These suits have been accepted in the majority of jurisdictions in which they have been tried.[5]

While there has been some controversy on the issue, the appropriate foundation for wrongful birth claims is the doctrine of informed consent.[6] If pregnancy is considered a medical condition, then pregnant women have the right under informed consent to receive information about the status of the pregnancy including the health of the fetus. Assuring the health of the fetus is a primary reason that many women seek prenatal care; thus informed consent to ongoing prenatal care must include information about both mother and child, and the available options to assess the health of the child. However, the concept of informed consent in any medical context has never required physicians to provide a comprehensive catalogue of information to patients. Disclosure of information has generally been limited to that information which other competent providers would offer in similar circumstances (the professional practice standard); or that information which a reasonable person would want in the situation at hand (the reasonable person standard). Any limitations on information pertain both to the options that are offered to patients, and to the information about a condition or treatment. The point here is that the right to information about the fetus can be limited on rational grounds if that right is based on informed consent. This analysis is consistent with current practice. For example, amniocentesis is usually not offered to pregnant women who are younger than 35 years of age.

This analysis suggests that the right to information about the fetus is not based on the right to privacy, but rather on the right to informed consent. This permits consideration of limits on information, but it does not offer any obvious guidelines for developing these limits for future technology. Clearly, the current professional standard for information provides little guidance for the use of technologies that have yet to be developed. Further, prenatal screening and selective abortion are so value laden that it is difficult to outline what a hypothetical "reasonable person" would want with respect to information about her fetus. In general terms, we can assume that reasonable people would want to know about conditions in a child that would result in significant harm to them and their family.

One solution to the dilemma of establishing appropriate standards would be to recognize the value-laden aspect of prenatal diagnosis and to carve out a unique niche for this technology that would require complete disclosure. A full disclosure standard would require that the pregnant woman be informed about and offered the complete range of genetic tests currently available. Further, any facts about the fetus that might be detected with screening or testing would be disclosed to the parents. Failure to offer testing followed by the birth of an affected child could result in a wrongful birth claim.

Such a broad standard would have several undesirable effects. First, it would be difficult for physicians to keep up to date on testing and screening technology as a large number of genetic conditions are mapped in the genome. A doctrine of full disclosure would require that physicians be aware of the full range of diagnostic capabilities, not just those emerging tests that detect common and/or severe conditions. Patients would need to be informed of the full range of tests as well. This would place a substantial, and probably unrealistic burden on medical professionals for both knowledge and time, and it would be difficult for couples to come to meaningful decisions. Second, the expense of laboratory services and counseling might become substantial if prenatal genetic testing and screening became widespread. Third, as long as the primary reason for obtaining prenatal genetic information is to decide about a pregnancy termination, the provision of some information may be contrary to the moral standards of some physicians. For pro-choice and pro-life individuals alike, the termination of a pregnancy for any reason carries significant moral weight. Many health care providers would be deeply troubled by the use of professional services for the termination of a pregnancy for mild or non-health-related conditions.

Fourth, and perhaps most importantly, there must be a concern for the basic integrity of the individual. In this case, it is the individual that the fetus will become. This concern arises primarily in those circumstances in which parents will have control over the choice of embryos or, eventually, over the specific genetic attributes of their embryo. The richness of human variety is genetic in part. Much of what we are can be seen in our parents, which is attributable to genes, parenting efforts, and modeling behaviors. Parents have significant control over the social and physical environment of the child, but no control over their own genetic influences. The question that is emerging is whether it is desirable to permit parents social, environmental, and biologic control over children. The issue is one of independence and individuality in their deepest senses. Such control may have a powerful psychological effect. It is certainly common enough now that children of all ages blame their parents for their faults. Oscar Wilde observed, "Children begin by loving their parents. After a time they judge them. Rarely, if ever, do they forgive them." We must be seriously concerned about the psychological implications for both children and parents of the knowledge (or fear) that we were carefully selected or even made to be the way we are. While there might be satisfaction all around for a child well made, there may also be a loss of full authorship in victory, and broader grounds for resentment in failure.

Further, there are potential harms even if genetic information is not used to terminate the pregnancy or to select the "ideal" embryo. Simple knowledge of the child's genetic makeup may profoundly alter the parent–child relationship. Children may be channeled into, or away from, certain activities or lifestyles without regard to the child's interests or demonstrated aptitudes. Strong parental expectations based on genetic testing may significantly limit a child's personal freedom. Children who are perceived as "predisposed" to certain health problems or behaviors may be excessively controlled or treated as fragile. A belief in "genetic determinism" by parents may severely limit the child's ability to find and chart his or her own course in life. For these reasons, detailed genetic information about the fetus or embryo may lead to a variety of harms beyond the destruction of a fetus from pregnancy termination.

Through this discussion, I have suggested that prospective parents do not have a right under informed consent to all information they might desire about their fetus. Further, there are significant harms to the fetus, the future child, the parent–child relationship in general, and the medical profession from a policy of full disclosure. These harms go beyond harms to the aborted fetus, and so the interests involved cannot be narrowly framed as a right to choice versus a right to life. The parents' interest in obtaining information about their prospective child must be balanced against society's interest (on behalf of the fetus) in limiting the amount and kind of information about the fetus that is made available to prospective parents. In short, it is appropriate to consider some information about the fetus as private and confidential.

Fetal Privacy and Confidentiality

The principles of privacy and confidentiality are familiar in medicine. Medical histories include a wealth of information of a personal nature, but information that is not relevant to the individual's health or presenting problem is considered private and should not be pursued. Personal information that is shared is considered confidential unless there are compelling reasons to reveal this information to others. Respect for privacy is a reflection of respect for the dignity and independence of others. Confidentiality has several foundations, including respect for the individual, prevention of harm if sensitive information is revealed to third parties, and the need to foster honest dialogue between the physician and the patient.[7] The most compelling reason to breach confidentiality in medicine is when the information can prevent a significant harm to a third party. Familiar cases arise when, for example, the patient has a sexually transmissible disease, or is thought to pose an imminent threat of violence to others. If we extend considerations of privacy and confidentiality to the fetus, we might conclude that information about the fetus can only be sought and revealed when the information can prevent a significant harm to the parents.

An objection might be raised here that respect for privacy and confidentiality are based on respect for persons only, and is not relevant to ambiguous entities such as fetuses or embryos. It might be claimed that confidentiality arises from the mutual expectations of physician and patient—the patient reveals truthful information to the physician with the expectation that the information will remain within that relationship. Yet such a framework for privacy and confidentiality is too restricted. Patients need not be persons capable of mutual expectations for physicians to respect their confidentiality. The traditional respect for privacy and confidentiality covers all patients, including those with profound cognitive impairments who never had the ability to form expectations. Of particular relevance is the growing domain of privacy and confidentiality for young children—most notably in the arena of genetic testing. The current standard is not to test children unless there are effective treatments or preventive measures, precisely for some of the reasons outlined above: there is not a sufficient benefit to be gained for the child in light of the significant risks of stigma and discrimination.[8] Any claimed benefit to the parents in knowing whether their child is a Huntington gene carrier, for example, has not been deemed sufficient to override the child's interests. Respect for privacy and confidentiality are not driven by promises or mutual expectations, but rather by the presumption that this respect is an obligation owed to all patients that can be overridden when significant benefits can be achieved or significant harms averted.

This logic can be extended prenatally. Fetuses and embryos have individual characteristics that can be revealed through medical technology. Harm results to the fetus if information is revealed that leads to the termination of the pregnancy. Further, fetuses may become persons who have a clear interest in what personal genetic information has been revealed to others. Whether it is appropriate to obtain such information and reveal it to others (like parents) should be driven by the relative benefits and harms to all concerned. As long as the embryo or fetus is a potential person, we can be concerned about breaching the bounds of privacy and confidentiality that will result in the termination of the fetus or embryo, or harm to the future individual or others. Thus privacy and confidentiality are not proposed as fetal "rights," but rather as applicable principles justified by utilitarian considerations. Respect for parental autonomy is a strong traditional value in reproductive services and it was appropriate as the guiding value when prenatal screening and testing were available almost exclusively for serious congenital or hereditary conditions. As medical capabilities expand to detect less severe conditions, respect for fetal privacy and confidentiality emerge as countervailing considerations to parental autonomy.

Just as our protections for the life of the fetus are not equivalent to our protections for persons, our respect for the privacy and confidentiality of the fetus or embryo may not be as strong as it is for born individuals. In most clinical contexts, we would expect that the potential harm to a third party would have to be relatively severe or life threatening in order to justify the breach of patient confidentiality. The question in prenatal screening and testing is how severe the potential harm to parents needs to be in order to justify disclosure of information about the prospective child. We need not expect the harm to be life threatening since society has justified abortion for maternal harms that are less than potentially fatal. The harms to the mother of an unwanted pregnancy have been recognized by the majority in society as sufficient to justify abortion. It is reasonable then to use the severity of these harms as a tough measure of severity for the harms required to justify the breach of fetal privacy or confidentiality. The proposition is offered that

the standard of disclosure for prenatal information be designed to prevent harms to parents that are of approximately the same magnitude as the harms of an unwanted pregnancy.

Limits on Disclosure

. . . To place rational limits on the standard disclosure of prenatal information, we need to explore the characteristics of hereditary and congenital conditions that may produce harm for the parents of an affected child. In doing so, we must define what sorts of harms are legitimate and determine what level of harm is sufficient to justify a breach of fetal privacy and confidentiality. Joel Feinberg defines harm as a setback to interests.[9] So what interests are legitimate in bearing a child? If we take the legality of abortion as indicative of the legitimacy of the harm of bearing an unwanted child, then we can begin by determining what interests unwanted children impinge upon for parents. First is simply control over one's body—whether to be pregnant or not. Second, there are the physical risks, burdens, and expenses of pregnancy and delivery. Third, there are the physical, emotional, and financial burdens of raising a child to adulthood, including the lost opportunities for other pursuits. Fourth are the social burdens of bearing a child for those who are not married, and for those bearing a child from a man to whom one is not married. In the separate context of prenatal screening and testing, several of these interests do not apply. The woman retains the interest in deciding whether she wishes to remain pregnant at all, thus precluding the first and second considerations. In addition, the social burdens of an unplanned pregnancy are not relevant. This leaves as the primary interest the personal burdens of raising a child.

The burdens of raising a healthy child are considerable. In the context of prenatal screening and testing, because the parents presumably want a child with all of the normal burdens involved, we will be concerned about the increased burdens associated with the condition tested for. To justify a breach of fetal privacy or confidentiality, we will expect these increased burdens to be significant—impinging on a similar set of interests parents have in raising any child, that is, emotional burdens, time, effort, freedom, and expense. Of course, the benefits of children for parents are tremendous as well, and are derived principally from a close, loving relationship. These benefits are usually not reduced by serious health problems for the child and, indeed, they may be increased for some parents.

The benefits of children will not be discussed further here on the assumption that the benefits are often less tangible than harms and less variable from one child to the next. The calculus of harms to parents is not intended to denigrate the benefits that all children confer to families, but rather to say that, in some circumstances, the additional problems created by a health condition may lead some reasonable parents to forgo those benefits.

Different hereditary conditions will have different impacts on family life. Conditions can be described with respect to four characteristics. First, there is the likely severity of the condition with respect to health. Second is the age of onset of the condition, and third is the probability that the child's genotype will manifest as a significant clinical disease. Fourth is the probability that the condition will occur in those without specific risk factors. Since this discussion is focused on parental interests, severity in this context will mean severity to the parents. However, the more severe the condition is for the child, generally the greater the harm will be to the parents. The parent's harms are different in many respects from the child's, but include emotional pain and suffering, loss of a child, loss of opportunities, loss of freedom, isolation, loneliness, fear, guilt, stigmatization, and financial expenses.[10]

The magnitude of the parents' harm need not correlate directly with the harm experienced by the child. Some conditions that are often considered severe may not be associated with any experience of harm for the child. Down syndrome is a prime example. Parents in this circumstance are not harmed by the suffering of a child with Down (unless, of course, the child has other serious congenital anomalies that may be associated with Down), but rather by their time, efforts, and expenses to support the special needs of an individual with Down syndrome. It might also be added that parents are harmed by their unfulfilled expectations with the birth of an impaired child. However, we must consider claims for unfulfilled expectations carefully, as expectations for children may be unrealistically high. At the extreme, there may be circumstances in which the parents consider themselves to be seriously harmed by a child with a minor medical condition or even a child of the "wrong" gender. The disappointment parents may feel in these circumstances is real, but disappointment from unrealistic or inappropriate expectations need not be considered a harm worth preventing. Respecting idiosyncratic or highly subjective expectations will undermine any

rational conception of parental harm and permit no limits to be placed on the use of prenatal diagnostic technology.

In general terms, the claim is that parents suffer a sufficient harm to justify prenatal testing or screening when the severity of a child's condition raises problems for the parents of a similar magnitude to the birth of an unwanted child. Of course, the comparison of the harms of a healthy, unwanted child with the harms of a child with significant impairments must be crude at best. People differ greatly, such that even the same medical condition in two individuals may produce substantially different harms. Conversely, people's interests may experience similarly setbacks from very different conditions. Breaking your leg and "totaling" your car are two very different events that, nevertheless, may produce similar types of harms (expenses, wasted freedom, loss of mobility, etc.). What is of primary concern here is the magnitude of harms, and not necessarily the specific nature of those harms. However, the nature of the harms will be similar in many circumstances because most parents have a similar set of interests in life to pursue that are largely independent of their children. Parents of an unwanted child have their interests impinged upon by the necessary efforts, time, emotional burdens, and expenses of the child. The parents of a child with an unwanted disability have their interests impinged upon by the efforts, time, emotional burdens, and expenses added by the disability that they would not have otherwise experienced with the birth of a healthy child. Thus a rough comparison of harms to these similar parental interests is being made in these different experiences of parenthood. Of course, there is nothing in this argument to suggest that parents should feel harm in many of these circumstances. As noted, many parents of seriously impaired children recognize only benefit from the relationship with their child. The argument is not for what people should experience, but for what reasonable parents might experience by way of harm.

What sorts of conditions might meet this general standard? First, there are conditions that are often fatal in childhood. Obviously the death of a child is a devastating emotional harm to parents. The emotional harm here is substantially different in kind from the emotional harm of an unwanted child, but a commonsense comparison of the magnitude of the harms suggests that harm of a fatal childhood illness is greater than the harm of an unwanted child. Second are conditions that result in a child who is chronically ill or who has recurrent illnesses of sufficient gravity to require repeated hospitalization. Such illnesses generally are associated with suffering, and relative isolation for the child, and burdens of suffering, time, effort, and expense for the parents. Third are conditions that will not permit the child to achieve independence in his or her adult years. Parents are harmed if a child has a disability that precludes such independence and this harm is roughly similar in kind to the harm of the unwanted child—time, effort, and loss of independence. Finally, there are disabilities of such severity that there are constant demands on the parents for time, effort, and financial resources. The dedication many parents have for children with serious disabilities makes the loss to their other interests in life substantial. (It is worth emphasizing here that some of the burdens to parents outlined above are burdens that our society could choose to shoulder. Universal coverage by health insurance that covered comprehensive services for those with disabilities or chronic illnesses would significantly reduce the harm to parents of bearing children with such conditions.)

The diseases that fit the above criteria for harm to parents include many of the conditions for which prenatal testing or screening is now offered, such as hemophilia, Down syndrome, sickle cell anemia, Menkes syndrome, Fanconi's syndrome, fragile X syndrome, muscular dystrophy, osteogenesis imperfecta, Hurler's syndrome, cystic fibrosis, Tay–Sachs disease, many cases of spina bifida, and many inborn errors of metabolism. The burdens of these conditions for the parents are roughly similar, if not much greater, than the burdens of an unwanted child in terms of the effort, time, and financial resources necessary to care for these children, not to mention the tragic early deaths caused by some of these diseases.

For what types of medical conditions should offers of prenatal testing and screening not be required as a standard of care? At least five classes of conditions can be distinguished on the basis of likely availability and effectiveness of therapy, age of onset, and likelihood of manifestation of the disease. Group one includes any condition affecting children that can be cured or effectively treated so that the affected individual does not experience significant mental or physical impairments and in which the cure or treatment does not cause a serious financial burden to the family. Examples would include PKU, galactosemia, polydactyly, hypothyroidism, most cases of asthma, and cleft lip and palate.

As more hereditary conditions become amenable to treatment, this category of conditions will expand. (This category does not include conditions that can be treated prenatally for which prenatal testing or screening may be justified on a therapeutic basis.)

In group two are those conditions affecting children that may not be amenable to cure or effective treatment, but for which some treatments may be available or the conditions usually have a limited impact on the life of the child and family in terms of effort, time, and financial resources. These are conditions generally not associated with repeated hospitalizations and burdensome medical interventions. Examples include G6PD deficiency, many of the thalassemias, Tourette syndrome, spherocytosis, Marfan syndrome, and icthyosis vulgaris. These conditions may require episodic medical care, but not constant care and support. Included in this category are conditions that are not diseases or disabilities, including gender, and personality and physical traits that fall within the range of normal human variation.

A third group of conditions for which prenatal screening or testing need not be offered as a standard of care are those conditions that do not affect children. There are a variety of late-onset genetic conditions, including Huntington disease, polycystic kidney disease, and many of the hereditary predispositions to cancer, such as those secondary to the BRCA1 gene. These conditions will not affect the gene carrier for three, four, perhaps five decades. Parents can anticipate life with a healthy child for this period of time (healthy at least by virtue of freedom from the effects of the genetic condition in question). Certainly there is a significant possibility that one or both parents would not survive to experience the illness of their adult child, or the child may experience death or disability from a condition entirely unrelated to the hereditary disease. Further, rapid advances in the medical care of genetic conditions means that there is a possibility that effective medical care or cure will be available before current newborns reach their age of risk. For these reasons, adult onset conditions do not constitute a burden to parents on the same magnitude as an unwanted child.

A fourth group includes those genes that are unlikely to manifest as significant disease at any age. Penetrance is the likelihood that a given gene will be expressed in the individual. Some genes, such as the gene for Huntington, have a penetrance of virtually 100% if the carrier lives long enough. Other conditions, like schizophrenia, appear to have a hereditary component, but there must be an interaction with other genes and/or the environment before the genotype is manifested as illness. A second aspect of probability is the chance that, given the expression of the gene, the condition will be of significant severity. Many genetic conditions have a wide variability in severity. Neurofibromatosis is an example in which some individuals are virtually asymptomatic, while others are seriously disabled. As genetic knowledge expands, it may be possible to predict severity based on the nature of the mutation or by the presence of other modulating genetic factors. If such specific predictions are not possible, then I will suggest, arbitrarily, that if the presence of a gene will lead to a sufficiently severe manifestation of the disease (by the above criteria) in greater than 1% of gene carriers, then the provision of testing is justified. These considerations are relevant when a family history reveals a high likelihood that the gene will be present in those tested.

Finally, the last variable relates to the incidence at birth of conditions in the general population. The presumption is that discussion about conditions and disclosure of screening tests to prospective parents is not necessary when conditions are rare, but appropriate for more common conditions. What might be a reasonable cutoff above which screening should be offered? A discussion of this issue is beyond the scope of this paper. Assuming that the condition in question was sufficiently severe by the above criteria, whether a population-based screening program is appropriate would depend on a variety of additional factors, including the accuracy, safety, and cost of the screening test, and the subsequent evaluations necessary to confirm the diagnosis. Current standards of care include offering amniocentesis to women at thirty-five years of age and older, and offering alpha-fetoprotein screening to all pregnant women. The incidence of chromosome anomalies in older mothers is one to two percent,[11] and the incidence of neural tube defects at birth is one to two per thousand.[12] Whether population-based screening for conditions with a lower incidence than these is reasonable and desirable will be an important subject of public policy development.

As prenatal diagnostic capabilities expand, there will be many difficult decisions about whether testing for specific conditions should be provided. The rough framework offered here will not answer all of these dilemmas, but will provide a basis for further analysis and discussion.

The emerging power to characterize the genetic makeup of children early in their prenatal development will have profound social implications. The divisiveness of the abortion debate, the strong tradition of respect for parental autonomy in regard to reproductive services, and the wide spectrum of conditions amenable to prenatal diagnosis have inhibited the discussion of limitations on prenatal information about the fetus or embryo. The rapid advance of technology in this area means that clear decisions must be made by society and standards developed. While respect for the autonomy of couples is a strong value, it should not be the sole value that guides the application of this powerful technology. We only need to envision a future in which a few technical generations seek to enhance life through biology while other critical social institutions, like education, are allowed to disintegrate. The most important individual and social problems are not secondary to flawed human biology. Beyond prenatal testing, there are many other decisions that relate to the care and support of families that we as a society can make that will more effectively enhance the quality of life for us and our descendants.

References

1. Benjamin S. Wilfond and Kathleen Nolan, "National Policy Development for the Clinical Application of Genetic Diagnostic Technologies: Lessons from Cystic Fibrosis," *JAMA* 270 (1993): 2848–54.

2. *Roe v. Wade*, 410 U. S. 113 (1973), at p. 10.

3. Laurie Nsiah-Jefferson, "Access to Reproductive Genetic Services for Low-Income Women and Women of Color," *Fetal Diagnosis and Therapy* 8, Supp. 1 (1993): 107–27.

4. Nancy A. Press and C. H. Browner, "Collective Fictions: Similarities in Reasons for Accepting Maternal Serum Alpha-Fetoprotein Screening among Women of Diverse Ethnic and Social Class Backgrounds," *Fetal Diagnosis and Therapy* 8, Supp. 1 (1993): 97–106.

5. Jeffrey R. Botkin and Maxwell J. Mehlman, "Wrongful Birth: Legal, Medical and Philosophic Issues," *American Journal of Law Medicine & Ethics* 22 (1994): 21–28; Lori B. Andrews, "Torts and the Double Helix: Malpractice Liability for Failure to Warn of Genetic Risks," *Houston Law Review* 29 (1992): 149–84.

6. Botkin and Mehlman, *"Wrongful Birth."*

7. LeRoy Walters, "Ethical Aspects of Medical Confidentiality," in *Contemporary Issues in Bioethics*, 2nd ed., ed. Tom Beauchamp and LeRoy Walters (Belmont, Calif.: Wadsworth Publishing Co., 1982), p. 19.

8. Lori B. Andrews, Jane J. Fullerton, Neil A. Holtzman, and Arno G. Motulsky, Editors, *Assessing Genetic Risks: Implications for Health and Social Policy* (Washington, D.C.: National Academy Press, 1994), p. 10.

9.   Joel Feinberg, *Harm to Others: The Moral Limits of the Criminal Law* (New York: Oxford University Press, 1984), pp. 31–65.

10.   J. A. Boss, "The Family Burden Justification for Selective Abortion," in *The Birth Lottery: Prenatal Diagnosis and Selective Abortion. Values and Ethics Series*, Vol. 5 (Chicago: Loyola University Press, 1993), 19.5–229.

11.   Lillian Y. F. Hsu, "Prenatal Diagnosis of Chromosome Abnormalities" in *Genetic Disorders and the Fetus*, ed. Aubrey Milunsky (New York: Plenum Press, 1986), pp. 115–83.

12.   Aubrey Milunsky, "The Prenatal Diagnosis of Neural Tube and other Congenital Defects," in *Genetic Disorders and the Fetus*, pp. 453–519.

Implications of Prenatal Diagnosis for the Human Right to Life

Leon R. Kass

Leon Kass expresses concern that the practice of "genetic abortion" will strongly affect our attitudes toward all who are "defective" or abnormal. Those who escape the net of selective abortion might receive less care and might even come to think of themselves as second-class specimens. Furthermore, on Kass view, genetic abortion might encourage us to accept the general principle that "defectives" of any kind ought not to be born. This in turn would threaten our commitment to the basic moral principle that each person, despite any physical or mental disability, is the inherent equal of every other person.

Kass presents six criteria that he suggests ought to be satisfied to justify the abortion of a fetus for genetic reasons. In the remainder of his paper, he focuses on the question raised by the last criterion: according to what standards should we judge a fetus with genetic abnormalities unfit to live? As candidates for such standards, Kass examines the concepts of social good, family good, and the "healthy and sound" fetus. He finds difficulty with all, and in the end he professes himself unable to provide a satisfactory justification for genetic abortion.

I wish to focus on the special ethical issues raised by the abortion of "defective" fetuses (so-called "abortion for fetal indications"). I shall consider only the cleanest cases, those cases where well-characterized genetic diseases are diagnosed with a high degree of certainty by means of amniocentesis, in order to sidestep the added moral dilemmas posed when the diagnosis is suspected or possible, but unconfirmed. However, many of the questions I shall discuss could also be raised about cases where genetic analysis gives only a statistical prediction about the genotype of the fetus, and also about cases where the defect has an infectious or chemical rather than a genetic cause (e.g. rubella, thalidomide)....

Precisely because the quality of the fetus is central to the decision to abort, the practice of genetic abortion has implications which go beyond those raised by abortion in general. What may be at stake here is the belief that all human beings possess equally and independent of merit certain fundamental rights, one among which is, of course, the right to life.

To be sure, the belief that fundamental human rights belong equally to all human beings has been but an ideal, never realized, often ignored, sometimes shamelessly. Yet it has been perhaps the most powerful moral idea at work in the world for at least two centuries. It is this idea and ideal that animates most of the current political and social criticism

Reprinted from *Ethical Issues in Human Genetics: Genetic Counseling and the Use of Genetic Knowledge*, edited by Bruce Hilton, Daniel Callahan, Maureen Harris, Peter Condliffe, and Burton Berkely (New York: Plenum, 1973), pp. 186–199. A revised version of this essay ("Perfect Babies: Prenatal Diagnosis and the Equal Right to Life") appears in Kass's book, *Toward a More Natural Science: Biology and Human Affairs* (New York: Free Press, 1985). (Notes omitted).

around the globe. It is ironic that we should acquire the power to detect and eliminate the genetically unequal at a time when we have finally succeeded in removing much of the stigma and disgrace previously attached to victims of congenital illness, in providing them with improved care and support, and in preventing, by means of education, feelings of guilt on the part of their parents. One might even wonder whether the development of amniocentesis and prenatal diagnosis may represent a backlash against these same humanitarian and egalitarian tendencies in the practice of medicine, which, by helping to sustain to the age of reproduction persons with genetic disease has itself contributed to the increasing incidence of genetic disease, and with it, to increased pressures for genetic screening, genetic counseling, and genetic abortion.

No doubt our humanitarian and egalitarian principles and practices have caused us some new difficulties, but if we mean to weaken or turn our backs on them, we should do so consciously and thoughtfully. If, as I believe, the idea and practice of genetic abortion points in that direction, we should make ourselves aware of it. And if, as I believe, the way in which genetic abortion is described, discussed, and justified is perhaps of even greater consequence than its practice for our notions of human rights and of their equal possession by all human beings, we should pay special attention to questions of language and in particular, to the question of justification. Before turning full attention to these matters, two points should be clarified.

First, my question "What decision, and why?" is to be distinguished from the question "Who decides, and why?" There is a tendency to blur this distinction and to discuss only the latter, and with it, the underlying question of private freedom versus public good. I will say nothing about this, since I am more interested in exploring what constitutes "good," both public and private. Accordingly, I would emphasize that the moral question—What decision, and why?—does not disappear simply because the decision is left in the hands of each pregnant woman. It is the moral question she faces. I would add that the moral health of the community and of each of its members is as likely to be affected by the aggregate of purely private and voluntary decisions on genetic abortions as by a uniform policy imposed by statute. We physicians and scientists especially should refuse to finesse the moral question of genetic abortion and its implications and to take refuge behind the issue, "Who decides?" For it is we who are responsible for choosing to develop the technology of prenatal diagnosis, for informing and promoting this technology among the public, and for the actual counseling of patients.

Second, I wish to distinguish my discussion of what ought to be done from a descriptive account of what in fact is being done, and especially from a consideration of what I myself might do, faced with the difficult decision. I cannot know with certainty what I would think, feel, do, or want done, faced with the knowledge that my wife was carrying a child branded with Down's syndrome or Tay–Sachs disease. But an understanding of the issues is not advanced by personal anecdote or confession. We all know that what we and others actually do is often done out of weakness, rather than conviction. It is all-too-human to make an exception in one's own case (consider, e.g., the extra car, the "extra" child, income tax, the draft, the flight from cities). For what it is worth, I confess to feeling more than a little sympathy with parents who choose abortions for severe genetic defect. Nevertheless, as I shall indicate later, in seeking for reasons to justify this practice, I can find none that are in themselves fully satisfactory and none that do not simultaneously justify the killing of "defective" infants, children, and adults. I am mindful that my arguments will fall far from the middle of the stream, yet I hope that the oarsmen of the flagship will pause and row more slowly, while we all consider whither we are going.

Genetic Abortion and the Living Defective

The practice of abortion of the genetically defective will no doubt affect our view of and our behavior toward those abnormals who escape the net of detection and abortion. A child with Down's syndrome or with hemophilia or with muscular dystrophy born at a time when most of his (potential) fellow sufferers were destroyed prenatally is liable to be looked upon by the community as one unfit to be alive, as a second-class (or even lower) human type. He may be seen as a person who need not have been, and who would not have been, if only someone had gotten to him in time.

The parents of such children are also likely to treat them differently, especially if the mother would have wished but failed to get an amniocentesis because of ignorance, poverty, or distance from the testing station, or if the prenatal diagnosis was in error. In such cases, parents are especially likely to resent the child. They may be disinclined to give it the kind of care they might have before the advent of amniocentesis and genetic abortion, rationalizing that a second-class specimen is not entitled to first-class treatment. If pressed to do so, say by physicians, the parents might refuse, and the courts may become involved. This has already begun to happen.

In Maryland, parents of a child with Down's syndrome refused permission to have the child operated on for an intestinal obstruction present at birth. The physicians and the hospital sought an injunction to require the parents to allow surgery. The judge ruled in favor of the parents, despite what I understand to be the weight of precedent to the contrary, on the grounds that the child was Mongoloid; that is, had the child been "normal," the decision would have gone the other way. Although the decision was not appealed to and hence not affirmed by a higher court, we can see through the prism of this case the possibility that the new powers of human genetics will strip the blindfold from the lady of justice and will make official the dangerous doctrine that some men are more equal than others.

The abnormal child may also feel resentful. A child with Down's syndrome or Tay–Sachs disease will probably never know or care, but what about the child with hemophilia or with Turner's syndrome? In the past decade, with medical knowledge and power over the prenatal child increasing and with parental authority over the postnatal child decreasing, we have seen the appearance of a new type of legal action, suits for wrongful life. Children have brought suit against their parents (and others) seeking to recover damages for physical and social handicaps inextricably tied to their birth (e.g., congenital deformities, congenital syphilis, illegitimacy). In some of the American cases, the courts have recognized the justice of the child's claim (that he was injured due to parental negligence), although they have so far refused to award damages, due to policy considerations. In other countries, e.g., in Germany, judgments with compensation have gone for the plaintiffs. With the spread of amniocentesis and genetic abortion, we can only expect such cases to increase. And here it will be the soft-hearted rather than the hard-hearted judges who will establish the doctrine of second-class human beings, out of compassion for the mutants who escaped the traps set out for them.

It may be argued that I am dealing with a problem which, even if it is real, will affect very few people. It may be suggested that very few will escape the traps once we have set them properly and widely, once people are informed about amniocentesis, once the power to detect prenatally grows to its full capacity, and once our "superstitious" opposition to abortion dies out or is extirpated. But in order even to come close to this vision of success, amniocentesis will have to become part of every pregnancy—either by making it mandatory, like the test for syphilis, or by making it "routine medical practice," like the Pap smear. Leaving aside the other problems with universal amniocentesis, we would expect that the problem for the few who escape is likely to be even worse precisely because they will be few.

The point, however, should be generalized. How will we come to view and act toward the many "abnormals" that will remain among us—the retarded, the crippled, the senile, the deformed, and the true mutants—once we embark on a program to root out genetic abnormality? For it must be remembered that we shall always have abnormals—some who escape detection or whose disease is undetectable *in utero*, others a result of new mutations, birth injuries, accidents, maltreatment, or disease—who will require our care and protection. The existence of "defectives" cannot be fully prevented, not even by totalitarian breeding and weeding programs. Is it not likely that our principle with respect to these people will change from "We try harder" to "Why accept second best?" The idea of "the unwanted because abnormal child" may become a self-fulfilling prophecy, whose consequences may be worse than those of the abnormality itself.

Genetic and Other Defectives

The mention of other abnormals points to a second danger of the practice of genetic abortion. Genetic abortion may come to be seen not so much as the prevention of genetic disease, but as the prevention of birth of defective or abnormal children—and, in a way, understandably so. For in the case of what other diseases does preventive medicine consist in the elimination of the patient-at-risk? Moreover, the very language used to discuss genetic disease leads us to the easy but wrong conclusion that the afflicted fetus or person is rather than has a disease. True, one is partly defined by his genotype, but only partly. A person is more than his disease. And yet we slide easily from the language of possession to the language of identity, from "He has hemophilia" to "He is a hemophiliac," from "She has diabetes" through "She is diabetic" to "She is a diabetic," from "The fetus has Down's syndrome" to "The fetus is a Down's." This way of speaking supports the belief that it is defective persons (or potential persons) that are being eliminated, rather than diseases.

If this is so, then it becomes simply accidental that the defect has a genetic cause. Surely, it is only because of the high regard for medicine and science, and for the accuracy of genetic diagnosis, that genotypic defectives are likely to be the first to go. But once the principle, "Defectives should not be born," is established, grounds other than cytological and biochemical may very well be sought. Even ignoring racialists and others equally misguided—of course, they cannot be ignored—we should know that there are social scientists, for example, who believe that one can predict with a high degree of accuracy how a child will turn out from a careful, systematic study of the socio-economic and psycho-dynamic environment into which he is born and in which he grows up. They might press for the prevention of socio-psychological disease, even of "criminality," by means of prenatal environmental diagnosis and abortion. I have heard a rumor that a crude, unscientific form of eliminating potential "phenotypic defectives" is already being practiced in some cities, in that submission to abortion is allegedly being made a condition for the receipt of welfare payments. "Defectives should not be born" is a principle without limits. We can ill-afford to have it established.

Up to this point, I have been discussing the possible implications of the practice of genetic abortion for our belief in and adherence to the idea that, at least in fundamental human matters such as life and liberty, all men are to be considered as equals, that for these matters we should ignore as irrelevant the real qualitative differences amongst men, however important these differences may be for other purposes. Those who are concerned about abortion fear that the permissible time of eliminating the unwanted will be moved forward along the time continuum, against newborns, infants, and children. Similarly, I suggest that we should be concerned lest the attack on gross genetic inequality in fetuses be advanced along the continuum of quality and into the later stages of life.

I am not engaged in predicting the future; I am not saying that amniocentesis and genetic abortion will lead down the road to Nazi Germany. Rather, I am suggesting that the principles underlying genetic

abortion simultaneously justify many further steps down that road . . .

Perhaps I have exaggerated the dangers; perhaps we will not abandon our inexplicable preference for generous humanitarianism over consistency. But we should indeed be cautious and move slowly as we give serious consideration to the question "What price the perfect baby?"

Standards for Justifying Genetic Abortion

. . . According to what standards can and should we judge a fetus with genetic abnormalities unfit to live, i.e., abortable? It seems to me that there are at least three dominant standards to which we are likely to repair.

The first is societal good. The needs and interest of society are often invoked to justify the practices of prenatal diagnosis and abortion of the genetically abnormal. The argument, full blown, runs something like this. Society has an interest in the genetic fitness of its members. It is foolish for society to squander its precious resources ministering to and caring for the unfit, especially for those who will never become "productive," or who will never in any way "benefit" society. Therefore, the interests of society are best served by the elimination of the genetically defective prior to their birth.

The societal standard is all-too-often reduced to its lowest common denominator: money. Thus one physician, claiming that he has "made a cost–benefit analysis of Tay–Sachs disease," notes that "the total cost of carrier detection, prenatal diagnosis and termination of at-risk pregnancies for all Jewish individuals in the United States under 30 who will marry is $5,730,281. If the program is setup to screen only one married partner, the cost is $3,122,695. The hospital costs for the 990 cases of Tay–Sachs disease these individuals would produce over a thirty-year period in the United States is $34,650,000." Another physician, apparently less interested or able to make such a precise audit has written: "Cost–benefit analyses have been made for the total prospective detection and monitoring of Tay–Sachs disease, cystic fibrosis (when prenatal detection becomes available for cystic fibrosis) and other disorders, and in most cases, the expenditures for hospitalization and medical care far exceed the cost of prenatal detection in properly selected risk populations, followed by selective abortion." Yet a third physician has calculated that the costs to the state of caring for children with Down's syndrome is more than three times that of detecting and aborting them. (These authors all acknowledge the additional non-societal "costs" of personal suffering, but insofar as they consider society, the costs are purely economic.)

There are many questions that can be raised about this approach. First, there are questions about the accuracy of the calculations. Not all the costs have been reckoned. The aborted defective child will be "replaced" by a "normal" child. In keeping the ledger, the "costs" to society of his care and maintenance cannot be ignored—costs of educating him, or removing his wastes and pollutions, not to mention the "costs" in non-replaceable natural resources he consumes. Who is the greater drain on society's precious resources, the average inmate of a home for the retarded or the average graduate of Harvard College? I am not sure we know or can even find out. Then there are the costs of training the physicians and genetic counselors, equipping their laboratories, supporting their research, and sending them and us to conferences to worry about what they are doing. An accurate economic analysis seems to me to be impossible, even in principle. And even if it were possible, one could fall back on the words of that ordinary language philosopher, Andy Capp, who, when his wife said that she was getting really worried about the cost of living, replied: "Sweet 'eart, name me one person who wants t'stop livin' on account of the cost."

A second defect of the economic analysis is that there are matters of social importance that are not reducible to financial costs, and others that may not be quantifiable at all. How does one quantitate the costs of real and potential social conflict, either between children and parents, or between the community and the "deviants" who refuse amniocentesis and continue to bear abnormal children? Can one measure the effect on racial tensions of attempting to screen for and prevent the birth of children homozygous (or heterozygous) for sickle cell anemia? What numbers does one attach to any decreased willingness or ability to take care of the less fortunate, or to cope with difficult problems? And what about the "costs" of rising expectations? Will we become increasingly dissatisfied with anything short of the "optimum baby"? How does one quantify anxiety? humiliation? guilt? Finally, might not the medical profession pay an immeasurable price if genetic abortion and other revolutionary activities bring about changes in medical ethics and medical

practice that lead to the further erosion of trust in the physician?

An appeal to social worthiness or usefulness is a less vulgar form of the standard of societal good. It is true that great social contributions are unlikely to be forthcoming from persons who suffer from most serious genetic diseases, especially since many of them die in childhood. Yet consider the following remarks of Pearl Buck (1968) on the subject of being a mother of a child retarded from phenylketonuria:

"My child's life has not been meaningless. She has indeed brought comfort and practical help to many people who are parents of retarded children or are themselves handicapped. True, she has done it through me, yet without her I would not have had the means of learning how to accept the inevitable sorrow, and how to make that acceptance useful to others. Would I be so heartless as to say that it has been worthwhile for my child to be born retarded? Certainly not, but I am saying that even though gravely retarded it has been worthwhile for her to have lived.

"It can be summed up, perhaps, by saying that in this world where cruelty prevails in so many aspects of our life, I would not add the weight of choice to kill rather than to let live. A retarded child, a handicapped person, brings its own gift to life, even to the life of normal human beings. That gift is comprehended in the lessons of patience, understanding, and mercy, lessons which we all need to receive and to practice with one another, whatever we are."

The standard of potential social worthiness is little better in deciding about abortion in particular cases than is the standard of economic cost. To drive the point home, each of us might consider retrospectively whether he would have been willing to stand trial for his life while a fetus, pleading only his worth to society as he now can evaluate it. How many of us are not socially "defective" and with none of the excuses possible for a child with phenylketonuria? If there is to be human life at all, potential social worthiness cannot be its entitlement.

Finally, we should take note of the ambiguities in the very notion of societal good. Some use the term "society" to mean their own particular political community, others to mean the whole human race, and still others speak as if they mean both simultaneously, following that all-too-human belief that what is good for me and mine is good for mankind. Who knows what is genetically best for mankind, even with respect to Down's syndrome? I would submit that the genetic heritage of the human species is largely in the care of persons who do not live along the amniocentesis frontier. If we in the industrialized West wish to be really serious about the genetic future of the species, we would concentrate our attack on mutagenesis, and especially on our large contribution to the pool of environmental mutagens.

But even the more narrow use of society is ambiguous. Do we mean our "society" as it is today? Or do we mean our "society" as it ought to be? If the former, our standards will be ephemeral, for ours is a faddish "society." (By far the most worrisome feature of the changing attitudes on abortion is the suddenness with which they changed.) Any such socially determined standards are likely to provide too precarious a foundation for decisions about genetic abortion, let alone for our notions of human rights. If we mean the latter, then we have transcended the societal standard, since the "good society" is not to be found in "society" itself, nor is it likely to be discovered by taking a vote. In sum, societal good as a standard for justifying genetic abortion seems to be unsatisfactory. It is hard to define in general, difficult to apply clearly to particular cases, susceptible to overreaching and abuse (hence, very dangerous), and not sufficient unto itself if considerations of the good community are held to be automatically implied.

A second major alternative is the standard of parental or familial good. Here the argument of justification might run as follows. Parents have a right to determine, according to their own wishes and based upon their own notions of what is good for them, the qualitative as well as the quantitative character of their families. If they believe that the birth of a seriously deformed child will be the cause of great sorrow and suffering to themselves and to their other children and a drain on their time and resources, then they may ethically decide to prevent the birth of such a child, even by abortion.

This argument I would expect to be more attractive to most people than the argument appealing to the good of society. For one thing, we are more likely to trust a person's conception of what is good for him than his notion of what is good for society. Also, the number of persons involved is small, making it seem less impossible to weigh all the relevant factors in determining the good of the family. Most powerfully, one can see and appreciate the possible harm done to

healthy children if the parents are obliged to devote most of their energies to caring for the afflicted child.

Yet there are ambiguities and difficulties perhaps as great as with the standard of societal good. In the first place, it is not entirely clear what would be good for the other children. In a strong family, the experience with a suffering and dying child might help the healthy siblings learn to face and cope with adversity. Some have even speculated that the lack of experience with death and serious illness in our affluent young people is an important element in their difficulty in trying to find a way of life and in responding patiently yet steadily to the serious problems of our society (Cassell, 1969). I suspect that one cannot generalize. In some children and in some families, experience with suffering may be strengthening, and in others, disabling. My point here is that the matter is uncertain, and that parents deciding on this basis are as likely as not to be mistaken.

The family or parental standard, like the societal standard, is unavoidably elastic because "suffering" does not come in discontinuous units, and because parental wishes and desires know no limits. Both are utterly subjective, relative, and notoriously subject to change. Some parents claim that they could not tolerate having to raise a child of the undesired sex; I know of one case where the woman in the delivery room, on being informed that her child was a son, told the physician that she did not even wish to see it and that he should get rid of it. We may judge her attitude to be pathological, but even pathological suffering is suffering. Would such suffering justify aborting her normal male fetus?

Or take the converse case of two parents, who for their own very peculiar reasons, wish to have an abnormal child, say a child who will suffer from the same disease as grandfather or a child whose arrested development would preclude the threat of adolescent rebellion and separation. Are these acceptable grounds for the abortion of "normals"?

Granted, such cases will be rare. But they serve to show the dangers inherent in talking about the parental right to determine, according to their wishes, the quality of their children. Indeed, the whole idea of parental rights with respect to children strikes me as problematic. It suggests that children are like property, that they exist for the parents. One need only look around to see some of the results of this notion of parenthood. The language of duties to children would be more in keeping with the heavy responsibility we bear in affirming the continuity of life with life and in trying to transmit what wisdom we have acquired to the next generation. Our children are not our children. Hopefully, reflection on these matters could lead to a greater appreciation of why it is people do and should have children. No better consequence can be hoped for from the advent of amniocentesis and other technologies for controlling human reproduction.

If one speaks of familial good in terms of parental duty, one could argue that parents have an obligation to do what they can to ensure that their children are born healthy and sound. But this formulation transcends the limitation of parental wishes and desires. As in the case of the good society, the idea of "healthy and sound" requires an objective standard, a standard in reality. Hard as it may be to uncover it, this is what we are seeking. Nature as a standard is the third alternative.

The justification according to the natural standard might run like this. As a result of our knowledge of genetic diseases, we know that persons afflicted with certain diseases will never be capable of living the full life of a human being. Just as a no-necked giraffe could never live a giraffe's life, or a needle-less porcupine would not attain true "porcupine-hood," so a child or fetus with Tay– Sachs disease or Down's syndrome, for example, will never truly be human. They will never be able to care for themselves, nor have they even the potential for developing the distinctively human capacities for thought or self-consciousness. Nature herself has aborted many similar cases, and has provided for the early death of many who happen to get born. There is no reason to keep them alive; instead, we should prevent their birth by contraception or sterilization if possible, and abortion if necessary.

The advantages of this approach are clear. The standards are objective and in the fetus itself, thus avoiding the relativity and ambiguity in societal and parental good. The standard can be easily generalized to cover all such cases and will be resistant to the shifting sands of public opinion.

This standard, I would suggest, is the one which most physicians and genetic counselors appeal to in their heart of hearts, no matter what they say or do about letting the parents choose. Why else would they have developed genetic counseling and amniocentesis? Indeed, the notions of disease, of abnormal, of defective, make no sense at all in the absence of a natural norm of health. This norm is the foundation of the art of the physician and of the inquiry of the health scientist. Yet, as Motulsky and others [1971] . . . have pointed out, the standard is elusive. Ironically, we are gaining

increasing power to manipulate and control our own nature at a time in which we are increasingly confused about what is normal, healthy, and fit.

Although possibly acceptable in principle, the natural standard runs into problems in application when attempts are made to fix the boundary between potentially human and potentially not human. Professor Lejeune (1970) has clearly demonstrated the difficulty, if not the impossibility, of setting clear molecular, cytological, or developmental signposts for this boundary. Attempts to induce signposts by considering the phenotypes of the worst cases is equally difficult. Which features would we take to be the most relevant in, say, Tay–Sachs disease, Lesch–Nyhan syndrome, Cri du chat, Down's syndrome? Certainly, severe mental retardation. But how "severe" is "severe"? As . . . I argued earlier, mental retardation admits of degree. It too is relative. Moreover it is not clear that certain other defects and deformities might not equally foreclose the possibility of a truly or fully human life. What about blindness or deafness? Quadriplegia? Aphasia? Several of these in combination? Not only does each kind of defect admit of a continuous scale of severity, but it also merges with other defects on a continuous scale of defectiveness. Where on this scale is the line to be drawn after mental retardation? blindness? muscular dystrophy? cystic fibrosis? hemophilia? diabetes? galactosemia? Tumer's syndrome? XYY? club foot? Moreover, the identical two continuous scales—kind and severity—are found also among the living. In fact, it is the natural standard which may be the most dangerous one in that it leads most directly to the idea that there are second-class human beings and sub-human human beings.

But the story is not complete. The very idea of nature is ambiguous. According to one view, the one I have been using, nature points to or implies a peak, a perfection. According to this view, human rights depend upon attaining the status of humanness. The fetus is only potential; it has no rights, according to this view. But all kinds of people fall short of the norm: children, idiots, some adults. This understanding of nature has been used to justify not only abortion and infanticide, but also slavery.

There is another notion of nature, less splendid, more humane and, though less able to sustain a notion of health, more acceptable to the findings of modern science. Animal nature is characterized by impulses of self-preservation and by the capacity to feel pleasure and to suffer pain. Man and other animals are alike on this understanding of nature. And the right to life is ascribed to all such self-preserving and suffering creatures. Yet on this understanding of nature, the fetus—even a defective fetus—is not potential, but actual. The right to life belongs to him. But for this reason, this understanding of nature does not provide and may even deny what it is we are seeking, namely a justification for genetic abortion, adequate unto itself, which does not simultaneously justify infanticide, homicide, and enslavement of the genetically abnormal.

There is a third understanding of nature, akin to the second, nature as sacrosanct, nature as created by a Creator. Indeed, to speak about this reminds us that there is a fourth possible standard for judgments about genetic abortion: the religious standard. I shall leave the discussion of this standard to those who are able to speak of it in better faith.

Now that I am at the end, the reader can better share my sense of frustration. I have failed to provide myself with a satisfactory intellectual and moral justification for the practice of genetic abortion. Perhaps others more able than I can supply one. Perhaps the pragmatists can persuade me that we should abandon the search for principled justification, that if we just trust people's situational decisions or their gut reactions, everything will turn out fine. Maybe they are right. But we should not forget the sage observation of Bertrand Russell: "pragmatism is like a warm bath that heats up so imperceptibly that you don't know when to scream." I would add that before we submerge ourselves irrevocably in amniotic fluid, we take note of the connection to our own baths, into which we have started the hot water running.

References

Buck, P. S. (1968). Foreword to *The Terrible Choice: The Abortion Dilemma*. New York: Bantam Books, pp. ix–xi.

Cassell, E. (1969). "Death and the Physician," *Commentary* (June), pp. 73–79.

Lejeune, J. (1970). *American Journal of Human Genetics*, 22, p. 121.

Lincoln, A. (1854). In *The Collected Works of Abraham Lincoln*, R. P. Basler, editor. New Brunswick, N.J.: Rutgers University Press, Vol II, p. 222.

Motulsky, A.G., G.R. Fraser, and J. Felsenstein (1971). In Symposium on Intrauterine Diagnosis, D. Bergsma, editor. *Birth Dejects: Original Article Series*, Vol. 7, No. 5.

Neel, J. (1972). In *Early Diagnosis of Human Genetic Defects: Scientific and Ethical Considerations*, M. Harris, editor. Washington, D.C.: U.S. Government Printing Office, pp. 366–380.

Section 4: Embryonic Stem Cells: End of the Battle?

Stem Cells from Skin Cells: The Ethical Questions

Insoo Hyun

Hyun argues that the genetic modifications of human skin cells to be like embryonic stem cells, though exciting, will not remove the ethical problems of stem cell research. First, induced pluripotent stem cell (iPS cell) research will have to be carried out in conjunction with embryonic stem cell research in order to determine their value and safety for clinical applications. Second, the use of iPS cells will raise complicated issues of informed consent because they will be solicited from gravely ill patients whose hopes might easily be exploited, as might those of future patients who may seek treatments with iPS cells.

Finally, iPS cell research may come up against the same questons about personhood as embryonic stem cells if it turns out that somatic cells can be programmed to generate supporting extraembryonic (placental) tissues needed for the embryo to develop into a fetus or if iPS cells can be programmed to generate human sex cells.

Recently, research teams led by Shinya Yamanaka and James Thomson published separate reports that they had genetically modified human skin cells to behave like embryonic stem cells.[1] Like their embryonic counterparts, these induced pluripotent stem cells (iPS cells) were capable of forming all three germ layers both in vitro and in immunodeficient mice, demonstrating their remarkable pluripotential character. Furthermore, the two teams' iPS cell colonies were genetically matched to the human skin cells from which they were derived, thus enlivening the possibility that one day (perhaps soon) patient- and disease-specific pluripotent stem cells could be generated for research that could later yield downstream clinical benefits.

Now that human iPS cells have arrived, many will wonder whether the thorny ethical challenges surrounding stem cell research can be fortuitously bypassed. This is hardly the case. While the scientific possibilities of iPS cells are enormously exciting, human iPS cell research raises both new ethical complexities and old philosophical problems.

As colleagues and I have noted elsewhere, it would be a serious mistake to conclude that iPS cell research averts the need for human embryonic stem cells.[2] Human iPS cell research must proceed together with human embryonic stem cell research for many important reasons.

Ongoing research on human embryonic stem cells is necessary to inform scientists' growing understanding and analyses of human IPS cells. Much more work is needed on both iPS cells and embryonic stem cells to determine whether these two kinds of stem cells differ in biologically and clinically significant ways.[3] As a matter of fact, we do not know at this point which of the possible sources of disease-specific pluripotent human stem cells—genetically screened IVF embryos, iPS cells, somatic cell nuclear transfer into enucleated oocytes,[4] or somatic cell chromosome transfer into zygotes and blastomeres that have had their own chromosomes removed[5]—will prove to be the best for clinical applications, all other things considered.

Safety is also a major concern for human iPS cells since the retroviruses used to insert the pluripotency-inducing genes might themselves lead to cancer and other harmful mutations (one of the pluripotency-inducing factors Yamanaka's group used was c-Myc, a gene commonly associated with tumor formation). In contrast, human embryonic stem cells are the only pluripotent human cells that are genetically unmodified; they are pluripotent stem cells in their purest, unadulterated form. Thus, in addition to possessing enormous scientific value in their own right, embryonic stem cells will be needed to serve as controls for examining the safety and efficacy of human iPS cells.[6]

Prudence calls for all research alternatives to be pursued simultaneously if possible. The idea that iPS cell research can (and should) proceed by itself is not a hope that makes much scientific sense. Good science is supposed to leave no stone unturned, subject to rigorous standards of research ethics.

This brings us to my next point. The pursuit of human iPS cells raises new challenges for the process of informed consent in biomedical research. That a person must provide voluntary and informed consent before participating in a scientific study is a well-known international principle of research ethics. According to stem cell research guidelines issued last year by the International Society for Stem Cell Research, all body cell donors or their legally authorized guardians must give their contemporaneous informed consent for the use of the donors' somatic tissues in stem cell research, with a few notable exceptions.[7] These exceptions largely pertain to the use of stored tissue samples, which would be a desirable and convenient resource for iPS cell studies. According to ISSCR guidelines, tissue samples may be used for research without contemporaneous informed consent only if researchers procure somatic cells from a tissue bank whose consent documents specifically designate nuclear reprogramming methods for stem cell research as one of the possible uses of the donor's tissues, and if donors have specifically agreed to this possible use. Only in extremely rare cases may the requirement for specified informed consent be waived. In these exceptional cases, there must be no reasonable and adequate alternative source for the unique characteristics of the tissue donor's somatic cells, such that another donor could be found who might offer contemporaneous informed consent.

The ISSCR guidelines were drafted prior to any published work in iPS cell research, however, and the ISSCR will have to revisit them to determine whether blanket consent forms from tissue banks or exception from specified tissue donor consent is appropriate for iPS cell research. Regardless of how the ISSCR decides this issue, the concepts of blanket consent and specified donor consent are currently hot issues in the ethics of genetic research on stored human tissues. Thus, human iPS cell researchers may find themselves getting swept into this ongoing debate if they decide to use stored somatic cells.

On the other hand, obtaining contemporaneous informed consent from tissue donors is not a simple proposition either. A chief aim of iPS cell research is to produce patient- and disease-specific stem cells for study and for the eventual development of clinical applications. As a result, iPS cell researchers will be especially interested in collecting skin biopsies from people who suffer from a range of seriously debilitating diseases and injuries for which we have not yet found cures. Researchers must be extremely careful not to take unfair advantage of these patients and their families. Unlike stem cell studies that use IVF embryos, human iPS cell research would leave a survivor behind who is the genetic source of an iPS cell line. Moreover, these individuals are likely to suffer from grave medical conditions. Those who volunteer to donate their own or their ill children's somatic cells for iPS cell research may do so in the hopes of directly or indirectly benefiting themselves or their loved ones through downstream therapeutic applications of these genetically-matched stem cell lines.[8] Given these possible motivations and the dire circumstances in which many patients and their families may find themselves, it is crucial that researchers not inadvertently exploit their donors' hopes and aspirations.

To guard against this danger, due care must be taken during the informed consent process to protect the liberty interests of patients providing tissue samples for iPS cell research. As with all human materials donors in stem cell research, somatic cell donors must be adequately informed of the aspects of the research that reasonable people would typically find relevant to their decision to participate.[9] Especially pertinent may be the fact that iPS cell lines would be genetically matched to their original tissue donors and that they will likely be shared with researchers at different institutions for academic and commercial purposes, most of which are unknown at this time. Donors should also be aware that their resulting iPS cells will likely be transplanted into laboratory animals for human-to-animal chimera experiments, first to assess the cells' developmental capabilities and later to conduct preclinical proof of concept studies in animal models. Because some tissue donors may be uneasy with the idea that their genetically-matched iPS cells could be used

to develop human biological characteristics in laboratory animals, they should be given an opportunity early in the consent process to refuse to donate their tissues for IPS cell research.

These are just a few examples of the factors that must be addressed during the informed consent process. My main point here is that, given the unique nature of iPS cell research, the ethical challenges of ensuring rigorous informed consent and of preventing the excessive lure of "therapeutic hope"[10] may be especially acute.

Another ethical factor to consider involves the welfare interests of patients who in the foreseeable future may seek our clinical research involving human iPS cells or their direct derivatives. These human studies could include first-time research volunteers or original donors for autologous transplantation studies. In either case, the potential for abuse is great. Unlike attempting to generate patient-specific pluripotent stem cells via somatic cell nuclear transfer (cloning), iPS cell research is relatively easy. There are no scarce human eggs to procure or micromanipulation techniques to master, as in human research cloning. Almost any competent cell biologist or geneticist can attempt to produce human iPS cells. This fact alone may compound the ever-present and very real threat that some researchers or clinicians could move too quickly to human clinical trials or offer unproven "treatments" using human stem cells. Again, the keen exploitability of desperate patients and their families should not be casually shrugged off. Presently the ISSCR is in the process of organizing a multinational, multidisciplinary task force to draft international guidelines for the clinical translation of stem cells. Undoubtedly, the implications of these recent breakthroughs in iPS cell research will be a major issue for this new task force.

Admittedly, some observers will argue that the majority of the concerns I have raised here are manageable as long as rigorous standards of informed consent are upheld and strict guidelines for translational research are followed. Some may even find reassurance in the belief that human iPS cell research should be capable of producing valuable patient- and disease-specific stem cell lines without resorting to human research cloning and ushering in all its perceived social consequences. Others may applaud the apparent ability of iPS cells to preserve some people's conceptions of the sanctity of potential or nascent human life. From certain moral and theological points of view, isn't human iPS cell research superior to all other methods for deriving pluripotent stem cells?

Perhaps not—at least not according to the very same value suppositions of the public that I just described. It is worth noting that human iPS cell research carries the familiar ring of old philosophical questions about reproduction, life, and what it means to be human. The Yamanaka and Thomson research teams have shown that ordinary skin cells can be driven back to a primitive, embryonic state of pluripotency. But no one knows yet exactly where the limits of this reprogramming technique lie. Perhaps iPS cell researchers will discover that skin cells can be driven back even further in development to a totipotent state—that is, to a single zygote-like cell capable of generating not only all three germ layers but also all the supporting extra-embryonic tissues. If this were happen, then one could argue that any cell in a person's body has the biological potential to give rise to another complete human being under the right circumstances, regardless of whether the original person is alive or recently deceased. Such a circumstance would be truly equivalent to human cloning in the original, horticultural sense of the Greek word *klon*—that is "twig."

Even if this bizarre scenario is deemed scientifically impossible, there is still another, perhaps more realistic possibility worth considering. Human iPS cells, if they are truly pluripotent, should be capable of generating human sex cells. But then this would entail that ordinary skin cells could be transformed into human sperm and eggs. This fact could radically alter our commonsense notions of human fertility and infertility. New biological categories and entities could result, and these have historically disrupted some of society's longstanding philosophical assumptions.

Without doubt, these recent breakthroughs in human iPS cell research are of monumental importance for both science and society, but the ethical issues corresponding to iPS cell research are much more complex than many might initially believe and should not be glossed over. Some may wonder whether we will soon enter a "Brave New World" with unimaginable scientific possibilities. I believe we are already standing in that world, and that researchers, patient advocacy groups, and the public should be both happy and cautious about it.

References

1. K. Takahashi, K. Tanabe, M, Ohnuki, et al., "Induction of Pluripotent Stem Cells from Adult Human Fibroblasts by Defined Factors," *Cell* 131 (2007): 861– 72; J. Yu, M.A. Vodyanik, K. Smuga-Otto, et al., "Induced Pluripotent Stem Cell Lines Derived from Human Somatic Cells," *Science*, published online November 20, 2007.

2. I. Hyun, K. Hochedlinger, R. Jaenisch, and S. Yamanaka, "New Advances in iPS Cell Research Do Not Obviate the Need for Human Embryonic Stem Cells," *Cell Stem Cell* 1 (2007): 367– 68.

3. Takahashi et al., "Induction of Pluripotent Stem Cells from Adult Human Fibroblasts by Defined Factors"; Yu et al., "Induced Pluripotent Stem Cell Lines Derived from Human Somatic Cells."

4. J.A. Byrne, D.A. Pedersen, L.L. Clepper, et al., "Producing Primate Embryonic Stem Cells by Somatic Cell Nuclear Transfer," *Nature* 450 (2007): 497– 502.

5. D. Egli, J. Rosains, G. Birkhoff, and K. Eggan, "Developmental Reprogramming after Chromosome Transfer into Mitotic Mouse Zygotes," *Nature* 447 (2007): 679– 85.

6. Hyun, Hochedlinger, Jaenisch, and Yamanaka, "New Advances in iPS Cell Research."

7. International Society for Stem Cell Research, "Guidelines for the Conduct of Human Embryonic Stem Cell Research,"http://www.isscr.org /guidelines / ISSCRhESCguidelines2006.pdf (2006).

8. I. Hyun, "Magic Eggs and the Frontier of Stem Cell Science," *Hasting Center Report* 36, no. 2 (2006): 16–19.

9. International Society for Stem Cell Research, "Guidelines for the Conduct of Human Embryonic Stem Cell Research."

10. Hyun, "Magic Eggs."

Ontological and Ethical Implications of Direct Nuclear Reprogramming

Gerard Magill and William B. Neaves

Magill and Neaves argue that the 2007 scientific breakthrough of producing induced pluripotent stem cells (iPS cells) from human skin cells has ethical implications for how we regard natural human

Magill, Gerard and William B. Neaves. From "Ontological and Ethical Implications of Direct Nuclear Reprogramming," *Kennedy Institute of Ethics*, Vol. 19, no. 1, (2009): 23–32. © 2009 The Johns Hopkins University Press. Reprinted with permission of The Johns Hopkins University Press.

embryos, as well as embryos produced by cloning (i.e., somatic cell nuclear transfer).

The iPS cells share with embryos the potential to develop, given the right conditions, into a late-term fetus. Further research may show that iPS cells, like embryos, can also make their own placentas. This would make them indistinguishable in relevant ways from embryos (however produced). Thus, logically speaking, those who consider an embryo the moral equivalent of a person and seek to protect them must either extend the same protection to iPS cells or change the criteria for personhood to ones that rely on features from a later state of embryonic development. Otherwise, defenders of the embryo-as-person view must reject using iPS cells for therapeutic purposes, in the same way that they reject the destruction of embryos and cloning.

A combination of two recent scientific breakthroughs may transform the ethical landscape of stem cell research. The discoveries deal with direct nuclear reprogramming of human skin cells and with the progression of reprogrammed mouse cells into fetuses. The laboratories of Yamanaka (Takahashi et al. 2007) and of Thomson (Yu et al. 2007) crossed a threshold to highlight a crucial aspect of cellular life. They demonstrated that direct nuclear reprogramming can drive back the development of human skin cells to yield induced pluripotent stem (iPS) cells—i.e., cells that resemble and behave like embryonic stem cells in their developmental potential, despite not being derived from embryos. The production of human iPS cells resulted from a prior breakthrough in reprogramming mouse cells (Okita, Ichisaka, and Yamanaka 2007).

A simultaneously published study on reprogrammed mouse cells by the Jaenisch laboratory in Boston demonstrated that these cells can develop into live late-term fetuses if provided a placenta by injecting them into a tetraploid blastocyst four cell and implanting the resulting cell mass in a uterus (Wernig et al. 2007). This procedure, also known as tetraploid complementation, was developed by Andras Nagy and Janet Rossant to characterize the full developmental potential of embryonic stem cells (Nagy et al. 1990). Tetraploid complementation combines ordinary diploid embryonic stem cells with developmentally compromised tetraploid blastocysts, which are formed by fusing the two diploid cells from the first cell division after fertilization and growing the resulting tetraploid cell into a blastocyst. When these aggregates composed of embryonic stem cells inserted into tetraploid blastocysts are implanted in a uterus, the embryo proper forms entirely from the diploid embryonic stem cells,

while the tetraploid component contributes only to the extraembryonic membranes and placenta (Tanaka, Hadjantonakis, and Nagy 2001).

The tetraploid complementation procedure has become the definitive method for proving cellular pluripotency (Nagy et al. 1993), and it was in this context that the Jaenisch lab employed it to demonstrate pluripotency of mouse iPS cells (Wernig et al. 2007). It would be impractical and unethical to ascertain if human iPS cells could develop into a late-term fetus. However, the combined results of these studies provide persuasive evidence that reprogrammed human cells could develop into a human fetus if they were placed in an environment that would provide a placenta and uterine support. No evidence indicates that anyone has attempted tetraploid complementation with primate cells, but there is likewise no basis for believing it would not work.

This new science reveals that every cell in the human body has the biological capacity or natural potentiality, given appropriate supportive interventions and the right circumstances, of becoming a fetus. Previously, the beginning of early human life was associated with the process of fertilization. The technology known as somatic cell nuclear transfer (SCNT) made it possible to unlock the developmental potential of an ordinary body cell by exposing its nucleus to factors found in an unfertilized egg, a zygote, or embryonic stem cells. Now with direct reprogramming, pluripotent cells can be generated with the potential to form a clone of the cell donor if the reprogrammed cells are placed in an environment that would allow formation of a placenta and are gestated in a uterus. Hence, directly reprogrammed cells can form cloned organisms capable of developing into fetuses just as can occur in the case of SCNT. Of course, no responsible scientist would try to reproduce a human being from either SCNT or from direct nuclear reprogramming—there is no substantive dispute over that issue.

The significance of reprogrammed cells, whether produced by SCNT or by the direct method of Yamanaka, is that the beginning of what could become personal human life is associated with any ordinary cell in the body. This reality reflects the presence of the entire human genome—the genetic code for the development of a completely formed human being—inside the nucleus of each of trillions of cells in the adult human body. The genes responsible for embryonic and fetal development reside in every ordinary body cell (Gurdon, Byrne, and Simonsson 2003; Hyun 2008). The technology of direct nuclear reprogramming can unlock the expression of these genes and with appropriate manipulation such as that employed by the Jaenisch lab (Okita, Ichisaka, and Yamanaka 2007), enable any body cell to become a fetus that is a clone of the donor of the reprogrammed skin cell. Therefore, iPS cells have the biological capacity to develop into a fetus and indeed possibly to be born as an individual person.

This natural capacity can be construed as referring to what is described in the philosophical argument of natural potentiality as "the potential encoded in, and expressive of, one's nature or kind" (DeGrazia 2007. p. 303), or "basic natural capacity" (George 2008, p. 23).

Now ordinary body cells can develop into a fetus without involving an enucleated egg. Because it is technically possible to develop a fetus from reprogrammed human cells, the question of their ontological status arises with ensuing ethical implications for research. By ontological status we mean the assignment of either personal or potentially personal life in the sense of having full moral respect. The new scientific data on iPS cells raises fundamental philosophical questions about the ontological status of cellular activity at the beginning of human life. Addressing these questions within the framework of an ethical analysis that focuses upon consistency could challenge philosophical arguments to assign full moral respect for human cellular development from its inception.

Ethical Analysis

Proponents of the philosophical argument of natural potentiality seek to protect human cellular development from its inception as personal. The basic rationale for this stance is that a human embryo directs its own integral organismic function from its beginning, developing its underlying natural potentiality by virtue of the entity it is. From the point at which it comes into being, there is a whole, albeit immature, and distinct human organism that is intrinsically valuable with the status of inviolability and deserving full moral respect (understanding inviolability and moral respect synonymously). The basis for this moral respect is the embryo's inherent natural capacity, or natural potentiality, as described above. Hence, it is argued that the human embryo is an end in itself and should not be used merely as a means to benefit others such as occurs in research that entails its destruction (Gómez-Lobo 2007, p. 312; George and Gómez-Lobo 2005). Proponents of this stance prohibit research on embryos arising from natural fertilization, somatic cell nuclear transfer, and "other cloning technologies" (George and Gómez-Lobo 2005, p. 206). The question is whether the consistency that has appeared so robust in this stance is placed in jeopardy by the demonstration of the Jaenisch lab that iPS cells can produce a cloned fetus.

The realization that any adult body cell could engender a fetus was first established by SCNT. This knowledge is now reinforced by the new cloning technology using iPS cells. Both technologies show that any ordinary body cell has the potential to become a late-term fetus. This information provides sharper contours to the consistency challenge that the natural potentiality argument must address.

The critical question is whether the natural potentiality argument pertains to the use of iPS cells as a cloning technology. A leading proponent of the natural potentiality argument explains as follows: In SCNT scientists "are doing more than merely placing the somatic cell in an environment hospitable to its continuing maturation and development. They are generating a wholly distinct, self-integrating, entirely new organism—an embryo" (George 2008. p. 30). The same argument pertains to iPS cells. Direct reprogramming, like SCNT, initiates a cellular process that, with appropriate supportive interventions, can generate an organism intrinsically capable of developing into a late-term fetus.

If the natural potentiality argument applies to cells produced by SCNT, consistency appears to demand its application to iPS cells. However, accepting natural potentiality in the case of cells made either by SCNT or by direct reprogramming leads logically to the conclusion that these cells merit ethical protection. But if the natural potentiality argument should be invoked to prohibit research on iPS cells because they have the biological capacity or natural potentiality of becoming a late-term fetus, such a prohibition is likely to appear absurd given its reach to every cell in the body. The appearance of absurdity lies in preventing science from exploiting the potential of ordinary body cells through direct nuclear reprograming for life-saving medical research.

It may be argued that human iPS cells do not merit ethical protection because they are merely pluripotent and must be artificially provided with a placenta to develop into a fetus, unlike fertilized eggs and cells made by SCNT that are totipotent and can develop their own placenta. But that argument may not be convincing for at least two reasons. First, although the placenta provides sustenance and a supportive environment that includes growth factor signals to the inner cell mass, such interaction is bidirectional and typical of signaling between cells and tissues throughout embryonic development. Indeed, the trophoblast depends on signals from the inner cell mass to proliferate and differentiate into the placenta. Most significantly, the placenta contributes no genetic or cellular elements to the substance of the embryo or fetus, and it is completely discarded at the end of gestation. Second, the natural potentiality argument that requires protection of IVF embryos also seems to apply to iPS cells. The former need artificial support during cultivation *in vitro* and insertion into the uterus as the indispensable environment for their natural potential to be realized, while the latter also would need to be supported artificially by the provision of a placenta via tetraploid complementation.

A reprogrammed human cell is not fundamentally different from a nuclear-transfer or natural fertilization zygote in its ability to become a fetus. The zygote makes its own placenta, while the reprogrammed skin cell must be provided with one, but the placenta never becomes part of the embryo itself. Both the reprogrammed skin cells and the cells of the blastocyst's inner cell mass solely form the respective embryos. That is, reprogrammed skin cells have the same developmental potential as do the cells of the inner cell mass of the blastocyst formed by a zygote. Hence, an iPS cell in an appropriate environment can from its beginning direct its own integral organismic development into a fully-formed, late-term fetus, which is the basic rationale of the natural potentiality argument.

Furthermore, one must recognize that efforts at direct reprogramming of adult somatic cells have focused on making pluripotent cells, not totipotent cells. The research community has devoted intense effort to making induced pluripotent stem cells (iPS cells) because of the therapeutic potential offered by their ability to develop into any ordinary body cell. No known effort has been directed to making induced totipotent stem cells (iTS cells), since there is no apparent therapeutic advantage gained by adding the ability to make a placenta. If the objective were to study development of the placenta's precursor, the trophoblast, this can be accomplished by treating either human embryonic stem cells or human iPS cells with a specific cell signaling factor, bone morphogenetic protein 4. If the only advantage of induced totipotent cells were in facilitating reproductive cloning, scientists would universally condemn such an objective in the context of human application.

However, if making totipotent cells by direct reprogramming were seriously attempted for future research purposes, it is likely that a combination of transcription factors could be found that would activate the genes required for making a placenta as well as an embryo. Each somatic cell does, after all, contain the complete human genome, including the genes required for making the trophoblast, which becomes the placenta, as well as the inner cell mass, which becomes the embryo proper. The fact that human iPS cells can be induced to differentiate into trophoblastic cells makes this point clearly. Some might argue that iPS cells are morally different from embryonic stem cells made by SCNT because they are merely pluripotent while the latter are totipotent. However, such an argument will fail as soon as someone discovers a combination of transcription factors and chemical agents that directly activate a somatic cell's genes for making both trophoblast and inner cell mass simultaneously.

Hence, for the natural potentiality argument, consistency must recognize a continuum between natural fertilization, SCNT, and iPS cells. And applying the natural potentiality argument here would also extend to totipotent derivatives if iTS cells were developed. Each involves similar personal ontological status and entails similar claims to protection from research that disrupts their cellular development. The recent production of iPS cells enhances the awareness of this continuum, but in so doing, it highlights a *prima facie* absurdity for the natural potentiality argument, as described previously.

Consistency also suggests a challenging alternative to the natural potentiality argument. An alternative to protecting human embryonic development along this continuum—natural fertilization, SCNT, iPS cells, and iTS cells if ever developed—avoids the concern about *prima facie* absurdity by applying insights gained from reprogrammed human cells back across the continuum to SCNT and to natural fertilization. The production of reprogrammed human cells may provide support for a philosophical viewpoint opposed by the natural potentiality argument—a viewpoint that earliest human embryogenesis basically deals with the biological matter of cellular development, matter that is inadequate for the so-called form of human personhood. This nuanced idea is supported by the commonsense recognition that manipulating body cells to exploit their inherent pluripotency for medical research is justifiable and laudable. Indeed, that common-sense recognition seems initially to have been the basis of nearly universal public support for iPS cell research, even among proponents of the so-called natural potentiality argument who advocate protecting human life as personal from its inception.

This alternative viewpoint does not oppose the ethical protection of the early stages of human life, but it postpones the beginning of that protection to a point later than its cellular inception. Of course, determining when that subsequent point of protection should begin continues to be a debated question in secular and religious discourse that relates science, ethics, and policy.

Mistaken or Insightful Relief

The initial relief over the direct reprogramming of human cells voiced by some who protect human life from its earliest stages of cellular development appears to have been premised on a mistaken assumption that iPS cells were unrelated to embryogenesis. The misplaced relief was motivated by the desire to find an escape hatch for obtaining embryonic-like stem cells without destroying embryos. However, it is now clear that reprogrammed human cells have the integral potential to become an embryo and, in due course, a fetus. Hence, direct nuclear reprogramming can be placed on a continuum with the processes

of natural fertilization and SCNT. And each process on this continuum should be addressed with consistency.

Perhaps the most significant breakthrough resulting from direct nuclear reprogramming of human cells may not be an alternative source of embryonic-like stem cells, although that is indeed a superb accomplishment. Rather, the greatest significance might be its clarification of the ontological status of all forms of early cellular development along the continuum of natural potentiality that can result in the formation of a fetus. From this perspective, there may have been instinctive perspicacity in the initial sense of relief occasioned by the discovery of how ordinary body cells can be reprogrammed into iPS cells.

References

1. DeGrazia, David. 2007. Must We Have Full Moral Status throughout Our Existence? A Reply to Alfonso Gómez-Lobo. *Kennedy Institute of Ethics Journal* 17: 297–310.

2. George, Robert P. 2008. Embryo Ethics. *Daedalus* 137 (1): 23–35.

3. —and Gómez-Lobo, Alfonso. 2005. The Moral Status of the Human Embryo. *Perspectives in Biology and Medicine* 48: 201–10.

4. Gómez-Lobo, Alfonso. 2007. Inviolability at Any Age, *Kennedy Institute of Ethics Journal* 17: 311–20.

5. Hyun, Insoo. 2008. Stem Cells from Skin Cells: The Ethical Questions. *Hastings Center Report* 38 (1): 20–22.

6. Nagy, A; Gocza, E; Diaz, E. M.; et al. 1990. Embryonic Stem Cells Alone Are Able to Support Fetal Development in the Mouse. *Development* 110: 815–21.

7. Nagy, Andràs; Rossant, Janet; Nagy, Rèka; et al. 1993. Derivation of Completely Cell Culture-Derived Mice from Early-Passage Embryonic Stem Cells. *Proceedings of the National Academy of Sciences USA* 90: 8424–28.

8. Okita, Keisuke; Ichisaka, Tomoko; and Yamanaka, Shinya. 2007. Generation of Germline-Competent Induced Pluripotent Stem Cells. *Nature* 448:313–17.

9. Takahashi, Kazutoshi; Tanabe, Koji; Ohnuki, Mari; et al. 2007. Induction of Pluripotent Stem Cells from Adult Human Fibroblasts by Defined Factors. *Cell* 131:861–72.

10. Tanaka, Mika; Hadjantonakis, Anna-Katerina; and Nagy, Andràs. 2001. Aggregation Chimeras: Combining ES Cells, Diploid and Tetraploid Embryos. In *Gene Knockout Protocols*, ed. Martin Tymms and Ismail Kola, Series: Methods in Molecular Biology, Vol. 158, pp. 135–54. Totowa, NJ: Humans Press Inc.

11. Wernig, Marius; Meissner, Alexander; Foreman, Ruth; et al. 2007. In Vitro Reprogramming of Fibroblasts into a Pluripotent ES-Cell-Like State. *Nature* 448:318–24.

12. Yu, Junying; Vodyanik, Maxim; Smuga-Otto, Kim; et al. 2007. Induced Pluripotent Stem Cell Lines Derived from Human Somatic Cells. *Science* 318: 1917–20.

Declaration on the Production and the Scientific and Therapeutic Use of Human Embryonic Stem Cells

Pontifical Academy for Life

The declaration by the Pontifical Academy sets out the official Roman Catholic position on the moral aspects of acquiring and using human embryonic stem cells. The Academy declares it is not morally legitimate to produce or use human embryos as a source of stem cells, nor is it acceptable to use stem cells from cell lines already established. The Academy endorses the idea of directing research toward using adult stem cells to achieve the benefits that it is hoped embryonic stem cells might achieve. In 2008, the congregation for the Doctrine of the Faith issued "Instruction *Dignitas Personae* on Certain Bioethical Questions," in which it reaffirmed these positions and justifications.

Given the nature of this article, the key ethical problems implied by these new technologies are presented briefly, with an indication of the responses which emerge from a careful consideration of the human subject from the moment of conception. It is this consideration which underlies the position affirmed and put forth by the Magisterium of the Church.

The ***first ethical problem***, which is fundamental, can be formulated thus: *Is it morally licit to produce and/or use living human embryos for the preparation of ES cells?*

The answer is negative, for the following reasons:

1. On the basis of a complete biological analysis, the living human embryo is—from the moment of the union of the gametes—a *human subject* with a well defined identity, which from that point begins its own *coordinated, continuous and gradual development*, such that at no later stage can it be considered as a simple mass of cells.

2. From this it follows that as a *"human individual"* it has the *right* to its own life; and therefore every intervention which is not in favour of the embryo is an act which violates that right. Moral theology has always taught that in the case of *"jus certum tertii"* the system of probabilism does not apply.

3. Therefore, the ablation of the inner cell mass (ICM) of the blastocyst, which critically and

Pontifical Academy for Life, Vatican City, August 25, 2000.

irremediably damages the human embryo, curtailing its development, is a *gravely immoral* act and consequently is *gravely illicit.*

4. *No end believed to be good,* such as the use of stem cells for the preparation of other differentiated cells to be used in what look to be promising therapeutic procedures, *can justify an intervention of this kind.* A good end does not make right an action which in itself is wrong.

5. For Catholics, this position is explicitly confirmed by the Magisterium of the Church which, in the Encyclical *Evangelium Vitae,* with reference to the Instruction *Donum Vitae* of the Congregation for the Doctrine of the Faith, affirms: "The Church has always taught and continues to teach that the result of human procreation, from the first moment of its existence, must be guaranteed that unconditional respect which is morally due to the human being in his or her totality and unity in body and spirit: The human being is to be respected and treated as a person from the moment of conception; and therefore from that same moment his rights as a person must be recognized, among which in the first place is the inviolable right of every innocent human being to life."

The ***second ethical problem*** can be formulated thus: *Is it morally licit to engage in so-called "therapeutic cloning"* by producing cloned human embryos and then destroying them in order to produce ES cells?

The answer is negative, for the following reason: Every type of therapeutic cloning, which implies producing human embryos and then destroying them in order to obtain stem cells, is illicit; for there is present the ethical problem examined above, which can only be answered in the negative.

The **third ethical problem** can be formulated thus: *Is it morally licit to use ES cells, and the differentiated cells obtained from them, which are supplied by other researchers or are commercially obtainable?*

The answer is negative, since: prescinding from the participation—formal or otherwise—in the morally illicit intention of the principal agent, the case in question entails a proximate material cooperation in the production and manipulation of human embryos on the part of those producing or supplying them.

In conclusion, it is not hard to see the seriousness and gravity of the ethical problem posed by the desire to extend to the field of human research the production and/or use of human embryos, even from an humanitarian perspective.

The possibility, now confirmed, of using **adult stem cells** to attain the same goals as would be sought with embryonic stem cells—even if many further steps in both areas are necessary before clear and conclusive results are obtained—indicates that adult stem cells represent a more reasonable and humane method for making correct and sound progress in this new field of research and in the therapeutic applications which it promises. These applications are undoubtedly a source of great hope for a significant number of suffering people.

DECISION SCENARIOS

The questions following each decision scenario are intended to prompt reflection and discussion. In considering how to answer them, you should consider the information in the Briefing Session, the ethical theories and principles presentation in Part V, "Foundations of Bioethics," and the arguments and criticisms offered in the relevant readings in this chapter.

DECISION SCENARIO 1

Improving the Society One Embryo at a Time

"The concept behind the bill is very simple, Senator," said Jill Laude."We want to improve the nation, and we know how to begin. Thousands of couples each year rely on assisted reproduction, and they can tell the specialists to implant only embryos with genes for traits like intelligence and musical talent."

"So we can increase the number of smart and talented people who are born?"

"Exactly," Laude said."Over time, those numbers will add up. Then those talented kids will start having their own talented kids."

"I see what you mean, but how does the bill you want me to sponsor make that possible?"

"By a system of financial incentives," Laude said. "We start by paying half the costs of assisted reproduction for those who agree to choose the way the legislation specifies."

"I'm guessing that at stage two we pay the full amount."

"Good guess."Laude smiled. "Then after ten years we start rewarding people for using assisted reproduction, even when they don't need to."

"This will be very controversial, you know,"said the senator.

"We know,"Laude said. "But we think it's the most important piece of legislation imaginable. We need to keep our society competitive, and in the long run the whole human race will benefit."

1. Given the state of genetic knowledge at this time, is such a program feasible?

2. If the program is feasible in principle, is there anything objectionable about it in principle?

3. If you needed to have a child by means of the techniques of assisted reproduction, would you want the embryos tested to be sure that they are free from serious genetic diseases before they are used?

4. If it were possible to test for traits you view as positive, would you want the embryos tested for these traits before they are used?

DECISION SCENARIO 2

A Child Like Us

"Carl and I wouldn't know how to raise a regular child," Olivia Padrone said, "We know what it's like to be dwarfs, and we could help a child who was a dwarf."

"So you want me to help arrange for the genetic test, then counsel you on the results?" Dallas Stratford asked.

"Exactly, we want a child just like us," Olivia said. "We're proud of being dwarfs, and we're both active in getting people to recognize that our culture and way of life is as good as anyone else's. Having a regular child would betray our ideals and be false to our view of life."

"I don't know what to say," Dallas said. "Usually, people want to avoid having a child with the mutation that produces dwarfism."

1. Genetic counselors have been "value neutral," not recommending that a woman have an abortion, no matter what tests revealed about the fetus. Yet their neutrality is challenged when a woman is willing to abort a normal child to have a child who has a specific birth "defect," such as dwarfism, deafness, or blindness. Are there circumstances in which value neutrality should be set aside?

2. On what grounds might a counselor turn down the request of someone for help in having a child with a particular "defect"?

3. If dwarfism, deafness, or blindness is a way of life and a culture, is it wrong to discourage the birth of more people who belong to the culture?

4. Do we have a duty to select embryos that will produce the best children possible?

DECISION SCENARIO 3

Screening for Marriage

In 1983, a group of Orthodox Jews in New York and Israel initiated a screening program with the aim of eliminating from their community diseases transmitted as recessive genes. The group called itself Dor Yeshorim, "the generation of the righteous."

Because Orthodox Jews do not approve of abortion in most instances, the program does not employ prenatal testing. Instead, people are given a blood test to determine whether they carry the genes for Tay–Sachs, cystic fibrosis, or Gaucher's disease. Each person is given a six-digit identification number, and if two people consider dating, they are encouraged to call a hotline. They are told either that they are "compatible" or that they each carry a recessive gene for one of the three diseases. Couples who are carriers are offered genetic counseling.

During 1993, 8000 people were tested, and eighty-seven couples who were considering marriage decided against it after they learned that they were both carriers of recessive genes. The number of people tested has steadily increased, and some view the Dor Yeshorim program as a model that might be followed by other groups or by society in general.

The tests were initially only for Tay–Sachs, but over time other diseases were added and by 2010 the organization was testing for ten diseases all of them lethal or severely debilitating. However, some critics regard it as a mistake to have moved from testing for almost invariably lethal, untreatable diseases such as Tay–Sachs to testing for cystic fibrosis. Individuals may feel pressured into being tested, and those who are carriers of one or more disease-predisposing genes may become unmarriageable social outcasts. Considering that genes for most diseases manifest themselves in various degrees of severity, many individuals may suffer social rejection for inadequate reasons. For example, Gaucher's disease, which involves an enzyme defect producing anemia and an enlarged liver and spleen, manifests itself only after age forty-five in half the diagnosed cases. Further, although the disease may be fatal, it often is not, and the symptoms can be treated.

1. Is the Dor Yeshorim screening program a form of eugenics? If so, does this make it unacceptable?

2. Is the program a good model for a national screening program? If not, why not?

3. Is it reasonable to screen for nonlethal genetic diseases?

4. What are the dangers inherent in any screening program?

DECISION SCENARIO 4

A Duty Not to Reproduce?

"I'm sorry I wasn't able to bring you better news," Dr. Valery Mendez said.

Timothy Schwartz shook his head. "We gambled and lost," he said. "We can't say we didn't know what we were doing."

"That doesn't make it much easier," Judith Schwartz said. "When you said we were both Tay–Sachs carriers, I thought, well, it won't happen to us. But I was wrong. What about this new test? Can we really trust the results?"

"I'm afraid so," said Dr. Mendez. "The fetal cells were cultured, and the chromosome study showed that the child you're carrying will have Tay–Sachs."

"What do you recommend?" Mr. Schwartz asked.

"It's not for me to recommend. I can give you some information—tell you the options—but you've got to make your own decision."

"Is abortion the only solution?" Mrs. Schwartz asked.

"If you call it a solution," Mr. Schwartz said.

"The disease is invariably fatal," Dr. Mendez said. "And there is really no effective treatment for it. A lot of people think there may be in the future, but that doesn't help right now."

"So what does it involve?" Mr. Schwartz asked. "At first your child will seem quite normal, but that's only because it takes time for a particular chemical to build up in the brain. After the first year or so, the child will start to show signs of deterioration. He'll start losing his sight. Then, as brain damage progresses, he'll lose control over his muscles, and eventually he will die."

"And we just have to stand by and watch that happen?" Mrs. Schwartz asked.

"Nothing can be done to stop it," Dr. Mendez said. "It's a terrible and sad disease."

"We certainly do want to have a child," Mr. Schwartz said. "But we don't want to have one that is going to suffer all his life. I don't think I could stand that."

1. In this case, how persuasive is the argument that "genetic abortion" constitutes a threat to the principle that all persons are of equal value?

2. Can the argument that every child deserves a normal opportunity for a good life be used to justify requiring abortion in a case such as this?

3. Some use the notion of a child's right to an "open future" as grounds for refusing to assist deaf parents in having a deaf child. Could this same notion be used to justify recommending that a woman pregnant with a fetus carrying the Tay–Sach gene have an abortion?

4. How unfavorably must the odds be against having a normal child before parents might be said to have a duty not to reproduce? In what way is the seriousness of the disease at issue relevant to the odds?

DECISION SCENARIO 5

Justified Test?

"Has any close relative, like your mother, sister, or a grandmother, ever died of breast cancer?" Dr. Susan Jolan asked.

"No one," Lola A'tibe said. "But I want to be tested for the gene anyway. I'm 40 years old and very health conscious, so I'd like to do everything I can to protect myself from breast cancer."

"I understand your motive," Dr. Jolan said. "I'll arrange for you to be tested for both the BRCA1 and BRCA2 genes as soon as possible."

1. Is Dr. Jolan responding properly to her patient's concerns? Why or why not?

2. Private companies have developed genetic tests that can be administered to whoever wants them and can pay for them. Why might critics object to this service?

3. If a woman is found to be the carrier of one of the mutated genes that cause breast cancer, this does not mean that she will develop breast cancer. It does mean that she is at greater risk than other women. Is this the sort of information a woman might find worth having?

DECISION SCENARIO 6

A Duty to Tell or to Remain Silent?

"Dr. Gress, two of the people we tested for heart disease also turned out positive for the APOe gene," Clara Chang said. "Do we have an obligation to notify them that they are at risk of developing Alzheimer's?"

"Absolutely not," Charles Gress said. "We have an obligation *not* to notify them. What good would it do for them to know they're at risk for a disease that can't be prevented and can't be treated? It would only cause them distress and unhappiness."

1. Is Dr. Gress's position morally legitimate?

2. Does the fact that the knowledge was acquired accidentally as part of a research program and not at the request of the individuals relieve the investigators of any obligation to inform the test subjects of any genetic discoveries about them?

3. Could Dr. Gress's position be considered paternalistic? If so, how might we recommend that the genetic information about individual patients be handled?

4. Some hold that sometimes patients have a duty to know their genetic status, even if they would prefer not to. Might an investigator have a duty to inform a patient of his status, even if the patient has said he doesn't want to know the outcome of a test?

DECISION SCENARIO 7

Tampering with Human Life?

"I don't see the problem," Harold Lucas said. "We have the opportunity to eliminate at least one form of hereditary blindness forever."

"I'm not exactly in favor of blindness," Amy Lamont said. "I know that many blind people have a hard time in our society."

"So, let's slice out the defective gene that causes it and splice in one that does the job right," Lucas said. "With germ-line therapy, we can modify the sex cell of the carriers and get rid of that form of the disease."

Lamont shook her head. "It sounds humane, but it's not so easy as that," she said. "Wanting to eliminate blindness suggests there's something wrong with blind people and that it's better for them not to be born."

"I think it's better for them not to be born *blind*."

"Also, getting rid of that gene means modifying human beings," Amy Lamont said. "If we start doing that, I don't know when we would stop. We might do anything at all with them."

"You're afraid of some kind of wild eugenics scheme?"

"That's one problem," Lamont said. "My objection is deeper than that, though. I don't like the idea of tampering with human life and human destiny. To change ourselves deliberately is, I think, to make us something less than human."

1. Rephrase Lamont's arguments so they are explicit.

2. Does wanting to eliminate hereditary blindness imply that blind people are less worthy or less human than sighted people? Why or why not?

3. Is Lamont's objection to eliminating hereditary blindness a slippery slope argument? If so, how? If not, why not?

4. How useful is it to consider the elimination of blindness therapeutic and any change going beyond the "normal" range of human abilities enhancement?

DECISION SCENARIO **8**

Embryonic Stem Cells

"Research with embryonic stem cells must go forward," Tina Cuella said."We owe it to people with spinal-cord injuries, Parkinson's, diabetes, and a hundred other diseases who might be helped by treatments using stem cells."

"Do you also favor taking hearts, livers, and kidneys from living infants and giving them to other people?" Howard Lain asked."Because that's exactly like what you're doing when you destroy an embryo to get stem cells."

"That's ridiculous. An embryo isn't like a baby."

1. Why, according to some, is it morally wrong to destroy a human embryo?

2. What status can be ascribed to the human embryo?

3. What, according to those opposed to research cloning, are the limits on what we owe to the sick?

4. Why do those endorsing research cloning reject the slippery slope argument against research using embryos?

Chapter **4**

Reproductive Control

CHAPTER CONTENTS

CASES AND CONTEXTS

CASE PRESENTATION

The Octomom and the McCaughey Septuplets: The Perils of Multiple Pregnancies

Multiple births were once greeted with amazement and the mothers of multiples applauded as having achieved something difficult and admirable. The role of reproductive medicine in causing multiple births, however, has altered the public's attitude toward them, and multiple births are now more likely to evoke criticism than admiration.

The two most extreme recent cases are Nadya Suleman, who gave birth to eight babies in 2009, and Bobbi McCaughey, who gave birth to seven in 1997. In both cases, the birth announcements were met with interest and approval, but as people began to understand more about what such extreme multiple births involved, much of the approval turned into criticism. This transformation took place faster in the Suleman case. This is likely due in part to differences in the women's personal circumstances, but it may also be that the public has now grown

more sophisticated about assisted reproduction and come to understand more about its costs and perils.

The Octomom

When Nadya Suleman gave birth to eight babies at Kaiser-Permanente Hospital in Bellflower, California, in January 2009, she attracted the world's attention and received an outpouring of warmth and good wishes.

People thought of the thirty-three-year-old Suleman as an infertile, single woman who wanted a child so badly that she had been forced to turn to a fertility specialist for help. She was, people imagined, as surprised by the results as they were: instead of having one baby, she had ended up with eight.

This portrait of Suleman was almost entirely a projection of the public's romantic imagination. Perhaps it is part of the reason that, when facts began to emerge that presented a less flattering image of Suleman, much of the public turned against her with an indignation so severe, it amounted to spite. Nearly everything the public assumed to be true of her tuned out to be false.

What shocked people most was that Suleman already had six children—all born with the help of fertility specialist Tien C. Chieu. She was married at the time these children were born, but her husband, Marcus Gutierrez, wasn't their father. She apparently used sperm donated by her friend David Solomon to conceive all fourteen children. She collected the sperm herself and took it to Dr. Chieu's clinic. Chieu used it to fertilize eggs that he removed from Suleman. The resulting embryos were frozen.

Suleman had six pregnancies using the embryos, and in each instance six embryos were transferred to her uterus. Her first five pregnancies, which were presided over by Chieu, resulted in the birth of a single child in four cases and fraternal twins in one. "She wanted to have many, many babies," Chieu told reporter Stephanie Saul.

Suleman's mother, Angela, a retired teacher, begged Dr. Chieu not to help her daughter get pregnant again. Although Chieu agreed, Suleman was not satisfied with only six children, so she sought help from Dr. Michael M. Kamrava of the West Coast IVF Clinic in Beverly Hills. Suleman wanted to use up the remainder of her frozen embryos, so she asked Kamrava to transfer all six at the same time.

Kamrava agreed to this, even though it violated the guidelines of the American Society for Assisted Reproduction. Not only did all six embryos develop in Suleman's uterus, two of them split into twins. Thus, she gave birth to eight babies.

State Support

The public was also shocked to learn that Suleman, who had divorced her husband in 2008, was unemployed and lived with her parents. Her only income was money she received from public welfare programs. She was thus unable to pay even a small fraction of the $1.3 million hospital costs that resulted from delivering her eight fragile, low-birth-weight babies and providing them with the intensive care they required. What's more, Suleman had no way to support her fourteen children. For the foreseeable future, she and her children would be dependent on state and federal assistance programs for food, shelter, clothing, and medical care.

The services of fertility specialists are rarely covered by insurance and are not covered by Medicaid, and each round of treatment costs at least $12,000–15,000. So where did Suleman get the money to pay Chieu and Kamrava? Apparently, she used her worker's compensation benefits. She had been employed as a psychiatric technician at Metropolitan State Hospital, and in 1999 she filed a claim alleging that she had suffered a back injury in performing her duties. She took her case to the Workers Compensation Appeals Board in 2001 and eventually received about $167,000.

Hostile Public

Public attention turned hostile as these facts emerged. Some people suggested that Suleman was deliberately exploiting the welfare system, having children to guarantee that she would never have to work again. Others thought she might be suffering from some unusual psychiatric disorder, such as a compulsion to have children. She acquired an agent, gave a long interview to NBC-TV, and seemed to be angling for a media deal. The tabloid media reflected the new public attitude toward Suleman by dubbing her "the Octomom."

Suleman deflected all criticisms. She loved children, she said, and she wanted a large family because she had been lonely growing up. Also, she planned to go back to work and support her children as soon as she was able.

Nothing Suleman said seemed to convince her critics, for what sort of job could Suleman, with her limited education, get that would pay enough to support fourteen children? Everyone who paid taxes would be paying for her foolish whim, a whim abetted by medical professionals who should have known better and refused to help her take such irrevocable steps. Instead, they accepted her money and violated professional guidelines.

A few people came to Suleman's defense. She didn't deserve to be vilified, they argued, because she didn't do anything wrong. Having a lot of children was neither illegal nor immoral. A number of people pointed out that the McCaughey family had escaped public condemnation when they had decided to go through with a pregnancy that would leave them with seven children. Like Suleman, the McCaugheys also couldn't pay their medical bills, nor could they afford to house, care for, feed, and educate their children.

McCaughey Septuplets

Shortly before noon on November 19, 1997, in Des Moines, Iowa, twenty-nine-year-old Bobbi McCaughey gave birth to seven babies by cesarean section.

McCaughey had set what was then a world record for the number of live babies born in a single pregnancy. The family was immediately bathed in the glare of worldwide media attention, and for a while they became emblems of the American family: hardworking, religious, and committed to the welfare of their children. Bobbi McCaughey was admired for her courage and fortitude for coping so well with a difficult thirty-one-week pregnancy.

To help prevent a miscarriage, she had been confined to bed in the nineteenth week, and for the last two months she had been hospitalized. Although all the babies had a lower than normal birth weight, ranging from 2.5 to 3.4 pounds, with the help of the more than forty obstetricians, neonatologists, pediatricians, and other specialists who attended the birth, the babies all survived. Some suffered difficulties, but eventually even they were pulled to safety by aggressive medical management.

Fertility Drugs

Because the McCaugheys had experienced difficulty conceiving their first child, Mikayla, they sought help from an infertility clinic when they were ready to have another. Bobbi McCaughey was treated with Pergonal to increase her chances of becoming pregnant, which she soon did.

Pergonal is one of several fertility drugs associated with multiple pregnancies. The drugs increase the likelihood of pregnancy by causing more than one egg to be released per menstrual cycle, and this also increases the likelihood that more than one egg will be fertilized.

Early in Mrs. McCaughey's pregnancy, her physician informed the couple that she was carrying seven fetuses and recommended that some of them be terminated. The elimination procedure, called *selective reduction*, involves deliberately destroying and removing fetuses and is performed to increase the chances that the remaining fetuses will develop into healthy babies. The McCaugheys rejected the recommendation on the ground that their religious beliefs made abortion unacceptable. "God gave us those babies," Mrs. McCaughey told a reporter. "He wants us to raise them."

Dangers

A multiple pregnancy increases the risk of a miscarriage. Mark Evans, a fertility expert at Wayne State Hospital, estimates that a woman pregnant with quadruplets has a twenty-five percent chance of a miscarriage in the first trimester; a woman pregnant with quintuplets has a fifty percent chance. Cases of pregnancies with a larger number of fetuses are too few to permit significant generalizations.

The risk of losing all fetuses to a miscarriage was sadly illustrated by the case of Mary Atwood in England. Pregnant with eight fetuses, she arranged to sell her story to a tabloid, with the amount she would be paid dependent on the number of surviving babies. All eight were lost in a miscarriage.

Even when a miscarriage doesn't occur, multiple pregnancies rarely reach the end of a full forty-week term. Triplets are born after an average of 33.5 weeks and quadruplets after thirty-one weeks. The result is that babies born as multiples often suffer from one or more of the many problems of prematurity: retinal damage causing blindness, bleeding into the brain producing permanent brain damage, retardation, learning disabilities, impaired motor skills, chronic lung problems, or cerebral palsy.

Irresponsible?

The McCaugheys, like Nadya Suleman, were luckier than Mary Atwood, but fertility specialists who permit multiple pregnancies to continue have many critics. Some believe Bobbi McCaughey's specialists should have stopped the fertility drugs sooner and perhaps prevented the release of so many eggs. Others think the specialists should have required the McCaugheys to agree to a selective reduction of multiple fetuses before starting Mrs. McCaughey's treatment. Also, when it became apparent how many fetuses were present, they should have pressed the McCaugheys harder to eliminate some of them.

Critics also see the McCaugheys as having acted irresponsibly. If they weren't prepared to accept selective reduction, they shouldn't have sought help from an infertility clinic. Also, because they were lucky enough to have a good outcome, their example may suggest that multiple pregnancies are now safe and reliable, and thus others may be encouraged to believe they can safely have multiple babies.

Costs

The cost of medical care for Mrs. McCaughey and her children is estimated to be around $1.5 million. This was the money the McCaugheys couldn't afford to pay, so it had to be picked up in some way by the health care system and the society. With so much medical need unmet, society cannot afford to indulge the wishes of others like Nadya Suleman and the McCaugheys.

Responsible Specialists

Responsible infertility specialists discourage multiple pregnancies. Their aim is to assist a woman in having one or at most two healthy babies. A multiple pregnancy carried to term is viewed not so much as a mark of success as a sign of failure. In 2009, in an effort to reduce the number of multiple pregnancies, the American Society for Reproductive Medicine and the Society for Assisted Reproduction offered revised guidelines regarding the number of embryos that should be transferred into the uterus. For women younger than 35 and likely to become

pregnant, the recommended number is no more than two. For women 35–37 and less likely to become pregnant, the number is two to three; for women between 38 and 40 and even less likely to become pregnant, the number is no more than four. For women older than 40 the recommend number is five for fewer.

Infertility clinics are almost completely self-regulated, however, and the guidelines are not binding. Thus, the penalty for the failure to prevent multiple births is borne by the woman, her babies, the family, and the society, but not by the clinic treating her. This situation has led many critics to demand that the fertility industry, an industry worth a billion dollars a year, be brought under the law and reasonable regulations enforced.

Figures published in 2010 showed that the number of multiple births has leveled off. Even so, they still occur with sufficient frequency that infertility clinics are likely to remain under pressure either to reduce the number or become subject to government regulation. Births are almost always occasions for joy, but almost invariably multiple births are occasions for trouble and tragedy.

SOCIAL CONTEXT
Shopping the Sperm Supermarket

Jane Nuffield (as we will call her) is a thirty-four-year-old product-liability attorney who has risen to the rank of partner in her law firm. She owns a large house in a gated community in a Chicago suburb and spends a month every year in Paris. She earns a mid-six-figure income and regularly receives bonuses.

Jane works hard, but she is generally happy with her life. Although she had hoped to be married by her age, nothing ever quite worked out with the men she dated. They had expected her either to act deferential and dependent, which she wasn't about to do, or to support them in comfort and leisure, which she wasn't about to do either. Now she was in no particular hurry to get married, but she did want to have a baby.

She wanted it enough that she decided to become a single mother. She had always gotten what she wanted out of life by her own efforts, and she saw no reason why having a baby should be any different. Her first step, before she even consulted a fertility expert, was to go online and do a Google search, then explore the offerings of the various sperm banks that turned up.

A New Breed

Jane was one of the many women taking a new road. Traditionally, single mothers in our society haven't been treated with respect. More likely than not, they have been young adults with little education, no money, and few job skills. Thus, as a group, they have been regarded as presenting a social problem, and the most effective way of addressing the problem, reformers have claimed, is to introduce policies and educational programs to reduce the number of single mothers.

The new breed of single mothers that is emerging runs completely counter to this social stereotype. Like Jane, they are women from their late twenties to mid-thirties who occupy the upper tiers of income, education, and occupations. They are lawyers, psychologists, physicians, and executives. They aren't women who find themselves accidentally pregnant and then decide to have the child and cope with the ensuing problems of poverty and unemployment. Rather, like Jane, they decide they want to become mothers and then set out in a deliberate fashion to achieve that aim.

Mothers by Choice

Women wanting to become pregnant have traditionally planned on getting married first. Yet many professional women now don't see marriage as a necessary or even particularly desirable step to take. Those who are like Jane and well along in their careers might once have settled for marrying Mr. Okay if they had failed to find Mr. Right. Now, however, they are unwilling to make such a compromise.

The increase in the number of physicians specializing in reproductive medicine and easy access to the technology of assisted reproduction, particularly sperm banking, makes it possible for single women to exercise more control over their own procreation than has ever before been possible. If they are in good health and have the financial resources required, they can guarantee themselves a good chance at having a child without directly involving a man.

Employing easily available fertility services is a new way for women to take control of their own reproduction without becoming involved in any personal complications. A single woman wanting to become pregnant without getting married might once have approached a male friend with the idea of making him (with or without his consent) the father of her child. Now she doesn't need to ask any man for a favor or engage in either deception or bargaining. If she can afford to, she can seek out medical methods for becoming pregnant.

This approach has the advantage of allowing her to avoid the emotional entanglements of having a child with a man she knows. Also, she can avoid the possibility that the man might either discover that the child is also his or change his mind about remaining silent and letting her have custody of the child. In either case, he may decide that he wants joint or even complete custody.

In addition, some lesbian couples are now deciding that one of them should become pregnant so that they can have a child and form a family. They need not spend time attempting to locate a sympathetic and obliging man willing both to become a father and to relinquish all claims on the child. Like Jane or any other single woman, the would-be lesbian mother with the financial resources need only locate a sperm bank that will accept her as a candidate for insemination.

Numbers?

No one knows exactly how many "choice moms" (as some call themselves) there are or whether they represent a trend that is increasing. Some evidence suggests that the number is going up. For example, reporter Amy Harmon learned that the local chapters of Single Mothers by Choice, a support group, doubled from twelve to twenty-five over a three-year period and that about 3000 of its 4000 members had used donor sperm. Some evidence also comes from census figures. The latest census found that more than 150,000 women with college degrees are single mothers who have never been married and are heads of their households. This is triple the number from the 2000 census. It is unlikely that even half these women used a sperm donor to become pregnant, but the large increase suggests that the number of choice moms is also on the increase.

Browsing the Catalogue

Some women deciding to become choice moms are enthusiastic about the possibilities that commercial sperm banks offer. Rather than selecting a mate, they get to select from a range of genetic material, often guided by the sort of background genetic information that is not available when a woman chooses a mate. (How many women ask potential mates to submit to a genetic analysis?)

Most commercial sperm banks have websites that allow potential mothers to browse through a catalogue of sperm donors and choose the one they prefer. The sperm banks typically provide detailed information about a donor, including age, race, medical history, family history, appearance, interests, educational attainments, and occupation. Some, with the permission of donors, include photographs, either baby pictures or recent ones. Other services offered, such as listening to a recording of a donor's voice, generally cost more.

Some sperm banks also offer ways for donors to reveal aspects of their personality. Thus, donors may write a personal essay or a letter about themselves that can be read by a prospective purchaser–recipient. Later, the letter can be given to a child conceived by the use of the donor's sperm. Donors are sometimes even asked to indicate their willingness to meet their biological child in the future if the child requests it.

Rather than browsing, women using the websites of some sperm banks can use a search function to see if the bank has available sperm from donors possessing particular characteristics. The traits sought range from race and blood type to level of education, eye and hair color, height, build, and physical appearance.

Some choice moms worry about having a child who will develop a severe mental illness like schizophrenia. Thus, they make a point of selecting donors who are past the age of the early to mid-twenties, when such illnesses usually appear. Other choice moms see selecting sperm as a chance of having a child who has physical characteristics (auburn hair, gray-green eyes, a tall stature) that they admire. By contrast, some women try to choose characteristics more like their own, so that their child will be more likely to resemble them, rather than an anonymous donor.

Other choice moms look for evidence of outstanding intelligence. They choose sperm acquired from men with advanced academic degrees who are in occupations requiring a high level of intellectual achievement. But for almost all choice moms, the very fact that they are free to make a choice is regarded as empowering. Although they may regret not having met a man to marry and father their child, they are pleased that this doesn't mean that they must give up their idea of motherhood.

A woman can learn only a limited amount from the description of a sperm donor, and if she knew the person, she might not have chosen his sperm. This was illustrated in 2007 when fifty-year-old Jeffrey Harrison responded to a newspaper ad placed by two teenagers. The young women had discovered that their mothers had both bought the sperm of Donor 150, and they asked him to get in touch with them.

Harrison, who sold his sperm frequently to California Cryobank in the late 1980s, had been described to potential clients as someone with blue eyes who was six feet tall and interested in philosophy, music, and drama. They were also told that Donor 150 was one of the sperm bank's most requested donors. Some two decades after his stint as a donor, Harrison was living in an RV with four dogs near Venice Beach in Los Angeles and scraping out a living by doing odd jobs and taking care of people's dogs. After meeting him, one of his biological daughters described him as "a free spirit."

Why Now?

Assisted reproduction has found a niche in our society. Its accomplishments are well publicized, and its techniques have become more sophisticated. Also, the stigma once attached to it as a producer of "test-tube babies" has mostly dissipated, and it has become a recognized medical specialty. Thus, single women wanting to have a child are likely to be aware of the possibility of using a sperm donor and to feel no shame about doing so. Becoming a single mother with the help of assisted reproduction no longer brings with it the taint of social disapproval.

Not only are women now free to control their own procreation, but the experiences of other women may prompt them to do so. A widely read book published in 2002 by economist Sylvia Hewlett found that about a third of professional women in their forties had no children. Hewlett later suggested to reporter Amy

Harmon that women in their fifties had more regrets about not having a child than they did about not having a partner. Thus, choice moms may be reacting to the experiences of women a generation older: those who set aside the traditional wife-and-mother role to pursue opportunities offered to them by a more open society.

The choice moms may be determined to have professional success while also preserving the option of motherhood, even if this means that they must exercise this option by making use of commercial sperm donors and the techniques of assisted reproduction. In an ironic social twist, women are now more able to create their own brave new world than men are.

The Price of Eggs—Egg Donors: Rewards, Risks, and Exploitation

Amanda Criswell (as we will call her) was a twenty-six-year-old nursing student when she saw the ad in her college paper:

Earn Up to $10,000!

Help infertile couples have a family by becoming an egg donor. If you are between the ages of 20 and 30 and in good health, you may be a candidate. Height and weight are important.

Amanda had borrowed all the money she could from the student loan program, and her part-time job as a receptionist at a restaurant didn't pay enough to let her stay in school. Dropping out and getting a full-time job meant giving up her dream.

Amanda called the number in the ad. She became an egg donor, and somewhat to her surprise, she discovered that being a donor was personally satisfying as well as financially rewarding. She liked the idea that she could help people have a family. The second time she donated eggs was easier than the first, because she knew what to expect. The experience wasn't

pleasant, but she found it satisfying. It also let her stay in school and complete her degree.

Advertising

An ad in the Columbia University student newspaper several years ago offered students $35,000 for becoming an egg donor, and similar offers have appeared in publications at Harvard, Princeton, and other Ivy League institutions. Ads in college newspapers throughout the country typically offer fees of up to $10,000–15,000 to recruit young women students to donate eggs, and some of the same ads appear on Craigslist and Facebook. In large cities, it is not unusual to see billboards with the headline "EGG DONORS NEEDED," followed by a telephone number and a promise of confidentiality.

Such advertisements have become so common that most people screen them out as just more litter in the media landscape. Even so, their frequency is an indicator that human donor ova are more in demand than ever before. The Centers for Disease Control reported that in

2006 (the most recent figures) donor eggs were used in the birth of some 10,000 children in the United States alone. This is almost double the number just a year earlier, and it is reasonable to believe that the number of children born from donor eggs has continued to increase since 2006.

In addition to donor eggs needed by fertility clinics, centers specializing in privately funded stem-cell research need eggs so that researchers can produce the embryos required to acquire embryonic stem cells. No agency keeps a count of how many eggs have been acquired from donors, but the number appears to be very low. The 2005 guidelines of the National Academy of Sciences discourages paying donors, and the California Institute for Regenerative Medicine pays only for a donor's travel expenses and lost wages. New York's Empire State Stem Cell Board, by contrast, adopted a policy in 2009 allowing researchers to pay up to $10,000 to an ovum donor. Fertility clinics, rather than research labs, are by far the main recruiters of egg donors.

Donor Risks

The significant increase in the use of "donated" eggs raises ethical and social issues about the process by which eggs are acquired and about the risks their acquisition poses to the donors. All are young women, many are college students, and most are motivated to contribute their eggs for the money they are promised. In the past, egg donors were sisters, relatives, or close friends, and money was not involved.

Age, relative inexperience, and the need for money may make potential ova donors vulnerable to exploitation: they may not be adequately informed about foreseeable risks or warned about the possibility of unknown risks. Also, young women, particularly those under financial pressure, may discount the seriousness of the risks they will be taking or not appreciate the serious nature of the commitment they are making. In addition to running the risk of serious injury or even death, a potential donor must accept the prospect of having a biological child born to another woman, a child she most likely will never meet.

Sperm donors (see Briefing Session) usually receive only about $50 to $200, but the process of making the donation is virtually risk free. By contrast, women who become egg donors must invest a couple of weeks of their time, experience pain and discomfort, and put their health and very lives at risk. They must agree to be injected with a series of hormones to stimulate their ovaries, and the hormones are likely to produce such symptoms as nausea, bloating, weight gain, moodiness, and fatigue. Such side effects are temporary, but the hormones may also cause ovarian hyperstimulation syndrome, a condition that can result in blood clots, kidney failure, and even death.

Donors must also submit to frequent blood tests and ultrasound scans to determine when the ova are ready to be harvested. They must then be anesthetized and the eggs retrieved from their follicles. This may be done by a small surgical incision or (most often) by aspiration through a hollow needle inserted through the vagina into the follicles.

The risks of the process include a bad (potentially fatal) reaction to the anesthesia, the possibility of damaging an organ, and the possibility of uncontrollable bleeding.

The entire donation process takes about two weeks. The chance that an egg donor may be injured by the procedures used in causing ovulation and in retrieving the eggs may be relatively small, but it is real. The risks of donation have not been scientifically studied, but five deaths have been reported in Britain.

Some critics express concern about the long-term cancer risk the ovary-stimulating hormones pose to the donor. This risk has not been studied, but a 2009 Danish study followed 54,362 women who had been given fertility drugs to help them become pregnant. The study found that after fifteen years the women were no more at risk for developing ovarian cancer than other women experiencing infertility.

(The exception was women who had taken the drug clomiphene citrate; they had a sixty-seven percent increase in serious ovarian cancer tumors.)

The extent to which these results apply to egg donors is uncertain, however, because women experiencing problems with fertility already have a higher rate of ovarian cancer. So far, no studies have compared the cancer risks of women without fertility problems who are given hormones with the risks of women in the general population. Also, no studies have been done to determine whether ovum donors are at a higher risk for other kinds of cancer.

Informed consent for potential ovum donors is usually limited to mentioning the possibility of immediate harms. Is a donor likely to have trouble conceiving her own child? This isn't known. Will she later suffer from depression or remorse? This has not been studied. Will she increase her chances of developing ovarian cancer, breast cancer, kidney cancer, or liver cancer? The studies needed to answer this question haven't been carried out.

Knowledge of the long-term risks of being an ovum donor is almost exclusively anecdotal. The result is that even when the informed consent process is carried out in an unobjectionable manner, the "informed" part consists of such limited information that a woman who agrees to be a donor is taking unknown risks. This issue, too, needs to be emphasized in the consent process, but the anecdotal evidence suggests that it rarely is.

Personal Eugenics

Ova are now being marketed the way that sperm has been for the last twenty years. The counterpart to advertisements soliciting donors are those directed at would-be parents. Fertility clinics and "donor agencies" solicit clients with online videos and photo galleries of egg donors. Thus, just as women may shop (and pay more for) sperm they consider "superior" in particular respects, women and couples may shop for "superior" ova.

What do they look for? Traits sought include an unproblematic family medical history (no schizophrenia, breast cancer, diabetes, sickle cell, and so on), evidence of intellectual accomplishment (admission to a highly selective college and high SAT scores serve as markers), and physical attributes such as height, weight, hair and eye color, and attractiveness.

As with the sperm market, the ovum market brings up questions about whether society is prepared to accept personal eugenic practices. We decisively reject the institutional practice of eugenics, but is the attempt to find an egg donor who embodies characteristics we would like our children to possess different in an ethically relevant way from choosing a partner with whom we would like to have children? (See the Social Context, "Shopping the Sperm Supermarket" for more discussion.)

Money is paid for donor eggs, and often the more desirable the traits the egg appears to represent, the greater is the amount of money offered. In a 2010 study, Aaron Levine reviewed more than a hundred ads in sixty-three college newspapers recruiting egg donors and found that more than half offered fees larger than the $10,000 maximum recommended in the guidelines of the American Society for Reproductive Medicine. ASRM guidelines state that compensation over $5000 above a donor's medical and living expenses "requires justification" and amounts above $10,000 "are not appropriate." So why the higher fees?

Some ads, Levine suggested, might be using a bait-and-switch tactic to encourage potential donors to make an initial contact, after which a lower fee could be negotiated. Other ads, however, appeared to be making offers designed to attract women who would donate "superior" or "extraordinary" ova. Thus, Levine discovered that every 100-point increase above a university's SAT score average was associated with a $2000 increase in the donor fee advertised in the campus newspaper. College ads, in particular, frequently exceeded the limit in the ASRM guidelines. One such ad offered $50,000 for "an extraordinary egg donor," an amount ten times that the ASRM deems "not appropriate."

Self-Regulation

Fertility clinics, Levine learned, tend to follow the ARM guidelines in their advertising. Egg-donor agencies, however, were more likely to advertise higher payments. The agencies are entrepreneurial, for-profit businesses, and they make their money from the fees they charge. Thus, they are highly motivated to secure the services of donors who will please their clients. Unlike the fertility clinics, agencies are not affiliated with organizations like ASRM: thus, they are under no obligation to follow the professional guidelines.

Several states prohibit the sales of human ova, most ignore the practice, and Virginia explicitly permits it. In 2009, California passed a law requiring that potential donors be informed of the risks as part of an informed-consent process. Nevertheless, for the most part, the states ignore the practice of recruiting ovum donors, leaving the medical and professional organizations to police the practices of their members.

Fertility clinics, assisted-reproduction physicians, and agencies that earn fees by matching donors with clients all operate in a way that is usually described as self-regulating. Critics find it easy to point to cases in which self-regulation has failed to work to protect the interests of individuals. Guidelines can be violated without real penalties, because they lack the force of law. If a physician is censured or kicked out of the professional organization, however, he can still continue to practice. In the fertility business, success in producing pregnancies, not professional status, is what counts.

Flawed Consent

Even if the guidelines are followed, anecdotal evidence suggests that the process of informed consent for ovum donors is often flawed. Too often, it seems, they are not given adequate information about the potential long-term harms they may suffer by becoming a donor. In addition, no one has a clear idea of exactly what those risks are, because relevant studies haven't been conducted.

The donation process is complicated by the fact that everyone involved—clinics, physicians, donor agencies, and donors—has a financial stake in the donation. Without a donor, the clinics, physicians, and agencies can't earn fees by providing services to their clients, and if the potential donor does not become an actual one, she is paid nothing. The clients who pay the money have their own agenda—they need donor ova to become pregnant—so their interest is in conflict with that of the potential donor.

A potential donor is likely motivated by the prospect of earning a comparatively large sum of money. That may make it more probable that she will ignore or downplay the risks of becoming a donor, that the money will serve as such a strong inducement that it will compromise her consent. Then, too, she will have the fertility clinic representative, the physician, and the egg-donor agency hoping and perhaps encouraging her to become a donor.

Envoi

Critics regard the entire ovum-donation process as one in which young women in need of money lack the protection of the law and risk being exploited by those who offer them money and encourage them to consent to become donors. As matters stand, only the moral principles and good intentions of those who recruit donors regulate the practice. This may be a barrier too weak to protect the interests of young and vulnerable women.

Advances in Reproductive Cloning

On February 3, 1997, Ian Wilmut of the Roslin Institute in Edinburgh, Scotland, made public the information that he and his research group had successfully produced a clone of an adult sheep. The younger genetic twin, the clone they named Dolly, had been born about seven months earlier and appeared to be healthy and normal in every respect.

The procedure Wilmut followed had a cookbook simplicity but was scientifically highly sophisticated. He took cells from the mammary tissue of a Finn Dorset ewe and got them to stop going through the ordinary process of cell division by culturing them in a medium with a low level of nutrients. Retrieving egg cells from a Scottish Blackface ewe, he removed their nuclei (hence the DNA) and then mixed them with the mammary cells. By passing a weak current of electricity through the mixture, Wilmut got some of the egg cells and mammary cells to fuse together. He then used a second pulse of electricity to activate the machinery responsible for cell division. (The process of transferring the nucleus of a somatic cell into an egg cell from which the nucleus has been evacuated is now called *somatic-cell nuclear transfer*. The phrase is more descriptive, but it also allows the word *cloning*, which has acquired controversial associations, to be avoided.)

Six days later, some of the fused cells had divided, becoming embryos in the way a fertilized egg develops into an embryo. Using the technology of embryo transfer, Wilmut succeeded in implanting one of the embryos in the uterus of a third sheep, another Blackface ewe. At the end of her pregnancy, the ewe gave birth to a lamb that was the genetic twin of the Finn Dorset sheep that supplied the mammary cells.

Wilmut and his group made 277 tries at fusing the nuclei of the body cells with the enucleated egg cells, but they managed to produce only twenty-nine embryos that lasted longer than six days, the usual time in vitro fertilization specialists allow for a fertilized egg to develop into an embryo before transferring it into the uterus. Of the embryos Wilmut implanted, Dolly was the sole success.

The great majority of biologists were amazed at Wilmut's achievement. Although they acknowledged that the DNA in the nucleus of a body cell contains a complete set of genes and so, in principle, could be used to produce another genetically identical individual, they didn't believe that our understanding of cells was detailed enough actually to do it. The view accepted by most researchers was that once a cell finds its place in the body, it switches off all the genes it contains, except those it needs to do its job and to reproduce itself. But to become an embryo, the genes must be switched on again. When the embryo is implanted in a uterus, they must be able to orchestrate the stunningly complicated process of development, changing the embryo into an offspring.

Wilmut demonstrated that what the majority of scientists considered only a distant possibility could be achieved in a relatively straightforward fashion. Placing the mammary cells in a culture low in nutrients seemed to return them to the state when their genetic potential is still open, and the pulse of electricity seemed to trigger them into dividing and developing. Wilmut showed that it wasn't necessary to understand the underlying biology of the process to control it. Under the right conditions, the DNA would reprogram itself to initiate and direct development.

Confirming Experiments

Wilmut's achievement was initially greeted with skepticism by some in the research community. Cloning was demonstrated as a phenomenon beyond doubt, however, in July 1998. Ryuzo Yanagimachi and his team at the University of Hawaii reported that they had produced more than fifty mouse clones. Some of the mice, moreover, were clones of clones.

Yanagimachi's technique was a variation of Wilmut's. Yanagimachi injected the genetic material from a mouse cumulus cell in the resting phase into an enucleated mouse egg and then used chemicals to get the cell to divide. After that, the cell was implanted into a surrogate mother and allowed to develop into a mouse. In one experiment, tan mice were used as genetic donors, black mice as egg donors, and white mice as gestational surrogates. The clones were all tan.

After Yanagimachi's demonstration, doubt about the reality of cloning evaporated. Scientists soon succeeded in cloning cows, goats, pigs, and cats. The first cat was cloned in 2002 only because researchers at Texas A&M failed (as others had) to clone a dog. Called cc, for "carbon copy" or "copycat," the kitten was the only successful result of attempts using eighty-seven cloned embryos transferred to gestational surrogates.

Drawbacks

Despite cc's name, cc really isn't an exact copy of her biological mother, a two-year-old calico cat named Rainbow. Although the two are genetically identical, the color and pattern of cc's coat is different. Coat color results from the separation and distribution of pigmented cells. This takes place during development and is not completely determined by genes.

Although cc is apparently healthy and normal, some cloned animals have not been so fortunate. A number die soon after birth, while others suffer from a variety of birth anomalies. Developmental delays, defective hearts, underdeveloped lungs, neurological deficits, and faulty immune systems are the

more common flaws. Some cloned mice appear normal; then, as they grow, they become extremely fat. Developing calves become oversized and die prematurely.

Scientists don't know exactly what happens to cause these adverse results. Apparently, however, cloning promotes the occurrence of random changes. During normal reproduction, both egg and sperm mature before they combine, but in cloning, eggs are harvested and the DNA in cells combined with them must all be reprogrammed during a period of minutes or hours. During the process, researchers think, genes are altered and random errors occur. These cause unpredictable problems that can crop up at any time during development or after birth.

That cloning works at all is surprising to some researchers, given what needs to happen to make it possible. Still, even under the best laboratory conditions and in skilled hands, only about three percent of attempts at cloning mammals are successful. Only about one attempt in a hundred results in a viable calf.

When Dolly was born, some scientists speculated that it was likely she would age prematurely. The cell from which the nuclear DNA was removed had already undergone a number of cell divisions and, given that cells divide only about fifty times before they die, perhaps the clock for Dolly had already been ticking before she was born. Experience with cloned animals, however, has so far not shown that they age prematurely.

Dolly herself died of a lung infection on February 14, 2003. She was six years old, and the infection appeared to have nothing to do with the fact that she was a clone. Her life was terminated with a lethal injection by the veterinarians treating her when they decided that they could not control her suffering and that she was unlikely to improve. The natural life span of a domestic sheep is not clear. They are usually slaughtered for food when they are nine months old, but those kept in pastures can live ten or twelve years.

Practical Uses

Cloning was developed to be the foundation of *pharming:* the use of animals to produce drugs. The Roslin Institute is an agricultural research center, and a third of Wilmut's funding came from PPL Therapeutics, a biotechnology firm. Wilmut's aim, as well as PPL's, was to produce a flock of sheep genetically engineered to give milk containing such medically valuable and expensive substances as blood-clotting factor, insulin, and human growth hormone. If a single sheep able to secrete one of these substances in her milk could be created, cells from her could be cloned into a herd. Cloning would make it possible to produce whatever number of animal drug factories are needed, ensuring us a supply of useful substances at lower prices.

The interest in cloning cattle is to produce a line which has properties that are valued for commercial reasons. A cow that produces substantially more milk than usual, for example, could be cloned to produce a herd of dairy cows. The milk yield from such a herd would significantly reduce the cost of milk production and boost profits. Studies by the FDA in 2005 showed that milk and meat from cloned animals is safe to consume.

The research that produced cc, the cloned cat, was supported by Genetics Saving and Clone, a biotech company that aims to profit from cloning valued pets. The company is already storing, for a fee, DNA samples from pets, with the expectation that cloning technology will soon be adequate to produce a genetic replica of a beloved pet. Dogs were the first target, but when cloning them turned out to be intractable, the company turned to cats.

Critics object to the whole idea of the enterprise, pointing out that in the United States alone millions of dogs and cats are destroyed each years as an unwanted surplus. Thus, it is pointlessly cruel to create even more. Those who believe they will get an identical version of their cat or dog are simply mistaken. Cc's coat color was different from her mother's, and very likely her behavior and personality will also be different. Developmental factors, including environmental ones, are likely to result in a very different animal.

Most people are more enthusiastic about the possibility of using reproductive cloning to establish colonies of endangered species. In 2001, scientists in Italy reported that they had successfully cloned an endangered wild sheep known as a muflon. The sheep survived and was put into a wildlife sanctuary. Another research group cloned a gaur, a wild ox, in 2002, but the calf died from an infection. Zoos around the world are investigating the possibility of cloning animals like the Siberian tiger, Sumatran tiger, several species of antelope, and the giant panda to save them from extinction. Some research facilities are saving cell samples from many species in the hope that, if they become extinct, new populations can be established.

A more distant possibility is to discover a completely preserved nucleus of an extinct animal (or piece together enough DNA fragments to form a complete set of genes), then transfer the nucleus into an enucleated egg cell and implant the embryo into the uterus of a similar species. Some researchers believe, for example, that it might be possible to resurrect the woolly mammoth by using an elephant as a gestational surrogate.

In 2002, Advanced Cell Technologies announced that it had cloned cow eggs and, when the embryos developed into fetuses, had removed kidney cells and transferred them to a sponge like matrix. The cells developed into what researchers described as a small kidney. When the kidney was implanted into the cow contributing the DNA, it produced a small amount of urine. Although no one sees this as an acceptable procedure for use with human cells, it demonstrates the possibility of growing organs for transplantation without relying on stem cells. (For the controversy over embryonic stem cells, see the Social Context, "Stem Cells," in Chapter 3.)

The possibility of using human embryonic stem cells to treat diseases, repair organs, and even grow whole organs makes cloning extremely important. Embryonic stem cells are obtained from embryos. If someone with (say) diabetes needed stem cells for treatment, then, to overcome the problem of tissue rejection, her DNA could be used to replace the nucleus in a donor egg. When the egg formed a blastocyst, the stem cells could be removed. They would be a perfect genetic match with her own tissue. This is an example of *therapeutic cloning*. That is, the cloning is for the purpose of getting materials for treatment, not for the purpose of reproduction. Because embryos must be destroyed to secure the stem cells, those who consider human embryos to have the status of persons regard even therapeutic cloning as a serious moral wrong.

Cell Conversion

In 2007, Shinya Yamanaka showed that it is possible to use a retrovirus to insert four genes into a somatic cell and convert the cell into a pluripotent state. In effect, the genes can reprogram a skin cell into an embryonic stem cell. These so-called induced pluripotent stem cells may make it unnecessary to destroy embryos to acquire stem cells; thus, the major objection to cloning for therapeutic purposes may disappear. Indeed, it may be that converted cells may make it unnecessary to rely on somatic cell nuclear transfer even for reproductive purposes. Many difficulties must be overcome, however, before either of these possibilities can be realized in any practical way. (See the Social Context "Stem Cells" in Chapter 3 for more information.)

What about Humans?

Most of the public discussion of cloning since Wilmut's announcement has focused on human *reproductive cloning*. People have been quick to realize that if sheep, mice, cattle, and cats have been cloned, there seems to be no technical reason a human can't be also.

Assuming that reproductive cloning were perfected, here are a few of the possibilities it opens up that have been discussed:

1. When one of a couple carries a gene responsible for a devastating illness, such as Tay–Sachs disease, the couple could decide to have a child and use only the genetic material from the noncarrier.

2. Women who have entered menopause as a result of chemotherapy, had their ovaries removed for therapeutic reasons, or are postmenopausal could still have a genetically connected child by employing the DNA from their somatic cells. The child would be a genetically identical twin, as well as an offspring, of the woman.

3. Similarly, men who are sterile for any reason or who no longer are capable of producing undamaged sperm (e.g., as a result of cancer surgery or radiation treatments) may still father a child.

4. The parents of a dying child could decide to have another child who will be a genetically identical replacement.

5. A woman could decide to use the DNA of a dying (or just dead) partner to have a child who would be the partner's genetic twin. A man could achieve the same end by finding a woman who would agree to be a gestational surrogate.

6. A "family" could be made up of several offspring who are genetically identical with the mother or the father. The father would also be a twin brother, and the mother a twin sister, of their offspring, although separated from them by years.

These possibilities, which many regard as potential benefits, are shadowed by other possibilities that some see as offering serious objections to human cloning.

1. Rich and egocentric people might decide to clone themselves for no reason, except to perpetuate their unique combination of genes.

2. Dictators or powerful political leaders could replace themselves with a clone, thus promoting an indefinite continuation of their influence.

3. The cellular DNA from popular figures such as athletes and movie stars might become marketed as commodities. Or because cloning would make "popular" DNA valuable, it might be stolen and used to produce children without the consent of an unwitting and unwilling donor.

Not a Photocopy

Some fears about cloning seem to reflect the mistaken belief that the clone of an individual will grow up to be exactly the same as the individual—a sort of photocopy. But of course, genetic identity doesn't result in exact similarity: we already know that identical twins, even when brought up in the same family, may turn out to be quite distinct in personality, interests, and motivations.

A child who develops in a different uterine environment, then grows up in a world filled with different people, practices, events, and experiences, is unlikely to be exactly like the person cloned. Even individuals can themselves become "different people" with experience and education.

The most serious objection to human reproductive cloning at the moment is that it would lead to so many tragic outcomes. With a success rate with mice hovering around a mere three percent the number of failed pregnancies is not likely to be better. Also, the chance of children being born with either lethal or seriously debilitating impairments is unacceptably high. We know from cloned mammals that unpredictable genetic and developmental errors occur.

No serious researcher thinks it would be anything but premature and morally indefensible to attempt to clone a human at the moment. Even if it is not wrong in principle, it would be wrong to produce children who would most likely be severely impaired, assuming that they didn't die shortly after birth.

But what of the future? In what circumstances, if any, would the cloning of humans be legitimate? Are we willing to take the risks involved in the development of a clone? Are we prepared to accept the alterations in our society that successful human cloning would produce?

Politics

Research involving cloning human embryos has been controversial from the start. On February 4, 1997, the day after Wilmut announced the cloning of Dolly, President Clinton asked the National Bioethics Advisory Committee to report to him in ninety days "with recommendations on possible Federal actions" to prevent the "abuse" of cloning. Meanwhile, on March 4, President Clinton issued an executive order banning the use of federal funds to support research leading to the cloning of humans. On June 9, the committee made its report to the president, and he immediately called for legislation banning cloning "for the purpose of creating a child."

In August 2001, President George Bush announced that he was prepared to allow human embryonic stem-cell research supported by federal funds to continue on stem cells that had already been recovered from embryos. Federal money could not be used, however, to create new embryos. Thus, the decision not only prohibited the creation of new embryos, but offered no federal support for even therapeutic cloning. In March 2009, President Barack Obama issued an executive order instructing NIH to draft guidelines lifting some of the Bush rules governing stem-cell research. The most important change was to make thirteen new human embryonic stem-cell lines eligible for research receiving federal funding.

An August 23, 2010, injunction by the Federal District Court of the District of Columbia halted federal funding, but the injunction was set aside by the United States Court of Appeals on September 9, 2010. A final resolution will depend on how the underlying lawsuit against the use of federal funding for research involving these new cell lines is decided. Obama, as well as Bush and Clinton, allowed to stand several federal regulations that explicitly prohibit reproductive cloning.

Denounced in Principle

Cloning human embryos for the purpose of reproduction continues to be denounced, even in principle, by the entire scientific and medi-cal community. Researchers have repeatedly asserted that they have no plans to carry out experiments like those which have produced other mammals. The fundamental practical interest in human cloning is in therapeutic cloning: the creation of human embryos to acquire embryonic stem cells to treat diseases and injuries. (For an analysis of these issues, see the Case Presentation "Stem Cells," in Chapter 3.)

CASE PRESENTATION

Louise Brown: The First "Test-Tube Baby"

Under other circumstances, the birth announcement would have been perfectly ordinary, the sort appearing in newspapers every day: *Born to John and Lesley Brown: a baby girl, Louise, 5 lbs. 12 ozs., 11:47 P.M., July 25, 1978, Oldham (England) General Hospital.*

But the birth of Louise Brown was far from being an ordinary event, and the announcement of its occurrence made headlines throughout the world. For the first time in history, a child was born who was conceived outside the mother's body under controlled laboratory conditions. Louise Brown was the world's first "test-tube baby."

For John and Lesley Brown, the birth of Louise was a truly marvelous event. "She's so small, so beautiful, so perfect," her mother told a reporter. Her father said, "It was like a dream. I couldn't believe it."

The joy of the Browns was understandable. From the time of their marriage in 1969, they had both very much wanted to have a child. Then they discovered that Lesley Brown was unable to conceive because of blocked fallopian tubes—the ova would not descend, so fertilization could not occur. In 1970, she had surgery to correct the condition, but the procedure was unsuccessful.

The Browns decided they would adopt a child, because they couldn't have one of their own. After two years on a waiting list, they gave up that plan. But the idea of having their own child was rekindled when a nurse familiar with the work of embryologist Robert Edwards and gynecologist Patrick Steptoe referred the Browns to them.

New Methods

For the previous twelve years, Steptoe and Edwards had been working on the medical and biochemical techniques required for embryo transfer. Steptoe developed techniques for removing a ripened ovum from a woman's ovaries, then reimplanting it in the uterus after it has been fertilized. Edwards improved the chemical solutions needed to keep ova functioning and healthy outside the body and perfected a method of external fertilization with sperm.

Using their techniques, Steptoe and Edwards had successfully produced a pregnancy in one of their patients in 1975, but it had resulted in a miscarriage. They continued to refine their procedures and were confident their techniques could produce a normal pregnancy that would result in a healthy baby.

They considered Lesley Brown a superb candidate for an embryo transfer. She was in excellent general health; at thirty-one, she was within the usual age range for pregnancy; and she was highly fertile. In 1976, Steptoe did an exploratory operation and found that her fallopian tubes were not functional and could not be surgically repaired. He removed them so he would have unimpeded access to the ovaries.

In November 1977, Mrs. Brown was given injections of a hormone to increase the maturation rate of her egg cells. Then, in a small private hospital in Oldham, Dr. Steptoe performed a minor surgical procedure. Using a laparoscope—a tube with a built-in eyepiece and light source that is inserted through a tiny slit in the abdomen—to guide him, he extracted an ovum with a suction needle from a ripened follicle.

The ovum was then placed in a small glass vessel containing biochemical nutrients and sperm secured from John Brown. Once the egg was fertilized, it was transferred to another nutrient solution. More than fifty hours later, the ovum had reached the eight-cell stage of division. Guided by their previous experience and research, Steptoe and Edwards had decided that it was at this stage an ovum should be returned to the womb. Although in normal human development the ovum has divided to produce sixty-four or more cells before it completes its descent down the fallopian tube and becomes attached to the uterine wall, they had learned that attachment is possible at an earlier stage. The stupendous difficulties in creating and maintaining the proper biochemical environment for a multiplying cell made it reasonable to reduce the time outside the body as much as possible.

Lesley Brown had been given another series of hormone injections to prepare her uterus. Two and a half days after the ovum was removed, the fertilized egg—an embryo—was reimplanted. Using a laparoscope and a hollow plastic tube (*a cannula*), Dr. Steptoe introduced the small sphere of cells into Mrs. Brown's uterus. It successfully attached itself to the uterine wall.

Success

Lesley Brown's pregnancy proceeded normally. But, because of the special nature of her case, seven weeks before the baby was due she entered the Oldham Hospital maternity ward so she could be continuously monitored. About a week before the birth was expected, the baby was delivered by cesarean section. Mrs. Brown had developed toxemia, a condition associated with high blood pressure that can lead to stillbirth.

The baby was normal, and all concerned were jubilant. "The last time I saw the baby, it was just eight cells in a test tube," Dr. Edwards said. "It was beautiful then, and it's still beautiful now." After the delivery, Dr. Steptoe said, "She came out crying her head off, a beautiful normal baby."

John Brown almost missed the great event, because no one of the hospital staff had bothered to tell him that his wife was scheduled for the operation. Only when he had been gone from the hospital for about two hours and called to talk to his wife did he find out what was about to happen.

He rushed back and waited anxiously until a nurse came out and said, "You're the father of a wonderful little girl." As he later told a reporter, "Almost before I knew it, there I was, holding our daughter in my arms."

Like many ordinary fathers, he ran down the halls of the hospital telling people he passed, "It's a girl! I've got a baby daughter."

To calm down, he went outside and stood in the rain. It was there that a reporter from a London newspaper captured Mr. Brown's view of the event. "The man who deserves all the praise is Dr. Steptoe," he said. "What a man to be able to do such a wonderful thing."

Life as Usual

On July 25, 2003, Louise Brown celebrated her twenty-fifth birthday at a party with 3000 guests, 1000 of them were others also born by in vitro fertilization (IVF). Patrick Steptoe had died in 1988, but Robert Edwards, then 77, was there to mark the occasion. So was Louise's twenty-year-old sister, Natalie, who had the distinction of being the first person born by IVF to have children of her own. Louise, who married later that year, had once wanted three or four children, but she was no longer sure she wanted to start a family of her own.

Despite dire predictions by opponents of IVF, Louise didn't turn out to be either grossly abnormal or psychologically scarred. (This is not to say that questions have not been raised about the safety of IVF; see the Briefing Session for a discussion.) The main feature distinguishing her from most of her peers turns out to be her trust fund composed of earnings from a book by her parents and from various television projects over the years. Since her birth, more than a million other babies have been born through the techniques of assisted reproduction. Such births have become so common place that they no longer attract attention.

In December 2006, three years after her enormous birthday party, Louise Brown gave birth to a boy whom she and her husband named Cameron. Some observers had started to speculate that if she waited too long, she might have to rely on the assisted-reproduction techniques required for her own birth. Presumably, this wouldn't bother her. "I want to have my own children, whatever it takes," she told a reporter from London's *Daily Mail* when she was twenty-three. "I would use the in vitro method if I couldn't have a baby."

Savior Sibling

Anissa Ayala was fifteen years old in 1988 when she was diagnosed with chronic myelogenous leukemia. She received radiation and chemotherapy to destroy diseased bone marrow and blood cells, but the outcome of such treatments is that the patient's bone marrow is unable to produce enough normal blood cells to sustain life. Anissa's parents, Mary and Andy Ayala, were informed that without a bone-marrow transplant of blood-producing stem cells Anissa's chances of long-term survival were virtually zero, while with a transplant she would have a seventy to eighty percent chance.

Tests showed that neither the Ayalas nor their nineteen-year-old son, Airon, had bone marrow sufficiently compatible for them to be donors for Anissa. They then turned to a public bone-marrow registry, and for the next two years they searched for a donor. The odds of a match between two nonrelated people is only one in 20,000, and as time passed and no donor turned up, the Ayalas felt increasingly desperate. Anissa's health had stabilized, but that condition couldn't be counted on to last forever.

Radical Solution

Mary and Andy Ayala decided that the only way they could do more to help save their daughter's life was to try to have another child. Anissa's physician tried to discourage them, pointing out that the odds were only one in four that the child would have the right tissue type to be a stem-cell donor. Furthermore, the probability of their conceiving another child was very low: Andy Ayala was forty-five and had had a vasectomy sixteen years earlier; Mary was forty-two and thus well past the period of highest fertility. Nevertheless, the Ayalas decided to go ahead with their plan, and as the first step Andy Ayala had surgery to repair the vasectomy. Against all the odds, Mary Ayala became pregnant.

Response

When it became known that the Ayalas planned to have a child because their daughter needed compatible bone marrow, they became the subjects of intense media attention and received much harsh criticism. Critics claimed that they were treating the baby Mary was expecting as a means only and not as a person of unique worth. One commentator described their actions as "outrageous." Others said they were taking a giant step down the path that ultimately would lead to conceiving children merely to be sources of tissues and organs needed by others.

A few opposed this outpouring of criticism by noting that people decide to have children for many and complex reasons and sometimes for no reason at all. Also, no one observed that a reason for having a child need not determine how one regards the child. In addition, those who condemned the Ayalas often emphasized the "child-as-an-organ-bank" notion but never mentioned the relative safety of a bone-marrow transplant.

The Ayalas were hurt by the criticisms. Mary said she had wanted a third child for a number of years but had been unable to get her husband to agree. Andy admitted that he wouldn't have wanted another child if Anissa hadn't become ill, but he said he also had in mind the comfort a child would bring to the family if Anissa should die. The whole family said they would want and love the child, whether or not its bone marrow was a good match for Anissa's.

Against All Odds

In February 1990, the Ayalas found that they had beaten the odds once more. Tests of the developing fetus showed that the stem cells were nearly identical with Anissa's. During an interview after the results were known, Anissa said, "A lot of people think 'How can you do this? How can you be having this baby for your daughter?' But she's my baby sister and we're going to love her for who she is, not for what she can give me."

Then, on April 6, 1990, in a suburban Los Angeles hospital, more than a week before her due date, Mary Ayala gave birth to a healthy six-pound baby girl. The Ayalas named her Marissa Eve.

Anissa's physician, pediatric oncologist Patricia Konrad, collected and froze blood from the baby's umbilical cord. Umbilical blood contains a high concentration of stem cells, and she wanted the blood available should Anissa need it before Marissa was old enough to be a donor.

When Marissa Eve was fourteen months old and had reached an adequate weight, she was given general anesthesia and marrow was extracted from her hipbone. After preparation, the donated marrow was injected into one of Anissa's veins. The procedure was successful, and the stem cells migrated to Anissa's marrow and began to multiply. Anissa's own bone marrow began to produce normal blood cells.

Three years later, Anissa married Bryan Espinosa, and Marissa Eve was the flower girl at the wedding. Radiation treatments had destroyed Anissa's chances of having a child of her own, but she claimed that the bond between her and Marisa Eve was especially close. "Marissa is more than a sister to me," Anissa told reporter Anni Griffiths Belt. "She's almost like my child, too."

"I was struck by the extraordinary bond between the sisters," Belt said, "The fact is, neither one would be alive today without the other."

Easier Than Ever

Mary and Andy Ayala beat the odds in several ways: Andy's vasectomy was successfully reversed, Mary became pregnant without medical intervention, and Marissa Eve turned out to be a good bone-marrow match for her sister. The odds of the first two events remain about the same today, but no longer is it necessary to gamble against the odds where bone-marrow compatibility is concerned.

Using eggs and sperm, embryos can be produced in vitro by artificial insemination, then screened for compatibility with an intended bone-marrow recipient. Only those embryos compatible with the recipient will then be introduced into the uterus of the mother. Thus, the same techniques used in preimplantation genetic screening for the purpose of preventing the transmission of a heritable disease can also be employed to select for such positive traits as bone-marrow compatibility. (For a discussion see the Chapter 3, Briefing Session.)

Most often, this technique has been used to ensure that the umbilical-cord blood, which contains blood-producing stem cells, of the child is compatible with the tissue of the recipient. This procedure has been used in about 2,000 cases over the past decade. Those who object to preimplantation screening for genetic reasons also object when it is used to select for tissue donation.

The Calvert Case: A Gestational Surrogate Changes Her Mind

Disease forced Crispina Calvert of Orange County, California, to have a hysterectomy, but only her uterus was removed by surgery, not her ovaries. She and her husband, Mark, wanted a child of their own, but without a uterus Crispina would not be able to bear it. For a fee of $10,000, they arranged with Anna Johnson to act as a surrogate.

Unlike the more common form of surrogate pregnancy, Johnson would have no genetic investment in the child. The ovum that would be fertilized would not be hers. Mary Beth Whitehead, the surrogate in the controversial Baby M case, had received artificial insemination. Thus, she made as much genetic contribution to the child as did the biological father.

Johnson, however, would be the gestational surrogate. In an in vitro fertilization process, ova were extracted from Crispina Calvert and mixed with sperm from Mark. An embryo was implanted in Anna Johnson's uterus, and a fetus began to develop.

Johnson's pregnancy proceeded in a normal course, but in her seventh month she announced she had changed her mind about giving up the child. She filed suit against the Calverts to seek custody of the unborn child. "Just because you donate a sperm and an egg doesn't make you a parent," said Johnson's attorney. "Anna is not a machine, an incubator."

"That child is biologically Chris and Mark's," said the Calverts' lawyer. "That contract is valid."

Critics of genetic surrogate pregnancy are equally critical of gestational surrogate pregnancy. Both methods, some claim, exploit women, particularly poor women. Further, in gestational pregnancy the surrogate is the one who must run the risks and suffer the discomforts and dangers of pregnancy. She has a certain biological claim to be the mother, because it was her body that produced the child according to the genetic information supplied by the implanted embryo.

Defenders of surrogate pregnancy respond to the first criticism by denying that surrogates are exploited. They enter freely into a contract to serve as a surrogate for pay, just as anyone might agree to perform any other service for pay. Pregnancy has hazards and leaves its marks on the body, but so do many other paid occupations. As far as gestational surrogacy is concerned, defenders say, since the surrogate makes no genetic contribution to the child, in no reasonable way can she be regarded as the child's parent.

The Ethics Committee of the American Fertility Society has endorsed a policy opposing surrogate pregnancy "for nonmedical reasons." The apparent aim of the policy is to permit the use of gestational surrogate pregnancy in cases like that of Mrs. Calvert, while condemning it when its motivation is mere convenience or an unwillingness to be pregnant. When a woman is fertile but, because of diabetes, uncontrollable hypertension, or some other life-threatening disorder, is unable to bear the burden of pregnancy, gestational surrogacy would be a legitimate medical option.

Birth and Resolution

The child carried by Anna Johnson, a boy, was born on September 19, and for a while, under a court order, Johnson and the Calverts shared visitation rights. Then, in October 1990, a California Superior Court denied Johnson the parental right she had sought. Justice R. N. Parslow awarded complete custody of the child to the Calverts and terminated Johnson's visitation rights.

"I decline to split the child emotionally between two mothers," the judge said. He said Johnson had nurtured and fed the fetus in the way a foster parent might take care of a child, but she was still a "genetic stranger" to the boy and could not claim parenthood because of surrogacy.

Justice Parslow found the contract between the Calverts and Johnson to be valid, and he expressed doubt about Johnson's contention that she had "bonded" with the fetus she was carrying. "There is substantial evidence in the record that Anna Johnson never bonded with the child till she filed her lawsuit, if then," he said. While the trial was in progress, Johnson had been accused of planning to sue the Calverts from the beginning to attempt to make the case famous so she could make money from book and movie rights.

"I see no problem with someone getting paid for her pain and suffering," Parslow said. "There is nothing wrong with getting paid for nine months of what I understand is a lot of misery and a lot of bad days. They are not selling a baby; they are selling pain and suffering."

The Calverts were overjoyed by the decision.

SOCIAL CONTEXT
Postmenopausal Motherhood

In late 1996, sixty-three-year-old Arceli Keh gave birth to a healthy baby girl. This made her the oldest woman ever to become a first-time mother.

This highly unusual event was not an accident of nature, but the result of deliberate planning and technological manipulation. Even so, Dr. Richard Paulson, the physician at the

University of Southern California infertility clinic who treated Keh, hadn't known her true age. She had lied to her previous doctors, and the age on her chart was recorded as fifty.

Fifty was already five years over the clinic's limit for in vitro fertilization, but Keh was in excellent health and did well on tests for strength and endurance. Paulson approved her for IVF, and by the time he discovered her true age, she was pregnant with an embryo formed by a donor egg fertilized with sperm provided by her sixty-year-old husband Isagani Keh.

The Kehs, who had immigrated from the Philippines, lived in Highland, California, about sixty miles east of Los Angeles. Although they had been married sixteen years, they had been unsuccessful in conceiving a child.

"I wasn't trying to make history," Arceli told a reporter for the London newspaper *The Express*. "We are working people," she said. "I only retired to have my baby." Isagani was still working as a carpenter to help pay the more than $60,000 they spent on the procedures resulting in the birth of their daughter, whom they named Cynthia.

Keh was the oldest postmenopausal woman to bear a child, but she wasn't the first. On Christmas Day, 1993, a fifty-nine-year-old British woman, identified only as Jennifer F., gave birth to twins. Jennifer F. was married and highly successful in business, but even though she was a millionaire, there came a time when she realized she regretted not having a child. By then she had undergone menopause, making it impossible for her to conceive.

Refusing to surrender her dream, Jennifer F. visited a National Health Service fertility clinic in London and asked for help. She wanted to be made pregnant with an embryo produced from her husband's sperm and a donor egg. Physicians at the clinic declined to perform the procedure, telling her she was too old to cope with the physical and emotional stress required to be a mother.

Determined to do everything possible to have a child, Jennifer F. then went to the clinic

operated by Severino Antinori in Rome. Antinori agreed to accept her as a patient and performed the in vitro fertilization and embryo transfer procedure. Antinori claims he has assisted more than fifty women over the age of fifty to become pregnant.

Although both Arceli Keh and Jennifer F. attracted much media attention, other postmenopausal women had earlier become pregnant and borne children. In 1993, Geraldine Wesolowski, fifty-three, gave birth to a baby who was both her child and her grandchild. She was the gestational surrogate for her son, Mark, and his wife Susan. As a result of an accident, Susan had undergone a hysterectomy, but she and Mark were able to provide the embryo that was then transferred to Wesolowski.

A year earlier, Mary Shearing, also fifty-three, gave birth to twin girls. She was made pregnant with embryos produced by donated eggs and sperm from her thirty-two-year-old husband. Even though Mary Shearing was no longer ovulating, she and her husband had decided to have a child of their own.

Since 1987, it has been technologically possible for a postmenopausal woman to become pregnant with donor eggs, and during the last few years, the number of older (usually first-time) mothers has been increasing. In the United States in 2000, there were 255 births to women between the ages of fifty and fifty-four, a significant increase from 174 in 1999. (Statistics on births to women over the age of fifty-four are not collected by the Centers for Disease Control.)

The increase may be due partly to changes in the policies of infertility clinics. Until recently, most clinics in the United States would not accept as patients women past their early or mid-forties. Experts suspected that older women not only would have a low success rate but also would be putting their health at greater risk. A large study released in 2002 provides grounds to question both claims.

The study was carried out at the University of Southern California and involved seventy-seven postmenopausal women treated at the university's reproductive clinic from 1991 to 2001; forty-two of the women gave birth. The study showed that healthy women in their fifties using donor eggs have rates of pregnancy that are comparable to those of younger women. Further, although older women face higher rates of pregnancy-induced diabetes and hypertension, the conditions are temporary. Older women are, however, more likely to have a cesarean section than younger women.

While clinics are making it easier for postmenopausal women to attempt motherhood, critics argue that, given the scarcity of donor eggs, they ought to be reserved for younger women. It is best for a child, critics claim, to have physically and mentally active parents. Older parents may be unable to keep up with the demands of growing children, and the children will thus be cheated by not having parents who do things with them. Also, older parents are more likely to die, leaving behind young children still in need of guidance and financial support.

Defenders of granting access to fertility services to older women argue that it is pure gender bias to deny them the possibility of having a child. Men often father children well into their old age and are often admired for doing so. Charlie Chaplin was seventy-three when he had his last child, and Senator Strom Thurmond had four children during his sixties and seventies.

The actor Tony Randall became a father for the first time when he was seventy-seven. By contrast, a woman no longer ovulating, even if she has a younger husband, has no way to have a child without relying on assisted reproduction.

Also, just because a woman is relatively young does not mean she will be a better mother. On the contrary, it seems likely that an older woman with more psychological and financial security will be a better parent than many young women. Besides, younger women do not have to prove that they will be good mothers before they are allowed to have children, so why should older women? Finally, babies born to older women using eggs obtained from younger women do just as well as babies born to younger women, and now the evidence suggests that older mothers are not risking their health to a significant extent.

The number of women past menopause wishing to become pregnant is never expected to become great. Even so, the conflict between those who argue that older women are entitled to access to assisted reproduction and those who argue that access should be denied to them is likely to continue. Now that a number of children have been born to older mothers, some relevant factual questions about safety have been settled. Yet ethical and social questions about postmenopausal motherhood remain.

CASE PRESENTATION
Baby M and Mary Beth Whitehead: Surrogate Pregnancy in Court

On March 30, 1986, Elizabeth Stern, a professor of pediatrics, and her husband William accepted from Mary Beth Whitehead a baby who had been born four days earlier. The child's biological mother was Whitehead, but she had been engaged by the Sterns as a surrogate mother. Even so, it was not until almost exactly a year later that the Sterns were able to claim legal custody of the child.

The Sterns, working through the Infertility Center of New York, had first met with Whitehead and her husband

Richard in January of 1985. Whitehead, who already had a son and a daughter, had indicated her willingness to become a surrogate mother by signing up at the Infertility Center. "What brought her there was empathy with childless couples who were infertile," her attorney later stated. Her own sister had been unable to conceive.

According to court testimony, the Sterns considered Mrs. Whitehead a "perfect person" to bear a child for them. Mr. Stern said it was "compelling" for him to have children, for he had no relatives "anywhere in the world." He and his wife planned to have children, but they put off attempts to conceive until his wife completed her medical residency in 1981. In 1979, however, she was diagnosed as having an eye condition indicating that she probably had multiple sclerosis. When she learned that the symptoms of the disease might be worsened by pregnancy and that she might become temporarily or even permanently paralyzed, the Sterns "decided the risk wasn't worth it." It was this decision that led them to the Infertility Center and to Mary Beth Whitehead.

The Sterns agreed to pay Whitehead $10,000 to be artificially inseminated with Mr. Stern's sperm and to bear a child. Whitehead would then turn the child over to the Sterns, and Elizabeth Stern would be allowed to adopt the child legally. The agreement was drawn up by a lawyer specializing in surrogacy. Mr. Stern later testified that Whitehead seemed perfectly pleased with the agreement and expressed no interest in keeping the baby she was to bear. "She said she would not come to our doorstep," he said. "All she wanted from us was a photograph each year and a little letter on what transpired that year."

Birth and Strife

The baby was born on March 27, 1986. According to Elizabeth Stern, the first indication that Whitehead might not keep the agreement was her statement to the Sterns in the hospital two days after the baby's birth. "She said she didn't know if 'I can go through with it,'" Dr. Stern testified. Although Whitehead did turn the baby over to the Sterns on March 30, she called a few hours later. "She said she didn't know if she could live any more," Elizabeth Stern said. She called again the next morning and asked to see the baby, and she and her sister arrived at the Sterns' house before noon.

According to Elizabeth Stern, Whitehead told her she "woke up screaming in the middle of the night" because the baby was gone, her husband was threatening to leave her, and she had "considered taking a bottle of Valium." Stern quoted Whitehead as saying, "I just want her for a week, and I'll be out of your lives forever." The Sterns allowed Mrs. Whitehead to take the baby home with her.

Whitehead then refused to return the baby and took the infant with her to her parents' home in Florida. The Sterns obtained a court order, and on July 31 the child was seized from Whitehead. The Sterns were granted temporary custody. Then Mr. Stern, as the father of the child, and Mrs. Whitehead, as the mother, each sought permanent custody from the Superior Court of the State of New Jersey.

Trial

The seven-week trial attracted national attention, for the legal issues were without precedent. Whitehead was the first to challenge the legal legitimacy of surrogate agreement in a U.S. court. She argued that the agreement was "against public policy" and violated New Jersey prohibitions against selling babies. In contrast, Mr. Stern was the first to seek a legal decision to uphold the "specific performance" of the terms of a surrogate contract. In particular, he argued that Whitehead should be ordered to uphold her agreement and to surrender her parental rights and permit his wife to become the baby's legal mother. In addition to the contractual issues, the judge had to deal with the "best interest" of the child as required by New Jersey child-custody law. In addition to being a vague concept, the "best interest" standard had never been applied in a surrogacy case.

On March 31, 1987, Judge Harvey R. Sorkow announced his decision. He upheld the legality of the surrogate-mother agreement between the Sterns and Whitehead and dismissed all arguments that the contract violated public policy or prohibitions against selling babies.

Immediately after he read his decision, Judge Sorkow summoned Elizabeth Stern into his chambers and allowed her to sign documents permitting her to adopt the baby she and her husband called Melissa. The court decision effectively stripped Mary Beth Whitehead of all parental rights concerning this same baby, the one she called Sara.

Appeal

The Baby M story did not stop with Judge Sorkow's decision. Whitehead's attorney appealed the ruling to the New Jersey Supreme Court, and on February 3, 1988, the seven members of the court, in a unanimous decision, reversed Judge Sorkow's ruling on the surrogacy agreement.

The court held that the agreement violated the state's adoption laws, because it involved a payment for a child. "This is the sale of a child, or at the very least, the sale of a mother's right to her child," Chief Justice Wilentz wrote. The agreement "takes the child from the mother regardless of her wishes and her maternal fitness . . . ; and it accomplishes all of its goals through the use of money."

The court ruled that surrogacy agreements might be acceptable if they involved no payment and if a surrogate mother voluntarily surrendered her parental rights. In the present case, though, the court regarded paying for surrogacy as "illegal, perhaps criminal, and potentially degrading to women."

The court let stand the award of custody to the Sterns, because "their household and their personalities promise a much more likely foundation for Melissa to grow and thrive." Mary Beth Whitehead, having divorced her husband three months earlier, was romantically involved with a man named Dean Gould and was pregnant at the time of the court decision.

Despite awarding custody to the Sterns, the court set aside the adoption agreement signed by Elizabeth Stern. Whitehead remained a legal parent of Baby M, and the court ordered a lower court hearing to consider visitation rights for the mother.

The immediate future of the child known to the court and to the public as Baby M was settled. Neither the Sterns nor Mary Beth Whitehead had won exactly what they had sought, but neither had they lost all.

BRIEFING SESSION

"Oh, brave new world that has such people in it!" exclaims Miranda in Shakespeare's *The Tempest*.

This is the line from which Aldous Huxley took the title for his dystopian novel *Brave New World*. A dystopia is the opposite of a utopia, and the future society depicted by Huxley is one we're invited to view with shock and disapproval.

In Huxley's dystopia, "pregnancy" is a dirty word, sex is purely recreational, and children are produced according to explicit genetic standards in the artificial wombs of state "hatcheries." Furthermore, one's genetic endowment determines the social position and obligations one has within the society, and everyone is conditioned to believe that the role she finds herself in is the best one to have.

In significant ways, that future society is now. The new and still developing technologies of human reproduction have reached a stage in which the innovations imagined by Huxley in 1932 to make such a society possible are well within the limits of feasibility.

We have no state hatcheries and no artificial uteruses. But we do have sperm banks, donor ova, artificial insemination, frozen embryos, and surrogate pregnancies. We have it within our power to remove an ovum from a woman's body, fertilize it, then place it in her uterus so that it may develop into a child. We can remove one or more of the cells of a growing embryo and allow them to develop into separate embryos. Because we have the power to clone mammals, producing a genetically identical twin, we most likely also have the power to clone humans.

The new technology of human-assisted reproduction is so powerful, it differs only in degree from that of Huxley's dystopian world. What we have yet to do is to employ the technology as part of a deliberate social policy to restructure our world along the lines imagined by Huxley.

Yet the potentiality is there. Perhaps more than anything else, it is the bleak vision of such a mechanistic and dehumanized future that has motivated much of the criticism of current reproductive technology. The "brave new world" of Huxley is one in which traditional values associated with reproduction and family life, values based on individual autonomy, have been replaced by values of a purely social kind. In such a society, it is the good of the society or the species, not the good of individuals, that is the touchstone of justification.

The possible loss of personal values is a legitimate and serious concern. The technologies of human reproduction are sometimes viewed as machines that may be employed to pave the road leading to a world of bleakness and loss. Yet it is important to remember that these same technologies also promise to enhance the lives of those presently living and prevent potential suffering and despair.

Thousands of women (as well as a lesser number of men) unable to have children may find it possible to do so through the use of reproductive technology. It offers a means of conception when biological dysfunction makes the normal means unlikely or impossible. Women past the age of ovulation, or who have lost their ovaries to surgery, and men with a low sperm count are among those who have an opportunity where not long ago none existed.

These are all potentialities that have become actualities. But in the view of some, current methods merely mark a beginning, and the possibilities inherent in reproductive technology remain relatively unrealized. It may be possible before long, for example, to avoid sexual reproduction and use in vitro fertilization and surrogate pregnancy to reproduce clones of an individual. The technology is so powerful that, if we wish, we can employ it to change the basic fabric and pattern of our society.

Should we do that? Or will the use of the technology promote the development of a dystopia? One way of thinking about these general questions is to turn once more to Huxley.

In 1962, Huxley published a utopian novel, *Island*. Like the society in *Brave New World*, Huxley's ideal society also relies on the principles of science, but they are used to promote autonomy and personal development. For more than a hundred years, the society on the island of Pala has shaped itself in accordance with the principles of reason and science. Living is communal, sexual repression is nonexistent, children are cared for by both biological parents and other adults, drugs are used to enhance perceptual awareness, and social obligations are assigned on the basis of personal interest and ability.

Reproductive technology is one of the means the society uses to achieve its ends. It practices contraception, eugenics, and artificial insemination. Negative eugenics to eliminate genetic diseases is considered only rational. But more than this, by the use of deep freeze and artificial insemination (DF and AI), sperm from donors with superior genetic endowments are available for the use of couples who wish to improve their chances of having a child with special talents or higher-than-usual intelligence.

Huxley's ideal society is not above criticism, even from those sympathetic toward the values he endorses. Yet *Brace New World* is such a powerful cautionary tale of what might happen if science were pressed into the service of repressive political goals that it makes it difficult to imagine other possible futures in which some of the same technology plays a more benign role. *Island* is an attempt to present such an alternative future, so in thinking about the possibilities inherent in reproductive technology, fairness demands that we also consider Palinese society and not restrict our attention to the world of soma and state hatcheries.

Techniques of Assisted Reproduction

The birth of Louise Brown in 1978 (see the Case Presentation in this chapter) was a major media event. Photographs, television coverage, interviews, and news stories presented the world with minute details of the lives of the people involved and close accounts of the procedures leading to Louise's conception.

Despite the unprecedented character of the event, few people seemed surprised by it. The idea of a "test-tube baby" was one already familiar from fiction and folklore. Medieval alchemists were thought capable of generating life in their retorts, and hundreds of science fiction stories depicted a future in which the creation of life in the laboratory was an ordinary occurrence. Thus, in some ways, the birth of Louise Brown was seen as merely a matter of science and medicine catching up with imagination. Indeed, they didn't quite catch up, for the "test tube" contained sperm and an egg, not just a mixture of chemicals.

While it's doubtful that the public appreciated the magnitude of the achievement which resulted in the birth of Louise Brown, it was one of considerable significance. The first embryo transfer was performed in rabbits in 1890, but it wasn't until the role of hormones in reproduction, the nutritional requirements of developing cells, and the reproductive process itself were better understood that it became possible to consider seriously the idea of fertilizing an egg outside the mother's body and then returning it for ordinary development.

An estimated 200,000 babies are born worldwide each year through the use of assisted reproduction. The number has increased by twenty-five percent since 2000–2002 (the most recent figures), and since the birth of Louise Brown, as many as four million "test-tube babies" have entered the world. In the United States, a leader in fertility treatments, about 60,000 infants a year are born with the help of the techniques of assisted reproduction. The number of such babies doubled from 1996 to 2004, and the available evidence suggests that the increase is continuing. This is not surprising, given that, by 2010, twelve to fifteen percent of women ages 15–44 were seeking fertility treatments. The world we live in is more like the one Huxley wrote about than most people imagine.

IVF

In vitro is a Latin phrase that means "in glass," and in embryology, it is used in contrast with *in utero*, or "in the uterus." Ordinary human fertilization takes place in utero (strictly speaking, in the fallopian tubes) when a sperm cell unites with an ovum. In vitro fertilization, then, is fertilization that is artificially performed outside the woman's body—in a test tube, so to speak.

The ovum that produced Louise Brown was fertilized in vitro. But the remainder of the process involved *embryo transfer*. After the ovum from her mother's body was fertilized and had become an embryo, it was transferred—returned for in utero development.

Robert Edwards and Patrick Steptoe, who were responsible for developing and performing the techniques that led to the birth of Louise Brown, followed a process that, allowing for technical improvements, is basically the same as the one still employed.

The patient is given a reproductive hormone to cause her ova to ripen. Several mature eggs are extracted from the ovarian follicles and placed in a nutrient solution to which sperm is then added. With luck, sperm cells penetrate several ova, fertilizing them. The fertilized eggs are transferred to another nutrient solution where they undergo cell division. The embryo (also called a zygote or, by some, pre-embryo) is then transferred to the woman, who has been given injections of hormones to prepare her uterus to receive it.

Numerous modifications and extensions of Steptoe and Edwards's techniques have been introduced since 1978. It's now common to employ a nonsurgical procedure for securing ova. After hormones stimulate the ovarian follicles, ultrasound is used to locate the follicles, and a hollow needle is inserted through the vaginal wall and into a follicle. Fluid is withdrawn and egg cells are identified under the microscope. They are then fertilized with the sperm and cultured, and the resulting embryos implanted.

Also, it's now not unusual to implant two, three, or even four fertilized ova at a time. (Implanting more than two is coming to be viewed as not good medical practice.) This makes it more likely that at least one will attach to the uterine wall and so eliminates the need for a woman to have eggs removed another time. Yet the practice also has the disadvantage of increasing the chances of multiple births. (See the Case Presentation "The Octomom and the McCaughey Septuplets: The Perils of Multiple Pregnancy," earlier in this chapter.)

GIFT, ZIFT, IVC, ULER, PZD, ICSI, DNA Transfer, CD, and IUI

Gamete intrafallopian transfer, or GIFT, uses some of the same manipulative techniques as IVF. It involves inserting both ova and sperm into the fallopian tubes through a small abdominal incision, so if fertilization takes place, it does so inside the woman's body. Some regard the procedure as being more "natural" than in vitro fertilization.

Zygote intrafallopian transfer, or ZIFT, involves culturing eggs and sperm outside the body and then placing the zygotes into a woman's fallopian tubes. If the transfer is done at a particular developmental stage, it is called *pronuclear stage tubal transfer,* or PROST. Both are variants of *tubal embryo transfer,* or TET, and reflect the view that the fallopian tubes provide the most protective environment for embryo development.

Intravaginal culture, or IVC, is another attempt at naturalness. Ova are placed in a tube into which sperm cells are added, and the tube is then inserted into the vagina and kept next to the cervix by a diaphragm. Normal sexual intercourse can take place with the tube in place. Two days later, the tube is removed, the contents decanted, and any fertilized ova transferred into the uterus.

Uterine lavage embryo retrieval, or ULER, is a method for assisting pregnancy in a woman with a functioning uterus but who is either incapable of ovulation or, for some reason (e.g., she knows she is the carrier of a lethal gene), doesn't wish to use her own ova. An ovulating woman is inseminated with donor sperm. Then, after around five days, the fertilized egg is washed out of the uterus (this is the lavage) before it becomes implanted in the uterine wall. Once retrieved, the embryo is implanted in the woman being assisted. Because fertilization takes place in vivo, instead of in vitro, a potential difficulty is that the embryo may not be washed out before it becomes embedded in the uterine wall. If this happens, the donor must then decide whether to have an abortion.

Partial zona dissection, or PZD, involves using microtechniques to drill holes in the *zona,* or protective membrane surrounding an ovum, to facilitate the passage of sperm into the interior. This increases the chances of fertilization by reducing the egg's resistance to penetration, which is particularly useful when the sperm involved may be constitutionally weak.

Intracytoplasmic sperm injection, or ICSI, is a technique that can help fifty to sixty percent of infertile men become fathers. Sperm are examined microscopically and one that seems best shaped and most active is injected directly into the egg cell.

DNA transfer involves replacing the nucleus of an older egg with one taken from a younger donor egg. The aim is to take advantage of the cellular mechanisms of the younger egg, while keeping the maternal genetic material. (The technique was used in China in 2003 to make an infertile woman pregnant, although she later miscarried.) Critics charge that the technique is too similar to human cloning to be employed.

Cytoplasmic donation, or CD, involves removing the cytoplasm from a younger donor egg and injecting it into an older egg. Some data indicate that this will increase the developmental success of the recipient egg.

Intrauterine insemination (IUI) involves administering hormones to stimulate the production of ova by the ovaries and then, when ovulation occurs, injecting semen into the uterus. IUI is less expensive ($2000–3000) than IVF ($12,000–15,000), and it is more likely to be covered by insurance. The pregnancy rate is lower, however, and the hormones used in IUI are more likely to lead to a pregnancy involving multiple fetuses.

IUI is responsible for 20 percent of multiple births (8 percent of which involve triplets, quadruplets, or more), and it is a major cause of the 12.8 percent rate of premature births. (IUI resulted in the sextuplets born to Jon and Kate Gosselin and featured in the 2010 TV program *Jon & Kate Plus 8.*) If some of the multiple embryos produced by IUI are not eliminated by selective reduction, the likelihood of harm to the mother and the babies is considerable.

New techniques to assist reproduction are being developed at a rapid rate, and not all those in use are mentioned here. That so many techniques are available means that if one doesn't work, a woman may try another. Yet having so many possibilities makes it difficult for some women who wish to become pregnant to give up the attempt, even after repeated failure.

Need and Success Rates

In 2002 (the latest year for which complete data are available), the U.S. population included about 62 million women of reproductive age. About ten percent of them received fertility treatment at some point in their lives. By some estimates, at least 5 million men are infertile, and one in nine married couples has difficulty conceiving a child. In 2002 alone, about 1.2 million women sought assistance at clinics specializing in treating infertility.

In 2010, the Centers for Disease Control reported the results of the agency's study (the most recent) of the effectiveness of assisted reproductive technology as employed in 430 infertility clinics. Attempts to produce pregnancy involve one-month cycles, and during 2007 the clinics intervened in 142,435 cycles. The interventions resulted in 43,412 live births (some of them multiple), for a success rate of 30.5 percent.

Also in 2007, thirty-five percent of interventions led to pregnancy and 81.9 percent of the pregnancies resulted in live births. (These figures exclude the use of donor eggs or frozen embryos.) Single births occurred in sixty-nine percent of the cases, twins in thirty-two percent, and triplets or more in two percent. (Apart from twins, the percentage of multiple births dropped by two-thirds.)

The chance of a woman's becoming pregnant with the help of reproductive technology is roughly the same (by some estimates) as that of a normal, healthy couple attempting conception during the woman's regular monthly cycle. But of course, not all the pregnancies result in births and almost three-quarters of the

women treated in infertility programs never become pregnant.

Costs

The financial cost of an attempt to become pregnant can be staggering. Each fertilization cycle costs from $12,000 to $15,000, and most women who get pregnant go through three or four cycles before pregnancy occurs. (The average cost of a single in vitro fertilization attempt was $12,400 in 2007.) Only about fifteen states require insurers to cover infertility treatments, and many people go deeply into debt to pay for them.

It is not unusual for someone to spend $25,000 to $35,000 attempting to get pregnant, and a few people spend as much as $200,000 or $300,000. By some estimates, the money spent on fertility-related medical services exceeds $3 billion to $5 billion a year. The cost of treatment has led some women to visit clinics in South Africa, Italy, or Germany, where prices are significantly lower, even though the success rate may also be lower.

Although some clinics discourage women from repeated attempts at pregnancy to improve their own success rates, others are willing to go far beyond reasonable efforts. Not only is providing fertility assistance lucrative, but some specialists are motivated by the hope that they can meet the needs of their patients. Women desperate to have a child sometimes press their physicians to employ techniques of unproven value.

Drawbacks

Cost is not the only drawback to assisted reproduction. Both the consequences of the methods used and the methods themselves are associated with a variety of moral and social difficulties.

Potential Risk to Child

An increasing number of studies indicate that a child conceived by some reproductive technologies may be at risk for serious birth defects. A study published in the *New England Journal of*

Medicine in 2002 found that babies conceived by IVF or intracytoplasmic sperm injection (ISI, see earlier) have an 8.6 percent risk of heart abnormalities, cleft palate, and undescended testicles, whereas the risk in unassisted pregnancies is 4.2 percent. A second study in the same journal found that IVF and ISI babies have 2.6 times the usual risk of low birth weight, a condition associated with heart and lung problems and poor cognitive development.

The range of risks was confirmed and extended by a 2009 Centers for Disease Control study that compared 281 IVF–ISI babies with 14,095 babies whose conception was unassisted. IVF–ISI babies were more than twice as likely to have defects in the septum of the heart (a hole between the chambers), a cleft lip or cleft palate, or an incompletely developed esophagus. Such babies were also more than four times as likely to have a malformed rectum.

We need to keep in mind, though, that the chance of any baby having some sort of birth defect is about three percent, and no study has yet been done large enough to establish the absolute risk of an IVF baby having a birth defect. The risks have been established on a comparative basis. Even so, a number of scientists think that growing embryos in the lab and manipulating sperm have consequences that are harmful to babies. In particular, IVF conditions may affect how genes are expressed and how embryonic development occurs.

The best evidence for this hypothesis comes from the prevalence of some rare diseases in IVF babies. One of the most studied is Beckwith–Wiedemann syndrome (BWS), which occurs in one of every 15,000 live births. Children with BWS have a greater chance of developing various forms of cancer (kidney cancer, in particular), show excessive growth of cells in certain organs, and display such anomalies as an oversized tongue. Researchers Andrew Feinberg and Michael DeBrun found that BWS is caused by the way a group of genes is expressed, and children with this form of gene expression have a one in two chance of developing cancer, whereas normal children have

a one in 10,000 chance. The researchers also found that the mothers of children with BWS were ten times more likely to have used IVF in getting pregnant than would be expected.

Other studies have drawn similar conclusions. One found, for example, that retinoblastoma, a cancerous eye tumor, occurs from five to seven times more often in children conceived with reproductive technology.

One current line of thought is that the culture medium in which embryos are grown contains chemicals that cause epigenetic changes—that is, changes in the way genes are expressed. The medium may add methyl groups, which act as switches to turn genes on or off. Epigenetic changes are known to cause disorders such as BWS and are also associated with low-birth-weight babies.

Studies comparing the behavior of mice born from IVF embryos with mice born without such assistance suggest that epigenetic changes can also produce behavioral differences.

Some IVF mice demonstrated memory problems, while others showed themselves lacking in normal caution and fear.

To keep the various risks in perspective, however, the actual number of children conceived by the use of reproductive technology who develop birth defects or suffer rare disease is relatively small. Also, some specialists question comparing data about IVF babies with data about babies conceived without technological assistance. Women who seek such assistance, they point out, are usually having difficulty getting pregnant, and whatever causes that difficulty may also influence their babies. Additional studies are proceeding, so new data may eventually provide a clearer picture.

Multiple Births

One of the hazards of assisted reproduction is that the fertility drugs given to women to speed up the production of ova can increase the chances that the women will become pregnant with multiple fetuses. Also, if in vitro fertilization is employed, the practice of transferring several embryos into a woman's fallopian tubes to improve the probability that at least one will implant in the uterus may result in the implanting of several embryos.

Unless selective abortion (called *fetal reduction*) is performed, a pregnancy with multiple fetuses puts the pregnancy at risk for miscarriage. A woman carrying quadruplets has a twenty-five percent chance of a miscarriage in the first trimester; a woman carrying quintuplets has a fifty percent chance.

Also, even if a miscarriage doesn't occur, a multiple pregnancy puts the infants at risk. Normal pregnancies last about forty weeks, but multiple pregnancies rarely go full term. Triplets are born around 33.5 weeks and quadruplets after thirty-one weeks. Because of their prematurity, babies born as multiples often suffer from such problems as blindness, stroke, brain damage, and impaired motor skills. Recent evidence indicates that even if impairments are not obvious, premature babies often grow up to have more difficulties in school and in life than those who were full-term babies.

The number of women taking fertility drugs tripled in the decade 1995–2005, rising from about one million to three million, and the number of multiple births *quadrupled*, from about 1980 to 2000. In 1995, 4973 children were born in groups of three or more. Triplets were most common, but quadruplets and even sextuplets were not uncommon.

A 2009 report from the National Center for Health Statistics showed that the number of multiple births has now leveled off. Twins are born at a rate of 32.1 per thousand births, and the number of triplets and other multiples declined by five percent in 2006, to 1.53 per thousand. This represents a twenty-one percent decline since 1998. Just as the increase in multiple births can be attributed to the rise in the use of reproductive technology, the decline can most likely be attributed to the guidelines that the American Society for Reproductive Medicine established in 1999. A major aim of the guidelines was to reduce the rate of triplet and higher pregnancies. Also, procedures for producing and selecting embryos have improved over the years, reducing the need to implant several embryos to achieve a pregnancy. Although success rates in producing a pregnancy are higher with multiple embryos, studies show that the chance of having a child is better with two embryos than with three.

In 1996, seven percent of births involved triplets or higher multiples, but by 2006, the figure dropped to two percent. Even so, about one-third of births in which reproductive technology is used are multiple ones. Infertility specialists are under a great deal of pressure to produce results. The procedures they offer are expensive, and the women seeking to have a child often pressure the specialists into making them pregnant as fast as possible. The specialists also put themselves under similar pressure, because if they don't produce results, they will lose out in the competition for patients. The fertility business is a billion-dollar industry, and the incentives to violate professional guidelines are considerable.

The costs of multiple pregnancies include a social cost, along with the personal costs of the mother or the parents. As many as twenty percent of the babies in some neonatal intensive care units are babies conceived by reproductive technology and born prematurely. Society may not only have to take care of the babies when they are premature; it may also have to provide them with special educational and social programs.

That so many multiple births still occur, despite industry guidelines, raises questions about what society's response should be. Should we allow women who become pregnant with multiple fetuses to try to carry them all to term? Or should we require that any woman who wants to use assisted reproductive techniques agree beforehand to a selective reduction of fetuses? (See the Case Presentation of the Octomom and the McCaughey septuplets in this chapter.) Fertility clinics can now violate the professional guidelines for limiting the chances of multiple pregnancy without suffering a legal penalty. Perhaps giving the guidelines the force of law would solve the problems that multiple births cause to children, their mothers, their families, and the society.

Embryos, Eggs, and Transplants

An important development in assisted reproduction was the perfection of techniques for freezing embryos. One advantage of the procedure is that it eliminates the need for a woman to undergo the lengthy and uncomfortable process required to secure additional ova. If a woman fails to become pregnant in a first attempt, embryos saved from the initial fertilization can be employed in another effort.

The technique also makes it possible to delay an embryo transplant until the potential mother has reached the most favorable time in her menstrual cycle. Furthermore, because embryos survive storage very well, when a woman who wants to preserve her option to have a child undergoes chemotherapy, she may have her ova fertilized and the embryos preserved. Evidence to date indicates that embryos can be stored in a frozen condition and then unfrozen and implanted without any damage to the chromosomes.

New techniques now allow ova, as well as sperm and embryos, to be frozen and banked until needed. In 1998, Sydney Grace-Louise Murdoch became the first child born in the United States from an egg that had been frozen. Since then, several hundred children around the world have been born from frozen ova, and entrepreneurs have established fertility centers that specialize in storing the eggs of women not yet ready to have a child who worry that, by the time they are ready, they will be too old to ovulate. Also, because not every woman has a male partner or wants to use a sperm donor, banking eggs against the day that they are wanted seems a good alternative to the expense and risks of fertility treatments.

Critics charge, however, that the process of freezing eggs is so unreliable that counting on using them is a high-risk gamble. Eggs have a watery composition, and the formation of ice crystals can destroy the cell membrane or damage the chromosomes. Defenders argue that new processes avoid these problems, and that the success rate of producing a pregnancy

after the eggs are thawed is about twenty percent, which is comparable to the success rate of using frozen embryos.

Ova, embryos, and sperm are not the only reproductive materials that can be successfully frozen. In 2004, a woman gave birth to a child conceived from an ovum produced by an *ovary* that had been frozen and stored for six years. The woman had been treated for breast cancer with chemotherapy, and before the treatment started, she had had an ovary removed and frozen. Years later, when the ovary was thawed and implanted under the skin of her abdomen, it began producing ova. An embryo was produced in vitro with her husband's sperm and then implanted in her uterus.

In another development in 2004, ovarian *tissue* was frozen and then successfully transplanted: Belgian physicians removed ovarian tissue from Ouarda Touirat and stored it while she was treated for lymphoma. After the effects of her chemotherapy dissipated, the tissue was reimplanted, and, without medical help, she became pregnant and had a child. In 2005, also in Belgium, physicians sewed two strips of (never-frozen) ovarian tissue donated by SephanieYarber's identical twin to each of her ovaries. The strips produced eggs, and Yarber became the first woman to give birth to a child by means of transplanted tissue.

Freezing eggs and ovaries and transplanting ovarian tissue raise questions about the reliability of the procedures and informed consent by participants. Are the procedures sufficiently effective to be offered to patients? Do patients understand the potential risks, as well as the benefits, of the procedures? The issues that have been most pressing and publicly discussed, however, are ones connected with frozen embryos.

Each year about 40,000 embryos are frozen at fertility clinics. Not all the embryos are implanted, and this raises what many consider to be the serious question of what should be done with them. What if a couple whose embryos are stored gets divorced? What if both die? What if the woman changes her mind about wanting to be pregnant? What if no surrogate is found?

Because more embryos are usually stored than are used to produce a pregnancy, what should be done with the leftovers? Fertility clinics typically offer the options of having excess embryos destroyed, used for research, or offered to an infertile couple. Often, though, couples cannot be traced, and centers are unwilling to give away an embryo without their permission. When embryos are unclaimed in this way or the bills for storage are left unpaid, frozen embryos are usually destroyed simply by being allowed to thaw. (A frozen embryo is only a tiny speck, because development is at the four-to eight-cell stage.)

A British law requires the destruction of unclaimed embryos after five years. The law took effect in August 1996, and in the face of some protest, about 3300 frozen embryos were destroyed. The courts had refused to set aside the law, and the prime minister ignored appeals that he intervene. Protesters held a vigil outside Westminster Cathedral, and the Vatican newspaper denounced the destruction as a "prenatal massacre."

At some fertility centers, another layer of complexity has been added by the practice of creating embryos from donated eggs and sperm from commercial sperm banks. The rationale is that donor eggs are scarce, and when more are available than are needed in a particular case, they shouldn't be wasted. Having on hand a collection of embryos that don't belong to any person or couple allows the centers to offer what fertility specialists call *embryo adoption*. This means that a woman or couple can choose ("adopt") an embryo for transfer on the basis of a description of the social and educational background and physical characteristics of the gamete donors. A couple can thus try for a resemblance between them and their potential child.

Some critics are troubled by the move from the creation of embryos in order to help particular people to the production of embryos on the speculation that someone who wants one may appear at the clinic. The practice is open to the charge that reproductive technology is a step nearer treating human embryos as commercial products to be offered to discriminating consumers.

At present, no laws govern the preservation or destruction of frozen embryos. Fertility centers set their own policies, and the rules followed by various centers are not uniform. (The situation is changing, though, as professional organizations such as the Society for Reproductive Technologies offer guidelines that are coming to function as regulations.)

Most recently, proponents of the development of an embryonic-stem-cell technology have argued that unused embryos should be used as a source of stem cells, rather than simply discarded. Although those who ascribe no special status to embryos find the view persuasive, those who consider embryos to have the moral status of persons regard it as unacceptable.

Gestational Surrogates and Donor Ova

This is perhaps the most dramatic possibility opened up by in vitro fertilization. A woman whose uterus has been removed, making her incapable of normal pregnancy, can contribute an ovum that, after being fertilized in vitro, is implanted in the uterus of a second woman whose uterus has been prepared to receive it. The "host" or gestational surrogate then carries the baby to term.

In a similar procedure, when a woman is incapable of producing ova, as the result of disease, injury, or normal aging, a donor ovum may be fertilized in vitro and implanted into her uterus, and she then carries the child to term. Thus, postmenopausal women or many women once considered hopelessly barren may now become pregnant and give birth to a baby, even though they are genetically unrelated to the child.

Gestational surrogacy is a relatively new practice, and it opens up a number of possibilities that may have significant social consequences. That women past the natural age of childbearing can now become mothers is a stunning possibility that has already given rise to ethical and policy questions.

(For a discussion, see the Social Context "Postmenopausal Motherhood," in this chapter.) Second, women using the services of a gestational surrogate do so at present because they are unable to bear children themselves. However, it is only a short step from being unable to bear children to being *unwilling* to bear children.

Thus, it is easy to imagine that some women might choose to free themselves from the rigors of pregnancy by hiring a gestational surrogate. The employer would be the source of the ovum, which would then be fertilized in vitro and implanted as an embryo in the uterus of the surrogate. Women who could afford to do so could have their own genetic children without ever having to be pregnant.

Criticisms of Assisted-Reproduction Practices

While admitting the present and potential values of reproductive technology in assisting women who want to have children, many critics think the technology has been oversold. Despite their hopes, the majority of women who must rely on it don't become pregnant. Also, women aren't always properly informed about their chances. A particular clinic may have a success rate of twenty-five percent, but for a woman in her early forties, the rate may be only a one percent to two percent chance per month of trying. (Only about a quarter of those who seek assistance overcome their infertility.)

Critics also point out that the expense of trying to become pregnant can be quite high. Each attempt costs $12,000 or more, and several attempts are usually required for success. Further, the procedures involve anxiety and discomfort. Although the risk of injury and infection isn't great, it is real. In addition, the safety of the fertility drugs used to trigger ovulation and to prepare the uterus for implantation has been questioned. Also, there is a possibility that the high hormone levels in the blood the drugs produce may increase a woman's risk of breast cancer.

Donated ova are a scarcer commodity than sperm, and fertility clinics and egg brokers make a concerted effort to recruit donors to meet the needs of their patients and clients. Critics regard the situation as one in which young women who need money are not provided with adequate information about the risks involved and are induced to become donors, even though doing so may not be in their interest. Professional guidelines, critics say, offer insufficient protection, and the billion-dollar fertility industry should be regulated by laws. (See the Social Context "The Price of Eggs," in this chapter, for a fuller discussion.)

Benefits of IVF and Other Forms of Assisted Reproduction

Assisted reproduction is complicated, is expensive, and requires a great investment of skill, knowledge, and resources. An obvious question is, What is to be gained by it? What benefits might justify the use of the technically difficult and expensive medical procedures involved?

The most direct and perhaps most persuasive answer is that assisted reproduction makes it possible for many people to have children who wouldn't otherwise be able to do so. For those people, this is a decisive consideration. Some research shows that more than ten percent of married couples in the United States are infertile—that is, they have attempted to conceive a child for a year or longer without success. Infertility affects 6.1 million women and an estimated 4 million men. In 1995 alone, 1.2 million people sought professional help in conceiving a child.

Assisted reproduction isn't a solution to all problems of fertility, but it's the only solution possible in a large number of cases. Figures show that as many as forty-five percent of all cases of female infertility are caused by abnormal or obstructed fallopian tubes. Although normal ova are produced, they cannot move down the tubes to be fertilized. In some cases, tissue blocking the tubes can be removed or the tubes reconstructed. In other cases, however, the tubes may be impossible to repair or may be entirely absent. (Only forty to fifty percent of infertile women can be helped through surgery.) This means that the only way in which these women can expect to have a child of their own is by means of some sort of assisted reproduction. This is also true when the woman has no uterus or is postmenopausal and must rely on a donated ovum. Thus, technology offers a realistic possibility of becoming parents to many people who once had no hope of having a child.

Critics of assisted reproduction often claim there is no *right* to have a child and suggest that those unable to conceive should simply accept the fact and perhaps adopt a child. Proponents don't justify assisted reproduction in terms of rights, however. They refer primarily to the strong desire some people have to become parents, and some point out that assisted reproduction, as it is most often employed, is nothing more than a means of facilitating a natural function that can't be carried out because of some sort of biological failure.

Ethical and Social Difficulties

Several aspects of the technology of assisted reproduction and the way it can be employed are regarded by some observers as troublesome. Discussed briefly next are a few sources of uneasiness not mentioned earlier.

Incest potential

Clinics typically refuse to reveal the names of sperm donors to their clients or to the children born from sperm supplied by the clinics. Yet protecting the privacy of donors has an unintended consequence: because most clinics provide information about donors (physical appearance, height, education) and some even offer pictures, some donors are wildly popular, and their sperm may be chosen by a dozen or more potential mothers. This means that the children of these mothers will be half-siblings. If many of them live in the same geographical area, there is a small but real risk of their unknowingly engaging

in incest. The same potential exists for children conceived from donor eggs, and it is less likely only because the number of children born from donated sperm is much larger. One estimate puts the number at 30,000 a year.

Eugenics

The use of reproductive technology may encourage the development of eugenic ideas about improving the species. Rather than having children of their own, would-be parents might be motivated to seek out ova and sperm from people who possess physical and intellectual characteristics that are particularly admired. Thus, even without an organized plan of social eugenics (see Chapter 5), individuals might be tempted to follow their own eugenic notions. These include the tendency to try to have "the perfect baby," and this cheapens human life by promoting the view that human babies are commodities produced to order.

Sex Selection

Similarly, would-be parents might be inclined to exercise the potential for control over the sex of their offspring. Only males contain both an X and a Y chromosome, and their presence is detectable in the cells of the developing embryo. Determination of the sex of the embryo would allow the potential parents to decide whether they wish to have a male or female child. Consequently, a potential human being (the developing embryo) might be destroyed for what is basically a trivial reason. No fertility clinic permits sex selection, but this is a matter of policy, not law.

Weakening of Family

Reproductive technology may promote a social climate in which having children becomes severed from the family. The procedures emphasize the mechanics of conception and so minimize the significance of the shared love and commitments of the parents of a child conceived by intercourse.

Similarly, the technology dilutes the notion of parenthood by making possible peculiar relationships. For example, as many as five people may become involved in having a child, for a couple can use donor sperm and donor eggs and rely on the services of a surrogate for pregnancy. Because there is no clear sense in which the child belongs to any of them, parenthood is radically severed from conception.

Attitudes of IVF Children

In 2010, the politically conservative Institute for American Values published the results of a study based on a survey of adults 18–45 who had been conceived by the use of donor sperm. The results, as Ross Douthat reports, depict a group of people who are thankful for the technology that made their lives possible, yet feel regret about being the products of a technological and financial transaction.

IVF offspring are more likely to endorse the idea that everyone has a right to have a child, and they support the practice of assisted reproduction. (Indeed, some twenty percent say they are sperm or egg donors.) However, a substantial minority report that they are bothered by "the circumstances of my conception" and that "money was exchanged to conceive me." A larger percentage than in the general population disapprove of the practice of paying for sperm or eggs and agree with the statement "It is wrong to deliberately conceive a fatherless/ motherless child." A large minority say that if a friend were planning to get pregnant by paying for donor sperm, they would discourage her.

IVF offspring are almost twice as likely as adopted children to report envying those who knew their biological parents, twice as likely to worry that their parents "might have lied to me about important matters," and three times as likely to report feeling "confused about who is a member of my family and who is not." Not surprisingly, the children of sperm donors are also more likely than adopted children to agree that "when I see someone who resembles me, I often wonder if we are related." For similar reasons, they worry more than adopted children about becoming involved in a romantic relationship with someone who is related to them biologically.

Douthat, among others, recommends that U.S. laws be revised to give sperm and egg donation the status and protections it deserves. As a medical procedure, assisted reproduction may resemble a blood transfusion, but its social and personal consequences more closely resemble adoption. Britain, Sweden, Norway, and Switzerland are among the countries that have banned anonymous sperm and egg donation. When children who are born as a result of assisted reproduction turn 18, they have the legal right to gain access to their biological parents.

These difficulties and ones discussed earlier are not likely to be considered equally serious by everyone. Those who do not believe that human life begins at conception will hardly be troubled by the discarding of unimplanted embryos. The chance of inadvertent incest among children born from donated sperm is small. Sex choice is possible now by the use of amniocentesis, so it's not a problem unique to reproductive technology, and the same is true of the implementation of eugenic ideas.

Whether assisted reproduction leads to a weakening of the values associated with the family is partly an empirical question that only additional experience will show. Even if childbearing does become severed from current family structure, it still must be shown that this is in itself something of which we ought to disapprove. It's not impossible that alternative social structures for childbearing and childrearing might be superior to ones currently dominant in Western culture.

Little information is available about the psychological and social well-being of children born with the help of assisted reproduction. Like Louise Brown, many are on the brink of middle age, but many more are still young and growing. The Institute for American Values report suggests that more research should be done to understand the needs, attitudes, and problems of this increasingly large segment of the population. Also, drawing on the experiences of other countries, the United States should consider changing its laws to allow children born from donated sperm, eggs, or embryos to find out about their biological parentage.

Cloning and Twinning

Cloning produces individuals that are exact genetic copies of the donor from whom the DNA was obtained. Some animal cells have been cloned for more than five decades, but it wasn't until 1997 that the first mammal (a sheep) was cloned. Nothing in principle seems to stand in the way of cloning a human, but if human cloning became a practical reality, it would present serious moral and social issues. (See the Case Presentation "Hello, Dolly," in Chapter 3.)

Many issues raised in a speculative way by cloning are raised in a more immediate way by the procedure known as *twinning*. In 1993, Jerry Hall and Robert Stillman took seventeen two- to eight-cell human embryos, separated the blastomeres (the individual cells) and coated them with artificial zona pellucida (the protective coat surrounding egg cells), and then placed them in various nutrient solutions. The outcome was the production of forty-eight new embryos from the original ones.

The cells continued to divide, but development stopped after six days, partly because the embryos were abnormal—the originals were chosen just because they were defective. The work was purely experimental, and it was never intended that the embryos would be implanted.

The immediate advantage of the techniques developed by Hall and Stillman (as well as many others) is to increase the supply of implantable embryos for couples with fertility problems. If a couple's embryos, produced by in vitro fertilization, can be used to produce several more embryos, these can be used in repeated implantation attempts. Thus, the woman does not have to undergo repetitions of the unpleasant, expensive, and somewhat risky procedures involved in triggering ovulation, and then retrieving ova for in vitro fertilization.

Regarded from this point of view, the techniques may make having a child easier, cheaper, and less time-consuming for some couples.

The process used by Hall and Stillman was, strictly speaking, not actually cloning, which requires taking a somatic cell from a developed organism, extracting the DNA, and then growing an embryo from it in an enucleated egg cell. Even so, the process of *twinning* they employed showed that it would take very little more technically to use the techniques of assisted reproduction to produce a number of genetically identical humans.

Such techniques, when combined with the freezing of embryos, open up a number of social possibilities as surprising and controversial as those which cloning would make possible:

1. The production of several identical embryos would make a market in embryos possible. If a child had already been born and could be shown to have desirable qualities, the couple who had produced the embryos might sell them at high prices. It would then be possible for someone to have a child genetically identical to the one with the desirable qualities.

2. Parents could have a family in which all their children were genetic copies of one another. The oldest and the youngest would have the same genetic endowment. If several gestational mothers were employed, it would be possible to produce a dozen or more genetically identical children of the same age.

3. A couple might have a child, while also freezing an embryo twin as a spare. If the child should die, then the genetic twin could be grown from the embryo. The twin would be as much like the lost child as genetics makes possible.

4. If embryo twins were frozen and stored, they could be implanted in gestational mothers years apart. Thus, one twin might be sixty, while the other is only six.

5. Twins of an individual might be stored so that if the person needed something like

a bone-marrow or kidney transplant, the twin could be implanted in a gestational surrogate and allowed to develop. The tissue match from the twin would be perfect, and the problem of rejection would not arise.

The issues raised by twinning differ little from those raised by cloning, and twinning is already a practical reality. Some of the uses are so benign as to be hardly debatable, while others may result in such a cheapening or commercialization of human life as to be undesirable options.

Artificial Insemination

In 1909, an unusual letter appeared in the professional journal *Medical World*. A.D. Hard, the author of the letter, claimed that when he was a student at Jefferson Medical College in Philadelphia, a wealthy businessman and his wife consulted a physician on the faculty about their inability to conceive a child. A detailed examination showed that the man was incapable of producing sperm. The case was presented for discussion in a class of which Hard was member. According to Hard, the class suggested that semen be taken from the "best-looking member of the class" and used to inseminate the wife.

The letter claimed that this was done while the woman was anesthetized and that neither the husband nor the wife was told about the process. The patient became pregnant and gave birth to a son. The husband was then told how the pregnancy was produced, and, although he was pleased with the result, he asked that his wife not be informed.

The event described by Hard took place in 1884, and Hard was probably "the best-looking member of the class."

The Philadelphia case is the first recorded instance of the artificial insemination of donor sperm in a human patient, but the process itself has a much longer history. Arab horsemen in the fourteenth century inseminated mares with semen-soaked sponges, and in the eighteenth century the Italian physiologist Spallansani

documented experiments in which he fertilized dogs, reptiles, and frogs.

The Procedure

Artificial insemination is a basic technique of assisted reproduction. It is initiated when the woman's body temperature indicates that ovulation is to take place in one or two days, then is repeated once or twice more until her body temperature shows that ovulation is completed. Typically, three inseminations are performed during a monthly cycle.

The procedure is simple. The patient is usually placed in a position so that her hips are raised. A semen specimen, collected earlier through masturbation or taken from a sperm bank, is placed in a syringe attached to a catheter. The catheter is inserted into the cervical canal and the semen slowly injected into the uterus. The patient stays in her position for fifteen or twenty minutes to increase the chances that the sperm will fertilize an ovum.

The overall success rate is about eighty-five to ninety percent. Success on the first attempt is rare, and the highest rate occurs in the third month. Efforts may be made every month for as long as six months or a year. Such efforts are continued, however, only when a detailed examination shows that the woman is not suffering from some unrecognized problem preventing her from becoming pregnant.

When sperm taken from donors is used, the rate of congenital abnormalities is slightly lower than that for the general population. There is no evidence that manipulating the sperm causes any harm, but as mentioned earlier, some evidence suggests that a woman's use of reproductive technology can lead to children with a higher than usual number of genetic impairments.

Reasons for Seeking Artificial Insemination

Artificial insemination may be sought for a variety of reasons. When a man and woman are involved, the reasons are almost always associated with factors that make it impossible for them to conceive a child in the usual sexual way. About ten percent of all married couples are infertile, and forty percent of those cases are due to factors involving the male.

The male may be unable to produce any sperm cells (a condition called *asospermia*), or the number he produces may be too low to make impregnation of the female likely (a condition called *oligospermia*). In other cases, adequate numbers of sperm cells may be produced, but they may not function normally. They may not be sufficiently motile to make their way through the vaginal canal to reach the uterus. Hence, their chances of reaching and fertilizing an ovum are slight. Finally, the male may suffer from a neurological condition that makes ejaculation impossible or from a disease (such as diabetes) that renders him impotent. His sperm can be removed and used in artificial insemination.

If the female cannot ovulate or if her fallopian tubes are blocked so that ova cannot descend, artificial insemination can accomplish nothing. (See the earlier section on in vitro fertilization.) Yet there are factors affecting the female that artificial insemination can be helpful in overcoming. For example, if the female has a vaginal environment that is biochemically inhospitable to sperm, artificial insemination may be successful. Because the sperm need not pass through the vagina, their chance of surviving is better. Also, if the female has a small cervix (the opening to the uterus) or if her uterus is in an abnormal position, then artificial insemination may be used to deliver the sperm to an advantageous position for fertilization.

A couple might also seek artificial insemination for genetic reasons. Both may be carriers of a recessive gene for a genetic disorder (e.g., Tay–Sachs disease), or the male may be the carrier of a dominant gene for a genetic disorder (e.g., Huntington's disease). In either case, they may not want to run the statistical risk of their child's being born with a genetic disease, yet may also not be willing to accept prenatal testing and abortion or embryo screening.

To avoid the possibility they fear, they may choose to make use of artificial insemination with sperm secured from a donor.

The traditional recipient of artificial insemination is a married woman who, in consultation with her husband, has decided to have a child. Some physiological or physical difficulty in conceiving leads them to turn to artificial insemination.

But the traditional recipient is no longer the only recipient. Recipients now include many single women who wish to have a child and view artificial insemination as a way of taking charge of their own reproduction. In buying sperm from a sperm bank, some see an opportunity to increase the chance that their child will have genetically influenced characteristics they value. (See the Social Context "Shopping the Sperm Supermarket," in this chapter.) Also, lesbian couples are now more often deciding that one of them should become pregnant. Even if they cannot marry, they say, having a child will allow them to become a family, albeit a nontraditional one.

Sperm Donors

Sperm donors are often medical or university students. Commercial sperm banks typically recruit more widely, but effort is made to employ donors who are in excellent health, with a high level of intellectual ability. Their family histories are reviewed to reduce the possibility of transmitting a genetic disorder, and their blood type is checked to determine its compatibility with that of the recipient. Also, a potential donor must be known to be fertile. Thus, he must already be a biological parent or he must fall within the normal range in several semen analyses.

Donors are paid $50 to $200 for their services, and typically their identity is kept secret from the recipient and any resulting children. A coding system is ordinarily used both to preserve the anonymity of the donor and to ensure that the same donor is used in all inseminations.

The semen stored in sperm banks is not necessarily that of anonymous donors. For a variety of reasons, individuals may wish to have their sperm preserved and pay a fee to a sperm-bank operator for this service. For example, a man planning a vasectomy or one expecting to become sterile because of a progressive disease may store his sperm in the event that he may later want to father a child. Lance Armstrong, seven-time winner of the Tour de France, banked sperm before undergoing treatment for testicular cancer, and this enabled him to have biological children afterwards.

Issues in Artificial Insemination

Artificial insemination (AI) presents a variety of moral, legal, and social issues that have not been addressed in a thorough fashion. Legal scholars have explored some of the consequences that AI has for traditional legal doctrines of paternity, legitimacy, and inheritance. They have also made recommendations for formulating new laws (or reformulating old ones) to take into account the reality of the practice of AI.

Critics of AI have focused mostly on its potential for altering the relationship between husbands and wives and for producing undesirable social changes. They argue that AI will take the love out of sexual procreation and make it a purely mechanical process, that AI will promote eugenics and so denigrate the worth of babies that fall short of some ideal, and that AI is just another step down the road toward the society of *Brave New World*. AI, they say, has the potential for destroying the family by allowing single women and lesbian couples to have children.

Some of the issues that need close attention from philosophers concern individual rights and responsibilities. For example, does a man who has served as a sperm donor have any special moral responsibilities? He certainly must have some responsibilities. For example, it would be wrong for him to lie about any genetic diseases in his family history. But does he have any responsibilities to the child that is produced by AI employing his sperm? If

donating sperm is no different from donating blood, then perhaps he does not. But is such a comparison apt?

Can a child born as a result of AI legitimately demand to know the name of his biological father? We need not assume that mere curiosity might motivate such a request. Someone could need to know her family background in order to determine how likely it is that a potential child might have a genetic disorder. Also, some may want to be sure that they are avoiding inadvertent incest if their potential partner was also conceived by AI. Perhaps the current practice of maintaining the anonymity of sperm donors is not one that can stand critical scrutiny.

Should a woman be allowed to order sperm donated by someone who approximates her concept of an ideal person? Should she be able to request a donor from a certain ethnic group, with particular eye and hair color, a certain minimum or maximum height, physical attractiveness, with evidence of intelligence, and so on? A number of other ethical questions are easily raised about AI: Does any woman (married or single, of any age) have the right to demand AI? Should a physician make AI by donor available to a married women if her husband is opposed?

Other questions concerning the proper procedures to follow in the practice of AI are also of considerable significance. For example, how thoroughly must sperm donors be screened for genetic defects? What standards of quality must sperm as a biological material be required to satisfy? What physical, educational, or general social traits (if any) should individual donors possess? Should records be maintained and shared through an established network to prevent the marriage or mating of individuals born from AI with the same biological father?

At present, these questions have been answered only by individual physicians or clinics, if at all. No general medical or legal policies govern the practice of AI, although the professional organizations offer ethical guidelines.

Even if present practices are adequate, most people would agree that we need to develop uniform policies to regulate AI.

Ovum Donors

The use of donor ova presents virtually the same set of issues as those raised by artificial insemination. Unlike AI, however, egg donation raises questions about the exploitation of donors. Typically, they are young women who agree to donate ova because they want to earn the several thousand dollars fertility clinics are willing to pay.

To earn the money, they must put themselves through an uncomfortable process involving treatment with powerful drugs and retrieval of the eggs by a small surgical incision or a needle puncture. The immediate risk to their health is small but real. Critics point out that women who are willing to submit themselves to the process must be young and are likely to be naive and vulnerable. A need for money will thus make them ripe for exploitation. (See the Social context "The Price of Eggs," in this chapter, for a fuller discussion.)

Surrogate Pregnancy

A *gestational surrogate* (see the earlier discussion) is a "host mother," a woman who is implanted with an embryo produced by AI from the ovum of another woman. *Surrogate mothers* are women who agree to become pregnant by means of artificial insemination. The surrogate mother carries the baby to term, then turns the baby over for adoption to the couple or individual with whom she made the agreement.

Surrogate mothers are typically sought by couples who wish to have a child with whom at least the man has a genetic link and who have been unsuccessful in conceiving a child themselves. A woman unable to conceive but wanting a child may also arrange for the services of a gestational surrogate using donor sperm.

Various legal complications surround surrogate pregnancy, and at least eighteen states have passed laws regulating surrogacy arrangements. Some laws, like those in Michigan and New Jersey, make it illegal for couples to adopt a child born to a surrogate mother. The aim is to discourage surrogacy.

When surrogacy arrangements are allowed, a major problem is finding a way to pay women who agree to be surrogates. Adoption laws forbid the selling of children or even the payment of money to one of the biological parents in connection with adoption. The child must be freely surrendered. Because a child born to a surrogate mother is, in the absence of laws to the contrary, legally her child, the child must be adopted by the couple securing her services. How then can the surrogate mother be paid?

Some women have simply volunteered to be surrogate mothers in these cases, so the issue of payment would not arise. In general, however, the difficulty has been resolved by paying the mother to compensate her for her inconvenience and the loss of her time. Technically, then, she is not being paid for conceiving and bearing a child, nor is she being paid for the child, who is handed over for adoption. Hence, laws against selling a child are not violated, and the surrogate is paid from $10,000 to $25,000.

A second problem is finding a way to permit surrogacy while avoiding turning it into a commercial operation resembling the breeding of horses or show dogs. Surrogacy is often arranged by an attorney acting as a broker on behalf of a couple that wants a child. The attorney finds the surrogate and draws up a contract between her and the couple. (The contract can include such items as a prorated fee if the surrogate miscarries or a requirement that the surrogate have an abortion if prenatal tests reveal a fetal abnormality.) The surrogate must agree to relinquish her maternal rights and not stand in the way of adoption by the contracting couple. For arranging the surrogacy, as well as for drawing up the contract, the broker receives a fee of $15,000 to $20,000.

Despite the claim that a surrogate is being paid for her time and inconvenience, some critics charge that surrogacy arrangements are no more than "baby selling." To avoid this appearance, New York State passed a law with the aim of removing the profit motive from surrogacy arrangements and making them completely noncommercial. The state kept it legal for a woman to become a surrogate but made it illegal to pay a broker to handle the arrangements. Further, the state made it illegal to pay a surrogate for anything more than her medical expenses. A contract agreeing to pay a fee to a broker or to a woman acting as a surrogate would have no legal standing in court.

Some of the same reasons offered to justify assisted reproduction can also be offered for surrogate pregnancy. Fundamentally, couples who wish to have a child of their own but are unable to do so because of some uncorrectable medical difficulty experienced by the woman view surrogate pregnancy as the only hope remaining to them. Some rule out adoption because of the relative shortage of available infants, and some simply want a genetic connection between them and the child. Many people are quite desperate to have a child of their own.

Critics have charged that surrogate pregnancy is no more than a specialized form of prostitution. A woman, in effect, rents out her body for a period of time and is paid for doing so. Such a criticism rests on the assumption that prostitution is morally wrong, and this is a claim at least some would deny is correct. Furthermore, the criticism fails to take into account the differences in aims. Some surrogate mothers have volunteered their services with no expectation of monetary reward, and some women have agreed to be surrogate mothers at the request of a sister, friend, daughter, or son. Even those who are paid mention that part of their motivation is to help those couples who so desperately want a child. Far from condemning surrogate mothers as acting immorally, it is possible to view at least some as acting in a morally heroic way by contributing to the good of others through their actions.

Perhaps the most serious objection to the use of surrogate mothers is that they are likely to be recruited from the ranks of those most in need of money. Women of upper-and middle-income groups are not likely to serve as surrogate mothers. Women with low-paying jobs or no jobs at all are obviously the prime candidates for recruiters. It might be charged, then, that women who become surrogate mothers are being exploited by those who have money enough to pay for their services.

Merely paying someone in need of money to do something does not constitute exploitation, however. To make such a charge stick, it would be necessary to show that women who become surrogate mothers are under a great deal of social and economic pressure and have no other realistic options. Furthermore, it could be argued that, within limits, individuals have a right to do with their bodies as they choose. If a woman freely decides to earn money by serving as a surrogate mother, then we have no more reason to object to her decision than we would have to object to a man's decision to earn money by working as a laborer.

As the population ages and women with careers postpone having children, the employment of surrogate mothers is likely to increase. The practice is now well established, but the ethical and social issues are far from being resolved to the general satisfaction of our society.

Ethical Theories and Reproductive Control

One of the themes of Mary Shelley's famous novel *Frankenstein* is that it is both wrong and dangerous to tamper with the natural forces of life. It is wrong because it disturbs the natural order of things, and it is dangerous because it unleashes forces beyond human control. The "monster" that is animated by Dr. Victor Frankenstein stands as a warning and reproach to all who seek to impose their will on the world through the powers of scientific technology.

The fundamental ethical question about the technology of human reproductive control is whether it ought to be employed at all. Is it simply wrong for us to use our knowledge of human biology to exercise power over the processes of human reproduction?

The natural law view, as represented by currently accepted doctrines of the Roman Catholic Church, suggests that all the techniques for controlling human reproduction that we have discussed here are fundamentally wrong.

Children may ordinarily be expected as a result of sexual union within marriage. However, if no measures are wrongfully taken to frustrate the possibility of their birth (contraception, for example), then a married couple has no obligation to attempt to conceive children by means such as artificial insemination or in vitro fertilization. Certainly, the couple has no reason to resort to anything as extreme as cloning or using donor embryos.

Indeed, many of the technological processes are themselves inherently objectionable. Artificial insemination, for example, requires male masturbation, which is prima facie wrong, since it is an act that can be considered to be unnatural, given the natural end of sex. AI, even when semen from the husband is used, tends to destroy the values inherent in the married state. It makes conception a mechanical act.

In vitro fertilization is open to the same objections. In addition, the process itself involves the destruction of fertilized ova. On the view that human conception takes place at the moment of fertilization, this means that the discarding of unimplanted embryos amounts to the destruction of human life.

On the utilitarian view, no reproductive technology is in itself objectionable. The question that has to be answered is whether the use of any particular procedure, in general or in a certain case, is likely to lead to

more good than not. In general, it is reasonable to believe that a utilitarian would be likely to approve of all the procedures we've discussed here.

A rule utilitarian, however, might oppose any or all of the procedures. If there is strong evidence to support the view that the use of reproductive technology will lead to a society in which the welfare of its members will not be served, then a rule utilitarian would be on firm ground in arguing that reproductive technology ought to be abandoned.

According to Ross's ethical theory, we have prima facie duties of beneficence. That is, we have an obligation to assist others in bettering their lives. This suggests that the use of reproductive technology may be justified as a means to promote the well-being of others. For example, if a couple desires to have a child but is unable to conceive one, then either in vitro fertilization procedures or artificial insemination might be employed to help them satisfy their shared desire. Twinning might be used to increase the number of embryos, and even cloning seems prima facie unobjectionable.

Kantian principles don't seem to supply grounds for objecting to assisted reproduction or reproductive technology in general as inherently wrong. However, the maxim involved in each action must always be one that satisfies the categorical imperative. Consequently, some instances of in vitro fertilization, artificial insemination, twinning, and cloning would no doubt be morally wrong.

The technology of reproduction is a reality of ordinary life. So far it has made our society into neither a dystopia nor a utopia. It's just one set of tools among the many that science and medicine have forged.

Yet the tools are powerful ones, and we should beware of allowing familiarity to produce indifference. The moral and social issues raised by reproductive technology are just as real as the technology. So far, we have not treated some of them with the seriousness they deserve.

READINGS

Section 1: Assisted Reproduction and the Limits of Autonomy

The Octomom and the Duties of the Fertility Specialists

Howard Minkoff and Jeffrey Ecker

Minkoff and Ecker use the controversy surrounding the birth of octuplets to Nadya Suleman (they don't refer to her by name) as an occasion to address some of the criticisms of her reproductive endocrinologists (fertility specialists). The authors deal with three specific questions about the responsibilities of reproductive endocrinologists: (1) Should reproductive endocrinologists consider the economic interest of society? (2) Should they consider the parenting abilities of their potential patients? (3) Should the number of embryo transfers be limited?

Minkoff and Ecker argue that the economic interest of society is not a concern of reproductive specialists, that in some cases they should refuse to provide reproductive help, and that there should be a limit on the number of embryos transferred.

In January, the world's second set of living octuplets was born in California, and the mother and her babies quickly became the focus of unrelenting media attention. As the mother disclosed details of her pregnancy (in vitro fertilization [IVF] with 6 embryos transferred) and reporters discovered more about her and her family (a single, unemployed mother with 6 other children at home), the public and media reaction shifted from awe to outrage. Reproductive endocrinologists similarly voiced concern about the birth of these higher-order multiples.[1]

However, closer consideration of the indignation of the public and of health professionals suggests that the causes of their concerns were quite disparate. The public's focus was on economic considerations and the social well-being of the children ("Why did they let her get pregnant?"). In contrast, infertility specialists focused on the risks of transferring excess embryos during an IVF cycle and the consequent biologic risks throughout in utero and neonatal life ("How could

Howard Minkoff and Jeffrey Ecker, From "The Octomom and the Fertility Specialists: The California octuplets and the duties of Reproductive endocrinologists." *American Journal of Obstetrics and Gynecology*, Vol. 201, no. 1, (2009): 15e1–15e3. Copyright © 2009 Elsevier, Inc. Reprinted by permission.

they have put 6 back?"). In this article we will discuss these alternate concerns, what this difference in focus reflects, and whether it suggests a need to reconsider the ethical obligations of reproductive endocrinologists to their patients as well as their obligation to evaluate a patient's fitness to parent.

We recognize that, although these discussions appear to include considerations of duties owed to children who might result from assisted reproduction, at the time decisions about the appropriateness of IVF are made, these children do not exist. In some cases there are preimplantation embryos frozen and awaiting transfer; in others there are gametes awaiting fertilization.

But in all cases the pregnancy, much less a child who may result, is still no more than an idea, a potential. The issue of the moral standing—the rights and respect—due these tissues or ideas is quite contentious and it is unlikely that all parties considering the questions raised by the recent octuplet pregnancy would find agreement on that subject. For example, some may see in vitro embryos as similar to ex utero children. Others would describe them as deserving respect but fundamentally different from a pregnancy. Reconciling alternate views of gametes, embryos, and as-yet-unconceived children is beyond the scope of this article and a task deeply encumbered by the politics and passion of abortion. Instead of entering this debate, we center our discussion on those whose rights are not in dispute and to whom provider obligations are clear—women anticipating pregnancy—although, we will also comment on what role, if any, reproductive endocrinologist[s] should play in appraising the parenting abilities of their patients.

What is the duty of reproductive endocrinologists to evaluate a patient's fitness to parent?

When society bestows privileges on the profession of medicine (the power to train, discipline, and dismiss its members), it does so with an expectation that in return physicians will render care to individual members of society rather than act in pursuit of society's broader aims. As a result, physicians' obligations have focused more on the good of the individual with whom they have a fiduciary responsibility than on society as a whole, although there are notable exceptions. Several professional organizations have asserted that the principle of primacy of patient welfare should not waver in the face of "market forces, *societal pressures* or administrative exigencies."[2] Accordingly, most professional organizations hold that physicians are under no ethical obligation to factor the cost to society of the ongoing care of a patient into decisions about whether to render service in the first place. For example, if an individual on welfare or a prison inmate had a myocardial infarction, physicians would not be expected to withhold care even if the patient's survival would impose a continuing cost to society (in fact, ethics would mandate they work to restore the individual's health). That is not to say there are not instances in which the physician rightly subsumes the interests of his/her patient to the greater good of society. The psychiatric commitment of a person thought to represent a threat to others, the quarantine of infectious individuals, and the warning of individuals of threats revealed during confidential conversations with patients[3] are but three examples. However, in general, society does not depend on individual providers to accomplish public health aims; it has other tools to accomplish policy goals (eg, quarantine laws and guaranteed payments for all dialysis).

Although society could, in theory, choose to limit IVF to families who could afford to raise their children without public assistance, reproductive endocrinologists have not considered future burdens on society as

criteria for eligibility for assisted reproductive technology (ART). A reasonable question then is whether reproductive endocrinologists should factor in economic circumstance in deciding whether an individual is an appropriate candidate for ART. In addressing this question it is important to consider separately the potential financial impact on society of assisting poor people to have children, and the consequence of the parents' financial circumstances on their parenting ability. In regard to the former, as just noted, the provider should not have as his/her primary obligation the protection of community interests. The provider's focus should be on the patient and, possibly, although to a much lesser degree and only in rare circumstance (to be discussed), the interests of children who might result. In regard to the latter, financial status is merely one measure, and not a particularly apt one, of "child-rearing abilities," ie, one of an untold number of characteristics that might reflect the life into which a child would be born.

There are many problems in thinking of reproductive endocrinologists as being best suited to parse these characteristics, ie, to serve as gatekeepers, evaluating economic and other factors as they consider who should have access to ART. In the first instance, most infertility physicians are not trained to perform such evaluations. Judging patients as potential parents is inherently subjective and may be flavored by individual opinions and, potentially, prejudices. Consequently, attempts to limit access to couples matching some concept of idealized parents could devolve into a Pandora's box of personal criteria (eg, family size and religion) used to select candidates for IVF. Even if guidelines were narrowly crafted to protect potential children from only *serious* risks, for example from having parents who have harmed children, it still might open the door to a cascade of standards that would block access to parents about whom there were much less substantive concerns. Previous attempts to exclude groups from childbearing are now justly regarded as shameful chapters in medical history.[4]

However, this case does provide an opportunity for a conversation about, on the one hand, the vital right of people to have children without fear of societal intrusions and, on the other, the right of physicians not to render requested care in extreme circumstances (eg, to couples with a history of abusing a child and who have not undergone rehabilitation). Great caution would be warranted in these deliberations lest "protecting the interests of children" becomes a pretext for introducing bias based on income, sexual orientation, or race into considerations of eligibility for ART. These are issues with which the Ethics Committee of the American Society of Reproductive Medicine (ASRM) has wrestled for some time, concluding that if reproductive endocrinologists "have a substantial, non-arbitrary basis for thinking that parents will provide inadequate child-rearing, they should be free to refuse to provide treatment services."[5] In the relevant committee opinion, however, the group went on to carefully circumscribe that right by noting that services should be denied "only after investigation shows that there is a substantial basis for such judgments" and admonishing their members not to engage in unjustified discrimination.[5] In trying to determine if that "substantial basis" exists, physicians must rely more on their training in evidence-based reasoning than on personal preference or social convention. However, because bias is universal, often unconscious and unintentional, and difficult to erase[6] (even with evidence), the goal of any screening should not be to weed out imperfect parents (which would put all prospective parents at risk), but rather only potentially dangerous ones.

In that regard the California octuplet case is less a cry for action than a cautionary tale. The "facts" that have roused the public's fury (ie, her income, her marital status, and her other 6 children) are examples of characteristics that should not be disqualifying, even if some individuals might decide that they themselves would not want children in those circumstances. The method of conception (natural or ART) should have minimal bearing on the requisites for parenting. Otherwise, questions of justice would be raised by the inequitable burden borne by a particular group, in this case infertile patients (although parity with naturally conceiving parents still would allow, in extreme circumstances, consideration of the appropriateness of a home environment for children). Recognizing all these challenges, reproductive endocrinologists have set a very low bar for admission into infertility programs or, to put it another way, they have set an extremely high threshold for disallowing access. This reflects a belief articulated by Robertson[7] that, "procreative liberty should enjoy presumptive primacy when conflicts about its exercise arise because. . . [it] is central to personal identity, to dignity and to the meaning of one's life," and, accordingly, a heavy onus should be placed on those who would deprive someone of that right. The Ethics Committee of ASRM recognizes that "offspring welfare" is a "valid consideration" as fertility

programs evaluate who to treat but cautions that programs should not discriminate based on "disability or other impermissible factors" and concludes that programs are not "morally obligated to withhold such services except when significant harm to future children is likely."[5]

Should the number of embryos returned be limited?

The risks of multiple gestations are real and well described. Those risks—mortality and complications associated with prematurity—have led professional organizations to establish guidelines that limit the number of embryos transferred in any one IVF cycle, because that number is directly correlated with the likelihood of multiple gestation including higher-order multiples. In other countries the number that may be transferred is limited by statute.

In the United States, no such statute exists and, in spite of guidelines, the decision is ultimately left to patient and provider. Those decisions are informed by how they collectively value the importance of achieving pregnancy and of avoiding multiple gestations, considerations no doubt influenced by what most patients pay for IVF. Single embryo transfer, for example, may reduce multiple gestations but will maintain success rates only if patients have access to (and can pay for) a subsequent cycle in which frozen embryos are transferred. This system for decision making in IVF suggests that patient autonomy is paramount. Yet although respect for autonomy is a central tenet of a principle-based approach to providing ethically appropriate medical care, there are important differences between "negative" and "positive" autonomy.[2] Pregnant or not, a patient may decline any procedure or treatment offered her; she may not, however, demand and receive treatment that her provider feels (or in the case of embryo transfer, has been linked by a wealth of data to higher-order multiples and the morbidities attendant thereto) is inappropriate or that is an undue risk to her health. Thus, patients alone should not choose the number of embryos transferred, and reproductive endocrinologists should (and in the California case should have) appropriately set limits. Any perceived conflict between what the patient wants and what the provider recommends should be mitigated by a focus on a shared goal, a healthy pregnancy. Both parties should recognize that transferring too many embryos increases risks to both the mother and to any pregnancies conceived. The

American College of Obstetricians and Gynecologists has suggested that multifetal pregnancy reduction should be discussed with patients *before* the initiation of any treatment that could increase the risk of multifetal pregnancy.[8]

What is to be done?

The public's response to the birth of the octuplets reflects a seemingly common belief that access to assisted reproductive services should be limited. Based on media reports one could even infer that the public is less concerned about implanting 6 embryos than assisting a poor unwed mother to have 14 children. In contrast, reproductive endocrinologists have focused on the excess embryo transfer.[1] It could even be argued that had it been revealed that the children were the result of 14 separate courses of IVF, much of the concern of reproductive endocrinologists would have been assuaged, whereas the resentment of the general public might have been stoked. Although it may not be possible to reconcile these differences, a few conclusions about the responsibilities of reproductive endocrinologists seem reasonable.

First, setting a limit on the number of embryos transferred is justified on ethical and medical grounds and we believe that the time has come to transform guidelines into regulations congruent with those in other countries such as the United Kingdom. Second, the characteristics of the mother of the octuplets that inflamed the public—her income, marital status, and other children—are examples of factors that should *not* be used to disqualify someone as a parent. That is not to say that providers and others cannot raise questions and concerns about other "parenting" issues as they counsel patients with or without infertility who are planning pregnancies. The fact that a couple who abused their children in the past might not be constrained legally from naturally conceiving other children does not provide an ethical justification for providing them with access to IVF. Even in less extreme circumstances, professionals may have experience or perspective that may lead potential parents to reconsider their plans or accept (rarely) that there are insurmountable obstacles. All involved, however, need be mindful that conversations with those planning pregnancy not become opportunities for imputing one group's values on another, extending prejudices

regarding who are appropriate parents, and unjustly burdening certain groups by limiting their ability to become parents. Finally, although some lay voices have railed against the costs to society of helping parents to conceive, that issue, if it need be addressed at all, should be the responsibility of government, not individual physicians. Instead, respecting the autonomy of parents and tending to their health needs should continue to be the fundamental professional obligations of providers.

The birth of the California octuplets has been a "Rashomon"-like experience for Americans, reinforcing competing beliefs about everything from poor people having children to the suitability of single parenting. For reproductive endocrinologists it offers a rare opportunity to rise above the public clamor, to reaffirm the primacy of their commitment to the health of those who seek their care, and to reconsider the manner in which their unique and valued services are rendered. For the public it offers an opportunity to reconsider how we as a society value parenthood and provide education, counseling, and support for those who are, or are planning to become, parents.

References

1. American Society for Reproductive Medicine. ASRM reacts to the latest news about California octuplets [press release]. Feb. 9, 2009. Available at: http://www.asrm.org/Media/Press/CA_octuplets2.html. Accessed Feb. 27, 2009.

2. American Board of Internal Medicine Foundation, American College of Physicians–American Society of Internal Medicine Foundation, European Federation of Internal Medicine. Medical professionalism in the new millennium: a physician charter. Ann Intern Med 2002;136:243–6.

3. *Tarasoff v. Regents of the University of California*, 17 Cal. 3d 425, 551 P.2d 334, 131 Cal. Rptr. 14 (Cal. 1976).

4. Currell S, Cogdell C. Popular eugenics: national efficiency and American mass culture in the 1930s. Athens, OH: Ohio University Press; 2006.

5. Ethics Committee of the American Society of Reproductive Medicine. Child-rearing ability and the provision of fertility services. Fertil Steril 2004;82:564–7.

6. Baron AS, Banaji MR. The development of implicit attitudes: evidence of race evaluations from ages 6 and 10 and adulthood. Psychol Sci 2006;17:53–8.

7. Robertson JA. Children of choice: freedom and the new reproductive technologies. Princeton, NJ: Princeton University Press; 1994.

8. American College of Obstetricians and Gynecologists. Multifetal pregnancy reduction: ACOG committee opinion no. 369. Obstet Gynecol 2007;109:1511–5.

"Give Me Children or I Shall Die!" New Reproductive Technologies and Harm to Children

Cynthia B. Cohen

Cynthia Cohen points to evidence suggesting that the use of reproductive technologies produces serious deficits in a small number of children and asks whether, if this is so, it would be wrong to continue to use them. Cohen focuses on the "Interest in Existing" argument, which holds that producing deficits wouldn't necessarily be wrong because, except in extreme cases, it's better to be alive than not exist.

A flaw in the argument, Cohen claims, is that it assumes children are waiting in a world of nonexistence, where they are worse off than if they were born. A second flaw is that the argument justifies the use of technology to produce any harm in children, as long as it is not so bad as to make death preferable (produce a "wrongful life"). Cohen argues that this is to view the nonexistence of not being born (which is neither good nor bad) as the same as the nonexistence produced by death (which may be preceded by devastating or serious deficits).

Cohen addresses the issue of what counts as a serious deficiency and claims such judgments must be made in specific circumstances in particular cultures. She ends by considering how obligations to actual children differ from those to potential children and why potential parents must make informed choices about using reproductive technologies. (Compare Cohen's views with those of Laura Purdy and Dena Davis in the previous chapter.)

"Be fruitful and multiply," God urged newly created humans. Those who take this command to heart cherish the opportunity to procreate and nurture children, to pass on their individual traits and family heritage to their offspring. Having children, for many, is a deeply significant experience that offers overall meaning for their lives. Not all who wish to do so, however, can fulfill the biblical injunction to multiply. Those who cannot often experience a terrible sense of loss. Rachel, in Genesis, felt such despair over her failure to conceive that she cried out to Jacob, "Give me children, or I shall die!" Some who echo her cry today turn to the new reproductive technologies.

There are ethical limits, however, to what may be done to obtain long-sought offspring. Having a deep desire and even a need for something does not justify doing anything whatsoever to obtain it. If the means used to bring children into the world were to create substantial harm to others or to these very children, this

would provide strong moral reason not to employ them. It would be wrong, for instance, for infertile couples to place women at risk of substantial harm by enticing those who are not in peak physical condition to "donate" eggs with handsome sums of money. By the same token, it would be wrong to use reproductive technologies to create children if this bore a significant chance of producing serious disease and impairments in these very children. Questions are being raised about whether in vitro fertilization (IVF) and other reproductive technologies do, in fact, create serious illness and deficits in a small but significant proportion of children who are born of them. If these technologies were found to do so, it would be wrong to forge ahead with their use.

Yet advocates of procreative liberty reject this seemingly inescapable conclusion. They contend that even if children were born with serious disorders traceable to their origin in the new reproductive technologies, this would not, except in rare cases, provide moral reason to refrain from using them. Those who conclude otherwise, they maintain, do not understand the peculiar sort of substantial harm to which children born of these novel reproductive means are susceptible. Surely,

John Robertson and like-minded thinkers claim, it is better to be alive—even with serious disease and deficits—than not. And these children would not be alive, but for the use of the new reproductive techniques. Therefore, they argue, these children cannot be substantially harmed by the use of these means to bring them into the world. Only if they are caused by these technologies to suffer devastating illness that makes life worse than nonexistence can they be said to be substantially harmed by them.

This startling claim raises intriguing questions. What do we mean by substantial harm—particularly when children who might experience it have not yet been conceived? What degree of disease and suffering that a child would experience as a result of the application of these novel means of conception would make it wrong to use them? Would it be wrong if the child's life would be so terrible that nonexistence would be better? Few conditions would be excluded by this standard. Would it be wrong if the child's life would not be awful, but would include major physical impairments, severe mental disability, and/or considerable pain and suffering?

In responding to such questions, we must consider the possibility that different standards of substantial harm may apply to children at the time when we consider conceiving them and after conception and birth. If so, we must develop a standard of substantial harm that applies to children who might be conceived that is distinct from one that applies to those already born—and must explain how children who are not born can be harmed. We must also address the concern that decisions not to conceive children because they would have serious deficits devalue the lives of those already living who were born with such deficits. Finally, we must grapple with the question of what parents and infertility specialists ought to do in the current state of inadequate knowledge about the effects of the new reproductive technologies on the children who result from their use.

The Harm to Children Argument

To ask what it means to attribute substantial harm to children who result from the new reproductive technologies is not just to pose an interesting abstract question. Studies indicate this may be a very practical, real question, as they raise the possibility that these technologies may create serious deficits in some proportion of the children born of them. To get a sense of the harms at issue, let us consider the claims of critics of the use of these technologies about their effect on the children born of them.

A primary harm that they attribute to the use of the new reproductive technologies is physical damage. Few long-term studies have been undertaken of the kinds and rates of physical diseases and abnormalities incurred by children born of the new reproductive technologies. Moreover, the evidence these investigations provide is conflicting. Australia is the only country that has kept statistics on the condition at birth *and* subsequent progress of children born of IVF since the inception of this technique in the late 1970s. Data from that country indicate that these children are two or three times more likely to suffer such serious diseases as spina bifida and transposition of the great vessels (a heart abnormality). The Australian data also suggest that some drugs used to stimulate women's ovaries to produce multiple oocytes in preparation for IVF increase the risk of serious birth impairments in the resulting children. Other investigations and commentators support this finding.[1] Still other reports, however, suggest that there is no increase in disorders at birth among children resulting from the use of the new reproductive technologies.[2] One small American follow-up study of the health status of children born of IVF and gamete intrafallopian transfer (GIFT) could find no significant differences in the rate of physical or neurological abnormalities in children born of techniques of assisted conception.[3] No controlled study to date, however, has incorporated an adequate sample size or sufficiently long follow-up monitoring period to determine accurately the risk of physical disorders associated with children born of IVF.

And little is known about the physiological impact on children who result from such other procedures as embryo freezing, gamete donation, zona drilling, and intracytoplasmic sperm injection.

It is well known that the higher rate of multiple births in IVF due to the implantation of several embryos in the uterus at a time contributes to an increased rate of preterm and low birth-weight babies. This, in turn, is associated with a higher incidence of perinatal, neonatal, and infant mortality in children conceived by IVF than those conceived coitally.[4] In France, for instance, the rates of prematurity and intrauterine growth retardation among IVF births in a two-year period were 16 percent and 14 percent respectively, whereas the expected rates for the general population were 7 percent and 3 percent.[5] An analysis of IVF outcome data from France between 1986 and 1990 indicated that perinatal mortality among IVF births also was higher than that in the general population, even when data were stratified according to gestational number. French neonatologists who had worked to prevent low birth weight, congenital anomalies, and genetic disorders among newborns observed that "[n]ow, we suddenly find our NICU filled with high-risk newborns . . . [as a result of the expansion of IVF services]."

Critics also express concern that the new reproductive technologies may jeopardize the psychological and social welfare of the children who result from them, particularly when they involve third parties in donor or surrogacy arrangements and depend on secrecy.[6] These children, they hypothesize, will view themselves as manufactured products, rather than distinctive individuals born of love between a man and a woman.[7] They will be denied the stable sense of identity that comes from knowing their biological heritage and family lineage should their rearing parents differ from their genetic parents.[8] Moreover, the social stigma these children will experience when others learn that they were conceived by these novel means will increase their difficulties, opponents contend. Little research is available on the effect of the use of assisted reproduction on the psychosocial development of the resulting children. In the first controlled study of family relationships and the psychological development of children created by the new reproductive technologies, no group differences in the emotions, behavior, or relationships with parents between children born of assisted reproduction and children conceived naturally or adopted could be found.[9]

One commentator summarizes the issues of harm raised by the use of the new reproductive technologies as follows:

> *The technology for both IVF and GIFT as well as adjunct technologies such as zona drilling, embryo freezing, and gamete donation have not been accompanied by careful scrutiny and analysis of the risks involved. Indeed, even when risks are clearly established (as with multiple pregnancy), there has been no discernible attempt to reduce these risks by altering procedures and protocols. There also has been an appalling lack of follow-up studies to determine the long-term health, psychological, and social consequence of these procedures.[10]*

In view of the current lack of systematic knowledge about difficulties these methods may create in children born of them, opponents of the new reproductive technologies maintain it is wrong to use them. Those who resort to these techniques, they claim, bear the burden of proof of their safety. They have an obligation to establish whether these ever-increasing methods of assisted reproduction do, in fact, harm a small but significant proportion of children before they are used. For ease of reference, we will call their claims the Harm to Children Argument against the use of the new reproductive technologies.

The Interest in Existing Argument

The basic response to the Harm to Children Argument by several proponents of the use of the new reproductive technologies,[11] of whom John Robertson is a respected spokesperson, is that even if children born of the new reproductive technologies were to suffer serious impairments as a result of their origin, this would not necessarily render it wrong to use these techniques. We might call this response the Interest in Existing Argument: since it is, in almost all cases, better to be alive than not, and these children would not be alive but for the employment of these techniques, using them to bring these children into the world is justified. Robertson writes:

> *[A] higher incidence of birth defects in such offspring would not justify banning the technique in order to protect the offspring, because without these techniques these children would not have been born at all. Unless their lives are so full of suffering as to be worse than no life at all, a very unlikely supposition, the defective children of such a union have not been harmed if they would not have been born healthy.[12]*

Only where "from the perspective of the child, viewed solely in light of his interests as he is then situated, any life at all with the conditions of his birth would be so harmful to him that from his perspective he would prefer not to live,"[13] could it be said to be a substantial harm to have been brought into existence by means of the new reproductive technologies.

Robertson here implicitly distinguishes between *devastating harm*—harm that brings such suffering into a person's life that this life is worse than no life at all—[and] *serious harm*—harm that does not render life worse than death, but that includes such detriments as major physical impairments, severe mental disability, and/or considerable pain and suffering. He labels only the former *substantial harm*. Indeed, at certain points, Robertson maintains that children damaged by their origin in the new reproductive technologies cannot be said to suffer harm at all, since their birth is an overriding benefit.

The Harm to Children Argument is logically flawed, Robertson and like-minded thinkers maintain, because the benefit of life that children born of these techniques receive outweighs almost any detriment they might experience as a result of their origins. Robertson notes:

> *Preventing harm would mean preventing the birth of the child whose interests one is trying to protect. Yet a child's interests are hardly protected by preventing the child's existence. If the child has no way to be born or raised free of that harm, a person is not injuring the child by enabling her to be born in the circumstances of concern.*[14]

It is not open to children damaged by the use of the new reproductive technologies to live free of impairment, since they could not have existed without the use of these technologies. The alternative for them would have been not to live at all, a state which is not in their interests. Consequently, according to the Interest in Existing Argument, it is, in almost all instances, in the interests of children who might be born of the new reproductive technologies to be brought into the world by these means, even if this would risk serious harm to them.

This argument applies only to children who suffer harm that is a necessary result of the use of these techniques. Thus, if it were claimed that contract surrogacy creates psychological harm for a child because the biological mother and rearing parents would be in a constant state of conflict with each other, the Interest in Existing Argument could not be used in response. This is because the warring trio could behave in a different manner less likely to cause this sort of harm to the child. According to advocates of the Interest in Existing Argument it was not a necessary condition of the child's very existence that the conflict among these various parents occur.

The Harm of Not Existing

The Interest in Existing Argument assumes that children with an interest in existing are waiting in a spectral world of nonexistence where their situation is less desirable than it would be were they released into this world. This presupposition is revealed by such observations as "a child's interests are hardly protected by preventing the child's existence" and that it is a disadvantage to such children that they "have no way of being born." In the Interest in Existing Argument children who might be conceived are pictured as pale preexisting entities with an interest in moving into the more full-blooded reality of this world. Their admission into this realm is thwarted by the failure to use available new reproductive technologies. This failure negates their interest in existing and thereby harms them.

Before a person exists, however, he or she does not reside in some other domain. Prior to conception, there is *no one who waits to be brought into this world*. Joel Feinberg argues, "Since it is necessary to *be* if one is to *be better off*, it is a logical contradiction to say that someone could be better off though not in existence."[15] To say that it was good for someone already in existence to have been born does not imply that his existence in this world is better than his life in some other realm. Nor does it imply that if he had not been caused to exist, this would have been bad for him.[16] Although a wealth of possible children can be conceived, their interests cannot be diminished if they are not. Therefore, it cannot be coherently argued that it is "better" for children to be created by means of the new reproductive technologies, even when this would result in serious disorders to them, since there is no alternative state in which their lot could be worse.

Part of the confusion at the heart of the Interest in Existing Argument stems from an incoherence found in tort actions for "wrongful life," to which this argument has an acknowledged debt. In these suits, children born with impairments claim that their current condition is worse than the state of nonexistence they would have had were it not for negligence on the part of physicians, hospitals, or testing laboratories. The wrong done to them, they contend, is not that their impaired condition was negligently caused, but that their very existence was negligently caused. This, they maintain, is a serious injury, since they would have been better off not being born at all. They ask for compensation for the injury of being brought into this world.

In an early wrongful life case, *Gleitman v. Cosgrove,* a child born with impairments whose mother had been told erroneously that her exposure to German measles during pregnancy would not harm the fetus, brought suit for damages for the injury of being born.[17] The traditional method of measuring damages in tort is to compare the condition of the plaintiff before and after an injury and to compensate for the difference. When the putative wrong done to the plaintiff is to have been brought into existence in an impaired state, the court must measure the difference between nonexistence and existence with impairments. In *Gleitman*, the court found it "logically impossible" to "weigh the value of life with impairments against the nonexistence of life itself." We cannot, according to the court, conceptualize a world in which the plaintiff did not exist and ask what benefits and burdens he experienced in that world in order to compare it with his situation in this world.

Even so, the *Gleitman* court concluded that the value of life, no matter how burdened, outweighs the disvalue of not existing, and that damages therefore could not be awarded to the child for "wrongful life." In drawing this conclusion, the court implicitly compared the world of existence with that of nonexistence and declared the former always preferable to the latter. Yet this is precisely the step the court had said it could not take. Similarly, in another leading case, *Berman v. Allan,* the court ruled against recognition of a "wrongful life" claim on grounds that "life—whether experienced with or without a major physical handicap—is more precious than non-life."[18] These courts were concerned that awarding damages for being alive would diminish the high value that the law places on human life. This public policy concern, however, caused them to lapse into incoherence. They claimed that the world of existence cannot be measured against that of nonexistence. However, if existence is better than nonexistence, as they also declared, nonexistence must be conceptually accessible in some sense so that an intelligible comparison can be made between it and existence.

Proponents of the Interest in Existing Argument adopt the two-world view underlying the logically impossible thesis of the early wrongful life cases when they claim that children are harmed if they are not brought out of the world of nonexistence into the world of existence. This leaves them with two problems: (1) explaining how to conceptualize and comprehend nonexistence and (2) justifying the claim that it is better to exist than not. Moreover, their dependence on the wrongful life decisions causes them to overlook an essential feature of their opponents' argument. The Harm to Children Argument is a *before-the-fact* one that applies to the time when a decision must be made about whether to employ the new reproductive technologies. *At this time, unlike the wrongful life cases, no child exists who could be harmed.* The Harm to Children Argument holds that at this preconception time, the morally right decision is not to use such technologies until further research establishes the degree of harm this might do to children who result. The Interest in Existing Argument, however, is an after-the-fact argument meant to apply at a time when children are already born. It must be used as a response to those who object to having already brought children into the world. Since the harm posited by the critics has not yet occurred when the decision is made whether to employ them, it is not an adequate response to say that without these technologies the resulting children

would not have been born.[19] That is precisely what is at issue—*whether these children ought to have been conceived and born.*

A further difficulty is that the Interest in Existing Argument justifies allowing the new reproductive technologies to create almost any harm to children conceived as a result of their use—as long as this is not devastating harm in which death is preferable to life with it. As Bonnie Steinbock and Ron McClamrock observe, "Very few lives meet the stringent conditions imposed by the wrongful life analysis. . . . Even the most dismal sorts of circumstances of opportunity (including, for example . . . an extremely high chance of facing an agonizing death from starvation in the early years of life, severe retardation plus quadriplegia) fail to be covered"[20] by the standard of devastating harm. Yet it would strike many as ethically objectionable to proceed with reproductive techniques should such serious, but not devastating harms result from them in a significant proportion of cases.

The "Wrongful Life" Standard of Substantial Harm

Those who present the Interest in Existing Argument, adopting the standard applied in wrongful life cases, describe substantial harm as that which, in Robertson's words, puts one in a condition that renders life so "horrible"[21] and so "full of unavoidable suffering" (p. 169) that it is worse than "no life at all."[22] Robertson does not give a more precise definition of substantial harm, nor does he present specific examples of conditions which fall under that rubric in his discussion of harm to children and the new reproductive technologies. Feinberg expands on the "wrongful life" standard of substantial harm:

> Surely in most cases of suffering and impairment we think of death as even worse. This is shown by the widespread human tendency to "cling to life at all costs." And even for severe genetic handicaps and inherited maladies, most competent persons who suffer from them will not express regret that they were born in the first place. . . . In the most extreme cases, however, I think it is rational to prefer not to have come into existence at all, and while I cannot prove this judgment, I am confident that most people will agree that it is at least plausible. I have in mind some of the more severely victimized sufferers from brain malformation, spina bifida, Tay–Sachs disease, polycystic kidney disease, Lesch–Nyhan syndrome, and those who,

from whatever cause, are born blind and deaf,
permanently incontinent, severely retarded, and
in chronic pain or near-total paralysis, with life-
expectancies of only a few years.[23]

To talk about death, both Feinberg and Robertson assume, is the same as to talk about "not coming into existence at all." They assimilate nonexistence before life and nonexistence after having lived. This is a mistake. *Nonexistence before coming into being* and *nonexistence after having lived* are two distinct concepts.

Lucretius observed that we do not express concern about nonexistence before creation, but we do fear our nonexistence after death. Why is this? The reason we perceive death as bad, Thomas Nagel proposes, is that it causes us to have fewer goods of this life than we would have had if we had continued to live.[24] Frances Kamm further observes that it is not only the absence of future goods in this life that leads us to fear death, but that death "takes away what already was and would have continued to be."[25] Preconception nonexistence, however, does not deprive us of what was ours already. In it there is no particular individual whose life ends and who thereby loses out on life's goods. Consequently, nonexistence before conception and birth does not seem as bad as death. We are indifferent to it.

Several other features of death that are also not characteristic of preconception nonexistence contribute to our assessment of it as bad. Death, for instance, happens to a person, whereas preconception nonexistence does not include an event in which nonexistence happens to a person. Death reveals our vulnerability in that through it a person is destroyed and deprived of life's goods. If a person does not exist, in contrast, this does not reflect negatively on "his" or "her" capacities.[26] Because of significant differences between them, preconception and posthumous nonexistence are qualitatively distinct concepts that are not interchangeable. Death has characteristics that lead us to evaluate it as bad, whereas preconception nonexistence strikes us as neither good nor bad.

Do we, too, fall into the trap of positing a shadowy world of nonexistence by distinguishing between preconception and posthumous nonexistence? We do not claim that either of these forms of nonexistence is a metaphysical locale. Instead, we view both as logical constructs built out of what we know about being alive. For both Nagel and Kamm, the meaning of death is derived from what we know about our existence in this world. The same is true of preconception nonexistence. Although the multitude of children whom it is possible for us to bring into the world do not exist, we can conceptualize certain things about them and what their lives would be like were we to conceive and bear them. We can also comprehend certain things about the negation of their existence were they to be born. That is, we can understand what they would lose if we decided not to conceive them and bring them into the world. Thus, we can meaningfully compare preconception nonexistence with life. We can consider children who might be brought into existence and ask whether we ought to conceive them without having to postulate a separate sphere of nonexistence in which they wait as we ponder the question.

While we can make sense of the notion of preconception nonexistence, can we also intelligibly claim that children who have not yet been conceived can have interests? It might be argued that those who do not exist cannot have interests and that therefore possible children can have no interest in not being conceived and brought into the world with serious disorders. Yet possible children can have interests, if these are taken in the sense of what contributes to their good, rather than as psychological states. We can conceive of what would promote their welfare were they to be brought into the world. To deny them such interests is mistakenly to reason by analogy with the dead. It has been supposed that the dead can have no interests because we cannot perform any actions that will affect the condition of their lives.[27] We cannot causally impinge on them for better or worse, it has been argued, for their lives have been completed. But this is not the case with possible children. We can affect them causally for better or worse by our present actions. Thus, we can ascribe to possible children certain interests that can be thwarted or fulfilled by actions that we take.

The interests of children who might be born of the new reproductive technologies are not adequately captured by the "wrongful life" standard. The comparison that parents and physicians must make when they assess whether use of these technologies would negatively affect the good of children who might result is not between *death* and the condition of these children were they to be born with certain deficits. The appropriate comparison is between *preconception nonexistence* and their condition were they to be born with certain deficits. If preconception nonexistence, unlike death, is neither good nor bad, then any life that will be worse than it *will not have to be as bad as the life of devastating deficits set out in the wrongful life standard.* A life with serious, but not devastating, deficits could be bad and therefore worse than preconception nonexistence, which is neither good nor bad. Therefore, we must modify the wrongful life standard of substantial harm to indicate that if new reproductive technologies were shown to cause a significant proportion of children born of them to suffer either devastating *or* serious deficits, they would cause substantial harm to these children and consequently ought not be used.

The Inadequate Opportunity for Health Standard of Substantial Harm

How are we to identify the serious deficits that—along with devastating deficits—would constitute substantial harm to these children? The boundary between moderate, serious, and devastating deficits is sufficiently blurred that reasonable people can disagree about where it lies in particular cases. Many would disagree with Feinberg that children knowingly conceived with such disorders as spina bifida, blindness, deafness, severe retardation, or permanent incontinence should be considered to be suffering from devastating deficits that make their lives worse than death. However, they might well view these disorders as amounting to serious deficits that make their lives worse than preconception nonexistence. What is needed is a conceptual framework that marks off those deficits that have such a negative impact on children that reasonable people would agree that knowingly to conceive children with these disorders would be to impose substantial harm on them in the vast majority of cases.

Laura Purdy suggests that we cause substantial harm to future children and therefore ought not knowingly conceive them "when there is a high risk of transmitting a serious disease or defect [of a sort that would deny them] a normal opportunity for health."[28] At points in Purdy's discussion, as when she states that "every parent should try to ensure normal health for his child," she can be taken to mean that having an abnormal state of health would constitute a disorder sufficiently serious to warrant not conceiving a child who would have it. On this approach, children with a particular biological, chemical, or mental state different from the norm would be said to lack "normal health" and therefore to suffer from a "serious disease or defect" that would justify not conceiving them. Yet it would not strike us as wrong knowingly to conceive children who are not "normal" because they have myopia or albinism. Normality does not appear to provide an adequate standard for deciding that a disorder is a serious deficit that substantially harms a child knowingly conceived with it.

At other points, however, Purdy seems to suggest that the focus for defining a serious deficit that falls under the substantial harm rubric should be on the failure to provide an adequate opportunity for a healthy life, as this is defined within a culture. Here she seems on the right track, for notions of health and disease—for better and for worse—are embedded within a society. What constitutes health and what represents a serious falling away from it varies from culture to culture and changes from time to time. As the notion of health and of an adequate opportunity for health vary according to the cultural context and conditions, so, too, does the meaning of a serious disease or deficit. Moreover, access to health services and the resulting opportunity for health—or lack of it—also affect what is meant by health, serious disorder, and substantial harm.

In our society, children who are color-blind are considered to have only a mild deficit and no diminution of their opportunity for health. However, in certain African cultures in which the capacity to distinguish a great variety of shades of green is needed to function at a minimal level for survival, color blindness is a serious deficit. Children born with this condition in such cultures do not have an adequate opportunity for health because their condition cannot be remedied. Thus, cultural values affect the meanings of health and of serious disorders. Stanley Hauerwas observes that "disease descriptions and remedies are relative to a society's values and needs. Thus 'retardation' might not 'exist' in a society which values cooperation more than competition and ambition."[29] Further, medical practices in different cultures reflect different views of what constitutes health and serious disorders. In Germany children with blood pressure that differs from the norm for their age on both the high and low end are suspected to be at risk of serious disease, whereas in America only high blood pressure is considered an indicator of serious disease.

What makes a disorder serious, however, is not only a matter of cultural needs, expectations, constructions, and practices. Some children are born with remediable conditions that are transformed into serious deficits when they are not ameliorated due to circumstances of injustice and neglect within a culture. The child born with spina bifida to poor parents in the hills of Appalachia has a minimal opportunity for health and a more serious disorder than the child born with this same condition to professional parents in Los Angeles. It might not be unfair to a child knowingly to conceive him or her with paralysis of the lower limbs if that child, once born, would have access to support structures giving him or her adequate mobility.[30] Nor would we have grounds for considering it wrong for parents knowingly to conceive a blind child if that child would receive compensatory education and ameliorative instruments enabling him or her to have an adequate opportunity for health within a society.

This relativity of the notion of health and of an adequate opportunity for health means that no definition of serious disease or disorder amounting to substantial harm that would apply across all cultures, times, and places can be given. Instead, the assessment of serious disease amounting to substantial harm must be made under specific circumstances within particular cultures. It must be defined not only in terms of a given physical or mental condition that damages a child's ability to function within a culture, but also in terms of the failure or inability of a culture to provide a child with access to ameliorative resources.

Sidney Callahan maintains that a principle of proportionality should be applied when making decisions concerning reproduction.[31] This would mean that the lower the risk and gravity of impairment to the child and the more would-be parents, family, and the institutional structures of a society are able and willing to ameliorate the impairment, the less the likelihood that a child would suffer a serious deficit and the more ethically justifiable it would be to conceive him or her. Should the probability and gravity of impairment be great, however, and the would-be parents, family, and social structure unwilling or unable to provide ameliorative measures for the child with such impairment, the higher the likelihood the child would suffer a serious deficit and the less ethically justifiable it would be to conceive that child. We do not end up with a black letter definition of a deficit serious enough to be termed substantial harm on this approach, but one that requires us to consider the nature of the disorder from which the child would suffer, the circumstances into which the child would be brought, and the ameliorative resources available for that child. Under current circumstances in our culture in which children born with disabling disorders have inadequate support, it would be morally questionable, at least, knowingly to conceive a child suffering from some of the deficits listed by Feinberg above.

Obligations to Actual and Possible Children

Although we consider it ethically necessary to provide treatment to keep children alive who have serious illnesses, we do not consider it ethically necessary

knowingly to conceive children with those same disorders. Why is this? Why do we assume that our obligations to children who already exist differ from our obligations to children whom we might conceive?

The difference between an actual and possible child and between our evaluations of preconception nonexistence and death help to explain this distinction. Since we view death as an evil in relation to being alive, we tend to maintain that once children are born, only if they suffer devastating harms that make life worse than death would we be justified in not doing what we can to prevent their death. Being alive is better than being dead, except in rare circumstances. However, we do not believe that we have an obligation to do everything we can to conceive and bring into the world possible children who would suffer serious or devastating illness as a result. This is because no one exists who is wronged by not being conceived and also because preconception nonexistence does not strike us as being either bad or good. To fail to actualize a possible child, therefore, does not put that child in a worse situation or wrong that child.

Furthermore, we have no obligation to conceive children if this would detrimentally affect the good of the family or culture into which they would be born. We have no obligation, for instance, to conceive a sixth child if we believe our family can only function adequately with five. And we need not bring children into the world when this would contribute to a problem of overpopulation or of limited resources. It is morally acceptable, indeed, some would say, morally required, that *before* we bring children into the world, we consider not only their well-being were they to be born, but the good of those who would be affected by their birth. *After* birth, however, the interest in existing of the living child comes into play and morally outweighs remnants of a parental or societal interest in not having had that child.

These conclusions may appear to intimate that the lives of children born with serious or even devastating disorders are not valued or valuable. This conclusion does not follow from the preceding argument. Should parents, after receiving convincing evidence that use of the new reproductive technologies would harm the resulting children, decide against employing them, this could say one of two things to living children with serious or devastating disorders. It could suggest that it would have been better for their families if a different child had been born without these disorders and she was not. Or it could imply that it would have been better for this child to have been born without these disorders.[32] The first implication suggests that it would be better for others if children with these disorders were not born, whereas the second maintains that it would be better for the children themselves if they had not been born with them. The first implies that it is regrettable that these children are alive instead of "normal" children. The second implies that it is regrettable that these children have these disorders. The second implication is the one on which we tend to act. This is exhibited by efforts we make to avoid serious or devastating disorders in children during pregnancy and to treat and care for children with such disorders after they are born. All of this suggests that it is not the children we disvalue, but the disorders that they have sustained. Consequently, it is not necessarily a reproach to disabled children who are already born if decisions are made against knowingly conceiving children who would have the same disabilities.

It is, however, a reproach to us and to our social institutions that once children with serious and devastating disorders are born, we provide woefully insufficient services and resources to them and their families. Does this contradict the claim that we value living children with disabilities and have their interests at heart? Hauerwas provides one perceptive explanation of our ambivalent and complex attitude toward those who live with serious disabilities in the course of discussing those who are developmentally delayed. He observes:

> *After all, what we finally seek is not simply to help the retarded better negotiate their disability but to be like us: not retarded. Our inability to accomplish that frustrates and angers us, and sometimes the retarded themselves become the object of our anger. We do not like to be reminded of the limits of our power, and we do not like those who remind us.*[33]

We wish to remedy the disabilities with which children may be born, but find it difficult to cope with the recognition of our own vulnerability that they inadvertently call forth. Therefore, we relegate them to a separate domain within the world of existence where we believe unknown others will assist them to meet the special challenges they face. This is uncharitable and unjust. We have a responsibility to overcome our misplaced frustration about being unable to render those who have serious or devastating disorders more like those who do not. We have a responsibility to assist them to make their own way in the world unhampered by our irrational fears.

Taking Harms Seriously

The biblical injunction to multiply does not exhort us to do anything whatsoever to have children. It would be wrong to have children if it were known before conception that the means used to bring this about could inflict serious or devastating deficits on those very children. Yet the logic of the Interest in Existing Argument leads its proponents to brush aside the question whether these technologies might create such serious impairments. The thrust of this argument is that use of the new reproductive technologies provides its own justification—it produces children. This claim disregards the welfare of these children. Moreover, it creates a barrier to more extensive and detailed investigations of the effect of the new reproductive technologies on children born of them.

On the approach presented here, if it were known ahead of time that children conceived with the assistance of the new reproductive technologies would not have an adequate opportunity for health, it would be wrong to use them. Assessment of when and whether this would be the case would be carried out in light of the personal, familial, and social circumstances into which these children would be born. This means that would-be parents who consider resorting to the new reproductive technologies must be informed about the risks these techniques would present to the children born as a result of their use, the means available for ameliorating deficits these children might experience, and what social support would be available should they lack the resources to address such deficits on their own. Only then can they decide whether they ought to proceed with these techniques. To implement this recommendation, evidence for and against the contention that the new reproductive technologies cause serious or devastating physical, psychological, or social harm to the resulting children should be investigated more thoroughly than at present. Because of limited knowledge of the possible effects of these measures on their children, those who repeat Rachel's cry today face an agonizingly difficult decision when they consider whether to use the new reproductive technologies.

References

1.   National Perinatal Statistics Unit, Fertility Society of Australia, *In Vitro Fertilization Pregnancies. Australia and New Zealand 1979–1985*, Sydney, Australia, 1987; Paul L. Lancaster, "Congenital Malformations after In-Vitro Fertilisation," [letter] *Lancet 2* (1987): 1392–93; see also AIHW National Perinatal Statistics Unit, Fertility Society of Australia, *Assisted Conception in Australia and New Zealand 1990*

(Sydney; AIHW National Perinatal Statistics Unit, 1992); Gail Vines, "Shots in the Dark for Infertility," *New Scientist* 140 (1993): 13–15; Lene Koch, "Physiological and Psychosocial Risks of the New Reproductive Technologies," in *Tough Choices: In Vitro Fertilization and the Reproductive Technologies*, ed. Patricia Stephenson and Marsden G. Wagner (Philadelphia: Temple University Press, 1993), pp. 122–34.

2.   U.B. Wennerholm et al., "Pregnancy Complications and Short-Term Follow-Up of Infants Born after In Vitro Fertilization and Embryo Transfer," *Acta Obstetrics et Gynecologicia Scandinavian* 70 (1991): 565–73; B. Rizk et al., "Perinatal Outcome and Congenital Malformations in In-Vitro Fertilization Babies from the Bourn–Hallam Group," *Human Reproduction* 6 (1991): 1259–64; S. Friedler, S. Mashiach, and N. Laufer, "Births in Israel Resulting from In-Vitro Fertilization/Embryo Transfer, 1982–1989: National Registry of the Israeli Association for Fertility Research," *Human Reproduction* 7 (1992): 1159–63; Society for Assisted Reproductive Technology, American Society for Reproductive Medicine, Assisted Reproductive Technology in the United States and Canada, "1993 Results Generated from the American Society for Reproductive Medicine/Society for Assisted Reproductive Technology Registry," *Fertility and Sterility* 64 (1995): 13–21.

3.   Norma C. Morin et al., "Congenital Malformations and Psychosocial Development in Children Conceived by In Vitro Fertilization," *Journal of Pediatrics* 115 (1989): 222–27.

4.   V. Beral et al., "Outcome of Pregnancies Resulting from Assisted Conception," *British Medical Bulletin* 46, no. 3 (1990): 753–68; I. Craft and T. al-Shawaf, "Outcome and Complications of Assisted Reproduction," *Current Opinion in Obstetrics and Gynecology* 3 (1991): 668–73; Rizk et al., "Perinatal Outcome and Congenital Malformations in In-Vitro Fertilization Babies from the Bourn–Hallam Group"; P. Doyle, V. Beral, and N. Maconochie, "Preterm Delivery, Low Birthweight and Small-for-Gestational-Age in Liveborn Singleton Babies Resulting from In-Vitro Fertilization," *Human Reproduction* 7 (1992): 425–28; Friedler et al., "Births in Israel," pp. 1160–63.

5.   Jean-Pierre Reller, Michele Couchard, and Catherine Huon, "The Neonatologists's Experience of In Vitro Fertilization Risks," *Tough Choices*, pp. 135–143; see also P. Rufat et al., "Task Force Report on the Outcome of Pregnancies and Children Conceived by In Vitro Fertilization (France: 1987 to 1989)," *Fertility and Sterility* 61 (1994): 324–30; FIVNAT (French In Vitro National), "Pregnancies and Births Resulting from In Vitro Fertilization: French National Registry, Analysis of Data 1986 to 1990," *Fertility and Sterility* 64 (1995): 746–56.

6.   Cynthia B. Cohen, "Reproductive Technologies: Ethical Issues," in *Encyclopedia of Bioethics*, ed. Warren Thomas Reich (New York Simon and Schuster Macmillan, 1995), vol. 4, pp. 2233–41; A. Baran and R. Pannor, *Lethal Secrets: The Shocking Consequences and Unsolved Problems of Artificial Insemination* (New York; Warner Books, 1989); D.N. Mushin, J. Spensley, and M. Barreda-Hanson, "In Vitro Fertilization Children: Early Psychosocial Development," *Journal of In Vitro Fertilization and Embryo Transfer* 4 (1986): 247–52.

7.   Margaret Radin, "Market-Inalienability," *Harvard Law Review* 100 (1987): 1921–36; Sidney Callahan, "The Ethical Challenges of the New Reproductive Technologies," in *Medical Ethics: A Guide for Health Professionals*, ed. J. Monagle and David Thomas (Rockville, Md.; Aspen, 1988), pp. 26–37.

8.   Leon Kass, *Toward a More Natural Science: Biology and Human Affairs* (New York: Free Press, 1985), p. 113; Lisa Sowle Cahill, "The Ethics of Surrogate Motherhood: Biology, Freedom, and Moral Obligation," *Law, Medicine and Health Care*

16, nos. 1–2 (1988): 65–71, at 69; Cynthia B. Cohen, "Parents Anonymous," in *New ways of Making Babies: The Case of Egg Donation*, ed. Cynthia B. Cohen (Bloomington: Indiana University Press, 1996).

9.   Susan Golombok et al., "Parents and Their Children Happy with Assisted Conception," [letter] *British Medical Journal* 307 (1994): 1032.

10.   Lene Koch, "Physiological and Psychosocial Risks of the New Reproductive Technologies," p. 128.

11.   Ruth F. Chadwick, "Cloning," *Philosophy* 57 (1982): 201–9; John A. Robertson, "Procreative Liberty and the Control of Conception, Pregnancy, and Childbirth," *University of Virginia law Review* 69 (1983): 405–462, at 434; John A. Robertson, "Embryos, Families, and Procreative Liberty: The Legal Structure of the New Reproduction," *Southern California Law Review* 59 (1986): 942–1041, at 958, 988; John A. Robertson, "Procreative Liberty, Embryos, and Collaborative Reproduction: A Legal Perspective," in *Embryos, Ethics, and Women's Rights: Exploring the New Reproductive Technologies*, ed. E.F. Baruch, A.F. Adamo, Jr., and J. Seager (New York: Howarth Press, 1988), pp. 179–94; John A. Robertson, "The Question of Human Cloning," *Hastings Center Report* 24, no. 3 (1994): 6–14; John A. Robertson, *Children of Choice: Freedom and the New Reproductive Technologies* (Princeton, N.J.: Princeton University Press, 1994), pp. 75–76, 110–11, 122–23, 152, 169–70; Ruth Macklin, "Splitting Embryos on the Slippery Slope," *Kennedy Institute of Ethics Journal* 4 (1994): 209–25, at 219–20.

12.   Robertson, "Procreative Liberty and the Control of Conception, Pregnancy, and Childbirth," p. 434.

13.   Robertson, *Children of Choice*, pp. 75–76.

14.   Robertson, *Children of Choice*, pp. 75–76.

15.   Joel Feinberg, "Wrongful Life and the Counterfactual Element in Harming," *Social Philosophy and Policy* 4 (1988): 145–78, at 158.

16.   Derek Parfit, *Reasons and Persons* (Oxford: Oxford University Press, 1985), p. 487.

17.   *Gleitman v. Cosgrove*, 49 N.J. 22, 227 A. 2d 689 (1967).

18.   *Berman v. Allan*, 80 N.J. 421, 404 A. 2d 8 (1979).

19.   Robertson, *Children of Choice*, pp. 75, 117; "Embryos, Families, and Procreative Liberty," pp. 958, 988.

20.   Bonnie Steinbock and Ron McClamrock, "When Is Birth Unfair to the Child?" *Hastings Center Report* 24, no. 6 (1994): 16–22, at 17.

21.   Robertson, *Children of Choice*, pp. 82, 85.

22.   Robertson, "Procreative Liberty and the Control of Conception, Pregnancy, and Childbirth," p. 434.

23.   Feinberg "Wrongful Life," p. 159.

24.   Thomas Nagel, "Death," in *Mortal Questions* (Cambridge: Cambridge University Press, 1979), pp. 1–10.

25.   Frances M. Kamm, *Morality, Mortality, Volume I. Death and Whom to Save from It* (New York: Oxford University Press, 1993), p. 40.

26.   Kamm, *Morality, Mortality*, pp. 40–41.

27.   Joan Callahan, "On Harming the Dead," *Ethics* 97 (1987): 341–52; Ernest Partridge, "Posthumous Interests and Posthumous Respect," *Ethics* 91 (1981): 243–64.

28.   Laura Purdy, "Genetic Diseases: Can Having Children Be Immoral?" in *Genetics Now: Ethical Issues in Genetic Research*, ed. John Buckly, Jr. (Washington, D.C.: University Press of America, 1978), pp. 25–89, at 25.

29.   Stanley Hauerwas, "Suffering the Retarded: Should We Prevent Retardation?" in *Suffering Presence; Theological Reflections on Medicine, the Mentally Handicapped, and the*

Church, ed. Stanley Hauerwas (Notre Dame: University of Notre Dame Press, 1986), pp. 159–81.

30.   Steinbock and McClamrock, "When Is Birth Unfair to the Child?" and Sidney Callahan, "An Ethical Analysis of Responsible Parenthood," in *Genetic Counseling: Facts, Values, and Norms*, ed. Alexander M. Capron, Marc Lappé and

Robert F. Murray (New York: Alan R. Liss, 1979), pp. 217–38.

31.   Callahan, "An Ethical Analysis of Responsible Parenthood."

32.   Mary Warnock, "Ethical Challenges in Embryo Manipulation," *British Medical Journal* 304 (1992): 1045–49, at 1047.

33.   Hauerwas, "Suffering the Retarded," p. 176.

The Right to Lesbian Parenthood

Gillian Hanscombe

Gillian Hanscombe sees the possibility of becoming a single parent as a major advantage of reproductive technology. She argues that homosexual parents are entitled to the same treatment from physicians and institutions as heterosexual ones. The objection that lesbian women should not be allowed to reproduce by artificial insemination is not one that can be supported by relevant evidence, Hanscombe claims. No studies have demonstrated that lesbian mothering is any different from heterosexual mothering or that children of lesbian mothers "fall victim to negative psychosexual developmental influences." She mentions instances of what she considers to be groundless prejudice against lesbian women by the medical establishment.

Anyone daring to address the subject of human rights faces both an appalling responsibility and being accused of an unnatural arrogance of utterance. I accept these risks not because I think myself expert on the subject of human rights, but because my experience is that human rights in the domain of parenthood are so very often denied existence.

I refer to a large minority in our population, that of lesbian women and gay men. Even at the most conservative estimate—which is that at least 1 in 20 adult people are homosexual—a group comprising 5 percent—we are dealing with a group larger than the 4 percent ethnic minorities group which already receives, as indeed it deserves to do, special attention. Lesbian women and gay men have to date, in all matters of social policy, been traditionally regarded as a deviant group.

It is the case, nonetheless, that the pathologising of this group is increasingly questioned, not only by members of the gay community themselves, but also by the agencies of our institutional life: that is, by medical practitioners, by teachers and social workers, and by working parties of religious and/or political orientation.

I am the co-author of a book about lesbian mothers.[1] It is written for the general public, rather than for

specialists, but is nevertheless the only book to date on the subject which I know of. It records the experiences of a selected group of lesbian mothers—selected to range over the varieties of social existence these parents and their children experience—from divorced women to single women who have deliberately chosen to conceive their children by artificial insemination by donor (AID).

The question asked by many heterosexual professionals who are charged with the theory or practice of social policy, is whether lesbian women, for example, should be (a) allowed, and (b) aided, to become mothers.

Objections to lesbian women being *allowed* to reproduce can only be social, since no physiological studies seeking to find physical differences between lesbian and non-lesbian women have ever succeeded in demonstrating such a difference.

Social objections fall into two categories: (a) the extent to which the psychopathology of the lesbian mother is assumed or demonstrated to deviate negatively from the norm. No studies to date have demonstrated that lesbian mothering is either significantly different from heterosexual mothering or that the lesbian mother is psychologically inadequately equipped to mother;[2] (b) the extent to which the children of lesbian mothers are assumed to fall victim to negative psychosexual developmental influences. No study to date has succeeded in demonstrating such a phenomenon.[3] There remain social objections issuing from prejudice, which in turn issues from ignorance. Since the medical profession forms a professional part of our social policy-making institutional life, it is required that medical practitioners do not form judgments based on ignorance. A mere assumption that because, historically, lesbian women have been pathologised this somehow proves that they are "not normal" (and that in a negative sense) is, of course, unacceptable.

A good way of thinking about this is to begin with what is known about female sexuality. In the first place, it is clear that women, unlike men, are able to separate their sexual practice from their reproductive practice. It is possible, that is, for a woman (a) to become sexually aroused and reach orgasm without any possibility that she will become pregnant and (b) for a woman to be inseminated—either naturally or artificially—and become pregnant whether or not at the same time, she experiences any sexual pleasure. Whatever might be thought, therefore, about lesbian sexual practice, it is clear that lesbian women are able to conceive and bear children in the same way as non-lesbian women do.

Hence, attempting not to allow them to do so would be highly problematic, even apart from the massive dilemma—were such a decision taken—of not being able to enforce the sanction. Contrary to popular prejudice, it is the case that lesbian women, like other women, are quite capable of engaging in sexual intercourse with a man and, like other women, often solely for the reason that they intend to become pregnant.

Prejudice is not only rife within what are called the "helping professions," it is rife, too, in the courts. Lesbian mothers in dispute with husbands almost all lose custody of their children solely on the grounds of their lesbianism.[4] Because of this, as well as for many other reasons, young women in the last decade have turned increasingly to the alternative of AID. They have found, by and large, that medical practitioners are not willing to provide AID for them, again solely on the grounds of their lesbianism. They have decided, increasingly, in response to this attitude, to conduct AID by themselves, with the assistance of sympathetic men. This is neither technically difficult nor is it illegal. Many AID daughters and sons of lesbian women are now in our nurseries and schools.

There are over two million lesbian mothers in the United States. Calculations for Britain are well-nigh impossible, owing to the professional nonrecognition of the existence of the group, together with the mothers' reticence in the face of prejudice. They are rightly anxious to conceal their sexuality since, like nearly all mothers, they love their children and will not willingly give them up, either to the courts or to any other social agency.

We might consider one case in particular. A lesbian woman, of middle-class background and professional standing in her own right, decided that she wanted to become a mother. It was, for her, a natural fulfillment of her womanhood, just as it is for millions of other women.

She became pregnant, deliberately, but unfortunately suffered a miscarriage, accompanied by much distress and depression. The usual practice of the hospital treating her was that, following the customary D & C, the patient should report to her own general practitioner. This she did, some six weeks later, wanting very much to know whether there were any clinical reasons why she might suffer further miscarriages. She asked the GP whether the hospital had sent her report.

"Yes, why?" came the reply.

"I want to know whether there is anything wrong with me which explains why I lost the baby," the woman explained.

"Why do you want to know?" persisted the GP.

"Because if there isn't, I want to become pregnant again," said the woman. "It was so dreadful losing the baby that I wouldn't knowingly go through it again. But if I can have a normal, full-term pregnancy, I want to try."

"But you can't have a baby," replied the GP, appalled; "you're not married!"

"What's that got to do with it?" asked the woman. And so ensued an embarrassing session of moralistic instruction from the GP to the silent woman. Her question remained unanswered.

She asked a friend who was a GP in a different area to write to the hospital for the information. This was done. There was no clinical reason for the miscarriage and the woman was pronounced normal and healthy.

The woman became pregnant again. But instead of feeling she could be cared for by her GP, she felt forced to opt for ante-natal care in the impersonal atmosphere of the hospital, where hundreds of women attended the clinic and where the same practitioner hardly ever appeared twice. At each visit, she was seen by different staff, which was comfortless but which at least ensured minimal questioning.

When she was nearly three months pregnant, the sister-in-charge said she must see the social worker. It was "hospital policy." But only, of course, for the unmarried. The woman felt angry and hurt, but didn't want to be accused of "making trouble." The social worker was sympathetic. "Just for the record, do you want your baby?" she asked. "Just for the record," the woman replied, "I planned my baby."

After delivery, she and her baby were not placed in an ordinary ward, but in one where mothers with handicapped babies were placed, together with mothers who had not had normal deliveries. In addition, she was "strongly advised" to stay for the full period, rather than go home after 48 hours. And yet both she and her baby were fit and healthy.

This mother keeps away from the "helping professionals." She is not open with her present GP, her child's school or the para-medical services, either about the circumstances of her child's birth or about her own sexuality. When she is offered contraception during her cervical smear tests, she simply declines it, not daring to explain that she is one of thousands of lesbian women who don't need it.

This woman is a proud and independent mother.[5] And her story is only one among scores. There is the mother who was refused AID by her local medical services and who then answered an advertisement in a lonely hearts column in order to find a man who would make her pregnant. She [charted] her ovulation cycle, and when she was fertile, dated the man, who only and clearly wanted casual sex. Her "experiment" worked and she bore a healthy child. There is the mother who came home from work one day to find a weeping partner who had to tell her that both her children—a son aged nine and a daughter aged seven—had been taken into care, because someone had told the social worker that the two women were lesbians.[6]

Hardly any histories of lesbian mothers and their children are on the record. But they are amongst us and they deserve the same care from professional caregivers as do other mothers and their children.

There are, too, gay men who parent and there are lesbian women and gay men who, though not biological parents themselves, are necessarily involved in childcare by virtue of their partners' parenthood. And there are men who donate semen for the insemination of women who take on themselves the responsibility of conception in order to exercise their rights to reproduce and bring up children. None of the considered and intricate planning undertaken by all these people is mentioned in the vast literature about the family, either in professional or popular publications. Hardly any of this material finds its way into discussions and seminars about family policy, about education, about poverty and so on.

In addition, cruel and heartless lobbying from powerful religious and political quarters—aimed against the human rights of adult homosexual women and men—is ongoing, despite its lack of scientific objectivity. Such pressure is also richly funded. The onus is therefore on the rational, well-informed and compassionate professionals in our caring institutions to consider how they will respond to those of our number born to homosexual parents. Removing the right to reproduce is both immoral and impractical. Neglecting the need of parents for normal support is both discriminatory and cruel. Removing their children from the natural custody of their parents—merely on grounds of the parents' sexuality—is a monstrous interference, with consequences for the children which are no better than the fate of children who are unwanted by their natural mothers. What is needed is education, not legislation.

There are no data—scientific, psychological, or social—which could support the thesis that homosexual people should not have the right to reproduce and to bring up their children. There are only differing opinions and prejudices, which are not capable of sustaining the rigorous intellectual analysis upon which any given body of knowledge must rest. Hitler didn't like homosexuals. Or the handicapped. Or Jews. His answer was to attempt to exterminate them. Our cruelties are not so extreme. What we do is simply to ignore groups of people whose existence troubles us.

I submit, humbly but confidently, that using an argument to exclude adult people from parenthood which is based solely on the definition of an individual's sexual practice, is untenable and uncivilized. Adult people have in their gift the right to dispose of their own reproductive potential as they themselves think suitable. And the rest of us share, all of us, in the responsibility to care for all those committed to parenting and for the children for whom they care.

Notes

1. Hanscombe, G. E., Farster, J. *Rocking the cradle*. London: Peter Owen, 1981 and Sheba Feminist Publishers, 1982.

2. Green, R. Sexual identity of 37 children raised by homosexual or transsexual parents. *American Journal of Psychiatry* 1978; 6: 692–697.

3. See projects comparing the psychosexual development of lesbians' children with that of single non-lesbians' children, undertaken by Michael Rutter, Susan Golombok and Ann Spencer, of the Institute of Psychiatry in London. Not all the data is yet published—to my present knowledge—but see reference (1) 85–87.

4. In February of this year the Court of Appeal ruled in favour of a lesbian mother retaining custody of her two daughters. The case made newspaper headlines, not least because such rulings have been so rare.

5. Identity and details withheld.

6. Identities and details withheld.

Instruction on Respect for Human Life in Its Origin and on the Dignity of Procreation: Replies to Certain Questions of the Day

Congregation for the Doctrine of the Faith

This "Instruction" was issued on February 22, 1987. It was approved and ordered published by Pope John Paul II and thus may be taken as representing the official position of the Roman Catholic Church on the issues addressed.

The document takes the position that a number of current or potential practices connected with reproductive technology are morally illegitimate. Included are the following:

- The use of human genetic material in procedures like cloning, parthenogenesis, and twin fission (the splitting of gametes)
- Attempts to manipulate genetic material for the purpose of sex selection or to promote desirable characteristics
- Artificial insemination involving unmarried individuals or the artificial insemination of an unmarried woman or a widow, even if the sperm is that of her deceased husband
- Acquiring sperm by means of masturbation
- Surrogate motherhood

Some techniques and practices, according to the document, are morally legitimate. Included are the following:

- Medical intervention to remove the causes of infertility
- The prescription of drugs to promote fertility

The document also makes a number of specific recommendations to governments to establish laws and policies governing reproductive technologies. It asks that civil laws be passed to prohibit the donation of sperm or ova between unmarried people. Laws should "expressly forbid" the use of living embryos for experimentation and protect them from mutilation and destruction. Further, legislation should prohibit "embryo banks, postmortem insemination and 'surrogate motherhood.'"

Some Roman Catholic theologians disagreed sharply with parts of the document. "The document argues that a child can be born only from a sexual act," Richard McCormick pointed out. "The most that can be argued is that a child should be born within a marriage from a loving act. Sexual intercourse is not the only loving act." Some suggested that individuals would make up their own minds on the issues, quite apart from the Vatican position. The significance of the document to non-Catholics is that the positions taken and the arguments for them are likely to affect the character of the discussion about reproductive technology and have an impact on legislation that will place restraints on research and practices many currently consider legitimate.

Notes and references are omitted in this excerpt.

From "Instructions for the Congregation for the Doctrine of the Faith", February 22, 1987.

Interventions upon Human Procreation

By "artificial procreation" or "artificial fertilization" are understood here the different technical procedures directed towards obtaining a human conception in a manner other than the sexual union of man and woman. This Instruction deals with fertilization of an ovum in a test-tube (in vitro fertilization) and artificial insemination through transfer into the woman's genital tracts of previously collected sperm.

A preliminary point for the moral evaluation of such technical procedures is constituted by the consideration of the circumstances and consequences which those procedures involve in relation to the respect due the human embryo. Development of the practice of in vitro fertilization has required innumerable fertilizations and destructions of human embryos. Even today, the usual practice presupposes a hyper-ovulation on the part of the woman: a number of ova are withdrawn, fertilized and then cultivated in vitro for some days. Usually not all are transferred into the genital tracts of the woman; some embryos, generally called "spare," are destroyed or frozen. On occasion, some of the implanted embryos are sacrificed for various eugenic, economic or psychological reasons. Such deliberate destruction of human beings or their utilization for different purposes to the detriment of their integrity and life is contrary to the doctrine on procured abortion already recalled.

The connection between in vitro fertilization and the voluntary destruction of human embryos occurs too often. This is significant: through these procedures, with apparently contrary purposes, life and death are subjected to the decision of man, who thus sets himself up as the giver of life and death by decree. This dynamic of violence and domination may remain unnoticed by those very individuals who, in wishing to utilize this procedure, become subject to it themselves. The facts recorded and the cold logic which links them must be taken into consideration for a moral judgment on IVF and ET (in vitro fertilization and embryo transfer): the abortion-mentality which has made this procedure possible, thus leads, whether one wants it or not, to man's domination over the life and death of his fellow human beings and can lead to a system of radical eugenics.

Nevertheless, such abuses do not exempt one from a further and thorough ethical study of the techniques of artificial procreation considered in themselves, abstracting as far as possible from the destruction of embryos produced in vitro.

The present Instruction will therefore take into consideration in the first place the problems posed by heterologous artificial fertilization (II, 1–3),* and subsequently those linked with homologous artificial fertilization (II, 4–6).†

Before formulating an ethical judgment on each of these procedures, the principles and values which determine the moral evaluation of each of them will be considered.

A. Heterologous Artificial Fertilization

1. WHY MUST HUMAN PROCREATION TAKE PLACE IN MARRIAGE? *Every human being is always to be accepted as a gift and blessing of God. However, from the moral point of view a truly responsible procreation vis-a-vis the unborn child must be the fruit of marriage.*

For human procreation has specific characteristics by virtue of the personal dignity of the parents and of the children: the procreation of a new person, whereby the man and the woman collaborate with the power of the Creator, must be the fruit and the sign of the mutual self-giving of the spouses, of their love and of their fidelity. *The fidelity of the spouses in the unity of marriage involves reciprocal respect of their*

---

*By the term heterologous artificial fertilization or procreation, the Instruction means techniques used a to obtain a human conception artificially by the use of gametes coming from at least one donor other than the spouses who are joined in marriage. Such techniques can be of two types:

a. Heterologous IVF and ET: the technique used to obtain a human conception through the meeting in vitro of gametes taken from at least one donor other than the two spouses joined in marriage.

b. Heterologous artificial insemination: the technique used to obtain a human conception through the transfer into the genital tracts of the woman of the sperm previously collected from a donor other than the husband.

†By artificial homologous fertilization or procreation, the Instruction means the technique used to obtain a human conception using the gametes of the two spouses joined in marriage. Homologous artificial fertilization can be carried out by two different methods:

a. Homologous IVF and ET: the technique used to obtain a human conception through the meeting in vitro of the gametes of the spouses joined in marriage.

b. Homologous artificial insemination: the technique used to obtain a human conception through the transfer into the genital tracts of a married woman of the sperm previously collected from her husband.

right to become a father and a mother only through each other.

The child has the right to be conceived, carried in the womb, brought into the world and brought up within marriage: it is through the secure and recognized relationship to his own parents that the child can discover his own identity and achieve his own proper human development.

The parents find in their child a confirmation and completion of their reciprocal self-giving: the child is the living image of their love, the permanent sign of their conjugal union, the living and indissoluble concrete expression of their paternity and maternity.

By reason of the vocation and social responsibilities of the person, the good of the children and of the parents contributes to the good of civil society; the vitality and stability of society require that children come into the world within a family and that the family be firmly based on marriage.

The tradition of the Church and anthropological reflection recognize in marriage and in its indissoluble unity the only setting worthy of truly responsible procreation.

2. Does heterologous artificial fertiliza-tion conform to the dignity of the couple and to the truth of marriage? Through IVF and ET and heterologous artificial insemination, human conception is achieved through the fusion of gametes of at least one donor other than the spouses who are united in marriage. *Heterologous artificial fertilization is contrary to the unity of marriage, to the dignity of the spouses, to the vocation proper to parents, and to the child's right to be conceived and brought into the world in marriage and from marriage. . . .*

These reasons lead to a negative moral judgment concerning heterologous artificial fertilization: consequently fertilization of a married woman with the sperm of a donor different from her husband and fertilization with the husband's sperm of an ovum not coming from his wife are morally illicit. Furthermore, the artificial fertilization of a woman who is unmarried or a widow, whoever the donor may be, cannot be morally justified.

The desire to have a child and the love between spouses who long to obviate a sterility which cannot be overcome in any other way constitute understandable motivations; but subjectively good intentions do not render heterologous artificial fertilization conformable to the objective and inalienable properties of

marriage or respectful of the rights of the child and of the spouses.

3. Is "surrogate"‡ Motherhood morally licit? *No, for the same reasons which lead one to reject heterologous artificial fertilization: for it is contrary to the unity of marriage and to the dignity of the procreation of the human person.*

Surrogate motherhood represents an objective failure to meet the obligations of maternal love, of conjugal fidelity and of responsible motherhood; it offends the dignity and the right of the child to be conceived, carried in the womb, brought into the world and brought up by his own parents; it sets up, to the detriment of families, a division between the physical, psychological and moral elements which constitute those families.

B. Homologous Artificial Fertilization

Since heterologous artificial fertilization has been declared unacceptable, the question arises of how to evaluate morally the process of homologous artificial fertilization: IVF and ET and artificial insemination between husband and wife. First a question of principle must be clarified.

4. What connection is required from the moral point of view between procreation and conjugal act? . . . In reality, the origin of a human person is the result of an act of giving. The one conceived must be the fruit of his parents' love. He cannot be desired or conceived as the production of an intervention of medical or biological techniques; that would be equivalent to reducing him to an object of scientific technology. No one may subject the coming of a child into the world to conditions of technical efficiency

---

‡By "surrogate mother" the Instruction means:

a. the woman who carries in pregnancy an embryo implanted in her uterus and who is genetically a stranger to the embryo because it has been obtained through the union of the gametes of "donors." She carries the pregnancy with a pledge to surrender the baby once it is born to the party who commissioned or made the agreement for the pregnancy.

b. the woman who carries in pregnancy an embryo to whose procreation she has contributed the donation of her own ovum, fertilized through insemination with the sperm of a man other than her husband. She carries the pregnancy with a pledge to surrender the child once it is born to the party who commissioned or made the agreement for the pregnancy.

which are to be evaluated according to standards of control and dominion.

The moral relevance of the link between the meanings of the conjugal act and between the goods of marriage, as well as the unity of the human being and the dignity of his origin, demand that the procreation of a human person be brought about as the fruit of the conjugal act specific to the love between spouses. The link between procreation and the conjugal act is thus shown to be of great importance on the anthropological and moral planes, and it throws light on the positions of the Magisterium with regard to homologous artificial fertilization.

5. IS HOMOLOGOUS "IN VITRO" FERTILIZATION MORALLY LICIT?

The answer to this question is strictly dependent on the principles just mentioned. Certainly one cannot ignore the legitimate aspirations of sterile couples. For some, recourse to homologous IVF and ET appears to be the only way of fulfilling their sincere desire for a child. The question is asked whether the totality of conjugal life in such situations is not sufficient to insure the dignity proper to human procreation. It is acknowledged that IVF and ET certainly cannot supply for the absence of sexual relations and cannot be preferred to the specific acts of conjugal union, given the risks involved for the child and the difficulties of the procedure. But it is asked whether, when there is no other way of overcoming the sterility which is a source of suffering, homologous in vitro fertilization may not constitute an aid, if not a form of therapy, whereby its moral licitness could be admitted.

The desire for a child—or at the very least an openness to the transmission of life—is a necessary prerequisite from the moral point of view for responsible human procreation. But this good intention is not sufficient for making a positive moral evaluation of in vitro fertilization between spouses. The process of IVF and ET must be judged in itself and cannot borrow its definitive moral quality from the totality of conjugal life of which it becomes part nor from the conjugal acts which may precede or follow it.

It has already been recalled that, in the circumstances in which it is regularly practiced, IVF and ET involves the destruction of human beings, which is something contrary to the doctrine on the illicitness of abortion previously mentioned. But even in a situation in which every precaution were taken to avoid the death of human embryos, homologous IVF and ET dissociates from the conjugal act the actions which are directed to human fertilization. For this reason the very nature of homologous IVF and ET also must be taken into account, even abstracting from the link with procured abortion.

Homologous IVF and ET is brought about outside the bodies of the couple through actions of third parties whose competence and technical activity determine the success of the procedure. Such fertilization entrusts the life and identity of the embryo into the power of doctors and biologists and establishes the domination of technology over the origin and destiny of the human person. Such a relationship of domination is in itself contrary to the dignity and equality that must be common to parents and children.

Conception in vitro is the result of the technical action which presides over fertilization. *Such fertilization is neither in fact achieved nor positively willed as the expression and fruit of specific acts of the conjugal union. In homologous IVF and ET, therefore, even if it is considered in the context of "de facto" existing sexual relations, the generation of the human person is objectively deprived of its proper perfection: namely, that of being the result and fruit of a conjugal act* in which the spouses can become "co-operators with God for giving life to a new person.". . .

Certainly, homologous IVF and ET fertilization is not marked by all that ethical negativity found in extra-conjugal procreation; the family and marriage continue to constitute the setting for the birth and upbringing of the children. Nevertheless, in conformity with the traditional doctrine relating to the goods of marriage and the dignity of the person, *the Church remains opposed from the moral point of view to homologous "in vitro" fertilization. Such fertilization is in itself illicit and in opposition to the dignity of procreation and of the conjugal union, even when everything is done to avoid the death of the human embryo.*

Although the manner in which human conception is achieved with IVF and ET cannot be approved, every child which comes into the world must in any case be accepted as a living gift of the divine Goodness and must be brought up with love.

6. HOW IS HOMOLOGOUS ARTIFICIAL INSEMINATION TO BE EVALUATED FROM THE MORAL POINT OF VIEW?

Homologous artificial insemination within marriage cannot be admitted except for those cases in which the technical means is not a substitute for the conjugal act but serves to facilitate and to help so that the act attains its natural purpose.

The teaching of the Magisterium on this point has already been stated. This teaching is not just an expression of particular historical circumstances but is based on the Church's doctrine concerning the connection between the conjugal union and procreation and on a consideration of the personal nature of the conjugal act and of human procreation."In its natural structure, the conjugal act is a personal action, a simultaneous and immediate cooperation on the part of the husband and wife, which by the very nature of the agents and the proper nature of the act is the expression of the mutual gift which, according to the words of Scripture, brings about union 'in one flesh.'"Thus moral conscience"does not necessarily proscribe the use of certain artificial means destined solely either to the facilitating of the natural act or to insuring that the natural act normally performed achieves its proper end."If the technical means facilitates the conjugal act or helps it to reach its natural objectives, it can be morally acceptable. If, on the other hand, the procedure were to replace the conjugal act, it is morally illicit.

Artificial insemination as a substitute for the conjugal act is prohibited by reason of the voluntarily achieved dissociation of the two meanings of the conjugal act. Masturbation, through which the sperm is normally obtained, is another sign of this dissociation: even when it is done for the purpose of procreation, the act remains deprived of its unitive meaning. "It lacks the sexual relationship called for by the moral

order, namely the relationship which realizes 'the full sense of mutual self-giving and human procreation in the context of true love.'"...

7. THE SUFFERING CAUSED BY INFERTILITY IN MARRIAGE. *The suffering of spouses who cannot have children or who are afraid of bringing a handicapped child into the world is a suffering that everyone must understand and properly evaluate.*

On the part of the spouses, the desire for a child is natural: it expresses the vocation to fatherhood and motherhood inscribed in conjugal love. This desire can be even stronger if the couple is affected by sterility which appears incurable. Nevertheless, marriage does not confer upon the spouses the right to have a child, but only the right to perform those natural acts which are per se ordered to procreation.

A true and proper right to a child would be contrary to the child's dignity and nature. The child is not an object to which one has a right, nor can be considered as an object of ownership: rather, a child is a gift, "the supreme gift" and the most gratuitous gift of marriage, and is a living testimony of the mutual giving of his parents. For this reason, the child has the right, as already mentioned, to be the fruit of the specific act of the conjugal love of his parents; and he also has the right to be respected as a person from the moment of his conception. . . .

Section 2:   Saviour Siblings

Should Selecting Saviour Siblings Be Banned?

Sally Sheldon and Stephen Wilkinson

Sally Sheldon and Stephen Wilkinson review the case against using pre-implantation genetic diagnosis plus human leucocyte antigen (HLA) matching to choose an embryo that, when implanted, will develop into a child who can supply tissue to save the life of a brother or sister in need—hence the "saviour sibling" label. The authors limit consideration to cases in which the tissue supplied is umbilical-cord tissue, not that of a vital organ. Cord blood contains the blood-producing stem cells needed to replenish the bone marrow in patients with leukemia whose marrow is destroyed as part of their treatment. Bone-marrow transplants can also use marrow taken from compatible siblings, as well as others. (See the Case Presentation "Saviour Sibling," in this chapter.)

The authors review arguments for prohibiting the use of reproductive technology to produce savior siblings: (a) the child would be treated as a commodity; (b) the practice is a step down the slippery slope leading to "designer babies"; (c) the child would be physically or psychologically harmed by being a savior sibling. They reject all three arguments as flawed and conclude that the selection of savior siblings should be permitted, particularly considering that the lives of a large number of children might be saved.

Recent high profile cases in Australia,[1] the UK,[2] and the USA[3] have brought to the public's attention a new kind of embryo selection. By using HLA (human leucocyte antigen) typing, popularly known as "tissue typing," in conjunction with preimplantation genetic diagnosis (PGD), doctors are now able to pick an embryo for implantation which, if all goes well, will become a "saviour sibling,"[4] a brother or sister capable of donating life-saving tissue to an existing child. In the UK, the most recent case to reach the courts and the newspapers is that of the Hashmis.[5] Their son, Zain, has ß-thalassaemia, a blood disorder which could be cured using tissue from the umbilical cord of a sibling, but only if the sibling is a tissue match. The Human Fertilisation and Embryology Authority gave permission for the Hashmis to select a saviour sibling for Zain. This decision was swiftly challenged in the courts, with the UK High Court finding that the selection of a saviour sibling was unlawful.[6] In May 2003, the Court of Appeal overturned this decision, declaring that tissue typing can be authorised under current legislation.[7]

Prior to the recent Court of Appeal ruling, it looked as if this form of preimplantation selection might be prohibited in the UK and our aim in this paper is to assess whether this and similar bans are defensible.

. . . We will concentrate on critically assessing the arguments for prohibition (rather than, for example, positive arguments for reproductive liberty). This is because banning the use of PGD to create saviour siblings will lead to the death of a number of children who could have been saved by sibling donation. And given that a ban will be fatal for a section of the population, the onus of proof rests clearly with the prohibitionists who must demonstrate that these children's deaths are less terrible than the consequences of allowing this particular use of PGD. As Glover puts it:[8] "You have got to have a very powerful reason to resist the means by which a child's life can be saved."

In what follows, we divide the prohibitionist arguments into three categories. First, there is the idea that saviour siblings would be wrongfully instrumentalised, treated as mere means rather than ends-in-themselves, or treated as commodities. Secondly, there are arguments according to which the creation of saviour siblings would either cause or constitute a move towards the creation of "designer babies." Finally, there are arguments which focus on the welfare of saviour siblings.

Means, Ends, and Commodification

The idea of deliberately creating a saviour sibling often provokes comments like these:

> It is totally unethical. You are not creating a child for itself.[9]
>
> We would have very serious concerns that he is a commodity rather than a person.[10]
>
> The trouble really is that this child as it grows up has been brought into the world because it is a commodity.[11]

Such comments run together two distinct worries: concerns about people having children for the wrong reasons, on the one hand, and concerns about the way in which the child will be treated by his or her parents, on the other. Thoughts of the second kind are really concerns about the welfare of the resultant child and so we will discuss these in a later section, focusing for the time being on the idea that deliberately conceiving a child is wrong if done for certain kinds of reason. Clearly, conceiving *can* be wrong if done for the wrong reasons. Conceiving a child in order later to eat it or torture it would be uncontentious, if extreme, supporting examples for this principle. The real question then is: Which reasons are the wrong reasons? One answer is that a child should be wanted *for his or her own sake* and not for some other purpose:[12]

> The commonest objection to this procedure is that it is wrong to bring children into existence "conditionally." This objection finds its philosophical foundation in Immanuel Kant's famous dictum, "Never use people as a means but always treat them as an end."

As an argument against selecting saviour siblings, though, this is defective in at least two ways (as Boyle and Savulescu, quoted above, go on to point out). First, it relies on a misreading of Kant's "famous dictum." This does not prohibit treating people as means, but rather prohibits treating them *merely* or *solely* as means. As Harris notes:[13] "We all . . . [treat people as means] perfectly innocuously much of the time. In medical contexts, anyone who receives a blood transfusion has used the blood donor as a means to their own ends. . . ."So there is nothing objectionable about creating a baby as a "means to an end" provided that it is also viewed and treated as a human being.

A second more practical objection to this argument is that it does not adequately distinguish between creating a child as a saviour sibling and creating a child for some other "instrumental" purpose—for example, "completing a family," being a playmate for an existing child, saving a marriage, delighting prospective grandparents, or providing an heir. Perhaps these things are different from creating a saviour sibling but, if they are, the difference *isn't* that they are any less "instrumental" for in all these cases, the child is used as a means.

The concern then cannot really be about having a child as a means since people frequently do this and it is not in itself objectionable. What might be objectionable, from the Kantian view, is creating a child *solely* to advance some further end. For example, it would obviously be wrong to create a saviour sibling and then just to discard him or her once it had "served the purpose." But this is clearly not what is proposed and so, overall, this argument fails, as a purely ethical argument and *a fortiori* as a case for legal prohibition.

Designer Babies and Slippery Slopes

A second argument against permitting the deliberate creation of saviour siblings is that to do so would be to step onto a slippery slope towards allowing "designer babies." This argument combines two distinct objections. The general form of the first is that if we allow something to happen which, considered in itself, is either acceptable or only slightly bad, it will later cause something else to happen which is very bad or clearly wrong (this being what is at the bottom of the proverbial slope). So applied to saviour siblings, it says that if we allow the creation of saviour siblings (which is only slightly bad) this will lead to something much worse: the creation of fully-fledged designer babies. As Quintavalle puts it "the new technique is a dangerous

first step towards allowing parents to use embryo testing to choose other characteristics of the baby, such as eye colour and sex."[14]

So the claim is that we will start off by allowing the deliberate creation of saviour siblings and "slide down the slope" towards permitting the selection of embryos on wholly frivolous grounds.

The second version of the slippery slope argument is either a point about consistency or a *reductio ad absurdum*—that is, an attempt to refute a position by showing that it has absurd implications. Lying behind it is the following argument:

1. Allowing the selection of saviour siblings isn't morally different from allowing people to choose "designer" characteristics (for example, hair, colour).

2. *Therefore;* (from (1)) if we ban one, we should ban the other. Conversely, if we allow one, we should allow the other.

3. Allowing people to choose designer characteristics is wrong and should be banned.

4. *Therefore:* (from (2) and (3)) allowing the selection of saviour siblings is wrong and should be banned.

This kind of argument can be used in two closely related ways. First, it is asserted that people who oppose designer babies but not saviour siblings are inconsistent and should really oppose both. Secondly, there is an attempted *reductio* of the view that selecting saviour siblings should be permitted: the idea being that this has the (supposedly absurd, or at least unpalatable) implication that selecting embryos with designer characteristics should also be permitted.

The objections to these "slope" arguments fall into three main categories. First, one could reject the premise (shared by both arguments) that allowing people to choose embryos with designer characteristics is wrong. Secondly (specifically in relation to the consequence based argument), one could argue that allowing the selection of saviour siblings won't, or needn't, cause us to become "permissive" about designer babies. Finally (specifically in relation to the consistency or *reductio* argument), one could argue that saviour siblings and designer babies are relevantly different and therefore one can oppose the latter and not the former without inconsistency.

Purely for the sake of argument, we will grant that allowing people to choose embryos with designer characteristics is wrong and should be prohibited and move straight onto the second objection.[15] This says that allowing the selection of saviour siblings won't, or needn't, cause us to become permissive about designer babies. There are at least three reasons for supporting this objection. The first is that those who propound the empirical slippery slope argument rarely, if ever, support it with any hard evidence. *Merely asserting* that saviour siblings are the "first step towards allowing parents to use embryo testing to choose other characteristics" is inadequate. The second is that it is very easy to envisage how, through careful regulation, a "slide down the slope" might be averted. In particular, there is no reason why selection can't be allowed for some purposes but not others. Indeed, that is the present position and there is no reason to believe that such a position couldn't be maintained, if Parliament (or a regulatory body such as the UK's Human Fertilisation and Embryology Authority) decided that that is what it wanted. So a slide is not inevitable. Thirdly, and finally, there is the fact that to get a fully-fledged designer baby—that is, one in whom numerous traits were selected for—a very large pool of preimplantation embryos would be required from which to select, thus imposing considerable extra cost, discomfort, and inconvenience on would-be "designer parents," and acting as a deterrent.

The third objection to the slippery slope argument is that saviour siblings and designer babies are morally different, and therefore there is nothing inconsistent about opposing one but not the other. Obviously there is a preliminary complication about what exactly counts as a "designer baby" but, for the sake of argument, let us just stipulate that a designer baby is one selected for his or her superficial characteristics (for example brown eyes, black hair, or tallness). Given this definition, is selecting a saviour sibling relevantly different from selecting a designer baby?

One reason for answering "yes" is the following. In the saviour sibling case, but not in designer babies case, there is a very weighty reason for using PGD—saving an existing child's life. But the same cannot be said of designer babies because the reasons for choosing a designer baby (insofar as there are reasons at all) are generally trivial—such as a mere fondness for [a] particular hair colour. So the *prima facie* case for permitting saviour sibling selection is much stronger than that for permitting designer baby selection because there are important reasons for the first but not the second. This constitutes a relevant difference between them and explains why one could without

inconsistency oppose the latter but not the former. There is of course much more to be said about how we might in general distinguish important from trivial reasons and we do not claim that this will always be a straightforward matter. But at least in this case the distinction seems relatively clear and unproblematic, for it is hard to deny that saving a child's life is a much more weighty consideration than getting a child with one's preferred hair colour.

We conclude therefore that the slippery slope or designer babies objection fails to justify a ban on the creation [of] saviour siblings because: (*a*) even if there is a "slope" there is no reason to believe that a "slide" down it is inevitable and (*b*) there are important differences between saviour siblings and designer babies which the slippery slope argument overlooks.

The Welfare of the Child

Finally those who oppose the deliberate creation of saviour siblings often make claims about the welfare of those children who will be thus created. These claims are based on a widely held moral belief (one enshrined in English Law) that, when making decisions about the use of reproductive technologies, we are under an obligation to take into account the welfare of any child created.[16]

The fundamental empirical premise of the child welfare argument is that saviour siblings will, on average, have worse lives than either (*a*) children conceived "naturally" or (*b*) other children created using PGD. The second comparator, (*b*), is of particular relevance if what is argued is that there is nothing wrong with PGD per se but that its use in this context is wrong. Given that the use of PGD for other purposes (that is, screening for a variety of genetic disorders) has been widely accepted, it seems appropriate to take the latter as our main focus.

Two types of damage are suggested by the proponents of the child welfare objection: harm to physical health caused directly by the PGD process and psychological harm. Let's start with physical health. Given that we are considering only the use of umbilical cord stem cells, any physical health problems for the saviour sibling must be caused by the PGD process itself (since no postnatal intervention using the child is envisaged). Is PGD physically harmful to the child thus selected? A recent editorial in *The Lancet* suggests that "embryo biopsy for PGD does not seem to produce adverse physical effects in the short term, but it is too early to exclude the possibility of later effects."[17] What we *can* say though is that, as far as direct effects on physical health are concerned, there is no reason to think that saviour siblings will be any worse off than other children created using PGD. So a child welfare argument based on physical health considerations will either simply fail (because the evidence of harm is inadequate) or will prove too much, counting not only against the creation of saviour siblings but against *all* uses of PGD. Either way, the argument doesn't successfully single out saviour sibling selection for especially restrictive treatment.

An obvious response to this is to claim that a future child should be exposed to the risks of PGD only if she will probably derive enough benefits to outweigh those risks—a view that we will call the *net benefit principle*. On this view, the potential person is rather like an existing patient and doctors should expose her to risk only if, on the balance of probabilities, she will be a net beneficiary. If this principle is accepted, then (it is argued) there is an important difference between using PGD to select a saviour sibling and using it to screen for a serious genetic disorder since only the latter procedure benefits the child created, and so only the latter can be ethically acceptable.

However, this net benefit argument relies on some confused thinking about what it means to "benefit an embryo." It appears to depend on something like the following model. When we screen for a disorder, an embryo (D) is subjected to an intervention (T) which has the following effects:

1. T prevents D from having a serious genetic disorder.

2. T involves as yet unknown long term health risks for D.

So subjecting D to T can (according to this model) be justified solely by reference to D's interests because the benefit of (1) outweighs the harm or risk involved in (2). In saviour sibling cases, however, things seem importantly different. For an embryo (S) is subjected to an intervention (T*) [with] the following effects:

1. T* will make S (more likely to be) a donor for an existing child.

2. T* involves as yet unknown long term health risks for S.

T* cannot be justified by reference to S's interests since there is no benefit for S and some risk and so, if we accept the net benefit principle, including T* on S is wrong. This then provides the (supposed) ethical basis for allowing preimplantation screening for genetic disorders, while not allowing saviour sibling selection—

namely, that only the former conforms to the net benefit principle.

What's wrong with this model? The main difficulty is that it is *not* the case that T (PGD) *prevents* D from having a serious genetic disorder. Rather, D was selected because it did not have the genetic disorder in question (and so had D been naturally implanted, rather than implanted as a result of T, D still would not have had the disorder). So we cannot think of T as benefiting D in a straightforwardly causal way, because T has not cured D or removed a disorder. Rather, T involved choosing D on the grounds that it was *already* a "healthy" embryo.

Given this, what can it mean to say that D has been benefited by T? The only way to make sense of this claim is to say that D derives benefit because T causes D to be implanted, and being implanted is better for D than not being implanted (assuming that, if implanted, D will go on to have a "life worth living" and that the alternative to implantation is destruction). So, if there is any benefit at all for D, it is not "being healthy rather than having a genetic disorder." Rather, the benefit is "existing rather than not existing."

This style of argument raises a number of thorny philosophical problems which we cannot explore in any depth here. One obvious difficulty, for example, is the question of whether it really makes sense to say of an individual that they were benefited by events that caused them to exist. But there are more practical and more decisive objections too. The most relevant for our purposes is that the argument just outlined applies equally to screening for genetic disorders and saviour sibling selection. For if the relevant benefit is being caused to exist (rather than being cured of a genetic disorder) then clearly both D and S stand to gain more or less equally in this respect—since both are caused to exist by the selection process and probably would not have existed without it. And furthermore this will apply (again, more or less equally) to *all* selected embryos, except in those few cases where the life in question is so bad that it is "not worth living." So the net benefit principle (even if true) fails to justify drawing a moral distinction between screening for genetic disorders and saviour sibling selection.

We turn now to the idea that saviour siblings will be psychologically scarred. There seem to be two linked but analytically separate concerns here: first, that a future child may suffer psychological harm if she finds out that she were wanted not for herself, but as a means to save the life of a sibling; and second, that a child conceived for this reason is likely to enjoy a less close and loving relationship with its parents who are less likely to value and nurture the child given that they wanted it primarily to save the life of the sibling.[18] However, even if we concede for the sake of argument that it would be hurtful or upsetting for a specially selected sibling (A) to discover that she had been conceived for the primary purpose of saving the life of an existing child (B), it seems unlikely that A would be *less* happy than another, randomly selected sibling (C) who was unable to act as a tissue donor. For it could surely be argued here that A would benefit from B's company and may well derive pleasure from knowing that[19] she has saved B's life. Furthermore, as Robertson *et al* point out:

> the fact that the parents are willing to conceive another child to protect the first suggests that they are highly committed to the well-being of their children, and that they will value the second child for its own sake as well.

In contrast, imagine the psychological impact on C, born into a bereaved family and later to discover that she was a huge disappointment to her parents because of her inability to save B's life. Of course, a full consideration of the issue of psychological harm would involve marshalling substantial bodies of empirical evidence (not something that we can do here). But while this discussion remains entirely speculative, we can at least say that it is far from obvious that considerations of child welfare should count against, rather than for, the practice of saviour sibling selection.

Next we want to look at a more philosophical response to the child welfare argument and ask: If it were established that saviour siblings were (on average) less happy than other children, would this fact be sufficient to justify banning the selection of saviour siblings?

We need to start by making a general distinction between two kinds of policy. First, there are "make people happier" policies; these aim to make actual (present or future) people happier than they otherwise would be.[20] Secondly, there are "prevent unhappy people" policies, which aim to prevent unhappy people from coming into existence. Make people happier policies are ubiquitous. Prevent unhappy people policies, on the other hand, are much rarer and often highly controversial because they are seen as "eugenic." An example of a prevent unhappy people policy would be encouraging the termination of fetuses with severe physical impairments (or at least this is one possible rationale for such a policy).[21]

Within this category (prevent unhappy people policies) a further distinction can be drawn. First there are policies that aim to prevent the creation of A so that B (who will be more happy than A would have been) can be created instead. B, in a manner of speaking, takes A's place. Kuhse and Singer provide what seems to be a clear example of this way of thinking (emphasis added).[22]

> *If the test shows that the foetus does have Down's syndrome, the woman is able to have an abortion. The same happens with women who are shown to be carriers of the gene for haemophilia: the foetus can be checked to see if it has the disease. If it does, the woman can have an abortion, and then try again, so that she can have a normal baby. Why do we regard this as a reasonable thing to do, even when the handicap is one like haemophilia, which is quite compatible with a worthwhile life?... [Because] we are offsetting the loss of one possible life against the creation of another life with better prospects.*

Secondly, there are policies that simply aim to prevent the creation of A (without any appeal to "substitution")—the thought being that, if A were to be born, she'd have a not merely low, but a *negative* quality of life, one such that she'd be "better off dead." As Glover puts it:[23]

> *some kinds of life are perhaps worse than not being alive at all—if it makes sense for people to see death as in their interests, there seems a parallel possibility of parents or doctors thinking that not being born may be in the interests of a potential child.*

Many regulations governing reproduction are of the "make people happier" kind. Other legislation, though, is not about making actual children happier but is, rather, about reducing the number of "disadvantaged" children born—either directly, through prohibition, or indirectly, through measures which are calculated to discourage. Such legislation clearly falls into the "prevent unhappy people" category. But can child welfare considerations justify such restrictions?

These restrictions could be defended in one (or both) of two ways. The first justification is that they lead to the "replacement" of less happy future people with more happy ones. The second is that they prevent misery and suffering by stopping the births of people with "negative quality lives." Let's take the second justification first. This is extremely unlikely to work against saviour sibling selection, even if any children created face very severe psychological problems. For, in the absence of other unconnected problems (for example severe painful illness) the chances of saviour siblings having *negative* quality lives are remote. Are we *really* expected to believe that these children will live lives that are worse than not being alive at all? Also relevant here are thoughts about how our attitudes to saviour siblings cohere with our attitudes to children with disabilities. For in the debate about prenatal screening, selective termination, eugenics and suchlike, the thought that people with severe and painful disabilities are "glad to be alive" is (rightly) taken seriously. If we allow (as we should) that these people, faced with extraordinarily unfavourable circumstances, have lives worth living, then surely we must also allow that most saviour siblings will have lives worth living too.

So proponents of restrictive regulation are forced to fall back on the first justification: selecting saviour siblings should be banned because this will lead to the children who would otherwise have been created in this way being "replaced" by a roughly equal number of other "happier" children (children who would not have existed at all if saviour sibling selection had been allowed). This, though, is problematic because there are general theoretical reasons for not allowing *any* arguments of this sort (replacement arguments) to influence the regulation of reproduction. The main one is that if arguments of this type are acceptable, then there seems no reason to restrict their application to particular practices like saviour sibling selection. Once we start thinking in this way, it is hard to limit the scope of such arguments because, as Glover suggests:[24]

> *If someone with a handicap is conceived instead of a normal person, things turn out less well than they might have done. It would have been better if the normal person had been conceived. But things of this sort can be said about almost any of us. If my own conception was an alternative to the conception of someone just like me except more intelligent, or more athletic or more musical, it would have been better if that person had been conceived.*

This has troubling implications. The main one is that *if* a replacement argument is deemed sufficient to justify prohibiting saviour sibling selection then (other things being equal) parallel arguments should, for reasons of consistency, be deemed sufficient to justify (amongst other things) making compulsory the use of prenatal screening or PGD so as to reduce the amount of disease in the world, and making women impregnate themselves with enhanced donor sperm rather than the "normal" sperm of their partners. The replacement justification of these coercive state actions would be fundamentally the same as the one lying behind

the prohibition of saviour sibling selection—that is, people's procreative autonomy would be restricted on the grounds that it would be better if a "happier" group of future persons came into existence instead of a "less happy" group.[25]

Our contention is not that all of these practices are exactly the same; they are not. But we would argue that there is something troubling about allowing this style of reasoning to underpin restrictions on procreative liberty. We would be the first to admit that this argument needs much more fleshing out (not something there is space to do here). However, what is clear, even from this short version is that there is something problematic about using replacement arguments to justify coercive state action. Hence, this justificatory strategy is not one on which prohibitionists should rely.

Conclusion

In this paper, we have critically assessed the three main arguments for prohibiting the use of PGD and tissue typing to select saviour siblings. These arguments are (*a*) that saviour siblings would be wrongfully treated as means rather than ends, (*b*) that they would cause or constitute a slide towards designer babies, and (*c*) that they would suffer physically and/or emotionally. We have found each of these arguments to be flawed and therefore conclude that the selection of saviour siblings should be permitted, especially given that prohibiting it would result in the preventable deaths of a number of existing children.

References

1. Spriggs M, Savulescu J. "Saviour siblings." *J Med Ethics* 2002; 28:289. Davies J-A, "'Designer' baby goes ahead." *The Age* 12 March 2003, www.theoge.com.au/articles/2003//03/11/1047144972401.html.
2. BBC News. *Hashmi decision sparks ethics row,* 22 February 2002, http://news.bbc.co.uk/1/hi/health/1836827.stm.
3. BBC News. *Genetics storm girl "responding well,"* 19 October 2002, http://news.bbc.co.uk/hi/health/979884.stm.
4. This term is taken from Spriggs M. Savulescu J. "Saviour siblings." *J Med Ethics* 2002;28:289.
5. Robertson JA, Kahn JP, Wogner JE. Conception to obtain hematopoietic stem cells. *Hastings Cent Rep* 2002;32:34–40.
6. R (Quintavalle) v Human Fertilisation and Embryology Authority [2003] EWHC 2785 (Admin).
7. R (Quintavalle) v Human Fertilisation and Embryology Authority [2003] EWCA Civ 667.
8. Glover J. Quoted in: BBC News. *Doctor plans "designer baby" clinic.* 11 December 2001, http://news.bbc.co.uk/1/hi/health/1702854.stm.
9. Quintavalle J. Quoted in: BBC News. *Doctor plans "designer baby" clinic.* 11 December 2001, http://news.bbc.co.uk/1/hi/health/1702854.stm. Quintavelle is a leading member of the group, Comment on Reproductive Ethics, which

brought the judicial review action described in reference 5 above.

10. Nathanson V. Quoted in: BBC News. *Baby created to save older sister.* 4 October 2000, http://news.bbc.co.uk/1/hi/health/1702854.stm.

11. Winston R. Quoted in: BBC *News_Go-ahead for "designer babies."* 13 December 2001, http://news.bbc.co.uk/1/hi/health/1706926.stm.

12. Boyle R, Savulescu J. Ethics of using preimplantation genetic diagnosis to select a stem cell donor for an existing person. *BMJ* 2001;323:1240–3, 1241.

13. Harris J. *The Value of Life.* London: Routledge, 1985:143.

14. Attributed to Josephine Quintavalle by BBC News. *Pro-life challenge to embryo testing,* 12 July 2002, http://news.bbc.co.uk/1/hi/health/2125482.stm.

15. This is partly because contesting this would take us too far from the issue at hand and into very complex territory, and partly because we don't need to contest it to undermine the slippery slope argument.

16. Under s. 13, Human Fertilisation and Embryology Act 1990, we are directed that: "A woman shall not be provided with treatment services unless account has been taken of the welfare of any child who may be born as a result of the treatment (including the need of that child for a father), and of any other child who may be affected by the birth." It should be noted here that this section also explicitly invites us to consider the welfare of existing children. Whilst it is probable that the architects of the 1990 Act were thinking here of the prevention of harm rather than the according of benefits to existing children, the wording of the law is clearly broad enough also to include the latter. This was recognised by the Court of

17. Appeal in its consideration of the Hashmi case, see the judgment of Mance LJ at 133.

18. Preimplantation donor selection [editorial]. *Lancet* 2001;358:1195.

19. This possibility was specifically denied by both the Hashmis and the Whitakers, who claimed that they wanted another child in any case.

20. These kinds of arguments are routinely advanced by the courts in allowing parents to consent to allow one sibling to act as a donor to another. Such donation is held to be in the donor's best interests, notwithstanding the pain and physical risks associated with the procedure, because of the donor's interest in a continued relationship with his or her sibling. Strunk v Strunk (1969) 445 SW 2d 145 (Ky CA).

21. We use terms like "happy" and "unhappy" here as a shorthand for quality of life (as perceived from the perspective of the person living that life).

22. Sheldon S, Wilkinson S. Termination of pregnancy for reason of foetal disability: are there grounds for a special exception in law? *Med Law Rev* 2001;9:85–109.

23. Kuhsa H, Singer P. *Should the Baby Live?* Oxford: Oxford University Press, 1985:158.

24. Glover J. *Fertility and the Family: the Glover Report on reproductive technologies to the European Commission.* London: Fourth Estate, 1989, 129.

25. Glover J. *Causing Death and Saving Lives.* Harmondsworth: Penguin, 1977:148.

26. Sheldon S, Wilkinson S. Termination of pregnancy for reason of foetal disability: are there grounds for a special exception in law? *Med Law Rev* 2001;9:85–109.

Section 3:   Human Reproductive Cloning

The Wisdom of Repugnance

Leon R. Kass

Leon Kass argues that the repulsion many people feel about the possibility of human cloning springs from a recognition that it violates our nature as embodied, engendered, and engendering beings and the social relations we have because of that nature. First, cloning would distort the cloned person's sense of individuality and social identity. Second, like IVF and prenatal genetic testing, cloning would transform procreation into manufacture and children into commodities. Third, cloning would encourage parents to regard children as property.

In contrast to those who see cloning as simply another technique, like AI and IVF, for helping individuals exercise their "right" to reproduce, Kass regards cloning as a significant slide down the slippery slope toward the "sperm to term" production of genetically designed children. In view of all these considerations, Kass urges an international legal ban on human cloning.

From *The New Republic*, 2 June 1997, pp. 17–26. Reprinted by permission of the author.

..."Offensive." "Grotesque." "Revolting." "Repugnant." "Repulsive." These are the words most commonly heard regarding the prospect of human cloning. Such reactions come both from the man or woman in the street and from the intellectuals, from believers and atheists, from humanists and scientists. Even Dolly's creator has said he "would find it offensive" to clone a human being.

People are repelled by many aspects of human cloning. They recoil from the prospect of mass production of human beings, with large clones of look-alikes, compromised in their individuality, the idea of father–son or mother–daughter twins; the bizarre prospects of a woman giving birth to and rearing a genetic copy of herself, her spouse or even her deceased father or mother; the grotesqueness of conceiving a child as an exact replacement for another who has died; the utilitarian creation of embryonic genetic duplicates of oneself, to be frozen away or created when necessary, in case of need for homologous tissues or organs for transplantation; the narcissism of those who would clone themselves and the arrogance of others who think they know who deserves to be cloned or which genotype any child-to-be should be thrilled to receive; the Frankensteinian hubris to create human life and increasingly to control its destiny; man playing God. Almost no one finds any of the suggested reasons for human cloning compelling; almost everyone anticipates its possible misuses and abuses. Moreover, many people feel oppressed by the sense that there is probably nothing we can do to prevent it from happening. This makes the prospect all the more revolting.

Revulsion is not an argument; and some of yesterday's repugnances are today calmly accepted—though, one must add, not always for the better. In crucial cases, however, repugnance is the emotional expression of deep wisdom, beyond reason's powerfully to articulate it. Can anyone really give an argument fully adequate to the horror which is father–daughter incest (even with consent), or having sex with animals, or mutilating a corpse, or eating human flesh, or even just (just!) raping or murdering another human being?

Would anybody's failure to give full rational justification for his or her revulsion at these practices make that revulsion ethically suspect? Not at all. On the contrary, we are suspicious of those who think that they can rationalize away our horror, say, by trying to explain the enormity of incest with arguments only about the genetic risks of inbreeding.

The repugnance at human cloning belongs in this category. We are repelled by the prospect of cloning human beings not because of the strangeness or novelty of the undertaking, but because we intuit and feel, immediately and without argument, the violation of things that we rightfully hold dear. Repugnance, here as elsewhere, revolts against the excesses of human willfulness, warning us not to transgress what is unspeakably profound. Indeed, in this age in which everything is held to be permissible so long as it is freely done, in which our given human nature no longer commands respect, in which our bodies are regarded as mere instruments of our autonomous rational wills, repugnance may be the only voice left that speaks up to defend the central core of our humanity. Shallow are the souls that have forgotten how to shudder.

The goods protected by repugnance are generally overlooked by our customary ways of approaching all new biomedical technologies. The way we evaluate cloning ethically will in fact be shaped by how we characterize it descriptively, by the context into which we place it, and by the perspective from which we view it. The first task for ethics is proper description. And here is where our failure begins.

Typically, cloning is discussed in one or more of three familiar contexts, which one might call the technological, the liberal and the meliorist. Under the first, cloning will be seen as an extension of existing techniques for assisting reproduction and determining the genetic makeup of children. Like them, cloning is to be regarded as a neutral technique, with no inherent meaning or goodness, but subject to multiple uses, some good, some bad. The morality of cloning thus depends absolutely on the goodness or badness of the motives and intentions of the cloners: as one bioethicist defender of cloning puts it, "the ethics must be judged [only] by the way the parents nurture and rear their resulting child and whether they bestow the same love and affection on a child brought into existence by a technique of assisted reproduction as they would on a child born in the usual way."

The liberal (or libertarian or liberationist) perspective sets cloning in the context of rights, freedoms and personal empowerment. Cloning is just a new option for exercising an individual's right to reproduce or to have the kind of child that he or she wants. Alternatively, cloning enhances our liberation (especially women's liberation) from the confines of nature, the vagaries of chance, or the necessity for sexual mating. Indeed, it liberates women from the need for men altogether, for the process requires only eggs, nuclei and (for the time being) uteri—plus, of course, a healthy dose of our (allegedly "masculine") manipulative science that likes to do all these things to mother nature and nature's mothers. For those who hold this outlook, the only moral restraints on cloning are adequately informed consent and the avoidance of bodily harm. If no one is cloned without her consent, and if the clonant is not physically damaged, then the liberal conditions for licit, hence moral, conduct are met. Worries that go beyond violating the will or maiming the body are dismissed as "symbolic"—which is to say, unreal. . . .

The meliorist perspective embraces valetudinarians and also eugenicists. The latter were formerly more vocal in these discussions, but they are now generally happy to see their goals advanced under the less threatening banners of freedom and technological growth. These people see in cloning a new prospect for improving human beings—minimally, by ensuring the perpetuation of healthy individuals by avoiding the risks of genetic disease inherent in the lottery of sex, and maximally, by producing "optimum babies," preserving outstanding genetic material, and (with the help of soon-to-come techniques for precise genetic engineering) enhancing inborn human capacities on many fronts. Here the morality of cloning as a means is justified solely by the excellence of the end, that is, by the outstanding traits or individuals cloned— beauty, or brawn, or brains. . . .

The technical, liberal and meliorist approaches all ignore the deeper anthropological, social and, indeed, ontological meanings of bringing forth new life. To this more fitting and profound point of view, cloning shows itself to be a major alteration, indeed, a major violation, of our given nature as embodied, gendered and engendering beings—and of the social relations built on this natural ground. Once this perspective is recognized, the ethical judgment on cloning can no longer be reduced to a matter of motives and intentions, rights and freedoms, benefits and harms, or even means and ends. It must be regarded primarily as a matter of meaning: Is cloning a fulfillment of human begetting and belonging? Or is cloning rather, as I contend, their pollution and perversion? To pollution and perversion, the fitting response can only be horror and revulsion; and conversely, generalized horror and revulsion are prima facie evidence of foulness and violation. The burden of moral argument must fall entirely on those who want to declare the widespread repugnances of humankind to be mere timidity or superstition.

Yet repugnance need not stand naked before the bar of reason. The wisdom of our horror at human cloning can be partially articulated, even if this is finally one of those instances about which the heart has its reasons that reason cannot entirely know. . . .

The Perversities of Cloning

Cloning creates serious issues of identity and individuality. The cloned person may experience concerns about his distinctive identity not only because he will be in genotype and appearance identical to another human being, but, in this case, because he may also be twin to the person who is his "father" or "mother"—if one can still call them that. What would be the psychic burdens of being the "child" or "parent" of your twin? The cloned individual moreover, will be saddled with a genotype that has already lived. He will not be fully a surprise to the world. People are likely always to compare his performances in life with that of his alter ego. True, his nurture and his circumstance in life will be different; genotype is not exactly destiny. Still, one must also expect parental and other efforts to shape this new life after the original—or at least to view the child with the original version always firmly in mind. Why else did they clone from the star basketball player, mathematician and beauty queen—or even dear old dad—in the first place?. . .

Troubled psychic identity (distinctiveness), based on all-too-evident genetic identity (sameness), will be made much worse by the utter confusion of social identity and kinship ties: For, as already noted, cloning radically confounds lineage and social relations, for "offspring" as for "parents." As bioethicist James Nelson has pointed out, a female child cloned from her "mother" might develop a desire for a relationship to her "father," and might understandably seek out the father of her "mother," who is after all also her biological twin sister. Would "Grandpa," who thought his paternal duties concluded, be pleased to discover that the clonant looked to him for paternal attention and support?

Social identity and social ties of relationship and responsibility are widely connected to, and supported by, biological kinship. Social taboos on incest (and adultery) everywhere serve to keep clear who is related to whom (and especially which child belongs to which parents), as well as to avoid confounding the social identity of parent-and-child (or brother-and-sister) with the social identity of lovers, spouses and co-parents. True, social identity is altered by adoption (but as a matter of the best interest of already living children: we do not deliberately produce children for adoption). True, artificial insemination and in vitro fertilization with donor sperm, or whole embryo donation, are in some way forms of "prenatal adoption"—a not altogether unproblematic practice. Even here, though, there is in each case (as in all sexual reproduction) a known male source of sperm and a known single female source of egg—a genetic father and a genetic mother—should anyone care to know (as adopted children often do) who is genetically related to whom.

In the case of cloning, however, there is but one "parent." The usually sad situation of the "single-parent child" is here deliberately planned, and with a vengeance. In the case of self-cloning, the "offspring" is, in addition, one's twin; and so the dreaded result of incest—to be parent to one's sibling—is here brought about deliberately, albeit without any act of coitus. Moreover, all other relationships will be confounded. What will father, grandfather, aunt, cousin, sister mean? Who will bear what ties and what burdens? What sort of social identity will someone have with one whole side—"father's" or "mother's"—necessarily excluded? It is no answer to say that our society, with its high incidence of divorce, remarriage, adoption, extramarital childbearing and the rest, already confounds lineage and confuses kinship and responsibility for children (and everyone else), unless one also wants to argue that this is, for children, a preferable state of affairs.

Human cloning would also represent a giant step toward turning begetting into making, procreation into manufacture (literally, something "handmade"), a process already begun with in vitro fertilization and genetic testing of embryos. With cloning, not only is the process in hand, but the total genetic blueprint of the cloned individual is selected and determined by the human artisans. To be sure, subsequent development will take place according to natural processes; and the resulting children will still be recognizably human. But we here would be taking a major step into making man himself simply another one of the man-made things. Human nature becomes merely the last part of nature to succumb to the technological project, which turns all of nature into raw material at human disposal, to be homogenized by our rationalized technique according to the subjective prejudices of the day.

How does begetting differ from making? In natural procreation, human beings come together, complementarily male and female, to give existence to another being who is formed, exactly as we were, *by what we are*: living, hence perishable, hence aspiringly erotic, human beings. In clonal reproduction, by contrast, and in the more advanced forms of manufacture to which it leads, we give existence to a being not by what we are but by what we intend and design. As with any product of our making, no matter how excellent, the artificer stands above it, not as an equal but as a superior, transcending it by his will and creative prowess. Scientists who clone animals make it perfectly clear that they are engaged in instrumental making; the animals are, from the start, designed as means to serve rational human purposes. In human cloning, scientists and prospective "parents" would be adopting the same technocratic mentality to human children: human children would be their artifacts.

Such an arrangement is profoundly dehumanizing, no matter how good the product. Mass-scale cloning of the same individual makes the point vividly; but the violation of human equality, freedom and dignity are present even in a single planned clone. And procreation dehumanized into manufacture is further degraded by commodification, a virtually inescapable result of allowing babymaking to proceed under the banner of commerce. Genetic and reproductive biotechnology companies are already growth industries, but they will go into commercial orbit once the Human Genome Project nears completion. Supply will create enormous demand. Even before the capacity for human cloning arrives, established companies will have invested in the harvesting of eggs from ovaries obtained at autopsy or through ovarian surgery, practiced embryonic genetic alteration, and initiated the stock-piling of prospective donor tissues. Through the rental of surrogate-womb services, and through the buying and selling of tissues and embryos, priced according to the merit of the donor, the commodification of nascent human life will be unstoppable.

Finally, and perhaps most important, the practice of human cloning by nuclear transfer—like other anticipated forms of genetic engineering of the next generation—would enshrine and aggravate a profound and mischievous misunderstanding of the meaning of having children and of the parent–child relationship. When a couple now chooses to procreate, the partners are saying yes to the emergence of new life in its novelty, saying yes not only to having a child but also, tacitly, to having whatever child this child turns out to be. In accepting our finitude and opening ourselves to our replacement, we are tacitly confessing the limits of our control. In this ubiquitous way of nature, embracing the future by procreating means precisely that we are relinquishing our grip, in the very activity of taking up our own share in what we hope will be the immortality of human life and the human species. This means that our children are not *our* children: they are not our property, not our possessions. Neither are they supposed to live our lives for us, or anyone else's life but their own. To be sure, we seek to guide them on their way, imparting to them not just life but nurturing love, and a way of life; to be sure, they bear our hopes that they will live fine and flourishing lives, enabling us in small measure to transcend our own limitations. Still, their genetic distinctiveness and independence are the natural foreshadowing of the deep truth that they have their own and never-before-enacted life to live. They are sprung from a past, but they take an uncharted course into the future.

Much harm is already done by parents who try to live vicariously through their children. Children are sometimes compelled to fulfill the broken dreams of unhappy parents; John Doe Jr. or the III is under the burden of having to live up to his forebear's name. Still, if most parents have hopes for their children, cloning parents will have expectations. In cloning, such overbearing parents take at the start a decisive step which contradicts the entire meaning of the open and forward-looking nature of parent–child relations. The child is given a genotype that has already lived, with full expectation that this blueprint of a past life ought to be controlling of the life that is to come. Cloning is inherently despotic, for it seeks to make one's children (or someone else's children) after one's own image (or an image of one's choosing) and their fixture according to one's will. In some cases, the despotism may be mild and benevolent. In other cases, it will be mischievous and downright tyrannical. But despotism—the control of another through one's will—it inevitably will be.

Meeting Some Objections

The defenders of cloning, of course, are not wittingly friends of despotism. Indeed, they regard themselves mainly as friends of freedom: the freedom of individuals to reproduce, the freedom of scientists and inventors to discover and devise and to foster "progress" in genetic knowledge and technique. They want large-scale cloning only for animals, but they wish to preserve cloning as a human option for exercising our "right to reproduce"—our right to have children, and children with "desirable genes." As law professor John Robertson points out, under our "right to reproduce" we already practice early forms of unnatural, artificial and extramarital reproduction, and we already practice early forms of eugenic choice. For this reason, he argues, cloning is no big deal.

We have here a perfect example of the logic of the slippery slope, and the slippery way in which it already works in this area. Only a few years ago, slippery slope arguments were used to oppose artificial insemination and in vitro fertilization using unrelated sperm donors. Principles used to justify these practices, it was said, will be used to justify more artificial and more eugenic practices, including cloning. Not so, the defenders retorted, since we can make the necessary distinctions. And now, without even a gesture at making the necessary distinctions, the continuity of practice is held by itself to be justificatory.

The principle of reproductive freedom as currently enunciated by the proponents of cloning logically embraces the ethical acceptability of sliding down the entire rest of the slope—to producing children ectogenetically from sperm to term (should it become feasible) and to producing children whose entire genetic makeup will be the product of parental eugenic planning and choice. If reproductive freedom means the right to have a child of one's own choosing, by whatever means, it knows and accepts no limits.

But, far from being legitimated by a "right to reproduce," the emergence of techniques of assisted reproduction and genetic engineering should compel us to reconsider the meaning and limits of such a putative right. In truth, a "right to reproduce" has always been a peculiar and problematic notion. Rights generally belong to individuals, but this is a right which (before cloning) no one can exercise alone. Does the right then inhere only in couples? Only in married couples? Is it a (woman's) right to carry or deliver or a right (of one or more parents) to nurture and rear? Is it a right to have your own biological child? Is it a right only to attempt reproduction, or a right also to succeed? Is it a right to acquire the baby of one's choice?

The assertion of a negative "right to reproduce" certainly makes sense when it claims protection against state interference with procreative liberty, say, through a program of compulsory sterilization. But surely it cannot be the basis of a tort claim against nature, to be made good by technology, should free efforts at natural procreation fail. Some insist that the right to reproduce embraces also the right against state interference with the free use of all technological means to obtain a child. Yet such a position cannot be sustained: for reasons having to do with the means employed, any community may rightfully prohibit surrogate pregnancy, or polygamy, or the sale of babies to infertile couples, without violating anyone's basic human "right to reproduce." When the exercise of a previously innocuous freedom now involves or impinges on troublesome practices that the original freedom never was intended to reach, the general presumption of liberty needs to be reconsidered.

We do indeed already practice negative eugenic selection, through genetic screening and prenatal diagnosis. Yet our practices are governed by a norm of health. We seek to prevent the birth of children who suffer from known (serious) genetic diseases. When and if gene therapy becomes possible, such diseases could then be treated, in utero or even before implantation—I have no ethical objection in principle to such a practice (though I have some practical worries), precisely because it serves the medical goal of healing existing individuals. But therapy, to be therapy, implies not only an existing "patient." It also implies a norm of health. In this respect, even germline gene "therapy," though practiced not on a human being but on egg and sperm, is less radical than cloning, which is in no way therapeutic. But once one blurs the distinction between health promotion and genetic enhancement, between so-called negative and positive eugenics, one opens the door to all future eugenic designs. "To make sure that a child will be healthy and have good chances in life": this is Robertson's principle, and owing to its latter clause it is an utterly elastic principle, with no boundaries. Being over eight feet tall will likely produce some very good chances in life, and so will having the looks of Marilyn Monroe, and so will a genius-level intelligence. . . .

Ban the Cloning of Humans

What, then, should we do? We should declare that human cloning is unethical in itself and dangerous in its likely consequences. In so doing, we shall have the backing of the overwhelming majority of our fellow Americans, and of the human race, and (I believe) of most practicing scientists. Next, we should do all that we can to prevent the cloning of human beings. We should do this by means of an international legal ban if possible, and by a unilateral national ban, at a minimum. Scientists may secretly undertake to violate such a law, but they will be deterred by not being able to stand up proudly to claim the credit for their technological bravado and success. Such a ban on clonal baby-making, moreover, will not harm the progress of basic genetic science and technology. On the contrary, it will reassure the public that scientists are happy to proceed without violating the deep ethical norms and intuitions of the human community. . . .

The president's call for a moratorium on human cloning has given us an important opportunity. In a truly unprecedented way, we can strike a blow for the human control of the technological project, for wisdom, prudence and human dignity. The prospect of human cloning, so repulsive to contemplate, is the occasion for deciding whether we shall be slaves of unregulated progress, and ultimately its artifacts, or whether we shall remain free human beings who guide our technique toward the enhancement of human dignity.

The Ethics of Human Reproductive Cloning

Carson Strong

Carson Strong addresses the question of whether, if human cloning were a procedure that didn't produce birth defects, it would be morally legitimate for some infertile couples to employ cloning to have a genetically related child. The objections to human reproductive cloning, he claims, are of three kinds: those that appeal to the interest of the child, those based on the consequences to society, and those arising from teleological views. Strong examines objections of all three types and argues that each objection involves problems so serious as to keep it from being sufficiently compelling. He concludes that human reproductive cloning could be ethically justifiable in at least some instances.

Carson Strong, From "The Ethics of Human Reproductive Cloning," *Ethics, Law and Moral Philosophy of Reproductive Biomedicine*, Vol. 1, no. 1, (2005): 45–49. Copyright © 2005 Elsevier, Inc. Reprinted by permission.

Introduction

Many hold that human reproductive cloning would be wrong under any circumstances. Others have maintained that in certain situations reproductive cloning would be ethically permissible. One type of case in which it has been claimed that it would be permissible involves infertile couples. This paper focuses on infertility cases in order to address the question of whether human reproductive cloning could at least sometimes be ethically justifiable.

A caveat should be stated at the outset. The risk of congenital anomalies in the offspring makes it reasonable to hold that it would be wrong to attempt human reproductive cloning at this time (National Academy of Sciences, 2002). In the future, however, it might be possible to carry out cloning with no more risk of anomalies than the background risk in procreation by sexual intercourse. Let us assume, for sake of argument, that cloning technology has advanced to that point. Given this assumption, would cloning in infertility cases be ethically permissible? . . .

An example of the type of case in question is a scenario in which the woman is unable to produce ova and the man is unable to produce spermatozoa. Like many couples, they want to have a child genetically related to at least one of them. One approach to having genetically related children would involve using sperm and ova donated by family members, but suppose that no family members are available in this case. Let us assume, in other words, that cloning using a cell nucleus from one member of the couple is the only way they could have a child genetically related to one of them. . . .

Whether cloning in such scenarios is ethically justifiable rests on the following question: which should be considered weightier, infertile couples' freedom to use cloning or the arguments against human reproductive cloning? To address this question, let us begin with the importance of the freedom of infertile couples to use cloning.

Cloning and Procreative Freedom

Some have claimed that cloning is not procreation because it does not involve the joining of male and female gametes (Massey *et al.*, 2001: Shuster, 2003). In reply, to assess whether cloning in the infertility cases is procreation, we should compare it to the paradigm of procreation—what I shall call "ordinary procreation." I refer to the type of procreation in which a couple begets, by sexual intercourse, a child

whom they then rear. In making this comparison, we need to look not only at the differences but also at the similarities, and it turns out that a number of similarities can be identified (Robertson, 1998). First, in both types of situation there is a genetic connection between the child and at least one member of the couple. Second, assuming that the woman can gestate, there is gestating and childbirth. Third, the child is raised by the couple. Fourth, in both types of case, the overall purpose is to create a family or add a child to the family. So, the similarities between the two situations are quite substantial. They both involve central features of the project of having children: genetic connection, gestation, childbirth, and rearing. Because of these similarities, it is reasonable to regard the use of cloning by infertile couples as procreation, even though it does not consist of the union of male and female gametes.

Based on these considerations, it is reasonable to hold that the freedom of infertile couples to use cloning is a form of procreative freedom. Procreative freedom is worthy of respect in part because freedom in general is worthy of respect. But more than this, procreative freedom is an especially important freedom because of the significance that procreative decisions can have for persons' lives (Strong, 1997). For these reasons, the freedom of infertile couples to use cloning is worthy of respect.

It might be objected that the desire to have genetically related children should be given relatively little weight. One might argue that this desire is a mere expression of vanity and is too frivolous to outweigh the objections to reproductive cloning, given that there are other options such as adoption or donor pre-embryos. . . . Let us consider whether there are reasons for desiring genetically related children that are not easy to dismiss.

To explore this, one strategy is to try to understand why having genetic children might be meaningful to people in "ordinary procreation" and then use this understanding in addressing reproductive cloning. It turns out that there are a number of reasons why people might find it meaningful to have genetic offspring in the ordinary type of procreation (Strong, 1997). It will suffice to discuss two of these reasons. First, having a genetic child might be valued because it involves participation in the creation of a person. When one has a child in ordinary procreation, a normal outcome is the creation of an individual with self-consciousness. Philosophers have regarded the phenomenon of self-consciousness with wonder. . . . One might say that in having children we participate in the mystery of the creation of self-consciousness. For this reason, some might regard creating a person as an important event, perhaps one with spiritual overtones.

Turning to the second reason, having genetic children in the ordinary situation might be valued as an affirmation of a couple's mutual love and acceptance. It can be a deep expression of acceptance to say to another, in effect."I want your genes to contribute to the genetic makeup of my children." Moreover, in such a context there might be an anticipation that the emotional bond between the couple will grow stronger because of common children to whom each has a biological relationship. To intentionally seek the strengthening of their personal bond in this manner can be a further affirmation of mutual love and acceptance. In stating these two reasons, I do not mean to imply that one ought to desire to have genetic offspring, but only that the desire can be defended. These are examples of reasons that are not silly or confused. Rather, they are reasons that deserve consideration.

Now let us consider the applicability of these reasons to cloning. Would it be reasonable for the infertile couple to want to use cloning in part because it would enable them to participate in the creation of a person? It can be argued that it would be. The member of the couple who provides a somatic cell nucleus for cloning would participate by providing the nuclear genetic material for the new person, and regardless of who provides the cell nucleus, if the woman is capable of gestating, then she could participate by gestating and giving birth to the child. If she has ova, then she could participate genetically by providing mitochondrial DNA. In addition, the couple might value cloning because they interpret it as an affirmation of mutual love and acceptance. A biological partnership in creating the child is possible if a cell nucleus from the man is used and the woman is the gestational mother. In that situation, the child comes forth from their two bodies.

Assuming mutual love, the woman bears a child having the genes of the man who loves her and is loved by her. Alternatively, suppose that a cell nucleus from the woman is used. The man then can become the social father of a child having the genes of the woman who loves him and is loved by him. To seek to become social parents in this manner can be an affirmation of mutual acceptance. These considerations show that some of the important reasons for valuing the having of genetic children in the ordinary scenario also apply when cloning is used. Although not everyone in the infertile couple's situation would want to use cloning in order to have a genetically related child, some might.

Objections to Human Reproductive Cloning

A number of objections have been raised against human reproductive cloning, and they generally fall into three main categories—those that appeal to the interests of the child, those based on consequences for society, and those arising from teleological views. First we shall consider objections that focus on the child's interests. The main ones are of two kinds, consequentialist and deontological. Let us begin with the consequentialist type.

Harm to the Child

Consequentialist child-centred objections claim that cloning will harm the child. An example is the "life in the shadow" argument (Holm, 1998). It claims that people will expect the child to lead a life that follows in the footsteps of the older person who has the same DNA. These expectations will pressure her to follow in that person's footsteps, and this will be harmful because it will prevent her from following a different path that might be more conducive to her wellbeing. Another example is the argument that there will be confusion over family lineage and kinship (President's Council on Bioethics, 2002). The nucleus donor will be both the social parent and the twin sibling of the child. This unusual relationship could result in some type of family turmoil that is harmful to the child, so the argument goes.

These consequentialist objections sometimes rest on the belief that persons with identical nuclear DNA will be identical. This belief is mistaken. For one thing, the imprinting of the DNA of parent and child might differ, resulting in phenotypic differences even though they have the same DNA (Simpson, 2003). Even if the imprinting is the same, the parent and child will be exposed to different environments *in utero* and will be raised in different social environments. Different environments can result in different outlooks, ambitions, and life choices. In addition, cloning does not duplicate the brain. As a child's brain develops, neural connections are made in response to environmental stimuli. Different stimuli result in different patterns of connections (Eisenberg, 2000). The child's brain will differ in many ways from the parent's.

Some authors who put forward these consequentialist objections acknowledge that the parent and child will not be identical (Holm, 1998). However, they hold that there will be a widespread *perception* that the parent and child are identical, based on the mistaken belief that people with identical nuclear DNA are identical, and that this perception will cause the harm in question. In reply, it is difficult to predict what people's perceptions will be when and if reproductive cloning becomes safe and feasible. That might be some distance into the future. Perhaps by then many people will have come to understand that genes alone do not determine who one is. If there is a concern that some infertile couples who use cloning might expect the child to follow in the footsteps of the parent, this concern could be addressed by means of prepregnancy counselling. Psychological counselling is already widely used in preparing infertile couples for various methods of assisted reproduction. Couples planning to use cloning could be counselled about the psychosocial dimensions of this method of procreation, including a possible tendency to assume, erroneously, that genetics determine who the child will be.

There is an even more serious problem with this objection, a problem that all versions of the objection that have been put forward share in common. Namely, the objection focuses exclusively on harms to the child, without consideration of benefits to the child. It makes this mistake precisely because it overlooks the fact that without the cloning the child in question would not exist. If one holds that bringing a child into existence through cloning can result in harms to her, then one must also hold that bringing a child into existence through cloning can result in benefits to her. It would be arbitrary to make one claim but deny the other. In assessing the objection, we need to consider the benefits as well as the harms and there would be benefits in the infertility cases. After all, cloning gives the child a life. Life generally is a good thing. It is expected that the child will experience pleasures associated with being alive and that she will have many good experiences. Moreover, what counts in a consequentialist argument is the overall balance of harms and benefits, and it is reasonable to expect that the benefits are going to outweigh the harms—that the child is going to have a good life on balance. If the child benefits on balance, then no wrong is done in creating her, at least as far as harms and benefits are concerned.

Perhaps the opponents of cloning will claim that cloning is wrong because *some* harms will occur, although admittedly not a net harm. However, the claim that it is wrong to create children who will experience some harms, although not a net harm, leads to

unacceptable conclusions. We would have to say, for example, that it is wrong for minorities who are subject to discrimination to have children because the children would experience harms caused by discrimination. Surely, this would be an incorrect conclusion. The objection amounts to saying that it is wrong to procreate when some ideal involving freedom from harm cannot be met (Pennings, 1999). But there is no obligation to have children only if their lives will be free from harm, as this counterexample illustrates.

Deontological Objections

Deontological child-centred objections hold that creating a child through cloning amounts to treating her with insufficient respect. This might be expressed in various ways. Some claim that the child has a *right* to a unique genetic make-up (National Bioethics Advisory Commission, 1997, p. 67; Williamson, 1999), or a *right* to ignorance of the effect of one's genome on one's future (Jonas, 1974). Others assert that cloning violates the Kantian categorical imperative by treating the child as a mere means (Kahn, 1997; Shuster, 2003). In reply, several points can be made. First, merely asserting that there is a right to a unique genetic make-up does not make it convincing, much less true, that there is such a right. An argument is needed supporting the claim that there is such a right, but opponents of reproductive cloning have not provided a successful argument for this. In the absence of a justification for the claim that there is such a right, the claim should be rejected. Second, to create a child through cloning can be consistent with respect for persons. It can be an instance of treating another as an end in herself and not as a mere means. We can imagine that the couple has purposes such that, in creating the child, they are not using her as a mere means but are acting, in part at least, in order to give her a life that will be her own. Third, in making a judgement about whether a child is treated with disrespect, it is not enough to look only at the technique of creation. It is also necessary to look at how the child is treated after she is born. Suppose she is brought into a loving family, with parents who nurture her, foster her discovery of her own interests and talents, and help her develop her autonomy as she grows older. In that scenario, the child is treated with respect. To put it differently, the problem with the objections that appeal to the categorical imperative is that they commit the fallacy of assuming that every case would be an instance of the worst case scenario—that every case would involve using the child as a mere means. This assumption seems rather extreme, and it is not reasonable.

Consequences for Society

Let us consider the objections that focus on adverse consequences for society. These too are expressed in various ways. It is argued that cloning and designing our children will transform procreation into a process similar to manufacturing, thereby altering the attitudes of parents toward their children and harming society (National Bioethics Advisory Commission, 1997, pp. 69–70). Another version is the argument that abuses might occur if cloning is used by totalitarian regimes or other unscrupulous persons (Massey *et al.*, 2001). In reply, when these various objections are applied to the specific context of helping infertile couples, they lose whatever persuasiveness they might initially have had (Strong, 1998). The purpose of cloning in these cases is not to choose the characteristics of the child, but to have a genetically related child. There is no genetic manipulation to make the child "better" in some sense. In this context, cloning is not about designing the child. It is about helping the couple experience the personal meaning that procreation can have when it involves having genetically related children. If there were a plausible concern that a widespread practice of cloning would be harmful to society, there would be a middle ground that we could take. Cloning could be restricted to a relatively small number of cases, such as cases involving infertile couples. In that event it would be doubtful that the particular adverse consequences in question would occur.

Teleological Arguments

Finally, there are teleological objections (Häyry, 2003). These too can be expressed in several ways. It is claimed that cloning is contrary to human dignity or contrary to the essence of being human. These objections are based on the view that humans have a natural essence or telos which they are meant to fulfill or strive for in order to be genuinely human. It is claimed that cloning prevents a human from achieving that essence and therefore it is contrary to human dignity.

In reply, several points are worth noting. First, within secular bioethics, teleological theories have become suspect, and for good reason. Teleological world views have been displaced by our scientific understanding of the world (Munson, 1979). Science gives us ways of understanding the workings of living organisms without appeal to a telos. One can see the consequences of this when one looks at secular bioethics. Approaches such as casuistry and principalism are widely discussed, and teleology is rarely mentioned. Second, even if one accepts a teleological world view, there are serious problems in specifying what the essence of a human is and in achieving a consensus on this matter.

Conclusion

None of the objections to human reproductive cloning discussed above appear to provide good reasons for claiming that cloning is wrong in the cases considered. The objections fail and therefore do not [outweigh] the procreative freedom of infertile couples to use cloning in the cases considered. Assuming these are the main objections, it appears that reproductive cloning would be ethically justifiable in at least some cases involving infertile couples.

References and Further Reading

Eisenberg L. 2000 Would cloned humans really be like sheep? In: McGee G (ed) *The Human Cloning Debate*. Berkeley Hills Books. Berkeley, USA, pp. 170–183.

Häyry M. 2003 Philosophical arguments for and against human reproductive cloning. *Bioethics* 17, 447–459.

Holm S. 1998 A life in the shadow: one reason why we should not clone humans. *Cambridge Quarterly of Healthcare Ethics* 7, 160–162.

Jonas H. 1974 *Philosophical Essays: from Ancient Creed to Technological Man*. Prentice Hall, Englewood Cliffs, USA.

Kahn A. 1997 Clone mammals . . . clone man? *Nature* 386, 119.

Kass L. 2000 The wisdom of repugnance: Why we should ban the cloning of humans. In: McGee G (ed) *The Human Cloning Debate*. Berkeley Hills Books, Berkeley, USA, pp. 68–106.

Massey JB, Slayden S, Shapiro DM *et al.* 2001 Unnatural deeds do breed unnatural troubles (Macbeth: Act V. Scene 1). *Fertility and Sterility* 76, 1083–1084.

Munson R. 1979 *Intervention and Reflection: Basic Issues in Medical Ethics*. Wadsworth Publishing Co., Inc., Belmont, California, USA, pp. 36–37.

National Academy of Sciences 2002 *Scientific and Medical Aspects of Human Reproductive Cloning*. National Academy Press, Washington, DC, USA, pp. 39–42, www.nap.edu.

National Bioethics Advisory Commission 1997 *Cloning Human Beings*. Rockville, Maryland, USA. www.georgetown.edu/research/nrcbl/nbac/pubs.html.

Pennings G. 1999 Measuring the welfare of the child: in search of the appropriate evaluation principle. *Human Reproduction* 14, 1146–1150.

President's Council on Bioethics 2002 *Human Cloning and Human Dignity: an ethical inquiry*, Washington, D.C., USA, pp. 110–111. www.bioethics.gov.

Robertson JA, 1998 Liberty, identity, and human cloning. *Texas Law Review* 76, 1371–1456.

Shuster E. 2003 Human cloning: category, dignity, and the rule of bioethics, *Bioethics* 17, 517–525.

Simpson JL., 2003 Toward scientific discussion of human reproductive cloning, *Reproductive BioMedicine Online* 7, 10–11.

Strong C. 1997 *Ethics in Reproductive and Perinatal Medicine: a New Framework.* Yale University Press, New Haven, USA.

Strong C. 1998 Cloning and infertility. *Cambridge Quarterly of Healthcare Ethics* 7, 279–293.

Williamson R. 1999 Human reproductive cloning is unethical because it undermines autonomy: commentary on Savulescu. *Journal of Medical Ethics* 25, 96–97.

Section 4: Surrogate Pregnancy

Surrogate Motherhood as Prenatal Adoption

Bonnie Steinbock

Bonnie Steinbock reviews the Baby M case and maintains that the court decision was inconsistent in considering the best interest of the child. The aim of legislation, she claims, should be to minimize potential harms and prevent cases like that of Baby M from happening again. This can be so only if surrogacy is not intrinsically wrong.

This leads Steinbock to examine three lines of argument and attempt to show that neither paternalism of the sort outlined by Gerald Dworkin (see Chapter 2) nor such considerations as threats of exploitation, loss of dignity, or harm to the child are adequate to show that surrogacy is inherently objectionable. In Steinbock's view, regulating surrogacy—and protecting liberty—is preferable to prohibiting it.

The recent case of "Baby M" has brought surrogate motherhood to the forefront of American attention. Ultimately, whether we permit or prohibit surrogacy depends on what we take to be good reasons for preventing people from acting as they wish. A growing number of people want to be, or hire, surrogates; are there legitimate reasons to prevent them? Apart from its intrinsic interest, the issue of surrogate motherhood provides us with an opportunity to examine different justifications for limiting individual freedom.

In the first section, I examine the Baby M case, and the lessons it offers. In the second section, I examine claims that surrogacy is ethically unacceptable because it is exploitive, inconsistent with human dignity, or harmful to the children born of such arrangements. I conclude that these reasons justify restrictions on surrogate contracts, rather than an outright ban.

I. Baby M

Mary Beth Whitehead, a married mother of two, agreed to be inseminated with the sperm of William Stern,

Bonnie Steinbock, From "Surrogate Motherhood as Prenatal Adoption," *Law Medicine and Health Care.*" Vol. 16, no. 1 (1988): 44–50.

and to give up the child to him for a fee of $10,000. The baby (whom Mrs. Whitehead named Sara, and the Sterns named Melissa) was born on March 27, 1986. Three days later, Mrs. Whitehead took her home from the hospital, and turned her over to the Sterns.

Then Mrs. Whitehead changed her mind. She went to the Sterns' home, distraught, and pleaded to have the baby temporarily. Afraid that she would kill herself, the Sterns agreed. The next week, Mrs. Whitehead informed the Sterns that she had decided to keep the child, and threatened to leave the country if court action was taken.

At that point, the situation deteriorated into a cross between the Keystone Kops and Nazi storm troopers. Accompanied by five policemen, the Sterns went to the Whitehead residence armed with a court order giving them temporary custody of the child. Mrs. Whitehead managed to slip the baby out of a window to her husband, and the following morning the Whiteheads fled with the child to Florida, where Mrs. Whitehead's parents lived. During the next three months, the Whiteheads lived in roughly twenty different hotels, motels, and homes to avoid apprehension. From time to time, Mrs. Whitehead telephoned Mr. Stern to discuss the matter: He taped these conversations on advice of counsel. Mrs. Whitehead threatened to kill herself, to kill the child, and falsely to accuse Mr. Stern of sexually molesting her older daughter.

At the end of July 1986, while Mrs. Whitehead was hospitalized with a kidney infection, Florida police raided her mother's home, knocking her down, and seized the child. Baby M was placed in the custody of Mr. Stern, and the Whiteheads returned to New Jersey, where they attempted to regain custody. After a long and emotional court battle, Judge Harvey R. Sorkow ruled on March 31, 1987, that the surrogacy contract was valid, and that specific performance was justified in the best interests of the child. Immediately after reading his decision, he called the Sterns into his chambers so that Mr. Stern's wife, Dr. Elizabeth Stern, could legally adopt the child.

This outcome was unexpected and unprecedented. Most commentators had thought that a court would be unlikely to order a reluctant surrogate to give up an infant merely on the basis of a contract. Indeed, if Mrs. Whitehead had never surrendered the child to the Sterns, but had simply taken her home and kept her there, the outcome undoubtedly would have been different. It is also likely that Mrs. Whitehead's failure to obey the initial custody order angered Judge Sorkow, and affected his decision.

The decision was appealed to the New Jersey Supreme Court, which issued its decision on February 3, 1988. Writing for a unanimous court, Chief Justice Wilentz reversed the lower court's ruling that the surrogacy contract was valid. The court held that a surrogacy contract which provides money for the surrogate mother, and which includes her irrevocable agreement to surrender her child at birth, is invalid and unenforceable. Since the contract was invalid, Mrs. Whitehead did not relinquish, nor were there any other grounds for terminating, her parental rights. Therefore, the adoption of Baby M by Mrs. Stern was improperly granted, and Mrs. Whitehead remains the child's legal mother.

The Court further held that the issue of custody is determined solely by the child's best interests, and it agreed with the lower court that it was in Melissa's best interests to remain with the Sterns. However, Mrs. Whitehead, as Baby M's legal as well as natural mother, is entitled to have her own interest in visitation considered. The determination of what kind of visitation rights should be granted to her, and under what conditions, was remanded to the trial court.

The distressing details of this case have led many people to reject surrogacy altogether. Do we really want police officers wrenching infants from their mothers' arms, and prolonged custody battles when surrogates find they are unable to surrender their children, as agreed? Advocates of surrogacy say that to reject the practice wholesale, because of one unfortunate instance, is an example of a "hard case" making bad policy. Opponents reply that it is entirely reasonable to focus on the worst potential outcomes when deciding public policy. Everyone can agree on at least one thing: This particular case seems to have been mismanaged from start to finish, and could serve as a manual of how not to arrange a surrogate birth.

First, it is now clear that Mary Beth Whitehead was not a suitable candidate for surrogate motherhood. Her ambivalence about giving up the child was recognized early on, although this information was not passed on to the Sterns.[1] Second, she had contact with the baby after birth, which is usually avoided in "successful" cases. Typically, the adoptive mother is actively involved in the pregnancy, often serving as the pregnant woman's coach in labor. At birth, the baby is given to the adoptive, not the biological, mother. The joy of the adoptive parents in holding their child serves both to promote their bonding, and to lessen the pain of separation of the biological mother.

At Mrs. Whitehead's request, no one at the hospital was aware of the surrogacy arrangement. She and her husband appeared as the proud parents of "Sara Elizabeth Whitehead," the name on her birth certificate. Mrs. Whitehead held her baby, nursed her, and took her home from the hospital—just as she would have done in a normal pregnancy and birth. Not surprisingly, she thought of Sara as her child, and she fought with every weapon at her disposal, honorable and dishonorable, to prevent her being taken away. She can hardly be blamed for doing so.[2]

Why did Dr. Stern, who supposedly had a very good relation with Mrs. Whitehead before the birth, not act as her labor coach? One possibility is that Mrs. Whitehead, ambivalent about giving up her baby, did not want Dr. Stern involved. At her request, the Sterns' visits to the hospital to see the newborn baby were unobtrusive. It is also possible that Dr. Stern was ambivalent about having a child. The original idea of hiring a surrogate was not hers, but her husband's. It was Mr. Stern who felt a "compelling" need to have a child related to him by blood, having lost all his relatives to the Nazis.

Furthermore, Dr. Stern was not infertile, as was stated in the surrogacy agreement. Rather, in 1979 she was diagnosed by two eye specialists as suffering from optic neuritis, which meant that she "probably" had multiple sclerosis. (This was confirmed by all four experts who testified.) Normal conception was ruled out by the Sterns in late 1982, when a medical colleague told Dr. Stern that his wife, a victim of multiple sclerosis, had suffered a temporary paralysis during pregnancy. "We decided the risk wasn't worth it," Mr. Stern said.[3]

Mrs. Whitehead's lawyer, Harold J. Cassidy, dismissed the suggestion that Dr. Stern's "mildest case" of multiple sclerosis determined their decision to seek a surrogate. He noted that she was not even treated for multiple sclerosis until after the Baby M dispute had started. "It's almost as though it's an afterthought," he said.[4]

Judge Sorkow deemed the decision to avoid conception "medically reasonable and understandable." The Supreme Court did not go so far, noting that "her anxiety appears to have exceeded the actual risk, which current medical authorities assess as minimal."[5] Nonetheless the court acknowledged that her anxiety, including fears that pregnancy might precipitate blindness and paraplegia, was "quite real." Certainly, even a woman who wants a child very much, may reasonably wish to avoid becoming blind and paralyzed as a result of pregnancy. Yet is it believable that a woman who really wanted a child would decide against pregnancy *solely* on the basis of *someone else's* medical experience? Would she not consult at least one specialist on her *own* medical condition before deciding it wasn't worth the risk? The conclusion that she was at best ambivalent about bearing a child seems irresistible.

This possibility conjures up many people's worst fears about surrogacy: That prosperous women, who do not want to interrupt their careers, will use poor and educationally disadvantaged women to bear their children. I will return shortly to the question of whether this is exploitive. The issue here is psychological: What kind of mother is Dr. Stern likely to be? If she is unwilling to undergo pregnancy, with its discomforts, inconveniences, and risks, will she be willing to make the considerable sacrifices which good parenting requires? Mrs. Whitehead's ability to be a good mother was repeatedly questioned during the trial. She was portrayed as immature, untruthful, hysterical, overly identified with her children, and prone to smothering their independence. Even if all this is true—and I think that Mrs. Whitehead's inadequacies were exaggerated—Dr. Stern may not be such a prize either. The choice for Baby M may have been between a highly strung, emotional, over-involved mother, and a remote, detached, even cold one.

The assessment of Mrs. Whitehead's ability to be a good mother was biased by the middle-class prejudices of the judge and mental health officials who testified.

Mrs. Whitehead left school at 15, and is not conversant with the latest theories on child rearing: She made the egregious error of giving Sara teddy bears to play with, instead of the more "age-appropriate," expert-approved pans and spoons. She proved to be a total failure at patty-cake. If this is evidence of parental inadequacy, we're all in danger of losing our children.

The Supreme Court felt that Mrs. Whitehead was "rather harshly judged" and acknowledged the possibility that the trial court was wrong in its initial award of custody. Nevertheless, it affirmed Judge Sorkow's decision to allow the Sterns to retain custody, as being in Melissa's best interests. George Annas disagrees with the "best interests" approach. He points out that Judge Sorkow awarded temporary custody of Baby M to the Sterns in May 1986 without giving the Whiteheads notice or an opportunity to obtain legal representation. That was a serious wrong and injustice to the Whiteheads. To allow the Sterns to keep the child compounds the original unfairness: ". . . justice requires that reasonable consideration be given to returning Baby M to the permanent custody of the Whiteheads."[6]

But a child is not a possession, to be returned to the rightful owner. It is not fairness to all parties that should determine a child's fate, but what is best for her. As Chief Justice Wilentz rightly stated, "The child's interest comes first: We will not punish it for judicial errors, assuming any were made."[7]

Subsequent events have substantiated the claim that giving custody to the Sterns was in Melissa's best interests. After losing custody, Mrs. Whitehead, whose husband had undergone a vasectomy, became pregnant by another man. She divorced her husband and married Dean R. Gould last November. These developments indicate that the Whiteheads were not able to offer a stable home, although the argument can be made that their marriage might have survived, but for the strains introduced by the court battle, and the loss of Baby M. But even if Judge Sorkow had no reason to prefer the Sterns to the Whiteheads back in May 1986, he was still right to give the Sterns custody in March 1987. To take her away then, at nearly eighteen months of age, from the only parents she had ever known, would have been disruptive, cruel, and unfair to her.

Annas's preference for a just solution is premised partly on his belief that there is no "best interest" solution to this "tragic custody case." I take it that he means that however custody is resolved, Baby M is the loser. Either way, she will be deprived of one parent. However, a best interests solution is not a perfect solution.

It is simply the solution which is on balance best for the child, given the realities of the situation. Applying this standard, Judge Sorkow was right to give the Sterns custody, and the Supreme Court was right to uphold the decision.

The best interests argument is based on the assumption that Mr. Stern has at least a *prima facie* claim to Baby M. We certainly would not consider allowing a stranger who kidnapped a baby, and managed to elude the police for a year, to retain custody on the grounds that he was providing a good home to a child who had known no other parent. However, the Baby M case is not analogous. First, Mr. Stern is Baby M's biological father and, as such, has at least some claim to raise her, which no non-parental kidnapper has. Second, Mary Beth Whitehead agreed to give him their baby. Unlike the miller's daughter in *Rumpelstiltskin*, the fairy tale to which the Baby M case is sometimes compared, she was not forced into the agreement. Because both Mary Beth Whitehead and Mr. Stern have *prima facie* claims to Baby M, the decision as to who should raise her should be based on her present best interests. Therefore we must, regretfully, tolerate the injustice to Mrs. Whitehead, and try to avoid such problems in the future.

It is unfortunate that the Court did not decide the issue of visitation on the same basis as custody. By declaring Mrs. Whitehead Gould the legal mother, and maintaining that she is entitled to visitation, the Court has prolonged the fight over Baby M. It is hard to see how this can be in her best interests. This is no ordinary divorce case, where the child has a relation with both parents which it is desirable to maintain. As Mr. Stern said at the start of the court hearing to determine visitation, "Melissa has a right to grow and be happy and not be torn between two parents."[8]

The court's decision was well-meaning but internally inconsistent. Out of concern for the best interests of the child, it granted the Sterns custody. At the same time, by holding Mrs. Whitehead Gould to be the legal mother, with visitation rights, it precluded precisely what is most in Melissa's interest, a resolution of the situation. Further, the decision leaves open the distressing possibility that a Baby M situation could happen again. Legislative efforts should be directed toward ensuring that this worse-case scenario never occurs.

II. Should Surrogacy Be Prohibited?

On June 27, 1988, Michigan became the first state to outlaw commercial contracts for women to bear children for others. Yet making a practice illegal does not necessarily make it go away: Witness black market adoption. The legitimate concerns which support a ban on surrogacy might be better served by careful regulation. However, some practices, such as slavery, are ethically unacceptable, regardless of how carefully regulated they are. Let us consider the arguments that surrogacy is intrinsically unacceptable.

A. Paternalistic Arguments

These arguments against surrogacy take the form of protecting a potential surrogate from a choice she may later regret. As an argument for banning surrogacy, as opposed to providing safeguards to ensure that contracts are freely and knowledgeably undertaken, this is a form of paternalism.

At one time, the characterization of a prohibition as paternalistic was a sufficient reason to reject it. The pendulum has swung back, and many people are willing to accept at least some paternalistic restrictions on freedom. Gerald Dworkin points out that even Mill made one exception to his otherwise absolute rejection of paternalism: He thought that no one should be allowed to sell himself into slavery, because to do so would be to destroy his future autonomy.

This provides a narrow principle to justify some paternalistic interventions. To preserve freedom in the long run, we give up the freedom to make certain choices, those which have results which are "far-reaching, potentially dangerous and irreversible."[9] An example would be a ban on the sale of crack. Virtually everyone who uses crack becomes addicted and, once addicted, a slave to its use. We reasonably and willingly give up our freedom to buy the drug, to protect our ability to make free decisions in the future.

Can a Dworkinian argument be made to rule out surrogacy agreements? Admittedly, the decision to give up a child is permanent, and may have disastrous effects on the surrogate mother. However, many decisions may have long-term, disastrous effects (e.g., postponing childbirth for a career, having an abortion, giving a child up for adoption). Clearly we do not want the state to make decisions for us in all these matters. Dworkin's argument is rightly restricted to paternalistic interferences which protect the individual's autonomy or ability to make decisions in the future. Surrogacy does not involve giving up one's autonomy, which distinguishes it from both the crack and selling-oneself-into-slavery examples. Respect for individual freedom requires us to permit people to make choices which they may later regret.

B. Moral Objections

Four main moral objections to surrogacy were outlined in the Warnock Report.[10]

1. It is inconsistent with human dignity that a woman should use her uterus for financial profit.

2. To deliberately become pregnant with the intention of giving up the child distorts the relationship between mother and child.

3. Surrogacy is degrading because it amounts to child-selling.

4. Since there are some risks attached to pregnancy, no woman ought to be asked to undertake pregnancy for another in order to earn money.

We must all agree that a practice which exploits people or violates human dignity is immoral. However, it is not clear that surrogacy is guilty on either count.

1. EXPLOITATION. The mere fact that pregnancy is *risky* does not make surrogate agreements exploitive, and therefore morally wrong. People often do risky things for money; why should the line be drawn at undergoing pregnancy? The usual response is to compare surrogacy and kidney-selling. The selling of organs is prohibited because of the potential for coercion and exploitation. But why should kidney-selling be viewed as intrinsically coercive? A possible explanation is that no one would do it, unless driven by poverty. The choice is both forced and dangerous, and hence coercive.

The situation is quite different in the case of the race car driver or stuntman. We do not think that they are *forced* to perform risky activities for money: They freely choose to do so. Unlike selling one's kidneys, these are activities which we can understand (intellectually, anyway) someone choosing to do. Movie stuntmen, for example, often enjoy their work, and derive satisfaction from doing it well. Of course they "do it for the money," in the sense that they would not do it without compensation; few people are willing to work "for free." The element of coercion is missing, however, because they enjoy the job, despite the risks, and could do something else if they chose.

The same is apparently true of most surrogates. "They choose the surrogate role primarily because the fee provides a better economic opportunity than alternative occupations, but also because they enjoy being pregnant and the respect and attention that it draws."[11] Some may derive a feeling of self-worth from an act they regard as highly altruistic: providing a couple with a child they could not otherwise have. If these motives are present, it is far from clear that the surrogate is being exploited. Indeed, it seems objectionably paternalistic to insist that she is.

2. HUMAN DIGNITY. It may be argued that even if womb-leasing is not necessarily exploitive, it should still be rejected as inconsistent with human dignity. But why? As John Harris points out, hair, blood and other tissue is often donated or sold; what is so special about the uterus?[12]

Human dignity is more plausibly invoked in the strongest argument against surrogacy, namely, that it is the sale of a child. Children are not property, nor can they be bought or sold. It could be argued that surrogacy is wrong because it is analogous to slavery, and so is inconsistent with human dignity.

However, there are important differences between slavery and a surrogate agreement. The child born of a surrogate is not treated cruelly or deprived of freedom or resold; none of the things which make slavery so awful are part of surrogacy. Still, it may be thought that simply putting a market value on a child is wrong. Human life has intrinsic value; it is literally priceless. Arrangements which ignore this violate our deepest notions of the value of human life. It is profoundly disturbing to hear the boyfriend of a surrogate say, quite candidly in a television documentary on surrogacy, "We're in it for the money."

Judge Sorkow accepted the premise that producing a child for money denigrates human dignity, but he denied that this happens in a surrogate agreement. Mrs. Whitehead was not paid for the surrender of the child to the father: She was paid for her willingness to be impregnated and carry Mr. Stern's child to term. The child, once born, is his biological child. "He cannot purchase what is already his."

This is misleading, and not merely because Baby M is as much Mrs. Whitehead's child as Mr. Stern's. It is misleading because it glosses over the fact that the surrender of the child was part—indeed, the whole point—of the agreement. If the surrogate were paid merely for being willing to be impregnated and carrying the child to term, then she would fulfill the contract upon giving birth. She could take the money *and* the child. Mr. Stern did not agree to pay Mrs. Whitehead merely to *have* his child, but to provide him with a child. The New Jersey Supreme Court held that this violated New Jersey's laws prohibiting the payment or acceptance of money in connection with adoption.

One way to remove the taint of baby-selling would be to limit payment to medical expenses associated with the birth or incurred by the surrogate during pregnancy (as is allowed in many jurisdictions, including New Jersey, in ordinary adoptions). Surrogacy could be seen, not as baby-selling, but as a form of adoption. Nowhere did the Supreme Court find any legal prohibition against surrogacy when there is no payment, and when the surrogate has the right to change her mind and keep the child. However, this solution effectively prohibits surrogacy, since few women would become surrogates solely for self-fulfillment or reasons of altruism.

The question, then, is whether we can reconcile paying the surrogate, beyond her medical expenses, with the idea of surrogacy as prenatal adoption. We can do this by separating the terms of the agreement, which include surrendering the infant at birth to the biological father, from the justification for payment. The payment should be seen as compensation for the risks, sacrifice, and discomfort the surrogate undergoes during pregnancy. This means that if, through no fault on the part of the surrogate, the baby is stillborn, she should still be paid in full, since she has kept her part of the bargain. (By contrast, in the Stern–Whitehead agreement, Mrs. Whitehead was to receive only $1,000 for a stillbirth.) If, on the other hand, the surrogate changes her mind and decides to keep the child, she would break the agreement, and would not be entitled to any fee, or compensation for expenses incurred during pregnancy.

C. The Right of Privacy

Most commentators who invoke the right of privacy do so in support of surrogacy. However, George Annas makes the novel argument that the right to rear a child you have borne is also a privacy right, which cannot be prospectively waived. He says:

> [Judge Sorkow] grudgingly concedes that [Mrs. Whitehead] could not prospectively give up her right to have an abortion during pregnancy.... This would be an intolerable restriction on her liberty and under *Roe* v. *Wade*, the state has no constitutional authority to enforce a contract that prohibits her from terminating her pregnancy.
>
> But why isn't the same logic applicable to the right to rear a child you have given birth to? Her constitutional rights to rear the child she has given birth to are even stronger since they involve even more intimately, and over a lifetime, her privacy rights to reproduce and rear a child in a family setting.[13]

Absent a compelling state interest (such as protecting a child from unfit parents), it certainly would be an intolerable invasion of privacy for the state to take

children from their parents. But Baby M has two parents, both of whom now want her. It is not clear why only people who can give birth (i.e., women) should enjoy the right to rear their children.

Moreover, we do allow women to give their children up for adoption after birth. The state enforces those agreements, even if the natural mother, after the prescribed waiting period, changes her mind. Why should the right to rear a child be unwaivable before, but not after birth? Why should the state have the constitutional authority to uphold postnatal, but not prenatal, adoption agreements? It is not clear why birth should affect the waivability of this right, or have the constitutional significance which Annas attributes to it.

Nevertheless, there are sound moral and policy, if not constitutional, reasons to provide a postnatal waiting period in surrogate agreements. As the Baby M case makes painfully clear, the surrogate may underestimate the bond created by gestation, and the emotional trauma caused by relinquishing the baby. Compassion requires that we acknowledge these feelings, and not deprive a woman of the baby she has carried because, before conception, she underestimated the strength of her feelings for it. Providing a waiting period, as in ordinary postnatal adoptions, will help protect women from making irrevocable mistakes, without banning the practice.

Some may object that this gives too little protection to the prospective adoptive parents. They cannot be sure that the baby is theirs until the waiting period is over. While this is hard on them, a similar burden is placed on other adoptive parents. If the absence of a guarantee serves to discourage people from entering surrogacy agreements, that is not necessarily a bad thing, given all the risks inherent in such contracts. In addition, this requirement would make stricter screening and counseling of surrogates essential, a desirable side effect.

D. Harm to Others

Paternalistic and moral objections to surrogacy do not seem to justify an outright ban. What about the effect on the offspring of such contracts? We do not yet have solid data on the effects of being a "surrogate child." Any claim that surrogacy creates psychological problems in the children is purely speculative. But what if we did discover that such children have deep feelings of worthlessness from learning that their natural mothers deliberately created them with the intention of giving them away? Might we ban surrogacy as posing an unacceptable risk of psychological harm to the resulting children?

Feelings of worthlessness are harmful. They can prevent people from living happy, fulfilling lives. However, a surrogate child, even one whose life is miserable because of these feelings, cannot claim to have been harmed by the surrogate agreement. Without the agreement, the child would never have existed. Unless she is willing to say that her life is not worth living because of these feelings, that she would be better off never having been born, she cannot claim to have been harmed by being born of a surrogate mother.

Children can be *wronged* by being brought into existence, even if they are not, strictly speaking, *harmed*. They are wronged if they are deprived of the minimally decent existence to which all citizens are entitled. We owe it to our children to see that they are not born with such serious impairments that their most basic interests will be doomed in advance. If being born to a surrogate is a handicap of this magnitude, comparable to being born blind or deaf or severely mentally retarded, then surrogacy can be seen as wronging the offspring. This would be a strong reason against permitting such contracts. However, it does not seem likely. Probably the problems arising from surrogacy will be like those faced by adopted children and children whose parents divorce. Such problems are not trivial, but neither are they so serious that the child's very existence can be seen as wrongful.

If surrogate children are neither harmed nor wronged by surrogacy, it may seem that the argument for banning surrogacy on grounds of its harmfulness to the offspring evaporates. After all, if the children themselves have no cause for complaint, how can anyone else claim to reject it on their behalf? Yet it seems extremely counter-intuitive to suggest that the risk of emotional damage to the children born of such arrangements is not even relevant to our deliberations. It seems quite reasonable and proper—even morally obligatory—for policymakers to think about the possible detrimental effects of new reproductive technologies, and to reject those likely to create physically or emotionally damaged people. The explanation for this must involve the idea that it is wrong to bring people into the world in a harmful condition, even if they are not, strictly speaking, harmed by having been brought into existence. Should evidence emerge that surrogacy produces children with serious psychological problems, that would be a strong reason for banning the practice.

There is some evidence on the effect of surrogacy on the other children of the surrogate mother. One woman reported that her daughter, now 17, who was 11 at the time of the surrogate birth,"... is still having

problems with what I did, and as a result she is still angry with me." She explains, "Nobody told me that a child could bond with a baby while you're still pregnant. I didn't realize then that all the times she listened to his heartbeat and felt his legs kick that she was becoming attached to him."[14]

A less sentimental explanation is possible. It seems likely that her daughter, seeing one child given away, was fearful that the same might be done to her. We can expect anxiety and resentment on the part of children whose mothers give away a brother or sister. The psychological harm to these children is clearly relevant to a determination of whether surrogacy is contrary to public policy. At the same time, it should be remembered that many things, including divorce, remarriage, and even moving to a new neighborhood, create anxiety and resentment in children. We should not use the effect on children as an excuse for banning a practice we find bizarre or offensive.

Conclusion

There are many reasons to be extremely cautious of surrogacy. I cannot imagine becoming a surrogate, nor would I advise anyone else to enter into a contract so fraught with peril. But the fact that a practice is risky, foolish, or even morally distasteful is not sufficient reason to outlaw it. It would be better for the state to regulate the practice, and minimize the potential for harm, without infringing on the liberty of citizens.

Notes

1. Had the Sterns been informed of the psychologist's concerns as to Mrs. Whitehead's suitability to be a surrogate, they might have ended the arrangement, costing the Infertility Center its fee. As Chief Justice Wilentz said, "It is apparent that the profit motive got the better of the Infertility Center." In the matter of Baby M, Supreme Court of New Jersey, A–39, at 45.

2. "[W]e think it is expecting something well beyond normal human capabilities to suggest that this mother should have parted with her newly born infant without a struggle. . . . We . . . cannot conceive of any other case where a perfectly fit mother was expected to surrender her newly born infant, perhaps forever, and was then told she was a bad mother because she did not." *Id.* at 79.

3. Father recalls surrogate was "perfect." *New York Times*, January 6, 1987, B2.

4. *Id.*

5. In the matter of Baby M, *supra* note 1, at 8.

6. Annas, G.J.: Baby M: babies (and justice) for sale. *Hastings Center Report* 17 (3): 15, 1987.

7. In the matter of Baby M, *supra* note 1, at 75.

8. Anger and Anguish at Baby M Visitation Hearing, *New York Times*, March 29, 1988, 17.

9. Dworkin, G.: Paternalism. In Wasserstrom, R. A., ed.: *Morality and the Law.* Belmont, Calif., Wadsworth, 1971;

reprinted in Feinberg, J., Gross, H., eds., *Philosophy of Law*, 3rd ed. Wadsworth, 1986, p. 265.

10. Warnock, M., chair: *Report of the committee of inquiry into human fertilisation and embryology*. London: Her Majesty's Stationery Office, 1984.

11. Robertson, J. A.: Surrogate mothers: not so novel after all. *Hastings Center Report* 13 (5): 29, 1983. Citing Parker, P.:

Surrogate mother's motivations: initial findings. *American Journal of Psychiatry* (140): 1, 1983.

12. Harris, J.: *The Value of Life*. London: Routledge & Kegan Paul, 1985, 144.

13. Annas, *supra* note 6.

14. Baby M case stirs feelings of surrogate mothers. *New York Times*, March 2, 1987, B1.

Is Women's Labor a Commodity?

Elizabeth S. Anderson

Elizabeth Anderson argues that commercial surrogacy should not be allowed. The practice of paying women to be surrogate mothers involves a "commodification" of both children and women. It treats women and their children as things to be used, instead of as persons deserving respect. Hence, surrogacy contracts should be unenforceable, and those who arrange them should be subject to criminal penalties.

Anderson holds that the introduction of market values and norms into a situation previously based on respect, consideration, and unconditional love has the effect of harming children and degrading and exploiting women. The values of the market contribute to a tendency to view children as property. When this happens, they are no longer valued unconditionally (as is the case with parental love), but are valued only because they possess characteristics with a market value.

Market values require that surrogate mothers repress whatever parental love they may feel for their children. Hence, the feelings of women are manipulated, degraded, and denied legitimacy. Further, women are exploited by having the personal feelings that incline them to become surrogates turned into something that can be marketed as part of a commercial enterprise.

In the past few years the practice of commercial surrogate motherhood has gained notoriety as a method for acquiring children. A commercial surrogate mother is anyone who is paid money to bear a child for other people and terminate her parental rights, so that the others may raise the child as exclusively their own. The growth of commercial surrogacy has raised with new urgency a class of concerns regarding the proper scope of the market. Some critics have objected to commercial surrogacy on the ground that it improperly

Elizabeth S. Anderson, From "Is Women's Labor a Commodity," *Philosophy & Public Affairs*. Vol. 19, no. 1 (1990): 71–87, 91–92. Copyright © John Wiley & Sons-Blackwell. Reprinted by permission.

treats children and women's reproductive capacities as commodities.[1] The prospect of reducing children to consumer durables and women to baby factories surely inspires revulsion. But are there good reasons behind the revulsion? And is this an accurate description of what commercial surrogacy implies? This article offers a theory about what things are properly regarded as commodities which supports the claim that commercial surrogacy constitutes an unconscionable commodification of children and of women's reproductive capacities.

What Is a Commodity?

The modern market can be characterized in terms of the legal and social norms by which it governs the production, exchange, and enjoyment of commodities. To say that something is properly regarded as a commodity is to claim that the norms of the market are appropriate for regulating its production, exchange, and enjoyment. To the extent that moral principles or ethical ideals preclude the application of market norms to a good, we may say that the good is not a (proper) commodity.

Why should we object to the application of a market norm to the production or distribution of a good? One reason may be that to produce or distribute the good in accordance with the norm is to *fail to value it in an appropriate way*. Consider, for example, a standard Kantian argument against slavery, or the commodification of persons. Slaves are treated in accordance with the market norm that owners may use commodities to satisfy their own interests without regard for the interests of the commodities themselves.

To treat a person without regard for her interests is to fail to respect her. But slaves are persons who may not be merely used in this fashion, since as rational beings they possess a dignity which commands respect. In Kantian theory, the problem with slavery is that it treats beings worthy of *respect* as if they were worthy merely of *use*. "Respect" and "use" in this context denote what we may call different *modes of valuation*. . . .

These considerations support a general account of the sorts of things which are appropriately regarded as commodities. Commodities are those things which are properly treated in accordance with the norms of the modern market. We can question the application of market norms to the production, distribution, and enjoyment of a good by appealing to ethical ideals which support arguments that the good should be valued in some other way than use. Arguments of the latter sort claim that to allow certain market norms to govern our treatment of a thing expresses a mode of valuation not worthy of it. If the thing is to be valued appropriately, its production, exchange, and enjoyment must be removed from market norms and embedded in a different set of social relationships.

The Case of Commercial Surrogacy

Let us now consider the practice of commercial surrogate motherhood in the light of this theory of commodities. Surrogate motherhood as a commercial enterprise is based upon contracts involving three parties: the intended father, the broker, and the surrogate mother. The intended father agrees to pay a lawyer to find a suitable surrogate mother and make the requisite medical and legal arrangements for the conception and birth of the child, and for the transfer of legal custody to himself.[2] The surrogate mother agrees to become impregnated with the intended father's sperm, to carry the resulting child to term, and to relinquish her parental rights to it, transferring custody to the father in return for a fee and medical expenses. Both she and her husband (if she has one) agree not to form a parent–child bond with her child and to do everything necessary to effect the transfer of the child to the intended father. At current market prices, the lawyer arranging the contract can expect to gross $15,000 from the contract, while the surrogate mother can expect a $10,000 fee.[3]

The practice of commercial surrogacy has been defended on four main grounds. First, given the shortage of children available for adoption and the difficulty of qualifying as adoptive parents, it may represent the only hope for some people to be able to raise a family. Commercial surrogacy should be accepted as an effective means for realizing this highly significant good. Second, two fundamental human rights support commercial surrogacy; the right to procreate and freedom of contract. Fully informed autonomous adults should have the right to make whatever arrangements they wish for the use of their bodies and the reproduction of children, so long as the children themselves are not harmed. Third, the labor of the surrogate mother is said to be a labor of love. Her altruistic acts should be permitted and encouraged.[4] Finally, it is argued that commercial surrogacy is no different in its ethical implications from many already accepted practices which separate genetic, gestational, and social parenting, such as artificial insemination by donor, adoption, wet-nursing and day care. Consistency demands that society accept this new practice as well.[5]

In opposition to these claims, I shall argue that commercial surrogacy does raise new ethical issues, since it represents an invasion of the market into a new sphere of conduct, that of specifically women's labor—that is, the labor of carrying children to term in pregnancy. When women's labor is treated as a commodity, the women who perform it are degraded. Furthermore, commercial surrogacy degrades children by reducing their status to that of commodities. Let us consider each of the goods of concern in surrogate motherhood—the child, and women's reproductive labor—to see how the commercialization of parenthood affects people's regard for them.

Children as Commodities

The most fundamental calling of parents to their children is to love them. Children are to be loved and cherished by their parents, not to be used or manipulated by them for merely personal advantage. Parental love can be understood as a passionate, unconditional commitment to nurture one's child, providing it with the care, affection, and guidance it needs to develop its capacities to maturity. This understanding of the way parents should value their children informs our interpretation of parental rights over their children. Parents' rights over their children are trusts, which they must always exercise for the sake of the child. This is not to deny that parents have their own aspirations in raising children. But the child's interests beyond subsistence are not definable independently of the flourishing of the family, which is the object of specifically parental aspirations. The proper exercise of parental rights includes those acts which promote their shared life as a family, which realize the shared interests of the parents and the child.

The norms of parental love carry implications for the ways other people should treat the relationship between parents and their children. If children are to be loved by their parents, then others should not attempt to compromise the integrity of parental love or work to suppress the emotions supporting the bond between parents and their children. If the rights to children should be understood as trusts, then if those rights are lost or relinquished, the duty of those in charge of transferring custody to others is to consult the best interests of the child.

Commercial surrogacy substitutes market norms for some of the norms of parental love. Most importantly, it requires us to understand parental rights no longer as trusts but as things more like property rights—that is, rights of use and disposal over the things owned. For in this practice the natural mother deliberately conceives a child with the intention of giving it up for material advantage. Her renunciation of parental responsibilities is not done for the child's sake, nor for the sake of fulfilling an interest she shares with the child, but typically for her own sake (and possibly, if "altruism" is a motive, for the intended parents' sakes). She and the couple who pay her to give up her parental rights over her child thus treat her rights as a kind of property right. They thereby treat the child itself as a kind of commodity, which may be properly bought and sold.

Commercial surrogacy insinuates the norms of commerce into the parental relationship in other ways. Whereas parental love is not supposed to be conditioned upon the child having particular characteristics, consumer demand is properly responsive to the characteristics of commodities. So the surrogate industry provides opportunities to adoptive couples to specify the height, I.Q., race, and other attributes of the surrogate mother, in the expectation that these traits will be passed on to the child.[6] Since no industry assigns agents to look after the "interests" of its commodities, no one represents the child's interests in the surrogate industry. The surrogate agency promotes the adoptive parents' interests and not the child's interests where matters of custody are concerned. Finally, as the agent of the adoptive parents, the broker has the task of policing the surrogate (natural) mother's relationship to her child, using persuasion, money, and the threat of a lawsuit to weaken and destroy whatever parental love she may develop for her child.[7]

All of these substitutions of market norms for parental norms represent ways of treating children as commodities which are degrading to them. Degradation occurs when something is treated in accordance with a lower mode of valuation than is proper to it. We value things not just "more" or "less," but in qualitatively higher and lower ways. To love or respect someone is to value her in a higher way than one would if one merely used her. Children are properly loved by their parents and respected by others. Since children are valued as mere use-objects by the mother and the surrogate agency when they are sold to others, and by the adoptive parents when they seek to conform the child's genetic makeup to their own wishes, commercial surrogacy degrades children insofar as it treats them as commodities.[8]

One might argue that since the child is most likely to enter a loving home, no harm comes to it from permitting the natural mother to treat it as property. So the purchase and sale of infants is unobjectionable, at least from the point of view of children's interests.[9] But the sale of an infant has an expressive significance which this argument fails to recognize. By engaging in the transfer of children by sale, all of the parties to the surrogate contract express a set of attitudes toward children which undermine the norms of parental love. They all agree in treating the ties between a natural mother and her children as properly loosened by a monetary incentive. Would it be any wonder if a child born of a surrogacy agreement feared resale by parents who have such an attitude? And a child who knew how anxious her parents were that she have the "right" genetic makeup might fear that her parents' love was contingent upon her expression of these characteristics.[10]

The unsold children of surrogate mothers are also harmed by commercial surrogacy. The children of some surrogate mothers have reported their fears that they may be sold like their half-brother or half-sister, and express a sense of loss at being deprived of a sibling.[11] Furthermore, the widespread acceptance of commercial surrogacy would psychologically threaten all children. For it would change the way children are valued by people (parents and surrogate brokers)—from being loved by their parents and respected by others, to being sometimes used as objects of commercial profit-making.[12]

Proponents of commercial surrogacy have denied that the surrogate industry engages in the sale of children. For it is impossible to sell to someone what is already his own, and the child is already the father's own natural offspring. The payment to the surrogate mother is not for her child, but for her services in carrying it to term.[13] The claim that the parties to the surrogate contract treat children as commodities, however, is based on the way they treat the *mother's* rights over her child. It is irrelevant that the natural father also has some rights over the child; what he pays for is exclusive rights to it. He would not pay her for the "service" of carrying the child to term if she refused to relinquish her parental rights to it. That the mother regards only her labor and not her child as requiring compensation is also irrelevant. No one would argue that the baker does not treat his bread as property just because he sees the income from its sale as compensation for his labor and expenses and not for the bread itself, which he doesn't care to keep.[14]

Defenders of commercial surrogacy have also claimed that it does not differ substantially from already accepted parental practices. In the institutions of adoption and artificial insemination by donor (AID), it is claimed, we already grant parents the right to dispose of their children.[15] But these practices differ in significant respects from commercial surrogacy. The purpose of adoption is to provide a means for placing children in families when their parents cannot or will not discharge their parental responsibilities. It is not a sphere for the existence of a supposed parental right to dispose of one's children for profit. Even AID does not sanction the sale of fully formed human beings. The semen donor sells only a product of his body, not his child, and does not initiate the act of conception.

Two developments might seem to undermine the claim that commercial surrogacy constitutes a degrading commerce in children. The first is technological: the prospect of transplanting a human embryo into the womb of a genetically unrelated woman. If commercial surrogacy used women only as gestational mothers and not as genetic mothers, and if it was thought that only genetic and not gestational parents could properly claim that a child was "theirs," then the child born of a surrogate mother would not be hers to sell in the first place. The second is a legal development: the establishment of the proposed "consent–intent" definition of parenthood.[16] This would declare the legal parents of a child to be whoever consented to a procedure which leads to its birth, with the intent of assuming parental responsibilities for it. This rule would define away the problem of commerce in children by depriving the surrogate mother of any legal claim to her child at all, even if it was hers both genetically and gestationally.[17]

There are good reasons, however, not to undermine the place of genetic and gestational ties in these ways.

Consider first the place of genetic ties. By upholding a system of involuntary (genetic) ties of obligation among people, even when the adults among them prefer to divide their rights and obligations in other ways, we help to secure children's interests in having an assured place in the world, which is more firm than the wills of their parents. Unlike the consent–intent rule, the principle of respecting genetic ties does not make the obligation to care for those whom one has created (intentionally or not) contingent upon an arbitrary desire to do so. It thus provides children with a set of preexisting social sanctions which give them a more secure place in the world. The genetic principle also places the children in a far wider network of associations and obligations than the consent–intent rule sanctions. It supports the roles of grandparents and other relatives in the nurturing of children, and provides children with a possible focus of stability and an additional source of claims to care if their parents cannot sustain a well-functioning household.

In the next section I will defend the claims of gestational ties to children. To deny these claims, as commercial surrogacy does, is to deny the significance of reproductive labor to the mother who undergoes it and thereby to dehumanize and degrade the mother herself. Commercial surrogacy would be a corrupt practice even if it did not involve commerce in children.

Women's Labor as a Commodity

Commercial surrogacy attempts to transform what is specifically women's labor—the work of bringing forth children into the world—into a commodity. It does so by replacing the parental norms which usually govern the practice of gestating children with the economic norms which govern ordinary production processes. The application of commercial norms to women's labor reduces the surrogate mothers from persons worthy of respect and consideration to objects of mere use.

Respect and consideration are two distinct modes of valuation whose norms are violated by the practices of the surrogate industry. To respect a person is to treat her in accordance with principles she rationally accepts—principles consistent with the protection of her autonomy and her rational interests. To treat a person with consideration is to respond with sensitivity to her and to her emotional relations with others, refraining from manipulating or denigrating these for one's own purposes. . . .

The application of economic norms to the sphere of women's labor violates women's claims to respect and consideration in three ways. First, by requiring the surrogate mother to repress whatever parental love she feels for the child, these norms convert women's labor into a form of alienated labor. Second, by manipulating and denying legitimacy to the surrogate mother's evolving perspective on her own pregnancy, the norms of the market degrade her. Third, by taking advantage of the surrogate mother's noncommercial motivations without offering anything but what the norms of commerce demand in return, these norms leave her open to exploitation. The fact that these problems arise in the attempt to commercialize the labor of bearing children shows that women's labor is not properly regarded as a commodity.

The key to understanding these problems is the normal role of the emotions in noncommercialized pregnancies. Pregnancy is not simply a biological process but also a social practice. Many social expectations and considerations surround women's gestational labor, marking it off as an occasion for the parents to prepare themselves to welcome a new life into their family. For example, obstetricians use ultrasound not simply for diagnostic purposes but also to encourage maternal bonding with the fetus.[18] We can all recognize that it is good, although by no means inevitable, for loving bonds to be established between the mother and her child during this period.

In contrast with these practices, the surrogate industry follows the putting-out system of manufacturing. It provides some of the raw materials of production (the father's sperm) to the surrogate mother, who then engages in production of the child. Although her labor is subject to periodic supervision by her doctors and by the surrogate agency, the agency does not have physical control over the product of her labor as firms using the factory system do. Hence, as in all putting-out systems, the surrogate industry faces the problem of extracting the final product from the mother. This problem is exacerbated by the fact that the social norms surrounding pregnancy are designed to encourage parental love for the child. The surrogate industry addresses this problem by requiring the mother to engage in a form of emotional labor.[19] In the surrogate contract, she agrees not to form or to attempt to form a parent–child relationship with her offspring.[20] Her labor is alienated, because she must divert it from the end which the social practices of pregnancy rightly promote—an emotional bond with her child. The surrogate contract thus replaces a norm of parenthood, that during pregnancy one create a loving attachment to one's child, with a norm of commercial production, that the producer shall not form any special emotional ties to her product. . . .

Commercial surrogacy is also a degrading practice. The surrogate mother, like all persons, has an independent evaluative perspective on her activities and relationships. The realization of her dignity demands that the other parties to the contract acknowledge rather than evade the claims which her independent perspective makes upon them. But the surrogate industry has an interest in suppressing, manipulating, and trivializing her perspective, for there is an ever-present danger that she will see her involvement in her pregnancy from the perspective of a parent rather than from the perspective of a contract laborer.

How does this suppression and trivialization take place? The commercial promoters of surrogacy commonly describe the surrogate mothers as inanimate objects: mere "hatcheries," "plumbing," or "rented property"—things without emotions which could make claims on others.[21] They also refuse to acknowledge any responsibility for the consequences of the mother's emotional labor. Should she suffer psychologically from being forced to give up her child, the father is not liable to pay for therapy after her pregnancy, although he is liable for all other medical expenses following her pregnancy.[22]

The treatment and interpretation of surrogate mothers' grief raises the deepest problems of degradation. Most surrogate mothers experience grief upon giving up their children—in 10 percent of cases, seriously enough to require therapy.[23] Their grief is not compensated by the $10,000 fee they receive. Grief is not an intelligible response to a successful deal, but rather reflects the subject's judgment that she has suffered a grave and personal loss. Since not all cases of grief resolve themselves into cases of regret, it may be that some surrogate mothers do not regard their grief, in retrospect, as reflecting an authentic judgment on their part. But in the circumstances of emotional manipulation which pervade the surrogate industry, it is difficult to determine which interpretation of her grief more truly reflects the perspective of the surrogate mother. By insinuating a trivializing interpretation of her emotional responses to the prospect of losing her child, the surrogate agency may be able to manipulate her into accepting her fate without too much fuss, and may even succeed in substituting its interpretation of her emotions for her own. Since she has already signed a contract to perform emotional labor—to express or repress emotions which are dictated by the interests of the surrogate industry—this might not be a difficult task.[24] A considerate treatment of the mothers' grief, on the other hand, would take the evaluative basis of their grief seriously.

Some defenders of commercial surrogacy demand that the provision for terminating the surrogate mother's parental rights in her child be legally enforceable, so that peace of mind for the adoptive parents can be secured.[25] But the surrogate industry makes no corresponding provision for securing the peace of mind of the surrogate. She is expected to assume the risk of a transformation of her ethical and emotional perspective on herself and her child with the same impersonal detachment with which a futures trader assumes the risk of a fluctuation in the price of pork bellies. By applying the market norms of enforcing contracts to the surrogate mother's case, commercial surrogacy treats a moral transformation as if it were merely an economic change.[26]

The manipulation of the surrogate mother's emotions which is inherent in the surrogate parenting contract also leaves women open to grave forms of exploitation. A kind of exploitation occurs when one party to a transaction is oriented toward the exchange of "gift" values, while the other party operates in accordance with the norms of the market exchange of commodities. Gift values, which include love, gratitude, and appreciation of others, cannot be bought or obtained through piecemeal calculations of individual advantage. Their exchange requires a repudiation of a self-interested attitude, a willingness to give gifts to others without demanding some specific equivalent good in return each time one gives. The surrogate mother often operates according to the norms of gift relationships. The surrogate agency, on the other hand, follows market norms. Its job is to get the best deal for its clients and itself, while leaving the surrogate mother to look after her own interests as best as she can. The situation puts the surrogate agencies in a position to manipulate the surrogate mothers' emotions to gain favorable terms for themselves. For example, agencies screen prospective surrogate mothers for submissiveness, and emphasize to them the importance of the motives of generosity and love. When applicants question some of the terms of the contract, the broker sometimes intimidates them by questioning their character and morality: if they were really generous and loving they would not be so solicitous about their own interests.[27]...

Many surrogate mothers see pregnancy as a way to feel "adequate," "appreciated," or "special." In other words, these women feel inadequate, unappreciated, or unadmired when they are not pregnant.[28] Lacking the power to achieve some worthwhile status in their own right, they must subordinate themselves to others' definitions of their proper place (as baby factories) in order to get from them the appreciation they need to attain a sense of self-worth. But the sense of self-worth one can attain under such circumstances is precarious and ultimately self-defeating. For example, those who seek gratitude on the part of the adoptive parents and some opportunity to share the joys of seeing their children grow discover all too often that the adoptive parents want nothing to do with them.[29] For while the surrogate mother sees in the arrangement some basis for establishing the personal ties she needs to sustain her emotionally, the adoptive couple sees it as an impersonal commercial contract, one of whose main advantages to them is that all ties between them and the surrogate are ended once the terms of the contract are fulfilled.[30] To them, her presence is a threat to marital unity and a competing object for the child's affections.

These considerations should lead us to question the model of altruism which is held up to women by the surrogacy industry. It is a strange form of altruism which demands such radical self-effacement, alienation from those whom one benefits, and the subordination of one's body, health, and emotional life to the independently defined interests of others.[31]

The primary distortions which arise from treating women's labor as a commodity—the surrogate mother's alienation from loved ones, her degradation, and her exploitation—stem from a common source. This is the failure to acknowledge and treat appropriately the surrogate mother's emotional engagement with her labor. Her labor is alienated, because she must suppress her emotional ties with her own child, and may be manipulated into reinterpreting these ties in a trivializing way. She is degraded, because her independent ethical perspective is denied, or demoted to the status of a cash sum. She is exploited, because her emotional needs and vulnerabilities are not treated as characteristics which call for consideration, but as factors which may be manipulated to encourage her to make a grave self-sacrifice to the broker's and adoptive couple's advantage. These considerations provide strong grounds for sustaining the claims of women's labor to its "product," the child. The attempt to redefine parenthood so as to strip women of parental claims to the children they bear does violence to their emotional engagement with the project of bringing children into the world.

Commercial Surrogacy, Freedom, and the Law

In the light of these ethical objections to commercial surrogacy, what position should the law take on the practice? At the very least, surrogate contracts should not be enforceable. Surrogate mothers should not be forced to relinquish their children if they have formed emotional bonds with them. Any other treatment of women's ties to the children they bear is degrading.

But I think these arguments support the stronger conclusion that commercial surrogate contracts should be illegal, and that surrogate agencies—which arrange such contracts should be subject to criminal penalties. Commercial surrogacy constitutes a degrading and harmful traffic in children, violates the dignity of women, and subjects both children and women to a serious risk of exploitation. . . .

If commercial surrogate contracts were prohibited, this would be no cause for infertile couples to lose hope for raising a family. The option of adoption is still available, and every attempt should be made to open up opportunities for adoption to couples who do not meet standard requirements—for example, because of age. While there is a shortage of healthy white infants available for adoption, there is no shortage of children of other races, mixed-race children, and older and handicapped children who desperately need to be adopted. Leaders of the surrogate industry have proclaimed that commercial surrogacy may replace adoption as the method of choice for infertile couples who wish to raise families. But we should be wary of the racist and eugenic motivations which make some people rally to the surrogate industry at the expense of children who already exist and need homes.

The case of commercial surrogacy raises deep questions about the proper scope of the market in modern industrial societies. I have argued that there are principled grounds for rejecting the substitution of market norms for parental norms to govern the ways women bring children into the world. Such substitutions express ways of valuing mothers and children which reflect an inferior conception of human flourishing. When market norms are applied to the ways we allocate and understand parental rights and responsibilities, children are reduced from subjects of love to objects of use. When market norms are applied to the ways we treat and understand women's reproductive labor, women are reduced from subjects of respect and consideration to objects of use. If we

are to retain the capacity to value children and women in ways consistent with a rich conception of human flourishing, we must resist the encroachment of the market upon the sphere of reproductive labor. Women's labor is *not* a commodity.

Notes

The author thanks David Anderson, Steven Darwall, Ezekiel Emanuel, Daniel Hausman, Don Herzog, Robert Nozick, Richard Pildes, John Rawls, Michael Sandel, Thomas Scanlon, and Howard Wial for helpful comments and criticisms.

1. See, for example, Gena Corea, *The Mother Machine* (New York: Harper and Row, 1985), pp. 216, 219; Angela Holder; "Surrogate Motherhood: Babies for Fun and Profit" *Case and Comment* 90 (1985): 3–11; and Margaret Jane Radin, "Market Inalienability," *Harvard Law Review* 100 (June 1987): 1849–1937.

2. State laws against selling babies prevent the intended father's wife (if he has one) from being a party to the contract.

3. See Katie Marie Brophy, "A Surrogate Mother Contract to Bear a Child," *Journal of Family Law* 20 (1981–82): 263–91, and Noel Keane, "The Surrogate Parenting Contract," *Adelphia Law Journal* 2 (1983): 45–53, for examples and explanations of surrogate parenting contracts.

4. Mary Warnock, *A Question of Life* (Oxford: Blackwell, 1985), p. 45. This book reprints the Warnock Report on Human Fertilization and Embryology, which was commissioned by the British government for the purpose of recommending legislation concerning surrogacy and other issues. Although the Warnock Report mentions the promotion of altruism as one defense of surrogacy, it strongly condemns the practice overall.

5. John Robertson, "Surrogate Mothers: Not So Novel After All," *Hastings Center Report*. October 1983, pp. 28–34; John Harris, *The Value of Life* (Boston: Routledge and Kegan Paul, 1985).

6. See "No Other Hope for Having a Child," *Time*, 19 January 1987, pp. 50–51. Radin argues that women's traits are also commodified in this practice. See "Market Inalienability," pp. 1932–35.

7. Here I discuss the surrogate industry as it actually exists today. I will consider possible modifications of commercial surrogacy in the final section below.

8. Robert Nozick has objected that my claims about parental love appear to be culture-bound. Do not parents in the Third World, who rely on children to provide for the family subsistence, regard their children as economic goods? In promoting the livelihood of their families, however, such children need not be treated in accordance with market norms—that is, as commodities. In particular, such children usually remain a part of their families and hence can still be loved by their parents. But insofar as children are treated according to the norms of modern capitalist markets, this treatment is deplorable wherever it takes place.

9. See Elizabeth Landes and Richard Posner, "The Economics of the Baby Shortage," *Journal of Legal Studies* 7 (1978): 323–48, and Richard Posner, "The Regulation of the Market in Adoptions," *Boston University Law Review* 67 (1987): 59–72.

10. Of course, where children are concerned it is irrelevant whether these fears are reasonable. One of the greatest fears of children is separation from their parents. Adopted children are already known to suffer from separation anxiety more acutely than children who remain with their natural mothers, for they feel that the original mother did not love them. In adoption, the fact that the child would be even worse off if the mother did not give it up justifies her severing of ties and can help to rationalize this event to the child. But in the case of commercial surrogacy, the severing of ties is done not for the child's sake, but for the parents' sakes. In the adoption case there are explanations for the mother's action which may quell the child's doubts about being loved which are unavailable in the case of surrogacy.

11. Kay Longcope, "Surrogacy: Two Professionals on Each Side of Issue Give Their Argument for Prohibition and Regulation," *Boston Globe*, 23 March 1987, pp. 18–19; and Iver Peterson, "Baby M Case: Surrogate Mothers Vent Feelings, *New York Times*, 2 March 1987, pp. B1, B4.

12. Herbert Krimmel, "The Case Against Surrogate Parenting," *Hastings Center Report*, October 1983, pp. 35–37.

13. Judge Sorkow made this argument in ruling on the famous case of Baby M. See *In Re Baby M*, 217 N.J. Super 313. Reprinted in *Family Law Reporter* 13 (1987): 2001–30. Chief Justice Wilentz of the New Jersey Supreme Court overruled Sorkow's judgment. See *In the Matter of Baby M*, 109 N.J. 396, 537 A. 2d 1227 (1988).

14. Sallyann Payton has observed that the law does not permit the sale of parental rights, only their relinquishment or forced termination by the state, and these acts are subject to court review for the sake of the child's best interests. But this legal technicality does not change the moral implications of the analogy with baby-selling. The mother is still paid to do what she can to relinquish her parental rights and to transfer custody of the child to the father. Whether or not the courts occasionally prevent this from happening, the actions of the parties express a commercial orientation to children which is degrading and harmful to them. The New Jersey Supreme Court ruled that surrogacy contracts are void precisely because they assign custody without regard to the child's best interests. See *In the Matter of Baby M*, p. 1246.

15. Robertson, "Surrogate Mothers: Not So Novel After All, p. 32; Harris, *The Value of Life*, pp. 144–45.

16. See Philip Parker, "Surrogate Motherhood: The Interaction of Litigation, Legislation and Psychiatry," *International Journal of Law and Psychiatry* 5 (1982): 341–54.

17. The consent–intent rule would not, however, change the fact that commercial surrogacy replaces parental norms with market norms. For the rule itself embodies the market norm which acknowledges only voluntary, contractual relations among people as having moral force. Whereas familial love invites children into a network of unwilled relationships broader than those they have with their parents, the willed contract creates an exclusive relationship between the parents and the child only.

18. I am indebted to Dr. Ezekiel Emanuel for this point.

19. One engages in emotional labor when one is paid to express or repress certain emotions. On the concept of emotional labor and its consequences for workers, see Arlie Hochschild, *The Managed Heart* (Berkeley and Los Angeles: University of California Press, 1983).

20. Noel Keane and Dennis Breo, *The Surrogate Mother* (New York: Everest House, 1981), p. 291; Brophy, "A Surrogate Mother Contract," p. 267. The surrogate's husband is also required to agree to this clause of the contract.

21. Corea, *The Mother Machine*, p. 222.

22. Keane and Breo, *The Surrogate Mother*, p. 292.

23. Kay Longcope, "Standing Up for Mary Beth," *Boston Globe*, 5 March 1987, p. 83; Daniel Goleman, "Motivations of Surrogate Mothers," *New York Times*, 20 January 1987, p. C1; Robertson, "Surrogate Mothers: Not So Novel After All," pp. 30, 34 n. 8. Neither the surrogate mothers themselves nor psychiatrists have been able to predict which women will experience such grief.

24. See Hochschild, *The Managed Heart*, for an important empirical study of the dynamics of commercialized emotional labor.

25. Keane and Breo, *The Surrogate Mother*, pp. 236–37.

26. For one account of how a surrogate mother who came to regret her decision viewed her own moral transformation, see Elizabeth Kane: *Birth Mother: The Story of America's First Legal Surrogate Mother* (San Diego: Harcourt Brace Jovanovich, 1988). I argue below that the implications of commodifying women's labor are not significantly changed even if the contract is unenforceable.

27. Susan Ince, "Inside the Surrogate Industry," in *Test-Tube Women*, ed. Rita Ardith, Ranate Duelli Klein, and Shelley Minden (Boston: Pandora Press, 1984), p. 110.

28. The surrogate broker Noel Keane is remarkably open about reporting the desperate emotional insecurities which shape the lives of so many surrogate mothers, while displaying little sensitivity to the implications of his taking advantage of these motivations to make his business a financial success. See especially Keane and Breo, *The Surrogate Mother*, pp. 247ff.

29. See, for example, the story of the surrogate mother Nancy Barrass in Arlene Fleming, "Our Fascination with Baby M," *New York Times Magazine*, 29 March 1987, p. 38.

30. For evidence of these disparate perspectives, see Peterson, "Baby M Case: Surrogate Mothers Vent Feelings," p. B4.

31. The surrogate mother is required to obey all doctor's orders made in the interests of the child's health. (See Brophy, "A Surrogate Mother Contract"; Keane, "The Surrogate Parenting Contract"; and Ince, "Inside the Surrogate Industry.") These orders could include forcing her to give up her job, travel plans, and recreational activities. The doctor could confine her to bed, and order her to submit to surgery and take drugs. One can hardly exercise an autonomous choice over one's health if one could be held in breach of contract and liable for $35,000 damages for making a decision contrary to the wishes of one's doctor.

DECISION SCENARIOS

The questions following each decision scenario are intended to prompt reflection and discussion. In deciding how to answer them, you should consider the information in the Briefing Session; the ethical theories and principles presented in Part V, "Foundations of Bioethics," and the arguments and criticisms offered in the relevant readings in this chapter.

DECISION SCENARIO 1

Child of a Civil Union

Lisa Miller and Janet Jenkins visited Vermont briefly in 2000 to take advantage of the state law that permitted them to join together in a civil union—the legal counterpart of marriage for same-sex couples. Wanting a family of their own, Lisa Miller moved to Virginia and was artificially inseminated with donor sperm. In September 2002, she gave birth to a little girl. The couple named her Isabella Miller-Jenkins, and the three of them lived together in Vermont for more than a year.

Yet, within the year of Isabella's birth, Miller and Jenkins decided to split up. In November 2003, Lisa Miller filed papers in Vermont to dissolve the union. At the time, she claimed that Isabella was a "child of the union" with Janet and asked that the court allow Janet to have contact with the child. The Vermont judge, William D. Cohen, ruled that the couple "should be treated no differently than a husband and wife" and established a visiting schedule. Lisa, the biological mother, would be in contempt of court if she failed to follow the schedule.

Lisa moved to Virginia, renounced homosexuality, and became an evangelical Christian. She had been living in Virginia when she filed for a dissolution of the union with Janet. A 2004 Virginia law makes same-sex unions from other states "void in all respects in Virginia." Lisa then asked a Virginia court that she be given sole custody of Isabella, saying that she had been confused when she said that Isabella was a child of her union with Janet. She asked for sole custody of Isabella, and it was granted in Virginia.

In November 2009, Judge Cohen of Vermont found Lisa Miller in contempt of court for denying Janet

Jenkins access to Isabella. He then awarded custody of the child to Jenkins. The Supreme Courts of Virginia and Vermont ruled in favor of Jenkins on visitation rights, holding that the case was the same as a custody dispute by a heterosexual couple. The rulings were appealed to the U.S. Supreme Court by Miller, but the court declined to hear the case.

Miller was supposed to surrender Isabella to Jenkins' custody according to Judge Cohen's order, but she failed to do so. As of January 2, 2010, she had defied the court order.

Legal experts see the case as the first in what is likely to be a series of similar cases. Once more, reproductive technologies have presented a practical challenge to established laws and practices. Concepts as fundamental as who counts as a parent and what constitutes a family are now matters of debate.

1. In what way does it make sense to consider Janet a parent of Isabella?

2. If, while in her union with Lisa, Janet, had adopted Isabella, would this give her any more moral standing (as distinct from legal standing) in claiming to be Isabella's parent?

3. Lisa said she no longer wants "to live the homosexual lifestyle" and that is why she split up with Janet. Is this sufficient reason to deny Janet regular access to Isabella?

4. Should the fact that Lisa is Isabella's biological mother give her any special status in disputes about the welfare of the child?

DECISION SCENARIO 2

Donor Responsibility

"I'm going to sell my sperm for the simple reason that I need the money," John Lolton said. "It's no big deal."

"I think it is," Jane Cooper said. "You seem to think its like selling your blood, but it isn't. If somebody is transfused with your blood, that's an end to things. But if a woman is inseminated with your sperm, a child may result."

"I don't have any responsibilities for what people do with my sperm," Lolton replied. "It's just a product."

"Not so," Cooper said. "It's a product all right, but if its used in artificial insemination, that means that you're the father of a child. And if you're the father of a child, that means you have to be willing to accept responsibility for that child."

"That is absolute nonsense," Lolton said.

1. If sperm is just a product, is Lolton correct in saying that he has no responsibilities for its use?

2. State as explicitly as possible Cooper's argument that a sperm donor is responsible for any child resulting from AI with his donated sperm.

3. We expect biological parents to take responsibility for their offspring. Can a departure from this standard be justified when the child is born as a result of donated sperm or a donated egg?

4. Are there instances in which AI would be morally wrong? What is the moral status of a child conceived by AI?

5. Ova as well as sperm may be donated. Although women get paid more, on what grounds might one argue that they are exploited while men are not?

DECISION SCENARIO 3

Looking for the Family Tree

The Donor Sibling Registry makes it possible for people who were conceived from donated sperm by artificial insemination to establish contact with their half-siblings—those whose mothers used the same sperm donor. Some donors are much more popular than others; reporter Amy Harmon found that dozens of women bought Donor 150's sperm from the California Cryobank. (See Social Context "Shopping the Sperm Supermarket.")

So far the Registry's website has connected more than 1000 half-siblings. The site makes it possible for a donor to shed his anonymity and make contact with his biological offspring. This doesn't happen very often, however.

The half-siblings connected through the site say that it helps them develop a sense of family that is missing. By entering the name of a sperm bank and a donor number on the website, the offspring of a donor can sometimes find a match with others. When this happens, some of them say, they feel as if they are now closer to filling in the missing half of their family.

About 30,000 children are born each year with donated sperm, and the sperm of a single donor may be chosen dozens of times. It is possible that the donor has dozens of children, and it isn't likely that they will know that they had the same biological father. Thus, the possibility that some of the offspring will become involved in incest with a half-sibling is genuine.

1. Should a sperm donor be required to agree to reveal his identity to his biological children when they turn 18?

2. Mothers have no legal obligation to reveal to their children that they were born by the use of donor sperm. Should this fact be included on a child's birth certificate?

3. Should sperm banks be required to keep a registry of children born by the use of the sperm they supplied? If they did, then children born by AI would be able to find out easily whether they were related, even if they didn't know the number of the donor who provided the sperm used by their mothers.

DECISION SCENARIO **4**

Embryo = Person?

"I'm curious," Lois Ramer said. "What happens to the eggs you take from me that get fertilized but not implanted?"

"We donate them to other women," Dr. Martha Herman said.

"Oh," Lois Ramer said, sounding surprised. "I don't want that to happen."

"Why is that?"

"Because they belong to my husband and me, and implanting them into other women would be like giving our children away."

"But an egg isn't a person," Dr. Herman said.

1. Is it necessary to think that a fertilized egg is equivalent to a person to agree with Lois Ramer's objection? Construct an argument supporting her position.

2. What position does the Vatican "Instruction" take on the question of the status of an egg that is fertilized for the purpose of implantation, but then not used?

3. If every egg fertilized was implanted, would this make the procedure of embryo transfer morally legitimate according to the Vatican "Instruction"?

DECISION SCENARIO **5**

Allowable Discrimination?

"I'm sorry we can't help you," Patricia Spring said, "but what you want is simply against our policy."

Charles Blendon and Carla Neuman didn't try to hide their disappointment. The San Diego Reproductive Clinic had been their last hope. They badly wanted to have a child, but Carla's fallopian tubes had been surgically removed as part of a successful effort to treat precancerous growths.

"In fact," Patricia Spring continued, "you don't meet at least two of our criteria."

"We can afford to pay," Charles said.

"That's not it. First of all, Carla is forty-five, and we set forty as the upper limit. And second, you two aren't married, and we require that the donor and the patient be husband and wife."

"Who makes those rules?" Carla asked. "If we want to have a child, that's our business and nobody else's."

"The clinic makes the rules," Patricia Spring said. "You see, there is an increasing number of birth defects in older women. There are sound medical reasons for our criteria."

"But what if we're willing to take the risk?" Charles asked.

"You can't take a risk that's likely to affect a child."

"But I'm willing to have tests," Carla said. "And neither of us is against abortion. If there's something wrong with the fetus, then I'll have an abortion."

"And what sort of medical basis is there for the marriage requirement?" Charles asked. "It seems to me that the clinic is just imposing its own moral standards on Carla and me."

"Look," Patricia Spring said, "I know you're both upset and disappointed. But the clinic operates in a community, and our criteria reflect both good medical judgment and the standards of the community."

1. Is the clinic justified in setting an age limit on the women it will accept as patients? If so, why?

2. How might a rule utilitarian justify the clinic's requirement that a couple be married in order for the woman to be accepted as a patient?

3. If the clinic receives public funds, would that provide any reason to believe its services should be open to everyone?

DECISION SCENARIO 6

The Ambiguous Status of Surrogacy

In January 1985, the British High Court took custody of a five-day-old girl, the first child known to be born in Britain to a woman paid to be a surrogate mother.

An American couple, known only as "Mr. and Mrs. A," were reported to have paid about $7500 to a twenty-eight-year-old woman who allowed herself to be artificially inseminated with sperm from Mr. A. The woman, Kim Cotton, was prevented from turning the child over to Mr. and Mrs. A by a court order issued because of the uncertainty over the legal status of a surrogate mother.

The court permitted "interested parties, including the natural father" to apply for custody of the child. Mr. A applied, and Judge Sir John Latey ruled that the couple could take the baby girl out of the country be-cause they could offer her the chance of "a very good upbringing."

1. Are there moral reasons that might have made the court hesitate before turning over the child to her biological father? For example, could it be persuasively argued that Kim Cotton was in effect selling her baby to Mr. and Mrs. A?

2. Kim Cotton agreed to be a surrogate mother for the sake of the money. Is surrogate pregnancy a practice that tends to exploit the poor? Or is it a legitimate way to earn money by providing a needed service?

3. Is serving as a surrogate mother essentially the same as prostitution? If it is not, then what are the relevant differences?

DECISION SCENARIO 7

Just a Matter of Autonomy?

Dr. Charles Davis quickly scanned the data sheet on his desk, then looked at the woman seated across from him. Her name was Nancy Callahan. She was twenty-five years old and worked as a print conservator at an art museum.

"I see you aren't married," Dr. Davis said.

"That's right," Nancy Callahan said. "That's basically the reason I'm here." When Dr. Davis looked puzzled, she added, "I still want to have a child."

Dr. Davis nodded and thought for a moment. Nancy Callahan was the first unmarried person to come to the Bayside Fertility Clinic to request AID. As the legal owner and operator of the clinic, as well as the chief of medical services, Dr. Davis was the one ultimately responsible for the clinic's policies.

"You're not engaged or planning to get married?"

"No, but I don't want to rule out the possibility that I will want to get married someday."

"Don't you know anybody you would want to have a child with in the ordinary sexual way?"

"I might be able to find someone," Nancy Callahan said. "But you see, I don't want to get involved with anybody right now. I'm ready to be a mother, but I'm not ready to get into the kind of situation that having a child in what you call 'the ordinary sexual way' would require."

"It's just somewhat unusual," Dr. Davis said.

"But it's not illegal, is it?"

"No," Dr. Davis said. "It's not illegal."

"So what's the problem? I'm healthy. I'm financially sound and mentally stable, and I'm both able and eager to accept the responsibility of being a mother."

"It's just that at the moment the policy of our clinic requires that patients be married and that both husband and wife agree to the insemination procedure."

"But there's nothing magical about a policy," Nancy Callahan said. "It can be changed for good reasons, can't it?"

"Perhaps so," said Dr. Davis.

1. Suppose that Ms. Callahan is a lesbian. Should this be a relevant consideration in deciding whether she should receive AID?

2. How might it be argued that respect for Ms. Callahan's autonomy makes it wrong to deny here the service she requests, yet the same service is provided to a married woman?

DECISION SCENARIO 8

Inherently Wrong or Just Impracticable?

"You've got to help us," Clarence Woody said. "Keith is. . . . was . . . . our only child, and he meant the world to us. When the police came and told us he was dead, all Sara and I could think of was how we could get him back."

"But you can't get him back," Dr. Alma Lieu said. "Even if we prepared one of his cells and implanted it in your wife's uterus, the baby wouldn't be Keith."

"But he would be his genetic twin," Clarence said. "He would be as close as we can get to replacing our son." His eyes filled with tears. "Won't you help us?"

1. On what grounds do critics object to cloning a human?

2. Assuming the safety of the cloned person is not in question, would cloning in such a case as this be morally legitimate?

3. Does the cloning of a human necessarily lead to the commodification of human life?

4. How persuasive in a case like this is the objection that cloning is "repugnant" to us because it violates our nature as biological and social organisms?

DECISION SCENARIO 9

The Possibility of Impairment

"You realize that the drugs we'll be using in preparing you for implanting the embryos will involve a slight, but significant, risk to any child you might have?" Dr. Aaron asked.

"I certainly didn't," Stephanie Dalata said. "You mean I might have a child with a birth defect?"

"You might," Dr. Aaron said. "Or one who is premature or has a low birth weight. Or if we implant four embryos, all four of them might develop, and all the babies would be at risk."

"I don't think you should go through with the treatments," her partner Alice Stimmons said. "If assisted reproduction is going to produce a child with a serious birth defect, it's wrong."

"I'm going to go ahead anyway," Stephanie Dalata said. "I think it's better for a child to have even serious defects than not exist at all."

1. Ms. Dalata apparently endorses what some call the "Interest in Existing" argument. State the argument clearly and concisely.

2. How persuasive is this argument?

3. Even births that don't involve assisted reproduction are associated with risks of serious and perhaps devastating harm to the child. Do objections to the "Interest in Existing" argument also apply to ordinary sexual (non-assisted reproduction) pregnancies?

4. Dr. Aaron warns Ms. Dalata that if he implants four embryos, all four might develop. State and discuss what you consider to be the most serious issues about infertility treatments and multiple births.

Part III

Terminations

Chapter 5

Abortion

CHAPTER CONTENTS

CASES AND CONTEXTS

The Conflict Begins: *Roe v. Wade*

Norma McCorvey of Dallas was unmarried, poor, and pregnant. She was twenty-one years old and wanted to have an abortion, but under Texas law in 1970, abortion was a criminal offense, except when required to save the woman's life.

McCorvey's life had been hard. She was abused both sexually and emotionally as a child, then raped at a reform school when she was a teenager. She married at sixteen, was beaten by her husband, and was involved with drugs and alcohol. Her first child, a daughter, was taken to be raised by her mother, and the father of her second child, also a daughter, assumed responsibility for the child's welfare.

When McCorvey found herself pregnant for the third time, she knew she didn't want another child. The law in California was less restrictive than the law in Texas, and McCorvey believed she could get an abortion there. Unfortunately, she lacked the money for travel and expenses. She tried to visit an illegal abortion clinic in Dallas, but found it closed down.

The Case

While still pregnant, McCorvey was approached by Linda Coffee, a public-interest attorney who had been given McCorvey's name by a lawyer specializing in adoptions. Coffee and Sarah Weddington, also an attorney, met with McCorvey and asked her if she would agree to be the plaintiff in a class-action lawsuit. The suit would be filed against Henry Wade, the district attorney of Dallas County, and would challenge the constitutionality of the Texas abortion law. McCorvey readily consented. When the papers were filed, Norma McCorvey became "Jane Roe."

Although McCorvey was the plaintiff, the case was a class-action suit that Coffee and Weddington hoped would be decided in a way that would recognize that women had a constitutional right to seek an abortion. The federal courts ruled that the Texas statute was void, but Dallas District Attorney Henry Wade appealed the District Court decision to the U.S. Supreme Court.

The legal case took time as it wound through the courts, and despite McCorvey's explicit wish not to have another child, she bowed to legal necessity and carried the fetus to term. She gave birth to a third daughter, then immediately gave up the baby for adoption.

The Decision

The Supreme Court handed down its ruling in *Roe v. Wade* on January 23, 1973. In a 7-to-2 decision, written by Justice Harry A. Blackmun, the Court found the Texas law to be unconstitutional. This ruling had the effect of decriminalizing abortion in the United States, because abortion laws in most other states differed little from the Texas statute.

The *Roe* decision did not hold that states could not regulate abortion. Rather, it placed limits on the restrictions states could impose without violating a woman's constitutionally protected right to privacy. Physicians have traditionally divided the nine months of pregnancy into three three-month trimesters, and the Court made use of these divisions to guide states in determining to what extent they could legitimately restrict abortion.

The ruling held that, during the first twelve weeks (the first trimester) of pregnancy, states cannot restrict a woman's decision to have an abortion. During the second trimester, states may place restrictions on abortion to protect the health or safety of the pregnant woman. In the final trimester, because the fetus may be considered viable and capable of an independent existence, states may restrict abortions but only in ways that still preserve the health of the pregnant woman.

From Roe to McCorvey

"Jane Roe" went back to being Norma McCorvey, but her life didn't seem to improve. A high-school dropout with no vocational training, McCorvey supported herself with various unskilled jobs, working as a waitress and a bartender. In the 1980s she began to acknowledge in public that she had been "Jane Roe," and this led to a brief flurry of attention from abortion-rights groups. She was introduced at meetings, gave interviews to the media, and gave some public talks. She became somewhat of a celebrity for a time.

Yet her celebrity didn't pay the bills, and she continued to work at low-paying jobs. Her celebrity did help her get jobs in abortion clinics, however. While she was working in a women's clinic in Dallas, the antiabortion group Operation Rescue set up an office next door and protested the clinic's activities. McCorvey was hostile to them at first, but then she began to have conversations with Philip Benham, the group's director, during her cigarette breaks. Benham, an evangelical preacher, talked to her about Christianity, and McCorvey agreed to attend church with the daughter of one of the group's members.

McCorvey converted to Christianity on her first visit to the church. She was baptized by Benham on August 8, 1995, in a swimming pool belonging to one of Benham's followers. The event, considered a major publicity coup by Operation Rescue, was videotaped and released to the media. McCorvey renounced her previous support for abortion and took a job doing word processing for Operation Rescue.

With the help of a coauthor, Andy Meisler, she went public in 1994 with the details of her story up to that time in *I Am Roe: My Life, Roe v. Wade, and Freedom of Choice.* With the help of another coauthor, she wrote *Won by Love,* an account of her conversion. She founded a ministry called "Roe No More," and she hopes to oppose abortion in Dallas by operating a mobile counseling center to encourage pregnant women to choose another alternative.

The Debate Continues

Linda Coffee and Sarah Weddington, McCorvey's lawyers, had achieved their aim. The *Roe* decision made it possible for most women wanting an abortion to obtain one. Yet the decision also triggered a firestorm of controversy between proponents of relatively unregulated choice ("pro-choice" advocates) and opponents of so-called abortion on demand ("pro-life" or "right-to-life" advocates) that shows no sign of dying down.

Those who favor making abortion a matter of individual decision were pleased by the *Roe* decision, but those who consider abortion a serious moral wrong were not. Many of the opponents resolved to work for a constitutional amendment prohibiting abortion or, alternatively, get the Supreme Court ruling in *Roe v. Wade* overturned.

Within the limits of regulation imposed by the *Roe* decision, opponents of abortion have taken various legal measures over the years in an attempt to slow or halt its practice. Thus, they have often succeeded in getting laws passed that impose requirements making it difficult for women to get an abortion. In response, advocates of personal choice have often charged that the laws are unconstitutional and filed suits that have ended up before the Supreme Court. *Roe v. Wade* marked the beginning of the legal skirmishes and court fights centered on abortion, but even so many years later, the end of the war is not in sight.

CASE PRESENTATION
When Abortion was Illegal: Mrs. Sherri Finkbine and the Thalidomide Tragedy

Background Note: The following case concerns an event that took place before the U.S. Supreme Court decision in Roe v. Wade was handed down in 1973. That decision had the effect of legalizing abortion in the United States. Before the decision, most state laws permitted abortion only to save the life of the mother. The case presented here illustrates the kinds of problems faced by many women who sought an abortion for other reasons.

In 1962, Mrs. Sherri Finkbine of Phoenix, Arizona, the mother of four children, was pregnant. Her health was good, but she was having some trouble sleeping. Rather

than talking with her doctor, she simply took some of the tranquilizers that her husband had brought back from a trip to Europe. The tranquilizers were widely used there; like aspirin or cough syrup, they could be bought over the counter in any pharmacy.

A few weeks after she began taking the tranquilizers, Sherri Finkbine read an article that discussed the great increase in the number of deformed children being born in Europe. Some of the children's arms and legs failed to develop or developed so that they had malformed hands jutting out from their shoulders. Other children were blind and deaf or had seriously defective internal organs requiring major corrective surgery. The impairments had been traced to the use in pregnancy of a supposedly harmless and widely used tranquilizer. Its active ingredient was thalidomide.

Mrs. Finkbine was worried enough to ask her doctor to find out if the pills she had been taking contained thalidomide. They did. When her doctor learned this, he told her, "The odds are so against you that I am recommending termination of pregnancy." He explained that getting approval for an abortion should not be difficult. She had good medical reasons, and all she had to do was explain them to the three-member medical board of Phoenix.

Mrs. Finkbine agreed with her doctor's advice. But then she began to think that maybe it was her duty to inform other women who may have been taking thalidomide about its disastrous consequences. She called a local newspaper and told her story to the editor. He agreed not to use her name, but on a front page, bordered in black, he used the headline "Baby-Deforming Drug May Cost Woman Her Child Here."

The story was picked up by the wire services, and Mrs. Finkbine's identity soon became known. The medical board had already approved her request for an abortion, but because of the great publicity that her case received, the members grew skittish and canceled their approval. The Arizona abortion statute legally sanctioned abortion only when it was required to save the life of the mother. The board was afraid that their decision might be challenged in court and that it couldn't stand up to the challenge.

Sherri Finkbine became the object of a great outpouring of antiabortion feelings. *Il Osservatore Romano*, the official Vatican newspaper, condemned her and her husband as murderers. Although she received some letters of support, others were abusive. One writer said, "I hope someone takes the other four children and strangles them, because it is all the same thing." Another wrote from the perspective of the fetus: "Mommy, please dear Mommy, let me live. Please, please, I want to live. Let me love you, let me see the light of day, let me smell a rose, let me sing a song, let me look into your face, let me say Mommy."

Sherri Finkbine tried to obtain a legal abortion outside her own state, but she was unable to find a doctor who would help her. Eventually, she got on a plane to Sweden and consulted a physician at a Swedish hospital. After a rigorous investigation by a medical board, Sherri Finkbine received the abortion she had traveled so far and struggled so hard to get.

Sherri Finkbine's problem was solved. Even so, she continued to express sympathy for the thousands of pregnant women who had taken thalidomide but lacked the money to go to another country for an abortion. Whether they wanted to or not, state abortion laws forced them to continue with pregnancies that would end with the birth of seriously impaired children. She considered such restrictive laws inhumane.

SOCIAL CONTEXT

A Statistical Profile of Abortion in the United States

January 2011 marked the thirty-eighth anniversary of the Supreme Court decision legalizing abortion in the United States. Yet nearly four decades after the decision, abortion has not become a standard, uncontroversial medical procedure, as many abortion-rights advocates expected.

Even though some 1.2 million abortions are performed every year in the United States, Americans remain ambivalent and divided on abortion's moral acceptability. To an extent, abortion has become even less accepted than it was during the 1980s and 1990s.

The data that follow present a statistical profile of abortion in the United States. The picture that emerges reveals a strong commitment to the idea that abortion should remain a legal procedure, combined with a lesser, yet still strong, belief that abortion should be illegal.

Despite the enduring and often sharp political conflicts over abortion, public support for keeping the procedure legal, although perhaps stringently regulated, remains high. Abortion as a procedure is not going to go away, yet neither are the moral and political issues associated with it.

(The data cited here may sometimes be inconsistent from section to section. Some statistics are for the latest year for which complete data are available, while other numbers are for more recent years for which data are incomplete. The discrepancies are few and small, and don't substantially alter the general picture.)

How Many Abortions?

About twenty-two percent of all pregnancies among American women end with an abortion, according to a 2010 estimate. When the pregnancies aren't intended, this percentage rises to forty percent. Each year, more than twenty out of every 1000 women aged 15–44 have an abortion, and half of those who have an abortion have had one before.

In 2005 (the most recent statistics), 1.21 million abortions were performed. This was a decrease from 1.31 million in 2000, and reflects what may be a relatively constant number.

Public health experts estimate that during the 1950s and 1960s, before the 1973 Supreme Court decision in *Roe v. Wade* that legalized abortion, 200,000 to 1.2 million illegal abortions were performed each year. The number of abortions increased after the procedure was made legal, peaking at 1.6 million in 1990. Since then, abortions have been declining, measured both as an absolute number and as a percentage of women of childbearing age who have them. It's beginning to look as if the number of abortions has stabilized at between 1.0 and 1.3 million a year.

The reasons for this stabilization (if it's real) are unclear, but some believe it's connected with the aging of the population, the wider availability of contraception, and fewer unwanted pregnancies. Others think the decline reflects a change of attitude toward abortion, as well as changes in society that make it more difficult for a woman to secure an abortion. As evidence, they point to protests at clinics, the shrinking number of abortion providers, and stiffer regulation by the states.

While the number of abortions is likely to vary slightly from year to year, experts think it is unlikely that any increase will reach the 1996 high point. Some suggest that a less accepting public attitude toward abortion will keep the number even lower than might otherwise be expected.

Who Has an Abortion?

Age. More than half (52%) of women who have an abortion are in their twenties. Women ages 20–24 account for 33% of all abortions, and teenagers account for another 18%.

Race. European Americans have 36% of the abortions performed in the United States, African Americans, 30%, and Hispanics, 25%.

Religion. Of women who have abortions, 37% say they are Protestants and 28% identify themselves as Catholics.

Marital status. About 45% of all abortions are obtained by women who have never been married.

Children. More than 61% of abortions are among women who have previously given birth to at least one child.

Rape. Each year, about 12,000 women have abortions as a result of rape.

Why Abortion?

* Seventy-five percent of women say they are choosing to have an abortion because having a child would interfere with their education, work, or other responsibilities.

* Seventy-five percent say that they cannot afford to have a (or another) child for financial reasons.

* Fifty percent say they don't want to be a single parent or that they aren't getting along with their husband or partner and don't want to face the problems of adding a child to the situation.

Contraception and Abortion

Some critics of abortion claim that its availability encourages women to use it as a form of birth control. The statistics suggest, however, that the situation is more complicated than that. Nearly all women seeking an abortion have (at some time) used some form of contraception, and the majority used it during the month in which they became pregnant. The intention of the majority to avoid becoming pregnant is most often thwarted by their failure to use contraception properly and consistently.

* Eight percent of women having abortions have never used any form of birth control. Those who are young, poor, African American, unmarried, or poorly educated are most likely never to have used contraception.

* Fifty-four percent of women having abortions used some method of contraception during the month in which they became pregnant.

* Seventy-six percent of pill users and forty-nine percent of condom users said they were inconsistent in the way they used the methods. Those who said they used them correctly were, respectively, thirteen percent and fourteen percent.

Obtaining an Abortion

Drug-Induced Abortion

In 2000, the federal Food and Drug Administration approved the drug RU-486 (mifepristone) for inducing abortion, permitting women in the earlier stages of pregnancy to avoid a surgical abortion. About 560,000 drug-induced abortions were performed in 2006.

Safety

* Less than one percent of women who have abortions experience major complications.

* The risk of death associated with abortion increases with the length of pregnancy: up to 8 weeks, 1 death per million; 16–20 weeks, 1 per 29,000; 21+ weeks, 1 per 11,000.

* The risk of death associated with childbirth is 11 times as high as the risk associated with abortion.

Timing

The great majority of abortions (eighty-eight percent) take place during the first twelve weeks of pregnancy. About fifty percent of the women who have an abortion after the fifteenth week of pregnancy say the delay was

WHEN WOMEN HAVE ABORTIONS	
Before the 9th week	61.8%
9–10 weeks	17.1
11–12 weeks	9.1
13–15 weeks	6.2
16–20 weeks	4.2
21+ weeks	1.4

caused by problems in getting the money or in finding someone to perform the procedure. Teenagers are much more likely than older women to have an abortion after the fifteenth week.

Providers

* During the period 2000–2005, the number of hospitals, clinics, and physicians providing abortion declined by twelve percent.

* Eighty-seven percent of counties in the United States lacked an abortion provider in 2005.

* Thirty-five percent of all women 15–44 lived in a county without an abortion provider in 2005.

* In 2005, the cost of a surgical abortion in the tenth week of pregnancy carried out with local anesthesia in a clinic or doctor's office ranged from $90 to $1800. The average cost was $413.

Public Payment

* Federal law prohibits the use of Medicaid funds (the state–federal program for the poor) to pay for abortion, except in cases in which the mother's life is endangered or the pregnancy is the result of rape or incest.

* Some states (17) allow public funds to be used to pay for abortion when a woman meets a low-income requirement.

* Publicly funded family planning services prevent an estimated 1.3 million unplanned pregnancies a year. On the basis of the rate

at which unplanned pregnancies are terminated, more than 632,000 abortions a year are thus avoided.

Ambivalence Toward Abortion

That the country has mixed feelings about abortion is revealed in a May 2009 poll by the Gallup Organization. The poll also shows a slight swing in a conservative direction. When people were asked, "With respect to the abortion issue, would you consider yourself to be pro-choice or pro-life?" those answering pro-life rose to 51% from the 44% reported in 2005. Those describing themselves as pro-choice declined from 48% to 42%. This is the first time a majority of U.S. adults have identified themselves as pro-life since Gallup first asked the question in 1995.

This conservative shift was not accompanied, however, by a significant increase in the number of people wanting to see abortion outlawed. In 2009, only 23% endorsed the view that abortion should be illegal, while 53% said it should be legal under some circumstances. Another 22% said it should be legal in any circumstance. Thus about 75% of the population favors maintaining abortion's legal status.

In a second 2009 Gallup poll, 75% of the people surveyed expressed the view that abortion should be "always" or "sometimes" legal and only 23% endorsed the notion that it should always be "illegal." Once again, it seems that about three-quarters of the population accepts the legitimacy of abortion for at least some reasons.

Abortion and New Medical Technology

To some extent, the ambivalence about abortion and the public clash of opinions about its moral legitimacy may be due to the development of new reproductive and life-sustaining technology, as well as to an increase in awareness of the character of the fetus.

When a genetic disease like Tay–Sachs is present in a family, in vitro fertilization and the

ABORTION SHOULD BE . . .

Always legal	22%
Sometimes legal	53%
Always illegal	23%

Source: Gallup Poll, May 2–5, 2009

selection of an embryo free of the disease for implantation can avoid a problem that might lead to abortion. While for some, discarding unused embryos created by in vitro fertilization is equivalent to abortion, most people are more comfortable with the idea of destroying embryos than of aborting a fetus.

Reproductive technology has also made more familiar the concept of "selectively reducing" one or more developing fetuses in a multiple pregnancy resulting from the use of fertility drugs. For some, selective reduction is simply abortion by another name, but for others it is a procedure necessary to give the remaining fetuses a better chance to develop normally.

Also, statistics indicate that more than half the population (seventy percent) aren't troubled by preventing a pregnancy through the use of a "morning after" drug like Plan B or ending a pregnancy by using a drug like RU-486. This may be because most people don't think of a fertilized egg as a fetus until development in the uterus is well underway. Thus, they don't equate it with a baby.

The other relevant development in technology is the ability to keep alive babies who are so premature that, in important aspects, they are still developing fetuses. A baby is considered full term if it is born forty weeks after conception, but a state-of-the-art neonatal unit staffed with trained and experienced people can save the lives of infants who have had only twenty-three or twenty-four weeks of development.

These babies often do not do well and suffer serious lifelong problems. (See Chapter 6.) Even so, the fact that such small babies can survive outside the uterus has led many people to become more restrained in their endorsement of abortion or to favor restrictions on when it

ABORTION AND WOMEN'S CHARACTERISTICS	
Age (rate per 1000 women)	
Under 15	1
15–19	24
20–24	46
25–29	32
30–34	19
35–39	10
40–44	3
Race/Ethnicity (percent of all abortions)	
White	14%
Hispanic	21%
African American	38%
Race/Ethnicity and Marital Status (rate per 1000 women)	
White, married	6
White, unmarried	26
African American, married	20
African American, unmarried	71
Hispanic, married	12
Hispanic, unmarried	52

Source: Centers for Disease Control and Prevention, 2006

can be performed. After all, the second trimester ends at around twenty-five weeks. (See the discussion of the *Webster* decision in "Social Context: Supreme Court Abortion Decisions After *Roe v. Wade*" later in this chapter.)

The Difficult Middle

The abstract and absolute positions represented by statements like "A woman has a right to choose to have an abortion for any reason at all" and "A fertilized egg is as much a person as a born child and has just as much right to life" have become less representative of the beliefs of most people over the last few decades. The majority of people tend toward the view that the most reasonable position on abortion lies somewhere between these extremes.

To sum up in a phrase, Americans appear to think abortion should be "safe, legal, and rare." But of course, agreement to such a general proposition doesn't translate into agreement about what restrictions are appropriate. Although, abstract positions may have blurred for most people, debates over particular policies remain as divisive and acrimonious as ever.

SOCIAL CONTEXT

The Morning-After Pills (Plan B and Ella): Emergency Contraception and Politics

Every year, American women have three million unintended pregnancies. One-quarter of all pregnancies end in abortion, and when the pregnancy is unintended, the percentage increases to almost one-half (forty-nine percent). One in three young women under the age of twenty becomes pregnant, and eighty percent of those pregnancies are unintended. More than 25,000 women a year become pregnant as a result of sexual assault.

One way to decrease the number of abortions performed each year would be to decrease the number of unwanted pregnancies, and this could happen if women had available a drug they could use to prevent pregnancy even *after* intercourse.

Also, women who have been raped can gain immediate reassurance from such a drug.

Plan B

The emergency contraceptive called Plan B is one such drug. (Plan A is some form of ordinary contraception, including abstinence. The newer drug ella has advantages over Plan B that will be discussed later.) More properly, Plan B is a treatment regimen that consists of taking two pills containing high doses (.75 mg) of the birth-control drug levonorgestrel synthetic version of the hormone progesterone. To be effective, the first pill must be taken within seventy-two hours of having sex and the second twelve hours later. (The optimal time to take the first dose is within the first twenty-four hours after sex, and the sooner, the better.) When both doses are taken within the effective period, the chance of preventing a pregnancy becomes eighty-nine percent.

The major side effects of the double dose of Plan B are nausea and vomiting. From one- to two-thirds of women taking the drug experience nausea for about two days, and some twelve to twenty-two percent have episodes of vomiting. An antinausea drug taken at the same time as the contraceptives can reduce the side effects.

Plan B (and drugs like it) prevent pregnancy by delaying or preventing ovulation, inhibiting fertilization, or preventing a fertilized egg from implanting itself in the wall of the uterus. Several drugs that function in this way were already available before Plan B was proposed, and physicians knew that they could provide their patients with emergency contraception by using high doses of FDA-approved birth-control pills. (The drug RU-486 can also prevent pregnancy if used early enough; see "Social Context: The Abortion Pill.")

Because there is no way to tell when an egg becomes fertilized after intercourse, Plan B blurs the line between contraception and abortion. A majority of Americans have no objections to contraception or to very early abortion, so they tend to see emergency contraception as a legitimate way to prevent an unintended pregnancy. Those opposed to contraception or to abortion, however, reject the use of Plan B.

Alaska, California, Hawaii, Oregon, and Washington allow pharmacists to provide emergency contraception in the form of a double dose of birth-control pills without a doctor's prescription. In about thirty other countries, including Britain and France, pharmacists can also dispense drugs similar to Plan B without a prescription if the client declares an urgent need for them.

Emergency contraceptive drugs are available over the counter (OTC) in Norway and Sweden, and proponents of Plan B were hopeful that the FDA would approve

Barr Laboratories' application to make the regimen available in the same way throughout the U.S. Women's groups, in particular, saw Plan B as a way to give women more control over their reproductive potential by freeing them from accidental pregnancies. In 2000, emergency contraception is estimated to have prevented 51,000 abortions and perhaps a similar number of additional unwanted pregnancies.

Conflict

When the FDA received reports that standard birth-control drugs were being prescribed by doctors for emergency contraception, the agency invited manufacturers to submit proposals for relabeling the drugs for this use. The Women's Capital Corporation had been established to manufacture Plan B so that it would be available to women, and in 2003 it applied to the FDA for approval to sell Plan B OTC. Barr Laboratories acquired the assets of the Women's Capital Corporation that same year and took over the task of getting FDA approval.

Although Plan B was approved as safe and effective by the FDA in 1999, it was available only by prescription. The Barr application to sell Plan B as an OTC drug proposed that no age restriction be placed on who could buy it. The application was reviewed by an independent FDA advisory panel of scientists and physicians, and the panel voted 23–4 for approval.

The FDA had always taken the advice of its advisory panels, but this time the panel's recommendation was overruled by upper-level FDA officials. Plan B was controversial, and abortion opponents were lobbying administration officials to pressure the FDA to turn down Barr's application. Although the FDA's own scientific panel had already concluded that Plan B was a contraceptive agent, not an abortion drug, this finding was rejected by many social conservatives. They also objected to making the drug available OTC, because it might encourage sexual activity among young teens who might otherwise be kept in check by the fear of pregnancy. The United

States Conference of Catholic Bishops was among several groups that lobbied federal officials to use their influence to prevent the FDA from approving Barr's application.

On the other side of the reproductive divide, the American Medical Association, American College of Gynecologists and Obstetricians, American Academy of Family Physicians, and American Academy of Pediatricians endorsed OTC sales of Plan B as in the best medical interest of women. OTC sales also were supported by Planned Parenthood and a number of women's health groups, which lobbied for its approval and gained support from a number of members of Congress.

Plan B was the only one of twenty-three applications to change a drug from prescription-required status to OTC to be turned down in the period 1994–2004. When the application was rejected, however, the political controversy over the drug didn't end. Rumors soon surfaced that Steven Galson, the head of the FDA's drug-review center, had told staff members that it didn't matter what the independent advisory panel's recommendation was, because the decision would be made by top officials at the agency. He later denied making such a statement, but it was Galson himself who made the final decision about Plan B.

After the Plan B application was turned down, several members of Congress asked the Government Accountability Office (GAO) to conduct a review of what had taken place at the FDA. The GAO investigation discovered that the decision to reject the application was made before the FDA's own scientific review of the application was finished. This supported the charge that inappropriate influence had been at work in the drug-evaluation process.

The GAO report also characterized the FDA's grounds for rejecting the proposal as "novel." Galson claimed he had made the "non-approved" decision on the ground that only twenty-nine of the 585 participants in Barr's clinical trial of Plan B were between the ages of 14 and 16. Younger teenagers,

Galson said, might act differently from older teenagers. In particular, they might engage in riskier sex if they knew that an emergency contraceptive was easily available. Thus, he claimed, Barr needed to supply more data to show that young adolescents could use the drug properly.

What the GAO pointed out was that the FDA had always used the behavior of older adolescents to predict the behavior of younger ones, including predictions about how they were likely to use OTC drugs. Galson's reason for rejecting Plan B was "novel" because it was the opposite of the reasoning used by the FDA in all other cases.

New Application: 16+

Barr responded to the FDA's claim that not enough teens ages 14–16 were included in the initial study of Plan B by filing a new application in July 2004. It requested that the company be able to sell the drug OTC to females *older* than 16.

The FDA's own rules required it to act on Barr's application by January. However, it failed to take any action until August 2005, more than a year later. The agency then announced that it was delaying approval to allow time for public comment. This action provoked additional charges that political ideology within the FDA was derailing what should be a science-based decision.

Despite such protests, in February 2005 the FDA announced that, although Barr's application was scientifically sound, the agency needed to delay its decision *indefinitely* while it considered whether it had the regulatory authority to approve Barr's plan to sell Plan B OTC and whether the plan to limit sales to those over 16 could be enforced.

In September 2005, Susan Wood, director of the FDA's Office of Women's Health resigned to protest the agency's decision. "I feel very strongly that this shouldn't be about abortion politics," she said. "This is a way to prevent pregnancy and thereby prevent abortion. This should be something that we should all agree on." She told a reporter that she could no longer serve at the FDA "when scientific and clinical evidence, fully evaluated and recommended by approval by the professional staff here, has been overruled."

2006 Applications: 18+

Various members of Congress expressed outrage over the FDA's decision to do nothing about Plan B, but the stalemate continued until August 2006. Andrew von Eschenbach, acting commissioner of the FDA, was about to appear before congressional committees that would decide whether to recommend him for a regular appointment, when he announced that he had asked Barr for a complete plan for limiting sales of Plan B to women over 16. The announcement elicited a positive reaction from those who had been critical of the agency for dragging its feet on Plan B.

Later that month, however, the FDA announced that it had met with representatives of Barr Laboratories and asked the company to submit a new application that would make Plan B available OTC to women *18 or older*. Those younger than 18 would need a prescription to gain access to the drug. Also, Plan B would be available only at pharmacies and clinics holding a federal drug license. The FDA signaled to the company that its price for approving Plan B as an OTC drug was to make it available only to adults.

2009 Application: 17+ and No Prescription

In 2009, Judge Edward R. Korman of the New York Federal District Court ruled that the FDA's decision to limit access to Plan B to those 18 or older was determined by politics, not science. He gave the agency thirty days to lower the limit to age 17.

The FDA announced that it would appeal the decision, and it invited the drug's manufacturer to submit a plan to market Plan B

"without a prescription to women seventeen years of age or older." The announcement was praised by organizations promoting the reproductive autonomy of women and condemned by conservative groups on the grounds that easier access to Plan B would encourage more unprotected sex and more abortions.

The Pill Called Ella

In June 2010, a federal scientific advisory panel unanimously recommended that the FDA approve an emergency contraceptive drug called ella. Unlike Plan B, which must be taken within a seventy-two-hour period in order to be effective, ella remains effective up to five days after unprotected sex. Also, the effectiveness of Plan B declines with time, whereas ella is as effective on the fifth day as on the first. Ella blocks the effects of progesterone, the female hormone that triggers ovulation. The drug is similar in chemical structure to RU-486 (the "abortion pill"), but the exact mechanism of its action is still not known.

The lack of knowledge about how ella operates makes it controversial. Abortion opponents claim that it prevents a fertilized egg from implanting in the uterus and so must be regarded as a drug that *terminates* conception. The manufacturer claims, in contrast, that the drug works by delaying ovulation and so *prevents* conception. Some scientists suggest that it may do both. Unlike RU-486, the ella did not end established pregnancies in animal studies.

Ella was developed in the United States, although it is manufactured by HRA Pharma, a French company. It was approved for sale in Europe in 2009. Even if the FDA approves it for sale in the United States, most experts think it will have little effect on reducing the number of unwanted pregnancies. Women who have unprotected sex have a 1 in 20 chance of becoming pregnant. If they take Plan B within the prescribed time, this chance drops to 1 in 40, and if ella is used, the risk drops to 1 in 50. Thus, ella is not likely to make much of a practical difference.

Envoi

Many groups aiming to give women more control over their reproductive potential imagined a time when a pill would be available to allow women to prevent a pregnancy after a sexual encounter they had not wanted or for which they hadn't been prepared. They imagined a future in which a woman of childbearing age wouldn't have to consult a doctor or show proof of age to a pharmacist, but merely walk into a convenience store, a bar, or a gas station and buy a pill that would provide the protection from pregnancy that she wanted. With both Plan B and ella, this remains a distant prospect.

SOCIAL CONTEXT
The "Abortion Pill"

Sandra Crane, as we'll call her, decided she had missed her period. She was thirty-one years old, and ordinarily her menstrual cycle was as regular as clockwork. Because she was now a week overdue, she was sure she must be pregnant.

The feeling was familiar. She had two children already: six-year-old Jennifer and two-year-old Thomas. She and her husband had decided not to have any more kids, so if she got pregnant, she'd take steps to end the pregnancy.

Sandra Crane paid a visit to her gynecologist's office the next day, and the day after that Dr. Krantz's nurse practitioner called and told Sandra that the test was positive. She was likely to be about two weeks pregnant. Sandra explained that she wanted the pregnancy ended as soon as possible, and the nurse made an appointment for her to see a doctor at the Women's Clinic. Sandra discussed her decision with Dr. Tina Merida, then returned for a second visit. She was given two tablets to swallow—a 600-milligram dosage of Mifeprex, a drug better known by the generic names RU-486 and mifepristone—and told to come back in two days.

When Sandra returned to the clinic, she was given a 400-milligram oral dose of misoprostol. The drug, a prostaglandin, began to act three days later. It made her uterus contract, and she began to experience cramping and bleeding. Soon, however, the uterine lining was expelled, just as if she were having a miscarriage. Sandra felt some discomfort, but the process differed little from an unusually heavy menstrual period.

After a day of rest, she felt almost her usual self again. Two weeks later, she returned to the clinic for an examination to make sure the abortion was complete.

Background

RU-486 was developed by the French endocrinologist Étienne-Émile Baulieu. The drug works by blocking the action of progesterone, the hormone that prepares the uterine wall for the implantation of a fertilized egg. The dose of misoprostol (a kind of prostaglandin) taken two or three days later then induces uterine contractions that expel the sloughed-off lining, including the zygote or fetus.

To be safest and most effective, RU-486 must be taken during the first five to seven weeks of pregnancy. Most physicians urge that it be taken as early as possible, although some research suggests that its use might be extended even to the tenth week of pregnancy.

If RU-486 is taken soon after sexual intercourse, it blocks the action of progesterone, and as a result, a fertilized egg won't be able to implant itself in the uterine wall. Hence, the drug also has the possibility of serving as a "morning-after pill" for preventing pregnancy, even after fertilization. But the drug's major use lies in its power to induce an abortion. In initial testing, 100 women volunteers less than a month pregnant were given RU-486. Of these, eighty-five percent aborted within four days, without reporting the pain or psychological difficulties that can accompany surgical abortion. The later use of prostaglandin injections in conjunction with the drug increased the speed of the process. An oral dose of misoprostol later replaced the injection. Women tolerated this better, and the price was significantly lower.

Additional clinical trials in France and the use of the drug by more than 1.5 million women showed it to be safe and 95.5 percent effective. With the use of misoprostol, the effectiveness rises to 96.9 percent. Some women taking the drug bleed excessively, and a proportion do not abort as expected (about three percent, according to a French study) and require surgical intervention. For these reasons, the drug is intended for use only under close medical supervision.

Conflict

The drug was developed in 1980 by the pharmaceutical company Roussel-Uclaf and approved for use in France in September 1988. A month later, in response to a boycott of the company's products by abortion opponents, Roussel took the drug off the market. This provoked public protests, and Health Minister Claude Evin notified the company that if it did not release the drug, the government, which owned 36.25 percent of the company, would permanently transfer the patent to another company. "From the moment the governmental approval of the drug was granted, RU-486 became the moral property of women, not just the property of the drug company," Evin said. Two days later the company resumed marketing the drug.

United States

Roussel licensed the drug for use in China, Sweden, and Britain, but its plans to market the drug in the United States were abandoned because of opposition from abortion opponents. The general position was stated by a representative of the National Right to Life Committee, who characterized the use of RU-486 as "chemical warfare against an entire class of innocent humans."

The Population Council, a nonprofit research organization committed to making medical abortion available to U.S. women, was frustrated by Roussel's decision and persuaded the company to grant it a license to manufacture and distribute the drug in the United States. The Council conducted another clinical trial, getting results similar to those of the French study. The data were presented to the FDA, and in September 2000 the agency recognized RU-486 as safe and effective and approved it as a prescription drug.

Reactions to the approval were predictably mixed. Abortion opponents denounced the FDA decision, calling RU-486 a "baby poison" and vowing to lobby for legislation to prohibit its use. Pro-choice advocates praised the decision, saying the drug would allow women to keep abortion decisions private. Also, women living in rural areas without easy access to surgical abortion would now have a safe option.

In Practice

Only some of the hopes that pro-choice advocates pinned on RU-486 have materialized. Many physicians still prefer the speed and reliability of surgical abortions. A procedure takes only a few minutes, and then the patient is on the way to recovery. RU-486 is limited to use during the first seven weeks of pregnancy, and once a woman is given the drug, the protocol approved by the FDA requires that she return to the office two more times. The process takes about three weeks.

Many physicians who thought they were likely to prescribe RU-486 soon came to realize that abortion is regulated by a bewildering complexity of state laws. Many of the laws were lobbied for by abortion opponents who wanted to make it difficult for a women to get an abortion, and the approval of RU-486 didn't make it possible for physicians to ignore the laws.

Some states require, for example, that a physician performing abortions have an ultrasound machine, life-support equipment, and an operating suite available. Other states have laws stipulating specific standards the facility must satisfy, including hall width, temperature of running water, and amount of ventilation.

At least thirteen states require counseling before an abortion is performed and dictate a waiting period. Some states require that the fetal tissue be inspected, and others demand that it be disposed of by cremation or burying. The laws of some states regulate abortion in general, but those in other states specifically mention drug-induced abortion.

Under these circumstances, it's not surprising that the availability of RU-486 did not have the impact on abortion that those pressing to make the drug available had anticipated. Of the 1.3 million abortions performed in the United States in 2006, about 560,000 were drug induced. This is a significant number, but some women's groups had expected that virtually all abortions would become drug induced. To what extent the situation would be different without state laws passed to discourage abortion is a matter of speculation.

Unexplained Deaths

Chemical abortion continues to face a challenge that calls into question its future as a common medical procedure. The trouble began when researchers discovered that between January 2005 and March 2006 seven pregnant women died who had been given the combination of RU-486 and misoprostol. Five of the women died of toxic shock due to infection by the bacterium *Clostridium sordellii*. Four of them died in California. There was no obvious explanation for the infections. One hypothesis was that the pills were contaminated, and another, more alarming one, was that misoprostol itself was responsible for the infections.

The protocol approved by the FDA in 2000 required that, after getting RU-486, women return to the clinic in two days to get an oral dose of misoprostol. Soon after the FDA approval, however, Planned Parenthood and other clinics instructed women to skip the second visit and take the misoprostol at home as a vaginal

suppository. This way of administering the drug turned out to be just as effective, allowed a lower dose of misoprostol to be used, and required fewer visits to the clinic. Thus, vaginal insertion of the drug was both more convenient and less expensive than the oral dosing required by the FDA protocol.

Some researchers suggest that it was this shift to vaginal insertion that was responsible for most of the deaths. In inserting misoprostol, they hypothesized, women might accidentally contaminate the pill with fecal bacteria. Other researchers suggested that the drug itself was to blame for the deaths. They hypothesize that misoprostol might lower the effectiveness of the immune system, thus making pregnant women less able to fight off a *Clostridium sordellii* infection. (For unclear reasons, pregnant women, seem unusually vulnerable to this infection.)

Although comparatively small, the number of deaths was seen as statistically significant. The combination of RU-486 and misoprostol was used in about 560,000 out of 1.3 million abortions in 2006, and the deaths associated with the drug combination meant that a woman using it had a 1-in-100,000 chance of dying. This risk is low, but it is ten times greater than the one-in-a million risk of dying from a surgical abortion. A drug-induced abortion is also five to ten times as likely to fail and require follow-up surgery, and the greater the length of the pregnancy, the greater is the risk of failure.

For these and similar reasons, the majority of physicians who performed abortions continued to prefer to use surgical methods. Also, in many cases insurers insisted that clinics and physicians return to using the FDA protocol requiring that misoprostol be administered orally in a physician's office. That no deaths in Europe were reported as attributable to the drug combination suggested that the deaths in the United States were connected with bacterial contamination.

Planned Parenthood, the largest abortion provider in the United States, funded a study to determine what factors might be responsible for the potentially lethal infections associated with the RU-486 and misoprostol combination. The study analyzed the records of 227,823 women who had abortions at Planned Parenthood clinics from January 2005 to June 2008. The study, published in 2009 in the *New England Journal of Medicine*, found that ninety-two serious infections were present in this group, but that when the misoprostol was given vaginally or by mouth (dissolved before swallowing) and antibiotics were routinely prescribed, the infection rate dropped to 0.06 per 1,000 abortions from the previous 0.93 per 1,000.

The study suggests that the drug combination can be safely used and that antibiotics can reduce the chance of infection to an even lower level. It is not clear, however, that the findings will significantly alter the way abortion providers operate. Some physicians are reluctant to prescribe antibiotics as a matter of routine, because the rate of infection is already so low. (The drugs were used by about 184,000 women in 2009.) Also, in developing countries, where drug-induced abortion is more likely to be used antibiotics are often not available or are too expensive to be used for anything but life-threatening infections.

Envoi

The dream of many women's health groups in the 1980s was that RU-486 would make abortion safe, private, and easily secured by all women who wanted it. Despite the commitment of these groups and their long political struggles, the dream had been more approximated than realized.

TIMELINE

April 2003: The Women's Capital Corporation, license holder for manufacturing Plan B, applies to the FDA for OTC approval.

October 2003: Barr Laboratories buys the assets of the Women's Capital Corporation and assumes responsibility for the application.

December 2003: FDA's independent advisory committee votes in favor of allowing Plan B to be sold OTC.

May 2004: FDA decides that women under age 16 might not be able to use Plan B and rejects Barr's application.

July 2004: Barr applies to allow OTC sales only for women over age 16.

August 2005: FDA delays approval to allow public comment.

November 2005: FDA indefinitely delays a decision on Plan B to determine whether limiting OTC sales in the way Barr proposed was practical and enforceable.

August 2006: FDA asks Barr for a complete plan for limiting OTC sales of Plan B to women over age 16. Later, it asks Barr for an application that will limit OTC sales to women over age 18.

August 2009: FDA agrees to accept a New York Circuit Court decision and approve an application to sell Plan B to people ages 17 and older without a doctor's prescription.

SOCIAL CONTEXT
The "Partial-Birth Abortion" Controversy

In 1995, debate began to rage around abortion performed after twenty weeks of gestation, often focusing on a specific surgical procedure used to terminate a pregnancy. Technically known as intact dilation and extraction, the procedure was named "partial-birth abortion" by those opposed to abortion.

The debate, still raging after more than a dozen years, is characterized to an unusual extent by a lack of information and a reliance on misinformation by participants on both sides. Instead of laying out the issues as the opponents present them, it is more useful to begin by considering some of the facts relevant to evaluating the various positions taken.

Late-Term Abortion

While abortion opponents often portray "abortion doctors" as employing brutal procedures to destroy viable fetuses in order to satisfy the whims of pregnant women, those favoring abortion rights often present women as opting for such measures in only rare and extreme cases. The best estimates available suggest that neither picture is accurate.

The length of a normal pregnancy is forty weeks. More than half (59.1%) of all abortions are performed less than nine weeks after conception, and more than a quarter (29%) are performed in weeks nine through twelve. Indeed, 98.6% of all abortions are performed within twenty weeks of conception. Thus, late-term abortion, defined as abortion after twenty weeks, is relatively rare, accounting for only 1.4% of all abortions.

No statistics are available on the reasons women have late-term (instead of early) abortions. The best information comes from the congressional testimony of physicians who perform abortions. They suggest that one group of women has abortions because the woman's own health is threatened by pregnancy. For example, the pregnancy may have triggered an autoimmune disease, or the woman may have developed cancer and need treatment with chemotherapy and radiation.

A second group has late-term abortions because the fetus has developed a severe defect. For example, ultrasound may reveal that the growing child's cerebral hemispheres have failed to develop. If the pregnancy continues, the child that is born not only will lack all cognitive capacity, but will die within a few days or weeks.

The third and largest group comprises those who have failed to get an early abortion for a variety of mostly social reasons. The group includes teenagers in psychological denial about being pregnant until they (or a parent) had to face the undeniable fact. Also included are indigent women, who may be homeless, mentally retarded, or socially unskilled. Drug users, who engage in their own form of denial, are included in this third group, as are women

with menstrual periods so irregular that they don't suspect they are pregnant until several months have passed.

Proponents of abortion rights tend to overlook this third group and focus instead on the other two. Being able to cite the pressing need of a pregnant woman to save her life or the cruelty of forcing a pregnant woman to carry to term a fetus with a serious developmental defect makes it easier for them to defend their case.

Opponents of abortion, by contrast, tend to discuss late-term abortion as if it were the general rule, rather than very much the statistical exception. When 98.6 percent of all abortions are performed before twenty weeks, it is misleading to condemn all abortion by focusing on the 1.4 percent as representative. They also tend to ignore powerful reasons for having a late-term abortion, preferring to use cases producing the strongest negative emotional response.

Fetal Viability

Abortion opponents have focused on fetal viability as the crucial grounds for outlawing late-term abortion. In making their case, they have suggested that late abortions involve killing babies that otherwise would live and thrive. This has made the debate over late-term abortion particularly contentious, for determinations of viability cannot be made in definite and reliable ways.

Perinatologists (specialists in newborns) say that too many factors are involved in determining viability to make reliable generalizations about which fetuses will live and which will die at any given stage of development. In addition to characteristics such as a fetus's weight and the developmental stage of the organs, factors like the health of the mother, her socioeconomic status, and her access to health care also play a role. So do the race and gender of the fetus. In development, a white fetus generally lags a week behind an African American one of the same age and a male fetus lags the same amount behind a female.

The viability of a fetus is also connected with the state of medical technology and

TIMING OF ABORTIONS	
Before the 9th week	59.1%
9–10 weeks	19.0
11–12 weeks	10.0
13–15 weeks	6.2
16–20 weeks	4.2
21+ weeks	1.4

management. At the time of the *Roe v. Wade* decision in 1973, fetal viability was around 26 weeks, but now it is closer to 24, with 21–22 weeks being barely possible. A *micropremie* weighs 500 to 600 grams (a bit over a pound) and is hardly larger than the palm of a man's hand. Babies of this age and size, even if they survive, are likely to have irreversible physical and mental deficits. (See Chapter 10.)

The American College of Obstetrics and Gynecology estimates that lees than four percent of babies are born during weeks 23 to 25 of the normal 40-week gestation period, and their survival is conditional on the factors mentioned. Some experts doubt that even with aggressive intervention and intensive care, more than about one percent of 25-week fetuses would survive. Some hospitals and state laws make 23 or 24 weeks the cutoff point for elective abortions, while others follow a more restrictive policy and make 20 weeks the limit. After the cutoff, a factor such as the health and safety of the mother or a fetal abnormality must be present to justify an abortion.

How viable a fetus is and how likely it is to survive without serious and permanent mental and physical deficits is a clinical judgment that can be made only case by case. A claim to the effect that thousands or even hundreds of viable fetuses are destroyed by abortion is not supported by the evidence.

Methods

Opponents of abortion have focused attention on a method to perform late-term abortion known as intact dilation and extraction.

The procedure involves using a drug to dilate (widen) the pregnant woman's cervix, then manipulating the fetus by hand until it can be pulled through the birth canal. Usually, to ease the passage and make the procedure easier on the woman, the fetal brain is extracted by suction so that the skull can be collapsed (fenestrated). It is this procedure that abortion opponents have called "partial-birth abortion," a name coined for rhetorical purposes and not one used in medicine.

Intact dilation and extraction may also be performed by injecting digoxin into the uterus to stop the fetal heart. After the death of the fetus, the woman is induced into labor with a hormone injection and the fetus is delivered vaginally. Some obstetricians consider this form of the procedure too psychologically stressful for the woman. Others believe it is sufficiently well tolerated to make it the preferred method.

The third or classic method of dilation and extraction does not involve removing an intact fetus. After a woman's cervix is dilated, instruments are used to dismember the fetus and extract the parts through the birth canal. The fetus is killed either by a prior injection or by the process itself. Ultrasound may be used to guide the instruments, and the procedure may take twenty minutes or longer.

Surgeons who prefer intact dilation and extraction point to the time and risks associated with the classic procedure. The woman's uterus may be damaged by an instrument or punctured by a sharp bone fragment. It is safer for the woman if the intact fetus is pulled out by hand.

About eighty-six percent of abortions performed after twenty weeks are done by one of these three procedures. "Any procedure done at this stage is pretty gruesome," said one high-risk-pregnancy specialist.

Early Federal Attempts to Ban

In 1996, Congress passed legislation banning late-term abortion, along with intact dilation and extraction, but the bill was vetoed by President Clinton on the ground that it made no provision for protecting the health of the pregnant woman.

A second attempt at passing legislation began a year later. The House passed a bill by a margin large enough (295–136) to override a presidential veto. The Senate passed a similar ban, but by a margin (64–36) short of the votes needed to survive a veto. President Clinton announced he would veto any bill that did not allow an abortion to protect the health of a pregnant woman, but both the House and Senate bills would protect only the *life* of the pregnant woman. Abortion opponents claimed that allowing an exception for health would be virtually equivalent to no regulation at all, given the nebulous nature of claims about health, particularly mental health.

The final version of the Senate bill was revised to reflect a proposal framed and endorsed by the American Medical Association. In the first endorsement of any position on abortion, the AMA proposal made it clear that dilation and *evacuation*, the procedure most often used in early abortions, was not banned. Also, the proposal protected physicians from criminal penalties if they had to perform a dilation and extraction because of unforeseen circumstances during a delivery. Finally, the proposal allowed physicians accused of violating the ban to appear before a state medical board instead of a trial court.

In contrast with the AMA, the American College of Obstetricians and Gynecologists and the American Academy of Pediatrics both opposed any ban on dilation and extraction. Some saw a danger in the AMA's position, suggesting that it invited politicians to make decisions about what medical procedures are appropriate.

State Attempts to Ban

Impatient with the slowness of Congress in passing a law banning "partial-birth abortion," about twenty-two states had passed their own laws by 1997. By 2005, however, all these laws had been ruled unconstitutional by the courts.

The most common flaw was that the language of the laws was so broad that it would also apply to abortions performed before the fetus could even be viable. Also, like the original bill passed by Congress, the laws made no exception to protect the pregnant woman's health.

Ohio Decision

In 1995, the Ohio legislature passed a law banning all abortion past the point of fetal viability. Viability was presumed to occur twenty-four weeks after conception. The only exception to the ban was for abortions a physician decided needed to be performed to "prevent the death of the pregnant woman or a serious risk of the substantial and irreversible impairment of a major bodily function of the pregnant woman."

The law also included a provision making it a crime for a physician to end a pregnancy "by purposely inserting a suction device into the skull of a fetus to remove its brain."

In *Voinovich v. Women's Medical Professional Corporation*, a case brought to challenge the law, the U.S. Sixth Circuit Court of Appeals in Cincinnati ruled that the law unconstitutionally restricted a woman's right to abortion by defining the prohibited procedure so broadly that it had the consequence of banning the most common method of performing a surgical abortion during the second trimester.

The ruling was appealed to the Supreme Court. In a 1998 decision (6–3), the Court refused to hear the case, letting the Appeals Court decision stand. In the dissenting opinion, Justice Thomas made clear that the dissenters' concern was not with late-term abortion, but with whether the prohibition of late-term abortion except to protect the life and health of the mother could limit the health that was protected to physical health and exclude mental health. In the 1973 decision *Roe v. Bolton*, the Court had held that physicians may consider "emotional" and "psychological" factors in deciding whether an abortion after fetal viability is necessary to preserve the health of the pregnant woman.

Nebraska Decision

A 2000 ruling by the United States Supreme Court on a Nebraska law resulted in nullifying more than thirty state laws. The 1997 Nebraska law banned "an abortion procedure in which the person performing the abortion partially delivers vaginally a living unborn child before killing the unborn child and completing the delivery." The phrase "partial delivery" was defined as "deliberately and intentionally delivering into the vagina a living unborn child or a substantial proportion thereof."

In a 5–4 vote, the Supreme Court held that the government cannot prohibit physicians from employing an abortion procedure that may be the most medically appropriate way of terminating some pregnancies. The Nebraska law, the Court decided, did not contain provisions for protecting the health and safety of the mother. Justice Stevens wrote in the majority opinion that it was "impossible for me to understand how a state has any legitimate interest in requiring a doctor to follow any procedure other than the one he or she reasonably believes will best protect the woman" in exercising her constitutional right to abortion.

Partial-Birth Abortion Ban Act of 2003

Many observers believed that the Supreme Court decision effectively declared that all legislation, state or federal, aimed at regulating abortion by outlawing procedures would be unconstitutional. Even so, in 2003, Congress passed the Partial-Birth Abortion Ban Act. The law makes it a crime for a doctor to perform an abortion in which "the entire fetal head" or "any part of the fetal trunk past the navel" is outside the woman's uterus at the time the fetal life is terminated.

Opponents of the law immediately challenged it in court, so the law did not take effect. In 2005, the Eighth Circuit U.S. Court of Appeals in St. Louis ruled that the law was unconstitutional. The act, the court held, contained an exception to protect a pregnant woman's life, but it made no exception to protect her health. This decision was in keeping with the court's ruling overturning the 1997 Nebraska law.

Congress, in an attempt to avoid having the law overturned on just this ground, appended to the law a "finding" claiming that the "partial-birth" procedure is never needed to protect the health of a pregnant woman and that "there is no credible medical evidence that partial-birth abortions are safe or are safer than other abortion procedures." Both these claims have been challenged in court by expert medical testimony. One doctor testified, for example, that the fertility of some women could be preserved by avoiding such complications as the puncturing of the uterus by bone fragments.

The Bush administration immediately appealed the St. Louis ruling to the Supreme Court (*Gonzales v. Carhart*). The Court agreed to hear the case, and in 2007 it upheld the constitutionality of the Partial-Birth Abortion Ban Act of 2003. This came as a surprise to many observers, because the Court's 2000 decision had overturned a Nebraska law that was essentially the same as the 2003 Act.

Need for a Law?

Many observers believe there was never a need for laws banning late-term abortion. In keeping with the *Roe v. Wade* decision granting states the power to regulate abortion to protect the interest of the fetus after the first trimester, and in keeping with the *Webster* decision (see the Social Context "Supreme Court Decisions After *Roe v. Wade*" in this chapter), more than forty states passed laws banning abortion after fetal viability. The problem of determining viability, however, is vexing and perhaps unsolvable, but an additional law banning late-term abortion, even if constitutional, would not help resolve the issue.

Advocates for abortion rights and even some opponents of abortion have expressed the view that the controversy over late-term abortion is primarily a way to keep abortion issues at the forefront of political discussion and to pressure politicians to modify their endorsement of elective abortion. Some have also seen the controversy as a way to raise money for all antiabortion activities.

Although, these analyses may be inaccurate, or even cynical, it seems fair to say that the debate over late-term abortion introduces no new ethical issues into the discussion. The old problems remain as complex and perhaps intractable as before.

SOCIAL CONTEXT
Supreme Court Abortion Decisions After *Roe v. Wade*

The conflict over abortion has been expressed, in part, in a continuing series of legal skirmishes that have produced a number of Supreme Court decisions seeking to define abortion rights and limits. To get some sense of the way in which laws, regulations, and practices have changed since the *Roe* decision in 1973, it is useful to review a few Court decisions. They give a sense of the direction taken by public policy on abortion.

Roe v. Bolton (1973)

The Court rejected the requirement that abortions had to be performed in hospitals, thus opening the way for abortion clinics. The Court also found that physicians could consider emotional and psychological factors connected with the health of a pregnant woman in deciding whether an abortion after the first trimester was justifiable.

Planned Parenthood v. Danforth (1976)

The Missouri law requiring a husband's consent for an abortion was struck down. Also, parents of minor, unmarried girls were found not to have an absolute veto over their daughter's decision to have an abortion.

Maher v. Roe (1977)

The Court ruled that states don't have a constitutional obligation to pay for abortions for the poor. Hence, states can decide whether they

want to include abortion funding in their contribution to the Medicaid program.

Harris v. McRae (1980)

The Court upheld the Hyde Amendment, a federal law banning the use of federal Medicaid funds to pay for abortions. Hence, a woman who wants an abortion but is unable to pay for it must obtain the money from some other source. States may choose to provide the funds, but they have no constitutional obligation to do so.

City of Akron v. Akron Center for Reproductive Health (1983)

The Court struck down a law requiring that women seeking an abortion receive counseling that includes the statement that "the unborn child is a human life from the moment of conception," then wait a minimum of twenty-four hours before reaffirming their decision.

Webster v. Reproductive Health Services (1989)

The Missouri law in the *Webster* case is similar to laws the Court had ruled unconstitutional. However, the law was carefully crafted by pro-life advocates to avoid the specific difficulties that had led the Court to reject the law in *Webster*. The preamble of the law asserts that "life begins at conception," but at issue were three provisions restricting abortion: (1) Public employees, including physicians and nurses, are forbidden to perform an abortion, except when necessary to save a woman's life. (2) Tax-supported facilities, including public hospitals, cannot be used to perform abortions, unless one is necessary to save a woman's life. (3) Physicians are required to conduct tests to determine the viability of a fetus if they have reason to believe the woman has been pregnant for at least twenty weeks.

On July 3, 1989, in a 5-to-4 decision, the Supreme Court upheld the constitutionality of the law. Chief Justice William Rehnquist, writing for the majority, held that the Court did not have to rule against the claim that life begins at conception, for such language is only an expression of a permissible value judgment. Furthermore, "Nothing in the Constitution requires States to enter or remain in the business of performing abortions. Nor . . . do private physicians and their patients have some kind of constitutional right of access to public facilities for the performance of abortions."

So far as viability is concerned, Rehnquist saw a problem not with the Missouri law, but with *Roe v. Wade*'s "rigid trimester analysis of a pregnancy." He found the Missouri law more sensitive to the issue of viability than the trimester rule, which holds that the state can regulate abortion in the second trimester (i.e., during the second three-month period) to protect a woman's health and regulate it more stringently, down to prohibiting it, in the last trimester.

Justice Harry A. Blackmun, the author of the majority opinion in *Roe v. Wade*, wrote the dissenting opinion in *Webster*. He regarded the Court's decision as an outright attack on Roe. Rehnquist, he argued, failed to consider the case for viability on appropriate grounds—namely, the right to privacy or autonomy, on which *Roe* was decided. Instead, Rehnquist misread the Missouri law in a way that seemed to conflict with the trimester structure established in *Roe* to balance the state's interest in maternal health and potential life against the right to privacy.

Abortion opponents hoped that the Court would use the *Webster* case to overturn *Roe v.*

Wade. The Court stopped short of that, but the *Webster* decision made it clear that the Court was willing to approve restrictions on abortion of a sort that it had held unconstitutional until then. Various new state and local regulations were then formulated and passed into law.

Planned Parenthood v. Casey (1992)

The Pennsylvania Abortion Control Act was framed with the intention of making abortions more difficult to secure. It set forth the following restrictions: (1) A physician must inform a woman seeking an abortion about the procedure and its risks, the stage of her pregnancy, and the alternative of carrying the fetus to term. (2) The woman must wait at least twenty-four hours after receiving this information before having an abortion. (3) A girl under the age of eighteen must secure the informed consent of at least one parent before having an abortion, and a parent must accompany the girl to counseling. Alternatively, consent may be sought from a court. (4) A married woman must (except under certain circumstances) sign a statement that she has notified her husband of her intention to have an abortion.

The 5-to-4 Court ruling upheld most sections of the law, but it rejected the provision requiring a married woman to notify her husband of her intention. In the view of some, however, the most important result of the *Casey* decision was to reaffirm a constitutional right to an abortion, while introducing a new legal standard for testing the constitutional legitimacy of abortion regulations.

The Court considered the law's provisions in terms of whether they had the purpose or result of imposing an "undue burden" on a woman seeking an abortion. The Court defined a burden as "undue" if it places a "substantial obstacle in the path of a woman seeking an abortion before the fetus attains viability." Only the spousal notification requirement, the Court held, imposed such a burden. The undue-burden standard thus made clear the Court's view that laws attempting to prohibit abortions outright or reduce the frequency of abortions by making them extraordinarily difficult to obtain are unconstitutional.

The Court explicitly endorsed *Roe v. Wade* as having established "a rule of law and a component of liberty that we cannot renounce." It held that Roe has acquired such a "rare precedential force" that it could be repudiated only "at the cost of both profound and unnecessary damage to the Court's legitimacy and to the nation's commitment to the rule of law."

Until the *Webster* decision, abortion was considered a fundamental right that could not be restricted, except to serve a compelling state interest. Thus, during the first two trimesters of pregnancy, almost all restrictions were considered unconstitutional. After *Webster*, abortion opponents saw that it might be possible to impose more and heavier regulation. However, although the "undue-burden" standard introduced in *Casey* permits considerable regulation during that period, it does not allow the practice to be regulated so heavily as to make it virtually unavailable.

Madsen v. Women's Health Center (1994)

In 1993, a Florida Circuit Court issued an injunction to protect access to the clinic operated by the Aware Woman Center for Choice in Melbourne, Florida. Demonstrators from Operation Rescue and related organizations were made subject to the injunction. The order imposed a 300-foot protected zone around the clinic, forbade the display of signs that could be seen from inside the clinic, and barred demonstrators from making excessive noise.

The case was appealed, and in a 6-to-3 ruling the Supreme Court upheld the basic provisions of the injunction. It approved an approximately thirty-six-foot buffer zone to keep protesters away from the clinic's entrance and parking lot and off a public right-of-way. The buffer zone "burdens no more speech than necessary to accomplish the government's interest," Justice Rehnquist wrote.

Schenck v. Pro-Choice Network (1997)

In a New York State case in which a group opposed to abortion appealed an injunction ordering them to cease blockading the entrances to a clinic and stop harassing and intimidating the women seeking an abortion, the Supreme Court, in a 6-to-3 decision, upheld the lower court's decision to keep the protesters from blocking doorways and driveways.

The Court struck down (6–3) a section of the New York law that established a "floating" fifteen-foot buffer zone between protesters and people entering or leaving a clinic, because the indefinite character of the zone raised the prospect of suppressing more speech than necessary to protect the state's interest in public safety. Yet the Court upheld (6–3) a section of the injunction allowing only two protesters at a time to come within a fixed fifteen-foot buffer zone to talk to women in a nonthreatening way and to "cease and desist" and to withdraw outside the zone if asked to do so.

The Court's tacit endorsement of a fixed buffer zone around abortion clinics is significant, because about 300 of the 900 abortion clinics in the country are protected by buffer zones spelled out in court injunctions. Both the Florida and New York rulings are considered important indicators of the Court's view of the Freedom of Access to Clinic Entrances Act, which is designed to provide federal remedies, including criminal penalties, to restrict violent protests at abortion clinics.

Hill v. Colorado (2000)

In a 6-to-3 ruling, the Court held that a Colorado law aimed at protecting abortion clinic physicians, patients, and visitors from harassment by protestors did not violate the protestors' First Amendment rights to free expression. The law holds that within 100 feet of any health care facility, no one can approach anyone closer than eight feet to talk or pass out leaflets, unless the person approached permits it.

Stenberg v. Carhart (2000)

A Nebraska law directed at prohibiting late-term (past twenty weeks) abortion banned any "abortion procedure in which the person performing the abortion partially delivers vaginally a living unborn child before killing the unborn child and completing the delivery." In a 5–4 vote, the Court held that the government cannot prohibit physicians from employing whatever abortion procedure may be the most medically appropriate. Also, in trying to regulate abortion, the law failed to include any provisions for protecting the health and safety of the pregnant woman. Justice Stevens wrote in the majority opinion that it is "impossible for me to understand how a state has any legitimate interest in requiring a doctor to follow any procedure other than the one he or she reasonably believes will best protect the woman" in exercising her constitutional right to abortion.

Gonzales v. Carhart (2007)

Congress passed the *Partial-Birth Abortion Ban Act* in 2003, making it a crime to perform an abortion in which "the entire fetal head" or "any part of the fetal trunk past the navel" is outside the woman's uterus at the time fetal life is ended. The law was challenged before it went into effect, and a federal Appeals Court rulings in St. Louis found it to be unconstitutional. The rulings were immediately appealed to the Supreme Court, which upheld the law in a 5–4 decision. The ruling effectively negated the impact of the 2000 Nebraska decision, which had found unconstitutional a law with virtually the same prohibitions as the 2003 Partial-Birth Abortion Ban Act.

BRIEFING SESSION

Hardly more than three decades ago, most Americans considered abortion a crime so disgusting that it was rarely mentioned in public. Back-alley abortionists with dirty hands and unclean instruments were real enough, but they were also the villains of cautionary tales to warn women against being tempted into the crime. Abortion was the dramatic stuff of novels and movies portraying "girls in trouble" or women pushed to the brink. To choose to have an abortion was to choose to be degraded.

The Supreme Court decision in *Roe v. Wade* changed all that in 1973. The decision had the effect of legalizing abortion, and since then abortion has gained an ambivalent acceptance from a majority of the population. Yet controversy over the legitimacy of abortion continues to flare. Indeed, no other topic in medical ethics has attracted more attention or so polarized public opinion. The reason is understandable: in the abortion question, major moral, legal, and social issues are intertwined to form a problem of great subtlety and complexity.

Before focusing on some of the specific issues raised by abortion, it is useful to have in hand some of the relevant factual information about human developmental biology and the techniques of abortion.

Human Development and Abortion

Fertilization occurs when an ovum is penetrated by a sperm cell and the nuclei of the two unite to form a single cell containing forty-six chromosomes. This normally occurs in the fallopian tube (or oviduct), a narrow tube leading from the ovary into the uterus (womb). The fertilized ovum—zygote, or conceptus—continues its passage down the fallopian tube, and during its two- to three-day passage it undergoes a number of cell divisions that increase its size. (Rarely, the zygote does not descend but continues to develop in the fallopian tube, producing an ectopic pregnancy. Because the tube is so small, the pregnancy has to be terminated surgically.) After reaching the uterus, a pear-shaped organ, the zygote floats free in the intra-uterine fluid. Here it develops into a *blastocyst*, a ball of cells surrounding a fluid-filled cavity.

By the end of the second week, the blastocyst becomes embedded in the wall of the uterus. At this point and until the end of the eighth week, it is known as an embryo. During the fourth and fifth weeks, organ systems begin to develop, and the external features take on a definitely human shape. During the eighth week, brain activity usually becomes detectable. At this time, the embryo comes to be known as a fetus.

Birth generally occurs about nine months after fertilization or, to be more accurate, around forty-plus weeks. It is customary to divide this time into three three-month (thirteen-week) periods or trimesters.

At present, pregnancy can be diagnosed as early as seven to ten days after fertilization. Also, improvements in ultrasound imaging allow the gestational sac surrounding the embryo to be detected in its earliest stages. Hence, a woman may be found to be pregnant even before she has missed an expected period.

Abortion is the termination of pregnancy. It can occur because of internal biochemical factors or as a result of physical injury to the woman. Terminations from such causes are usually referred to as "spontaneous abortions," but they are also commonly called miscarriages.

Abortion can also be a deliberate process resulting from human intervention. The methods used in contemporary medicine depend to a great extent on the stage of the pregnancy. The earliest intervention involves the use of drugs (such as RU-486 or the hormones in birth control pills) to prevent the embedding of the blastocyst in the uterine wall.

Because the new tests and ultrasound make it possible to detect pregnancy as early as a week or ten days after fertilization, a pregnancy can be terminated at that point. A physician dilates (widens) the cervix (the narrow opening to the uterus), then uses a hand-operated syringe to suction out the contents of the uterus.

Subsequent intervention during the first trimester (up to about twelve weeks) commonly employs the same technique of uterine or vacuum aspiration. After the cervix is dilated, a small tube is inserted into the uterus and its contents are emptied by suction. The procedure is known as dilation and evacuation. The classical abortion procedure is dilation and curettage. The cervix is dilated, and its contents are gently scraped out by the use of a curette, a spoon-shaped surgical instrument. The procedure has been almost wholly replaced by evacuation in developed countries.

After twelve weeks, when the fetus is too large to make the other methods practical, the most common abortion technique involves dilating the cervix and extracting the fetus. (See the Social Context "The 'Partial-Birth Abortion' Controversy," earlier in this chapter, for discussion.)

These facts about pregnancy and abortion put us in a position to discuss some of the moral problems connected with them. We won't be able to untangle the skein of issues wrapped around the abortion question. We'll only attempt to state a few of the more serious ones and to indicate the lines of argument that have been offered to support positions taken with respect to them; afterward we'll sketch out some possible responses that might be offered on the basis of the ethical theories we discuss in Part V, "Foundations of Bioethics."

The Status of the Fetus

It is crucial for the application of the principles of any moral theory that we have a settled opinion about the objects and subjects of morality. Although principles are generally stated with respect to rational individuals, every theory recognizes that there are people who in fact cannot be considered rational agents. For example, mental and physical incapacities may diminish or destroy rationality. But ethical theories generally recognize that we still have duties to people who are so incapacitated.

The basic problem that this raises is this: Who or what is to be considered a person? Are there any characteristics that we can point to and say that it is by virtue of possessing these characteristics that an individual must be considered a person and thus accorded moral treatment?

The abortion issue raises this question most particularly with regard to the fetus. (We will use the term "fetus," for the moment, to refer to the developing organism at any stage.) Just what is the status of the fetus in the world? We must find a satisfactory answer to this question, some writers have suggested, before we can resolve the general moral problem of abortion.

Let's consider the possible consequences of answering the question one way or the other. First, if a fetus is a person, it has a serious claim to life. We must assert the claim on its behalf, for, like an unconscious person, the fetus is unable to do so. The claim of the fetus as a person must be given weight and respect in deliberating about any action that would terminate its life. Perhaps only circumstances as extreme as a threat to the life of the mother would justify abortion.

Assuming that the fetus is a person, then, an abortion would be a case of killing and something not to be undertaken without reasons sufficient to override the fetus's claim to life. In effect, only conditions of the same sort that would justify our killing an adult person (e.g., self-defense) would justify our killing a fetus. Thus, the moral burden in every case would be to demonstrate that abortion is not a case of wrongful killing.

By contrast, if a fetus is not a person in a morally relevant sense, then abortion need not be considered a case of killing equivalent to the killing of an adult. In one view, it might be said that an abortion is not essentially different from an appendectomy. According to this way of thinking, a fetus is no more than a complicated clump of organic material, and its removal involves no serious moral difficulty.

In another view, it could be argued that, even though the fetus is not a person, it is a potential person, and thus is a significant and morally relevant property. The fetus's very potentiality makes it unique and distinguishes it from a diseased appendix, a cyst, or any other kind of organic material. Thus, because the fetus can become a person, abortion does present a moral problem. A fetus can be destroyed only for serious reasons. Thus, preventing a person from coming into existence must be justified to an extent comparable to the justification required for killing a person. (Some have suggested that the justification does not have to be identical because the fetus is only a potential person. The justification we might present for killing a person would thus serve only as a guide for those who might justify abortion.)

So far we have used the word "fetus," and this usage tends to obscure the fact that human development is a process with many stages. Perhaps it is only in the later stages of development that the entity becomes a person. But exactly when might this happen?

The difference between a fertilized ovum and a fully developed baby just a few minutes before birth are considerable. The ovum and the blastocyst seem just so much tissue. But the embryo and the fetus present more serious claims to being persons. Should abortion be allowed until the fetus becomes visibly human, or until the fetus shows heartbeat and brain waves, or until the fetus can live outside the uterus (becomes viable)?

The process of development is continuous, and so far it has proved impossible to find differences between stages that can be generally accepted as morally relevant. Some writers on abortion have suggested that it is useless to look for such differences, because any place where the line is drawn will be arbitrary. Others have claimed that it is possible to draw the line by relying on criteria that can be rationally defended. A few have even argued that a reasonable set of criteria for determining who shall be considered a person might even deny the status to infants.

Pregnancy, Abortion, and the Rights of Women

Pregnancy and fetal development are normal biological processes, and most women who choose to have a child carry it to term without unusual difficulties. However, it is important to keep in mind that even a normal pregnancy involves changes and stresses that are uniquely burdensome. Once the process of fetal growth is initiated, a woman's entire physiology is altered by the new demands placed on it and by the biochemical changes taking place within her body. For example, the metabolic rate increases, the thyroid gland grows larger, the heart pumps more blood to meet fetal needs, and a great variety of hormonal changes take place. The growing fetus physically displaces the woman's internal organs and alters the size and shape of her body.

As a result of such changes, the pregnant woman may suffer a variety of ailments. More common ones include severe nausea and vomiting ("morning sickness"), muscle cramps, abdominal pain, anemia, tiredness, and headaches. For many women, such complaints are relatively mild or infrequent; for others, they are severe or constant. Nausea and vomiting can lead to dehydration and malnutrition so serious as to be life threatening. Women who suffer from diseases such as diabetes are apt to face special health problems as a result of pregnancy.

Partly because of hormonal changes, women are also more likely to experience psychological difficulties when pregnant, such as emotional lability (mood swings), severe depression, and acute anxiety. Such conditions are often accompanied by quite realistic concerns about the loss of freedom associated with becoming a parent, compromised job status, loss of sexual attractiveness due to the change in body shape, and the pains and risks of childbirth.

The woman who intends to carry a child to term is also likely to have to alter her behavior in many ways. She may have to curtail the time she spends working, take a leave of absence, or even quit her job. Any career plans she has are likely to suffer. She may be unable to participate in social activities to the extent that she previously did, and forced to give up some entirely. In addition, if she recognizes an obligation to the developing fetus and is well informed, she may have to alter her diet, stop smoking, and strictly limit the amount of alcohol she consumes.

In sum, the physical and emotional price paid by a woman for a full-term pregnancy is high. Even a normal pregnancy, one that proceeds without any special difficulties, exacts a toll of discomfort, stress, restricted activity, and worry.

Women who wish to have a child are generally willing to undergo the rigors of pregnancy to satisfy this desire. But is it a woman's duty to nurture and carry to term an unwanted child? Pregnancies resulting from rape and incest are the kinds of dramatic cases frequently mentioned to emphasize the seriousness of the burden imposed on women. But the question is also important when the conditions surrounding the pregnancy are more ordinary.

Suppose that a woman becomes pregnant unintentionally and decides that having a child will be harmful to her career or her way of life. Or suppose she simply does not wish to subject herself to the pains of pregnancy. Does a woman have a moral duty to see to it that the developing child comes to be born?

A number of writers have taken the position that women have an exclusive right to control their own reproductive function. In the view of these writers, such a right is based upon the generally recognized right to control what is done to our bodies. Since pregnancy is something that involves a woman's body, the woman concerned may legitimately decide whether to continue the pregnancy or terminate it. The decision is hers alone, and social or legal policies that restrict the free exercise of her right are unjustifiable.

Essentially the same point is sometimes phrased by saying that women own their bodies. Because their bodies are their own "property," women alone have the right to decide whether to become pregnant and, if pregnant unintentionally, whether to have an abortion.

Critics have pointed out that this general line of argument, taken alone, does not support the strong conclusion that women should be free from all constraints in making abortion decisions. Even granting that women's bodies are their own property, we nevertheless recognize restrictions on exercising property rights. We have no right to shoot trespassers, and we cannot endanger our neighbors by burning down our house. Similarly, if any legitimate moral claims can be made on behalf of the fetus, then the right of women to decide whether to have an abortion may not be unrestricted.

Some philosophers (e.g., Judith Jarvis Thomson) have taken the view that, although women are entitled to control their bodies and make abortion decisions, the decision to have an abortion must be supported by weighty reasons. They have suggested that, even if we grant that a fetus is a person, its claim to life cannot be given unconditional precedence over the woman's claim to control her own life. She is entitled to autonomy and the right to arrange her life in accordance with her own concept of the good. It would be wrong for her to destroy the fetus for a trivial reason, but legitimate and adequate reasons for taking the life of the fetus might be offered.

Others, by contrast, have argued that when a woman becomes pregnant, she assumes a responsibility for the life of the fetus. It is, after

all, completely dependent on her for its continued existence. She has no more right to take its life in order to seek her own best interest than she has to murder someone whose death may bring benefits to her.

Therapeutic Abortion

Abortion is sometimes required to save the life of the mother or in order to provide her with medical treatment considered essential to her health. Abortion performed for such a purpose is ordinarily regarded as a case of self-defense. For this reason, it is almost universally considered to be morally unobjectionable. (Strictly speaking, the Roman Catholic view condemns abortion in all of its forms. It does approve of providing medical treatment for the mother, even if this results in the death of the fetus, but the death of the fetus must never be intended.)

If the principle of preserving the life and health of the mother justifies abortion, then what conditions fall under that principle? If a woman has cancer of the uterus and her life can be saved only by an operation that will result in the death of the fetus, then this clearly falls under the principle. But what about psychological conditions? Is a woman's mental health relevant to deciding whether an abortion is justified? What if a psychiatrist believes that a woman cannot face the physical rigors of pregnancy or bear the psychological stresses that go with it without developing severe psychiatric symptoms? Would such a judgment justify an abortion? Or is the matter of psychological health irrelevant to the abortion issue?

Consider, too, the welfare of the fetus. Suppose that prenatal tests indicate that the developing child suffers from serious abnormalities. (This was the case of the "thalidomide babies.") Is abortion for the purpose of preventing the birth of such children justifiable?

It might be argued that it is not, that an impaired fetus has as much right to its life as an impaired person. We do not, after all, consider it legitimate to kill people who become seriously injured or suffer from diseases that render them helpless. Rather, we care for them and work to improve their lives—or at least we ought to.

Some might argue, however, that abortion in such cases is not only justifiable, but a duty. It is our duty to kill the fetus to spare the person it will become a life of unhappiness and suffering. We might even be said to be acknowledging the dignity of the fetus by doing what it might do for itself if it could—what any rational creature would do. Destroying such a fetus would spare future pain to the individual and his or her family and save the family and society from an enormous expense. Thus, we have not only a justification to kill such a fetus, but also the positive obligation to do so.

In this chapter, we will not deal explicitly with the issues that are raised by attempting to decide whether it is justifiable to terminate the life of an impaired fetus. Because such issues are directly connected with prenatal genetic diagnosis and treatment, we discuss them more fully in Chapter 10. Nonetheless, in considering the general question of the legitimacy of abortion, it is important to keep such special considerations in mind.

Abortion and the Law

Abortion in our society has been a legal issue as well as a moral issue. Until the Supreme Court decision in *Roe v. Wade,* nontherapeutic abortion was illegal in virtually all states. The Webster decision (see the Social Context "Supreme Court Decisions After *Roe v. Wade,*" in this chapter) is a recent indication that the Court is willing to accept more state restrictions than previously, but even so, abortions are far from being illegal. However, even though groups still lobby for a constitutional amendment to protect a fetus's "right to life" and prohibit elective abortion, the position has little popular support.

The rightness or wrongness of abortion is a moral matter, one whose issues can be resolved only by appealing to a moral theory. Different theories may yield incompatible answers, and even individuals who accept the same theory may arrive at different conclusions.

Such a state of affairs raises the question of whether the moral convictions or conclusions of some people should be embodied in laws that govern the lives of all people in the society. The question can be put succinctly: Should the moral beliefs of some people serve as the basis for laws that will impose those beliefs on everyone?

This question cannot be answered in a straightforward way. To some extent, which moral beliefs are at issue is a relevant consideration. So, too, are the political principles that we are willing to accept as basic to our society. Every ethical theory recognizes that there is a scope of action that must be left to individuals as moral agents acting freely on the basis of their own understanding and perceptions. Laws requiring the expression of benevolence or gratitude, for example, seem peculiarly inappropriate.

Yet, one of the major aims of a government is to protect the rights of its citizens. Consequently, a society must have just laws that recognize and enforce those rights. In a very real way, then, the moral theory we hold and the conclusions arrived at on the basis of it will determine whether we believe that certain types of laws are justified. They are justified when they protect the rights recognized in our moral theories—when political rights reflect moral rights. (See the Briefing Session in Chapter 8 for a fuller discussion of moral rights and their relation to political rights.)

An ethical theory that accords the status of a person to a fetus is likely to claim also that the laws of the society should recognize the rights of the fetus. A theory that does not grant the fetus this position is not likely to regard laws forbidding abortion as justifiable.

Ethical Theories and Abortion

Theories like those of Mill, Kant, Ross, and Rawls attribute autonomy, or self-direction to individuals. An individual is entitled to control his or her own life, and it seems reasonable to extend this principle to apply to one's own body. If so, then a woman should have the right to determine whether or not she wishes to have a child. If she is pregnant with an unwanted child, then, no matter how she came to be pregnant, she might legitimately decide on an abortion. Utilitarianism also suggests this answer, though on consequential grounds. In the absence of other considerations, if it seems likely that having a child will produce more unhappiness than an abortion would, then an abortion would be justifiable.

If the fetus is considered to be a person, however, the situation is different for some theories. The natural law view holds that the fetus is an innocent person and that direct abortion is never justifiable. Even if the pregnancy is due to rape, the fetus cannot be held at fault and made to suffer through its death. Even though she may not wish to have the child, the mother has a duty to preserve the life of the fetus.

For deontological theories like those of Kant and Ross, the situation becomes more complicated. If the fetus is a person, it has an inherent dignity and worth. It is an innocent life that cannot be destroyed except for the weightiest moral reasons. Those reasons may include the interests and wishes of the woman, but deontological theories provide no clear answer as to how these factors are to be weighed.

For utilitarianism, by contrast, even if the fetus is considered a person, the principle of utility may still justify an abortion. Killing a person is not, for utilitarianism, inherently wrong. (Yet it is compatible with rule utilitarianism to argue that permitting elective abortion as a matter of policy would produce more unhappiness than forbidding abortion altogether. Thus, utilitarianism does not offer a definite answer to the abortion issue.)

As we have already seen, both utilitarianism and deontological theories can be used to justify therapeutic abortion. When the mother's life or health is at stake, the situation may be construed as one of self-defense. Both Kant and Ross recognize that we each have a right to protect ourselves, even if it means taking the life of another person. For utilitarianism, preserving one's life is justifiable, for being alive is a necessary condition for all forms of happiness.

We have also indicated that abortion "for the sake of the fetus" can be justified by both utilitarianism and deontological theories. If by killing the fetus we can spare it a life of suffering, minimize the sufferings of its family, and preserve the resources of the society, then abortion is legitimate on utilitarian grounds. In the terms of Kant and Ross, destroying the fetus might be a way of recognizing its dignity. If we assume that it is a person, then by sparing it a life of indignity and pain, we are treating it in the way that a rational being would want to be treated.

The legitimacy of laws forbidding abortion is an issue that utilitarianism would resolve by considering their effects. If such laws promote the general happiness of the society, then they are justifiable. Otherwise, they are not. In general, Kant, Ross, Rawls, and natural law theory recognize intrinsic human worth and regard as legitimate laws protecting that worth, even if those holding this view are only a minority of the society. Thus, laws discriminating against blacks and women, for example, would be considered unjust on the basis of these theories. Laws enforcing equality, by contrast, would be considered just.

But what about fetuses? The Roman Catholic interpretation of natural law would regard the case as exactly the same. As full human persons, they are entitled to have their rights protected by law. Those who fail to recognize this are guilty of moral failure, and laws permitting abortion are the moral equivalent of laws permitting murder.

For Kant and other deontologists, the matter is less clear. As long as there is substantial doubt about the status of the fetus, it is not certain that it is legitimate to demand that the rights of fetuses be recognized and protected by law. It is clear that the issue of whether or not the fetus is considered a person is most often taken as the crucial one in the abortion controversy.

The battle over abortion is certain to continue in the courts, the streets, the media, and classrooms. The issues are of great social importance, yet highly personal and explosively emotional. The best hope for a resolution continues to rest with the condemnation of violence and an emphasis on the traditional strategies of verbal persuasion, rational argument, and the appeal to basic moral principles.

READINGS

Section 1: Abortion and the "Deprivation of Futures" Argument

Why Abortion Is Immoral

Don Marquis

Don Marquis offers what he considers to be an essentially new argument to establish the basic wrongness of abortion. The reason murder is wrong, according to Marquis, is that it deprives a person of the value of his or her future. Because a fetus, if not aborted, can be assumed to have a future like ours that is also of value, abortion, like any other kind of killing, can be justified only by the most compelling reasons. Contraception, by contrast, is not wrong, because there is no identifiable individual to be deprived of a future.

The view that abortion is, with rare exceptions, seriously immoral has received little support in the recent philosophical literature. No doubt most philosophers affiliated with secular institutions of higher education believe that the anti-abortion position is either a symptom of irrational religious dogma or a conclusion generated by seriously confused philosophical argument. The purpose of this essay is to undermine this general belief. This essay sets out an argument that purports to show, as well as any argument in ethics can show, that abortion is, except possibly in rare cases, seriously immoral, that it is in the same moral category as killing an innocent adult human being . . .

I

 . . . [A] necessary condition of resolving the abortion controversy is a more theoretical account of the

Don Marquis, From "Why Abortion is Immoral", *The Journal of Philosophy*, Vol. 86, no. 4, (1989):183–202. Copyright © 1989 THE JOURNAL OF PHILOSOPHY, INC. Reproduced by permission.

wrongness of killing. After all, if we merely believe, but do not understand, why killing adult human beings such as ourselves is wrong, how could we conceivably show that abortion is either immoral or permissible?

II

In order to develop such an account, we can start from the following unproblematic assumption concerning our own case: it is wrong to kill *us*. Why is it wrong? Some answers can be easily eliminated. It might be said that what makes killing us wrong is that a killing brutalizes the one who kills. But the brutalization consists of being inured to the performance of an act that is hideously immoral; hence, the brutalization does not explain the immorality. It might be said that what makes killing us wrong is the great loss others would experience due to our absence. Although such hubris is understandable, such an explanation does not account for the wrongness of killing hermits, or those whose lives are relatively independent and whose friends find it easy to make new friends.

A more obvious answer is better. What primarily makes killing wrong is neither its effect on the murderer nor its effect on the victim's friends and relatives, but its effect on the victim. The loss of one's life is one of the greatest losses one can suffer. The loss of one's life deprives one of all the experiences, activities, projects, and enjoyments that would otherwise have constituted one's future. Therefore, killing someone is wrong, primarily because the killing inflicts (one of) the greatest possible losses on the victim. To describe this as the loss of life can be misleading, however. The change in my biological state does not by itself make killing me wrong. The effect of the loss of my biological life is the loss to me of all those activities, projects, experiences, and enjoyments which would otherwise have constituted my future personal life. These activities, projects, experiences, and enjoyments are either valuable for their own sakes or are means to something else that is valuable for its own sake. Some parts of my future are not valued by me now, but will come to be valued by me as I grow older and as my values and capacities change. When I am killed, I am deprived both of what I now value which would have been part of my future personal life, but also what I would come to value. Therefore, when I die, I am deprived of all of the value of my future. Inflicting this loss on me is ultimately what makes killing me wrong. This being the case, it would seem that what makes killing *any* adult human being prima facie seriously wrong is the loss of his or her future . . .

The claim that what makes killing wrong is the loss of the victim's future is directly supported by two considerations. In the first place, this theory explains why we regard killing as one of the worst of crimes. Killing is especially wrong, because it deprives the victim of more than perhaps any other crime. In the second place, people with AIDS or cancer who know they are dying believe, of course, that dying is a very bad thing for them. They believe that the loss of a future to them that they would otherwise have experienced is what makes their premature death a very bad thing for them. A better theory of the wrongness of killing would require a different natural property associated with killing which better fits with the attitudes of the dying. What could it be?

The view that what makes killing wrong is the loss to the victim of the value of the victim's future gains additional support when some of its implications are examined. In the first place, it is incompatible with the view that it is wrong to kill only beings who are biologically human. It is possible that there exists a differ-ent species from another planet whose members have a future like ours. Since having a future like that is what makes killing someone wrong, this theory entails that it would be wrong to kill members of such a species. Hence, this theory is opposed to the claim that only life that is biologically human has great moral worth, a claim which many anti-abortionists have seemed to adopt. This opposition, which this theory has in common with personhood theories, seems to be a merit of the theory.

In the second place, the claim that the loss of one's future is the wrong-making feature of one's being killed entails the possibility that the futures of some actual nonhuman mammals on our own planet are sufficiently like ours that it is seriously wrong to kill them also. Whether some animals do have the same right to life as human beings depends on adding to the account of the wrongness of killing some additional account of just what it is about my future or the futures of other adult human beings which makes it wrong to kill us. No such additional account will be offered in this essay. Undoubtedly, the provision of such an account would be a very difficult matter. Undoubtedly, any such account would be quite controversial. Hence, it surely should not reflect badly on this sketch of an elementary theory of the wrongness of killing that it is indeterminate with respect to some very difficult issues regarding animal rights.

In the third place, the claim that the loss of one's future is the wrong-making feature of one's being killed does not entail, as sanctity of human life theories do, that active euthanasia is wrong. Persons who are severely and incurably ill, who face a future of pain and despair, and who wish to die will not have suffered a loss if they are killed. It is, strictly speaking, the value of a human's future which makes killing wrong in this theory. This being so, killing does not necessarily wrong some persons who are sick or dying. Of course, there may be other reasons for a prohibition of active euthanasia, but that is another matter. Sanctity-of-human-life theories seem to hold that active euthanasia is seriously wrong even in an individual case where there seems to be good reason for it independently of public policy considerations. This consequence is most implausible, and it is a plus for the claim that the loss of a future of value is what makes killing wrong that it does not share this consequence.

In the fourth place, the account of the wrongness of killing defended in this essay does straightforwardly entail that it is prima facie seriously wrong to kill children and infants, for we do presume that they have futures of value. Since we do believe that it is wrong to kill defenseless little babies, it is important that a theory of the wrongness of killing easily account for this. Personhood theories of the wrongness of killing, on the other hand, cannot straightforwardly account for the wrongness of killing infants and young children. Hence, such theories must add special ad hoc accounts of the wrongness of killing the young. The plausibility of such ad hoc theories seems to be a function of how desperately one wants such theories to work. The claim that the primary wrong-making feature of a killing is the loss to the victim of the value of its future accounts for the wrongness of killing young children and infants directly; it makes the wrongness of such acts as obvious as we actually think it is. This is a further merit of this theory. Accordingly, it seems that this value of a future-like-ours theory of the wrongness of killing shares strengths of both sanctity-of-life and personhood accounts while avoiding weaknesses of both. In addition, it meshes with a central intuition concerning what makes killing wrong.

The claim that the primary wrong-making feature of a killing is the loss to the victim of the value of its future has obvious consequences for the ethics of abortion. The future of a standard fetus includes a set of experiences, projects, activities, and such which are identical with the futures of adult human beings and are identical with the future of young children. Since the reason that is sufficient to explain why it is wrong to kill human beings after the time of birth is a reason that also applies to fetuses, it follows that abortion is prima facie seriously morally wrong.

This argument does not rely on the invalid inference that, since it is wrong to kill persons, it is wrong to kill potential persons also. The category that is morally central to this analysis is the category of having a valuable future like ours; it is not the category of personhood. The argument to the conclusion that abortion is prima [facie] seriously morally wrong proceeded independently of the notion of person or potential person or any equivalent . . .

Of course, this value of a future-like-ours argument, if sound, shows only that abortion is prima facie wrong, not that it is wrong in any and all circumstances. Since the loss of the future to a standard fetus, if killed, is, however, at least as great a loss as the loss of the future to a standard adult human being who is killed, abortion, like ordinary killing, could be justified only by the most compelling reasons. The loss of one's life is almost the greatest misfortune that can happen to one. Presumably abortion could be justified in some circumstances, only if the loss consequent on failing to abort would be at least as great. Accordingly, morally permissible abortions will be rare indeed unless, perhaps, they occur so early in pregnancy that a fetus is not yet definitely an individual. Hence, this argument should be taken as showing that abortion is presumptively very seriously wrong, where the presumption is very strong—as strong as the presumption that killing another adult human being is wrong.

III

How complete an account of the wrongness of killing does the value of a future-like-ours account have to be in order that the wrongness of abortion is a consequence? This account does not have to be an account of the necessary conditions for the wrongness of killing. Some persons in nursing homes may lack valuable human futures, yet it may be wrong to kill them for other reasons. Furthermore, this account does not obviously have to be the sole reason killing is wrong where the victim did have a valuable future. This analysis claims only that, for any killing where the victim did have a valuable future like ours, having that future by itself is sufficient to create the strong presumption that the killing is seriously wrong.

One way to overturn the value of a future-like-ours argument would be to find some account of the wrongness of killing which is at least as intelligible and which has different implications for the ethics of abortion. Two rival accounts possess at least some degree of plausibility. One account is based on the obvious fact that people value the experience of living and wish for that valuable experience to continue. Therefore, it might be said, what makes killing wrong is the discontinuation of that experience for the victim. Let us call this the *discontinuation account.* Another rival account is based upon the obvious fact that people strongly desire to continue to live. This suggests that what makes killing us so wrong is that it interferes with the fulfillment of a strong and fundamental desire, the fulfillment of which is necessary for the fulfillment of any other desires we might have. Let us call this the *desire account.*

Consider first the desire account as a rival account of the ethics of killing which would provide the basis for rejecting the anti-abortion position. Such an account will have to be stronger than the value of a future-like-ours account of the wrongness of abortion if it is to do the job expected of it. To entail the wrongness of abortion, the value of a future-like-ours account has only to provide a sufficient, but not a necessary, condition for the wrongness of killing. The desire account, on the other hand, must provide us also with a necessary condition for the wrongness of killing in order to generate a pro-choice conclusion on abortion. The reason for this is that presumably the argument from the desire account moves from the claim that what makes killing wrong is interference with a very strong desire to the claim that abortion is not wrong because the fetus lacks a strong desire to live. Obviously, this inference fails if someone's having the desire to live is not a necessary condition of its being wrong to kill that individual.

One problem with the desire account is that we do regard it as seriously wrong to kill persons who have little desire to live or who have no desire to live or, indeed, have a desire not to live. We believe it is seriously wrong to kill the unconscious, the sleeping, those who are tired of life, and those who are suicidal. The value-of-a-human-future account renders standard morality intelligible in these cases; these cases appear to be incompatible with the desire account.

The desire account is subject to a deeper difficulty. We desire life, because we value the goods of this life. The goodness of life is not secondary to our desire for it. If this were not so, the pain of one's own premature death could be done away with merely by an appropriate alteration in the configuration of one's desires. This is absurd. Hence, it would seem that it is the loss of the goods of one's future, not the interference with the fulfillment of a strong desire to live, which accounts ultimately for the wrongness of killing . . .

The discontinuation account looks more promising as an account of the wrongness of killing. It seems just as intelligible as the value of a future-like-ours account, but it does not justify an anti-abortion position. Obviously, if it is the continuation of one's activities, experiences, and projects, the loss of which makes killing wrong, then it is not wrong to kill fetuses for that reason, for fetuses do not have experiences, activities, and projects to be continued or discontinued. Accordingly, the discontinuation account does not have the anti-abortion consequences that the value of a future-like-ours account has. Yet, it seems as intelligible as the value of a future-like-ours account, for when we think of what would be wrong with our being killed, it does seem as if it is the discontinuation of what makes our lives worthwhile which makes killing us wrong.

Is the discontinuation account just as good an account as the value of a future-like-ours account? The discontinuation account will not be adequate at all, if it does not refer to the *value* of the experience that may be discontinued. One does not want the discontinuation account to make it wrong to kill a patient who begs for death and who is in severe pain that cannot be relieved short of killing. (I leave open the question of whether it is wrong for other reasons.) Accordingly, the discontinuation account must be more than a bare discontinuation account. It must make some reference to the positive value of the patient's experience. But, by the same token, the value of a future-like-ours account cannot be a bare future account either. Just having a future surely does not itself rule out killing the above patient. This account must make some reference to the value of the patient's future experience and projects also. Hence, both accounts involve the value of experiences, projects, and activities. So far we still have symmetry between the accounts.

The symmetry fades, however, when we focus on the time period of the value of the experiences, etc., which has moral consequences. Although both accounts leave open the possibility that the patient in our example may be killed, this possibility is left open only in virtue of the utterly bleak future for the patient. It makes no difference whether the patient's immediate past contains intolerable pain, or consists of being in a coma (which we can imagine is a situation of indifference), or consists in a life of value. If the patient's future is a future of value, we want our account to make it wrong to kill the patient. If the patient's future is intolerable, whatever his or her immediate past, we want our account to allow killing the patient. Obviously, then, it is the value of that patient's future which is doing the work in rendering the morality of killing the patient intelligible.

This being the case, it seems clear that whether one has immediate past experiences or not does no work in the explanation of what makes killing wrong. The addition the discontinuation account makes to the value of a human future is otiose. Its addition to the value-of-a-future account plays no role at all in rendering intelligible the wrongness of killing. Therefore, it can be discarded with the discontinuation account of which it is a part.

IV

The analysis of the previous section suggests that alternative general accounts of the wrongness of killing are either inadequate or unsuccessful in getting around the anti-abortion consequences of the value of a future-like-ours argument. A different strategy for avoiding these anti-abortion consequences involves limiting the scope of the value-of-a-future argument. More precisely, the strategy involves arguing that fetuses lack a property that is essential for the value-of-a-future argument (or for any anti-abortion argument) to apply to them.

One move of this sort is based upon the claim that a necessary condition of one's future being valuable is that one values it. Value implies a valuer. Given this one might argue that, since fetuses cannot value their futures, their futures are not valuable to them. Hence, it does not seriously wrong them deliberately to end their lives.

This move fails, however, because of some ambiguities. Let us assume that something cannot be of value unless it is valued by someone. This does not entail that my life is of no value unless it is valued by me. I may think, in a period of despair, that my future is of no worth whatsoever, but I may be wrong because others rightly see value—even great value—in it. Furthermore, my future can be valuable to me even if I do not value it. This is the case when a young person attempts suicide, but is rescued and goes on to significant human achievements. Such young people's futures are ultimately valuable to them, even though such futures do not seem to be valuable to them at the moment of attempted suicide. A fetus's future can be valuable to it in the same way. Accordingly, this attempt to limit the anti-abortion argument fails . . .

V

In this essay, it has been argued that the correct ethic of the wrongness of killing can be extended to fetal life and used to show that there is a stronger presumption that an abortion is morally impermissible. If the ethic of killing adopted here entails, however, that contraception is also seriously immoral, then there would appear to be a difficulty with the analysis of this essay.

But this analysis does not entail that contraception is wrong. Of course, contraception prevents the actualization of a possible future of value. Hence it follows from the claim that futures of value should be maximized that contraception is prima facie immoral.

This obligation to maximize does not exist, however; furthermore, nothing in the ethics of killing in this paper entails that it does. The ethics of killing in this essay would entail that contraception is wrong only if something were denied a human future of value by contraception. Nothing at all is denied such a future by contraception, however.

Candidates for a subject of harm by contraception fall into four categories: (1) some sperm or other, (2) some ovum or other, (3) a sperm and an ovum separately, and (4) a sperm and an ovum together. Assigning the harm to some sperm is utterly arbitrary, for no reason can be given for making a sperm the subject of harm rather than an ovum. Assigning the harm to some ovum is utterly arbitrary, for no reason can be given for making an ovum the subject of harm rather than a sperm. One might attempt to avoid these problems by insisting that contraception deprives both the sperm and the ovum separately of a valuable future like ours. On this alternative, too many futures are lost. Contraception was supposed to be wrong, because it deprived us of one future of value, not two. One might attempt to avoid this problem by holding that contraception deprives the combination of sperm and ovum of a valuable future like ours. But here the definite article misleads. At the time of contraception, there are hundreds of millions of sperm, one (released) ovum and millions of possible combinations of all of these. There is no actual combination at all. Is the subject of the loss to be a merely possible combination? Which one? This alternative does not yield an actual subject of harm either. Accordingly, the immorality of contraception is not entailed by the loss of a future-like-ours argument simply because there is no nonarbitrarily identifiable subject of the loss in the case of contraception.

VI

The purpose of this essay has been to set out an argument of the serious presumptive wrongness of abortion subject to the assumption that the moral permissibility of abortion stands or falls on the moral status of the fetus. Since a fetus possesses a property, the possession of which in adult human beings is sufficient to make killing an adult human being wrong, abortion is wrong . . .

The Morality of Abortion and the Deprivation of Futures

Mark T. Brown

Mark Brown rejects Don Marquis's argument that abortion is wrong for the same reason that killing an adult is wrong: it deprives the person of a future of value. Brown claims that the argument trades on the ambiguity of "future of value," which may mean either "potential future of value" or "self-represented future of value."

The first interpretation implies that we commit homicide whenever we fail to provide someone with whatever he needs to live, but not to provide someone with necessities (e.g., medical care) is not necessarily to treat him unjustly. A fetus could have a presumptive right to life only if women had no right to control their bodies. Marquis's argument fails for it "implausibly" assigns people "welfare rights to valuable futures" and "liberty rights not to be killed."

While the second interpretation makes Marquis's argument deductively valid, it cannot be sound (i.e., have all true premises), because the fetus lacks the neurological development required for imagining a future. Marquis's argument gains its force only by trading on the ambiguity of "future of value."

In an influential essay entitled "Why abortion is wrong," Donald Marquis presents an argument which purports to derive the immorality of abortion from a deceptively simple but intuitively compelling claim: it is presumptively wrong to kill us, competent adult human beings, because doing so destroys our most valuable possession, a future of value.[1] Marquis claims that killing actual persons is wrong because it unjustly deprives the victim of his or her future; that the fetus has a future similar in morally relevant respects to the future lost by a competent adult homicide victim, and that, as [a] consequence, abortion is justifiable only in the same special and extreme circumstances in which killing competent adult human beings is justifiable. Marquis presents the gist of the Future Like Ours (FLO) argument in this way:

> . . . we can start from the following unproblematic assumption: it is wrong to kill us . . . when I am killed I am deprived of all the value of my future. Inflicting this loss on me is ultimately what makes killing me wrong. The future of a standard fetus

> includes a set of experiences, projects, activities and such which are identical with the futures of adult human beings and the futures of young children. Since the reason that is sufficient to explain why it is wrong to kill human beings after the time of birth is a reason that also applies to fetuses, it follows that abortion is prima facie seriously wrong.[2]

The Future Like Ours argument has been criticised on the grounds that it ignores the point of view of the pregnant woman; that it is incompatible with contraception and abstinence; and that it understates the explanatory resources of the competing personhood theory while overstating its own explanatory power.[3] These objections make a powerful cumulative case that something is amiss in FLO, but none comes to grips with the metaphysical thesis at the heart of the argument: the claim that actual persons possess a future of value. What exactly does it mean to have a future of value?

The expression is ambiguous. It could mean that actual persons have a potential future of value in the sense that given favourable conditions they are likely to have a worthwhile life; or it could mean that actual persons have a self-represented future of value in the sense that they can construct mental representations of valuable futures. The FLO argument turns upon this ambiguity. The expression occurs twice in the argument, first in the claim that homicide is presumptively wrong because it deprives its victim of a future of value, and second in the claim that both actual persons and fetuses have a future of value. The Future Like Ours argument would be valid if "future of value" were used consistently to mean either "potential future of value" or "self-represented future of value," and FLO would be sound if one or the other interpretation supported both the moral claim and the metaphysical claim, but if any interpretation which makes the argument valid renders it unsound, then FLO must be rejected. I first argue that the potential future of value interpretation is unsound because it is not presumptively seriously wrong to deprive someone of a potential future of value. I then argue that the self-represented future of value interpretation is unsound because the fetus does not represent its future. The essay concludes with an analysis of the intuitive appeal of the Future Like Ours argument.

I

The Future Like Ours argument might be salvaged if homicide were presumptively wrong because it deprives a human being of a potential future of value, whether or not that human being ever imagined his or her future. In this case, the expression "a future of value" could be used consistently throughout the argument: killing persons is presumptively wrong because it deprives them of their potential future of value; a fetus has a potential future of value; thus killing a fetus is presumptively wrong. The second premise is plausible. In most cases the course of a pregnancy can be foreseen with enough confidence to predict that the fetus will be born as an infant who has the capacity to enjoy a life qualitatively similar to the lives of actual persons.

The first premise is implausible, in part because a potential future of value interpretation implies welfare rights which most people would reject in other spheres of life. If deprivation of potential futures of value is presumptively a form of culpable homicide, then culpable homicide is committed whenever a person is denied access to what he or she needs to live. A homeless man who dies of exposure, an elderly woman whose unheated apartment precipitates a fatal case of pneumonia, an injured child who dies for want of a suitable blood transfusion would all be homicide victims. Each case is tragic in its own way, but it is far from clear that these persons' rights have been violated. Persons can die in ways which do not violate their rights.[4] This is not to say that no harm is

done when a potential future of value is foreclosed. On the contrary, to prevent a person from acting upon a highly reliable anticipated future imposes upon them significant opportunity costs, but it does not necessarily treat him or her unjustly. Only if the person had a right to the favourable circumstances which make possible a potential future of value would depriving him or her of that future be presumptively wrong.

For example, the future quality of life of many actual persons depends critically upon whether they receive prompt and effective medical treatment. Many persons with end stage renal disease could expect bright futures if they were to receive a kidney transplant, but neither medical need nor therapeutic benefit entitles these persons to medical services. Patients have a right to life-enhancing medical interventions because they subscribe to a health care plan which covers the procedure or because they are citizens of a country which maintains a functioning system of universal health care or for some other reason, but they do not have a right to medical services, or to any other external good, simply because they would have a better future if someone were to provide for their needs.

The potential future of value of the fetus is no less dependent upon favourable external circumstances. Since the fetus will become a person who has the capacity to enjoy its life and derive meaning from it only if it has access to the reproductive system of a woman, abortion would be presumptively wrong only if women had no presumptive right to control access to their reproductive systems. The fetus certainly needs its uterine environment if it is to realise its potential, but persons do not in general have a right to satisfy their needs at the expense of the autonomy, bodily integrity and wellbeing of another person. If I need a bone marrow transplant in order to realise my potential future of value, I do not thereby gain a right to your bone marrow, even if you are my mother. Perhaps pregnancy creates more stringent duties than motherhood, but if so, an argument is needed to establish this claim, an argument notably absent from Marquis's presentation of the Future Like Ours argument.

A defender of FLO might object at this point that abortion kills the fetus and that killing a person does violate his or her rights in all but the most extreme circumstances, even if depriving him or her of life-sustaining services need not, but this is not a distinction that can be drawn within a potential future of value interpretation of FLO. Someone who has been killed and someone who has been denied access to life support have been deprived equally of their potential futures. The potential future of value interpretation fails because the moral premise if true implausibly entitles persons to welfare rights to valuable futures in addition to liberty rights not to be killed. A self-represented future of value interpretation is needed to distinguish between the right not to be killed and the right to valuable futures.

II

The Future Like Ours argument would be valid if the expression "a future of value" consistently meant "a self-represented future of value." Substituting in, the argument would look like this: killing persons is presumptively wrong because it deprives them of their self-represented future; fetuses have self-represented futures; thus, killing fetuses is presumptively wrong. The first premise is plausible. At any moment a person can project a representation of a self which extends over time, a self understood from the perspective of the present, reconstructed from present remnants of the past and projected from the present into many possible futures. Persons care about their self-represented futures and their memories, their self-represented past, because this self-conception defines who they are and confers meaning and significance upon what they think and do. In contrast with potential futures, self-represented futures do not depend upon outside agencies for their realisation. The value of a self-represented future resides within the person herself, as a feature of a richly complex mental life. Killing a person deprives her of this future: her hopes and dreams are dashed, her goals unfulfilled, her sins unforgiven, longed for reunions and reconciliations never occur. All of this happens in the present, to a person able to unite in a moment of self-consciousness a personal past, present and future. One reason why killing persons violates their rights, but depriving them of life support need not, is that killing persons deprives them of a future and a past which is rightfully their own because it is something they themselves have created.

Even if killing a person is presumptively wrong because it deprives its victim of his self-represented future, this cannot be a reason why it is wrong to kill a fetus because the fetus does not construct mental representations of its future. The neurological and embryological evidence of this issue is clear.[5] Higher order cognitive functioning of the type implicated in planning and memory is dependent upon massive cortical/sub-cortical conductivity. Sub-cortical thalamic fibres first begin to form synapses with cortical neurons at about twenty-five weeks' gestation and only at some point well after birth does conductivity reach a critical threshold sufficient for self-awareness. A third trimester fetus may be sentient but there is no medical reason to think it is capable of self-consciousness.

The Future Like Ours argument rests upon two substantive claims: (1) killing persons is presumptively wrong because it deprives them of a future of value; and (2) fetuses have futures of value. The plausibility of the first claim depends upon the intuition that persons suffer significant harm when prevented from experiencing their self-represented future, but since the fetus does not represent its future it cannot be harmed in this way. The plausibility of the second claim depends upon the proposition that both the fetus and actual persons have a potential future of value, but unless one has a right to the conditions under which this potential can be realised, neither homicide nor abortion is presumptively wrong for this reason. The self-represented future of value interpretation underwrites the moral claim about the wrongness of homicide but militates against the metaphysical claim that persons and fetuses are relevantly similar; the potential future of value interpretation uncovers a genuine commonality between persons and fetuses but not one which can support the moral claim that abortion is presumptively seriously wrong. We may conclude that the Future Like Ours argument retains its force only if one equivocates on the concept of a future of value . . .

Notes

1. Marquis D. "Why abortion is immoral." *Journal of Philosophy* 1989;86-4:183–202.

2. See reference 1: 189, 190, 202.

3. Cudd A. "Sensationalized philosophy: a reply to Marquis's Why abortion is immoral." *The Journal of Philosophy* 1990;87,5: 262–4. Norcross A. "Killing, abortion, and contraception." *The Journal of Philosophy* 1990;87,5:268–77. Paske G. "Abortion and the neo-natal right to life: a critique of Marquis's futurist argument." In Pojman L, Beckwith F, eds. *The abortion controversy.* Boston: Jones and Bartlett, 1994: 343–53. Similar criticisms were levelled against FLO by an anonymous referee for this journal.

4. Here I draw upon Thomson JJ. "A defense of abortion." *Philosophy and Public Affairs* 1971;1,1:47–56, and the enormous literature this essay has elicited over the years.

5. Flower M. "Neuromaturation of the human fetus." *Journal of Medicine and Philosophy* 1985;10:237–51. Grobstein C. *Science and the unborn.* New York: Basic Books, 1988:55, 130.

Section 2: Abortion and the Status of the Fetus: The Classic Arguments

An Almost Absolute Value in History

John T. Noonan, Jr.

John Noonan argues that at the moment of fertilization a developing human being becomes a person. Noonan reviews some distinctions used by abortion proponents who maintain that personhood is achieved at a later stage of development (viability, experience, and social visibility) and concludes that they are all illegitimate. Noonan argues that conception is the decisive moment of humanization because it is then that the new being receives a genetic code from its parents.

The basic principle that should govern our attitude toward the fetus, Noonan claims, is a theological and humanistic one: do not injure your fellow man without a sufficient reason. Thus, abortion is never right, except to save the mother's life. Abortion is immoral because it "violates the rational humanistic tenet of the equality of human lives."

The most fundamental question involved in the long history of thought on abortion is: How do you determine the humanity of a being? To phrase the question that way is to put in comprehensive humanistic terms what the theologians either dealt with as an explicitly theological question under the heading of "ensoulment" or dealt with implicitly in their treatment of abortion. The Christian position as it originated did not depend on a narrow theological or philosophical concept. It had no relation to theories of infant baptism. It appealed to no special theory of instantaneous ensoulment. It took the world's view on ensoulment as that view changed from Aristotle to Zacchia. There was, indeed, theological influence affecting the theory of ensoulment finally adopted, and, of course, ensoulment itself was a theological concept, so that the position was always explained in theological terms. But the theological notion of ensoulment could easily be translated into humanistic language by substituting "human" for "rational soul"; the problem of knowing when a man is a man is common to theology and humanism.

From "An Absolute Value in History", reprinted by permission of the publisher from The Morality of Abortion: Legal and Historical Perspectives, edited by John T. Noonan, Jr., pp. 51–59, Cambridge, Mass.: Harvard University Press, Copyright © 1970 by the President and Fellows of Harvard College.

If one steps outside the specific categories used by the theologians, the answer they gave can be analyzed as a refusal to discriminate among human beings on the basis of their varying potentialities. Once conceived, the being was recognized as man because he had man's potential. The criterion for humanity, thus, was simple and all-embracing: If you are conceived by human parents, you are human.

The strength of this position may be tested by a review of some of the other distinctions offered in the contemporary controversy over legalizing abortion. Perhaps the most popular distinction is in terms of viability. Before an age of so many months, the fetus is not viable, that is, it cannot be removed from the mother's womb and live apart from her. To that extent, the life of the fetus is absolutely dependent on the life of the mother. This dependence is made the basis of denying recognition to its humanity.

There are difficulties with this distinction. One is that the perfection of artificial incubation may make the fetus viable at any time: It may be removed and artificially sustained. Experiments with animals already show that such a procedure is possible. This hypothetical extreme case relates to an actual difficulty: there is considerable elasticity to the idea of viability. Mere length of life is not an exact measure. The viability of the fetus depends on the extent of its anatomical and functional development. The weight and length of the fetus are better guides to the state of its development than age, but weight and length vary. Moreover, different racial groups have different ages at which their fetuses are viable. Some evidence, for example, suggests that Negro fetuses mature more quickly than white fetuses. If viability is the norm, the standard would vary with race and with many individual circumstances.

The most important objection to this approach is that dependence is not ended by viability. The fetus is still absolutely dependent on someone's care in order to continue existence; indeed a child of one or three or even five years of age is absolutely dependent on another's care for existence; uncared for, the older fetus or the younger child will die as surely as the early fetus detached from the mother. The unsubstantial lessening in dependence at viability does not seem to signify any special acquisition of humanity.

A second distinction has been attempted in terms of experience. A being who has had experience, has lived and suffered, who possesses memories, is more human than one who has not. Humanity depends on formation by experience. The fetus is thus "unformed" in the most basic human sense.

This distinction is not serviceable for the embryo which is already experiencing and reacting. The embryo is responsive to touch after eight weeks and at least at that point is experiencing. At an earlier stage the zygote is certainly alive and responding to its environment. The distinction may also be challenged by the rare case where aphasia has erased adult memory: has it erased humanity? More fundamentally, this distinction leaves even the older fetus or the younger child to be treated as an unformed inhuman thing. Finally, it is not clear why experience as such confers humanity. It could be argued that certain central experiences such as loving or learning are necessary to make a man human. But then human beings who have failed to love or to learn might be excluded from the class called man . . .

Finally, a distinction is sought in social visibility. The fetus is not socially perceived as human. It cannot communicate with others. Thus, both subjectively and objectively, it is not a member of society. As moral rules are rules for the behavior of members of society to each other, they cannot be made for behavior toward what is not yet a member. Excluded from the society of men, the fetus is excluded from the humanity of men.

By force of the argument from the consequences, this distinction is to be rejected. It is more subtle than that founded on an appeal to physical sensation, but it is equally dangerous in its implications. If humanity depends on social recognition, individuals or whole groups may be dehumanized by being denied any status in their society. Such a fate is fictionally portrayed in *1984* and has actually been the lot of many men in many societies. In the Roman empire, for example, condemnation to slavery meant the practical denial of most human rights; in the Chinese Communist world, landlords have been classified as enemies of the people and so treated as nonpersons by the state. Humanity does not depend on social recognition, though often the failure of society to recognize the prisoner, the alien, the heterodox as human has led to the destruction of human beings. Anyone conceived by a man and a woman is human. Recognition of this condition by society follows a real event in the objective order, however imperfect and halting the recognition. Any attempt to limit humanity to exclude some group runs the risk of furnishing authority and precedent for excluding other groups in the name of the consciousness or perception of the controlling group in society.

A philosopher may reject the appeal to the humanity of the fetus because he views "humanity" as a secular view of the soul and because he doubts the existence of anything real and objective which can be identified as humanity. One answer to such a philosopher is to ask how he reasons about moral questions without supposing that there is a sense in which he and the others of whom he speaks are human. Whatever group is taken as the society which determines who may be killed is thereby taken as human. A second answer is to ask if he does not believe that there is a right and wrong way of deciding moral questions. If there is such a difference, experience may be appealed to: to decide who is human on the basis of the sentiment of a given society has led to consequences which rational men would characterize as monstrous.

The rejection of the attempted distinctions based on viability and visibility, experience and feeling, may be buttressed by the following considerations: Moral judgments often rest on distinctions, but if the distinctions are not to appear arbitrary *fiat*, they should relate to some real difference in probabilities. There is a kind of continuity in all life, but the earlier stages of the elements of human life possess tiny probabilities of development. Consider for example, the spermatozoa in any normal ejaculate: There are about 200,000,000 in any single ejaculate, of which one has a chance of developing into a zygote. Consider the oocytes which may become ova: there are 100,000 to 1,000,00 oocytes in a female infant, of which a maximum of 390 are ovulated. But once spermatozoa and ovum meet and the conceptus is formed, such studies as have been made show that roughly in only 20 percent of the cases will spontaneous abortion occur. In other words, the chances are about 4 out of 5 that this new being will develop. At this stage in the life of the being there is a sharp shift in probabilities, an immense jump in potentialities. To make a distinction between the rights of spermatozoa and the rights of the fertilized ovum is to respond to an enormous shift in possibilities. For about twenty days after conception the egg may split to form twins or combine with another egg to form a chimera, but the probability of either event happening is very small.

It may be asked, What does a change in biological probabilities have to do with establishing humanity? The argument from probabilities is not aimed at establishing humanity but at establishing an objective discontinuity which may be taken into account in moral discourse. As life itself is a matter of probabilities, as most moral reasoning is an estimate of probabilities, so it seems in accord with the structure of reality and the nature of moral thought to found a moral judgment on the change in probabilities at conception. The appeal to probabilities is the most commonsensical of arguments, to a greater or smaller degree all of us based our actions on probabilities, and in morals, as in law, prudence and negligence are often measured by the account one has taken of the probabilities. If the chance is 200,000,000 to 1 that the movement in the bushes into which you shoot is a man's, I doubt if many persons would hold you careless in shooting; but if the chances are 4 out of 5 that the movement is a human being's, few would acquit you of blame. Would the argument be different if only one out of ten children conceived came to term? Of course this argument would be different. This argument is an appeal to probabilities that actually exist, not to any and all states of affairs which may be imagined.

The probabilities as they do exist do not show the humanity of the embryo in the sense of a demonstration in logic any more than the probabilities of the movement in the bush being a man demonstrate beyond all doubt that the being is a man. The appeal is a "buttressing" consideration, showing the plausibility of the standard adopted. The argument focuses on the decisional factor in any moral judgment and assumes that part of the business of a moralist is drawing lines. One evidence of the nonarbitrary character of the line drawn is the difference of probabilities on either side of it. If a spermatozoon is destroyed, one destroys a being which had a chance of far less than 1 in 200 million of developing into a reasoning being, possessed of the genetic code, a heart and other organs, and capable of pain. If a fetus is destroyed, one destroys a being already possessed of the genetic code, organs, and sensitivity to pain, and one which had an 80 percent chance of developing further into a baby outside the womb who, in time, would reason.

The positive argument for conception as the decisive moment of humanization is that at conception the new being receives the genetic code. It is this genetic information which determines his characteristics, which is the biological carrier of the possibility of human wisdom, which makes him a self-evolving being. A being with a human genetic code is man.

This review of current controversy over the humanity of the fetus emphasizes what a fundamental question the theologians resolved in asserting the inviolability of the fetus. To regard the fetus as possessed of equal rights with other humans was not, however, to decide every case where abortion might be employed. It did decide the case where the argument was that the fetus should be aborted for its own good. To say a being was human was to say it had a destiny to decide for itself which could not be taken from it by another man's decision. But human beings with equal rights often come in conflict with each other, and some decision must be made as [to] whose claims are to prevail. Cases of conflict involving the fetus are different only in two respects: the total inability of the fetus to speak for itself and the fact that the right of the fetus regularly at stake is the right to life itself.

The approach taken by the theologians to these conflicts was articulated in terms of "direct" and "indirect." Again, to look at what they were doing from outside their categories, they may be said to have been drawing lines or "balancing values." "Direct" and "indirect" are spatial metaphors; "line-drawing" is another. "To weigh" or "to balance" values is a metaphor of a more complicated mathematical sort hinting at the process which goes on in moral judgments. All the metaphors suggest that, in the moral judgments made, comparisons were necessary, that no value completely controlled. The principle of double effect was no doctrine fallen from heaven, but a method of analysis appropriate where two relative values were being compared. In Catholic moral theology, as it developed, life even of the innocent was not taken as an absolute. Judgments of acts affecting life issued from a process of weighing. In the weighing, the fetus was always given a value greater than zero, always a value separate and independent from its parents. This valuation was crucial and fundamental in all Christian thought on the subject and marked it off from any approach which considered that only the parents' interests needed to be considered.

Even with the fetus weighed as human, one interest could be weighed as equal or superior: that of the mother in her own life. The casuists between 1450 and 1895 were willing to weigh this interest as superior. Since 1895, that interest was given decisive weight only in the two special cases of the cancerous uterus and the ectopic pregnancy. In both of these cases the fetus itself had little chance of survival even if abortion were not performed. As the balance was once struck in favor of the mother whenever her life was endangered, it could be so struck again. The balance reached between 1895 and 1930 attempted prudentially and pastorally to forestall a multitude of exceptions for interests less than life.

The perception of the humanity of the fetus and the weighing of fetal rights against other human rights constituted the work of the moral analysts. But what spirit animated abstract judgments? For the Christian community it was the injunction of Scripture to love your neighbor as yourself. The fetus as human was a neighbor; his life had parity with one's own. The commandment gave life to what otherwise would have been only rational calculation.

The commandment could be put in humanistic as well as theological terms: do not injure your fellow man without reasons. In these terms, once the humanity of the fetus is perceived, abortion is never right except in self-defense. When life must be taken to save life, reason alone cannot say that a mother must prefer a child's life to her own. With this exception, now of great rarity, abortion violates the rational humanist tenet of the equality of human lives.

For Christians the commandment to love had received a special imprint in that the exemplar proposed of love was the love of the Lord for his disciples. In the light given by this example, self-sacrifice carried to the point of death seemed in the extreme situations not without meaning. In the less extreme cases, preference for one's own interests to the life of another seemed to express cruelty or selfishness irreconcilable with the demands of love.

A Defense of Abortion

Judith Jarvis Thomson

Judith Jarvis Thomson, in this very influential article, avoids the problem of determining when the fetus becomes a person. For the sake of argument only, she grants the conservative view that the fetus is a person from the moment of conception. She points out, however, that the conservative argument using this claim as a premise actually involves an additional unstated premise. The argument typically runs as follows: The fetus is an innocent person; therefore, killing a fetus is always wrong. The argument requires that we assume that killing an innocent person is always wrong. But, Thomson claims, killing an innocent person is sometimes allowable. This is most clearly so when self-defense requires it.

Using several moral analogies, Thomson attempts to show that a fetus's right to life does not consist in the right not to be killed, but in the

Jarvis Thomson, From *Philosophy and Public Affairs*, Vol. 1, no. 1 (Fall 1971). Copyright © 1971 John Wiley & Sons-Blackwell. Reprinted by permission.

right not to be killed unjustly. The fetus's claim to life is not an absolute one that must always be granted unconditional precedence over the interests of its mother. Thus, abortion is not always permissible, but neither is it always impermissible. When the reasons for having an abortion are trivial, then abortion is not legitimate. When the reasons are serious and involve the health or welfare of the woman, then abortion is justifiable.

Most opposition to abortion relies on the premise that the fetus is a human being, a person, from the moment of conception. The premise is argued for, but, as I think, not well. Take, for example, the most common argument. We are asked to notice that the development of a human being from conception through birth into childhood is continuous; then it is said that to draw a line, to choose a point in this development and say "before this point the thing is not a person, after this point it is a person" is to make an arbitrary choice, a choice for which in the nature of things no good reason can be given. It is concluded that the fetus is, or anyway that we had better say it is, a person from the moment of conception. But this conclusion does not follow. Similar things might be said about the development of an acorn into an oak tree, and it does not follow that acorns are oak trees, or that we had better say they are. Arguments of this form are sometimes called "slippery slope arguments"—the phrase is perhaps self-explanatory—and it is dismaying that opponents of abortion rely on them so heavily and uncritically.

I am inclined to agree, however, that the prospects for "drawing a line" in the development of the fetus look dim. I am inclined to think also that we shall probably have to agree that the fetus has already become a human person well before birth. Indeed, it comes as a surprise when one first learns how early in its life it begins to acquire human characteristics. By the tenth week, for example, it already has a face, arms and legs, fingers and toes; it has internal organs, and brain activity is detectable.[1] On the other hand, I think that the premise is false, that the fetus is not a person from the moment of conception. A newly fertilized ovum, a newly implanted clump of cells, is no more a person than an acorn is an oak tree. But I shall not discuss any of this. For it seems to me to be of great interest to ask what happens if, for the sake of argument, we allow the premise. How, precisely, are we supposed to get from there to the conclusion that abortion is morally impermissible? Opponents of abortion commonly spend most of their time establishing that the fetus is a person, and hardly any time explaining the step from there to the impermissibility of abortion. Perhaps they think the step too simple and obvious to require much comment. Or perhaps instead they are simply being economical in argument. Many of those who defend abortion rely on the premise that the fetus is not a person, but only a bit of tissue that will become a person at birth; and why pay out more arguments than you have to? Whatever the explanation, I suggest that the step they take is neither easy nor obvious, that it calls for closer examination than it is commonly given, and that when we do give it this closer examination we shall feel inclined to reject it.

I propose, then, that we grant that the fetus is a person from the moment of conception. How does the argument go from here? Something like this, I take it. Every person has a right to life. So the fetus has a right to life. No doubt the mother has a right to decide what shall happen in and to her body; everyone would grant that. But surely a person's right to life is stronger and more stringent than the mother's right to decide what happens in and to her body, and so outweighs it. So the fetus may not be killed; an abortion may not be performed.

It sounds plausible. But now let me ask you to imagine this. You wake up in the morning and find yourself in bed with an unconscious violinist. A famous unconscious violinist. He has been found to have a fatal kidney ailment, and the Society of Music Lovers has canvassed all the available medical records and found that you alone have the right blood type to help. They have therefore kidnapped you, and last night the violinist's circulatory system was plugged into yours, so that your kidneys can be used to extract poisons from his blood as well as your own. The director of the hospital now tells you, "Look, we're sorry the Society of Music Lovers did this to you—we would never have permitted it if we had known. But still, they did it, and the violinist is now plugged into you. To unplug you would be to kill him. But never mind, it's only for nine months. By then he will have recovered from his ailment, and can safely be unplugged from you." Is it morally incumbent on you to accede to this situation? No doubt it would be very nice of you if you did, a great kindness. But do you *have* to accede to it? What if it were not nine months, but nine years? Or longer still? What if the director of the hospital says, "Tough luck, I agree, but now you've got to stay in bed, with the violinist plugged into you, for the rest of your life. Because remember this. All persons have a right to life, and violinists are persons. Granted you have a right to decide what happens in and to your body, but a person's right to life outweighs your right to decide what happens in and to your body. So you cannot ever be unplugged from him." I imagine you would regard this as outrageous, which suggests that something really is wrong with that plausible-sounding argument I mentioned a moment ago.

In this case, of course, you were kidnapped; you didn't volunteer for the operation that plugged the violinist into your kidneys. Can those who oppose abortion on the ground I mentioned make an exception for pregnancy due to rape? Certainly. They can say that all persons have a right to life, but that some have less of a right to life than others, in particular, that those who came into existence because of rape have less. But these statements have a rather unpleasant sound. Surely the question of whether you have a right to life at all, or how much of it you have, shouldn't turn on the question of whether or not you are a product of a rape. And in fact the people who oppose abortion on the ground I mentioned do not make this distinction, and hence do not make an exception in case of rape.

Nor do they make an exception for a case in which the mother has to spend the nine months of her pregnancy in bed. They would agree that would be a great pity, and hard on the mother; but all the same, all persons have a right to life, the fetus is a person, and so on. I suspect, in fact, that they would not make an exception for a case in which, miraculously enough, the pregnancy went on for nine years, or even for the rest of the mother's life.

Some won't even make an exception for a case in which continuation of the pregnancy is likely to shorten the mother's life; they regard abortion as impermissible even to save the mother's life. Such cases are nowadays very rare, and many opponents of abortion do not accept this extreme view. All the same, it is a good place to begin: a number of points of interest come out in respect to it.

1.

Let us call the view that abortion is impermissible even to save the mother's life "the extreme view." I want to suggest that it does not issue from the argument I mentioned earlier without the addition of some fairly powerful premises. Suppose a woman has become pregnant, and now learns that she has a cardiac condition such that she will die if she carries the baby to term. What may be done for her? The fetus, being a person, has a right to life, but as the mother is a person too, so has she a right to life. Presumably they have an equal right to life. How is it supposed to come out that an abortion may not be performed? If mother and child have an equal right to life, shouldn't we perhaps flip a coin? Or should we add to the mother's right to life her right to decide what happens in and to her body, which everybody seems to be ready to grant—the sum of her rights now outweighing the fetus's right to life?

The most familiar argument here is the following. We are told that performing the abortion would be directly killing[2] the child, whereas doing nothing would not be killing the mother, but only letting her die. Moreover, in killing the child, one would be killing an innocent person, for the child has committed no crime, and is not aiming at his mother's death. And then there are a variety of ways in which this might be continued. (1) But as directly killing an innocent person is always and absolutely impermissible, an abortion may not be performed. Or, (2) as directly killing an innocent person is murder, and murder is always and absolutely impermissible, an abortion may not be performed.[3] Or, (3) as one's duty to refrain from directly killing an innocent person is more stringent than one's duty to keep a person from dying, an abortion may not be performed. Or, (4) if one's only options are directly killing an innocent person or letting a person die, one must prefer letting the person die, and thus an abortion may not be performed.[4]

Some people seem to have thought that these are not further premises which must be added if the conclusion is to be reached, but they follow from the very fact that an innocent person has a right to life.[5] But this seems to me to be a mistake, and perhaps the simplest way to show this is to bring out that while we must certainly grant that innocent persons have a right to life, the theses in (1) through (4) are all false. Take (2) for example. If directly killing an innocent person is murder, and thus is impermissible, then the mother's directly killing the innocent person inside her is murder, and thus is impermissible. But it cannot seriously be thought to be murder if the mother performs an abortion on herself to save her life. It cannot seriously be said that she *must* refrain, that she *must* sit passively by and wait for her death. Let us look again at the case of you and the violinist. There you are, in bed with the violinist, and the director of the hospital says to you, "It's all most distressing, and I deeply sympathize, but you see this is putting an additional strain on your kidneys, and you'll be dead within the month. But you *have* to stay where you are all the same. Because unplugging you would be directly killing an innocent violinist, and that's murder, and that's impermissible." If anything in the world is true, it is that you do not commit murder, you do not do what is impermissible, if you reach around to your back and unplug yourself from that violinist to save your life.

The main focus of attention in writings on abortion has been on what a third party may or may not do in answer to a request from a woman for an abortion. This is in a way understandable. Things being as they are, there isn't much a woman can safely do to abort herself. So the question asked is what a third party may do, and what the mother may do, if it is mentioned at all, is deduced, almost as an afterthought, from what it is concluded that third parties may do. But it seems to me that to treat the matter in this way is to refuse to grant to the mother that very status of person which is so firmly insisted on for the fetus. For we cannot simply read off what a person may do from what a third party may do. Suppose you find yourself trapped in a tiny house with a growing child. I mean a very tiny house, and a rapidly growing child—you are already up against the wall of the house and in a few minutes you'll be crushed to death. The child on the other hand won't be crushed to death; if nothing is done to stop him from growing he'll be hurt, but in the end he'll simply burst open the house and walk out a free man. Now I could well understand it if a bystander were to say, "There's nothing we can do for you. We cannot choose between your life and his, we cannot be the ones to decide who is to live, we cannot intervene." But it cannot be concluded that you too can do nothing, that you cannot attack it to save your life. However innocent the child may be, you do not have to wait passively while it crushes you to death. Perhaps a pregnant woman is vaguely felt to have the status of house, to which we don't allow the right of self-defense. But if the woman houses the child, it should be remembered that she is a person who houses it.

I should perhaps stop to say explicitly that I am not claiming that people have a right to do anything whatever to save their lives. I think, rather, that there are drastic limits to the right of self-defense. If someone threatens you with death unless you torture someone else to death, I think you have not the right, even to save your life, to do so. But the case under consideration here is very different. In our case there are only two people involved, one whose life is threatened, and one who threatens it. Both are innocent: the one who is threatened is not threatened because of any fault, the one who threatens does not threaten because of any fault. For this reason we may feel that we bystanders cannot intervene. But the person threatened can.

In sum, a woman surely can defend her life against the threat to it posed by the unborn child, even if doing so involves its death. And this shows not merely that the theses in (1) through (4) are false; it shows also that the extreme view of abortion is false, and so we need not canvass any other possible ways of arriving at it from the argument I mentioned at the outset.

2.

The extreme view could of course be weakened to say that while abortion is permissible to save the mother's life, it may not be performed by a third party, but only by the mother herself. But this cannot be right either. For what we have to keep in mind is that the mother and the unborn child are not like two tenants in a small house which has, by an unfortunate mistake, been rented to both: the mother *owns* the house. The fact that she does adds to the offensiveness of deducing that the mother can do nothing from the supposition that third parties can do nothing. Certainly it lets us see that a third party who says "I cannot choose between you" is fooling himself if he thinks this is impartiality. If Jones has found and fastened on a certain coat, which he needs to keep him from freezing, but which Smith also needs to keep him from freezing, then it is not impartiality that says "I cannot choose between you" when Smith owns the coat. Women have said again and again "This body is *my* body!" and they have reason to feel angry, reason to feel that it has been like shouting into the wind. Smith, after all, is hardly likely to bless us if we say to him, "Of course it's your coat, anybody would grant that it is. But no one may choose between you and Jones who is to have it."

We should really ask what it is that says "no one may choose" in the face of the fact that the body that houses the child is the mother's body. It may be simply a failure to appreciate this fact. But it may be something more interesting, namely the sense that one has a right to refuse to lay hands on people, even where justice seems to require that somebody do so. Thus justice might call for somebody to get Smith's coat back from Jones, and yet you have a right to refuse to be the one to lay hands on Jones, a right to refuse to do the physical violence to him. This, I think, must be granted. But then what should be said is not "no one may choose," but only "*I cannot choose*," and indeed not even this, but "*I will not act*," leaving it open that somebody else can or should, and in particular that anyone in a position of authority, with the job of securing people's rights, both can and should. So this is no difficulty. I have not been arguing that any given third party must accede to the mother's request that he perform an abortion to save her life, but only that he may.

I suppose that in some view of human life the mother's body is only on loan to her, the loan not being one which gives her any prior claim to it. One who held this view might well think it impartiality to say "I cannot choose." But I shall simply ignore this possibility. My own view is that if a human being has any just, prior claim to anything at all, he has a just, prior claim to his own body. And perhaps this needn't be argued for here anyway, since, as I mentioned, the arguments against abortion we are looking at do grant that the woman has a right to decide what happens in and to her body.

But although they do grant it, I have tried to show that they do not take seriously what is done in granting it. I suggest the same thing will reappear even more clearly when we turn away from cases in which the mother's life is at stake, and attend, as I propose we now do, to the vastly more common cases in which a woman wants an abortion for some less weighty reason than preserving her own life.

3.

Where the mother's life is not at stake, the argument I mentioned at the outset seems to have a much stronger pull. "Everyone has a right to life, so the unborn person has a right to life." And isn't the child's right to life weightier than anything other than the mother's own right to life, which she might put forward as ground for an abortion?

This agreement treats the right to life as if it were unproblematic. It is not, and this seems to me to be precisely the source of the mistake.

For we should now, at long last, ask what it comes to, to have a right to life. In some views having a right to life includes having a right to be given at least the bare minimum one needs for continued life. But suppose that what in fact is the bare minimum a man needs for continued life is something he has no right at all to be given? If I am sick unto death, and the only thing that will save my life is the touch of Henry Fonda's cool hand on my fevered brow, then all the same, I have no right to be given the touch of Henry Fonda's cool hand on my fevered brow. It would be frightfully nice of him to fly in from the West Coast to provide it. It would be less nice, though no doubt well meant, if my friends flew out to the West Coast and carried Henry Fonda back with them. But I have no right at all against anybody that he should do this for me. Or again, to return to the story I told earlier, the fact that for continued life the violinist needs the continued use of your kidneys does not establish that he has a right to be given the continued use of your kidneys. He certainly has no right against you that *you* should give him continued use of your kidneys. For nobody has any right to use your kidneys unless you give him this right—if you do allow him to go on using your kidneys, this is a kindness on your part, and not something he can claim from you as his due. Nor has he any right against anybody else that *they* should give him continued use of your kidneys. Certainly he had no right against the Society of Music Lovers that they should plug him into you in the first place. And if you now start to unplug yourself, having learned that you will otherwise have to spend nine years in bed with him, there is nobody in the world who must try to prevent you, in order to see to it that he is given something he has a right to be given.

Some people are rather stricter about the right to life. In their view, it does not include the right to be given anything, but amounts to, and only to, the right not to be killed by anybody. But here a related difficulty arises. If everybody is to refrain from killing that violinist, then everybody must refrain from doing a great many different sorts of things. Everybody must refrain from slitting his throat, everybody must refrain from shooting him—and everybody must refrain from unplugging you from him. But does he have a right against everybody that they shall refrain from unplugging you from him? To refrain from doing this is to allow him to continue to use your kidneys. It could be argued that he has a right against us that *we* should allow him to continue to use your kidneys. That is, while he had no right against us that we should give him the use of your kidneys, it might be argued that he anyway has a right against us that we shall not now intervene and deprive him of the use of your kidneys. I shall come back to third-party inteventions later. But certainly the violinist has no right against you that *you* shall allow him to continue to use your kidneys. As I said, if you do allow him to use them it is a kindness on your part, not something you owe him.

The difficulty I point to here is not peculiar to the right to life. It reappears in connection with all the other natural rights, and it is something which an adequate account of rights must deal with. For present purposes it is enough just to draw attention to it. But I would stress that I am not arguing that people do not have a right to life—quite to the contrary, it seems to me that the primary control we must place on the acceptability of an account of rights is that it should turn out in that account to be a truth that all persons have a right to life. I am arguing only that having a right to life does not guarantee having either a right to be given the use of or a right to be allowed continued use of another person's body—even if one needs it for life itself. So the right to life will not serve the opponents of abortion in the very simple and clear way in which they seem to have thought it would.

4.

There is another way to bring out the difficulty. In the most ordinary sort of case, to deprive someone of what he has a right to is to treat him unjustly. Suppose a boy and his small brother are jointly given a box of chocolates for Christmas. If the older boy takes the box and refuses to give his brother any of the chocolates, he is unjust to him, for the brother has been given a right to half of them. But suppose that, having learned that otherwise it means nine years in bed with that violinist, you unplug yourself from him. You surely are not being unjust to him, for you gave him no right to use your kidneys, and no one else can have given him any such right. But we have to notice that in unplugging yourself, you are killing him; and violinists, like everybody else, have a right to life, and thus in the view we were considering just now, the right not to be killed. So here you do what he supposedly has a right you shall not do, but you do not act unjustly to him in doing it.

The emendation which may be made at this point is this: the right to life consists not in the right not to be killed, but rather in the right not to be killed unjustly.

This runs a risk of circularity, but never mind: it would enable us to square the fact that the violinist has a right to life with the fact that you do not act unjustly toward him in unplugging yourself, thereby killing him. For if you do not kill him unjustly, you do not violate his right to life, and so it is no wonder you do him no injustice.

But if this emendation is accepted, the gap in the argument against abortion stares us plainly in the face: it is by no means enough to show that the fetus is a person, and to remind us that all persons have a right to life—we need to be shown also that killing the fetus violates its right to life, i.e., that abortion is unjust killing. And is it?

I suppose we may take it as a datum that in a case of pregnancy due to rape the mother has not given the unborn person a right to the use of her body for food and shelter. Indeed, in what pregnancy could it be supposed that the mother has given the unborn person such a right? It is not as if there were unborn persons drifting about the world, to whom a woman who wants a child says "I invite you in."

But it might be argued that there are other ways one can have acquired a right to the use of another person's body than by having been invited to use it by that person. Suppose a woman voluntarily indulges in intercourse, knowing of the chance it will issue in pregnancy, and then she does become pregnant; is she not in part responsible for the presence, in fact the very existence, of the unborn person inside? No doubt she did not invite it in. But doesn't her partial responsibility for its being there itself give it a right to the use of her body?[6] If so, then her aborting it would be more like the boy's taking away the chocolates, and less like your unplugging yourself from the violinist—doing so would be depriving it of what it does have a right to, and thus be doing it an injustice.

And then, too, it might be asked whether or not she can kill it even to save her own life: If she voluntarily called it into existence, how can she now kill it, even in self-defense?

The first thing to be said about this is that it is something new. Opponents of abortion have been so concerned to make out the independence of the fetus, in order to establish that it has a right to life, just as its mother does, that they have tended to overlook the possible support they might gain from making out that the fetus is *dependent* on the mother, in order to establish that she has a special kind of responsibility for it, a responsibility that gives it rights against her which are not possessed by any independent person—such as an ailing violinist who is a stranger to her.

On the other hand, this argument would give the unborn person a right to its mother's body only if her pregnancy resulted from a voluntary act, undertaken in full knowledge of the chance a pregnancy might result from it. It would leave out entirely the unborn person whose existence is due to rape. Pending the availability of some further argument, then, we would be left with the conclusion that unborn persons whose existence is due to rape have no right to the use of their mothers' bodies, and thus that aborting them is not depriving them of anything they have a right to and hence is not unjust killing.

And we should also notice that it is not at all plain that this argument really does go even as far as it purports to. For there are cases and cases, and the details make a difference. If the room is stuffy, and I therefore open a window to air it, and a burglar climbs in, it would be absurd to say, "Ah, now he can stay, she's given him a right to the use of her house—for she is partially responsible for his presence there, having voluntarily done what enabled him to get in, in full knowledge that there are such things as burglars, and that burglars burgle." It would be still more absurd to say this if I had had bars installed outside my windows, precisely to prevent burglars from getting in, and a burglar got in only because of a defect in the bars. It remains equally absurd if we imagine it is not a burglar who climbs in, but an innocent person who blunders or falls in. Again, suppose it were like this: people-seeds drift about in the air like pollen, and if you open your windows, one may drift in and take root in your carpets or upholstery. You don't want children, so you fix up your windows with fine mesh screens, the very best you can buy. As can happen, however, and on very, very rare occasions does happen, one of the screens is defective, and a seed drifts in and takes root. Does the person-plant who now develops have a right to the use of your house? Surely not—despite the fact that you voluntarily opened your windows, you knowingly kept carpets and upholstered furniture, and you knew that screens were sometimes defective. Someone may argue that you are responsible for its rooting, that it does have a right to your house, because after all you could have lived out your life with bare floors and furniture, or with sealed windows and doors. But this won't do—for by the same token anyone can avoid a pregnancy due to rape by having a hysterectomy, or anyway by never leaving home without a (reliable!) army.

It seems to me that the argument we are looking at can establish at most that there are some cases in which the unborn person has a right to the use of its mother's body, and therefore *some* cases in which abortion is unjust killing. There is room for much discussion and argument as to precisely which, if any. But I think we should sidestep this issue and leave it open, for at any rate the argument certainly does not establish that all abortion is unjust killing.

5.

There is room for yet another argument here, however. We surely must all grant that there may be cases in which it would be morally indecent to detach a person from your body at the cost of his life. Suppose you learn that what the violinist needs is not nine years of your life, but only one hour: all you need do to save his life is to spend one hour in that bed with him. Suppose also that letting him use your kidneys for that one hour would not affect your health in the slightest. Admittedly you were kidnapped. Admittedly you did not give anyone permission to plug him into you. Nevertheless it seems to me plain you *ought* to allow him to use your kidneys for that hour—it would be indecent to refuse.

Again, suppose pregnancy lasted only an hour, and constituted no threat to life or health. And suppose that a woman becomes pregnant as a result of rape. Admittedly she did not voluntarily do anything to bring about the existence of a child. Admittedly she did nothing at all which would give the unborn person a right to the use of her body. All the same it might well be said, as in the newly amended violinist story, that she *ought* to allow it to remain for that hour—that it would be indecent of her to refuse.

Now some people are inclined to use the term "right" in such a way that it follows from the fact that you ought to allow a person to use your body for the hour he needs, that he has a right to use your body for the hour he needs, even though he has not been given that right by any person or act. They may say that it follows also that if you refuse, you act unjustly toward him. This use of the term is perhaps so common that it cannot be called wrong; nevertheless it seems to me to be an unfortunate loosening of what we would do better to keep a tight rein on. Suppose that box of chocolates I mentioned earlier had not been given to both boys jointly, but was given only to the older boy. There he sits, stolidly eating his way through the box, his smaller brother watching enviously. Here we are likely to say, "You ought not to be so mean. You ought to give your brother some of those chocolates." My own view is that it just does not follow from the truth of this that the brother has any right to any of the chocolates. If the boy refuses to give his brother any, he is greedy, stingy, callous—but not unjust. I suppose that the people I have in mind will say it does follow that the brother has a right to some of the chocolates, and thus that the boy does act unjustly if he refuses to give his brother any. But the effect of saying this is to obscure what we should keep distinct, namely the difference between the boy's refusal in this case and the boy's refusal in the earlier case, in which the box was given to both boys jointly, and in which the small brother thus had what was from any point of view clear title to half.

A further objection to so using the term "right" that from the fact that A ought to do a thing for B, it follows that B has a right against A that A do it for him, is that it is going to make the question of whether or not a man has a right to a thing turn on how easy it is to provide him with it; and this seems not merely unfortunate, but morally unacceptable. Take the case of Henry Fonda again. I said earlier that I had no right to the touch of his cool hand on my fevered brow, even though I needed it to save my life. I said it would be frightfully nice of him to fly in from the West Coast to provide me with it, but that I had no right against him that he should do so. But suppose he isn't on the West Coast. Suppose he has only to walk across the room, place a hand briefly on my brow—and lo, my life is saved. Then surely he ought to do it, it would be indecent to refuse. Is it to be said, "Ah, well, it follows that in this case she has a right to the touch of his hand on her brow, and so it would be an injustice in him to refuse"? So that I have a right to it when it is easy for him to provide it, though no right when it's hard? It's rather a shocking idea that anyone's rights should fade away and disappear as it gets harder and harder to accord them to him.

So my own view is that even though you ought to let the violinist use your kidneys for the one hour he needs, we should not conclude that he has a right to do so—we should say that if you refuse, you are, like the boy who owns all the chocolates and will give none away, self-centered and callous, indecent in fact, but not unjust. And similarly, that even supposing a case in which a woman pregnant due to rape ought to allow the unborn person to use her body for the hour he needs, we should not conclude that he has a right to do so; we should conclude that she is self-centered,

callous, indecent, but not unjust, if she refuses. The complaints are no less grave; they are just different. However, there is no need to insist on this point. If anyone does wish to deduce "he has a right" from "you ought," then all the same he must surely grant that there are cases in which it is not morally required of you that you allow that violinist to use your kidneys, and in which he does not have the right to use them, and in which you do not do him an injustice if you refuse. And so also for mother and unborn child. Except in such cases as the unborn person has a right to demand it—and we were leaving open the possibility that there may be such cases—nobody is morally *required* to make large sacrifices, of health, of all other interests and concerns, of all other duties and commitments, for nine years, or even for nine months, in order to keep another person alive.

6.

We have in fact to distinguish between two kinds of Samaritan: the Good Samaritan and what we might call the Minimally Decent Samaritan. The story of the Good Samaritan, you will remember, goes like this:

> *A certain man went down from Jerusalem to Jericho, and fell among thieves, which stripped him of his raiment, and wounded him, and departed, leaving him half dead.*
>
> *And by chance there came down a certain priest that way: and when he saw him, he passed by on the other side.*
>
> *And likewise a Levite, when he was at the place, came and looked on him, and passed by on the other side.*
>
> *But a certain Samaritan, as he journeyed, came where he was; and when he saw him he had compassion on him.*
>
> *And went to him, and bound up his wounds, pouring in oil and wine, and set him on his own beast, and brought him to an inn, and took care of him.*
>
> *And on the morrow, when he departed, he took out two pence, and gave them to the host, and said unto him, "Take care of him, and whatsoever thou spendest more, when I come again, I will repay thee." (Luke 10:30–35)*

The Good Samaritan went out of his way, at some cost to himself, to help one in need of it. We are not told what the options were, that is, whether or not the priest and the Levite could have helped by doing less than the Good Samaritan did, but assuming they could have, then the fact they did nothing at all shows they were not even Minimally Decent Samaritans, not because they were not Samaritans, but because they were not even minimally decent.

These things are a matter of degree, of course, but there is a difference, and it comes out perhaps most clearly in the story of Kitty Genovese, who, as you will remember, was murdered while thirty-eight people watched or listened, and did nothing at all to help her. A Good Samaritan would have rushed out to give direct assistance against the murderer. Or perhaps we had better allow that it would have been a Splendid Samaritan who did this, on the ground that it would have involved a risk of death for himself. But the thirty-eight not only did not do this, they did not even trouble to pick up a phone to call the police. Minimally Decent Samaritanism would call for doing at least that, and their not having done it was monstrous.

After telling the story of the Good Samaritan, Jesus said, "Go, and do thou likewise." Perhaps he meant that we are morally required to act as the Good Samaritan did. Perhaps he was urging people to do more than is morally required of them. At all events it seems plain that it was not morally required of any of the thirty-eight that he rush out to give direct assistance at the risk of his own life, and that it is not morally required of anyone that he give long stretches of his life—nine years or nine months—to sustaining the life of a person who has no special right (we were leaving open the possibility of this) to demand it.

Indeed, with one rather striking class of exceptions, no one in any country in the world is *legally* required to do anywhere near as much as this for anyone else. The class of exceptions is obvious.

My main concern here is not the state of law in respect to abortion, but it is worth drawing attention to the fact that in no state in this country is any man compelled by law to be even a Minimally Decent Samaritan to any person; there is no law under which charges could be brought against the thirty-eight who stood by while Kitty Genovese died. By contrast, in most states in this country women are compelled by law to be not merely Minimally Decent Samaritans, but Good Samaritans to unborn persons inside them. This doesn't by itself settle anything one way or the other, because it may well be argued that there should be laws in this country—as there are in many European countries—compelling at least Minimally Decent Samaritanism.[7] But it does show that there is a gross injustice in the existing state of the law. And it shows also that the groups currently working against liberalization of abortion laws, in fact working toward having it declared unconstitutional for a state to permit abortion, had better start working for the adoption of Good Samaritan laws generally, or earn the charge that they are acting in bad faith.

I should think, myself, that Minimally Decent Samaritan laws would be one thing, Good Samaritan laws quite another, and in fact highly improper. But we are not here concerned with the law. What we should ask is not whether anybody should be compelled by law to be a Good Samaritan, but whether we must accede to a situation in which somebody is being compelled—by nature, perhaps—to be a Good Samaritan. We have, in other words, to look now at third-party interventions. I have been arguing that no person is morally required to make large sacrifices to sustain the life of another who has no right to demand them, and this even where the sacrifices do not include life itself; we are not morally required to be Good Samaritans or anyway Very Good Samaritans to one another. But what if a man cannot extricate himself from such a situation? What if he appeals to us to extricate him? It seems to me plain that there are cases in which we can, cases in which a Good Samaritan would extricate him. There you are, you were kidnapped, and nine years in bed with that violinist lie ahead of you. You have your own life to lead. You are sorry, but you simply cannot see giving up so much of your life to the sustaining of his. You cannot extricate yourself, and ask us to do so. I should have thought that—in light of his having no right to the use of your body—it was obvious that we do not have to accede to your being forced to give up so much. We can do what you ask. There is no injustice to the violinist in our doing so.

7.

Following the lead of the opponents of abortion, I have throughout been speaking of the fetus merely as a person, and what I have been asking is whether or not the argument we began with, which proceeds only from the fetus's being a person, really does establish its conclusion. I have argued that it does not.

But of course there are arguments and arguments, and it may be said that I have simply fastened on the wrong one. It may be said that what is important is not merely the fact that the fetus is a person, but that it is a person for whom the woman has a special responsibility issuing from the fact that she is its mother. And it might be argued that all my analogies are therefore irrelevant—for you do not have that special kind of responsibility for that violinist, Henry Fonda does not have that special kind of responsibility for me. And our attention might be drawn to the fact that men and women both *are* compelled by law to provide support for their children.

I have in effect dealt (briefly) with this argument in section 4 above; but a (still briefer) recapitulation now may be in order. Surely we do not have any such "special responsibility" for a person unless we have assumed it, explicitly or implicitly. If a set of parents do not try to prevent pregnancy, do not obtain an abortion, but rather take it home with them, then they have assumed responsibility for it, they have given it rights, and they cannot *now* withdraw support from it at the cost of its life because they now find it difficult to go on providing for it. But if they have taken all reasonable precautions against having a child, they do not simply by virtue of their biological relationship to the child who comes into existence have a special responsibility for it. They may wish to assume responsibility for it, or they may not wish to. And I am suggesting that if assuming responsibility for it would require large sacrifices, then they may refuse. A Good Samaritan would not refuse—or anyway, a Splendid Samaritan, if the sacrifices that had to made were enormous. But then so would a Good Samaritan assume responsibility for that violinist; so would Henry Fonda, if he is a Good Samaritan, fly in from the West Coast and assume responsibility for me.

8.

My argument will be found unsatisfactory on two counts by many of those who want to regard abortion as morally permissible. First, while I do argue that abortion is not impermissible, I do not argue that it is always permissible. There may well be cases in which carrying the child to term requires only Minimally Decent Samaritanism of the mother, and this is a standard we must not fall below. I am inclined to think it a merit of my account precisely that it does *not* give a general yes or a general no. It allows for and supports our sense that, for example, a sick and desperately

frightened fourteen-year-old schoolgirl, pregnant due to rape, may *of course* choose abortion, and that any law which rules this out is an insane law. And it also allows for and supports our sense that in other cases resort to abortion is even positively indecent. It would be indecent in the woman to request an abortion, and indecent in a doctor to perform it, if she is in her seventh month, and wants the abortion just to avoid the nuisance of postponing a trip abroad. The very fact that the arguments I have been drawing attention to treat all cases of abortion, or even all cases of abortion in which the mother's life is not at stake, as morally on a par ought to have made them suspect at the outset.

Second, while I am arguing for the permissibility of abortion in some cases, I am not arguing for the right to secure the death of the unborn child. It is easy to confuse these two things in that up to a certain point in the life of the fetus it is not able to survive outside the mother's body; hence removing it from her body guarantees its death. But they are importantly different. I have argued that you are not morally required to spend nine months in bed, sustaining the life of that violinist; but to say that is by no means to say that if, when you unplug yourself, there is a miracle and he survives, you then have a right to turn around and slit his throat. You may detach yourself even if this costs him his life; you have no right to be guaranteed his death, by some other means, if unplugging yourself does not kill him. There are some people who will feel dissatisfied by this feature of my argument. A woman may be utterly devastated by the thought of a child, a bit of herself, put out for adoption and never seen or heard of again. She may therefore want not merely that the child be detached from her, but more, that it die. Some opponents of abortion are inclined to regard this as beneath contempt—thereby showing insensitivity to what is surely a powerful source of despair. All the same, I agree that the desire for the child's death is not one which anybody may gratify, should it turn out to be possible to detach the child alive.

At this place, however, it should be remembered that we have only been pretending throughout that the fetus is a human being from the moment of conception. A very early abortion is surely not the killing of a person, and so is not dealt with by anything I have said here.

Notes

1. Daniel Callahan, *Abortion: Law, Choice and Morality* (New York, 1970), p. 373. This book gives a fascinating survey of the available information on abortion. The Jewish tradition is surveyed in David M. Feldman, *Birth Control in Jewish Law* (New York, 1968), Part 5, the Catholic tradition in John

T. Noonan, Jr., "An Almost Absolute Value in History," in *The Morality of Abortion*, ed. John T. Noonan, Jr. (Cambridge, Mass., 1970).

2. The term "direct" in the arguments I refer to is a technical one. Roughly, what is meant by "direct killing" is either killing as an end in itself, or killing as a means to some end, for example, the end of saving someone else's life. See note 5 below, for an example of its use.

3. Cf. *Encyclical Letter of Pope Pius XI on Christian Marriage*, St. Paul Editions (Boston, n.d.), p. 32: "However much we may pity the mother whose health and even life is gravely imperiled in the performance of the duty allotted to her by nature, nevertheless what could ever be a sufficient reason for excusing in any way the direct murder of the innocent? This is precisely what we are dealing with here." Noonan (*The Morality of Abortion*, p. 43) reads this as follows: "What cause can ever avail to excuse in any way the direct killing of the innocent? For it is a question of that."

4. The thesis in (4) is in an interesting way weaker than those in (1), (2), and (3): they rule out abortion even in cases in which both mother *and* child will die if the abortion is not performed. By contrast, one who held the view expressed in (4) could consistently say that one needn't prefer letting two persons die to killing one.

5. Cf. the following passage from Pius XII, *Address to the Italian Catholic Society of Midwives*: "The baby in the maternal breast has the right to life immediately from God.—Hence there is no man, no human authority, no science, no medical, eugenic, social, economic or moral 'indication' which can establish or grant a valid juridical ground for a direct deliberate disposition of an innocent human life, that is a disposition which looks to its destruction either as an end or as a means to another end perhaps in itself illicit.—The baby, still not born, is a man in the same degree and for the same reason as the mother" (quoted in Noonan, *The Morality of Abortion*, p. 45).

6. The need for a discussion of this argument was brought home to me by members of the Society for Ethical and Legal Philosophy, to whom this paper was originally presented.

7. For a discussion of the difficulties involved, and a survey of the European experience with such laws, see *The Good Samaritan and the Law*, ed. James M. Ratcliffe (New York, 1966).

On the Moral and Legal Status of Abortion

Mary Anne Warren

Mary Anne Warren takes an even stronger position than Thomson (see preceding article), arguing that a woman's right to have an abortion is unrestricted. She attempts to show that there is no adequate basis for holding that the fetus has "a significant right to life" and that, whatever right can be appropriately granted to the fetus, it can never override a woman's right to protect her own interest and well-being. Accordingly, the laws that restrict access to abortion are an unjustified violation of a woman's rights.

Warren is critical of both Noonan (see earlier article) and Thomson. Noonan, she claims, fails to demonstrate that whatever is genetically human (the fetus) is also morally human (a person). Thomson, Warren argues, is mistaken in believing that it is possible both to grant that the fetus is a person and to produce a satisfactory defense of the right to obtain an abortion. Contrary to Thomson's aim, Thomson's central argument supports the right to abortion only in cases in which the woman is in no way responsible for her pregnancy.

Like Noonan, Warren conceives the basic issue in abortion to be the question of what properties something must possess to be a person in the moral sense. She offers five traits she believes anyone would accept as central and argues that the fetus, at all stages of development, possesses none of them. Since the fetus is not a person, it is not entitled to the full range of moral rights. That the fetus has the potential to become a person may give it a prima facie right to life, but the rights of an actual person always outweigh those of a potential person.

We will be concerned with both the moral status of abortion, which for our purposes we may define as the act which a woman performs in voluntarily terminating, or allowing another person to terminate, her pregnancy, and the legal status which is appropriate for this act. I will argue that, while it is not possible to produce a satisfactory defense of a woman's right to obtain an abortion without showing that a fetus is not a human being, in the morally relevant sense of that term, we ought not to conclude that the difficulties involved in determining whether or not a fetus is human make it impossible to produce any satisfactory solution to the problem of the moral status of abortion. For it is possible to show that, on the basis of intuitions which we may expect even the opponents of abortion to share, a fetus is not a person, hence not the sort of entity to which it is proper to ascribe full moral rights.

Of course, while some philosophers would deny the possibility of any such proof,[1] others will deny that there is any need for it, since the moral permissibility of abortion appears to them to be too obvious to require proof. But the inadequacy of this attitude should be evident from the fact that both the friends and foes of abortion consider their position to be morally self-evident. Because proabortionists have never adequately come to grips with the conceptual issues surrounding abortion, most if not all, of the arguments which they advance in opposition to laws restricting access to abortion fail to refute or even weaken the traditional antiabortion argument, i.e., that a fetus is a human being, and therefore abortion is murder.

These arguments are typically of one of two sorts. Either they point to the terrible side effects of the restrictive laws, e.g., the deaths due to illegal abortions, and the fact that it is poor women who suffer the most as a result of these laws, or else they state that to deny a woman access to abortion is to deprive her of her right to control her own body. Unfortunately, however, the fact that restricting access to abortion has tragic side effects does not, in itself, show that the restrictions are unjustified, since murder is wrong regardless of the consequences of prohibiting it; and the appeal to the right to control one's body, which is generally construed as a property right, is at best a rather feeble argument for the permissibility of abortion. Mere ownership does not give me the right to kill innocent people whom I find on my property, and indeed I am apt to be held responsible if such people injure themselves while on my property. It is equally unclear that I have any moral right to expel an innocent person from

my property when I know that doing so will result in his death . . .

John Noonan is correct in saying that "the fundamental question in the long history of abortion is, How do you determine the humanity of a being?"[2] He summarizes his own antiabortion argument, which is a version of the official position of the Catholic Church, as follows:

> . . . *it is wrong to kill humans, however poor, weak, defenseless, and lacking in opportunity to develop their potential they may be. It is therefore morally wrong to kill Biafrans. Similarly, it is morally wrong to kill embryos.*[3]

Noonan bases his claim that fetuses are human upon what he calls the theologians' criterion of humanity: that whoever is conceived of human beings is human. But although he argues at length for the appropriateness of this criterion, he never questions the assumption that if a fetus is human then abortion is wrong for exactly the same reason that murder is wrong.

Judith Thomson is, in fact, the only writer I am aware of who has seriously questioned this assumption; she has argued that, even if we grant the antiabortionist his claim that a fetus is a human being, with the same right to life as any other human being, we can still demonstrate that, in at least some and perhaps most cases, a woman is under no moral obligation to complete an unwanted pregnancy.[4] Her argument is worth examining, since if it holds up it may enable us to establish the moral permissibility of abortion without becoming involved in problems about what entitles an entity to be considered human, and accorded full moral rights. To be able to do this would be a great gain in the power and simplicity of the proabortion position, since, although I will argue that these problems can be solved at least as decisively as can any other moral problem, we should certainly be pleased to be able to avoid having to solve them as part of the justification of abortion.

On the other hand, even if Thomson's argument does not hold up, her insight, i.e., that it requires arguments to show that if fetuses are human then abortion is properly classified as murder, is an extremely valuable one. The assumption she attacks is particularly invidious, for it amounts to the decision that it is appropriate, in deciding the moral status of abortion, to leave the rights of the pregnant woman out of consideration entirely, except possibly when her life is threatened. Obviously, this will not do; determining what moral rights, if any, a fetus possesses is only the first step in determining the moral status of abortion. Step two, which is at least equally essential, is finding a just solution to the conflict between whatever rights the fetus may have, and the rights of the woman who is unwillingly pregnant. While the historical error has been to pay far too little attention to the second step, Ms. Thomson's suggestion is that if we look at the second step first we may find that a woman has a right to obtain an abortion *regardless* of what rights the fetus has.

Our own inquiry will also have two stages. In Section I, we will consider whether or not it is possible to establish that abortion is morally permissible even on the assumption that a fetus is an entity with a full-fledged right to life. I will argue that in fact this cannot be established, at least not with the conclusiveness which is essential to our hopes of convincing those who are skeptical about the morality of abortion, and that we therefore cannot avoid dealing with the question of whether or not a fetus really does have the same right to life as a (more fully developed) human being.

In Section II, I will propose an answer to this question, namely, that a fetus cannot be considered a member of the moral community, the set of beings with full and equal moral rights, for the simple reason that it is not a person, and that it is personhood, and not genetic humanity, i.e., humanity as defined by Noonan, which is the basis for membership in this community. I will argue that a fetus, whatever its stage of development, satisfies none of the basic criteria of personhood, and is not even enough *like* a person to be accorded even some of the same rights on the basis of this resemblance. Nor, as we will see, is a fetus's *potential* personhood a threat to the morality of abortion, since, whatever the rights of potential people may be, they are invariably overridden in any conflict with the moral rights of actual people.

I

We turn now to Professor Thomson's case for the claim that even if a fetus has full moral rights, abortion is still morally permissible, at least sometimes, and for some reasons other than to save the woman's life. Her argument is based upon clever, but I think faulty, thinking. She asked us to picture ourselves waking up one day, in bed with a famous violinist. Imagine that you have been kidnapped, and your bloodstream hooked up to that of the violinist, who happens to have an ailment which will certainly kill him unless he is permitted to share your kidneys for a period of nine months. No one else can save him, since you alone have the right type of blood. He will be unconscious all that time, and you will have to stay in bed with him, but after the nine months are over he may be unplugged, completely cured, that is provided that you have cooperated.

Now then, she continues, what are your obligations in this situation? The antiabortionist, if he is consistent, will have to say that you are obligated to stay in bed with the violinist: for all people have a right to life, and violinists are people, and therefore it would be murder for you to disconnect yourself from him and let him die.[5] But this is outrageous, and so there must be something wrong with the same argument when it is applied to abortion. It would certainly be commendable of you to agree to save the violinist, but it is absurd to suggest that your refusal to do so would be murder. His right to life does not obligate you to do whatever is required to keep him alive; nor does it justify anyone else forcing you to do so. A law which required you to stay in bed with the violinist would clearly be an unjust law, since it is no proper function of the law to force unwilling people to make huge sacrifices for the sake of other people toward whom they have no such prior obligation.

Thomson concludes that, if this analogy is an apt one, then we can grant the antiabortionist his claim that a fetus is a human being, and still hold that it is at least sometimes the case that a pregnant woman has the right to refuse to be a Good Samaritan towards the fetus, i.e., to obtain an abortion. For there is a great gap between the claim that *x* has a right to life, and the claim that *y* is obligated to do whatever is necessary to keep *x* alive, let alone that he ought to be forced to do so. It is *y*'s duty to keep *x* alive only if he has somehow contracted a *special* obligation to do so; and a woman who is unwillingly pregnant, e.g., who was raped, has done nothing which obligates her to make the enormous sacrifice which is necessary to preserve the conceptus.

This argument is initially quite plausible, and in the extreme case of pregnancy due to rape it is probably conclusive. Difficulties arise, however, when we try to specify more exactly the range of cases in which abortion is clearly justifiable even on the assumption that the fetus is human. Professor Thomson considers it a virtue of her argument that it does not enable us to conclude that abortion is *always* permissible. It would, she says, be "indecent" for a woman in her seventh month to obtain an abortion just to avoid having to postpone a trip to Europe. On the other hand, her argument enables us to see that "a sick and desperately frightened schoolgirl pregnant due to rape may *of course* choose abortion, and that any law which rules this out is an insane law" (p. 65). So far, so good; but what are we to say about the woman who becomes pregnant not through rape but as a result of her own carelessness, or because of contraceptive failure, or who gets pregnant intentionally and then changes her mind about wanting a child? With respect to such cases, the violinist analogy is of much less use to the defender of the woman's right to obtain an abortion.

Indeed, the choice of a pregnancy due to rape, as an example of a case in which abortion is permissible even if a fetus is considered a human being, is extremely significant; for it is only in the case of pregnancy due to rape that the woman's situation is adequately analogous to the violinist case for our intuitions about the latter to transfer convincingly. The crucial difference between a pregnancy due to rape and the normal case of an unwanted pregnancy is that in the normal case we cannot claim that the woman is in no way responsible for her predicament; she could have remained chaste, or taken her pills more faithfully, or abstained on dangerous days, and so on. If on the other hand, you are kidnapped by strangers, and hooked up to a strange violinist, then you are free of any shred of responsibility for the situation, on the basis of which it would be argued that you are obligated to keep the violinist alive. Only when her pregnancy is due to rape is a woman clearly just as nonresponsible.[6]

Consequently, there is room for the antiabortionist to argue that in the normal case of unwanted pregnancy a woman has, by her own actions, assumed responsibility of the fetus. For if *x* behaves in a way which he could have avoided, and which he knows involves, let us say, a 1 percent chance of bringing into existence a human being, with a right to life, and does so knowing that if this should happen then that human being will perish unless *x* does certain things to keep him alive, then it is by no means clear that when it does happen *x* is free of any obligation to what he knew in advance would be required to keep that human being alive.

The plausibility of such an argument is enough to show that the Thomson analogy can provide a clear and persuasive defense of a woman's right to obtain an abortion only with respect to those cases in which the woman is in no way responsible for her pregnancy, e.g., where it is due to rape. In all other cases, we would almost certainly conclude that it was necessary to look carefully at the particular circumstances in order to determine the extent of the woman's responsibility, and hence the extent of her obligation. This is an extremely unsatisfactory outcome, from the viewpoint of the opponents of restrictive abortion laws, most of whom are convinced that a woman has a right to obtain an abortion regardless of how and why she got pregnant.

Of course a supporter of the violinist analogy might point out that it is absurd to suggest that forgetting her pill one day might be sufficient to obligate a woman to complete an unwanted pregnancy. And indeed it is absurd to suggest this. As we will see, the moral right to obtain an abortion is not in the least dependent upon the extent to which a woman is responsible for her pregnancy. But unfortunately, once we allow the assumption that a fetus has full moral rights, we cannot avoid taking this absurd suggestion seriously. Perhaps we can make this point more clear by altering the violinist story just enough to make it more analogous to a normal unwanted pregnancy and less to a pregnancy due to rape, and then seeing whether it is still obvious that you are not obligated to stay in bed with the fellow.

Suppose, then, that violinists are peculiarly prone to the sort of illness the only cure for which is the use of someone else's bloodstream for nine months, and that because of this there has been formed a society of music lovers who agree that whenever a violinist is stricken they will draw lots and the loser will, by some means, be made the one and only person capable of saving him. Now then, would you be obligated to cooperate in curing the violinist if you had voluntarily joined this society, knowing the possible consequences, and then your name had been drawn and you had been kidnapped? Admittedly, you did not promise ahead of time that you would, but you did deliberately place yourself in a position in which it might happen that a human life would be lost if you did not. Surely this is at least a prima facie reason for supposing that you have an obligation to stay in bed with the violinist. Suppose that you had gotten your name drawn deliberately; surely *that* would be quite a strong reason for thinking that you had such an obligation.

It might be suggested that there is one important disanalogy between the modified violinist case and the case of an unwanted pregnancy, which makes the woman's responsibility significantly less, namely, the fact that the fetus *comes into existence* as the result of the woman's actions. This fact might give her a right to refuse to keep it alive, whereas she would not have had this right had it existed previously, independently, and then as a result of her actions become dependent upon her for its survival.

My own intuition, however, is that *x* has no more right to bring into existence, either deliberately or as a foreseeable result of actions he could have avoided, a being with full moral rights (*y*), and then refuse to do what he knew beforehand would be required to keep that being alive, than he has to enter into an agreement with an existing person, whereby he may be called upon to save that person's life, and then refuse to do so when so called upon. Thus *x*'s responsibility for *y*'s existence does not seem to lessen his obligation to keep *y* alive, if he is also responsible for *y*'s being in a situation in which only he can save him.

Whether or not this intuition is entirely correct, it brings us back once again to the conclusion that once we allow the assumption that a fetus has full moral rights it becomes an extremely complex and difficult question whether and when abortion is justifiable. Thus the Thomson analogy cannot help us produce a clear and persuasive proof of the moral permissibility of abortion. Nor will the opponents of the restrictive laws thank us for anything less; for their conviction (for the most part) is that abortion is obviously *not* a morally serious and extremely unfortunate, even though sometimes justified act, comparable to killing in self-defense or to letting the violinist die, but rather is closer to being a morally neutral act, like cutting one's hair.

The basis of this conviction, I believe, is the realization that a fetus is not a person, and thus does not have a full-fledged right to life. Perhaps the reason why this claim has been so inadequately defended is that it seems self-evident to those who accept it. And so it is, insofar as it follows from what I take to be perfectly obvious claims about the nature of personhood, and about the proper grounds for ascribing moral rights, claims which ought, indeed, to be obvious to both the friends and foes of abortion. Nevertheless, it is worth examining these claims, and showing how they demonstrate the moral innocuousness of abortion, since this apparently has not been adequately done before.

II

The question which we must answer in order to produce a satisfactory solution to the problem of the moral status of abortion is this: How are we to define

the moral community, the set of beings with full and equal moral rights, such that we can decide whether a human fetus is a member of this community or not? What sort of entity, exactly, has the inalienable rights to life, liberty, and the pursuit of happiness? Jefferson attributed these rights to all *men*, and it may or may not be fair to suggest that he intended to attribute them *only* to men. Perhaps he ought to have attributed them to all human beings. If so, then we arrive, first, at Noonan's problem of defining what makes a being human, and, second, at the equally vital question which Noonan does not consider, namely, What reason is there for identifying the moral community with the set of all human beings, in whatever way we have chosen to define that term?

1. On the Definition of "Human"

One reason why this vital second question is so frequently overlooked in the debate over the moral status of abortion is that the term "human" has two distinct, but not often distinguished, senses. This fact results in a slide of meaning, which serves to conceal the fallaciousness of the traditional argument that since (1) it is wrong to kill innocent human beings, and (2) fetuses are innocent human beings, then (3) it is wrong to kill fetuses. For if "human" is used in the same sense in both (1) and (2) then, whichever of the two senses is meant, one of these premises is question-begging. And if it is used in two different senses then of course the conclusion doesn't follow.

Thus, (1) is a self-evident moral truth,[7] and avoids begging the question about abortion, only if "human being" is used to mean something like "a full-fledged member of the moral community." (It may or may not also be meant to refer exclusively to members of the species *Homo sapiens*.) We may call this the *moral* sense of "human." It is not to be confused with what we will call the *genetic* sense; i.e., the sense in which *any* member of the species is a human being, and no member of any other species could be. If (1) is acceptable only if the moral sense is intended, (2) is non-question-begging only if what is intended is the genetic sense.

In "Deciding Who Is Human," Noonan argues for the classification of fetuses with human beings by pointing to the presence of the full genetic code, and the potential capacity for rational thought (p. 135). It is clear that what he needs to show, for his version of the traditional argument to be valid, is that fetuses are human in the moral sense, the sense in which it is analytically true that all human beings have full moral rights. But, in the absence of any argument showing that whatever is genetically human is also morally human, and he gives none, nothing more than genetic humanity can be demonstrated by the presence of the human genetic code. And, as we will see, the *potential* capacity for rational thought can at most show that an entity has the potential for becoming human in the moral sense.

2. Defining the Moral Community

Can it be established that genetic humanity is sufficient for moral humanity? I think that there are very good reasons for not defining the moral community in this way. I would like to suggest an alternative way of defining the moral community, which I will argue for only to the extent of explaining why it is, or should be, self-evident. The suggestion is simply that the moral community consists of all and *only* people, rather than all and only human beings;[8] and probably the best way of demonstrating its self-evidence is by considering the concept of personhood, to see what sorts of entity are and are not persons, and what the decision that a being is or is not a person implies about its moral rights.

What characteristics entitle an entity to be considered a person? This is obviously not the place to attempt a complete analysis of the concept of personhood, but we do not need such a fully adequate analysis just to determine whether and why a fetus is or isn't a person. All we need is a rough and approximate list of the most basic criteria of personhood, and some idea of which, or how many, of these an entity must satisfy in order to properly be considered a person.

In searching for such criteria, it is useful to look beyond the set of people with whom we are acquainted, and ask how we would decide whether a totally alien being was a person or not. (For we have no right to assume that genetic humanity is necessary for personhood.) Imagine a space traveler who lands on an unknown planet and encounters a race of beings utterly unlike any he has ever seen or heard of. If he wants to be sure of behaving morally toward these beings, he has to somehow decide whether they are people, and hence have full moral rights, or whether they are the sort of thing which he need not feel guilty about treating as, for example, a source of food.

How should he go about making this decision? If he has some anthropological background, he might look for such things as religion, art, and the manufacturing of tools, weapons, or shelters, since these factors have been used to distinguish our human from our prehuman ancestors, in what seems to be closer to the moral than the genetic sense of "human." And no doubt he would be right to consider the presence of such factors as good evidence that the alien beings were people, and morally human. It would, however, be overly anthropocentric of him to take the absence of these things as adequate evidence that they were not, since we can imagine people who have progressed beyond, or evolved without ever developing, these cultural characteristics.

I suggest that the traits which are most central to the concept of personhood, or humanity in the moral sense, are, very roughly, the following:

1. consciousness (of objects and events external and/or internal to the being), and in particular the capacity to feel pain;

2. reasoning (the developed capacity to solve new and relatively complex problems);

3. self-motivated activity (activity which is relatively independent of either genetic or direct external control);

4. the capacity to communicate, by whatever means, messages of an indefinite variety of types, that is, not just with an indefinite number of possible contents, but on indefinitely many possible topics;

5. the presence of self-concepts, and self-awareness, either individual or racial, or both.

Admittedly, there are apt to be a great many problems involved in formulating precise definitions of these criteria, let alone in developing universally valid behavioral criteria for deciding when they apply. But I will assume that both we and our explorer know approximately what (1)–(5) mean, and that he is also able to determine whether or not they apply. How, then, should he use his findings to decide whether or not the alien beings are people? We needn't suppose that an entity must have *all* of these attributes to be properly considered a person; (1) and (2) alone may well be sufficient for personhood, and quite probably (1)–(3), if "activity" is construed so as to include the activity of reasoning.

All we need to claim, to demonstrate that a fetus is not a person, is that any being which satisfies *none* of (1)–(5) is certainly not a person. I consider this claim to be so obvious that I think anyone who denied it, and claimed that a being which satisfied none of

(1)–(5) was a person all the same, would thereby demonstrate that he had no notion at all of what a person is—perhaps because he had confused the concept of a person with that of genetic humanity. If the opponents of abortion were to deny the appropriateness of these five criteria, I do not know what further arguments would convince them. We would probably have to admit that our conceptual schemes were indeed irreconcilably different, and that our dispute could not be settled objectively.

I do not expect this to happen, however, since I think that the concept of a person is one which is very nearly universal (to people), and that it is common to both proabortionists and antiabortionists, even though neither group has fully realized the relevance of this concept to the resolution of their dispute. Furthermore, I think that on reflection even the antiabortionists ought to agree not only that (1)–(5) are central to the concept of personhood, but also that it is a part of this concept that all and only people have full moral rights. The concept of a person is in part a moral concept; once we have admitted that *x* is a person we have recognized, even if we have not agreed to respect, *x*'s right to be treated as a member of the moral community. It is true that the claim that *x* is a *human being* is more commonly voiced as part of an appeal to treat *x* decently than is the claim that *x* is a person, but this is either because "human being" is here used in the sense which implies personhood, or because the genetic and moral sense of "human" have been confused.

Now if (1)–(5) are indeed the primary criteria of personhood, then it is clear that genetic humanity is neither necessary nor sufficient for establishing that an entity is a person. Some human beings are not people, and there may well be people who are not human beings. A man or woman whose consciousness has been permanently obliterated but who remains alive is a human being which is no longer a person; defective human beings, with no appreciable mental capacity, are not and presumably never will be people; and a fetus is a human being which is not yet a person, and which therefore cannot coherently be said to have full moral rights. Citizens of the next century should be prepared to recognize highly advanced, self-aware robots or computers, should such be developed, and intelligent inhabitants of other worlds, should such be found, as people in the fullest sense, and to respect their moral rights. But to ascribe full moral rights to an entity which is not a person is as absurd as to ascribe moral obligations and responsibilities to such an entity.

3. Fetal Development and the Right to Life

Two problems arise in the application of these suggestions for the definition of the moral community to the determination of the precise moral status of a human fetus. Given that the paradigm example of a person is a normal adult being, then (1) How like this paradigm, in particular how far advanced since conception, does a human being need to be before it begins to have a right to life by virtue, not of being fully a person as of yet, but of being *like* a person? and (2) To what extent, if any, does the fact that a fetus has the *potential* for becoming a person endow it with some of the same rights? Each of these questions requires some comment.

In answering the first question, we need not attempt a detailed consideration of the moral rights of organisms which are not developed enough, aware enough, intelligent enough, etc., to be considered people, but which resemble people in some respects. It does seem reasonable to suggest that the more like a person, in the relevant respects, a being is, the stronger is the case for regarding it as having a right to life, and indeed the stronger its right to life is. Thus we ought to take seriously the suggestion that, insofar as "the human individual develops biologically in a continuous fashion . . . the rights of a human person might develop in the same way."[9] But we must keep in mind that the attributes which are relevant in determining whether or not an entity is enough like a person to be regarded as having some of the same moral rights are no different from those which are relevant to determining whether or not it is fully a person—i.e., are no different from (1)–(5)—and that being genetically human, or having recognizably human facial and other physical features, or detectable brain activity, or the capacity to survive outside the uterus, are simply not among these relevant attributes.

Thus it is clear that even though a seven- or eight-month fetus has features which makes it apt to arouse in us almost the same powerful protective instinct as is commonly aroused by a small infant, nevertheless it is not significantly more personlike than is a very small embryo. It is *somewhat* more personlike; it can apparently feel and respond to pain, and it may even have a rudimentary form of consciousness, insofar as its brain is quite active. Nevertheless, it seems safe to say that it is not fully conscious, in the way that an infant of a few months is, and that it cannot reason, or communicate messages of indefinitely many sorts, does not engage in self-motivated activity, and has no self-awareness. Thus, in the *relevant* respects, a fetus, even a fully developed one, is considerably less personlike than is the average mature mammal, indeed the average fish. And I think that a rational person must conclude that if the right to life of a fetus is to be based upon its resemblance to a person, then it cannot be said to have any more right to life then, let us say, a newborn guppy (which also seems to be capable of feeling pain), and that a right of that magnitude could never override a woman's right to obtain an abortion, at any stage of her pregnancy.

There may, of course, be other arguments in favor of placing legal limits upon the stage of pregnancy in which an abortion may be performed. Given the relative safety of the new techniques of artificially inducing labor during the third trimester, the danger to the woman's life or health is no longer such an argument. Neither is the fact that people tend to respond to the thought of abortion in the later stages of pregnancy with emotional repulsion, since mere emotional responses cannot take the place of moral reasoning in determining what ought to be permitted. Nor, finally, is the frequently heard argument that legalizing abortion, especially late in the pregnancy, may erode the level of respect for human life, leading, perhaps, to an increase in unjustified euthanasia and other crimes. For this threat, if it is a threat, can be better met by educating people to the kinds of moral distinctions which we are making here than by limiting access to abortion (which limitation may, in its disregard for the rights of women, be just as damaging to the level of respect for human rights).

Thus, since the fact that even a fully developed fetus is not personlike enough to have any significant right to life on the basis of its personlikeness shows that no legal restrictions upon the stage of pregnancy in which an abortion may be performed can be justified on the grounds that we should protect the rights of the older fetus; and since there is no other apparent justification for such restrictions, we may conclude that they are entirely unjustified. Whether or not it would be *indecent* (whatever that means) for a woman in her seventh month to obtain an abortion just to avoid having to postpone a trip to Europe, it would not, in itself, be *immoral*, and therefore it ought to be permitted.

4. Potential Personhood and the Right to Life

We have seen that a fetus does not resemble a person in any way which can support the claim that it has even some of the same rights. But what about its *potential*, the fact that if nurtured and allowed to develop naturally it will very probably become a person?

Doesn't that alone give it at least some right to life? It is hard to deny that the fact that an entity is a potential person is a strong prima facie reason for not destroying it; but we need not conclude from this that a potential person has a right to life, by virtue of that potential. It may be that our feeling that it is better, other things being equal, not to destroy a potential person is better explained by the fact that potential people are still (felt to be) an invaluable resource, not to be lightly squandered. Surely, if every speck of dust were a potential person, we would be much less apt to conclude that every potential person has a right to become actual.

Still, we do not need to insist that a potential person has no right to life whatever. There may well be something immoral, and not just imprudent, about wantonly destroying potential people, when doing so isn't necessary to protect anyone's rights. But even if a potential person does have some prima facie right to life, such a right could not possibly outweigh the right of a woman to obtain an abortion, since the rights of any actual person invariably outweigh those of any potential person, whenever the two conflict. Since this may not be immediately obvious in the case of a human fetus, let us look at another case.

Suppose that our space explorer falls into the hands of an alien culture, whose scientists decide to create a few hundred thousand or more human beings, by breaking his body into its component cells, and using these to create fully developed human beings, with, of course, his genetic code. We may imagine that each of these newly created men will have all of the original man's abilities, skills, knowledge, and so on, and also have an individual self-concept, in short that each of them will be a bona fide (though hardly unique) person. Imagine that the whole project will take only seconds, and that its chances of success are extremely high, and that our explorer knows all of this, and also knows that these people will be treated fairly. I maintain that in such a situation he would have every right to escape if he could, and thus to deprive all of these potential people of their potential lives; for his right to life outweighs all of theirs together, in spite of the fact that they are all genetically human, all innocent, and all have a very high probability of becoming people very soon, if only he refrains from acting.

Indeed, I think he would have a right to escape even if it were not his life which the alien scientists planned to take, but only a year of his freedom, or, indeed, only a day. Nor would he be obligated to stay if he had gotten captured (thus bringing all these people-potentials into existence) because of his own carelessness, or even if he had done so deliberately, knowing the consequences. Regardless of how he got captured, he is not morally obligated to remain in captivity for *any* period of time for the sake of permitting any number of potential people to come into actuality, so great is the margin by which one actual person's right to liberty outweighs whatever right to life even a hundred thousand potential people have. And it seems reasonable to conclude that the rights of a woman will outweigh by a similar margin whatever right to life a fetus may have by virtue of its potential personhood.

Thus, neither a fetus's resemblance to a person, nor its potential for becoming a person provides any basis whatever for the claim that it has any significant right to life. Consequently, a woman's right to protect her health, happiness, freedom, and even her life,[10] by terminating an unwanted pregnancy, will always override whatever right to life it may be appropriate to ascribe to a fetus, even a fully developed one. And thus, in the absence of any overwhelming social need for every possible child, the laws which restrict the right to obtain an abortion, or limit the period of pregnancy during which an abortion may be performed, are a wholly unjustified violation of a woman's most basic moral and constitutional rights.[11]

Notes

1. For example, Roger Wertheimer, who in "Understanding the Abortion Argument" (*Philosophy and Public Affairs*, 1,

No. 1 [Fall, 1971], 67–95), argues that the problem of the moral status of abortion is insoluble, in that the dispute over the status of the fetus is not a question of fact at all, but only a question of how one responds to the facts.

2. John Noonan, "Abortion and the Catholic Church: A Summary History," *Natural Law Forum*, 12 (1967), 125.

3. John Noonan, "Deciding Who Is Human," *Natural Law Forum*, 13 (1968), 134.

4. "A Defense of Abortion."

5. Judith Thomson, "A Defense of Abortion," *Philosophy and Public Affairs*, 1, No. 1 (Fall, 1971), 47–66.

6. We may safely ignore the fact that she might have avoided getting raped, e.g., by carrying a gun, since by similar means you might likewise have avoided getting kidnapped, and in neither case does the victim's failure to take all possible precautions against a highly unlikely event (as opposed to reasonable precautions against a rather likely event) mean that he is morally responsible for what happens.

7. Of course, the principle that it is (always) wrong to kill innocent human beings is in need of many other modifications, e.g., that it may be permissible to do so to save a greater number of other innocent human beings, but we may safely ignore these complications here.

8. From here on, we will use "human" to mean genetically human, since the moral sense seems closely connected to, and perhaps derived from, the assumption that genetic humanity is sufficient for membership in the moral community.

9. Thomas L. Hayes, "A Biological View," *Commonweal*, 85 (March 17, 1967), 677–78; quoted by Daniel Callahan, in *Abortion, Law, Choice, and Morality* (London: Macmillan & Co., 1970).

10. That is, insofar as the death rate, for the woman, is higher for childbirth than for early abortion.

11. My thanks to the following people, who were kind enough to read and criticize an earlier version of this paper: Herbert Gold, Gene Glass, Anne Lauterbach, Judith Thomson, Mary Mothersill, and Timothy Binkley.

Section 3:   Emergency Contraception and Professional Responsibilities

---

Conscientious Objection and Emergency Contraception

Robert F. Card

Card argues that pharmacists, nurses, and doctors have a professional duty to inform women about emergency contraception (EC) and to provide it when requested. He rejects the standard solution to the problem EC

Robert Card, From "Conscientious Objection and Emergency Contraception", *The American Journal of BioEthics*, Vol. 7, no. 6 (2007): 8–14, Copyright © 2007 Taylor and Francis Group, LLC. Reprinted with permission.

poses to medical professionals who object to it on conscientious grounds—namely, referring patients to a willing provider. This solution, Card claims, can result in great harm to women, may compromise patient confidentiality, and fails to fulfill the obligations of a medical professional.

In Card's view, professionals can't legitimately object to EC on the same grounds as they might object to abortion, because EC prevents ovulation and thus operates before fertilization occurs. Professionals might try to object to EC on the grounds they would use to object to contraception, holding that EC is unacceptable either because it deprives reproductive cells of the opportunity to become persons or because it interferes with procreation, which is the only acceptable goal of intercourse.

Card counters the first objection with the non-identity argument of Purdy and Brock—namely, that possible persons cannot be harmed by being prevented from becoming persons. The second objection he dismisses as injurious to rape victims (procreation can hardly be their goal) and as inconsistent with the autonomy-based right of adults to make reproductive decisions (e.g., to have a sex without the goal of reproducing). If adults have a right to contraception, then medical professionals must offer and provide EC.

Unlike other contraceptives, EC must be used within 72 hours after sexual contact, so referral to a willing provider may delay EC beyond this time, particularly in rural areas with few providers and for disadvantaged patients who typically delay seeking help. For those reasons, Card concludes, medical professionals cannot ethically refuse to offer and provide EC. Referring women elsewhere will not let them escape their professional duty.

Decisions regarding health policy frequently involve a volatile mixture of medical science, politics, and ethical values. One of the most contentious recent issues concerns prescriptions for emergency contraception (EC), especially given the reticence of the United States Food and Drug Administration (FDA) to grant over-the-counter status to the EC levonorgestrel (Duramed Pharmaceuticals, Inc., Pomona, NY) and the resignation of one of the FDA's directors over this issue. On August 24, 2006, FDA announced approval of levonorgestrel as an over-the-counter medication for women age 18 and older,[1] yet a general moral question still remains: what is the scope of medical providers' right to refuse treatment based on their own ethical objections to this treatment? As it turns out, FDA's decision may simply make the relevant ethical issues more subtle—imagine cases in which a medical provider refuses to mention or discuss EC with a woman who is expressing her concern regarding an unplanned pregnancy. The FDA's recent plan still uses pharmacists as a gatekeeper because women younger than age 18 years must secure a prescription and women age 18 years and old must be able to prove their age to a pharmacist who keeps the drugs behind the counter. As observed in the *Washington Post*:

> *The FDA decision does not resolve other controversial issues swirling around the pills, including the refusal of hospitals run by religious organizations to offer them, of some pharmacies to stock them and of some antiabortion pharmacists to dispense them. "The FDA doing a stupid thing doesn't change anything for those of us who need to do the right thing," said Karen Brauer, president of the group Pharmacists for Life International, which opposes the use of the emergency contraceptive (Stein 2006, A06).*

There has been increased attention focused on this issue, given numerous reports (Greenberger and Vogelstein 2005; Stein 2005) that medical professionals have refused to honor women's requests for EC based on conscientious objection. This discussion broaches a relatively unexplored issue within biomedical ethics; conscientious objection raises interesting questions in other contexts such as abortion and physician-assisted suicide. A standard way to address this issue is to advocate referral of care to a willing provider. To cite just one such example, Dan Brock states in the context of active euthanasia that if performing the associated actions "conflicted with a particular physician's reasonable understanding of his or her moral or professional responsibilities, the care of a patient who requested euthanasia should be transferred to another" (Brock 1992 [2004], 215). This is a popular approach to managing conscientious refusals, yet as I will argue within this discussion of EC, it is not an unproblematic response.

I will understand conscientious objection as a refusal to comply with a request based on personal moral or religiously-inspired moral reasons (Childress 1985). This general moral question applies not only to pharmacists who refuse to dispense EC but also to physicians who refuse to discuss EC on moral grounds. This article focuses mainly on the former controversy because this is an issue of current relevance; 15 states have recently considered bills concerning conscientious objection in the pharmacy. (Greenberger and Vogelstein 2005, 1557). In what follows, a "critical examination will be conducted regarding the ethical duties of professionals with respect to hormonal EC (e.g., estrogen and progestin/levonorgestrel). In contrast to other thinkers that advocate the duty to refer patients, this paper argues that providers have a professional ethical obligation to inform women of this option and dispense EC when this treatment is requested.

The analysis presented is based on professional ethical obligations and should not be construed as necessarily supporting or denying legal or regulatory requirements. Professional ethics is a different and higher standard as compared with legality. Because not every moral obligation is (or ought to be) codified into law, the discussion of this article should be understood as centered on professional ethics.

The Moderate View of Conscientious Objection

In an influential article, Julie Cantor and Ken Baum (2004) focus on the objecting pharmacist's duty to refer patients requesting EC to another willing pharmacist. They note that the American Pharmacists Association (APhA) (Washington, DC) has endorsed referrals, and they hold that pharmacists do not have an absolute right to object nor do they lack a right to conscientious objection (Cantor and Baum 2004, 2011). There is no absolute right to object because autonomy rights are limited in their scope. Clearly, pharmacists cannot ethically refuse to provide treatment based on the patient's race or ethnicity. Mark Wicclair (2000, 212) points out that if a medical professional conscientiously objected to forgoing aggressive treatment on the grounds that it would deny her an opportunity to test a new drug, then this type of reason would properly be accorded no moral weight as a ground for conscientious refusal. Pharmacists have a right to object because the APhA has explicitly adopted a pharmacist conscience clause, [which] states that:

> [the] APhA recognizes the individual pharmacist's right to exercise conscientious refusal and supports the establishment of systems to ensure patients' access to legally prescribed therapy without compromising the pharmacist's right of conscientious refusal (APA, 2004).

As I view it, this clause grants a (defeasible) professional right on the part of pharmacists to engage in conscientious objection. Cantor and Baum believe that a position in the "vast middle ground" is most defensible. This moderate position, although reasonable on its face, is problematic on closer inspection.

Referrals may not be possible for economically disadvantaged patients and/or those who live in rural areas, thereby leaving such patients with no true access

to medical treatment. In the case of EC, time is of the essence, as such medication works best in the first 12 to 24 hours after sexual contact and must be administered within 72 hours (Greenberger and Vogelstein 2005, 1557). This position can therefore result in great harm to women. Further, by exercising the referral option, objecting pharmacists are not fulfilling their role responsibility. The precise role of pharmacists within the United States healthcare system is somewhat murky, but some plausible suggestions include the following: checking for drug interactions with the patient's prescription medications and instructing patients on using a medication. A pharmacist's role is not to second-guess an adult's decisions regarding the use of an approved pharmaceutical but is to provide convenient and safe access to medications. Additionally, the publicity of confrontations with objecting pharmacists, especially at the counters of large, chain pharmacies, compromises patient integrity and confidentiality.

While the moderate view stresses a duty to refer instead of a duty to dispense the medication as a way to strike a balance between the interests of patients and pharmacists, it is unclear what actual ethical difference exists between these two duties for the conscientiously objecting pharmacist. Cantor and Baum state, "[a] referral may also represent a break in causation between the pharmacist and distributing emergency contraception, a separation that the objecting pharmacist presumably seeks" (Cantor and Baum 2004, 2011). Is this really true, and do all objecting professionals support the referral option? Referring the patient to another willing pharmacist certainly does not remove the pharmacist from the causal chain of events that leads to the use of EC, an act that is considered morally wrong by such objecting pharmacists. Supporters of pharmacists' right to conscientious objection such as Karen Brauer, hold that such medical treatment violates the Hippocratic Oath by doing harm to human life (Stein 2005). Brauer defends pharmacists' rights to refuse to dispense medications themselves as well as to refuse to refer customers to other willing pharmacists. Brauer holds this position because she believes that referring customers makes no intrinsic moral difference:

> That's like saying, 'I don't kill people myself but let me tell you about the guy down the street who does.' What's that saying? 'I will not off your husband, but I know a buddy who will?' It's the same thing (Stein 2005, A01).

A staunch defender of pharmacists' right to conscientious objection (such as Brauer) clearly sees no ethical difference between dispensing the medication herself and allowing another willing pharmacist to do so. This presents a serious challenge to the moderate view. Because the proponents of the moderate view have not defended an intrinsic moral distinction between "doing" and "allowing," this argument by the staunch defender of conscientious objection remains unchallenged. At the very least, referrals are not as ethically unproblematic for objecting pharmacists as moderates think. In fact, because referrals are equally morally troublesome for these objecting pharmacists, Cantor and Baum have not provided the "respectful balance" between the interests of pharmacists and patients that they seek.

A Less Moderate View of Conscientious Refusals by Medical Practitioners

In this section, I critically analyze proposed objections to the dispensing of EC to arrive at a less moderate view on the reasonableness of conscientious objection in this context. Before beginning this task, however, I wish to briefly elaborate on how I have framed the issue in order to set the stage for the weighing of reasons that is to follow. From the outset of this article I have viewed this debate as involving the autonomy rights of medical professionals. Valuable insight into this debate is gained by taking seriously the notion that medical providers (e.g., physicians, pharmacists, nurses) are members of a profession. Writings by numerous thinkers (Arras 1988; Pellegrino 1987) suggest plausible characteristics of a profession that are satisfied by the medical field. Edmund Pellegrino makes some thought-provoking observations about why physicians (and, by extension, other healthcare providers) are members of a profession. To discuss just one of his points, Pellegrino views medical knowledge as a "public trust." This knowledge was gained by invasions of privacy and experimentation on human beings, and these decisions were justified because medicine should use this knowledge to reduce human suffering and serve humankind. This suggests that there are social obligations on the part of medical professionals that are not possessed by persons who are simply members of an occupation. The distinction between the concepts of a *profession* and an *occupation* is rough around the edges, but it

marks off a useful and important distinction. The issue at hand requires balancing the moral values of the medical professional and the patient. Medical professionals are persons who possess autonomy rights, and hence may refuse care in some circumstances, yet we cannot forget to take the patients' moral values into consideration as well.

To imagine just one concrete scenario, perhaps the woman seeking EC finds using contraception to be ethically unproblematic but does not morally agree with abortion at any stage. The professional's refusal may cause a delay in care which, given the circumstances of the woman, may then require her to have an abortion later. Are we then at a standoff in this conflict between the moral values of the patient and the provider? This is not the case, because refusals of care with respect to EC may jeopardize the health and the well-being of women. At the moral center of medical professionalism is the requirement that practitioners give primacy to their patients' interests. This is echoed in ethical codes, for instance, in statements of research ethics (e.g., the Declaration of Helsinki) proclaiming a professional's duties to safeguard subjects' well-being and to not treat subjects merely as a means to advancing the interests of society or medical science. Because EC must be used within 72 hours of sexual contact, time is of the essence. A refusal of care in this context may amount, in practical terms, to a right to impose their beliefs on their patients, yet professionals do not possess this right. This follows from the fact that patients possess autonomy rights and the point that providers should give primacy to patients' interests. The position of this article is that conscientious objection is different with respect to EC as compared with physician-assisted suicide, for example; the extremely narrow time frame for care is one such salient difference.

One may downplay the importance of the previous discussion by proposing that if pharmacists refer patients to other professionals who will give the patients timely access to EC, there is no significant threat to women's health or well-being. In response, I would ask the objector whether he or she accepts the position that the professional must dispense EC if a referral is not possible. I doubt this is the case. If the objector does not accept this position, then he or she fails to safeguard the patient's interests. If the objector does accept this position, then he or she agrees with the argument set out previously: that medical providers can be under a professional obligation with respect to EC that overrides their personal moral beliefs. Further, this objection is clearly premised upon a hypothetical scenario. If, for example, war is declared and there are so many able-bodied persons willing to enlist that conscription is not necessary, then it may be thought that conscientious objection becomes an issue that is of mere theoretical interest (if no injustice or bad consequences occur in such a state of affairs). But with respect to EC, unfairness and bad consequences do in fact occur,[2] and hence this objection is not realistic in the circumstances in which the debate regarding EC occurs.

Physicians who conscientiously refuse to provide EC object on the same basis offered by pharmacists—yet a critical examination of this basis may lead to a reconsideration of these reasons. This section focuses on examining this basis in general; after all, physicians' greater stature within the profession does not itself make their professed reasons more forceful. What are these reasons? Professionals may object to dispensing EC because a) s/he considers EC to be unethical since it is equivalent to abortion, or b) s/he considers contraception itself to be immoral. I will evaluate these versions of conscientious objection to dispensing EC in turn.

The first line of argument (a) is empirically questionable. There is no evidence that levonorgestrel and similar hormonal EC regimens have an effect on an established pregnancy (Glasier 1997, 1060). Conception represents the start of the process of becoming pregnant; as David Bainbridge says regarding conception, *conception* is "a term to include all the different mechanisms that must act for a pregnancy to be established, of which fertilisation is only one" (Bainbridge 2001, 278). His point is that pregnancy is not equivalent to fertilization. Another source states the following regarding EC: "By medical definition, the pills block rather than terminate pregnancy." (Editors of *Scientific American*, 2005) The scientific data suggest that hormonal EC operates mainly by inhibiting or disrupting ovulation (Glasier 1997, 1063). What this means is that EC inhibits follicular development and the maturation and/or the release of the ovum itself (Glasier 1997, 1058), thereby preventing pregnancy. As Anna Glasier puts the point, "it cannot be stressed too strongly that if hormonal emergency contraception works largely by interfering with ovulation, then it cannot be regarded as an abortifacient" (1997, 1063).

Why, then, would anyone regard hormonal EC as equivalent to abortion? One hypothesis is based on simple scientific ignorance of the mode of action of EC. A more interesting hypothesis is offered by Glasier: "Although it seems likely that the estrogen–progestin regimen works mainly by interfering with ovulation, it is nevertheless regarded by many as an abortifacient because it is taken after, rather than before, intercourse" (1997, 1063). This highlights a line of reasoning that is obviously mistaken because it involves a causal or temporal confusion. It is worth taking a moment to sort this out in order to see the mistake. If a woman has unprotected sexual intercourse, she may become pregnant. Sperm can remain in the female genital tract and are capable of fertilization for up to 5 days; the ovum appears to be capable of fertilization for only about 24 hours (Glasier 1997, 1058). If a woman's request for this medication is satisfied, EC may interfere with ovulation and hence fertilization does not occur. The point is that EC has lasting effects and could thereby prevent a pregnancy that might have otherwise occurred even after the 72-hour "window period"—the time during which EC must be taken in order to be effective. EC is a form of contraception, not an abortifacient.

An astute objecting pharmacist might object to the definition of pregnancy used in the previous discussion, suggesting instead that pregnancy is equivalent to fertilization (or, at least, that fertilization marks the point at which an individual with moral standing exists). On this understanding, if fertilization had occurred, then EC would terminate the pregnancy and is equivalent to abortion. Because the mode of action of currently available EC is not precisely known, it is possible that EC may interfere with the transport of the embryo to the uterus or inhibit its implantation into the endometrium (Dresser 2005, 9). A review of the literature suggests that there is no solid reason to believe that hormonal EC works in either the former or latter manner (Glasier 1997, 1059); recent scientific evidence (Croxatto et al. 2004) suggests that hormonal EC does not have post-fertilization effects.

Consider further that the astute pharmacist bases his or her objection to EC on the fact that a pregnancy has occurred, but this is an unknown within the 72-hour window period. Some basic facts about human pregnancy make this clear. Pregnancy can be detected in women by the measurement of human chorionic gonadotropin, a hormone produced by the placenta in early pregnancy. Bainbridge makes clear that the embryo has an aggressive approach to the maternal recognition of pregnancy (relative to other species); he reports that "the embryo can form a considerable bulk of placental tissue as early as five to seven days after fertilisation" (Bainbridge 2001, 93). However, even given this fact and the existence of sensitive and reliable pregnancy tests it is not possible to confirm a positive pregnancy within the 72-hour window period.

This is another way in which conscientious refusal within the context of EC differs from other cases in which medical professionals invoke such objections. In a case of conscientious objection regarding abortion, a physician knows whether or not a fetus exists. The same is true, *mutatis mutandis*, in cases of conscientious objection regarding assisted suicide. Yet there is a small and unknowable probability that dispensing EC during the window period would cause something morally wrong to occur (by the objecting professional's own beliefs). Since the objecting professional lacks relevant evidence for the very foundation of his or her conscientious objection, there is not sufficient reason to grant substantial weight to a refusal on this ground.

A very astute professional might accept the foregoing discussion, but respond by arguing that, while this probability is an unknown, there is a non-zero probability that pregnancy has occurred. If the professional dispenses EC, then there is a possibility that he or she has contributed to the commission of a morally wrong action (by his or her own beliefs). Or, in a slightly revised version, an objecting professional might state that by doing so in numerous instances, there would be a non-zero probability that he or she has contributed to the commission of a morally wrong action (by his or her own beliefs).

I will call this *the zero probability argument:* persons should not perform an action unless it is true that there is a zero probability that their action (or their contribution to an action) will issue in immoral results. The zero probability argument leads to absurd results because the mere possibility of contributing to immoral results exists with virtually anything a human being does—given the existence of spurious causal chains, this may be true of acts such as taking a walk or brushing one's teeth. More specifically, the mere possibility of contributing to wrongdoing applies to many acts performed by a medical professional (e.g., dispensing cold and sinus medicines that might be abused in various ways) and would suggest that such professionals should stop assisting patients in general. This is unacceptable; it is simply unreasonable to withhold medication because of the *mere possibility* that this may contribute to an immoral result.

In this portion of the discussion, we have discovered a general problem with conscientious objections to EC based on a comparison to abortion. If fertilization has occurred, because there is no evidence that

EC has post-fertilization effects, dispensing EC will not change the outcome. On the other hand, if fertilization has not occurred and EC acts to inhibit ovulation, thereby preventing a pregnancy that would have otherwise later occurred, nothing immoral happens even granting the objecting professional's beliefs as discussed. In either case, the basis for the professional's conscientious refusal with regard to dispensing EC is called into question. EC causes something ethically-problematic to occur only if contraception itself is considered morally unacceptable.

Perhaps members of Pharmacists for Life (Powell, OH) represent this remaining type of objecting professional; recall, they stated above that EC constitutes "doing harm to human life." If this notion is taken literally, then this implies that medical treatments such as chemotherapy are morally wrong in themselves. Chemotherapy destroys human cells and hence seemingly counts as doing harm to human life in some way. Yet it is absurd to think that chemotherapy is morally wrong in itself. It is more plausible to suppose, that the objecting professional believes that the human life in question is somehow limited specifically to individual sperm and ova. This professional might argue that reproductive cells are special because they possess the potential to become persons. Sperm and ova that are not given at least an opportunity to become persons are harmed.

The fact that this claim lacks a sound basis is made clear by referring to a version of the non-identity problem. Contraception, if effective, prevents conception; yet does not-being-conceived constitute a moral wrong to one who otherwise would have come into existence? Laura Purdy discusses the non-identity problem and addresses this question in the negative:

> [T]here seems to be no reason to believe that possible individuals are either deprived or injured if they do not exist . . . [if we had not been created] we would not exist and there would be nobody to be deprived of anything (Purdy 1978 [2004], 258).

This argument states that if an individual never comes into existence, then there is no one that is harmed because no one exists who is a subject of harm. This general argument is not beyond dispute; Dan Brock (1995) questions the dismissal of harms to "possible persons" by referring to the non-identity problem. Yet Brock's discussion centers on the case of genetically-transmitted handicaps, and his point is that the possible harm to a potential offspring should not be dismissed if one could have a different child without comparable burdens (Brock 1995, 271). Hence, the foregoing argument is not directly affected; even a critic of the non-identity argument such as Brock does not accept that being deprived of existence itself constitutes a moral harm. After all, if not being brought into existence were an injury and we were committed to a principle of minimizing harm, this would imply (in certain circumstances) the absurd result that failing to reproduce at a maximal rate is a moral wrong. In sum, before one is conceived, there is no individual of which to speak. If one was never brought into existence, it is not the case that harm occurs by virtue of the deprivation of "actualizing" the potential to become a person—there is no one who could be said to have been deprived of anything.

One may object that I have not properly interpreted the moral objection to contraception. One may instead think that contraception is wrong because intercourse is ethically acceptable only if the goal is procreation. In response, I call attention to the ambiguity of the term *goal* and critically analyze this proposed reason. If this reason is to be understood as "intercourse is ethically acceptable only if the natural 'goal' is procreation," then in this argument no contraception is morally permissible. This position is unreasonable because it is inconsistent with the compelling fundamental idea that adults possess a moral reproductive right founded in autonomy. This notion was first articulated as a legal right in *Griswold v. Connecticut* (1965). If the term *goal* is to be understood as "intercourse is ethically acceptable only if a person's 'goal' is procreation," then we must determine the subjective intentions or circumstances in which potentially procreative activity occurred. If a woman requests EC because of contraceptive failure, then obviously her goal was not procreation and EC should be dispensed. Yet this does not support the objecting professional's position. What if, instead, a woman who is a rape victim requests EC? Was the goal in the activity procreation? It is reasonable to say that she had no positive goal with respect to the intercourse because she was an unwilling participant. Notice that objecting providers do not distinguish cases of sexual assault from other cases in which women request EC, so this subjective understanding of the reason is not applicable to the situation at hand. This proposed reason based on the wrongness of contraception does not successfully support conscientious objection on the part of professionals with respect to EC.

Conclusion

Initially, there seem to be three relevant alternatives regarding this issue: an absolute right to object, no right to object, or a limited right to object. This article has argued that there is no absolute right to object because if would be immoral for a provider to deny medical treatment to a patient based solely on, for example, his or her race. There is a *prima facie* right regarding conscientious objection, founded in the notion that providers are persons with their own ethical values who exercise moral judgment, yet this right may be defeated in certain cases. Working strictly within the context of conscientious refusals to dispense EC, the argument in this article suggests that fewer options exist than appear on the face of things. A limited right to object, if it is manifested in a professional obligation to refer the patient to a willing provider, can be viewed as philosophically indistinguishable from the case of dispensing EC by the staunch objecting professional himself or herself. This is the case if no stock is put into an intrinsic moral distinction between "doing" and "allowing"; the defender of the moderate view on conscientious objection with respect to EC has not adequately recognized this point nor attempted to rebut it. For the staunch defender of the right to conscientious objection discussed in this article, either such providers have an absolute right to object or no right to conscientious objection regarding EC. As argued previously, providers are medical professionals who lack an absolute right to object. Further, I have argued that the reasons offered for refusals regarding EC do not withstand critical scrutiny. Hence, it is reasonable to think that even given their moral reservations, providers have a professional ethical obligation to dispense EC.

Notes

1. This announcement was made while this article was under review; however, this event does not change the basic philosophical issues and proposed objections to EC—the consideration of which is the focus of this discussion. For details on the FDA's approval and plan for distributing EC as an over-the-counter pharmaceutical, see FDA 2006.

2. In a compelling narrative, Dana L. discusses her difficulty acquiring levonorgestrel in Virginia and the subsequent choice regarding abortion she was forced to make as a result (L., Dana 2006).

References

American Pharmacists Association. 2004. House of Delegates *Report of the Policy Review Committee.* Available at http://www. aphanet. org/AM/Template.cfm? Section=Home&Template= /CM/ContentDisplay.cfm&ContentID=2472 (accessed October 20, 2005).

Arras, J. D. 1988. AIDS and the duty to treat. *Hastings Center Report* 18:10–18.

Bainbridge, D. 2001. *Making babies: The science of pregnancy.* Cambridge, MA: Harvard University Press.

Brock, D. W. 1992 [2004]. Voluntary active euthanasia. In *Critically thinking about medical ethics*, ed. R. F. Card, 214–223. Upper Saddle River, NJ: Prentice Hall.

Brock, D. W. 1995. The non-identity problem and genetic harms. *Bioethics* 9:269–275.

Cantor, J., and K. Baum. 2004. The limits of conscientious objection—may pharmacists refuse to fill prescriptions for emergency contraception? *New England Journal of Medicine* 351:2008–2012.

Croxatto, H. B., V. Brache, M. Pavez, et al. 2004 Pituitary–ovarian function following the standard levonorgestrel emergency contraceptive dose or a single 0.75-mg. dose given on the days preceding ovulation. *Contraception* 70:442–450.

Dresser, R. 2005. Professionals, conformity, and conscience. *Hastings Center Report* 35:9–10.

Editors of *Scientific American.* 2005. Fill this prescription. *Scientific American* September 26. Available at http://www.sciam.com (accessed on October 13, 2005).

FDA. 2006. Plan B (0.75 mg levonorgestrel) tablets information. Available at http://fda.gov/CDER/drug/infopage/planB/planBQandA.htm (accessed on August 24, 2005).

Glasier, A. 1997. Emergency postcoital contraception. *New England Journal of Medicine* 337:1058–1064.

Greenberger, M. D., and R. Vogelstein. 2005. Pharmacist refusals: A threat to women's health. *Science* 308:1557–1558.

Griswold v. Connecticut 381 U.S. 479 (1965).

Karasz, A., N. T. Kirchen, and M. Gold. 2004. The visit before the morning after: barriers to preprescribing emergency contraception. *Annals of Family Medicine* 2:345–350.

Dana, L. 2006. What happens when there is no Plan B? *Washington Post* June 4: B01.

Pellegrino, E. D. 1987 [2004]. Altruism, self-interest, and medical ethics. *Journal of the American Medical Association* 258:1939–1940.

Purdy, L. 1978. Can having children be immoral? In *Critically thinking about medical ethics*, ed. R. F Card, 255–261. Upper Saddle River, NJ: Prentice Hall.

Stein, R. 2005. Pharmacists' rights at the front of new debate. *Washington Post* March 28: A01.

Stein, R. 2006. FDA approves Plan B's over-the-counter sale. *Washington Post* March 28: A01.

Wicclair, M. R. 2000. Conscientious objection in medicine. *Bioethics* 14:205–227.

DECISION SCENARIOS

The questions following each decision scenario are intended to prompt reflection and discussion. In deciding how to answer them, you should consider the information in the Briefing Session; the ethical theories and principles presented in Part V, "Foundations of Bioethics," and the arguments and criticisms offered in the relevant readings in this chapter.

DECISION SCENARIO 1

Emergency Contraception

Samantha Williams was feeling desperate when she walked into Wall's Drugs and Sundries. She had failed to take any precautions when she had sex with Charlie, and Charlie hadn't been prepared either. Neither of them had been expecting what happened to happen.

But it had, and now she was going to have to do something about it. She was only seventeen, and she couldn't have a baby. It would change the rest of her life. She wouldn't be able to go to college, and she would have to get a job. She knew Charlie wasn't going to marry her. She barely knew him, anyway. Besides, what if they did get married? Charlie had no more way of supporting himself than she did, and his family was even poorer than hers. She had already waited too long. She should have gone to the drugstore immediately.

Samantha hung back, waiting until no one else was standing in the little nook the pharmacy had set aside for consultations. She was relieved to see that the pharmacist on duty was a young red-haired woman with a nice smile. The plastic plaque by the cash register identified her as Monique Marquesa.

"I need a package of Plan B," Samantha told her. She then quickly added, "Or a bottle or however it comes."

"You think you need it?" The pharmacist gave her an appraising glance. "You know what it is?"

"I absolutely need it." Samantha felt herself blushing. "And I know people call it a morning-after pill."

"How old are you?" Monique Marquesa asked the question in a curt way. "You know there's an age requirement?"

"I'm seventeen." Samantha was not going to let herself be bullied. "I know that's old enough to buy Plan B." She added, "I also have the money. In cash."

"I don't approve of girls your age taking Plan B." Maquesa gave Samanth a stern look, "You shouldn't need it, and I'm not going to sell it to you. For me, it's a matter of conscience."

"But I need it." Samantha was so stunned she couldn't think of what to say. "You have to sell it to me."

"No I don't," the pharmacist said. "If you want the drug, you can go to a Planned Parenthood clinic and get it. There's one at the Millennium Plaza."

"But that's miles from here." Samantha couldn't believe what the woman was telling her. "It's already been a couple of days, and I'm sure the clinic is closed this time of night. I don't know if I can even get there."

"I'm sorry." The pharmacist didn't sound sorry. "That's all I can do. I've sent you to a place where you can get what you want. I'm not going to go against my principles just to please you."

1. Is Monique Marquesa acting within her rights in refusing to sell Samantha Plan B for reasons of conscience?

2. Do pharmacists have a professional duty to provide patients with the drugs they request, so long as it is legal to do so?

3. Would it be legitimate for a taxi driver to refuse to drive Samantha to Planned Parenthood on the grounds that he objects to contraception and abortion?

4. Should pharmacists be required by law to stock and sell Plan B to those who meet the legal requirements for buying it?

DECISION SCENARIO 2

After The Concert

It happened after a concert. Sixteen-year-old Mary Pluski had gone with three of her friends to hear Bruce Springsteen at Chicago's Blanton Auditorium. After the concert, in a crowd estimated at 11,000, Mary became separated from the other three girls. She decided that the best thing to do was to meet them at the car.

But when she got to the eight-story parking building, Mary realized she wasn't sure what level they had parked on. She thought it might be somewhere in the middle, so she started looking on the fourth floor. While she was walking down the aisles of cars, two men in their early twenties, one white and the other black, stopped her and asked if she were having some kind of trouble.

Mary explained the situation to them, and one of the men suggested that they get his car and drive around inside the parking building. Mary hesitated, but both seemed so polite and genuinely concerned to help that she decided to go with them.

Once they were in the car, however, the situation changed. They drove out of the building and toward the South Side. Mary pleaded with them to let her out of the car. Then, some seven miles from the auditorium, the driver stopped the car in a dark area behind a vacant building. Mary was then raped by both men.

Mary was treated at Allenworth Hospital and released into the custody of her parents. She filed a complaint with the police, but her troubles were not yet over. Two weeks after she missed her menstrual period, tests showed that Mary was pregnant.

"How do you feel about having this child?" asked Sarah Ruben, the Pluski family physician.

"I hate the idea," Mary said. "I feel guilty about it, though. I mean, it's not the child's fault."

"Let me ask a delicate question," said Dr. Ruben. "I know from what you've told me before that you and your boyfriend have been having sex. Can you be sure this pregnancy is not really the result of that?"

Mary shook her head. "Not really. I use my diaphragm, but I know it doesn't give a hundred percent guarantee."

"That's right. Now, does it make any difference to you who the father might be, so far as a decision about terminating the pregnancy is concerned?"

"If I were sure it was Bob, I guess the problem would be even harder," Mary said.

"There are some tests we can use to give us that information," Dr. Ruben said. "But that would mean waiting for the embryo to develop into a fetus. It would be easier and safer to terminate the pregnancy now."

Mary started crying. "I don't want a child," she said. "I don't want any child. I don't care who's the father. It was forced on me, and I want to get rid of it."

"I'll make the arrangements," said Dr. Ruben.

1. If abortion can be justified in a case of rape, can a similar argument be used to justify it in a case in which the pregnancy was unintended?

2. Suppose the fetus is a person. Can abortion be justified on the grounds that a woman has a right to decide whether she wants to carry the child to term?

3. Is depriving the fetus of a future justified by the conditions under which the fetus was conceived?

DECISION SCENARIO 3

A Procedure by Another Name

In March 1995, Tammy Watts had been pregnant for eight months and was excited by the prospect of becoming a mother for the first time. Then her world fell apart. A routine ultrasound revealed that her baby had trisomy 13, a chromosomal abnormality that causes severe deformities and no hope of survival for the child.

Tammy Watts' child was dying inside her, and this put her own life at risk. Because she could not help her child and feared for her own life, she chose to have the procedure known as intact dilation and extraction. This is the procedure called "partial-birth abortion" by abortion opponents.

"Losing my baby at the end of my pregnancy was agonizing," Watts said in congressional testimony in 1995. "But the way the right deals with the procedure makes it even worse. When I heard [President] Bush mention 'partial-birth abortion' during the [presidential] debates, I thought, 'How dare you stand there and tell flat-out lies?' There is no such thing as this procedure."

Watts' testimony was accompanied by additional testimony from Viki Wilson, who had a late-term abortion because the brain of the fetus she was carrying was developing outside the skull. More testimony was given by Vikki Stella, whose fetus had developed without a brain (was an encephalic) and had seven other serious abnormalities.

The women all testified that they owed their own health to a late-term abortion and that a continuation of their ultimately futile pregnancies would have led to threats to their lives posed by strokes, blood clots, and infection. "No women have these procedures for trivial reasons," Stella testified. "They have them because it's their own choice."

1. "Partial-birth abortion" is a term coined by opponents of late-term abortion for its rhetorical power. Does the use of the term make it difficult to engage in informed public discussions of the relevant issues? (The so-called Partial-Birth Abortion Act of 2003 gave the term and the definition in the act a legal status.)

2. Stella testified that women did not choose late-term abortion for "trivial reasons." Statistics indicate, however, that some women with normally developing fetuses seek late-term abortions because, for whatever reason, they failed to seek an early abortion. Does this fact undercut the argument the three women are making in their testimony?

3. Does the testimony indicate that there is sufficient reason not to make late-term abortion illegal. (For a discussion of the Partial-Birth Abortion Act of 2003, see the Social Context "The 'Partial-Birth Abortion' Controversy," in this chapter.)

DECISION SCENARIO 4

A Pregnant Mental Child

Clare Macwurter was twenty-two years old chronologically, but mentally she remained a child. As a result of her mother's prolonged and difficult labor, Clare had been deprived of an adequate blood-oxygen supply during her birth. The consequence was that she suffered irreversible brain damage.

Clare enjoyed life and was generally a happy person. She couldn't read, but she liked listening to music and watching television, although she could rarely understand the stories. She was physically attractive and, with the help of her parents, she could care for herself.

Clare was also interested in sex. When she was seventeen, she and a fellow student at the special

school they attended had been caught having intercourse. Clare's parents had been told about the incident, but after Clare left the school the following year, they took no special precautions to ensure that Clare would not become sexually involved with anyone. After all, she stayed at home with her mother every day, and, besides, it was a matter they didn't much like to think about.

The Macwurters were both surprised and upset when Clare became pregnant. At first they couldn't imagine how it could have happened. They recalled that on several occasions Clare had been sent to stay at the house of Mr. Macwurter's brother and his wife while Mrs. Macwurter went shopping.

John Macwurter at first denied that he had had anything to do with Clare's pregnancy. But during the course of a long and painful conversation with his brother, he admitted that he had had sexual relations with Clare.

"I wasn't wholly to blame," John Macwurter said. "I mean, I know I shouldn't have done it. But still, she was interested in it, too. I didn't really rape her. Nothing like that."

The Macwurters were at a loss about what they should do. The physician they consulted told them that Clare would probably have a perfectly normal baby. But of course, Clare couldn't really take care of herself, much less a baby. She was simply unfit to be a mother. Mrs. Macwurter, for her part, was not eager to assume the additional responsibilities of caring for another child. Mr. Macwurter would be eligible to retire in four more years, and the couple had been looking forward to selling their house and moving back to the small town in Oklahoma where they had first met and then married. The money they had managed to save, plus insurance and a sale of their property, would permit them to place Clare in a long-term care facility after their deaths. Being responsible for another child would both ruin their plans and jeopardize Clare's future well-being.

"I never thought I would say such a thing," Mrs. Macwurter told her husband, "but I think we should arrange for Clare to have an abortion."

"That's killing," Mr. Macwurter said.

"I'm not so sure it is. I don't really know. But even if it is, I think it's the best thing to do."

Mrs. Macwurter made the arrangements with Clare's physician for an abortion to be performed. When Mr. Macwurter asked his brother to pay for the operation, John Macwurter refused. He explained that he was opposed to abortion and so it would not be right for him to provide money to be used in that way.

1. Could Thomson's defense of abortion be employed here to show that the proposed abortion is permissible?

2. Why would Noonan oppose abortion in this case? What alternatives might he recommend? What if it were likely that the baby would be impaired? Would this alter the situation for Noonan?

3. Do the traits Warren lists as central to the concept of personhood require that we think of Clare Macwurter as not being a person in a morally relevant sense?

4. Why would Marquis oppose this abortion?

DECISION SCENARIO 5

Fetal Reduction

Mrs. Lois Bishop (as we will call her) learned that she was carrying twins at the same time she learned that one of the twins had Down syndrome.

"There's no question in my mind," she said. "I want to have an abortion. I had the tests done in the first place to do what I could to guarantee that I would have a normal, healthy child. I knew from the first that there was a possibility that I would have to have an abortion, so I'm prepared for it."

Her obstetrician, Dr. George Savano, nodded. "I understand that," he said. "You are certainly within your rights to ask for an abortion, and I can arrange for you to have one. But there is another possibility, an experimental one, that you might want to consider as an option."

The possibility consisted of the destruction of the abnormally developing fetus. In the end, it was the possibility that Mrs. Bishop chose. A long, thin needle was inserted through Mrs. Bishop's abdomen and guided into the heart of the fetus. A solution was then injected directly into the fetal heart.

Although there was a risk that Mrs. Bishop would have a miscarriage, she did not. The surviving twin continued to develop normally, and Mrs. Bishop had an uneventful delivery.

Dr. Savano was criticized by some physicians as "misusing medicine," but he rejects such charges. Mrs. Bishop also has no regrets, for if the procedure had not been performed, she would have been forced to abort both twins.

1. What sort of utilitarian argument might be offered to justify Dr. Savano's experimental procedure in this case?

2. Would Marquis consider the destruction of the fetus with Down syndrome immoral? After all, it may be argued that persons with Down syndrome do not have "a future like ours."

3. The procedure leads to the death of a developing fetus, so one might say that it is morally equivalent to abortion. Are there any morally relevant factors that distinguish this case from more ordinary cases involving abortion?

DECISION SCENARIO **6**

A Family Tragedy

For months, doctors told eleven-year-old Visna (as we'll call her) and her parents that her abdominal pains were nothing but indigestion. Then, in July 1998, the truth finally emerged: Visna was twenty-seven weeks' pregnant.

Visna's family had emigrated from India to the Detroit suburb of Sterling Heights, Michigan, only the previous summer. Her parents found factory jobs and rented a two-bedroom apartment, and Visna shared one of the rooms with Hari, her sixteen-year-old brother. Sometime during the winter after their arrival, Visna told her parents, Hari raped her, but this emerged only after Visna, who had turned twelve, was found to be pregnant.

As soon as Visna's parents learned her condition, they made plans to take her to Kansas for an abortion. Visna would have to have a late-term abortion, and because Michigan law bans almost all abortions after twenty-four weeks, her family would have to take her out of state. But their plans were frustrated when they were leaked to a family court judge. Charges of parental negligence were filed by prosecutors against her parents, and the court immediately removed Visna from her family and made her a ward of the state.

At a court hearing, Visna's doctor argued that if her pregnancy were allowed to continue, it could cause her both physical and psychological damage. A psychologist testified that, because Visna was a Hindu, if she were forced to have an illegitimate child, it would make her unfit for marriage by another Hindu. Her parents also expressed their worry that if Visna had a child, the child might suffer from genetic abnormalities and, in particular, might be mentally retarded, because her brother would be the father.

At the end of the hearing, the prosecution announced that it was convinced that pregnancy might endanger Visna's life and dropped the negligence charge against her parents. Visna was reunited with her family, and her parents pursued their original plan of taking her to Kansas. In Wichita, Dr. George Tiller, who was later shot to death by a pro-life activist, stopped the fetus's heart and used drugs to induce labor, thus performing a "partial-birth" abortion.

1. In what circumstances, if any, should late-term abortions be legally permitted?

2. Should some sort of hearings board or court be established to decide on the legitimacy of cases of late-term abortion?

3. Is there a difference between late-term abortion and infanticide?

4. Assuming that late-term abortion is sometimes indistinguishable from infanticide, does that imply that late-term abortion is never justified?

DECISION SCENARIO **7**

Unexpected News

Helen and John Kent waited nervously in the small consulting room while Laurie Stent, their genetic counselor, went to tell Dr. Charles Blatz that they had arrived to talk to him.

"I regret that I have some bad news for you," Dr. Blatz told them. "The karyotyping that we do after amniocentesis shows a chromosomal abnormality."

He looked at them, and Helen felt that she could hardly breathe. "What is it?" she asked.

"It's a condition known as trisomy 21, and it produces a birth defect we call Down syndrome. You may have heard of it under the old name of mongolism."

"Oh, God," John said. "How bad is it?"

"Such children are always mentally retarded," Dr. Blatz said. "Some are severely retarded and others just twenty or so points below average. They have some minor physical deformities, and they sometimes have heart damage. They typically don't live beyond their thirties, but by and large they seem happy and have good dispositions."

Helen and John looked at each other with great sadness. "What do you think we should do?" Helen asked. "Should I have an abortion, and then we could try again?"

"I don't know," John said. "I really don't know. You've had a hard time being pregnant these last five months, and you'd have to go through that again. Besides, there's no guarantee this wouldn't happen again."

"But this won't be the normal baby we wanted," Helen said. "Maybe in the long run we'll be even unhappier than we are now."

1. Explain the nature of the conflict between the positions taken by Noonan and Warren that arises in this case.

2. If one accepts Thomson's view, what factors are relevant to deciding whether an abortion is justifiable in this instance?

3. Does feminist ethics suggest any way of dealing with this situation?

DECISION SCENARIO **8**

A Matter of Convenience

Ruth Perkins is twenty-four years old, and her husband, Carl Freedon, is four years older. Both are employed, Ruth as an executive for Laporte Gas Transmission and Carl as a systems analyst at a St. Louis bank. Their combined income is more than $240,000 a year.

Perkins and Freedon live up to their income. They have an eleven-room house with a tennis court in a high-priced suburb, they both dress well, and Carl is a modest collector of sports cars (three MG-TDs). Both like to travel, and they try to get out of the country at least twice a year—to Europe for a month in the summer and to Mexico or the Caribbean for a couple of weeks during the winter.

Perkins and Freedon have no children. They agreed when they were married that children would not be a part of their plan for life together. They were distressed when Ruth became pregnant and at first refused to face the problem. They worried about it for several months, considering arguments for and against abortion. At last they decided that Ruth should have an abortion.

"I don't see why I have to go through with this interview," Ruth said to the woman at the Morton Hospital Counseling Center.

"It's required of all who request an abortion," the counselor explained. "We think it's better for a person to be sure what she is doing so she won't regret it later."

"My husband and I are certain," Ruth said. "A child doesn't fit in at all with our lifestyle. We go out a lot,

and we like to do things. A child would just get in the way."

"A child can offer many pleasures," the woman said.

"I don't doubt it. If some want them, that's fine with me. We don't. Besides, we both have careers that we're devoted to. I'm not about to quit my job to take care of a child, and the same is true of my husband."

"How long have you been pregnant?"

Ruth looked embarrassed. "Almost six months," she said. "Carl and I weren't sure what we wanted to do at first. It took a while for us to get used to the idea."

"You don't think you waited too long?"

"That's stupid," Ruth said. She could hardly keep her voice under control. "I didn't mean that personally. But Carl and I have a right to live our lives the way we want. So far as we are concerned, a six-month fetus is not a person. If we want to get rid of it, that's our business."

"Would you feel the same if it were a child already born?"

"I might," Ruth said. "I mean, a baby doesn't have much personality or anything, does it?"

"I take it you're certain you want the abortion."

"Absolutely. My husband and I think it's the right thing for us. If others think we're wrong . . . well, it's their right to think what they please."

1. How might Warren's arguments be used to support Perkins' position?

2. Could someone who accepts Thomson's arguments consider abortion justified in this case?

3. If Brown's criticism of Marquis is correct, does this mean that abortion for any reason is justified?

DECISION SCENARIO **9**

Whose Life?

Daniel Bocker was worried. The message his secretary had taken merely said "Go to see Dr. Tai at 3:30 today." He hadn't been asked if 3:30 was convenient for him, and he hadn't been given a reason for coming in.

Mr. Bocker knew it would have to do with his wife, Mary. She had been suffering a lot of pain during her pregnancy, and the preceding week she had been examined by a specialist that Dr. Tai, her gynecologist, had sent her to see. The specialist had performed a thorough examination and taken blood, tissue, and urine samples, but he had told Mary nothing.

"Thank you for coming in," Dr. Tai said. "I want to talk to you before I talk to your wife, because I need your help."

"The tests showed something bad, didn't they?" Mr. Bocker said. "Something is wrong with the baby."

"The baby is fine, but there is something wrong with your wife, something very seriously wrong. She has what we call uterine neoplasia."

"Is that cancer?"

"Yes it is," said Dr. Tai. "But I don't want either of you to panic about it. It's not at a very advanced stage, and at the moment it's localized. If an operation is performed very soon, then she has a good chance to make a full recovery. The standard figures show about 80% success."

"But what about the baby?"

"The pregnancy will have to be terminated," Dr. Tai said. "And I should tell you that your wife will not be able to have children after the operation."

Mr. Bocker sat quietly for a moment. He had always wanted children; for him, a family without children was not a family at all. He and Mary had talked about having at least three, and the one she was pregnant with now was the first.

"Is it possible to save the baby?" he asked Dr. Tai.

"Mrs. Bocker is only in her fourth month; there is no chance that the child could survive outside her body."

"But what if she didn't have the operation? Would the baby be normal?"

"Probably so, but the longer we wait to perform the operation, the worse your wife's chances become. I don't want to seem to tell you what to do, but my advice is for your wife to have an abortion and to undergo the operation as soon as it is reasonably possible."

"But she might recover, even if she had the child and then had the operation, mightn't she?"

"It's possible, but her chances of recovery are much less. I don't know what the exact figures would be, but she would be running a terrible risk."

Mr. Bocker understood what Dr. Tai was saying, but he also understood what he wanted.

"I'm not going to encourage Mary to have an abortion," he said. "I want her to have a child, and I think she wants that, too."

"What if she wants to have a better chance to live? I think the decision is really hers. After all, it's her life that is at stake."

"But it's not just her decision," Mr. Bocker said. "It's a family decision, hers and mine. I'm not going to agree to an abortion, even if she does want one. I'm going to try to get her to take the extra risk and have the child before she has the operation."

1. Would the doctrine of double effect justify taking steps to treat Mrs. Bocker's illness, even at the cost of terminating her pregnancy?

2. Would both Noonan and Thomson see the situation as one in which considerations of self-defense are relevant?

3. It is sometimes said that the father of a child also has a right to decide whether an abortion is to be performed. Would Daniel Bocker be justified in urging his wife to take the risk of having the child?

DECISION SCENARIO 10

Reducing Abortion by Making It Legal?

A study published in 2009 by the Gutmacher Institute and the World Health Organization showed that a decline in the number of abortions took place worldwide during the period 1995–2003. (This period offered the most recent set of complete data.) The number fell from forty-six million in 1995 to thirty-two million in 2003.

The factor most responsible for the decline was access to contraception. The study also found that abortion occurs about as often in countries in which it is illegal as it does in countries that permit it. The aspect of abortion affected most by its legal status was its safety. "Where abortion is illegal, it is likely to be unsafe, performed under unsafe conditions by poorly trained providers," one of the researchers said.

In Uganda, abortion is illegal and sex education is limited to programs teaching abstinence. The estimated abortion rate for 2003 in Uganda was fifty-four per 1,000 women, about twice the U.S. rate of twenty-one per 1,000 for that year. The lowest abortion rate is in Western Europe (twelve per 1,000), where contraception is easily available and abortion is legal.

1. Can an argument be made that, paradoxically, those who oppose abortion ought to endorse its legal status and promote the use of contraception?

2. Why would those who endorse a natural law view (e.g., Roman Catholics) find this argument impossible to support?

3. Does the fact that abortion occurs about as often when it is illegal as when it is legal and that when abortion is illegal it is considerably more unsafe support the conclusion that abortion should be legal?

Chapter 6

Treating or Terminating: The Dilemma of Impaired Infants

CHAPTER CONTENTS

CASES AND CONTEXTS

The Agony of Bente Hindriks

Bente Hindriks was diagnosed at birth with a severe form of a rare genetic disorder called Hallopeau–Siemens syndrome. The disorder involves a genetic defect that affects the collagen fibers that anchor the epidermis to the overlying dermis.

The defect in the collagen results in the formation of large blisters on the skin's outer layer, and even a light touch can rupture the blisters and make the skin slough off, causing excruciating pain. When a baby with Hallopeau–Siemens syndrome is fed, the mechanical action of her sucking and swallowing can tear off the mucosal layer lining her mouth and esophagus. The scar tissue that then forms can block the esophagus and restrict the motion of the tongue. Feeding through a surgically implanted gastric tube is then necessary. The delicate membrane (the conjunctiva) covering the eye and lining the eyelids and the cornea may also be affected, and the heavy scarring of these tissues can result in blindness. Webbing may also develop between the fingers or toes, resulting in mitten-like fingers or toes.

The gene responsible for Hallopeau–Siemens syndrome is recessive, and it may affect babies of both genders. The disorder is expressed either at birth or very soon afterward, and children with the syndrome die early in their lives. They may live for three or four years or, when the disorder is not so severe, nine or ten. But they remain in constant pain throughout their lives, no matter how short or how long. The longer they live, the more they will need surgery and medical intervention to keep them alive and functioning. If they don't die of infection, they eventually die of invasive skin cancer.

Bente's problem was obvious from the moment of birth. Her skin blistered as if it had been severely burned, and the blisters broke open when she was moved to an isolette or lifted to be cleaned. She lost fluids and proteins from the ruptured blisters and had to be kept hydrated by IV fluids. The raw patches of flesh from which the skin had fallen away made her subject to bacterial infections, so she had to be given IV antibiotics. Because of the scar-

ring in her mouth and esophagus, she needed to be fed through a surgically implanted gastric tube.

Such problems were manageable, but the pain was not. Bente showed signs of extreme suffering: uncontrollable and unceasing shrieking, abnormally high blood pressure, a rapid pulse, and fast breathing. These are signs that experienced pediatricians recognize as indicating that a baby's body is under severe stress.

Does being under severe stress mean that the baby is experiencing severe pain? Because babies cannot say what they are feeling, answering the question requires drawing a conclusion from vital signs and behavior. The behavior that babies with the syndrome exhibit and the physiological signs that they manifest are the same as those displayed by older children and adults when they are suffering great pain. Thus, just as we conclude that cats, dogs, and monkeys that display similar signs are experiencing pain, we can conclude that the same holds for infants. Also, older children and adults have physiological equipment—brains, nerves, and neurotransmitters—that we believe produces the experience of pain, given certain stimuli, and babies and animals have similar equipment. So we conclude that babies and animals also experience pain. (This is an issue philosophers call the "problem of other minds.")

Bente was born in the Netherlands at Groningen University Medical Center. Her pediatrician, Eduard Verhagen, had no reasonable doubt that Bente was in unremitting pain. Yet, to his immense frustration, he could do nothing to help her. Even the most powerful painkilling drugs did no good. Day after day, Bente went on screaming in agony. The hospital staff bandaged her raw flesh where the skin had peeled away, but when they changed her bandages, they tore off even more skin. No medical intervention seemed to help.

"The diagnosis was extremely rare and impossible to treat," Dr. Verhagen recalled several years later. "We knew she would live a few years, but not more than five or six. Then she would die of skin cancer."

Karin and Edwin Hindriks, Bente's parents, could not bear to witness their daughter's unrelievable agony. Karin Hindriks asked Dr. Verhagen and the other physicians taking care of Bente to end her suffering. "We said we didn't want this for our daughter," Mrs. Hindriks recalled. "Such a horrendous life." But without running the risk of criminal prosecution, the doctors were powerless to act. "The doctors said, 'We understand, but we can't do anything, because if we did, then it's murder.'"

The Hindriks took their daughter home. "We saw her getting worse and worse," Mrs. Hindriks remembered. "After five or six months, her toes began to mesh, to grow together." Mr. Hindriks recalled that "It was painful to watch. You want it to stop." But they could do nothing to help Bente. Most babies with fatal disorders can be made comfortable while they are waiting for death, but not even this was possible for Bente.

The Hindriks thought about ending Bente's life themselves. In the end, though, she died in her father's arms, to both the relief and sadness of her parents. The death certificate says she died of natural causes, but the Hindriks acknowledge that Bente was given large doses of morphine in an effort to ease her pain. Most likely, her father believes, the drug ended her life, but he has no regrets about this. Bente's death, from the parents' point of view, was for the best, and the unfortunate aspect is that she had to suffer such a long and pointless agony.

Dr. Verhagen suspects that throughout the world physicians are injecting suffering infants with fatal diseases with large doses of morphine to try to ease their pain, even though the physicians know that the drug will cause the infants' death. What is unfortunate, he claims, is that this must be done in a fashion that is surreptitious and not subject to discussion and decision making that is both rational and compassionate.

Infants, Dr. Verhagen believes, are as much entitled to the benefit of euthanasia as adults. He wishes now that he had been able legally to act on the wishes of the Hindriks and provide Bente with a quick death to end her suffering.

SOCIAL CONTEXT
The Dilemma of Extreme Prematurity

When Jan Anderson went into labor, she was twenty-three weeks pregnant—seventeen weeks short of the normal forty-week pregnancy. "They told me I had a beautiful baby boy," she said. But her son, Aaron, weighed only a little more than 750 grams (about 1.5 pounds), and when she finally saw him, he was in the neonatal intensive-care unit. He was attached to a battery of monitors, intravenous lines, and a respirator. Surrounding him were people checking his heart and respiration rates, monitoring his blood gases, siphoning the mucus from his mouth and underdeveloped lungs, and injecting a variety of medications needed to keep his condition stable.

"It was pretty scary," Ms. Anderson, a single woman, told reporter Gina Kolata.

Aaron spent four months in the hospital before Ms. Anderson was allowed to take him home. Aaron's life was preserved, but despite all the treatment he received, he was left with permanent disabilities. By age 2 he was quadriplegic and virtually blind, had cerebral palsy, and was perhaps mentally impaired.

Statistical Profile of the Problem

Every year, more than 400,000 babies are born at least six weeks prematurely and about 62,000 of them weigh less than 1600 grams (about 3.5 pounds). In the United States, more than a thousand preterm babies are born each day, and from 1990 to 2006 (the latest figures, published in 2010), the preterm birthrate increased by twenty percent. (About thirteen percent of all births in the United States are preterm.) Thanks to the development of new procedures and the use of new drugs, almost eighty-five percent of premature infants live long enough to leave the hospital (though many must return), but only about twenty percent have no lasting major physical or mental impairment.

The more premature an infant and the lower the birth weight, the more likely it is that the infant will die soon after birth or be severely physically and mentally impaired. About half of premature infants in the 500- to 750-gram (1- to 1.5-pound) range fail to survive. From twenty-five to thirty-three percent of babies under 750 grams have irreversible neurological damage. The figure rises to between forty and fifty percent for those with a birth weight between 500 and 600 grams. About five to ten percent of these very low-birth-weight babies will have cerebral palsy, and a similar percentage will have IQs below 70, where 100 is average.

Survival rate is closely connected with gestation time. The technological limit for preserving the lives of premature infants is about twenty-three to twenty-four weeks. Estimates of an infant's developmental stage may be off by a week or so because it's impossible to be certain when conception took place. Premature girls have about a one-week developmental advantage over boys, and black infants have the same advantage over white infants. Thus, a white boy may be about two weeks behind in development compared with a black girl.

Underdeveloped

Premature babies have not spent enough time in the uterus, and as a result, they are physiologically underdeveloped. The more premature the infant, the more underdeveloped it is. Birth weight, generally, is an index of developmental prematurity. Extremely premature neonates are "fetal infants" that have spent hardly more than half of the forty-week gestation period in their mother's uterus.

Extremely premature infants are liable to life-threatening disorders. Many have problems eating, digesting food, and absorbing nutrients. Their lungs are small and brittle and fill up with secretions, making it impossible for them to breathe normally. They must be put on a mechanical ventilator, and they tend to suffer from respiratory infections.

Poor prenatal development also makes smaller infants prone to cerebral hemorrhages, or "brain bleeds," that can result in a variety of devastating consequences. Infants that have had brain bleeds are prone to seizure disorders, blindness, low vision, deafness, mental retardation, and various more subtle mental difficulties that may show up only years later.

About seventy percent of the babies in the 500- to 9000-gram range now survive. Before the 1970s, prior to the advent of neonatal intensive-care units (NICUs), a child with a birth weight under 900 grams (about 2 pounds) would not be likely to live for long. In the 1980s and the early 2000s, survival rose to about fifty percent and it has now reached the seventy to seventy-one percent level.

Because of aggressive intervention and the use of new drugs and technology, the survival rates of even the most premature infants have risen steadily. Laboratories can now perform dozens of biochemical tests on a few drops of blood, instead of the full-vial testing previously required. Newly developed artificial pulmonary surfactants can increase the breathing capacity of an infant's lungs and shorten the time a respirator is needed. Infants with underdeveloped lungs can benefit from extracorporeal membrane oxygenation (ECMO), a treatment in which a sort of artificial lung removes carbon dioxide from the blood and supplies it with oxygen. Better infection control and better nutrition have also contributed to survival.

Most important, corticosteroids are now used to treat pregnant women who are likely to give birth during the period from twenty-four to thirty-four weeks of gestation. The drug stimulates fetal development and speeds up the maturation of the lungs. The steroid therapy may reduce by as much as one-third the amount of time a premature infant must remain in intensive care.

As intervention strategies and technologies have improved, the need for them has increased. Babies born prematurely to women who have had no prenatal care and those born to drug-using mothers have placed heavy demands on NICUs.

After Prematurity

Statistics about the effects of prematurity on infants who survive and mature are often confusing. Results from small studies of special populations rarely match the results of large studies. Even so, the studies mentioned next sketch a similar picture.

A 2006 Canadian study followed 166 babies from 1977 to 1982 who weighed 1.1 to 2.2 pounds at birth and compared them with 145 babies of normal weight. The proportion of high-school graduates was similar in both groups, although a lower percentage of the low-birth-weight group attended college. Both groups had the same proportion of full and part-time employment. In every comparison, though, the low-birth-weight males did much less well than the females. Males had a lower survival rate, did less well in school, and had a higher percentage of neurological difficulties.

The study's results may not represent what happens to most low-birth-weight babies in the United States. The group studied was ninety-four percent white, and eighty-two percent of the children came from two-parent families. Also, because the Canadian medical system provides care for all citizens, the infants all received the best treatments available at specialized neonatal units.

A 2005 U.S. study followed into their early school years 219 children born prematurely (with birth weights of 2.2 pounds or less) from 1992 to 1995 at Cleveland's Children's Hospital. The study found that although 70% of the babies survived, compared with 50% in the 1970s and 1980s, they were just as likely to suffer from serious disabilities as those born in the earlier decades. Some 38% of the children had IQs below 85, compared with 14% of normal-weight children; 21% had asthma, compared with 9% of other children. The premature children were also much more likely to suffer from cerebral palsy, hearing and vision deficits, social difficulties, and poor school performance.

Because 61% of the premature infants in the Cleveland study were African Americans from poor, inner-city families, the results of the study may be no more accurate as a general portrait of the effects of prematurity than those of the Canadian study.

A study published in 2000 may provide a more accurate picture. Saroi Saigal followed 150 babies born two to three months prematurely between 1977 and 1982 until their teens. The children weighed from one pound, two ounces, to two pounds, four ounces, at birth. She found that at age eight 50% were receiving special educational help, compared with 10% of a population matched for gender, age, and social class. Some 25%, compared with 6%, had repeated a grade in school. Less than half of those in the lowest birth-weight category scored in the normal range on intelligence and achievement tests. Of the 150 teenagers, forty-two had neurological or sensory disorders, such as cerebral palsy, blindness, and deafness. The others, although lacking such deficits, still scored significantly lower on the tests than the control group.

What all the studies show is that premature infants who survive cannot be counted on to outgrow their initial problems. While some will, the majority will not.

The attitude of those who survive prematurity, however, may be positive. A 1996 study surveyed 150 surviving adolescents about the quality of their lives. Researchers found that, although twenty-seven percent of the group was disabled, they rated their quality of life about as high as a comparison group that had been born after full-term development. Only one of the 150 considered death preferable to his present condition.

Costs

The new success in "saving babies" has not come without financial costs. The cost of keeping alive a premature infant runs as much as $5000–8000 per day. A very low-birth-weight neonate may have to remain in intensive care for weeks or even months. The most premature infants may run up bills approaching $1 million. (The medical cost at birth for a preterm infant is $33,000, in contrast with $3,200 for a term birth.) These infants, despite having the highest treatment costs, are also the ones least likely to benefit from the care they are given.

Moreover, the cost of the care is most likely to be borne by the taxpayer, for the mothers of the very low-birth-weight babies are most often uninsured and unemployed women whose medical care is covered by the federal- and state-funded Medicaid program. Most of these women have received no prenatal care, and a substantial number are drug users.

Some critics believe that too much money is being spent trying to save infants who are not likely to gain significant benefits. According to Michael Rie, a neonatologist at the University of Kentucky, "The hundred highest users of Medicaid dollars in each state are preemies who end up for months on ventilators and end up with cerebral bleeds and extremely lousy outcomes." It costs three times as much to care for an infant under 750 grams as it does to care for a victim of serious burns in a burn unit. It costs twenty percent more to care for such an infant than it does to pay for heart transplant surgery. Most hospitals spend more money on very young patients than they do on the very old, the group often singled out in discussions of medical costs as consuming a disproportionate amount of health-care funds.

Treatment Decisions

Initiating Treatment

The basic moral question about extremely low-birth-weight infants is whether they ought to be treated at all. Some neonatologists regard the treatment of all infants as a moral obligation. They resuscitate fully any infant showing the slightest signs of life at delivery, regardless of its gestational age or weight. They believe this is the right course of action, even though they know that surviving infants will be likely to have severe mental and physical impairments.

Other neonatologists view the outcome of extraordinary efforts as likely to be so grim as to

make resuscitation an unacceptable option. As one NICU physician states the policy at his hospital for dealing with infants weighing less than 500 grams, "We generally keep them warm and let them expire by themselves. These are not viable babies, and it's crazy to do anything more."

Because of these differences in beliefs about the right way to act, a premature infant may be the object of an all-out medical effort to save his life at one hospital, while at another hospital he might be provided only the care needed to keep him comfortable. At some U.S. hospitals, physicians try to save infants as young as twenty-two weeks, but most European hospitals require a minimum of twenty-six weeks of gestation.

Discontinuing Treatment

The same divergence of views about withholding treatment is found in the question of discontinuing treatment. Some physicians say that they would go to court to secure an order if a parent asked that a respirator sustaining an infant be turned off. Others view the matter as one concerning the best interest of the child. As one physician put the point in a hypothetical case, "If a baby survives a major head bleed, we'll tell the parents he'll almost surely be damaged and he's suffering a great deal and we don't think we should do anything more."

Perhaps partly because of the development of NICUs and partly because of a misimpression of federal regulations, there has been an increased tendency for physicians to make the basic decisions about whether a premature infant is treated and the extent and limit of the treatment. Parents sometimes say that they were not even consulted about their child's treatment. Indeed, some report that although they did not want their child treated or wanted treatment discontinued, their wishes were disregarded by physicians, who did whatever they thought best.

Whose Decision?

This was the experience of Jan Anderson. Believing that the outcome of her premature baby's treatment would not be a good one, she twice asked Aaron's physicians to turn off the ventilator. But no one would even discuss the possibility with her. According to Ms. Anderson, one physician screamed at her, "We're trying to save your child, not kill him."

After four months of hospitalization, Aaron went home, but he was a virtually blind quadriplegic, with cerebral palsy and perhaps a permanent mental impairment. Although Ms. Anderson loves him and takes care of him, she says that if she had been given the opportunity, she would have discontinued her baby's life support when he was born. She also says that if she were pregnant and went into labor again at twenty-three weeks, then "I would make sure there was no discussion about saving the child." In her view, "There is no need for anyone to suffer like this."

Some physicians no doubt believe that it is their duty to preserve the lives of premature infants, no matter what the parents of the child might think. The parents, however, are the ones who usually must bear the financial, family, and emotional burdens that a severely impaired child imposes. The courts have often recognized this and allowed the final decision about treatment to rest with the parents. (See the Case Presentation "Baby Owens," in this chapter.)

Some physicians apparently still guide their conduct by the so-called Baby Doe laws passed in 1985. (See the Social Context "The Baby Doe Cases," in this chapter.) These federal regulations required that all newborns, regardless of the degree of their impairment or the likelihood of their survival, receive lifesaving treatment and support. Physicians were threatened with federal prosecution for not following strict guidelines issued by the surgeon general. A Supreme Court decision eventually overturned the regulations, and the practice of making treatment decisions on a case-by-case basis became acceptable once again.

Insurance companies or Medicaid typically pays the bills for premature infants that receive treatment in NICUs. Hence, physicians do not have to allow financial costs to play a major role in making treatment decisions. This may incline them to ignore the lifelong expenses that will have to be borne somehow by the family. Physicians can go on to the next case, but parents must remain with their child, no matter what the child's condition and prospects. Again, because parents must bear the burden, they have a good claim to be included in the decision-making process.

Does an NICU physician have an incentive, other than the best interest of a patient, to initiate or continue treatment of a low-birth-weight infant? One rarely mentioned reason for aggressive treatment is that neonatologists want to explore the limits of the modes of treatment and the technology currently used. Understanding the limits may make it possible to extend them so that smaller and smaller premature infants can be kept alive. Hence, some neonatologists, motivated by an interest in research, may not give parents an adequate opportunity to take part in treatment decisions.

Parents, however, do not always want to be included in the decision-making process. Some prefer to turn over to physicians all responsibility involving initiating or withdrawing medical treatment. Furthermore, physicians themselves don't always know when aggressive treatment is appropriate. They must make recommendations and decisions in an environment of crisis about a patient whose condition is in a constant state of change.

Some neonatologists and bioethicists argue that hospital ethics committees should play a crucial role in deciding how premature infants should be treated. Such committees, having no vested interest in the outcome of a decision, could weigh the issues more objectively than either the neonatologist or the parents.

Baby Owens: Down Syndrome and Duodenal Atresia

On a chilly December evening in 1976, Dr. Joan Owens pushed through the plate glass doors of Midwestern Medical Center and walked over to the admitting desk. Dr. Owens was a physician in private practice and regularly visited Midwestern to attend to her patients.

But this night was different. Dr. Owens was coming to the hospital to be admitted as a patient. She was pregnant, and shortly after 9:00 she began having periodic uterine contractions. Dr. Owens recognized them as the beginnings of labor pains. She was sure of this not only because of her medical knowledge but also because the pains followed the same pattern they had before her other three children were born.

While her husband, Phillip, parked the car, Dr. Owens went through the formalities of admission. She was not particularly worried, for the birth of her other children had been quite normal and uneventful. But the pains were coming more frequently now, and she was relieved when she completed the admission process and was taken to her room. Phillip came with her, bringing her small blue suitcase of personal belongings.

At 11:30 that evening, Dr. Owens gave birth to a 4.5-pound baby girl. The plastic bracelet fastened around her wrist identified her as Baby Owens.

Bad News

Dr. Owens was groggy from exhaustion and from the medication she had received. But when the baby was shown to her, she saw at once that it was not normal. The baby's head was misshapen and the skin around her eyes strangely formed.

Dr. Owens recognized that her daughter had Down syndrome.

"Clarence," she called to her obstetrician. "Is the baby mongoloid?"

"We'll talk about it after your recovery," Dr. Clarence Ziner said.

"Tell me now," said Dr. Owens. "Examine it!"

Dr. Ziner made a hasty examination of the child. He had already seen that Dr. Owens was right and was doing no more than making doubly certain. A more careful examination would have to be made later.

When Dr. Ziner confirmed Joan Owens's suspicion, she did not hesitate to say what she was thinking. "Get rid of it," she told Dr. Ziner. "I don't want a mongoloid child."

Dr. Ziner tried to be soothing. "Just sleep for a while now," he told her. "We'll talk about it later."

Four hours later, a little after 5:00 in the morning and before it was fully light, Joan Owens woke up. Phillip was with her, and he had more bad news to tell. A more detailed examination had shown that the child's small intestine had failed to develop properly and was closed off in one place—the condition known as duodenal atresia. It could be corrected by a relatively simple surgical procedure, but until surgery was performed the child could not be fed. Phillip had refused to consent to the operation until he had talked to his wife. Joan Owens had not changed her mind: she did not want the child.

"It wouldn't be fair to the other children to raise them with a mongoloid," she told Phillip. "It would take all of our time, and we wouldn't be able to give David, Sean, and Melinda the love and attention they need."

"I'm willing to do whatever you think best," Phillip said. "But what can we do?"

"Let the child die," Joan said. "If we don't consent to the surgery, the baby will die soon. And that's what we have to let happen."

Phillip put in a call for Dr. Ziner, and when he arrived in Joan's room, they told him of their decision. He was not pleased with it.

"The surgery has very low risk," he said. "The baby's life can almost certainly be saved. We can't tell how retarded she'll be, but most DS children get along quite well with help from their families. The whole family will grow to love her."

"I know," Joan said. "And I don't want that to happen. I don't want us to center our lives around a defective child. Phillip and I and our other children will be forced to lose out on many of life's pleasures and possibilities."

"We've made up our minds," Phillip said. "We don't want the surgery."

"I'm not sure the matter is as simple as that," Dr. Ziner said. "I'm not sure we can legally just let the baby die. I'll have to talk to the director and the hospital attorney."

Applying for a Court Order

At 6:00 in the morning, Dr. Ziner called Dr. Felix Entraglo, the director of Midwestern Medical Center, and Isaac Putnam, the head of the center's legal staff. They agreed to meet at 9:00 to talk over the problem presented to them by the Owenses.

They met for two hours. It was Putnam's opinion that the hospital would not be legally liable if Baby Owens were allowed to die because her parents refused to give consent for necessary surgery.

"What about getting a court order requiring surgery?" Dr. Entraglo asked. "That's the sort of thing we do when an infant requires a blood transfusion or immunization and his parents' religious beliefs make them refuse consent."

"This case is not exactly parallel," said Mr. Putnam. "Here we're talking about getting a court order to force parents to allow surgery to save the life of a defective infant. The infant will still be defective after the surgery, and I think a court would be reluctant to make a family undergo significant emotional and financial hardships when the parents have seriously deliberated about the matter and decided against surgery."

"But doesn't the child have some claim in this situation?" Dr. Ziner asked.

"That's not clear," said Mr. Putnam. "In general, we assume that parents will act for the sake of their child's welfare, and when they are reluctant to do so we look to the courts to act for the child's welfare. But in a situation like this . . . who can say? Is the Owens baby really a person in any legal or moral sense?"

"I think I can understand why a court would hesitate to order surgery," said Dr. Entraglo. "What sort of life would it be for a family when they had been pressured into accepting a child they didn't want? It would turn a family into a cauldron of guilt and resentment mixed in with love and concern. In this case, the lives of five normal people would be profoundly altered for the worse."

"So we just stand by and let the baby die?" asked Dr. Ziner.

"I'm afraid so," Dr. Entraglo said.

The Final Days

It took twelve days for Baby Owens to die. Her lips and throat were moistened with water to lessen her suffering, and in a small disused room set apart from the rooms of patients, she was allowed to starve to death.

Many nurses and physicians thought it was wrong that Baby Owens was forced to die such a lingering death. Some thought it was wrong for her to have to die at all, but such a protracted death seemed needlessly cruel. Yet they were cautioned by Dr. Entraglo that anything done to shorten the baby's life would probably constitute a criminal action. Thus, fear of being charged with a crime kept the staff from administering any medication to Baby Owens.

The burden of caring for the dying baby fell on the nurses in the obstetrics ward. The physicians avoided the child entirely, and it was the nurses who had to see to it that she received her water and was turned in her bed. This was the source of much resentment among the nursing staff, and a few nurses refused to have anything to do with the dying child. Most kept their ministrations to an absolute minimum.

But one nurse, Sara Ann Moberly, was determined to make Baby Owens's last days as comfortable as possible. She held the baby, rocked her, and talked soothingly to her when she cried. Doing all for the baby that she could do soothed Sara Ann as well.

But even Sara Ann was glad when Baby Owens died. "It was a relief to me," she said. "I almost couldn't bear the frustration of just sitting there day after day and doing nothing that could really help her."

SOCIAL CONTEXT
The Baby Doe Cases

In Bloomington, Indiana, in 1982, a child was born with Down syndrome and esophageal atresia. The parents and the physicians of the infant, who became known as Baby Doe, decided against the surgery that was needed to open the esophagus and allow the baby to be fed. The decision was upheld by the courts, and six days after birth Baby Doe died of starvation and dehydration.

A month later, in May 1982, the secretary of Health and Human Services (HHS) notified hospitals that any institution receiving federal funds could not lawfully "withhold from a handicapped infant nutritional sustenance or medical or surgical treatment required to correct a life-threatening condition if (1) the withholding is based on the fact that the infant is handicapped and (2) the handicap does not render treatment or nutritional sustenance contraindicated."

Baby Doe Hot Line

Ten months later, acting under instructions from President Reagan, an additional and more detailed regulation was issued. Hospitals were required to display a poster in NICUs and pediatric wards indicating that "discrimination" against handicapped infants was a violation of federal law. The poster also listed a toll-free, twenty-four-hour "hot-line" number for reporting suspected violations. In addition, the regulations authorized representatives of HHS to take "immediate remedial action" to protect infants. Further, hospitals were required to permit HHS investigators access to the hospital and to relevant patient records.

A group of associations, including the American Academy of Pediatrics, brought suit against HHS in an attempt to stop the regulations from becoming legally effective. Judge Gerhard Gesell of the U.S. District Court ruled, in April 1983, that HHS had not followed the proper procedures in putting the regulations into effect and so they were invalid. In particular, the regulations were issued without notifying and consulting with those affected by them, a procedure that is legally required to avoid arbitrary bureaucratic actions. The judge held that, although HHS had considered relevant factors in identifying a problem, it had failed to consider the effects of the use of the hot-line number. An "anonymous tipster" could cause "the sudden

descent of Baby Doe squads" on hospitals, and "monopolizing physician and nurse time, and making hospital charts and records unavailable during treatment, can hardly be presumed to produce quality care of the infant."

Furthermore, Judge Gesell held, the main purpose of the regulations was apparently to "require physicians treating newborns to take into account wholly medical risk–benefit considerations and to prevent parents from having any influence upon decisions as to whether further medical treatment is desirable." The regulations explored no other ways to prevent "discriminatory medical care." In his conclusion, Judge Gesell held that federal regulations dealing with imperiled newborns should "reflect caution and sensitivity" and that "wide public comment prior to rule-making is essential."

HHS responded to the court decision by drafting another regulation (July 5, 1983) that attempted to resolve the procedural objection that invalidated the first. Sixty days was allowed for the filing of written comments. Since the substance of the regulation was virtually the same, the proposal was widely contested, and on January 12, 1984, another set of regulations was published. They too became an object of controversy.

Baby Jane Doe

Meanwhile, a second Baby Doe case had become the focus of public attention and legal action. On October 11, 1983, an infant who became known as Baby Jane Doe was born in Port Jefferson (Long Island), New York. Baby Jane Doe suffered from meningomyelocele, anencephaly, and hydrocephaly. (See Briefing Session, this chapter, for an explanation of these conditions.) Her parents were told that without surgery she might live from two weeks to two years, but with surgery she might survive twenty years. However, she would be severely retarded, epileptic, paralyzed, and likely to have constant urinary and bladder infections. The parents consulted with neurologists, a Roman Catholic priest, nurses, and social workers. They decided surgery was not in the best interest of the child and opted, instead, for the use of antibiotics to prevent infection of the exposed spinal nerves. "We love her very much," her mother said, "and that's why we made the decision we did."

Lawrence Washburn, Jr., a lawyer who for a number of years had initiated lawsuits on behalf of the unborn and impaired, somehow learned that Baby Jane Doe was being denied surgery and entered a petition on her behalf before the New York State Supreme Court. Because Washburn was not related to the infant, his legal standing in the case was questionable, and the court appointed William Weber to represent the interest of Baby Jane Doe. After a hearing, the judge ruled that the infant was in need of surgery to preserve her life and authorized Weber to consent.

This decision was reversed on appeal. The court held that the parents' decision was in the best interest of the infant. Hence, the state had no basis to intervene. The ruling was then appealed to the New York Court of Appeals and upheld. The court held that the parents' right to privacy was invaded when a person totally unrelated and with no knowledge of the infant's condition and treatment entered into litigation in an attempt to challenge the discharge of parental responsibility. However, the main grounds for allowing the ruling to stand were procedural, for the suit had not followed New York law requiring that the state intervene in the treatment of children through the family court.

In the cases of both Baby Doe and Baby Jane Doe, the federal government went to court to demand the infants' medical records. The government charged that decisions against their treatment represented discrimination against the handicapped. However, the courts consistently rejected the government's demands. In June 1985, the Supreme Court agreed to hear arguments to decide whether the federal laws that protect the handicapped against discrimination also apply to the treatment of imperiled newborns who are denied life-prolonging treatment.

Final Regulations

On May 15, 1985, the third anniversary of the death of Baby Doe, HHS's final "Baby Doe" regulation went into effect. The regulation was an implementation of an amendment to the Child Abuse Prevention and Treatment Act that was passed into law in October 1984 and the result of negotiations among some nineteen groups representing right-to-life advocates, the disabled, the medical professions, and members of Congress.

The regulation extended the term "medical neglect" to cover cases of "withholding of medically indicated treatment from a disabled infant with a life-threatening condition." Withholding treatment, but not food and water, was not "medical neglect" in three kinds of cases:

1. The infant is chronically and irreversibly comatose.

2. The provision of such treatment would merely prolong dying, not be effective in ameliorating or correcting all the infant's life-threatening conditions, or otherwise be futile in terms of the survival of the infant.

3. The provision of such treatment would be virtually futile in terms of the survival of the infant, and the treatment itself under such circumstances would be inhumane.

The regulation defined "reasonable medical judgment" as "a medical judgment that would be made by a reasonably prudent physician knowledgeable about the case and the treatment possibilities with respect to the medical conditions involved." State child-protection service agencies were designated as the proper organizations to see to it that infants were not suffering "medical neglect," and, in order to receive any federal funds, such agencies were required to develop a set of procedures to carry out this function. Parents, physicians, and hospitals were thus no longer the direct subjects of the regulation.

Supreme Court Decision

On June 9, 1986, the Supreme Court, in a 5-to-3 ruling with one abstention, struck down the Baby Doe regulations. The Court held that there was no evidence that hospitals had discriminated against impaired infants or had refused treatments sought by parents. Accordingly, there was no basis for federal intervention.

Justice John Paul Stevens, in the majority opinion, stressed that no federal law requires hospitals to treat impaired infants without parental consent. Nor does the government have the right "to give unsolicited advice either to parents, to hospitals, or to state officials who are faced with difficult treatment decisions concerning handicapped children." Furthermore, state child-protection agencies "may not be conscripted against their will as the foot soldiers in a Federal crusade."

Hospitals and those directly involved in neonatal care were generally relieved by the Supreme Court decision. In their arguments before the Court, they had claimed that federal "Baby Doe squads arriving within hours after birth" had second-guessed the agonizing decisions made by parents and physicians and that this had "a devastating impact on the parents."

The Court decision once again placed the responsibility for making decisions about withholding life-sustaining treatment from imperiled newborns on families and physicians acting in consultation. Some hospitals use review committees to recommend whether infants ought to be treated, but what powers these committees should have and who should be on them continue to be a matter of dispute.

CASE PRESENTATION

Baby K: An Anencephalic Infant and a Mother's Request

The female child known in court records as Baby K was born in 1993 at Fairfax Hospital in Falls Church, Virginia. She was born with the catastrophic impairment called anencephaly. Her brain lacked both cerebral hemispheres, and she would never be capable of even a rudimentary form of thought. Only her brain stem was intact, and it would keep her breathing for a while.

The standard treatment for anencephalic infants is to make them comfortable, provide them with nourishment, and then wait until their organ systems fail and death ensues. Death usually comes within a few hours, days, or weeks from respiratory failure, because the brain stem does not adequately regulate breathing.

Baby K remained alive much longer than most babies with her impairment, primarily because of her mother's insistence that the baby's periodic respiratory crises be treated aggressively, including the use of a mechanical ventilator to breathe for her. The mother was described in one court document as "acting out of a firm Christian faith that all life should be protected."

At the age of sixteen months, Baby K lived, not at home with her mother, but in an extended-care facility so that she could receive the constant attention she needed. She left the nursing home only to have respiratory treatment at Fairfax Hospital. After her second admission, the hospital went to the federal district court to seek a ruling that it would not violate any state or federal law by refusing to provide Baby K with additional treatment. Physicians at the hospital held that further treatment would be futile, and a hospital ethics committee decided that withholding aggressive treatment would be legitimate. Nevertheless, the court ruled that the hospital had to provide the care required to preserve the infant's life.

Ruling Appealed

The hospital appealed the district court ruling to the U.S. Court of Appeals. The appeal was supported by Baby K's father (who was not married to her mother) and by a court-appointed guardian. However, the court ruled 2-to-1 that the 1986 Federal Emergency Medical Treatment and

Active Labor Act required the hospital to provide treatment for Baby K. The court held that, although providing assisted breathing for an anencephalic infant might not be expected to produce a medical benefit, the law, as passed by Congress, made no exceptions for situations in which the "required treatment would exceed the prevailing standard of medical care."

The appeals court's extension of the Emergency Medical Treatment Act to the Baby K case surprised most observers. The law was passed to keep private hospitals from "dumping" to public facilities patients with emergency problems (including pregnant women in labor) but no money and no health insurance to pay for the cost of their care. (The act is usually referred to as an antidumping law.) However, payment was not an issue in the Baby K case, for her mother was fully insured as a member of the Kaiser Permanente health maintenance organization.

According to the mother's attorney, Ellen Flannery, the court simply applied the law in a straightforward manner. "There's no dispute that the appropriate treatment for acute respiratory distress is ventilation," she said. "The care is not physiologically futile. It will achieve the result required by the mother, and that is to stabilize the baby." The physicians in the case, she claimed, based their decision on their judgment about the quality of life such a child might have, and the law does not address such issues.

Others saw the consequences of extending the law as threatening the power of physicians, hospitals, and ethics committees to have a say in decisions about treating infants with profound birth anomalies. Arthur Kohrman, head of the American Academy of Pediatrics ethics committee, was quoted as saying, "This is a profoundly important case, because it strips away the ability of physicians to act as moral agents and turns them into instruments of technology. [Anencephalic] babies are born dying, and the issue is not prolonging their death but supporting it in a humane and dignified way."

Robert Veatch, head of the Kennedy Institute for Bioethics, testifying on behalf of the mother, expressed the view that courts should not defer their judgment to that of physicians. "These are religious and philosophical judgments on which physicians have no more expertise than parents," he said. The impact that the extension of the antidumping law to cases of severe birth impairment may have on treatment decisions is not yet obvious. As the appeals court pointed out, Congress made no exceptions with respect to providing care above the accepted standard in cases judged to be futile. The law might be amended by Congress to include exceptions.

Potential Results

If the law is not amended, decisions to provide no more than standard treatment for impaired infants may turn out to have no effect in particular cases. When emergency medical attention is requested by a parent, the emergency treatment law may require that an earlier decision about limiting treatment be set aside.

BRIEFING SESSION

If we could speak of nature in human terms, we would often say that it is cruel and pitiless. Nowhere does it seem more heartless than in the case of babies born into the world with severe physical impairments and deformities. The birth of such a child transforms an occasion of expected joy into one of immense sadness. It forces the child's parents to make a momentous decision at a time when they are least prepared to reason clearly: Should they insist that everything be done to save the child's life? Or should they request that the child be allowed an easeful death?

Nor can physicians and nurses escape the burden that the birth of such a child delivers. Committed to saving lives, can they condone the death of that child? What will the physician say to the parents when they turn to him or her for advice? No one involved in the situation can escape the moral agonies that it brings.

To see more clearly what the precise moral issues are in such cases, we need to consider some of the factual details that may be involved in them. We also need to mention other kinds of moral considerations that may be relevant to deciding how an impaired newborn child is to be dealt with by those who have the responsibility to decide.

Genetic and Congenital Impairments

The development of a child to the point of birth is an unimaginably complicated process, and there are many ways in which it can go wrong. Birth defects are the leading cause of infant mortality in the United States. Although some can be successfully treated, many more either are fatal or lead to a lifetime of often serious disability.

Two kinds of errors are most frequently responsible for producing impaired children:

1. *Genetic errors.* The program of information that is coded into DNA (the genetic material) may be in some way abnormal because of the occurrence of a mutation. Consequently, when the DNA code is "read" and its instructions followed, the child that develops will be impaired. The defective gene may have been inherited, or it may be due to a new mutation. Single-gene defects are typically inherited. For example, phenylketonuria (PKU) results when the gene that encodes the enzyme phenylalanine hydroxylase that breaks down the amino acid phenylalanine is missing or faulty. Phenylalanine is produced when protein metabolizes, and if it is not broken down, the buildup results in brain damage. Other birth defects are produced by a combination of inherited genes and mutations. Most of these defects are not well understood and occur in a sporadic (i.e., unpredictable) way.

2. *Congenital errors.* "Congenital" means only "present at birth," and since genetic defects have results that are present at birth, the term is misleading. Ordinarily, however, the phrase is used to designate errors that result during the developmental process. The impairment, then, is not in the original code of genes, but results either from genetic damage or from the reading of the code. The "manufacture and assembly" of the materials that constitute the child's development are affected.

We know that many factors can influence fetal development. Radiation (such as X-rays), drugs (such as thalidomide), chemicals (such as mercury), and nutritional deficiencies (such as lack of folic acid) can all cause changes in an otherwise normal process. Also, biological disease agents, such as certain viruses or spirochetes, may intervene in development, altering the machinery of the cells, interfering with the formation of tissues, and defeating the carefully programmed process that leads to a normal child. In about half the cases in which a baby is born with an impairment, however, the cause is not known.

Specific Impairments

Once an impaired child is born, the medical and moral problems are immediate. Let us consider now some of the defects commonly found in newborn children. Our focus will be more on what they are than on what caused them, for, as far as the moral issue is concerned, how the child came to be impaired is of no importance.

Down Syndrome

This is a chromosomal disorder first identified in 1866 by the English physician J. L. H. Down. Normally, humans have twenty-three pairs of chromosomes, but Down syndrome results from the presence of an extra chromosome. The condition is called trisomy 21, for, instead of a twenty-first pair of chromosomes, the affected person has a twenty-first triple. (Less often, the syndrome is produced when the string of chromosomes gets twisted and chromosome pair number 21 sticks to number 15.)

In ways not wholly understood, the normal process of development is altered by the extra chromosome. The child is born with retardation and various physical abnormalities. Typically, the latter are relatively minor and include such features as a broad skull, a large tongue, and an upward slant of the eyelids. It is this last feature that led to the name "mongolism" for the condition, a name no longer in use in medicine.

Down syndrome occurs in about one of every 800 births. The risk of a baby's being born with the condition rises with the age of the mother, although it is not known why this is so. In young women, the syndrome occurs at a rate of one in every 2000 births; in women over 40, it increases to one in one hundred, and in women over 50, it rises to one in twelve. In 1984, researchers discovered that certain chromosomes sometimes contain an extra copy of a segment known as the *nucleolar organizing region*. This abnormality seems linked to Down's syndrome, and families in which either parent has the abnormality are twenty times more likely to have an afflicted child. Researchers hope to use such information to develop a reliable screening test.

There is no cure for Down syndrome—no way to compensate for the abnormality of the development process. Those with the defect generally have an IQ of about 50–80 and usually require the care and help of others. They can learn basic tasks and can follow routines. Despite their impairment, people with Down syndrome can live semi-independent lives and usually seem to be quite happy. Because they frequently have heart abnormalities and other problems, people with Down syndrome used to die in their twenties and thirties. With close medical attention, they now live into their fifties and beyond. In the United States, the life expectancy of someone with Down syndrome is 56. (See the following section for an account of prenatal tests for the syndrome.)

Spina Bifida

Spina bifida is a general name for birth impairments that involve an opening in the spine. In development, the spine of the child with spina bifida fails to fuse properly, and often the open vertebrae permit the membrane covering the spinal cord to protrude to the outside. The membrane sometimes forms a bulging, thin sac that contains spinal fluid and nerve tissue. When

nerve tissue is present, the condition is called *myelomeningocele*. This form of spina bifida is a very severe one and often has a harsh prognosis.

Complications arising from spina bifida must often be treated surgically. The opening in the spine must be closed, and in severe cases the sac must be removed and the nerve tissue inside placed within the spinal canal. Normal skin is then grafted over the area. The danger of an infection of the meninges (meningitis) is great; thus, treatment with antibiotics is also necessary.

Furthermore, a child with spina bifida is likely to require orthopedic operations to attempt to correct the deformities of the legs and feet that occur because of muscle weakness and lack of muscular control due to nerve damage. The bones of such children are thin and brittle, and fractures are frequent.

A child born with spina bifida is virtually always paralyzed to some extent, usually below the waist. Because of the nerve damage, the child will have limited sensation in the lower part of the body. This means he will have no control over his bladder or bowels. The lack of bladder control may result in infection of the bladder, urinary tract, and kidneys because the undischarged urine may serve as a breeding place for microorganisms. Surgery may help with the problems of bowel and urinary incontinence.

The incidence of spina bifida is between one and ten per 1000 births. Roughly 2000 babies a year are born with the disorder. For reasons that remain speculative, among whites the rate is three times higher in families of low socioeconomic status than in families of higher socioeconomic status. The rate in the black population is less than half that in the white population. In 1994, the federal government began requiring the addition of folic acid to enriched grain products, and a 2005 study showed that, during the period 1995–2002, there was a significant decrease in the prevalence of spina bifida and anencephaly. (See the discussion that follows.) Folic acid is a B vitamin found in green vegetables, beans, and orange juice, but how it might work to provide a protective effect is unknown. Spina bifida is almost always accompanied by hydrocephaly.

Hydrocephaly

"Hydrocephaly" literally means "water on the brain." When, for whatever reason, the flow of fluid through the spinal canal is blocked, the cerebro-spinal fluid produced within the brain cannot escape. Pressure buildup from the fluid can cause brain damage, and if it is not released, the child will die. Although hydrocephaly is frequently the result of spina bifida, it can have several other causes and can occur late in a child's development. Treatment requires surgically inserting a thin tube, or shunt, to drain the fluid from the skull to the heart or abdomen, where it can be absorbed. The operation can save the baby's life, but physical and mental damage is frequent. Placing the shunt and getting it to work properly are difficult tasks that may require many operations. If hydrocephaly accompanies spina bifida, it is treated first.

Anencephaly

This term literally means "without brain." In this invariably fatal condition, the cerebral hemispheres of the brain are totally absent. The defect is related to spina bifida, for in some forms the bones of the skull are not completely formed and leave an opening through which brain material bulges to the outside. There is never hope for improvement by any known means.

Esophageal Atresia

In medical terms, an atresia is the closing of a normal opening or canal. The esophagus is the muscular tube that extends from the back of the throat to the stomach. Sometimes the tube forms without an opening, or it does not completely develop so that it does not extend to the stomach. The condition must be corrected by surgery in order for the child to get food into its stomach. The chances of success in such surgery are very high.

Duodenal Atresia

The duodenum is the upper part of the small intestine. Food from the stomach empties into it. When the duodenum is closed off, food cannot pass through and be digested. Surgery can repair this condition and is successful in most cases.

Problems of Extreme Prematurity

A normal pregnancy lasts approximately forty weeks. Infants born after only twenty-six weeks of growth or less typically fail to live. Those born in the weeks after that time have extremely low birth weights. About half of those weighing from 1 to 1.5 pounds fail to survive, and those who do have a multiplicity of problems resulting from the fact that their bodies have simply not had the time to develop adequately to cope with the demands of life outside the uterus.

The undeveloped lungs of premature infant are inefficient and prone to infections. The mechanical ventilation needed to assist their breathing may result in long-term lung damage. Extremely premature infants are subject to cerebral hemorrhages ("brain bleeds") that may lead to seizures, blindness, deafness, retardation, and a variety of less noticeable disabilities. (For a discussion of extremely premature infants and the moral issues they present with respect to withholding or withdrawing treatment, see the Social Context "The Dilemma of Extreme Prematurity," in this chapter.)

Testing for Impairments

Genetic impairments are inherited; they are the outcome of the genetic endowment of the child. A carrier of defective genes who has children can pass on the genes. Congenital impairments are not inherited and cannot be passed on.

With proper genetic counseling, individuals belonging to families in which certain diseases "run" can assess the risk that their children might be impaired by examining patterns of inheritance. Also, some genetic diseases can be diagnosed before birth (or even in the embryo) by detecting the presence of the gene.

(See Chapter 8 for a discussion of screening for genetic diseases.) Some developmental anomalies, such as the chromosomal abnormality resulting in Down syndrome, can be detected by examining genetic material during fetal development. Large abnormalities in the developing fetus (such as anencephaly, or "missing brain") can often be detected by the use of images produced by ultrasound (sonography).

Amniocentesis and CVS

Until recently, the most used and most reliable methods of prenatal diagnosis were amniocentesis and chorionic villus sampling (CVS). Both involve direct cell studies. In amniocentesis, the amnion (the membrane surrounding the fetus) is punctured with a needle and some of the amniotic fluid is removed for examination. The procedure cannot be usefully and safely performed until fourteen to sixteen weeks into the pregnancy. Until that time, the amount of fluid is inadequate.

The risk to the woman and to the fetus from the procedure is relatively small, usually less than one percent. (The risk that the procedure will result in a miscarriage is about one in 200.) If amniocentesis is performed eleven to twelve weeks after conception, there is a small increase in the probability that the child will have a deformed foot.

Chorionic villus sampling (CVS) involves retrieving hair-like villi cells from the developing placenta. The advantage of the test is that it can be employed six to ten weeks after conception. Although the procedure is as safe as amniocentesis, a 1994 study by the Centers for Disease Control found that infants whose mothers had undergone CVS from 1988 to 1992 had a 0.03 percent risk of missing or undeveloped fingers or toes. A later study questioned this finding and found no reason to believe that the risk of fetal damage is greater than normal.

Amniocentesis came into wide use only in the early 1960s. At first, it was restricted mostly to testing fetuses in cases in which there was a risk of Rh incompatibility. When the mother lacks a group of blood proteins called the Rhesus (or Rh) factor, and the fetus has it, the immune system of the mother may produce antibodies against the fetus. The result for the fetus may be anemia, brain damage, and even death.

It was soon realized that additional information about the fetus could be gained from further analysis of the amniotic fluid and the fetal cells in it. The fluid can be chemically assayed, and the cells can be grown in cultures for study. An examination of the DNA can show whether there are any known abnormalities that are likely to cause serious physical or mental defects.

Some disorders (such as Tay–Sachs disease) can be detected by chemical analysis of the amniotic fluid. However, some of the more common genetic diseases, such as PKU, Huntington's, and muscular dystrophy, require an analysis of the genetic material. Because only males have a Y chromosome, it's impossible to examine fetal cells without also discovering the gender of the fetus.

Amniocentesis and CVS do pose slight hazards. Accordingly, neither is regarded as a routine procedure to be performed in every pregnancy. There must be some indication that the fetus is at risk from a genetic or developmental disorder. One indication is the age of the mother. Down syndrome is much more likely to occur in fetuses conceived in women over the age of thirty-five. Because the syndrome is produced by a chromosome abnormality, an examination of the chromosomes in the cells of the fetus can reveal the defect.

Alphafetoprotein

A test for Down syndrome introduced in the 1980s employs a blood sample taken from the pregnant woman. The sample is examined for the presence of three fetal proteins. About sixteen to eighteen weeks after gestation, fetuses with Down syndrome are known to produce abnormally small quantities of estriol and alphafetoprotein and abnormally large amounts of chorionic gonadotropin. The levels of the proteins, plus such factors as the woman's age, can be used to determine the statistical probability of a child with the syndrome. This test avoids the risks of amniocentesis and CVS.

A blood test for the presence of alphafetoprotein can also indicate the likelihood of neural tube defects characteristic of spina bifida. Ultrasound can then be used to confirm or detect these or other developmental anomalies.

New Noninvasive Tests

A 2005 study of 117 cases of Down syndrome occurring in some 38,000 pregnant women found that a combination of three noninvasive tests at eleven to thirteen weeks of gestation was eighty-seven percent accurate in predicting whether the fetus had Down syndrome. The tests were an ultrasound examination of the thickness of the fetal neck (nuchal translucency) and two blood tests. The first was a test for pregnancy-associated plasma protein A(PAPP-A), and the second was a test for beta human chorionic gonadotropin (HCG). If a second ultrasound to detect the presence or absence of a fetal nasal bone is added, the detection rate of Down syndrome rises to ninety-seven percent.

An estimated six percent of all live births, some 200,000 infants a year, require intensive neonatal care. The afflictions singled out for special mention are those which are most often the source of major moral problems. Those correctable by standard surgical procedures present no special moral difficulties. But even they are often associated with other impairments, such as Down syndrome, that make them important factors in moral deliberations.

Ethical Theories and the Problem of Birth Impairments

A great number of serious moral issues are raised by impaired newborns. Should they be given only ordinary care, or should special efforts be made to save their lives? Should they be given no care and allowed to die? Should they be killed in a merciful manner? Who should decide what is in the interest of the child? Might acting in the interest of the child require not acting to save the child's life?

A more basic question that cuts even deeper than these concerns the status of the newborn. It is virtually the same as the question raised in Chapter 9 about the fetus—namely, Are severely impaired newborns persons? It might be argued that some infants are so severely impaired that they should not be considered persons in a relevant moral sense. Not only do they lack the capacity to function, but they lack even the potentiality for ordinary psychological and social development. In this respect, they are worse off than most maturing fetuses.

If this view is accepted, then the principles of our moral theories do not require that we act to preserve the lives of impaired newborns. We might, considering their origin, be disposed to show them some consideration and treat them benevolently—perhaps in the same way we might deal with animals that are in a similarly hopeless condition. We might kill them or allow them to die as a demonstration of our compassion.

One major difficulty with this view is that it is not at all clear which impaired infants could legitimately be considered nonpersons. Birth defects vary widely in severity, and, unless one is prepared to endorse infanticide generally, it is necessary to have defensible criteria for distinguishing among newborns. Also, one must defend a general concept of a person that would make it reasonable to regard human offspring as occupying a different status.

By contrast, it might be claimed that the fact that a newborn is a human progeny is sufficient to consider it a person. Assuming that this is so, the question becomes, How ought we to treat a severely impaired infant person? Just because they are infants, impaired newborns cannot express wishes, make claims, or enter into deliberations. All that is done concerning them must be done by others.

A utilitarian might decide that the social and personal cost (the suffering of the infant, the anguish of the parents and family, the monetary cost to the family and society) of saving the life of such an infant is greater than the social and personal benefits that can be expected. Accordingly, such a child should not be allowed to live, and it should be killed as painlessly as possible to minimize its suffering. Yet a rule utilitarian might claim, on the contrary, that the rule "Save every child where possible" would, in the long run, produce more utility than disutility.

The natural law position of Roman Catholicism is that even the most defective newborn is a human person. Yet this view does not require that extraordinary means be used to save the life of such a child. The suffering of the family, great expense, and the need for multiple operations would be reasons for providing only ordinary care. Ordinary care does not mean that every standard medical procedure that might help should be followed. It means only that the defective newborn should receive care of the same type provided for a normal infant. It would be immoral to kill the child or to cause its death by withholding all care.

If the infant is a person, then Kant would regard it as possessing an inherent dignity and value. But the infant in its condition lacks the capacity to reason and to express its will. How, then, should we, acting as its agents, treat the infant? Kant's principles provide no clear-cut answer. The infant does not threaten our own existence, and we have no grounds for killing him. But, it could be argued, we should allow the child to die. We can imaginatively put ourselves in the place of the infant. Although it would be morally wrong to will our own death (which, Kant claimed, would involve a self-defeating maxim), we might express our autonomy and rationality by choosing to refuse treatment that would prolong a painful and hopeless life. If this is so, then we might act in this way on behalf of the defective child. We might allow the child to die. Indeed, it may be our duty to do so. A similar line of argument from Ross's viewpoint might lead us to decide that, although we have a prima facie duty to preserve the child's life, our actual duty is to allow him to die.

Another basic question remains: Who is to make the decision about how an impaired newborn is to be treated? Traditionally, the assumption has been that this is a decision best left to the infant's parents and physicians. Because they can be assumed to have the highest concern for the infant's welfare and the most knowledge about its condition and prospects, they are the ones who should have the primary responsibility for deciding her fate. If there is reason to believe that they are not acting in a responsible manner, then it becomes the responsibility of the courts to guarantee that the interests of the infant are served.

Hardly any responsible person advocates heroic efforts to save the lives of infants who are most severely impaired, and hardly anyone advocates not treating infants with relatively simple and correctable impairments. The difficult cases are those which fall somewhere along the continuum. Advances in medical management and technology can now save the lives of many infants who earlier would have died relatively quickly, and yet we still lack the power to provide those infants with a life that we might judge to be worthwhile. Yet a failure to treat such infants does not invariably result in their deaths, and a failure to provide them with early treatment may mean that they are even more impaired than they would be otherwise.

No one believes that we currently have a satisfactory solution to this dilemma. It is important to keep in mind that it is not a purely intellectual problem. The context in which particular decisions are made is one of doubt, confusion, and genuine anguish.

Envoi

In 1973, R. S. Duff and A. G. M. Campbell shocked the public by reporting that during a thirty-month period forty-three infants at the Yale–New Haven Hospital had been permitted to die. Each of the children suffered from one or more severe birth defects. Although the staff of the hospital took no steps to end the lives of the infants, treatment was withheld from them.

Such decisions had been made for years in hospitals throughout the world. Sometimes they were made by physicians acting alone and sometimes by physicians in consultation with families. But almost never had the situation been discussed openly and publicly.

Now there is more openness about the whole complex of moral and human problems presented by impaired newborns. There is a greater willingness to consider the possibility that saving the life of a child might not be the right act to perform—that it may even be our duty to assist the child's dying. The time of covert decisions and half-guilty conferences has passed. The issues are there, they are known to be there, and they must be faced.

We must also face questions about how we as a society will respond to the needs of children who are severely impaired and the associated needs of their families and caregivers. Medicine has become progressively more successful at keeping alive infants who might once have died, but as these infants grow older, they are likely to have an array of medical, social, educational, and pshychological problems. We have taken only small steps toward the goal of integrating impaired children and adults into our society.

We have done almost nothing to recognize that the people who care about, and (typically) care for, impaired children need help. The constant worry of aging parents responsible for a seriously impaired adult child is captured in the question "Who will take care of her when we are dead?" This is a question that we as a society have not answered.

READINGS

Section 1:   The Groningen Protocol

The Groningen Protocol: The Why and the What

James Lemuel Smith

J. L. Smith describes the problem faced by Dutch pediatrician Eduard Verhagen of dealing with infants who have a hopeless prognosis and intractable pain. Smith then presents the scheme for classifying infants with serious medical problems into three categories and the five conditions for legitimizing active infant euthanasia that make up the Groningen Protocol as developed by Verhagen and his collaborator Pieter Sauer.

Dr. Eduard Verhagen didn't start out to be an advocate for changing the law in Holland to allow active euthanasia for infants. More than anything else, it was his experience as a pediatrician forced to deal with the

intractable pain of Bente Hindriks, an infant with a severe form of the invariably fatal genetic disorder called Hallopeau–Siemens syndrome, that forced him to develop his ideas about infant euthanasia.

Hallopeau–Siemens is a disease that involves the blistering and peeling off of the upper layer of the skin and mucous membranes. The disorder has no effective treatment, and skin damage is accompanied by severe and unrelieveable pain. Although Bente's parents asked

Dr. Verhagen to terminate her life humanely to end her suffering, he was unable to do so without running the risk of being charged with homicide.

Dr. Verhagen felt that as a physician he had failed Bente and her parents. All three of them, he thought, had suffered more than was necessary, and his inability to help them remained a matter of self-reproach. As the father of three children, he knew what it was like to want to spare your child from pointless pain, but he could only imagine the horror of having to watch your child suffering such pain day after day while hoping she will die and be spared further torment. Also, Dr. Verhagen was accustomed to helping sick children, not denying them what they most needed. He helped them not only in his role as Head of Pediatrics at Holland's Groningen University Medical Center, but as a volunteer physician who had spent years providing medical care to children in underdeveloped countries.

Dr. Verhagen decided some four years after Bente's death that he had to do something to call attention to the problem presented by babies like her. His motive and his hope were that the law in the Netherlands would be eventually changed to permit infant euthanasia under certain strict conditions. Dutch law now allows euthanasia for those above the age of sixteen, but it makes no provision for younger children or infants. This leaves them, in Dr. Verhagen's view, without an option that others have, an option that, if available, could spare a certain number of them the intractable and pointless suffering that destroys the quality of their sad, brief lives.

Working toward changing the law, or at least helping pediatricians avoid being charged with a crime for an appropriate and compassionate act, Dr. Verhagen and his colleagues began to describe some of their most difficult cases to attorneys in the federal prosecutor's office in Groningen. Sometimes they even took the lawyers on medical rounds with them, giving them a sense of what it was like to be a pediatrician who has to deal with children who cannot be helped, cannot be expected to get better, and live out their lives in pain.

A Public Announcement

Although Dr. Verhagen had started his campaign to revise Dutch law around 2002, in 2005 he made public the information that he had participated in ending the lives of four infants. "All four babies had spina bifida," he said. "Not the usual type, but severely affected children where spina bifida was not the only problem. They were in constant pain."

He said that ending their suffering was worth the risk of getting charged with a crime. "In the last minutes or seconds, you see the pain relax and they fall asleep. . . . At the end after the lethal injection, their fists are unclenched, and there is relief for everyone in the room. Finally, they get what they should have been given earlier."

Dr. Verhagen's actions and his approval of active infant euthanasia produced a flood of mail, some of it quite virulent. Much of the mail comes from Christian right groups and social conservatives in the United States. Verhagen was called "Dr. Death" and described as a "second Hitler"; comparisons to the Holocaust were common. However, he also received mail from parents from various countries telling him that they were forced to end the life of their own child when the medical profession refused to assist them.

"We know the law says you are not allowed to kill anyone against their will," Dr. Verhagen said in an interview. "We also know that death can be more humane than continued life, if it involves extreme suffering. We are facing patients and their parents who we think should be given the option of ending their [children's] lives."

Verhagen had already called for a change in the way the legal system in the Netherlands views infant euthanasia. Indeed, he expressed a wish to see such changes made throughout the world. "It's time to be honest about the unbearable suffering endured by newborns with no hope of a future," he said. "All over the world doctors end lives discreetly out of compassion, without any kind of regulation. Worldwide, the U.S. included, many deaths among newborns are based on end-of-life decisions, after physicians reached the conclusion that there was no quality of life. This is happening more and more frequently."

Dr. Verhagen made clear that in endorsing active infant euthanasia he was not talking about infants in ordinary difficulties or even those with a treatable condition that might or might not live. Rather, he had in mind infants whose continued existence was a burden to them and their families, ones who "face a life of agonizing pain."

An example, he said, "may be a child with spina bifida with a sac of brain fluid attached where the nerves are floating around. This child is barely able to breathe, and would have to undergo at least sixty operations in the course of a year to temporarily alleviate its problems. Moreover, the child would suffer such unbearable pain that it has to be constantly anesthetized. The parents watch this in tears and beg the doctor to bring an end to such suffering."

Physicians in every country face the problem that concerns Dr. Verhagen. According to one study, 73 percent of the physicians in France reported using drugs to end the life of a newborn. Some 43 percent of Dutch physicians acknowledged having performed such an act, and 2–4 percent of physicians in the United Kingdom, Italy, Spain, Germany, and Sweden said they had taken measures to terminate the life of a suffering infant. While physicians in the United States say that this happens from time to time, no survey data are available to suggest how often.

Dr. Verhagen observes that the subject of infants who suffer from unendurable pain with no prospect of improvement or long-term survival, is not one people like to be reminded of. "But it is in the interest of newborns who have to endure unbearable suffering that we draw up a nationwide protocol that allows each pediatrician to treat this delicate question with due care, knowing he followed the criteria."

Need for a Protocol

Since 1997 Dutch medical groups have asked the government to establish a board of medical, legal, and ethical experts to encourage physicians to report cases in which they decided to perform active euthanasia. Although the government has thus far failed to act, some Dutch physicians have sometimes taken steps to end the lives of infants for humane reasons.

In the March 10, 2005, issue of the *New England Journal of Medicine* Dr. Verhagen and Dr. Pieter J. J. Sauer, his colleague at Groningen, reported that a review of legal records shows that from 1997 to 2004, about three cases a year were reported to the legal authorities, and no one was prosecuted. However, the authors point out, a national survey of Dutch doctors concluded that out of about 200,000 births a year, around 15 to 20 cases of active euthanasia occurred. These figures suggest that a number of physicians are making decisions without shared guiding principles, open discussion, or oversight. In the view of Verhagen and Sauer, all cases of deliberate termination need to be reported to prevent "uncontrolled and unjustified euthanasia," and actions should be in keeping with acknowledged guidelines and open to review by a knowledgeable group.

Three Categories of Infants

In the *New England Journal of Medicine* article, Verhagen and Sauer present a set of guidelines and procedures to allow pediatricians and parents to approach the problem presented by a special class of infants made up of those with no hope of recovery who also suffer severe and continuing pain. They divide newborns and infants who might be considered candidates for end-of-life decisions into three categories:

1. *Infants with no chance of survival who are likely to die soon after birth, even if they receive the best medical and surgical care available.* Usually, these will be infants with some underlying and untreatable medical problem, such as the absence or underdevelopment of the lungs or kidneys. No matter what is done for these infants, they will not survive.

2. *Infants who are sustained by intensive care but have a bleak prognosis.* Although these infants may continue to live after being removed from intensive care, they have a poor prognosis and a poor quality of life. Typically, these will be infants with severe brain abnormalities or severe organ damage caused by a loss of oxygen supply to fetal tissues during development.

3. *Infants who have a hopeless prognosis and experience unbearable suffering.* Even if these infants are not receiving intensive care, they have a prognosis of a poor quality of life accompanied by sustained suffering. This group includes infants with the worst forms of spina bifida (see Verhagen's description of such a case above). This group also includes infants still alive after intensive care who have a poor quality of life, continued suffering, and no hope of improvement.

When dealing with an infant in the third category, the authors say, pediatricians and medical consultants must be certain about the prognosis and discuss it with the child's parents. The physicians must also do all that they can to control the child's pain.

Even if every known pain-management step is taken, Verhagen and Sauer believe that there will be some infants whose suffering cannot be relieved and whose future holds no hope of improvement. In such cases as this, the physicians and the parents may decide that death would be a more humane prospect than the continuation of life. (Bente Hindriks, because of the ravages produced by Hallopeau–Siemens syndrome, her unrelievable pain, and her hopeless prognosis would qualify for inclusion in this category, although Verhagen and Sauer don't mention her name.) The authors estimate that only 15–20 infants a year in the Netherlands fall in the third group.

The Groningen Protocol

The Groningen Protocol consists of five medical requirements that must be fulfilled for the active euthanasia of infants to be justified:

1. The infant's diagnosis and prognosis must be certain.

2. The infant must be experiencing hopeless and unbearable suffering.

3. At least one independent physician must confirm that the first two conditions are met.

4. Both parents must give their informed consent.

5. The termination procedure must be performed in accord with the accepted medical standard.

The protocol is accompanied by a set of additional requirements that the authors describe as intended to "clarify the decision and facilitate assessment." These rules have the function of documenting particular cases of euthanasia and the grounds for them. The rules require the physician in charge to indicate what the child's medical condition was, why the decision to end its life was made, the names and qualifications of the other physicians involved, as well as the examinations they made, and their opinions about the child's condition and prognosis. The physician in charge must also describe the way in which the parents were informed and their opinions about what would be best for the child. The informed consent of the parents is required for euthanasia.

The rules also require that the physician indicate the circumstance of the child's death, who took part in the decision making, the justification for the death, when and where the procedure was carried out, what method was used (e.g., an injectable drug), and why it was chosen. A coroner must make a finding about the death, and all the information asked for in the requirements must then be reported to the office of the prosecuting attorney.

A version of the Groningen Protocol was first developed by Verhagen and Sauer in 2002. Part of the impetus behind the initial statement was the same as for the 2005 version. They wanted to transform a decision-making process that typically takes place in secret into one that is public and transparent. When the practice of infant euthanasia is standardized and brought out of the shadows, the authors believe, it becomes subject to the scrutiny of others and protects the interests of infants and their families.

Also, because infant euthanasia is still illegal in the Netherlands, the Groningen Protocol offers a way for pediatricians to provide what they consider to be appropriate help to infants and families, while also reducing the risk that they will be prosecuted for their actions. The authors admit, however, that following the protocol does not guarantee that prosecution will not occur.

Verhagen and Sauer observe that, although the Groningen Protocol suits Dutch legal and social culture, "it is unclear to what extent it would be transferable to other countries." Given the controversy in the United States over physician-assisted suicide in adults, it seems unlikely that the Groningen Protocol will be adopted any time soon. It has at the least, however, called attention to the crucially important matter of the unrelievable suffering of doomed infants.

If the Groningen Protocol is not adopted, then what is an acceptable alternative? May we assume that the present practice of allowing children with a bleak prognosis to experience intractable pain until they die is an *unacceptable* alternative?

Section 2: The Ashley Treatment

The "Ashley Treatment"

Ashley's Mom and Dad

The young girl known only as Ashley had an apparently normal birth, but she appears to have suffered damage to her brain from an unknown cause. Her mental and motor faculties have failed to develop, and as a result, she is completely dependent on others for her care. Although the growth of her body was proceeding along a normal developmental path, her mental and motor functions would never improve. Her parents, who identify themselves only as

"Ashley's Mom and Dad," argue on their blog about their daughter that the medical procedures they requested on the behalf of Ashley when she was nine ("the Ashley treatment") were all intended to improve the quality of her life, not that of their own as caretakers.

With or without the treatment, the parents claim, their intention has always been to keep Ashley at home. The growth attenuation by hormone injections will keep her small enough to ensure that she is frequently moved to be with the other family members, and the surgery to remove her uterus and breast buds will prevent menstrual cramps and the breast discomfort caused by lying down most of the time. The surgeries, including a preventive appendectomy, will also spare Ashley the dangers of breast and uterine cancer and unrecognized appendicitis. The Ashley treatment, her parents argue, is in her best interest and will improve the quality of her life.

Ashley's Story

Our daughter Ashley had a normal birth, but her mental and motor faculties did not develop. Over the years, neurologists, geneticists, and other specialists conducted every known traditional and experimental test, but still could not determine a diagnosis or a cause. Doctor's call her condition "static encephalopathy of unknown etiology," which means an insult to the brain of unknown origin or cause, and one that will not improve.

Now nine years old, Ashley cannot keep her head up, roll or change her sleeping position, hold a toy, or sit up by herself, let alone walk or talk. She is tube fed and depends on her caregivers in every way. We call her our Pillow Angel since she is so sweet and stays right where we place her—usually on a pillow.

Ashley is a beautiful girl whose body is developing normally with no external deformities; see photos. She is expected to live a full life and was expected to attain a normal adult height and weight. Ashley being in a stable condition is a blessing because many kids with similarly severe disabilities tend to deteriorate and not survive beyond five years of age.

Ashley is alert and aware of her environment; she startles easily. She constantly moves her arms and kicks her legs. Sometimes she seems to be watching TV intently. She loves music and often gets in celebration mode of vocalizing, kicking, and choreographing/conducting with her hands when she really likes a song (Andrea Boccelli is her favorite—we call him her boyfriend). She rarely makes eye-contact even when it is clear that she is aware of a person's presence next to her. Ashley goes to school in a classroom for special needs children, which provides her with daily bus trips, activities customized for her, and a high level of attention by her teachers and therapists.

Ashley brings a lot of love to our family and is a bonding factor in our relationship; we can't imagine life without her. She has a sweet demeanor and often smiles and expresses delight when we visit with her, we think she recognizes us but can't be sure. She has a younger healthy sister and brother. We constantly feel the desire to visit her room (her favorite place with special lights and colorful displays) or have her with us wanting to be in her aura of positive energy. We're often gathered around her holding her hand, thus sensing a powerful connection with her pure, innocent and angelic spirit. As often as we can we give her position changes and back rubs, sweet talk her, move her to social and engaging places, and manage her entertainment setting (music or TV). In return she inspires abundant love in our hearts, so effortlessly; she is such a blessing in our life!

To express how intensely we feel about providing Ashley with the best care possible, we would like to quote from a private email that we received from a loving mother with her own 6 year old Pillow Angel:

> "In my mind, I have to be immortal because I have to always be here on Earth to take care of my precious child. Taking care of him is difficult, but it is never a burden. I am [his] eyes, ears and voice. He is my best friend, and I have dedicated my life to providing joy and comfort to him. To my last breath, everything I will ever do will be for him or because of him. I cannot adequately put into words the amount of love and devotion I have for my child. I am sure that you feel the same way about Ashley."

The chance of Ashley having significant improvement, such as being able to change her position in bed, let alone walk, is non-existent. She has been at the same level of cognitive, mental and physical developmental ability since about three months of age. Ashley has aged and grown in size but her mental and physical abilities have remained and will remain those of an infant.

Faced with Ashley's medical reality, as her deeply loving parents, we worked with her doctors to do all we could to provide Ashley with the best possible quality of life. The result is the "Ashley Treatment."

Summary

The Ashley Treatment is the name we have given to a collection of medical procedures for the improvement of Ashley's quality of life. The treatment includes growth attenuation through high-dose estrogen therapy, hysterectomy to eliminate the menstrual cycle and associated discomfort to Ashley, and breast bud removal to avoid the development of large breasts and the associated discomfort to Ashley. We pursued this treatment after much thought, research, and discussions with doctors.

Nearly three years after we started this process, and after the treatment was published in October, 2006 by Dr. Gunther and Dr. Diekema in a medical journal[1] that resulted in an extensive and worldwide coverage by the press[2] and dozens of public discussion,[3] we decided to share our thoughts and experience for two purposes: first, to help families who might bring similar benefits to their bedridden Pillow Angels; second, to address some misconceptions about the treatment and our motives for undertaking it.

A fundamental and universal misconception about the treatment is that it is intended to convenience the caregiver; rather, the central purpose is to improve Ashley's quality of life. Ashley's biggest challenges are discomfort and boredom; all other considerations in this discussion take a back seat to these central challenges. The Ashley Treatment goes right to the heart of these challenges and we strongly believe that it will mitigate them in a significant way and provide Ashley with lifelong benefits.

Unlike what most people thought, the decision to pursue the Ashley Treatment was not a difficult one. Once we understood the options, problems, and benefits, the right course was clear to us. Ashley will be a lot more physically comfortable free of menstrual cramps, free of the discomfort associated with large and fully-developed breasts, and with a smaller, lighter body that is better suited to constant lying down and is easier to be moved around.

Ashley's smaller and lighter size makes it more possible to include her in the typical family life and activities that provide her with needed comfort, closeness, security and love: meal time, car trips, touch, snuggles, etc. Typically, when awake, babies are in the same room as other family members, the sights and sounds of family life engaging the baby's attention, entertaining the baby. Likewise, Ashley has all of a baby's needs, including being entertained and engaged, and she calms at the sounds of family voices. Furthermore, given Ashley's mental age, a nine and a half year old body is more appropriate and provides her more dignity and integrity than a fully grown female body.

We call it Ashley Treatment because:

1. As far as we know Ashley is the first child to receive this treatment,

2. We wanted a name that is easy to remember and search for,

3. The name applies to a collection of procedures that together have the purpose of improving Ashley's quality of life and well-being. Growth attenuation is only one aspect of the treatment.

The Ashley Treatment

In early 2004 when Ashley was six and a half years old, we observed signs of early puberty. In a related conversation with Ashley's doctor, Ashley's Mom came upon the idea of accelerating her already precocious puberty to minimize her adult height and weight. We scheduled time with Dr. Daniel F. Gunther, Associate Professor of Pediatrics in Endocrinology at Seattle's Children's Hospital, and discussed our options. We learned that attenuating growth is feasible through high-dose estrogen therapy. This treatment was performed on teenage girls starting in the 60's and 70's, when it wasn't desirable for girls to be tall, with no negative or long-term side effects.

The fact that there is experience with administering high-dose estrogen to limit height in teenage girls gave us the peace of mind that it was safe—no surprise side effects. Furthermore, people found justification in applying this treatment for cosmetic reasons while we were seeking a much more important purpose, as will be detailed below.

In addition to height and weight issues, we had concerns about Ashley's menstrual cycle and its associated cramps and discomfort. We also had concerns about Ashley's breasts developing and becoming a source of discomfort in her lying down position and while strapped across the chest area in her wheelchair, particularly since there is a family history of large breasts and other related issues that we discuss below. The estrogen treatment would hasten both the onset of the menstrual cycle and breast growth. Bleeding during the treatment would likely be very difficult to control.

It was obvious to us that we could significantly elevate Ashley's adult quality of life by pursuing the following three goals:

1. Limiting final height using high-dose estrogen therapy.

2. Avoiding menstruation and cramps by removing the uterus (hysterectomy).

3. Limiting growth of the breasts by removing the early breast buds.

The surgeon also performed an appendectomy during the surgery, since there is a chance of 5% of developing appendicitis in the general population, and this additional procedure presented no additional risk. If Ashley's appendix acts up, she would not be able to communicate the resulting pain. An inflamed appendix could rupture before we would know what was going on, causing significant complication.

Ashley was dealt a challenging life and the least that we can do as her loving parents and caregivers is to be diligent about maximizing her quality of life. The decision to move forward with the Ashley Treatment was not a difficult one for us as many seem to think. It was obvious to us that a reduction in Ashley's height (and therefore weight), elimination of the menstrual cycle, and avoidance of large breasts would bring significant benefits to her health and comfort. The only downside that we could think of was the surgery itself; however, the involved surgery is commonly done and is not complicated. Hysterectomy is a 1.5 hour surgery of less involvement and risk than a Fundoplication (wrapping and sewing the upper part of the stomach around the esophagus), which is commonly provided to children like Ashley to mitigate reflux and vomiting. The breast bud removal is a minor surgery with minimal risk. Furthermore, we're fortunate to have access to one of the best surgical facilities and teams at Seattle Children's Hospital. If we were in a less developed locale or country with higher risk of surgery, we would have looked at this part of the analysis differently.

Since the Ashley Treatment was new and unusual, Dr. Gunther scheduled us to present our case to the ethics committee at Seattle Children's Hospital, which we did on May 5th 2004. The committee includes about 40 individuals from different disciplines and is evenly composed of men and women. After we presented our case we waited outside while the committee deliberated the issue. The committee chairman along with Doctor Diekema, ethics consultant, conveyed the committee's decision to us, which was to entrust us with doing the right thing for Ashley. There was one legal issue that we needed to investigate related to "sterilization" of a disabled person. Upon consultation with a lawyer specializing in disability law, we found out that the law does not apply to Ashley's case due to the severity of her disability, which makes voluntary reproduction impossible. The law is intended to protect women with mild disability who might chose to become pregnant at some future point, and should have the right to do so. Furthermore, sterilization is a side effect of the Ashley Treatment and not its intent.

The combined hysterectomy, breast bud removal, and appendectomy surgery was performed without complications in July 2004. Ashley spent four days in the hospital under close supervision, and thanks to aggressive pain control her discomfort appeared minimal. In less than one month, Ashley's incisions healed and she was back to normal; it's remarkable how kids heal so much quicker than adults. Ashley's Mom had had a C-section and knew first hand how Ashley would feel after surgery; thankfully, the recovery went much better than Mom anticipated.

Shortly after the surgery and recovery, we started the high-dose estrogen therapy. We completed this treatment in December 2006 after two and a half years. During this whole period, we have observed no adverse consequences.

Expenses of the surgery and of the therapy that followed, which we estimate to be about $30,000, [were] fully covered by insurance. . . .

We hope that by now it is clear that the Ashley Treatment is about improving Ashley's quality of life and not about convenience to her caregivers. Ashley's biggest challenge is discomfort and boredom and the Ashley Treatment goes straight to the heart of this challenge. It is common for Ashley to be uncomfortable or to be bored. Even though Ashley's level of tolerance has increased along the years, she is helpless when bothered and her only recourse is to cry until someone comes to her rescue. These episodes are triggered by something as simple as sliding off the pillow, a sneeze, or a hair landing on her face and tickling/bothering her, let alone menstrual cramps, adult-level bed sores, and discomfort caused by large breasts and a constricting bra. Also, without the treatment, Ashley could not be moved as frequently or be as included in family life, and we would not experience the joy of being an intact family as often.

If people have concerns about Ashley's dignity, she will retain more dignity in a body that is healthier, more of a comfort to her, and more suited to her state of development as George Dvorsky, a member of the Board of Directors for the Institute for Ethics and Emerging Technologies, alludes to in a related article.[4] "If the concern has something to do with the girl's dignity being violated, then I have to protest by arguing that the girl lacks the cognitive capacity to experience any sense of indignity. Nor do I believe this is somehow demeaning or undignified to humanity in general; the treatments will endow her with a body that more closely matches her cognitive state—both in terms of her physical size and bodily functioning. The estrogen treatment is not what is grotesque here. Rather, it is the prospect of having a full-grown and fertile woman endowed with the mind of a baby."

Even though caring for Ashley involves hard and continual work, she is a blessing and not a burden. She brings a lot of love to our hearts as we're sure all Pillow Angels bring their families. In the words of a mother who lost her Pillow Angel: "While I would never want her to go through the discomfort she endured during her life, I would give all I have for one more snuggle, one more gaze from her radiant eyes." If there is a prize for those who have the record of how often they are told "I Love You", we're certain that these kids would win it effortlessly. Ashley's presence in our home kindles abundant feelings of love in all members of the family. It is a joy just being with her, she brings nourishment to our souls; it is a pleasure to visit with her and sweet talk her and observe her innocent and genuine smile. Ashley sets the barometer in our home: when she is happy we're happy and when she is not we're not.

We are very fortunate that Ashley is a healthy child, outside her abnormal mental development, and is in a stable condition. We're describing our unique experience which is not universal in this regard, and most likely not even representative. We fully understand that different Pillow Angels have different problems and pose different challenges to their caregivers, and that different families have different abilities and resources to provide for their special needs children.

The decision to move forward with this treatment, unlike what most have thought, was not difficult. Ever since we researched the idea and with Ashley's doctor's confirmation that it could be done, we focused squarely on getting it done as quickly as we could to maximize the benefits. It was clear to us that the lifelong benefits

to Ashley by far outweigh risk factors associated with the surgery. In contrast, the decision to insert the feeding tube into Ashley's stomach and associated surgery was a lot harder for us. Ashley's doctor suggested that we put the feeding tube in at 5 months of age because it was taking up to eight hours a day to get enough nutrition in her through a bottle. We delayed the tube insertion for years in order to spare Ashley the surgery. At five years of age we finally decided to go for the surgery, since almost every time Ashley would catch a cold she would completely refuse her bottle for days and end up dehydrated and in the emergency room.

Furthermore, we did not pursue this treatment with the intention of prolonging Ashley's care at home. We would never turn the care of Ashley over to strangers even if she had grown tall and heavy. In the extreme, even an Ashley at 300 pounds, would still be at home and we would figure out a way to take care of her.

The objection that this treatment interferes with nature is one of the most ridiculous objections of all; medicine is all about interfering with nature. Why not let cancer spread and nature takes its course. Why give antibiotics for infections? Even an act as basic as cutting hair or trimming nails is interfering with nature.

Some question how God might view this treatment. The God we know wants Ashley to have a good quality of life and wants her parents to be diligent about using every resource at their disposal (including the brains that He endowed them with) to maximize her quality of life. Knowingly allowing avoidable suffering for a helpless and disabled child can't be a good thing in the eyes of God. Furthermore, the God we know wants us to actively share our experience and learning with the rest of the world to help all Pillow Angels and other special need children in reaping the benefits of the Ashley Treatment.

We want to avoid sensationalism or philosophical debates about what we did and why we did it. We'd rather care for and enjoy Ashley than get into such endless debates. In our opinion, only parents with special-needs children are in a position to fully relate to this topic. Unless you are living the experience, you are speculating and you have no clue what it is like to be the bedridden child or their caregivers. Furthermore, in the case of the female aspects of the treatment, women are in a better position to relate to these aspects and the benefits for which they are intended. . . .

References

1.   "Attenuating Growth in Children with Profound Developmental Disability, A New Approach to an Old Dilemma," *Archives of Pediatrics & Adolescent Medicine*, Vol. 160, No.

10, October 2006, Daniel F. Gunther, MD, MA; Douglas S. Diekema, MD, MPH.

2. This story topped the Health section of Google News between January 5 and January 8—there have been more than 600 related articles worldwide.

3. "Pillow Angel Parents Deserve Credit, Not Blame," Blog: Sciam Observations, Opinions, arguments and

analyses from the editors of *Scientific American*, January 4, 2007.

4. "Helping families care for the helpless," George Dvorsky, Sentient Developments, Institute for Ethics and Emerging Technologies, November 6, 2006.

The Ashley Treatment: Best Interests, Convenience, and Parental Decision-Making

S. Matthew Liao, Julian Savulescu, and Mark Sheehan

Liao and his coauthors argue that although growth attenuation in a severely disabled child like Ashley may be justifiable, hysterectomy and the surgical removal of breast buds are not. Small size could be in Ashley's best interest, permitting her family to care for her at home. If the attenuation also promotes the interest of her parents, that should not count against it. Moral obligations do not typically require large sacrifices of health and all others interests and duties.

The benefit to Ashley of the removal of her uterus and breast buds, by contrast, is not as clear, and harms are more likely. Less invasive ways of protecting against cramps and the discomforts of having breasts might be found, and the risks of cancer and sexual abuse seem too unlikely to justify surgery. The authors also reject the argument that an immature body is more in keeping with Ashley's mental age and will give her greater dignity.

Finally, the authors encourage us to see that the right to be loved and cared for that Ashley shares with other children, disabled people, and the elderly should be recognized by society and supported by every able person by paying taxes and voting for policies that help parents and other caregivers.

The story of Ashley, a nine-year-old from Seattle, has caused a good deal of controversy since it appeared in the *Los Angeles Times* on January 3, 2007.[1] Ashley was born with a condition called static encephalopathy, a severe brain impairment that leaves her unable to walk, talk, eat, sit up, or roll over. According to her doctors, Ashley has reached, and will remain at, the developmental level of a three-month-old.[2]

In 2004, Ashley's parents and the doctors at Seattle's Children's Hospital devised what they called the "Ashley Treatment," which included high-dose estrogen therapy to stunt Ashley's growth, the removal of

Julian Savulescu, Mark Sheehan, and S. Matthew Liao, From "The Ashley Treatment: Best Interests, Convenience, and Parental Decision-Making," *Hastings Center Report*, Vol 37, no. 2 (2007): 16–20. Copyright © 2007 Hastings Center Report. All rights reserved. Reproduced by permission.

her uterus via hysterectomy to prevent menstrual discomfort, and the removal of her breast buds to limit the growth of her breasts. Ashley's parents argue that the Ashley Treatment was intended "to improve our daughter's quality of life and not to convenience her caregivers."[3] They also "decided to share our thoughts and experience . . . to help families who might bring similar benefits to their bedridden 'Pillow Angels,'" which means that this treatment has public policy implications.

In the case of incompetent children like Ashley, parents are the custodians of the child's interests and are required to make decisions that protect or promote those interests. Doctors should also offer treatments that are in Ashley's best interests. It would be wrong to offer a treatment that was against the interests of the child but in the parents' (or others') interests. The central questions in medical ethics in relation to this case are: Were these treatments in Ashley's best interests? Do they treat her as a person with dignity and respect, and were they likely to make her life go better?

Ashley's parents argue that they sought the Ashley treatment in order to alleviate Ashley's "discomfort and boredom." Their contention that stunting Ashley's growth was done for sake of improving "our daughter's quality of life and not to convenience her caregivers" is controversial.

According to her parents, keeping Ashley small—at around seventy-five pounds and four feet, five inches tall—means that Ashley can be moved considerably more often, held in their arms, be taken "on trips more frequently," "have more exposure to activities and social gatherings," and "continue to fit in and be bathed in a standard size bathtub." All this serves Ashley's health and well-being because, so the parents argue, "the increase in Ashley's movement results in better blood circulation, GI functioning (including digestion, passing gas), stretching, and motion of her joints," which means that Ashley will be less prone to infections.

Undoubtedly, the parents are right that Ashley will benefit in the manner they have proposed if they can do all these things for her. The claim about the value of small size in a particular social circumstance is certainly not unique. Dwarves have given the same argument as a justification for preferring to have short children. They have argued that parenting dwarves is desirable for them because of their own size and because they have made modifications to their homes and their surroundings to take into account their short stature.[4]

As a general point, it is entirely conceivable that in some natural, social, or psychological circumstances, having a normal body may be a disadvantage. In H.G. Wells' short story "The Country of the Blind," Nunez, a mountaineer in the Andes, falls and comes upon the Country of the Blind. Nunez has normal vision, but in this society of blind people, he is disadvantaged, and he eventually consents to have his eyes removed. Similarly, in a world of loud noise, being able to hear could be a disadvantage. In the case of apotemnophilia—a body dysmorphic disorder in which the patient feels incomplete possessing all four limbs—doctors justify amputation by reasoning that the patient's psychology demands it. In Ashley's case, having a normal-sized body could be a disadvantage. Stunting Ashley's growth may then be in her overall interest, given her likely natural and social circumstances.

Of course, Ashley's parents may have had other motives besides her benefit. Many critics have claimed that what her parents were really after was to make things easier or more convenient for themselves. Convenience may have been at least *part* of their motivation. Her parents could have found ways to take care of Ashley even if she had grown to her normal size of five feet, six inches. They argue that they were already near their limits when lifting Ashley; but if their own convenience was no consideration, they could have augmented their strength by hiring people to help them, or by going to the gym, or by taking steroids, and so on. We are not advocating any of these things; we are asserting only that since the parents *could* have taken these measures, part of the rationale for making Ashley smaller may have been their own convenience.

This said, acting out of the motive to convenience the caregivers or otherwise promote their interests is not necessarily wrong, for two reasons. First, motives may only form part of the justification of the treatment of children. Whether the treatment will benefit or harm them is just as important, and sometimes even more so. Imagine a parent who takes a child with appendicitis to a hospital merely hoping that the child will get admitted so that the parent can get some badly needed sleep. Does this make it wrong to perform an appendectomy? Obviously not. In such a case, the justification of the procedure depends on the interests of the child and not on the motives of the parents (though of course the two can be related).

Second, in any plausible moral theory, moral obligations should typically not be so demanding that one must make enormous sacrifices in order to fulfil them. As Judith Jarvis Thomson observes, "nobody is morally *required* to make large sacrifices, of health, of all other interests and concerns, of all other duties and commitments . . . in order to keep another person alive."[5] Exactly where the demands of morality stop, especially in the case of parents, is not easy to say. But, arguably, if Ashley's parents have to take steroids, which may have side effects, in order to move Ashley around, or if they will have to impoverish themselves in order to hire additional caregivers, then these alternatives might just be too demanding, and Ashley's parents would not be obligated to pursue them.

Of course, someone might accept that the demands of morality have limits but still question whether stunting Ashley's growth for her caregivers' convenience is justified. Indeed, many are worried that the Ashley Treatment might represent a return to the practices of the eugenics movement and be an affront to human dignity.[6] In particular, it has been asked whether, if it is permissible to stunt Ashley's growth to keep her small, why it is not also permissible surgically to remove her legs to keep her small. Needless to say, it is disturbing to think of a scenario in which severely disabled institutionalized children are subjected to mass surgery and growth-stunting to make the staff's work easier.

These questions raise issues concerning the ethics of body modification. Some forms of plastic surgery are performed on children: "bat ears" are sometimes corrected to prevent a child's being teased, and growth hormone or estrogen treatment is sometimes provided to children predicted to have short or tall stature.[7] However, other forms of body modification that might be allowed in adults are not permitted in children. A Scottish surgeon, Robert Smith, amputated the healthy legs of two patients suffering from apotemnophilia. The patients had received psychiatric and psychological treatment prior to the operation, but did not respond. Both operations were carried out with private funding, and the patients said they were satisfied with the results.[8] But this kind of surgery could not be ethically performed on healthy children because it is not plausibly in their interests, given the risks to, and the stress such an operation would impose on, their bodies. For this reason, surgically removing Ashley's legs just so she would be easier to care for would be unethical.

Giving Ashley estrogen to stunt her growth is obviously controversial but may be justifiable in this circumstance. Imagine that as a part of Ashley's condition, her body would grow to five times the size of other people. She would be enormous. In such a case, it does not seem too objectionable to arrest this kind of development through pharmacological means to allow her to be nursed and cared for, even if this is done partly for the caregivers' convenience. That is, suppose that if her development was not arrested, providing her with decent care would eventually require twenty people. If this is right, the question is not whether development *may* be arrested, but only *when* it may be arrested.

Here it is important to point out that decisions of this kind should be made on a case by case basis, with independent ethical review, such as occurred in this case through a hospital's clinical ethics committee. In general, it is inappropriate for institutions to biologically modify their patients to make them easier to manage, though clearly many demented people are sedated for this purpose. The benefits of being cared for at home by one's family may warrant imposing some burdens on incompetent dependants to enable them to remain at home and to make it possible for care to be delivered there. When the parents' resources are limited, the state, with its greater resources, should not resort to biological modification when the patient's quality of life can be preserved through social services.

***

The removal of Ashley's uterus and her breast buds is another matter. Ashley's parents argue that a hysterectomy will allow her to avoid the menstrual cycle and the discomforts commonly associated with it, eliminate "any possibility of pregnancy," and also eliminate the possibility "of uterine cancer and other common and often painful complications that cause women later in life to undergo the procedure." We find these arguments debatable.

For starters, it is unclear how much discomfort women suffer from the menstrual cycle, and whether the level of discomfort justifies hysterectomy. Also, even if Ashley will experience some discomfort, it is unclear why less invasive methods—such as giving Ashley pain killers whenever she experiences cramps—are not sufficient. Furthermore, removing Ashley's uterus may cause her ovaries not to function normally as a result of a compromised supply of blood.[9] This may result in Ashley's ovaries not producing enough of the hormones that would otherwise protect her against serious common diseases such as heart disease and osteoporosis.

Regarding unwanted pregnancies, while this does occur sometimes, the parents' statement gives the impression that sexual abuse is a given to one in Ashley's situation. Also, the parents may be in danger of blaming the victim. Ashley would get pregnant only through sexual abuse, but surely action should be taken against the offenders rather than Ashley. In any case, there are less invasive ways of avoiding pregnancy, such as putting Ashley on birth control pills.

Finally, regarding the possibility of uterine cancer and other painful complications, it seems premature to undertake a preventive measure when no one knows whether the symptoms will ever manifest. Giving Ashley regular health checkups seems to be much more appropriate and less invasive.

According to Ashley's parents, surgically removing Ashley's breast buds is justified because Ashley will not be breastfeeding. In addition, their presence "would only be a source of discomfort to her" because Ashley is likely to have large breasts, and "large breasts are uncomfortable lying down with a bra and even less comfortable without a bra." Moreover, they "impede securing Ashley in her wheelchair, stander, or bath chair, where straps across her chest are needed to support her body weight." Furthermore, removing her breasts also means that she can avoid the possibility of painful fibrocystic growth and breast cancer, which runs in Ashley's family. Finally, according to the parents, large breasts "could 'sexualize' Ashley towards her caregiver, especially when they are touched while she is being moved or handled, inviting the possibility of abuse." Again, we find these arguments problematic. We shall start with the ones that have been addressed previously.

In arguing that the breasts could "sexualize" Ashley, the parents are again in danger of blaming the victim for possible abuse. Moreover, someone might sexually abuse Ashley whether she has breasts or not. The focus should be on the potential sex offenders.

The argument that breasts would make securing Ashley in her wheelchair difficult, and so on, is an argument from convenience. Like the previous argument about size, it depends on how likely the harm to Ashley would be and how great the sacrifice of coping with management would be. Unlike Ashley's height and weight, in this case, it does not seem too demanding to require the parents to look for straps that would be more suitable for a larger breast size. Even if Ashley had been allowed to grow her breasts to their full potential, surely there are disabled persons with similar breast sizes, and their caregivers have apparently been able to use straps that are suitable for them (although the situation may be different when the patient's disability is as grave as Ashley's).

The possibility of painful fibrocystic growth and breast cancer is similar to the risk of uterine cancer; here, too, undertaking a preventive measure when the symptoms have not manifested seems premature. Even in the case of familial breast cancer, such as cancer linked to the genes BRCA 1 and 2, it is still not standard medical practice to offer prophylactic mastectomy to children, even those with a permanent intellectual disability that renders them incompetent. Many would argue that screening is preferable until there is more debate on the justification of prophylactic surgery in incompetent people.

The argument that Ashley does not need her breasts because she will not breastfeed (making her breasts only a "source of discomfort") assumes that the sole function of having breasts is for breastfeeding. Allowing Ashley to develop breasts may enable her to form and complete her gender identity. It is true that gender assignment surgery has been performed on children at birth in cases of intersex conditions,[10] but there is a growing consensus that surgery should be delayed until the child can make his or her own decision about it.[11] Ashley will never (on the evidence provided) be able to

decide for herself. But there is a difference between gender assignment and gender *elimination*. Ashley's parents argue that since Ashley has the mental state of a three-month-old, it is more fitting for her to have the body of an infant. They cite the statement of George Dvorsky, a member of the board of directors for the Institute for Ethics and Emerging Technologies, approvingly:

> *If the concern has something to do with the girl's dignity being violated, then I have to protest by arguing that the girl lacks the cognitive capacity to experience any sense of indignity. Nor do I believe this is somehow demeaning or undignified to humanity in general; the treatments will endow her with a body that more closely matches her cognitive state—both in terms of her physical size and bodily functioning. The estrogen treatment is not what is grotesque here. Rather, it is the prospect of having a full-grown and fertile woman endowed with the mind of a baby.*

This argument implies that anyone with the mind of a baby should have the body of a baby, but there's no reason to think this is true. Indeed, suppose a woman in her forties has such severe dementia that her mental state is reduced to that of a baby; to hold that she should no longer have breasts is absurd.

It is important to remember that surgical procedures like hysterectomy are not without risks. Anaesthetics are occasionally lethal, and the surgical complications can include perforation of the bowel, infection, and occasionally death. All told, drug treatment to stunt growth seems more justifiable than the surgical modifications.

* * *

Ashley's case calls to attention the fact that every able person in our society has at least a prima facie duty to provide support and assistance to those who are providing care, not just for the likes of Ashley, but also for all normal children, the elderly, and others in care. Because of their basic, biological need for love, children have a human right to be loved.[12] Successfully discharging the duty to love children requires considerable time and resources. Possibly some parents can successfully discharge this duty using their own resources. But for many others, it can be quite difficult, owing perhaps to the demands of employment or of other family members. However, if the right of children to be loved is a human right, and if the duties that stem from such a human right are applicable to all able persons in appropriate circumstances, then all other able persons in appropriate circumstances have associated duties to help parents discharge their duties to love their children. Such help might mean supporting better child care programs or advocating flexible workplace policies that would make it easier for parents to care for their children. It might also mean paying taxes and voting for policies that would help parents discharge their duties.[13]

This argument can be extended to the case of Ashley and others who require care, such as the elderly. Those who require care, like Ashley, have a fundamental need—and, therefore, a human right—to be cared for; and we, as members of society, have an associated duty to support policies that help their families care for them.

One of the main objections to the Ashley Treatment is that Ashley's disadvantage is socially constructed. If more resources were available for her care, then she could be nursed and cared for in a normal adult size. Those who defend the Ashley Treatment are right to respond that because these resources are not now adequately provided, Ashley's parents may be taking the only option open to them. Indeed, to deny her both the necessary social resources and medical treatment is to doubly harm her. If we as a society believe that it is undignified, as a matter of human rights, for Ashley to undergo these treatments, then we must be prepared to provide her caregivers with enough assistance and support that they would not have to resort to these means. Upholding human dignity comes with a price, and if it is what we should value as a society, then we must be prepared to pay to uphold it.

References

1. S. Verhovek, "Parents Defend Decision to Keep Disabled Girl Small," *Los Angeles Times*, January 3, 2007.

2. D. Gunther and D. Diekema, "Attenuating Growth in Children with Profound Developmental Disability: A New Approach to an Old Dilemma," *Archives of Pediatrics and Adolescent Medicine* 160, no. 10 (2006): 1013–17.

3. "The 'Ashley Treatment': Toward a Better Quality of Life for 'Pillow Angels,'" http://ashleytreatment.spaces.live.com/ (accessed February 15, 2007).

4. S. Baruch, D. Kaufman, and K. Hudson, "Genetic Testing of Embryos: Practices and Perspectives of U.S. IVF Clinics," *Fertility and Sterility*, forthcoming.

5. J.J. Thomson, "A Defense of Abortion," in *Ethics in Practice*, ed. by H. LaFollette (Oxford, U.K.: Blackwell, 1997), 69–78, at 77.

6. E. Cohen, "Disability Community Decries 'Ashley Treatment,'" http://www.cnn.com/2007/HEALTH/01/11/ashley.outcry/.

7. P. Louhiala, "How Tall Is Too Tall? On the Ethics of Oestrogen Treatment for Tall Girls," *Journal of Medical Ethics* 33, no. 1 (2007): 48–50.

8. C. Dyer, "Surgeon Amputated Healthy Legs," *British Medical Journal* 320 (2000): 332.

9. C. Garcia and W. Cutler, "Preservation of the Ovary: A Reevaluation," *Fertility and Sterility* 42, no. 4 (1984): 510–14.

10. M. Spriggs and J. Savulescu, "The Ethics of Surgically Assigning Sex for Intersex Infants," in *Cutting to the Core: The Ethics of Contested Surgeries*, ed. D. Benatar (Lanham, Md.: Rowman & Littlefield, forthcoming).

11. S.M. Liao, "The Ethics of Using Genetic Engineering for Sex Selection," *Journal of Medical Ethics* 31 (2005): 116–18.

12. S.M. Liao, "The Right of Children to Be Loved," *Journal of Political Philosophy* 14, no. 4 (2006): 420–40.

13. Strictly, these are prima facie duties: it is an open question whether justice requires this use of limited health resources or some other use that may more efficiently and effectively promote health.

Section 3:   The Status of Impaired Infants

Examination of Arguments in Favor of Withholding Ordinary Medical Care from Defective Infants

John A. Robertson

John Robertson defends a conservative natural law position in criticizing two arguments in favor of withholding "necessary but ordinary" medical care from impaired infants. He rejects the claim made by Michael Tooley that infants are not persons and argues that, on the contrary, there is no nonarbitrary consideration that requires us to

John A. Robertson, From "Examination of Arguments in Favor of Withholding Ordinary Medical Care from Defective Infants," *Stanford Law Review*, Vol. 27, (1975): 246–261. Copyright © 1975 Board of Trustees of the Leland Stanford Junior University. Reprinted by permission.

protect the past realization of conceptual capability but not its potential realization.

The second argument that Robertson considers is one to the effect that we have no obligation to treat defective newborns when the cost of doing so greatly outweighs the benefits (a utilitarian argument). In criticism, Robertson claims that we have no way of judging this. Life itself may be of sufficient worth to an impaired person to offset his or her suffering, and the suffering and cost to society are not sufficient to justify withholding care.

1. Defective Infants Are Not Persons

Children born with congenital malformations may lack human form and the possibility of ordinary, psychosocial development. In many cases mental retardation is or will be so profound, and physical incapacity so great, that the term "persons" or "humanly alive" have odd or questionable meaning when applied to them. In these cases the infants' physical and mental defects are so severe that they will never know anything but a vegetative existence, with no discernible personality, sense of self, or capacity to interact with others. Withholding ordinary medical care in such cases, one may argue, is justified on the ground that these infants are not persons or human beings in the ordinary or legal sense of the term, and therefore do not possess the right of care that persons possess.

Central to this argument is the idea that living products of the human uterus can be classified into offspring that are persons, and those that are not. Conception and birth by human parents does not automatically endow one with personhood and its accompanying rights. Some other characteristic or feature must be present in the organism for personhood to vest, and this the defective infant arguably lacks. Lacking that property, an organism is not a person or deserving to be treated as such.

Before considering what "morally significant features" might distinguish persons from nonpersons, and examining the relevance of such features to the case of the defective infant, we must face an initial objection to this line of inquiry. The objection questions the need for any distinction among human offspring because of

> the monumental misuse of the concept of "humanity" in so many practices of discrimination and atrocity throughout history. Slavery, witchhunts and wars have all been justified by their perpetrators on the grounds that they held

> their victims to be less than fully human. The insane and criminal have for long periods been deprived of the most basic necessities for similar reasons, and been excluded from society. . . .

> Even when entered upon with the best of intentions, and in the most guarded manner, the enterprise of basing the protection of human life upon such criteria and definitions is dangerous. To question someone's humanity or personhood is a first step to mistreatment and killing.

Hence, according to this view, human parentage is a necessary and sufficient condition for personhood, whatever the characteristics of the offspring, because qualifying criteria inevitably lead to abuse and untold suffering to beings who are unquestionably human. Moreover, the human species is sufficiently different from other sentient species that assigning its members greater rights on birth alone is not arbitrary.

This objection is indeed powerful. The treatment accorded slaves in the United States, the Nazi denial of personal status to non-Aryans, and countless other incidents, testify that man's inhumanity to man is indeed greatest when a putative nonperson is involved. Arguably, however, a distinction based on gross physical form, profound mental incapacity, and the very existence of personality or selfhood, besides having an empirical basis in the monstrosities and mutations known to have been born to women is a basic and fundamental one. Rather than distinguishing among the particular characteristics that persons might attain through the contingencies of race, culture, and class, it merely separates out those who lack the potential for assuming any personal characteristics beyond breathing and consciousness.

This reply narrows the issue: should such creatures be cared for, protected, or regarded as "ordinary" humans? If such treatment is not warranted, they may be treated as nonpersons. The arguments supporting care in all circumstances are based on the view that all living creatures are sacred, contain a spark of the divine, and should be so regarded. Moreover, identifying those human offspring unworthy of care is a difficult task and will inevitably take a toll on those whose humanity cannot seriously be questioned. At this point the argument becomes metaphysical or religious and immune to resolution by empirical evidence, not unlike the controversy over whether a fetus is a person. It should be noted, however, that recognizing all human offspring as persons, like recognizing the fetus to be a person, does not conclude the treatment issue.

Although this debate can be resolved only by reference to religious or moral beliefs, a procedural solution may reasonably be considered. Since reasonable people can agree that we ordinarily regard human offspring as persons, and further, that defining categories of exclusion is likely to pose special dangers of abuse, a reasonable solution is to presume that all living human offspring are persons. This rule would be subject to exception only if it can be shown beyond a reasonable doubt that certain offspring will never possess the minimal properties that reasonable persons ordinarily associate with human personality. If this burden cannot be satisfied, then the presumption of personhood obtains.

For this purpose I will address only one of the many properties proposed as a necessary condition of personhood—the capacity for having a sense of self—and consider whether its advocates present a cogent account of the nonhuman. Since other accounts may be more convincingly articulated, this discussion will neither exhaust nor conclude the issue. But it will illuminate the strengths and weaknesses of the personhood argument and enable us to evaluate its application to defective infants.

Michael Tooley has recently argued that a human offspring lacking the capacity for a sense of self lacks the rights to life or equal treatment possessed by other persons. In considering the morality of abortion and infanticide, Tooley considers "what properties a thing must possess in order to have a serious right to life," and he concludes that:

> [h]aving a right to life presupposes that one is capable of desiring to continue existing as a subject of experiences and other mental states. This in turn presupposes both that one has the concept of such a continuing entity and that one believes that one is oneself such an entity. So an entity that lacks such a consciousness of itself as a continuing subject of mental states does not have a right to life.

However, this account is at first glance too narrow, for it appears to exclude all those who do not presently have a desire "to continue existing as a subject of

experiences and other mental states." The sleeping or unconscious individual, the deranged, the conditioned, and the suicidal do not have such desires, though they might have had them or could have them in the future. Accordingly, Tooley emphasizes the capability of entertaining such desires, rather than their actual existence. But it is difficult to distinguish the capability for such desires in an unconscious, conditioned, or emotionally disturbed person from the capability existing in a fetus or infant. In all cases the capability is a future one; it will arise only if certain events occur, such as normal growth and development in the case of the infant, and removal of the disability in the other cases. The infant, in fact, might realize its capability long before disabled adults recover emotional balance or consciousness.

To meet this objection, Tooley argues that the significance of the capability in question is not solely its future realization (for fetuses and infants will ordinarily realize it), but also its previous existence and exercise. He seems to say that once the conceptual capability has been realized, one's right to desire continued existence permanently vests, even though the present capability for desiring does not exist, and may be lost for substantial periods or permanently. Yet, what nonarbitrary reasons require that we protect the past realization of conceptual capability but not its potential realization in the future? As a reward for its past realization? To mark our reverence and honor for someone who has realized that state? Tooley is silent on this point.

Another difficulty is Tooley's ambiguity concerning the permanently deranged, comatose, or conditioned. Often he phrases his argument in terms of a temporary suspension of the capability of conceptual thought. One wonders what he would say of someone permanently deranged, or with massive brain damage, or in a prolonged coma. If he seriously means that the past existence of a desire for life vests these cases with the right to life, then it is indeed difficult to distinguish the comatose or deranged from the infant profoundly retarded at birth. Neither will ever possess the conceptual capability to desire to be a continuing subject of experiences. A distinction based on reward or desert seems arbitrary, and protection of life applies equally well in both cases. Would Tooley avoid this problem by holding that the permanently comatose and deranged lose their rights after a certain point because conceptual capacity will never be regained? This would permit killing (or at least withholding of care from) the insane and comatose—doubtless an unappealing prospect.

Moreover, we do not ordinarily think of the insane, and possibly the comatose, as losing personhood before their death. Although their personality or identity may be said to change, presumably for the worse, or become fragmented or minimal, we still regard them as specific persons. If a "self" in some minimal sense exists here then the profoundly retarded, who at least is conscious, also may be considered a self, albeit a minimal one. Thus, one may argue that Tooley fails to provide a convincing account of criteria distinguishing persons and nonpersons. He both excludes beings we ordinarily think of as persons—infants, deranged, conditioned, possibly the comatose—and fails to articulate criteria that convincingly distinguish the nonhuman. But, even if we were to accept Tooley's distinction that beings lacking the potential for desire and a sense of self are not persons who are owed the duty to be treated by ordinary medical means, this would not appear to be very helpful in deciding whether to treat the newborn with physical or mental defects. Few infants, it would seem, would fall into this class. First, those suffering from malformations, however gross, that do not affect mental capabilities would not fit the class of nonpersons. Second, frequently even the most severe cases of mental retardation cannot be reliably determined until a much later period; care thus could not justifiably be withheld in the neonatal period, although this principle would permit nontreatment at the time when nonpersonality is clearly established. Finally, the only group of defective newborns who would clearly qualify as nonpersons is anencephalics, who altogether lack a brain or those so severely brain-damaged that it is immediately clear that a sense of self or personality can never develop. Mongols, myelomeningoceles, and other defective infants from whom ordinary care is now routinely withheld would not qualify as nonpersons. Thus, even the most coherent and cogent criteria of humanity are only marginally helpful in the situation of the defective infant. We must therefore consider whether treatment can be withheld on grounds other than the claim that such infants are not persons.

2. No Obligation to Treat Exists When the Costs of Maintaining Life Greatly Outweigh the Benefits

If we reject the argument that defective newborns are not persons, the question remains whether circumstances exist in which the consequences of treatment as compared with nontreatment are so undesirable that the omission of care is justified. As we have seen, the doctrine of necessity permits one to violate the criminal law when essential to prevent the occurrence of a greater evil. The circumstances, however, when the death of a nonconsenting person is a lesser evil than his continuing life are narrowly circumscribed, and do not include withholding care from defective infants. Yet many parents and physicians deeply committed to the loving care of the newborn think that treating severely defective infants causes more harm than good, thereby justifying the withholding of ordinary care. In their view the suffering and diminished quality of the child's life do not justify the social and economic costs of treatment. This claim has a growing commonsense appeal, but it assumes that the utility or quality of one's life can be measured and compared with other lives, and that health resources may legitimately be allocated to produce the greatest personal utility. This argument will now be analyzed from the perspective of the defective patient and others affected by his care.

a. The Quality of the Defective Infant's Life

Comparisons of relative worth among persons, or between persons and other interests, raise moral and methodological issues that make any argument that relies on such comparisons extremely vulnerable. Thus the strongest claim for not treating the defective newborn is that treatment seriously harms the infant's own interests, whatever may be the effect on others. When maintaining his life involves great physical and psychosocial suffering for the patient, a reasonable person might conclude that such a life is not worth living. Presumably the patient, if fully informed and able to communicate, would agree. One then would be morally justified in withholding lifesaving treatment if such action served to advance the best interests of the patient.

Congenital malformations impair development in several ways that lead to the judgment that deformed retarded infants are "a burden to themselves." One is the severe physical pain, much of it resulting from repeated surgery that defective infants will suffer. Defective children also are likely to develop other pathological features, leading to repeated fractures, dislocations, surgery, malfunctions, and other sources of pain. The shunt, for example, inserted to relieve hydrocephaly, a common problem in defective children, often becomes clogged, necessitating frequent surgical interventions.

Pain, however, may be intermittent and manageable with analgesics. Since many infants and adults experience great pain, and many defective infants do not, pain alone, if not totally unmanageable, does not sufficiently show that a life is so worthless that death is preferable. More important are the psychosocial deficits resulting from the child's handicaps. Many defective children never can walk even with prosthesis, never interact with normal children, never appreciate growth, adolescence, or the fulfillment of education and employment, and seldom are even able to care for themselves. In cases of severe retardation, they may be left with a vegetative existence in a crib, incapable of choice or the most minimal responses to stimuli. Parents or others may reject them, and much of their time will be spent in hospitals, in surgery, or fighting the many illnesses that beset them. Can it be said that such a life is worth living?

There are two possible responses to the quality-of-life argument. One is to accept its premises but to question the degree of suffering in particular cases, and thus restrict the justification for death to the most extreme cases. The absence of opportunities for schooling, career, and interaction may be the fault of social attitudes and the failings of healthy persons, rather than a necessary result of congenital malformations. Psychosocial suffering occurs because healthy, normal persons reject or refuse to relate to the defective, or hurry them to poorly funded institutions. Most nonambulatory, mentally retarded persons can be trained for satisfying roles. One cannot assume that a nonproductive existence is necessarily unhappy; even social rejection and nonacceptance can be mitigated. Moreover, the psychosocial ills of the handicapped often do not differ in kind from those experienced by many persons. With training and care, growth, development, and a full range of experiences are possible for most people with physical and mental handicaps. Thus, the claim that death is a far better fate than life cannot in most cases be sustained.

This response, however, avoids meeting the quality-of-life argument on its strongest grounds. Even if many defective infants can experience growth, interaction, and most human satisfactions if nurtured, treated, and trained, some infants are so severely retarded or grossly deformed that their response to love and care, in fact their capacity to be conscious, is always minimal. Although mongoloid and nonambulatory spina bifida children may experience an existence we would hesitate to adjudge worse than death, the profoundly retarded, nonambulatory blind, deaf infant who will spend his few years in the back-ward cribs of a state institution is clearly a different matter.

To repudiate the quality-of-life argument, therefore, requires a defense of treatment in even these extreme cases. Such a defense would question the validity of any surrogate or proxy judgments of the worth or quality of life when the wishes of the person in question cannot be ascertained. The essence of the quality-of-life argument is a proxy's judgment that no reasonable person can prefer the pain, suffering, and loneliness of, for example, life in a crib at an IQ level of 20, to an immediate, painless death.

But in what sense can the proxy validly conclude that a person with different wants, needs, and interests, if able to speak, would agree that such a life were worse than death? At the start one must be skeptical of the proxy's claim to objective disinterestedness. If the proxy is also the parent or physician, as has been the case in pediatric euthanasia, the impact of treatment on the proxy's interests, rather than solely on those of the child, may influence his assessment. But even if the proxy were truly neutral and committed only to caring for the child, the problem of egocentricity and knowing another's mind remains. Compared with the situation and life prospects of a "reasonable man," the child's potential quality of life indeed appears dim. Yet a standard based on healthy, ordinary development may be entirely inappropriate to this situation. One who has never known the pleasures of mental operation, ambulation, and social interaction surely does not suffer from their loss as much as one who has. While one who has known these capacities may prefer death to a life without them, we have no assurance that the handicapped person, with no point of comparison, would agree. Life, and life alone, whatever its limitations, might be of sufficient worth to him.

One should also be hesitant to accept proxy assessments of quality-of-life because the margin of error in such predictions may be very great. For instance, while one expert argues that by a purely clinical assessment he can accurately forecast the minimum degree of future handicap an individual will experience, such forecasting is not infallible, and risks denying care to infants whose disability might otherwise permit a reasonably acceptable quality-of-life. Thus given the problems in ascertaining another's wishes, the proxy's bias to personal or culturally relative interests, and the unreliability of predictive criteria, the quality-of-life argument is open to serious question. Its strongest appeal arises in the case of a grossly deformed, retarded, institutionalized child, or one with incessant unmanageable pain, where continued life is itself torture. But these cases are few, and cast doubt on the utility of any such judgment. Even if the judgment occasionally may be defensible, the potential danger of quality-of-life assessments may be a compelling reason for rejecting this rationale for withholding treatment.

b. The Suffering of Others

In addition to the infant's own suffering, one who argues that the harm of treatment justifies violation of the defective infant's right to life usually relies on the psychological, social, and economic costs of maintaining his existence to family and society. In their view the minimal benefit of treatment to persons incapable of full social and physical development does not justify the burdens that care of the defective infant imposes on parents, siblings, health professionals, and other patients. Matson, a noted pediatric neurosurgeon, states:

> [I]t is the doctor's and the community's responsibility to provide [custodial] care and to minimize suffering, but, at the same time, it is also their responsibility not to prolong such individual, familial, and community suffering unnecessarily, and not to carry out multiple procedures and prolonged, expensive, acute hospitalization in an infant whose chance for acceptable growth and development is negligible.

Such a frankly utilitarian argument raises problems. It assumes that because of the greatly curtailed orbit of his existence, the costs or suffering of others [are] greater than the benefit of life to the child. This judgment, however, requires a coherent way of measuring and comparing interpersonal utilities, a logical–practical problem that utilitarianism has never surmounted. But even if such comparisons could reliably show a net loss from treatment, the fact remains that the child must sacrifice his life to benefit others. If the life of one individual, however useless, may be sacrificed for the benefit of any person, however useful, or for the benefit of any number of persons, then we have acknowledged the principle that rational utility may justify any outcome. As many philosophers have demonstrated, utilitarianism can always permit the sacrifice of one life for other interests, given the appropriate arrangement of utilities on the balance sheet. In the absence of principled grounds for such a decision, the social equation involved in mandating direct, involuntary euthanasia becomes a difference of degree, not kind, and we reach the point where protection of life depends solely on social judgments of utility.

These objections may well be determinative. But if we temporarily bracket them and examine the extent to which care of the defective infant subjects others to suffering, the claim that inordinate suffering outweighs the infant's interest in life is rarely plausible. In this regard we must examine the impact of caring for defective infants on the family, health professionals, and society-at-large.

The Family. The psychological impact and crisis created by birth of a defective infant is devastating. Not only is the mother denied the normal tension release from the stresses of pregnancy, but both parents feel a crushing blow to their dignity, self-esteem, and self-confidence. In a very short time, they feel grief for the loss of the normal expected child, anger at fate, numbness, disgust, waves of helplessness, and disbelief. Most feel personal blame for the defect, or blame their spouse. Adding to the shock is fear that social position and mobility are permanently endangered. The transformation of a "joyously awaited experience into one of catastrophe and profound psychological threat" often will reactivate unresolved maturational conflicts. The chances for social pathology—divorce, somatic complaints, nervous and mental disorders—increase and hard-won adjustment patterns may be permanently damaged.

The initial reactions of guilt, grief, anger, and loss, however, cannot be the true measure of family suffering caused by care of a defective infant, because these costs are present whether or not the parents choose treatment. Rather, the question is to what degree treatment imposes psychic and other costs greater than would occur if the child were not treated. The claim that care is more costly rests largely on the view that parents and family suffer inordinately from nurturing such a child.

Indeed, if the child is treated and accepted at home, difficult and demanding adjustment must be made. Parents must learn how to care for a disabled child, confront financial and psychological uncertainty, meet the needs of other siblings, and work through their own conflicting feelings. Mothering demands are greater than with a normal child, particularly if medical care and hospitalization are frequently required. Counseling or professional support may be nonexistent or difficult to obtain. Younger siblings may react with hostility and guilt, older with shame and anger. Often the normal feedback of child growth that renders the turmoil of childrearing worthwhile develops more slowly or not at all. Family resources can be depleted (especially if medical care is needed), consumption patterns altered, or standards of living modified. Housing may have to be found closer to a hospital, and plans for further children changed. Finally, the anxieties, guilt, and grief present at birth may threaten to recur or become chronic.

Yet, although we must recognize the burdens and frustrations of raising a defective infant, it does not necessarily follow that these costs require nontreatment, or even institutionalization. Individual and group counseling can substantially alleviate anxiety, guilt, and frustration, and enable parents to cope with underlying conflicts triggered by the birth and the adaptations required. Counseling also can reduce psychological pressures on siblings, who can be taught to recognize and accept their own possibly hostile feelings and the difficult position of their parents. They may even be taught to help their parents care for the child.

The impact of increased financial costs also may vary. In families with high income or adequate health insurance, the financial costs are manageable. In others, state assistance may be available. If severe financial problems arise or pathological adjustments are likely, institutionalization, although undesirable for the child, remains an option. Finally, in many cases, the experience of living through a crisis is a deepening and enriching one, accelerating personality maturation, and giving one a new sensitivity to the needs of spouse, siblings, and others. As one parent of a defective child states: "In the last months I have come closer to people and can understand them more. I have met them more deeply. I did not know there were so many people with troubles in the world."

Thus, while social attitudes regard the handicapped child as an unmitigated disaster, in reality the problem may not be insurmountable, and often may not differ from life's other vicissitudes. Suffering there is, but seldom is it so overwhelming or so imminent that the only alternative is death of the child.

Health Professionals. Physicians and nurses also suffer when parents give birth to a defective child, although, of course, not to the degree of the parents. To the obstetrician or general practitioner the defective birth may be a blow to his professional identity. He has the difficult task of informing the parents of the defects, explaining their causes, and dealing with the parents' resulting emotional shock. Often he feels guilty for failing to produce a normal baby. In addition the parents may project anger or hostility on the physician, questioning his professional competence or seeking the services of other doctors. The physician also may feel that his expertise and training are misused when employed to maintain the life of an infant whose

chances for a productive existence are so diminished. By neglecting other patients, he may feel that he is prolonging rather than alleviating suffering.

Nurses, too, suffer role strain from care of the defective newborn. Intensive-care-unit nurses may work with only one or two babies at a time. They face the daily ordeals of care—the progress and relapses—and often must deal with anxious parents who are themselves grieving or ambivalent toward the child. The situation may trigger a nurse's own ambivalence about death and mothering, in a context in which she is actively working to keep alive a child whose life prospects seem minimal.

Thus, the effects of care on physicians and nurses are not trivial, and must be intelligently confronted in medical education or in management of a pediatric unit. Yet to state them is to make clear that they can but weigh lightly in the decision of whether to treat a defective newborn. Compared with the situation of the parents, these burdens seem insignificant, are short term, and most likely do not evoke such profound emotions. In any case, these difficulties are hazards of the profession—caring for the sick and dying will always produce strain. Hence, on these grounds alone it is difficult to argue that a defective person may be denied the right to life.

Society. Care of the defective newborn also imposes societal costs, the utility of which is questioned when the infant's expected quality of life is so poor. Medical resources that can be used by infants with a better prognosis, or throughout the health-care system generally, are consumed in providing expensive surgical and intensive-care services to infants who may be severely retarded, never lead active lives, and die in a few months or years. Institutionalization imposes costs on taxpayers and reduces the resources available for those who might better benefit from it, while reducing further the quality of life experienced by the institutionalized defective.

One answer to these concerns is to question the impact of the costs of caring for defective newborns. Precise data showing the costs to taxpayers or the trade-offs with health and other expenditures do not exist. Nor would ceasing to care for the defective necessarily lead to a reallocation within the health budget that would produce net savings in suffering or life; in fact, the released resources might not be reallocated for health at all. In any case, the trade-offs within the health budget may well be small. With advances in prenatal diagnosis of genetic disorders, many deformed infants who would formerly require care will be aborted beforehand. Then, too, it is not clear that the most technical and expensive procedures always constitute the best treatment for certain malformations. When compared with the almost seven percent of the GNP now spent on health, the money in the defense budget, or tax revenues generally, the public resources required to keep defective newborns alive seem marginal, and arguably worth the commitment to life that such expenditures reinforce. Moreover, as the Supreme Court recently recognized, conservation of the taxpayer's purse does not justify serious infringement of fundamental rights. Given legal and ethical norms against sacrificing the lives of nonconsenting others, and the imprecisions in diagnosis and prediction concerning the eventual outcomes of medical care, the social-cost argument does not compel nontreatment of defective newborns.

Ethical Issues in Aiding the Death of Young Children

H. Tristram Engelhardt, Jr.

H.T. Engelhardt contends that children are not persons in the full sense. They must exist in and through their families. Thus, parents, in conference with a physician who provides information, are the appropriate ones to decide whether to treat an impaired newborn when (1) there is not only little likelihood of a full human life but also the likelihood of suffering if the life is prolonged or (2) the cost of prolonging the life is very great.

Engelhardt further argues that it is reasonable to speak of a *duty* not to treat an impaired infant when this will only prolong a painful life or would only lead to a painful death. He bases his claim on the legal notion of a "wrongful life." This notion suggests that there are cases in which nonexistence would be better than existence under the conditions in which a person must live. Life can thus be seen as an injury, rather than as a gift.

Euthanasia in the pediatric age group involves a constellation of issues that are materially different from those of adult euthanasia. The difference lies in the somewhat obvious fact that infants and young children are not able to decide about their own futures and thus are not persons in the same sense that normal adults are. While adults usually decide their own fate, others decide on behalf of young children. Although one can argue that euthanasia is or should be a personal right, the sense of such an argument is obscure with respect to children. Young children do not have any personal rights, at least none that they can exercise on their own behalf with regard to the manner of their life and death. As a result, euthanasia of young children raises special questions concerning the standing of the rights of children, the status of parental rights, the obligations of adults to prevent the suffering of children, and the possible effects on society of allowing or expediting the death of seriously defective infants.

What I will refer to as the euthanasia of infants and young children might be termed by others infanticide, while some cases might be termed the withholding of extraordinary life-prolonging treatment. One needs a term that will encompass both death that results from active intervention and death that ensues when one simply ceases further therapy. In using such a term, one must recognize that death is often not directly but only obliquely intended. That is, one often intends only to treat no further, not actually to have death follow, even though one knows death will follow.

Finally, one must realize that deaths as the result of withholding treatment constitute a significant proportion of neonatal deaths. For example, as high as 14 percent of children in one hospital have been identified as dying after a decision was made not to treat further, the presumption being that the children would have lived longer had treatment been offered.

From *Beneficent Euthanasia*, edited by Marvin Kohl, published by Prometheus Books, Buffalo, N.Y. 1975.

Even popular magazines have presented accounts of parental decisions not to pursue treatment. These decisions often involve a choice between expensive treatment with little chance of achieving a full, normal life for the child and "letting nature take its course," with the child dying as a result of its defects. As this suggests, many of these problems are products of medical progress. Such children in the past would have died. The quandaries are in a sense an embarrassment of riches; now that one *can* treat such defective children, *must* one treat them? And, if one need not treat such defective children, may one expedite their death?

I will here briefly examine some of these issues. First, I will review differences that contrast the euthanasia of adults to euthanasia of children. Second, I will review the issue of the rights of parents and the status of children. Third, I will suggest a new notion, the concept of the "injury of continued existence," and draw out some of its implications with respect to a duty to prevent suffering. Finally, I will outline some important questions that remain unanswered even if the foregoing issues can be settled. In all, I hope more to display the issues involved in a difficult question than to advance a particular set of answers to particular dilemmas.

For the purpose of this paper, I will presume that adult euthanasia can be justified by an appeal to freedom. In the face of imminent death, one is usually choosing between a more painful and more protracted dying and a less painful or less protracted dying, in circumstances where either choice makes little difference with regard to the discharge of social duties and responsibilities. In the case of suicide, we might argue that, in general, social duties (for example, the duty to support one's family) restrain one from taking one's own life. But in the face of imminent death and in the presence of the pain and deterioration of a fatal disease, such duties are usually impossible to discharge and are thus rendered moot. One can, for example, picture an extreme case of an adult with a widely disseminated carcinoma, including metastases to the brain, who because of severe pain and debilitation is no longer capable of discharging any social duties. In these and similar circumstances, euthanasia becomes the issue of the right to control one's own body, even to the point of seeking assistance in suicide. Euthanasia is, as such, the issue of assisted suicide, the universalization of a maxim that all persons should be free, *in extremis*, to decide with regard to the circumstances of their death.

Further, the choice of positive euthanasia could be defended as the more rational choice: the choice of a less painful death and the affirmation of the value of a rational life. In so choosing, one would be acting to set limits to one's life in order not to live when pain and physical and mental deterioration make further rational life impossible. The choice to end one's life can be understood as a noncontradictory willing of a smaller set of states of existence for oneself, a set that would not include a painful death. That is, adult euthanasia can be construed as an affirmation of the rationality and autonomy of the self.

The remarks above focus on the active or positive euthanasia of adults. But they hold as well concerning what is often called passive or negative euthanasia, the refusal of life-prolonging therapy. In such cases, the patient's refusal of life-prolonging therapy is seen to be a right that derives from personal freedom, or at least from a zone of privacy into which there are no good grounds for social intervention.

Again, none of these considerations applies directly to the euthanasia of young children, because they cannot participate in such decisions. Whatever else pediatric, in particular neonatal, euthanasia involves, it surely involves issues different from those of adult euthanasia. Since infants and small children cannot commit suicide, their right to assisted suicide is difficult to pose. The difference between the euthanasia of young children and that of adults resides in the difference between children and adults. The difference, in fact, raises the troublesome question of whether young children are persons, or at least whether they are persons in the sense in which adults are. Answering that question will resolve in part at least the right of others to decide whether a young child should live or die and whether he should receive life-prolonging treatment.

The Status of Children

Adults belong to themselves in the sense that they are rational and free and therefore responsible for their actions. Adults are *sui juris.* Young children, though, are neither self-possessed nor responsible. While adults exist in and for themselves, as self-directive and self-conscious beings, young children, especially newborn infants, exist for their families and those who love them. They are not, nor can they in any sense be, responsible for themselves. If being a person is to be a responsible agent, a bearer of rights and duties, children are not persons in a strict sense. They are, rather, persons in a social sense: others must act on their behalf and bear responsibility for them. They are, as it were, entities defined by their place in social roles (for example, mother–child, family–child) rather than beings that define themselves as persons, that is, in and through themselves. Young children live as persons in and through the care of those who are responsible for them, and those responsible for them exercise the children's rights on their behalf. In this sense children belong to families in ways that most adults do not. They exist in and through their family and society.

Treating young children with respect has, then, a sense different from treating adults with respect. One can respect neither a newborn infant's or very young child's wishes nor its freedom. In fact, a newborn infant or young child is more an entity that is valued highly because it will grow to be a person and because it plays a social role as if it were a person. That is, a small child is treated as if it were a person in social roles such as mother–child and family–child relationships, though strictly speaking the child is in no way capable of claiming or being responsible for the rights imputed to it. All the rights and duties of the child are exercises and "held in trust" by others for a future time and for a person yet to develop.

Medical decisions to treat or not to treat a neonate or small child often turn on the probability and cost of achieving that future status—a developed personal life. The usual practice of letting anencephalic children (who congenitally lack all or most of the brain) die can be understood as a decision based on the absence of the possibility of achieving a personal life. The practice of refusing treatment to at least some children born with meningomyelocele can be justified through a similar, but more utilitarian, calculus. In the case of anencephalic children one might argue that care for them as persons is futile since they will never be persons. In the case of a child with meningomyelocele, one might argue that when the cost of cure would likely be very high and the probable lifestyle open to attainment very truncated, there is not a positive duty to make a large investment of money and suffering. One should note that the cost here must include not only financial costs but also the anxiety and suffering that prolonged and uncertain treatment of the child would cause the parents.

This further raises the issue of the scope of positive duties not only when there is no person present in a strict sense, but when the likelihood of a full human life is also very uncertain. Clinical and parental judgment may and should be guided by the expected life-style and the cost (in parental and societal pain

and money) of its attainment. The decision about treatment, however, belongs properly to the parents because the child belongs to them in a sense that it does not belong to anyone else, even to itself. The care and raising of the child falls to the parents, and when considerable cost and little prospect of reasonable success are present, the parents may properly decide against life-prolonging treatment.

The physician's role is to present sufficient information in a usable form to the parents to aid them in making a decision. The accent is on the absence of a positive duty to treat in the presence of severe inconvenience (costs) to the parents; treatment that is very costly is not obligatory. What is suggested here is a general notion that there is never a duty to engage in extraordinary treatment and that "extraordinary" can be defined in terms of costs. This argument concerns children (1) whose future quality of life is likely to be seriously compromised and (2) whose present treatment would be very costly. The issue is that of the circumstances under which parents would not be obliged to take on severe burdens on behalf of their children or those circumstances under which society would not be so obliged. The argument should hold as well for those cases where the expected future life would surely be of normal quality, though its attainment would be extremely costly. The fact of little likelihood of success in attaining a normal life for the child makes decisions to do without treatment more plausible because the hope of success is even more remote and therefore the burden borne by parents or society becomes in that sense more extraordinary. But very high costs themselves could be a sufficient criterion, though in actual cases judgments in that regard would be very difficult when a normal life could be expected.

The decisions in these matters correctly lie in the hands of the parents, because it is primarily in terms of the family that children exist and develop—until children become persons strictly, they are persons in virtue of their social roles. As long as parents do not unjustifiably neglect the humans in those roles so that the value and purpose of that role (that is, child) stands to be eroded (thus endangering other children), society need not intervene. In short, parents may decide for or against the treatment of their severely deformed children.

However, society has a right to intervene and protect children for whom parents refuse care (including treatment) when such care does not constitute a severe burden and when it is likely that the child could be brought to a good quality of life. Obviously, "severe burden" and "good quality of life" will be difficult to define and their meanings will vary, just as it is always difficult to say when grains of sand dropped on a table constitute a heap. At most, though, society need only intervene when the grains clearly do not constitute a heap, that is, when it is clear that the burden is light and the chance of a good quality of life for the child is high. A small child's dependence on his parents is so essential that society need intervene only when the absence of intervention would lead to the role "child" being undermined. Society must value mother–child and family–child relationships and should intervene only in cases where (1) neglect is unreasonable and therefore would undermine respect and care for children, or (2) where societal intervention would prevent children from suffering unnecessary pain.

The Injury of Continued Existence

But there is another viewpoint that must be considered: that of the child or even the person that the child might become. It might be argued that the child has a right not to have its life prolonged. The idea that forcing existence on a child would be wrong is a difficult notion, which, if true, would serve to amplify the foregoing argument. Such an argument would allow the construal of the issue in terms of the perspective of the child, that is, in terms of a duty not to treat in circumstances where treatment would only prolong suffering. In particular, it would at least give a framework for a decision to stop treatment in cases where, though the costs of treatment are not high, the child's existence would be characterized by severe pain and deprivation.

A basis for speaking of continuing existence as an injury to the child is suggested by the proposed legal concept of "wrongful life." A number of suits have been initiated in the United States and in other countries on the grounds that life or existence itself is, under certain circumstances, a tort or injury to the living person. Although thus far all such suits have ultimately failed, some have succeeded in their initial stages. Two examples may be instructive. In each case the ability to receive recompense for the injury (the tort) presupposed the existence of the individual, whose existence was itself the injury. In one case a suit was initiated on behalf of a child against his father alleging that his father's siring him out of wedlock was an injury to the child. In another case a suit on behalf of a child born of an inmate of a state mental hospital impregnated by rape in that institution was brought against the state of New York. The suit was brought on the grounds that being born with such historical antecedents was itself an injury for which recovery was due. Both cases presupposed that

nonexistence would have been preferable to the conditions under which the person born was forced to live.

The suits for tort for wrongful life raise the issue not only of when it would be preferable not to have been born but also of when it would be *wrong* to cause a person to be born. This implies that someone should have judged that it would have been preferable for the child never to have had existence, never to have been in the position to judge that the particular circumstances of life were intolerable. Further, it implies that the person's existence under those circumstances should have been prevented and that, not having been prevented, life was not a gift but an injury. The concept of tort for wrongful life raises an issue concerning the responsibility for giving another person existence, namely the notion that giving life is not always necessarily a good and justifiable action. Instead, in certain circumstances, so it has been argued, one may have a duty *not* to give existence to another person. This concept involves the claim that certain qualities of life have a negative value, making life an injury, not a gift; it involves, in short, a concept of human accountability and responsibility for human life. It contrasts with the notion that life is a gift of God and thus similar to other "acts of God" (that is, events for which no man is accountable). The concept thus signals the fact that humans can now control reproduction and that where rational control is possible humans are accountable. That is, the expansion of human capabilities has resulted in an expansion of human responsibilities such that one must now decide when and under what circumstances persons will come into existence.

The concept of tort for wrongful life is transferable in part to the painfully compromised existence of children who can only have their life prolonged for a short, painful, and marginal existence. The concept suggests that allowing life to be prolonged under such circumstances would itself be an injury of the person whose painful and severely compromised existence would be made to continue. In fact, it suggests that there is a duty not to prolong life if it can be determined to have a substantial negative value for the person involved. Such issues are moot in the case of adults, who can and should decide for themselves. But small children cannot make such a choice. For them it is an issue of justifying prolonging life under circumstances of painful and compromised existence. Or, put differently, such cases indicate the need to develop social canons to allow a decent death for children for whom the only possibility is protracted, painful suffering.

I do not mean to imply that one should develop a new basis for civil damages. In the field of medicine, the need is to recognize an ethical category, a concept of wrongful continuance of existence, not a new legal right. The concept of injury for continuance of existence, the proposed analogue of the concept of tort for wrongful life, presupposes that life can be of a negative value such that the medical maxim *primum non nocere* ("first do no harm") would require not sustaining life.

The idea of responsibility for acts that sustain or prolong life is cardinal to the notion that one should not under certain circumstances further prolong the life of a child. Unlike adults, children cannot decide with regard to euthanasia (positive or negative), and if more than a utilitarian justification is sought, it must be sought in a duty not to inflict life on another person in circumstances where that life would be painful and futile. This position must rest on the facts that (1) medicine now can cause the prolongation of the life of seriously deformed children who in the past would have died young and that (2) it is not clear that life so prolonged is a good for the child. Further, the choice is made not on the basis of costs to the parents or to society but on the basis of the child's suffering and compromised existence.

The difficulty lies in determining what makes life not worth living for a child. Answers could never be clear. It seems reasonable, however, that the life of children with diseases that involve pain and no hope of survival should not be prolonged. In the case of Tay–Sachs disease (a disease marked by a progressive increase in spasticity and dementia usually leading to death at age three or four), one can hardly imagine that the terminal stages of spastic reaction to stimuli and great difficulty in swallowing are at all pleasant to the child (even insofar as it can only minimally perceive its circumstances). If such a child develops aspiration pneumonia and is treated, it can reasonably be said that to prolong its life is to inflict suffering. Other diseases give fairly clear portraits of lives not worth living: for example, Lesch–Nyhan disease, which is marked by mental retardation and compulsive self-mutilation.

The issue is more difficult in the case of children with disease for whom the prospects for normal intelligence and a fair lifestyle do exist, but where these chances are remote and their realization expensive. Children born with meningomyelocele present this dilemma. Imagine, for example, a child that falls within Lorber's fifth category (an IQ of sixty or less, sometimes blind, subject to fits, and always incontinent). Such a child has little prospect of anything approaching a normal life, and there is a good chance of its dying even with treatment. But such judgments are statistical. And if one does not treat such children,

some will still survive and, as John Freeman indicates, be worse off if not treated. In such cases one is in a dilemma. If one always treats, one must justify extending the life of those who will ultimately die anyway and in the process subjecting them to the morbidity of multiple surgical procedures. How remote does the prospect of a good life have to be in order not to be worth great pain and expense? It is probably best to decide, in the absence of a positive duty to treat, on the basis of the cost and suffering to parents and society. But, as Freeman argues, the prospect of prolonged or even increased suffering raises the issue of active euthanasia.

If the child is not a person strictly, and if death is inevitable and expediting it would diminish the child's pain prior to death, then it would seem to follow that, all else being equal, a decision for active euthanasia would be permissible, even obligatory. The difficulty lies with "all else being equal," for it is doubtful that active euthanasia could be established as a practice without eroding and endangering children generally, since, as John Lorber has pointed out, children cannot speak in their own behalf. Thus although there is no argument in principle against the active euthanasia of small children, there could be an argument against such practices based on questions of prudence. To put it another way, even though one might have a duty to hasten the death of a particular child, one's duty to protect children in general could override that first duty. The issue of active euthanasia turns in the end on whether it would have social consequences that refraining would not, on whether (1) it is possible to establish procedural safeguards for limited active euthanasia and (2) whether such practices would have a significant adverse effect on the treatment of small children in general. But since these are procedural issues dependent on sociological facts, they are not open to an answer within the confines of this article. In any event, the concept of the injury of continued existence provides a basis for the justification of the passive euthanasia of small children—a practice already widespread and somewhat established in our society—beyond the mere absence of a positive duty to treat.

Conclusion

Though the lack of certainty concerning questions such as the prognosis of particular patients and the social consequence of active euthanasia of children prevents a clear answer to all the issues raised by the euthanasia of infants, it would seem that this much can be maintained: (1) Since children are not persons strictly but exist in and through their families, parents are the appropriate ones to decide whether or not to treat a deformed child when (a) there is not only little likelihood of full human life but also great likelihood of suffering if the life is prolonged, or (b) when the cost of prolonging life is very great. Such decisions must be made in consort with a physician who can accurately give estimates of cost and prognosis and who will be able to help the parents with the consequences of their decision. (2) It is reasonable to speak of a duty not to treat a small child when such treatment will only prolong a painful life or would in any event lead to a painful death. Though this does not by any means answer all the questions, it does point out an important fact—that medicine's duty is not always to prolong life doggedly but sometimes is quite the contrary.

Right to Life of the Handicapped

Alison Davis

Davis argues from her experience as a handicapped person against allowing doctors, within the first 28 days of the life of a severely disabled infant, to predict the infant's quality of life and decide the course of treatment on the basis. Davis points out that the prediction for her would have been a life without worthwhile quality, a prediction wholly at odds with her own experience of life. She rejects the notion of nonpersonhood during the first four weeks of life and expresses the fear that following predictions made during that period to justify nontreatment would lead to the decriminalization of killing handicapped people at later ages.

In reference to your items on the bill drafted by Mr and Mrs Brahams permitting doctors to withhold treatment from newborn handicapped babies, I would like to make the following points.

I am 28 years old, and suffer from a severe physical disability which is irreversible, as defined by the bill. I was born with myelomeningocele spina bifida. Mr and Mrs Brahams suggest several criteria for predicting the potential quality of life of people like me, and I note that I fail to fulfill most of them.

I have suffered considerable and prolonged pain from time to time, and have undergone over 20 operations, thus far, some of them essential to save my life. Even now my health is at best uncertain. I am doubly incontinent and confined to a wheelchair and thus, according to the bill, I should have 'no worthwhile quality of life'.

However, because I was fortunately born in rather more tolerant times, I was given the chance to defy the odds and live, which is now being denied to handicapped newborns. Even so, my parents were

encouraged to leave me in the hospital and 'go home and have another' and I owe my life to the fact that they refused to accept the advice of the experts.

Despite my disability I went to an ordinary school and then to university, where I gained an honours degree in sociology. I now work full-time defending the right to life of handicapped people. I have been married eight years to an able-bodied man, and over the years we have travelled widely in Europe, the Soviet Union and the United States. This year we plan to visit the Far East.

Who could say I have 'no worthwhile quality of life'? I am sure though that no doctor could have predicted when I was 28 days old (and incidentally had received no operation at all) that despite my physical problems I would lead such a full and happy life. I do not doubt that they were 'acting in good faith' when they advised my parents to abandon me, but that does not mean that their advice was correct.

I was pleased to see that Dr Havard considered [that] legislation was not the right way to solve the problem, though I suspect his disquiet was rather over an infringement of the liberty of doctors than out of any concern for the rights of the handicapped. Whatever his motives, though, I feel the medical profession could go a lot farther than it has to condemn the constant undermining of the rights of handicapped people at progressively later stages in their lives. There is nothing magical about the age of 28 days after all. It is simply the currently accepted boundary of 'non-personhood' for babies with congenital defects.

This notion of 'non-personhood' denies the right of handicapped people to be recognised as equal human beings in a caring society, and it makes a mockery of the goodwill which seemingly abounded in the International Year of Disabled People.

Legislation of the type proposed could well also lead to the *de facto* decriminalisation of the act of killing a handicapped person of any age, just as it did in Hitler's Germany. And if it does, woe betide any handicapped people who are too ill to defend their right to life by protesting that they are in fact happy. And woe betide us all, when we get too old to be considered 'useful' and all the friends who could have spoken in our defence have already been oh so lovingly 'allowed to die'.

DECISION SCENARIOS

The questions following each decision scenario are intended to prompt reflection and discussion. In deciding how to answer them, you should consider the information in the Briefing Session; the ethical theories and principles presented in Part V, "Foundations of Bioethics," and the arguments and criticisms offered in the relevant readings in this chapter.

DECISION SCENARIO **1**

Doing the Right Thing?

Susan Roth was looking forward to being a mother. She had quit her secretarial job three months before her baby was due so that she could spend the time getting everything ready. Her husband, David, was equally enthusiastic, and they spent many hours happily speculating about the way things would be when their baby came. It was their first child.

"I hope they don't mix her up with some other baby," Mrs. Roth said to her husband after the delivery.

She didn't know yet that there was little chance of confusion. The Roth infant was seriously deformed. Her arms and legs had failed to develop, her skull was misshapen, and her face deformed. Her large intestine emptied through her vagina, and she had no muscular control over her bladder.

When she was told, Mrs. Roth said, "We cannot let it live, for her sake and ours." On the day she left the hospital with the child, Mrs. Roth mixed a lethal dose of a tranquilizing drug with the baby's formula and fed it to her. The child died that evening.

Mrs. Roth and her husband were charged with infanticide. During the court proceedings, Mrs. Roth

admitted to the killing but said she was satisfied that she had done the right thing. "I know I could not let my baby live like that," she said. "If only she had been mentally abnormal, she would not have known her fate. But she had a normal brain. She would have known. Placing her in an institution might have helped me, but it wouldn't have helped her."

The jury, after deliberating for two hours, found Mrs. Roth and her husband guilty of the charge.

1. Would this child satisfy the criteria that would allow the Groningen Protocol to be followed?

2. Does the fact that the intelligence of the child is normal support the mother's claim that killing was justifiable? Might normal intelligence make the "injury of continued existence" even greater than subnormal intelligence?

3. Why might some consider the mother's action morally wrong?

4. Would the best-interest-of-the-infant standard offer any support for the mother's action?

DECISION SCENARIO 2

No Food, No Water?

Irene Towers had been a nurse for almost twelve years; for the last three of those years she had worked in the Neonatal Unit of Halifax County Hospital. It was a job she loved. Even when the infants were ill or required special medical or surgical treatment, she found the job of caring for them immensely rewarding. She knew that without her efforts many of the babies would simply die.

Irene Towers was on duty the night that conjoined twins were born to Corrine Couchers and brought at once to the Neonatal Unit. Even Irene, with all her experience, was distressed to see them. The twin boys were joined at their midsections in a way that made it impossible to separate them surgically. Because of the position of the single liver and the kidneys, not even one twin could be saved at the expense of the life of the other. Moreover, both children were severely deformed, with incompletely developed arms and legs and misshapen heads. As best as the neurologist could determine, both suffered severe brain damage.

The father of the children was Dr. Harold Couchers, a slightly built man in his early thirties who was a specialist in internal medicine with a private practice.

Irene felt sorry for him the night the children were born. When he went into the room with the obstetrician to examine his sons, he had already been told what to expect. He showed no signs of grief as he stood over the slat-sided crib, but the corners of his mouth were drawn tight, and his face was almost unnaturally empty of expression. Most strange for a physician, Irene thought—he merely looked at the children and did not touch them. She was sure that in some obscure way he must be blaming himself for what had happened to them.

Later that evening, Irene saw Dr. Couchers sitting in the small conference room at the end of the hall with Dr. Cara Rosen, Corrine Couchers' obstetrician. They were talking earnestly and quietly when Irene passed the open door. Then, while she was looking over the assignment sheet at the nursing station, the two of them walked up. Dr. Rosen took a chart from the rack behind the desk and made a notation. After returning the chart, she shook hands with Dr. Couchers, and he left.

It was not until the end of her shift that Irene read the chart; Dr. Rosen's note said that the twin boys were to be given neither food nor water. At first Irene couldn't believe the order. But when she asked her supervisor, she was told that the supervisor had telephoned Dr. Rosen and that the obstetrician had confirmed the order.

Irene said nothing to the supervisor or to anyone else, but she made her own decision. She believed it was wrong to let the children die, particularly in such a horrible way. They deserved every chance to fight for their lives, and she was going to help them the way she had helped hundreds of other babies in the unit.

For the next week and a half, Irene saw to it that the children were given water and fed the standard infant formula. She did it all herself, on her own initiative. Although some of the other nurses on the floor saw what she was doing, none of them said anything to her. One even smiled and nodded to her when she saw Irene feeding the children.

Apparently someone else also disapproved of the order to let the twins die. Thirteen days after their birth, an investigator from the state Family Welfare Agency appeared in the neonatal ward. The rumor was that his visit had been prompted by an anonymous telephone call.

Late in the afternoon of the day of that visit, the deformed twins were made temporary wards of the Agency, and the orders on the chart were changed—the twins were now to be given food and water. On the next day, the county prosecutor's office announced publicly that it would conduct an investigation of the situation and decide whether criminal charges should be brought against Dr. Couchers or members of the hospital staff.

Irene was sure that she had done the right thing. Nevertheless, she was glad to be relieved of the responsibility.

1. Is there a morally relevant distinction between not treating (and allowing to die) and not providing such minimal needs as food and water (and allowing to die)?

2. Does any line of reasoning support the action taken by Irene Towers?

3. Did Irene Towers exceed the limits of her responsibility, or did she act in a morally heroic way?

Murder or Temporary Insanity?

Dr. Daniel McKay and his wife, Carol, had only a few moments of joy at the birth of their son. They learned almost immediately that the child was severely impaired. Half an hour later, the infant was dead— Dr. McKay, a veterinarian, had slammed him onto the floor of the delivery room.

Mrs. McKay had had problems during pregnancy. An ultrasound test indicated excessive fluid in the uterus, a sign that something might be wrong. Dr. Joaquin Ramos assured the McKays that everything was all right and that the pregnancy should continue. On June 27, 1983, he ordered Mrs. McKay admitted to the Markham, Illinois, hospital so that labor could be induced.

"Don't do any heroic measures," Dr. McKay told Dr. Ramos when Dr. McKay learned that the infant was impaired. Dr. Ramos explained that that was not his choice, for hospital policy required that everything possible be done for babies, even ones like the McKay baby that might not live more than a few months. The child had webbed fingers, heart and lung malfunctions, and missing testicles. It was suspected that the child also had a genetic disorder that might mean kidney malfunctions, mental retardation, and death within months.

Dr. McKay smashed the infant's head against the floor several times, splattering the wall and floor with brain tissue and blood. "Dan, what have you done?" a nurse shouted. Dr. McKay later said that while holding the child, he asked himself, "Can I accept and love this child, or would it be better off dead?" He had just talked to his wife. "I said to Dan, 'Is it a boy or a girl?' He said it was a little boy. I said, 'Oh, Dan, we got our boy!' Dan really wasn't saying anything. He had tears in his eyes." She then realized that the baby was not crying and asked her husband to go see what was wrong.

Dr. McKay was charged with murder. Two defense psychiatrists testified that he had been temporarily insane. Two others said that he had succumbed to stress. A prosecution psychiatrist said that he was legally sane but that "he made a decision that he had a moral imperative to do what he did." The jury could not agree whether Dr. McKay was guilty, not guilty, guilty but not mentally ill, or not guilty by reason of insanity. A mistrial was declared, but another trial was scheduled.

1. How might the hospital policy of "doing everything possible" for all impaired infants be criticized in terms of the "best-interest" standard?

2. Would the McKay infant count as a potential person? How might the potential personhood of the infant affect the decision whether or not to withhold treatment?

3. Might one argue that Dr. McKay's action was morally right, whether or not it was legally justifiable?

4. Under what conditions, if any, ought the parents of an impaired infant be allowed to decide how the child is to be treated?

The Messenger Case

On February 8, 1984, Traci Messenger had an emergency cesarean section at the E. W. Sparrow Hospital in East Lansing, Michigan, and her son, Michael, was delivered after only a twenty-five-week gestation period—fifteen weeks prematurely. Michael weighed one pound, eleven ounces; was very likely to have serious brain damage; and was given a thirty to fifty percent chance of survival.

Before Traci Messenger's surgery, Michael's father, Dr. Gregory Messenger, a dermatologist on the staff of the hospital, had spoken with his wife's physicians and requested that no extraordinary measure be taken to prolong the child's life. However, after the child was born, the neonatologist, Dr. Padmoni Karna, insisted that the baby be given respiratory support and diagnostic tests.

About an hour after Michael was delivered, Dr. Messenger went into the child's room and asked the nurses to leave. He then disconnected the life-support system, setting off an alarm. The child died, and the hospital called the police. A short time later, the county prosecutor, Donald E. Martin, charged Dr. Messenger with manslaughter.

Although most states, including Michigan, allow parents to decide to withdraw life support from their ailing child, Mr. Martin said he had decided to prosecute because Dr. Messenger had not waited for the results of medical tests. "The father appeared to make a unilateral decision to end life for his infant son," Mr. Martin said.

Dr. Messenger's attorney replied that Dr. Messenger had several warnings of severe medical problems during delivery and immediately after birth. Monitoring of the baby suggested that he was not receiving sufficient oxygen and would be severely brain damaged. Blood tests at birth indicated that the baby had a 14 percent level of oxygen, and, as a physician testified at a preliminary hearing, five minutes at a less-than 50-percent level is enough to damage the brain. "The parents made a decision when the outcome was so grim and the prognosis was so bad; they indicated 'we do not want this intervention.' I think it was incumbent on hospital personnel to honor their directive, and they didn't do that."

Dr. Karna said that she would have agreed to removing the life support, given the blood-test results, but that Dr. Messenger had acted without consulting her.

1. Might Michael Messenger be considered likely to suffer "the injury of continued existence"?

2. On what grounds might one support the claim that the infant should be treated?

3. Suppose that after the test results the parents and Dr. Karna disagreed as to whether the infant should be treated. Whose opinion should be decisive?

4. Would considering the "best interest" of the infant be of help in resolving a conflict between the Messengers and Dr. Karna?

DECISION SCENARIO 5

Another Ashley?

Brookhaven, as we will call it, is a long-term health care institution in the Washington metropolitan area. Most of Brookhaven's patients are in residence there for only a few months; either they succumb to their ailments and die, or they recover sufficiently to return to their homes.

But for some patients, death has no immediate likelihood nor is recovery a possibility. They linger on at Brookhaven, day after day and year after year. Juli Meyers is such a patient, although that is not really her name.

Juli is seventeen and has been in Brookhaven for six years. But before Brookhaven, there were other institutions. In fact, Juli has spent most of her life in hospitals and special-care facilities. But Juli does not seem to be aware of any of this.

At Brookhaven, she spends her days lying in a bed surrounded with barred metal panels. The bars have been padded with foam rubber. Although most of the time Juli is curled tightly in a fetal position, she sometimes flails around wildly and makes guttural sounds. The padding keeps her from injuring herself.

Juli's body is thin and underdeveloped, with sticklike arms and legs. She is blind and deaf and has no control over her bowels and bladder. She is totally dependent on others to clean her and care for her. She can swallow the food put into her mouth, but she cannot feed herself. She makes no response to the people or events around her.

There is no hope that Juli will walk or talk, laugh or cry, or even show the slightest sign of intelligence or awareness. She is the victim of one of the forms of Schilder's disease. The nerve fibers that make up her central nervous system have mostly degenerated. The cause of the degeneration is not fully known, nor is it known how to halt the process. The condition is irreversible, and Juli will never be better than she is.

At birth Juli seemed perfectly normal and healthy, but at three months she began to lose her sight and hearing. She made the gurgling noises typical of babies less and less frequently. By the end of her first year, she made no sounds at all and was completely blind and deaf. Also, she was losing control of her muscles, and her head lolled on her shoulders, like a doll with a broken neck.

She became highly subject to infections, and more than once she had pneumonia. One time, when she was on the critical list, a specialist suggested to her mother that it would be pointless to continue treating her. Even if she recovered from the pneumonia, she would remain hopelessly impaired. Mrs. Meyers angrily rejected the suggestion and insisted that everything possible be done to save Juli's life.

Although not wealthy, the family bore the high cost of hospitalization and treatments. Mrs. Meyers devoted herself almost totally to caring for Juli at home, and the other four children in the family received little of her attention. Eventually, Mrs. Meyers began to suffer from severe depression, and when Juli was eight and a half, her parents decided that she would have to be placed in an institution. Since then, Juli has changed little. No one expects her to change. Her mother visits her three times a month and brings Juli freshly laundered and ironed clothes.

1. Whats arguments can be offered to support Mrs. Meyers's decision not to allow Juli to die?

2. Are there any grounds for supposing that Juli is being made to suffer "the injury of continued existence"?

3. Could Julie be regarded as an appropriate candidate for the "Ashley treatment"?

4. Is it possible to justify using society's limited medical resources to keep Juli alive?

5. Evaluate the following argument: Opponents of abortion oppose spending public funds for abortion on the grounds that they (the opponents) are being forced to support murder, which is a serious moral evil. Keeping Juli alive is a serious moral evil. Therefore, no public funds should be used for this purpose.

DECISION SCENARIO 6

Pointless Suffering?

Ginny Rutten was born with epidermolysis bullosa, a genetic disease involving the blistering and sloughing off of the skin and mucous membranes—the whole thickness, down to the fat and muscle. Ginny cannot drink, because the lining of her mouth is blistered and swollen, and so can take no nourishment by mouth. Areas of her skin have eroded, producing patches of raw flesh resembling third-degree burns. Because of the breakdown of her skin, she suffers constant pain, and the dehydration the skin breakdown produces leads to electrolyte imbalances that put her at risk of heart arrhythmia and death.

Ginny has a disease for which there is no cure and not even a treatment to prevent the blistering and peeling of her skin. In addition to enduring the pain from the skin loss, babies with the disease lose their fingers and suffer from a drawing up— contracture—of their arms and legs from scarring. They need total care their entire lives, which are likely to be only a few months or a few years. No case of a spontaneous cure or even a lengthy remission is on record.

Ginny screams in pain when she is awake. She is sedated by a morphine drip and sleeps in brief cycles. Her physicians and the hospital Ethics Committee debate the question of whether to feed Ginny artificially, either by an IV drip or through a surgical opening into her stomach, and so keep her alive. Her parents ask that Ginny's life be ended humanely by a lethal injection.

1. How would Ginny's case be classified within the categories of the Groningen Protocol?

2. What conditions must Ginny's case meet to satisfy the requirements spelled out in the Groningen Protocol?

3. Can Ginny's case be regarded as one involving the injury of continued existence?

4. If Ginny is neurologically normal, does this imply that she ought to be treated, even if treating her only prolongs her pain?

5. We routinely euthanize dogs, cats, and horses to protect them from pointless suffering which cannot be relieved. Is there some reason we shouldn't treat human babies the same way?

Chapter 7

Euthanasia and Assisted Suicide

CHAPTER CONTENTS

CASES AND CONTEXTS

Karen Quinlan: The Debate Begins

At two in the morning on Tuesday, April 14, 1975, Mrs. Julie Quinlan was awakened by a telephone call. When she hung up she was crying. "Karen is very sick," Mrs. Quinlan said to her husband, Joseph. "She's unconscious, and we have to go to Newton Hospital right away."

The Quinlans thought their twenty-one-year-old adopted daughter might have been in an automobile accident. But the doctor in the intensive-care unit told them that wasn't so. Karen was in a critical comatose state of unknown cause and was being given oxygen through a mask taped over her nose and mouth. She had been brought to the hospital by two friends who had been with her at a birthday party. After a few drinks, she had started to pass out, and her friends decided she must be drunk and put her to bed. Then someone checked on her later in the evening and found that Karen wasn't breathing. Her friends gave her mouth-to-mouth resuscitation and rushed her to the nearest hospital.

Blood and urine tests showed that Karen had not consumed a dangerous amount of alcohol. They also showed the presence of .6 milligram of aspirin and the tranquilizer Valium. Two milligrams would have been toxic, five lethal. Why Karen stopped breathing was mysterious. But it was during that time that part of her brain died from oxygen depletion.

After Karen had been unconscious for about a week, she was moved to St. Clare's Hospital in nearby Denville, where testing and life-support facilities were better. Dr. Robert J. Morse, a neurologist, and Dr. Arshad Javed, a pulmonary internist, became her physicians. Additional tests were made. Extensive brain damage was confirmed, and several possible causes of the coma were ruled out.

No Longer the Same

During the early days, the Quinlans were hopeful. Karen's eyes opened and closed, and her mother and her nine-teen-year-old sister, Mary Ellen, thought that they detected signs that Karen recognized them. But Karen's condition began to deteriorate. Her weight gradually dropped from 120 pounds to 70 pounds. Her body began to contract into a rigid fetal position, until her five-foot-two-inch frame was bent into a shape hardly longer than three feet. She was now breathing mechanically, by means of an MA-1 respirator that pumped air through a tube in her throat. By early July, Karen's physicians and her mother, sister, and brother had come to believe it was hopeless to expect her ever to regain consciousness.

Only her father continued to believe it might be possible. But when he told Dr. Morse about some encouraging sign he had noticed, Dr. Morse said to him, "Even if God did perform a miracle so that Karen would live, her damage is so extensive she would spend the rest of her life in an institution." Mr. Quinlan then realized that Karen would never again be as he remembered her. He now agreed with Karen's sister: "Karen would never want to be kept alive on machines like this. She would hate this."

Need to Go to Court

The Quinlans' parish priest, Father Thomas Trapasso, had also assured them that the moral doctrines of the Roman Catholic Church did not require the continuation of extraordinary measures to support a hopeless life. Before making his decision, Mr. Quinlan asked the priest, "Am I playing God?" Father Thomas said, "God has made the decision that Karen is going to die. You're just agreeing with God's decision, that's all."

On July 31, after Karen had been unconscious for three and a half months, the Quinlans gave Drs. Morse and Jared their permission to take Karen off the respirator. The Quinlans signed a letter authorizing the discontinuance of extraordinary procedures and absolving the hospital from all legal liability. "I think you have come to the right decision," Dr. Morse said to Mr. Quinlan.

But the next morning Dr. Morse called Mr. Quinlan. "I have a moral problem about what we agreed on last night," he said. "I feel I have to consult somebody else and see how he feels about it." The next day, Dr. Morse called again. "I find I will not do it," he said. "And I've informed the administrator at the hospital that I will not do it."

The Quinlans were upset and bewildered by the change in Dr. Morse. Later they talked with the hospital attorney and were told by him that, because Karen was over twenty-one, they were no longer her legal guardians. The Quinlans would have to go to court and be appointed to guardianship. After that, the hospital might or might not remove Karen from the respirator.

Mr. Quinlan consulted attorney Paul Armstrong. Because Karen was an adult without income, Mr. Quinlan explained, Medicaid was paying the $450 a day it cost to keep her alive. The Quinlans thus had no financial motive in asking that the respirator be taken away. Mr. Quinlan said that his belief that Karen should be allowed to die rested on his conviction that it was God's will, and it was for this reason that he wanted to be appointed Karen's guardian.

Legal Arguments

Mr. Armstrong filed a plea with Judge Robert Muir of the New Jersey Superior Court on September 12, 1975. He explicitly requested that Mr. Quinlan be appointed Karen's guardian so that he would have "the express power of authorizing the discontinuance of all extraordinary means of sustaining her life."

Later, on October 20, Mr. Armstrong argued the case on three constitutional grounds. First, he claimed that there is an implicit right to privacy guaranteed by the Constitution and that this right permits individuals or others acting for them to terminate the use of extraordinary medical measures, even when death may result. This right holds, Armstrong said, unless there are compelling state interests that set it aside.

Second, Armstrong argued that the First Amendment guarantee of religious freedom extended to the Quinlan case. If the court did not allow them to act in accordance with the doctrines of their church, their religious liberty would be infringed. Finally, Armstrong appealed to the "cruel and unusual punishment" clause of the Eighth Amendment. He claimed that "for the state to require that Karen Quinlan be kept alive, against her will and the will of her family, after the dignity, beauty, promise, and meaning of earthly life have vanished, is cruel and unusual punishment."

Karen's mother, sister, and a friend testified that Karen had often talked about not wanting to be kept alive by machines. An expert witness, a neurologist, testified that Karen was in a "chronic vegetative state" and that it was unlikely that she would ever regain consciousness. Doctors testifying for St. Clare's Hospital and Karen's physicians agreed with this. But, they argued, her brain still showed patterns of electrical activity, and she still had a discernible pulse.

Thus, she could not be considered dead by legal or medical criteria.

On November 10, Judge Muir ruled against Joseph Quinlan. He praised Mr. Quinlan's character and concern, but he decided that Mr. Quinlan's anguish over his daughter might cloud his judgment about her welfare, so he should not be made her guardian. Furthermore, Judge Muir said, because Karen is still medically and legally alive, "the Court should not authorize termination of the respirator. To do so would be homicide and an act of euthanasia."

Appeal

Mr. Armstrong appealed the decision to the New Jersey Supreme Court. On January 26, 1976, the court convened to hear arguments, and Mr. Armstrong argued substantially as before. But this time the court's ruling was favorable. The court agreed that Mr. Quinlan could assert a right of privacy on Karen's behalf and that whatever he decided for her should be accepted by society. It also set aside any criminal liability for removing the respirator, claiming that if death resulted, it would not be homicide, and that, even if it were homicide, it would not be unlawful. Finally, the court stated that if Karen's physicians believed that she would never emerge from her coma, they should consult an ethics committee to be established by St. Clare's Hospital. If the committee accepted their prognosis, then the respirator could be removed. If Karen's present physicians were then unwilling to take her off the respirator, Mr. Quinlan was free to find a physician who would.

Six weeks after the court decision, the respirator still had not been turned off. In fact, another machine, one for controlling body temperature, had been added. Mr. Quinlan met with Morse and Jared and demanded that they remove the respirator. They agreed to "wean" Karen from the machine, and soon she was breathing without mechanical assistance. Dr. Morse and St. Clare's Hospital were determined that Karen would not die while under their care. Although she was moved to a private room, it was next door to the intensive-care unit. They intended to put her back on the respirator at the first sign of breathing difficulty.

Because Karen was still alive, the Quinlans began a long search for a chronic-care hospital. Twenty or more institutions turned them away, and physicians expressed great reluctance to become involved in the case. Finally, Dr. Joseph Fennelly volunteered to treat Karen, and on June 9 she was moved from St. Clare's to the Morris View Nursing Home.

The End—After Ten Years

Karen Quinlan continued to breathe. She received high-nutrient feedings and regular doses of antibiotics to ward off infections. During some periods she was more active than at others, making reflexive responses to touch and sound.

On June 11, 1985, at 7:01 in the evening, ten years after she lapsed into a coma, Karen Quinlan finally died. She was thirty-one years old.

Her father died of cancer on December 10, 1996, at the Karen Quinlan Center of Hope, a hospice Joseph and Julia Quinlan had founded in 1980 with money they received from the film and book rights to their daughter's story. Joseph Quinlan continued to support the right of patients and their families to discontinue the use of life-sustaining technologies, but he opposed all forms of physician-assisted suicide.

SOCIAL CONTEXT

When the Diagnosis Is Death

Unlike our computers, our bodies aren't equipped with a tiny light that stops glowing when they stop functioning. Thus, no society has ever been quite sure when to declare someone dead. Some cultures in the Middle East don't consider people dead until three days after their hearts stop beating.

Parents are often faced with a terrible situation in which, in outward appearance, their child is still alive. Their son's blood is circulating, his temperature is normal, and his chest moves in and out. Yet what they are seeing is an illusion of life created by drugs and machines. Fifty years earlier, the parents wouldn't have had to deal with the emotional and conceptual challenge of accepting the fact that their son is dead and that stopping his treatment is the right thing to do.

Death as a Practical Matter

"When is someone dead?" didn't become a practical question until the rise of intensive-care medicine in the 1950s and the increasing success of organ transplantation in the 1970s. People began to ask, "If a physician switches off the ventilator that is keeping a patient's body supplied with oxygen, is this homicide?" and "If a surgeon removes the heart from a breathing patient, has she killed him?"

These questions became more than academic exercises for a few surgeons who were arrested and charged with homicide, and finding answers became more urgent for personal and practical reasons. If surgeons couldn't remove organs from a body with a beating heart without fearing a trial and a prison sentence, they would no longer perform transplants.

Discussions during the 1970s and 1980s about determining criteria for death led to the development of four basic ideas about what it means to be dead:

1. *Cardiopulmonary.* A person is dead when her heart stops beating and she is no longer breathing. This is the traditional definition of death as "the permanent cessation of breathing and blood circulation." It is akin to what people have in mind when they say, "He died twice while they were operating on him."

2. *Whole Brain.* Death is "the irreversible cessation of all brain functions." A person is dead when his brain displays no organized electrical activity and even the brain stem, which controls basic functions such as breathing and blood pressure, is electrically silent.

3. *Higher Brain.* Death is the permanent loss of consciousness. An individual in an irreversible coma is dead, even though her brain stem continues to regulate her heartbeat and blood pressure.

4. *Personhood.* Death occurs when someone ceases to be a person. Relevant to deciding whether this has happened is information about the absence of mental activities such as reasoning, remembering, experiencing an emotion, anticipating the future, and interacting with others.

These ideas remain the definitions at the focus of current debates.

Death as a Diagnosis

The definition of death in the 1985 federal Universal Determination of Death Act is a straightforward endorsement of the first two concepts:

An individual who has sustained either (1) irreversible cessation of circulatory and respiratory functions or (2) irreversible cessation of all functions of the entire brain, including the brain stem, is dead.

This definition is embodied in the laws of all fifty states, but that we accept both concepts can be confusing. Many people don't see how someone whose body is still working can be declared dead. But many others don't see how someone can be declared dead unless a doctor tests him to make sure that he is brain dead. The key to eliminating such confusions is recognizing that death is a diagnosis governed by two sets of criteria. In some circumstances, cardiopulmonary criteria are appropriate, while in others, brain death criteria are. Neither set trumps the other.

Diagnosis

A physician makes a diagnosis by confirming the hypothesis that the patient's disorder best fits into a particular category. Thus, a five-year-old girl who has a fever, light sensitivity, and a red, pustular rash has chicken pox. Symptoms and signs define the "chicken pox" category, and the data about the little girl confirm the hypothesis that these criteria are met. The same is so when "death" is the diagnostic category.

Cardiopulmonary

The cardiopulmonary criteria dictate that a patient is dead when his circulatory and respiratory functions have irreversibly ceased. To determine whether the data support this hypothesis, the physician examines the patient. She may feel for a pulse in the carotid or femoral artery and use a stethoscope to listen for heart and lung sounds. She may use an ophthalmoscope to see if the blood in the vessels in the retinas has broken into the stagnant segments which indicate that the blood isn't circulating. (This criterion is called the *boxcars sign*.) She may also perform an electrocardiogram to determine whether the heart is displaying any electrical activity. Using such data, the physician may conclude that the cardiopulmonary criteria are satisfied. That is, death is her diagnostic conclusion.

Whole Brain

The diagnosis of death by means of whole-brain criteria follows similar diagnostic logic, but two restrictions govern the use of such criteria. First, they don't apply to encephalic infants or children under two. Encephalic infants are born without brain hemispheres, and because they lack even the potential for consciousness, it makes no sense to test for its loss. Also, young children develop at such different rates neurologically that clinical and imaging tests can't be used to make reliable predictions. For these groups, only cardiopulmonary criteria are appropriate for determining death.

Second, before a physician pronounces someone in a coma dead, he must rule out reversible causes. He must establish that drugs, an internal chemical imbalance (as in diabetes), or hypothermia isn't the cause of the coma. Patients with these conditions may show clinical signs of death, yet recover consciousness. For example, fugu—puffer-fish liver—is a delicacy in Japan, but if a diner eats too much, its poison (a tetrodotoxin) may induce a state in which his pulse and respiration are so slow that they are difficult to detect. Some people have come awake to find themselves naked, cold, and shivering in the morgue. (It seems likely that others didn't come awake at the right time.) Thus, it's crucial for the examining physician to be sure that a patient hasn't consumed something that might cause a reversible coma.

Once these preliminary conditions are met, the physician examines the patient to determine whether her brain stem has suffered irreversible damage. She is removed briefly from a ventilator, at least once and often twice, to see if an increase in carbon dioxide in her blood will trigger her body to breathe. If it doesn't, then damage to the brain stem is indicated.

The physician tests other reflexes controlled by the brain stem. He strokes the back of the patient's throat to check her gag reflex, shines a light in her eyes to see if her pupils contract, touches her eyeball to test for a blink response, and sticks her with a needle to look for a pain response. He may turn her head to the side to see if her eyes move with it—the *"doll's eyes" sign.*

Clinical observations like these are the prime data used to determine death. Often, however, an MRI or a CT scan is obtained to look for the amount and location of the brain damage, and an electroencephalogram (EEG) is employed to confirm the clinical judgment that the patient's brain has undergone irreversible structural damage. (The brain probably will show some electrical activity, because isolated groups of cells remain active, but there must be no pattern of organized activity.) These tests are most likely to be used when a patient is young or was not expected to die from his injury or disease. The physician relies on the data they produce to decide whether they support the hypothesis that the patient's brain has suffered an irreversible loss of all functions. If so, death is the diagnosis.

Success

The cardiopulmonary criteria in the Uniform Determination of Death Act are traditional, but the brain-death criteria are modeled on those in the 1968 report of the Harvard Medical School's Ad Hoc Committee to Examine the Definition of Brain Death. The Committee was explicit about why a definition was needed: "Our primary purpose," the report stated, "is to define irreversible coma as a new criterion for death," because the cardiopulmonary criteria "can lead to controversy in obtaining organs for transplantation." Also, the Committee wanted to avoid wasting resources on patients who are unable to benefit from life-support measures and to spare their families the financial and emotional costs of supporting them.

More than ninety-nine percent of the people who die in hospitals are pronounced dead by traditional cardiopulmonary criteria. Those declared dead by brain-death criteria are always patients receiving intensive care. Once they are declared dead, they are taken off life support or, with the consent of their families, their organs are removed for transplantation.

The Harvard Committee was successful in both its aims. The concept of brain death freed many families from the doubt and guilt involved in deciding to remove someone from intensive care. The concept also improved the success rate of transplants by allowing surgeons to use undamaged organs from bodies kept functioning by intensive measures.

Higher Brain Function and PVS

Some would like to see society adopt the third concept and define death as the "irreversible loss of *higher* brain function." This would expand the criteria for determining death to include those in a persistent vegetative state (PVS).

Those diagnosed with PVS have damaged cerebral hemispheres, and this results in their not being aware of themselves or their surroundings. They are incapable of thinking or intentional movement, but if their brain stems are undamaged, their autonomic nervous system continues to control their reflexes.

Thus, PVS patients can breathe and excrete, their hearts beat, their muscles respond to stimuli, and they cycle through regular sleep–wake patterns. Although their eyelids may blink and their eyes move, they lack the brain capacity needed to see. They are like digital cameras with a functioning optical system but no microprocessor: information is supplied, but can't be used. Some PVS patients may smile or produce tears that run down their cheeks, but these are reflexes that are only accidentally connected with what's happening around them.

After six months to a year, PVS patients are not likely to recover even the most rudimentary form of consciousness. They aren't like patients diagnosed as "minimally conscious," who have some episodes of awareness and a small, yet real, possibility of waking up. PVS patients remain vegetative for as long as they live, which may be for decades. Karen Quinlan lived for almost ten years, and Nancy Cruzan was allowed to die after seven. Terri Schiavo slipped into a coma in 1990 and died in 2005, only after a protracted legal battle by her parents to keep her husband from ordering her removed from life support. (See the Case Presentation "Terri Schiavo," in this chapter.)

PVS patients require total care. They must be fed through a surgically implanted gastric tube, hydrated with IV fluids, bathed and toileted, kept on special mattresses and turned to avoid pressure sores, given antibiotics to prevent infections, and provided with around-the-clock nursing care.

If the "irreversible loss of higher brain function" were accepted as the third legal definition of death, PVS patients could be declared dead and no longer given life-support measures, including gastric feeding and IV hydration. Such acceptance wouldn't require a court decision or even a request from the family.

Adopting this criterion would mean that as many as fifty thousand PVS patients in the United States could be removed from life support. (No one is sure of the exact number of PVS patients.) This would result in immense savings, because it costs about one hundred thousand dollars a year to provide care for a PVS patient. The money, proponents of adopting the criterion argue, could be better spent on extending the lives of those who are conscious and play a role in the lives of their family and society.

Unlikely

The whole-brain definition of death was accepted in our society with little fuss. To most people, it made intuitive sense that someone whose brain isn't functioning at all and will never function again can't be alive. The criterion also seemed cut and dried: the EEG shows that the brain is electrically silent.

The higher brain definition is unlikely ever to be accepted. It lacks the precision and certainty that makes the whole-brain definition uncontroversial. Given the same data from brain scans and clinical tests, doctors can disagree about when higher brain functions have been permanently lost. Studies show further that PVS is frequently misdiagnosed, so many patients who are capable of recovery might fall victim to a bad diagnosis.

Also, the families of some PVS patients believe that, no matter how long the odds, the patient may eventually wake up from the coma. The thinking of these families is also probably representative of that of a large part of the population, even those who know no one with PVS.

Loss of Personhood

The definition of death as the loss of personhood has a resonance with most people. We understand what a friend means when she says her mother's progressive dementia has so destroyed her as a person that she might as well be dead.

We see how a woman with a degenerative neurological disorder like Alzheimer's or Huntington's may reach a later stage in which she has lost so much cognitive and emotional functioning that she may no longer be thought of as a person. If we could agree that she has lost whatever is essential to being a person, then, given the "loss of personhood" definition of death, it would be morally permissible for us to withdraw life support.

Understandable or not, the definition isn't likely to gain the support it would need to be adopted as a legal criterion. Exactly what attributes are required to qualify as a person is open to dispute, and we're unlikely to get general agreement on exactly when someone has lost so many of them that she has lost her personhood. Diagnosing death might thus come to be seen as arbitrary. Worse, critics charge, it could open the road to abuse: the old, the poor, and the poorly functioning might stop measuring up to personhood and not be given needed support.

A large number of people will always believe that an individual they care about, no matter how mentally and physically impaired, is the same person as before. Looking like a person and having a history as a person are seen by many as sufficient for being a person. This attitude is not likely to change.

Circle Completed

We end where we began: death can be defined as the permanent failure of heartbeat and respiration or as the permanent failure of the whole brain. These definitions, it is widely agreed, have served us well. That they are seen as objective and precise gives them a strength that the other two definitions can't match. Leaving well enough alone seems to most observers to be our best option.

We can hope that as the concept of brain death becomes more familiar, people faced with a situation in which a loved one has been diagnosed as brain dead won't have to suffer the pain of an unrealistic hope based on doubt. Whether diagnosed by cardiopulmonary criteria or whole-brain criteria, the diagnosis is the same death.

CASE PRESENTATION

Elizabeth Bouvia's Demand to Starve: A Request for Assisted Suicide?

On September 3, 1983, Elizabeth Bouvia was admitted, at her own request, to Riverside General Hospital in Riverside, California. She sought admission on the grounds that she was suicidal. She was twenty-six years old, a victim of cerebral palsy, and almost totally paralyzed. She had the partial use of one arm, could speak, and could chew her food if someone fed it to her. In addition to her paralysis, she suffered almost constant pain from arthritis.

Despite the severity of her handicap, Mrs. Bouvia had earned a degree in social work, been married, and lived independently with the assistance of relatives and others. Then matters became particularly difficult for her. She had not been successful in an attempt to have a child, her husband left her, and she lost the state grant that paid for her special transportation needs.

After her admission, Mrs. Bouvia announced to the hospital staff that she wished to starve herself to death. She asked to be provided with hygienic care and painkilling medicines but no food. She explained that she wanted the hospital to be a place where she would "just be left alone and not bothered by friends or family or anyone else" so that she could "ultimately starve to death" and be free from her "useless body."

Mrs. Bouvia refused to eat the solid food offered to her, and her attending physician stated that if she did not eat, he would have her declared mentally ill and a danger to herself. She could then be force-fed. She responded by calling local newspapers and asking for legal assistance. The American Civil Liberties Union agreed to provide her an attorney, and Richard Stanley Scott became her legal representative.

Mr. Scott convinced her to allow herself to be fed while he made efforts to secure a court order restraining the hospital from either discharging her or force-feeding her. At the court hearing, Mrs. Bouvia testified as to her reasons for refusing nourishment:

I hate to have someone care for every personal need . . . it's humiliating. It's disgusting, and I choose to no longer do that, no longer to be dependent on someone to take care of me in that manner. . . . I am choosing this course of action due to my physical limitation and disability.

Dr. Donald E. Fisher, head of psychiatry at the hospital, testified that he would force-feed Mrs. Bouvia, even if the court ordered him not to.

On behalf of his client, Mr. Scott argued that her decision to refuse nourishment was "exactly medically and morally analogous to the patient deciding to forgo further kidney dialysis," knowingly accepting death as the consequence.

Judge John H. Hews refused to grant the restraining order. He expressed the view that Mrs. Bouvia was a competent, rational, and sincere person whose decision was based on her physical condition and not upon her recent misfortunes. Nevertheless, allowing her to starve herself to death in the hospital would "have a profound effect" on the staff, other patients, and other handicapped people. Mrs. Bouvia, Judge Hews held, was "not terminal" and might expect to live another fifteen to twenty years. Accordingly, he held that "the established ethics of the medical profession clearly outweigh and overcome her own rights of self-determination" and "force-feeding, however invasive, would be administered for the purpose of saving the life of an otherwise nonterminal patient and should be permitted. There is no other reasonable option." In effect, in Judge Hews's view, Mrs. Bouvia had a right to commit suicide but she did not have the right to have others assist her.

Mrs. Bouvia later refused to eat, and Judge Hews authorized the hospital to feed her against her will. Her attorney argued that this was an unlawful invasion of her privacy and appealed to the California Supreme Court. The court unanimously refused to grant a hearing on the appeal, thus allowing the lower court ruling to stand.

In February 1986, Mrs. Bouvia was back in court. Through her attorney, she sought an injunction to stop High Desert Hospital of Lancaster, California, where she had become a patient, from using a nasogastric tube to feed her against her wishes. In a public statement, she asserted that she had no intention to attempt to starve herself to death but wished only to receive a liquid diet. The hospital's physicians and lawyers maintained that a liquid diet would be a form of starvation and that the law precluded them from agreeing to her demand. The eventual court decision was again in favor of Mrs. Bouvia, and in April the feeding tube was removed.

Elizabeth Bouvia eventually decided that she would begin to eat. The hospital resumed feeding her, and when her health was considered stable once more, she was released. She announced at the time of her release that she had changed her mind about dying, but in 1987 she again reversed herself. She tried starving herself to death but gave up the effort when doctors told her it might take several weeks. She felt she could not endure such side effects as the constant vomiting caused by taking painkilling medications without food. "Starving myself would take too long," she said. "I wish there were a quicker way."

She moved to Los Angeles and took up residence in a small cell-like room at the L.A. County–USC Medical Center. The cost of the room, more than $800 a day, was paid for by MediCal, the California version of the Medicaid program for those unable to pay for medical care. Her father and two sisters visited her a couple of times a year, and friends visited about once a week. Mostly, though, she remained in her bed and watched TV. "The thought of being here another ten years, I just can't fathom," she told a reporter. "I would rather be dead than lie here."

No one seems to know whether Elizabeth Bouvia is still lying in bed and waiting to die. On May 11, 2008, the *Los Angeles Times* mentioned that she was still alive, and in January 2010 the same newspaper referred to her in a story about the death of a judge in one of her court cases. Alive or dead, her initial plan to starve herself to death and the decision by Judge Hews that "the established ethics of the medical profession" outweighed her right to self-determination have continued to be an important part of the background in the debate about physician-assisted suicide.

The Cruzan Case: The Supreme Court Upholds the Right to Die

In the early morning of January 11, 1983, twenty-five-year-old Nancy Cruzan was driving on a deserted county road in Missouri. The road was icy and the car skidded, then flipped over and crashed. Nancy was thrown from the driver's seat and landed face down in a ditch by the side of the road.

An ambulance arrived quickly, but not quickly enough to save her from suffering irreversible brain damage. Nancy never regained consciousness, and her physicians eventually concluded that she had entered into what is known medically as a persistent vegetative state, awake but unaware. The higher brain functions responsible for recognition, memory, comprehension, anticipation, and other cognitive functions had all been lost.

Her arms and legs were drawn into a fetal position, her knees against her chest, and her body stiff and contracted. Only loud sounds and painful stimuli evoked responses, but even those were no more than neurological reflexes.

"We've literally cried over Nancy's body, and we've never seen anything," her father, Joe Cruzan, said. "She has no awareness of herself."

Nancy was incapable of eating, but her body was sustained by a feeding tube surgically implanted in her stomach. She was a patient at the Missouri Rehabilitation Center, but no one expected her to be rehabilitated. She could only be kept alive.

"If only the ambulance had arrived five minutes earlier—or five minutes later," her father lamented.

The cost of Nancy Cruzan's care was $130,000 a year. The bill was paid by the state. Because she was a legal adult when her accident occurred, her family was not responsible for her medical care. Had she been under twenty-one, the Cruzans would have been responsible for her medical bills, as long as they had any financial resources to pay them.

Eight Years Later

In 1991, eight years after her accident, Nancy was almost thirty-three years old, and her physicians estimated that she might live another thirty years. She was like some 10,000 other Americans who are lost in the dark, dimensionless limbo lying between living and dying. Those who love them can think of them only with sadness and despair. Given a choice between lingering in this twilight world and dying, most people find it difficult to imagine anyone would choose not to die.

Hope eventually faded even for Nancy Cruzan's parents. They faced the fact she would never recover her awareness, and the time came when they wanted their daughter to die, rather than be kept alive in her hopeless condition. They asked that the feeding tube used to keep her alive be withdrawn. Officials at the Missouri Rehabilitation Center refused, and Joe and Louise Cruzan were forced to go to court.

Lower Court Decisions

During the court hearings, the family testified that Nancy would not have wanted to be kept alive in her present condition. Her sister Christy said Nancy had told her that she never wanted to be kept alive "just as a vegetable." A friend testified that Nancy had said that if she were injured or sick she wouldn't want to continue her life, unless she could live "halfway normally." Family and friends spoke in general terms of Nancy's vigor and her sense of independence.

In July 1988, Judge Charles E. Teel of the Jasper County Circuit Court ruled that artificially prolonging the life of Nancy Cruzan violated her constitutional right. He wrote, "There is a fundamental right expressed in our Constitution as 'the right to liberty,' which permits an individual to refuse or direct the withholding or withdrawal of artificial death-prolonging procedures when the person has no cognitive brain function."

Missouri Attorney General William Webster said Judge Teel's interpretation of the Missouri living-will law was much broader than the legislature intended and appealed the ruling. In November 1988, in a 4-to-3 decision, the Missouri Supreme Court overruled the decision of the lower court: Nancy Cruzan's parents would not be allowed to disconnect the feeding tube.

The court focused on the state's living-will statute. The law permits the withdrawing of artificial life-support systems in cases in which individuals are hopelessly ill or injured and there is "clear and convincing evidence" that this is what they would want done. The act specifically forbids the withholding of food and water. Judge Teel's reasoning in the lower court decision was that the surgically implanted tube was an invasive medical treatment and that the Missouri law permitted her parents, as guardians, to order it withdrawn.

The Missouri Supreme Court held that the evidence as to what Nancy Cruzan would have wanted did not meet the "clear and convincing" standard required by the law. Also, the evidence did not show that the implanted feeding tube was "heroically invasive" or "burdensome." In the circumstance, then, the state's interest in preserving life should override other considerations.

The court found "no principled legal basis" to permit the Cruzans "to choose the death of their ward." Thus, "in the face of the state's strongly stated policy in favor of life, we choose to err on the side of life, respecting the right of incompetent persons who may wish to live despite a severely diminished quality of life." William Colby, the Cruzans' attorney, appealed the ruling to the U.S. Supreme Court, and for the first time the Court agreed to hear a case involving "right to die" issues.

Supreme Court Decision

On June 25, 1990, the Supreme Court issued a landmark ruling. In a 5-to-4 decision, it rejected Colby's argument that the Court should overturn as unconstitutional the State of Missouri's stringent standard requiring "clear and convincing evidence" as to a comatose patient's wishes. The decision came as a cruel disappointment to Nancy Cruzan's parents, because it meant that they had lost their case.

Yet, for the first time in U.S. judicial history, the Court recognized a strong constitutional basis for living wills and for the designation of another person to act as a surrogate in making medical decisions on behalf of another. Unlike the decisions in *Roe v. Wade* and *Quinlan,* which found a right of privacy in the Constitution, the Court decision in *Cruzan* appealed to a Fourteenth Amendment "liberty interest." The interest involves being free to reject unwanted medical treatment. The Court found grounds for this interest in the common-law tradition, according to which, if one person even touches another without consent or legal justification, then battery is committed.

The Court regarded the latter finding as the basis for requiring that a patient give informed consent to medical treatment. The "logical corollary" of informed consent, the Court held, is that the patient also possesses the right to withhold consent. A difficulty arises, though, when a patient is in no condition to give consent. The problem becomes one of knowing what the patient's wishes would be.

Justice Rehnquist, in the majority opinion, held that the Constitution permits states to decide on the standard that must be met in determining the wishes of a comatose patient. Hence, Missouri's rigorous standard that requires "clear and convincing proof" of the wishes of the patient was allowed to stand. The Court held that it was legitimate for the state to err on the side of caution, "because an erroneous decision not to terminate treatment results in the maintenance of the status quo," while an erroneous decision to end treatment "is not susceptible of correction."

Justice William Brennan dissented strongly from this line of reasoning. He pointed out that making a mistake about a comatose patient's wishes and continuing treatment also has a serious consequence. Maintaining the status quo "robs a patient of the very qualities protected by the right to avoid unwanted medical treatment."

Justice Stevens, in another dissent, argued that the Court's focus on how much weight to give previous statements by the patient missed the point. The Court should have focused on the issue of the best interest of the patient. Otherwise, the only people eligible to exercise their constitutional right to be free of unwanted medical treatment are those "who had the foresight to make an unambiguous statement of their wishes while competent."

One of the more significant aspects of the decision was that the Court made no distinction between providing nutrition and hydration and other forms of medical treatment. One argument on behalf of the state was that providing food and water was not medical treatment. However, briefs filed by medical associations made it clear that determining the formula required by a person in Nancy Cruzan's condition and regulating her feeding are medically complex procedures. The situation is more comparable to determining the contents of an intravenous drip than to giving someone food and water.

The Missouri living-will statute explicitly forbids the withdrawal of food and water. However, the law was not directly at issue in the *Cruzan* case, because Nancy Cruzan's accident occurred before the law was passed. The Court's treatment of nutrition and hydration as just another form of medical treatment has since served as a basis for challenging the constitutionality of the Missouri law, as well as laws in other states containing a similar provision.

The Supreme Court decision placed much emphasis on the wishes of the individual in accepting or reject-ing medical treatment. In doing so, it underscored the importance of the living will as a way of indicating our wishes if something should happen to render us inca-pable of making them known directly. In some states, though, living wills have a legal force only when the individual has a terminal illness (Nancy Cruzan did not) or when the individual has been quite specific about what treatments are unwanted. Because of such limita-tions, some legal observers recommend that individuals sign a durable power of attorney designating someone to make medical decisions for them if they become legally incompetent.

The Court decision left undecided the question of the constitutionality of assisted suicide. Some state courts have held that, although individuals have a right to die, they do not have a right to the assistance of others in killing themselves. While more than twenty states have passed laws against assisted suicide, only Oregon has made it legal for physicians to prescribe drugs to help patients end their lives.

A Final Court Ruling

What of Nancy Cruzan? The State of Missouri withdrew from the case, and both the family's attorney and the state-appointed guardian filed separate briefs with the Jasper County Circuit Court asking that the implanted feeding tube be removed. A hearing was held to consider both her medical condition and evidence from family and friends about what Nancy Cruzan would wish to be done. On December 14, 1990, Judge Charles Teel ruled that there was evidence to show that her intent, "if mentally able, would be to terminate her nutrition and hydration," and he authorized the request to remove the feeding tube.

Even after the tube was removed, controversy did not end. About twenty-five protesters tried to force their way into Nancy Cruzan's hospital room to reconnect the feeding tube. "The best we can do is not cooperate with anyone trying to starve an innocent person to death," one of the protest leaders said.

Twelve days after the tube was removed, on December 26, 1990, Nancy Cruzan died. Her parents, sisters, and grandparents were at her bedside. Almost eight years had passed since the accident that destroyed her brain and made the remainder of her life a matter of debate.

"We all feel good that Nancy is free at last," her father said at her graveside.

The *Cruzan* decision, by acknowledging a "right to die" and by finding a basis for it in the Constitution, pro-vides states with new opportunities to resolve the issues surrounding the thousands of cases as tragic as Nancy Cruzan's.

CASE PRESENTATION
Terri Schiavo

Michael Schiavo claimed that around four in the morning on February 26, 1990, he was awakened by a dull thud. Startled, he jumped out of bed, and it was then that he discovered his wife Terri sprawled on the floor. Michael knelt down and spoke to her, but she was obviously unconscious. He called 911, but by the time the paramedics arrived and resuscitated Terri, she had suffered damage from which she would never recover.

Teresa Marie Schindler was born on December 31, 1963, in Huntingdon Valley, Pennsylvania. Although over-weight during her childhood, she lost fifty pounds in her senior year in high school, and most of the rest of her life she struggled to keep her weight down. She and Michael Schiavo met when she was in her second semester at Bucks County Community College. They married in 1984 and soon moved to St. Petersburg, Florida. Michael worked as a restaurant manager, and Terri got a job as a clerk with an insurance company. Terri's parents, Robert and Mary Schindler, also moved to Florida to be near their daughter and son-in-law. Relations between the parents and the young couple were friendly.

After Terri collapsed at home, she was rushed to the nearest hospital and treated for an apparent heart attack. A blood assay done at the hospital showed that she was suffering from a potassium imbalance, and her doctors thought that this had probably triggered the heart attack. The potassium imbalance, some physicians later suggested, might have been the result of bulimia, the eating disorder that had troubled her life since high school. The cycle of overeating, purging, and dieting characteristic of the disorder can produce a change in the electrolytes in the blood. Because this change disrupts the electrical signals controlling the heart, it may produce cardiac arrest. Terri had continued to work at losing weight in Florida, and at the time of her collapse she weighed only 120 pounds.

Diagnosis

Whatever the reason for Terri's collapse, she failed to re-gain consciousness. Once she was out of immediate danger, the hospital neurologists performed a series of tests and examinations: Did she respond to a simple command like "Squeeze my hand"? Did her eyes track moving objects? Did her pupils respond to light? Did she show any sign of recognizing Michael or her parents? The answers to these questions were always no.

Terri's neurological responses were distinctly abnormal, and she showed no signs of cognitive functioning. In addition, CT scans of her brain revealed that the disruption of the oxygen supply to her brain caused by the cardiac arrest had damaged the cerebral cortex. The more primitive parts of her brain were undamaged, but the parts responsible for even the most basic forms of thinking and self-awareness had been destroyed.

The neurologists, after reviewing all the evidence, reached the conclusion that Terri Schiavo had suffered damage to her brain that was both severe and irreversible. She was diagnosed as being in a persistent vegetative state.

Persistent Vegetative State

Persistent vegetative state (PVS) is a specific diagnosis, not to be confused with brain death. People diagnosed with PVS have damaged or dysfunctional cerebral

hemispheres, and this results in their not being aware of themselves or their surroundings. They are incapable of thinking and of deliberate or intentional movement. When the brain stem is undamaged, as it was in Terri's case, the autonomic nervous system and a range of bodily reflexes remain intact. (See the Social Context "When the Diagnosis Is Death," in this chapter.)

PVS patients are still able to breathe and excrete; their hearts beat, and their muscles behave reflexively. The patients cycle through regular sleep–wake patterns, but although their eyelids may blink and their eyes move, they lack the brain capacity to see. (They resemble a digital camera with a functioning optical system but no microprocessor—information is supplied, but it can't be used.) Some PVS patients may smile or tears may run down their cheeks, but these events are reflexive and thus are connected with circumstances in which smiling or crying would be appropriate only in an accidental way.

If a patient's brain is injured but not substantially destroyed, the patient may remain in a vegetative state for only a short time. Such a recovery is unusual, however. After a vegetative state lasts four weeks, neurologists consider it *persistent.* In most cases of PVS, if a change for the better has not occurred after three months, it's not likely to occur at all. When PVS lasts for six months, only about half of those with the diagnosis ever acquire any sort of interactive consciousness. Even then, it is only interactive consciousness of the "Squeeze my hand" variety. Such higher functions as talking or answering questions do not occur. (A study by Cambridge University scientists in September 2006 showed that MRI images might be used to make more reliable diagnoses. The study obtained images of conscious people asked to imagine walking around a room in their house or watching a tennis match, then compared them with the images of a brain of a patient who was given the same instructions. The same areas of the patient's brain lighted up. This suggested that her brain was responding to the command, but whether she was having any subjective experience can't be known. Nor is it clear whether the patient or others like her are likely to recover any interactive abilities.)

After six months, PVS patients virtually never recover even the most rudimentary form of consciousness. They remain vegetative as long as they live, which may be for decades. (Karen Quinlan lived almost ten years after lapsing into unconsciousness: see the Case Presentation

"Karen Quinlan: The Debate Begins," in this chapter.) PVS patients require complete care, including feeding through a gastric tube surgically implanted in the stomach and hydration through an IV line, for the remainder of their lives. Because they are prone to infections, they must be carefully monitored and given IV antibiotics prophylactically. They must be kept on special mattresses and moved regularly to prevent the development of bedsores, ulcers caused by the breakdown of the skin and underlying tissue from the constant pressure of the body's weight on the same area.

Neither Brain Dead nor Minimally Conscious

PVS patients have no higher level brain functioning, but they are not brain dead. To be considered brain dead, a patient must be diagnosed as lacking in any detectable brain activity. This means that even the brain stem (which keeps the heart beating and the lungs functioning) must show no functional or electrical activity.

PVS patients are also not in a *minimally conscious state*. Those who fit into this diagnostic category show at least some episodes of awareness. Their eyes may track movement from time to time, though not always. They may respond to commands like "Squeeze my hand for yes" by squeezing for no.

Neurologists consider this category an appropriate diagnosis when the available evidence supports the idea that the patient displays some glimmer of consciousness at least some of the time. Brain scans of minimally conscious patients, for example, show that their language areas respond when a loved one speaks to them. PVS patients display none of these characteristics. Also, minimally conscious patients have a much higher expectation of recovering more consciousness than do PVS patients. Even so, the expectation of any recovery is low, and if any recovery does occur, it is likely to be only slight.

Michael as Guardian

Michael Schiavo, as Terri's husband, became her legal guardian as soon as she was diagnosed as mentally incompetent. In 1992, he sued his wife's gynecologists for malpractice to get the money to pay for her private care. The theory behind the suit was that they had failed to detect the potassium imbalance that led to her heart

attack, which, in turn, led to the loss of oxygen that caused her brain damage. (After Terri Schiavo died, an autopsy showed no evidence that she had suffered a heart attack.) Michael won the suit. He was awarded $750,000 earmarked for Terri's extended care and another $300,000 to compensate him for his loss and suffering.

In 1993, a year later, Michael and his wife's parents, Robert and Mary Schindler, had a disagreement over the care Terri was receiving. Michael later claimed that the disagreement was really over money and that the Schindlers wanted to force him to give them a share of his $300,000 malpractice award. They filed a suit asking the court to remove Michael as Terri's guardian and appoint them in his place. The court found no reason to hold that the care Michael was providing Terri was inadequate, and the suit against him was dismissed.

Treatment Decisions: The Legal Battles

The course of events involving the struggle over the fate of Terri Schiavo became intricate and confusing after the falling-out between Michael and the Schindlers. The clearest way to follow the dispute is to consider the events in chronological order.

1994. Four years after Terri's PVS diagnosis, Michael met with the doctors taking care of her to ask about the likelihood of her ever regaining consciousness. He learned from them that this was unlikely ever to happen. Michael then told the long-term care facility where she was a patient that he didn't want her to be resuscitated if she suffered a heart attack or if some other life-threatening event occurred. (This is known as a "do not resuscitate," or DNR, order.)

Relations between Michael and the Schindlers continued to deteriorate, particularly after Michael and his girlfriend Jodi Centonze had two children together. (The Schindlers had originally encouraged Michael to move on with his life, and he started a relationship with Centonze only after Terri had been in a nursing home for four years.) Supporters of the Schindlers denounced Michael as an adulterer who was not fit to act as Terri's guardian.

1998–2003. Four years after Michael had authorized the DNR order and eight years after Terri was diagnosed as being in a PVS, Michael, in his role as Terri's guardian, filed a petition asking Florida's Pinellas–Pasco Circuit Court to authorize him to order the removal of her gastric tube and allow her to die. Michael argued that, even though Terri had left no written instructions, several times she had expressed to him the view that she would not want to be kept alive in her present condition. Robert and Mary Schindler opposed Michael's petition, claiming that Terri was capable of recovering consciousness.

The court found in favor of Michael, but between 1998 and 2003 the Schindlers continued to engage in legal maneuvers to block Michael's efforts to allow Terri to die. They filed civil suits against him, as well as accusations of abuse. They sought support from prolife groups and members of the religious right, urging them to appeal to elected officials for help in keeping Terri alive. In violation of a court order, they showed a videotape of Terri that convinced many viewers that she had some cognitive function.

When Terri's feeding tube was removed under court order on October, 15, 2003, the Florida state legislature quickly passed "Terri's Law" allowing the governor to order the tube replaced. Governor Jeb Bush signed the order, and President George Bush made a public statement praising the action.

Religious conservatives claimed that Terri's Law was the result of their prayer vigils, broadcasts on Christian radio, and thousands of email messages to Florida legislators. Some saw the result as a model for an approach they might take to get laws passed in other states to forbid removing feeding tubes, to allow prayer in school, and to post the Ten Commandments in courts and other public places. Terri's Law, some said, was a victory for conservatives nationally, for it showed that it was possible to use legislation to take away much of the power of the courts.

Vigils and demonstrations continued around Woodside Hospice, where Terri was a patient. Fundamentalist religious conservatives, both Catholic and Protestant, vied for media attention. Most had special agendas, some connected with promoting religious values, others with promoting disability rights. Still others seemed to focus only on Terri and the prospect of her death. Very few counterdemonstrators appeared in what was often a hostile, angry environment. Michael Schiavo was compared to Hitler and called a murderer.

Starting in 2001, the Schindlers began to file accusations of abuse against Michael. From 2001 to 2004, they made nine accusations that included neglect of hygiene, denial of dental care, poisoning, and physical harm. All were investigated by the Florida Department of Children and Families. (Agency reports released in 2005 concluded that there were no indications of any harm, abuse, or neglect.) The Schindlers continued to make clear their opinion that Terri's condition was not the result of a heart attack. In their view, Michael tried to strangle her but failed to kill her. They offered no evidence for this view, other than their speculation that Michael eventually established a relationship with another woman.

2005. When Terri's Law was ruled unconstitutional by a state court, the Florida attorney general appealed the case to the Florida Supreme Court, which upheld the lower court ruling. When the Schindlers appealed the decision to the U.S. Supreme Court, the case was again refused. On March 18, 2005, the Florida Circuit Court once more ordered the gastric tube removed.

Various members of the U.S. Congress were approached by a number of members of the religious right and asked to intervene in the Florida case. Speaker of the House Tom DeLay, a Texas Republican, said that the removal of Terri's feeding tube would be "an act of medical terrorism." One of the Schindlers' spiritual advisors said, "We pray that this modern-day crucifixion will not happen."

March 16. Congress initiated a debate over what could be done to allow the Schindlers to prevent Terri's feeding tube from being removed. The White House indicated that if Congress passed such a bill, the president would sign it.

March 18. While the debate was proceeding, Terri's feeding tube was removed, for the third time, in accordance with Judge Greer's order. The Schindlers visited Terri in the hospice afterward. They were accompanied by one of their spiritual advisors, Father Malinowski, who later said he had taken a scrap from a robe worn by Mother Teresa and touched Terri's throat, forehead, and cheek with it.

March 21. The House and Senate passed a bill that allowed the Schindlers' case against removing Terri's feeding tube to be heard in a federal court. They were thus given another opportunity to achieve what they had failed to accomplish in the state courts. "Every hour is incredibly important to Terri Schiavo," said House Majority Leader DeLay.

Senator Bill Frist, Republican of Tennessee, the Senate majority leader, said that Congress had to act on the bill because "These are extraordinary circumstances that center on the most fundamental of human values and virtues: the sanctity of human life." Frist, a transplant surgeon as well as a senator, had earlier claimed to be able to tell from the videotape of Terri that she was not in a persistent vegetative state. He received much criticism from the medical community for making a diagnosis without examining the patient or the medical records.

A number of legislators denounced the legislation. Representative Christopher Shays of Connecticut, one of four Republicans in the House to vote against it, objected that "this Republican party of Lincoln has become a party of theocracy."

President Bush signed the bill into law at his ranch in Texas around one in the morning. The next day, at a public appearance in Tucson, he praised Congress for "voting to give Terri's parents another chance to save their daughter's life." The statement was met with a roar of approval from the crowd of Republican supporters.

March 23–26. The bill passed by Congress and signed into law permitted the Schindlers to file a sequence of petitions and appeals in the federal courts. On Wednesday, March 23, they filed an emergency request with the U.S. Supreme Court to replace Terri's feeding tube. Republican leaders of the House and the Senate filed briefs in support of the Schindlers. The brief signed by Senator Frist argued that "the Court cannot permit Mrs. Schiavo to die" before the claims of her parents are reviewed by federal courts. But on Thursday, March 24, the Supreme Court rejected the Schindlers' petition.

In Florida, Governor Bush suggested on Wednesday, March 23, that he might send state agents to forcibly replace Terri's gastric tube. Judge Greer issued an emergency order barring the state from "taking possession of Theresa Marie Schiavo."

On Thursday, March 24, Governor Bush appealed the ruling. In court documents, he charged that Terri's medical condition might be due to abuse by her husband and filed an affidavit by a neurologist claiming that she had been misdiagnosed as being in a persistent vegetative state. The Schindlers also filed a petition on the same grounds.

The court-appointed neurologist who examined Terri rejected the possibility of a misdiagnosis. Judge Greer then turned down the petitions of both Governor Bush and the Schindlers. On the same day, a higher state court and the Florida Supreme Court also rejected appeals of the rulings.

A federal 11th Circuit Court of Appeal panel in Atlanta refused to reconsider the case. Further, Chief Judge J. L. Edmundson, a conservative Republican, wrote that federal courts had no jurisdiction in the case and that the law enacted by Congress and signed by President Bush allowing the Schindlers to seek a federal court review was unconstitutional. "If sacrifices to the independence of the judiciary are permitted today," Judge Edmundson wrote, "precedent is established for the constitutional transgressions of tomorrow." Having been turned down by the Appeals Court, the Schindlers made another emergency appeal to the U.S. Supreme Court. For the fifth time, however, the Supreme Court refused to intervene in the case. The Schindlers had reached the end of the legal line.

March 27–30. Reporter Rick Lyman described the mood of the protesters who maintained their post across the street from Woodside Hospice as one that was more somber and subdued than it had been earlier. Not Dead Yet, a disability rights organization that focuses on end-of-life issues, blocked the driveway leading to the hospice. A member of the group said that it hoped to make society change its view that a life with a severe disability is not worth living. One man at the scene blew a ram's horn from time to time, another chanted, and a young woman prayed into her cupped hands, then released the prayer toward the hospice.

Signs expressed in shorthand the views that protesters had often spelled out in interviews and speeches: *Hey, Judge. Who Made You God? Murder Is Legal in America, Hospice or Auschwitz?* Even Governor Bush wasn't immune from criticism, because he had said there was nothing else he could do within the law: *Where's Jeb?* Some protestors became angry, shouting "Nazi!" and "Murder!" but the Schindlers made it known that they wanted the crowd to remain calm.

Several protesters tried to carry cups of water into the hospice to give to Terri, but they were turned back by the police. Because Terri was unable to swallow, the attempts were symbolic. Some protesters continued to hold prayer vigils.

The End

On the morning of Thursday, March 31, 2005, just after nine o'clock, Terri Schiavo died at Woodside Hospice. Michael was at her bedside and cradled her head as life slipped away and she stopped breathing. At Michael's request, neither her parents nor her brother or sister was present, although all of them had paid her a last visit at the hospice. Thirteen days had passed since Terri's feeding tube had been withdrawn. The end came, as is typical in such cases, as a result of dehydration.

The acrimony toward Michael by the Schindlers and their supporters did not end with Terri's death. "After these recent years of neglect at the hands of those who were supposed to care for her, she is finally at peace with God for eternity," Terri's sister, Suzzane Vitadamo, said in a public statement. "His [Michael's] heartless cruelty continued until the very last moment," said a priest who had sided with the Schindlers.

Michael Schiavo neither appeared in public nor made any statement. His lawyer, speaking on his behalf, said that "Mr. Schiavo's overriding concern here was to provide for Terri a peaceful death with dignity. This death was not for the siblings and not for the spouse and not for the parents. This was for Terri."

Autopsy

Three months after Terri Schiavo's death, on June 15, 2005, the results of the extensive autopsy that was performed on her body were made public. The results revealed that her brain had shrunk to less than half its normal weight due to the destruction caused by a loss of oxygen ("anoxic-ischemic encephalopathy"). No treatment nor the passage of time could ever have restored Terri to even the lowest level of awareness or motor control. Her brain had shriveled and forever lost those capacities. The autopsy showed that the original diagnosis of persistent vegetative state had been correct.

The autopsy failed to find any signs of trauma or strangulation, undercutting the assertion by the Schindlers that Michael had abused Terri and thus was responsible for her condition. Also, no evidence was found suggesting that she had been neglected or received inadequate or inappropriate care.

What the autopsy could not establish, however, was the cause of the cardiac arrest that resulted in the oxygen deprivation that caused Terri's brain damage. "No one observed her taking diet pills, binging and purging or consuming laxatives," the autopsy report observes, "and she apparently never confessed to her family or friends about having an eating disorder." What is more, says the report, her potassium level was measured only after she had been treated with a number of drugs known to lower potassium in the blood, and this makes suspect the main piece of evidence supporting the idea that she suffered from bulimia. Thus, the evidence that Terri suffered "a severe anoxic brain injury" is certain, but what caused it is not. "The manner of death will therefore be certified as undetermined," the report concludes.

The Battles Continue

Incredibly, the conflict over Terri Schiavo did not end with her death. The Schindlers attempted to have independent experts witness the autopsy, but the Pinellas County Medical Examiner refused their request. Videotapes, photographs, and tissue samples from the autopsy were made available by the agency's office, however.

The Schindlers also petitioned a court for the right to determine the disposition of their daughter's body. They said that they wanted her to be buried in Pinellas County so that they could visit her grave. The court rejected the petition, holding that Michael Schiavo had the right to make such decisions.

Terri Schiavo's body was cremated on April 1, 2005. Michael's lawyer announced that Michael's plan was to bury Terri's ashes in Huntingdon Valley, Pennsylvania, where she had grown up and where they had met so many years earlier. In January 2006, Michael married Jodi Centonze, the woman he had met in 1994, four years after Terri had been placed in a nursing home. The newly married couple and their two children continued to live in Florida.

Jack Kevorkian: Moral Leader or Doctor Death?

On August 5, 1993, Thomas W. Hyde, Jr., a thirty-year-old Michigan construction worker with a wife and a two-year-old daughter, was taken inside a battered white 1968 Volkswagen bus parked behind the apartment building in the Detroit suburb of Royal Oak, where sixty-five-year-old retired pathologist Dr. Jack Kevorkian lived.

Dr. Kevorkian fitted a respiratory mask over Hyde's face and connected the plastic tubing leading from the mask to a short cylinder of carbon monoxide gas. Dr. Kevorkian placed a string in Hyde's hand. At the opposite end of the string was a paper clip crimping the plastic tubing and shutting off the flow of gas. Hyde jerked on the string, pulled loose the paper clip, then breathed in the carbon monoxide flowing into the mask. Twenty minutes later, he was dead.

Mr. Hyde suffered from amyotrophic lateral sclerosis (Lou Gehrig's disease), a degenerative and progressive neurological disorder. He was paralyzed, unable even to swallow, and, without suctioning, he would have choked to death on his own saliva. He reported that he was in great pain, and like hundreds before him, he approached Dr. Kevorkian to help him end his life.

In a videotape made on July 1, 1993, Mr. Hyde said to Dr. Kevorkian, "I want to end this. I want to die." Dr. Kevorkian agreed to help, and Mr. Hyde became the twentieth person since 1990 whom Dr. Kevorkian had assisted in committing suicide.

Trial

After the death of Thomas Hyde, Dr. Kevorkian was arrested and charged with violating the 1992 Michigan law that had been enacted specifically to stop his activities. The law applies to anyone who knows that another person intends to commit suicide and who either "provides the physical means" or "participates in a physical act" by which the suicide is carried out. However, the law explicitly excludes those administering medications or procedures that may cause death "if the intent is to relieve pain or discomfort."

On May 2, 1994, a jury found Dr. Kevorkian innocent of the charge of assisting suicide. As one juror said, "He

convinced us he was not a murderer, that he was really trying to help people out." According to another, Dr. Kevorkian had acted to relieve Mr. Hyde's pain, and that is allowed by the law.

Several jurors expressed skepticism and resentment at the attempt to legislate behavior falling within such a private sphere. "I don't feel it's our obligation to choose for someone else how much pain and suffering they can go through," one said. "That's between them and their God."

After the decision, Dr. Kevorkian reiterated his position that people have a right to decide when to end their lives. He acted, he said, to protect that right. "I want that option as I get older, and I want it unencumbered, unintimidated, free with my medical colleagues," he said. "So I did it for myself, too, just as any competent adult would want to do."

Kevorkian always insisted that he practiced physician-assisted suicide only in accordance with stringent safeguards. "You act only after it is absolutely justifiable," he said. "The patient must be mentally competent, the disease incurable." He maintained that other physicians should determine that a candidate for assisted suicide was incurable and that a psychiatrist assess the patient's mental state and determine that he or she was competent. In practice, Kevorkian did not proceed in this fashion, because other physicians refused to cooperate with him.

Critics. Critics charged that without the safeguard of a psychiatric evaluation, patients who sought out Kevorkian to help them kill themselves were likely to be suffering from depression. Hence, they couldn't be regarded as having made an informed, rational decision to end their lives.

Other critics worried that if physicians are allowed to play a role in terminating the lives of patients, that role could expand. Physicians might begin by assisting those who ask their help, but then move on to making their own decisions about who should live. Or they might even be recruited to carry out a government policy identifying those who should be "assisted" in dying. The potential for abuse is so serious that physicians should not be associated in any way with procedures intended to end the lives of patients.

Finally, some critics, though disagreeing with Kevorkian, believed he had successfully pointed out a major flaw in the health care system: the medical profession is so committed to preserving life that it has not developed ways of dealing with death in cases in which it is inevitable. Rather than help people kill themselves, critics said, physicians ought to surrender the idea of treatment and concentrate on making those with terminal illnesses pain free so that they can spend their remaining time receiving the comfort of their families and friends.

It was in keeping with such an aim that hospitals and other institutions set up hospices to provide nursing care and support for the dying. Even after decades, however, hospices remain at the margins of the medical establishment, and physicians associated with them are given little respect by their colleagues.

A Charge of Murder. In 1998, the Michigan Department of Consumer and Industry Services, the state agency responsible for licensing physicians, charged that Jack Kevorkian was practicing medicine without a license by assisting forty-two people in committing suicide. (Kevorkian said that he had assisted about 120 people.)

Although the agency had issued a cease-and-desist order, Kevorkian continued to help terminally ill people die. That same year, the Michigan legislature passed a law making assisting in suicide a crime, but Kevorkian announced that he would continue his activities despite the law.

In September 1998, Dr. Kevorkian administered a lethal injection to Thomas Youk, a fifty-two-year-old man in an advanced stage of the motor neuron disease amyotrophic lateral sclerosis (ALS). For the first time, Kevorkian, by his own direct action, caused the death of a person, thus moving from physician-assisted suicide to active euthanasia.

Kevorkian videotaped the event and offered the tape to the CBS program *Sixty Minutes,* which broadcast excerpts from the tape on national television on November 22. About 15.6 million households watched the program.

Kevorkian said he had given the tape to CBS in the hope that it would lead to his arrest and become a test case for assisted suicide and active euthanasia.

"I want a showdown," Kevorkian told a reporter. "I want to be prosecuted for euthanasia. I am going to prove that this is not a crime, ever, regardless of what words are written on paper."

On November 25, the prosecutor of Oakland County, Michigan, filed first-degree murder charges against Jack Kevorkian. David G. Gorcyca, the prosecutor, said that Dr. Kevorkian's actions clearly fit the definition of premeditated murder and that the consent of the man killed was no legal defense.

On April 13, 1999, Jack Kevorkian was found guilty of second-degree murder and sentenced to a prison term of ten to twenty-five years. "This trial was not an opportunity for a referendum," Judge Jessica Cooper said at the sentencing.

Follow-up

Kevorkian was denied parole in 2005, but in June 2007, after eight years in prison, he was paroled on the grounds of good behavior. Kevorkian had already announced that once he was free, he would not go back to assisting people in committing suicide, but would, rather, campaign to change laws to make such a practice legal. He kept this resolution, and since his parole, he has given lectures on college campuses, run for Congress, and published books advocating the view that people who are terminally ill should be allowed to decide when to end their lives and secure the help of a physician in achieving this goal.

Jack Kevorkian continues to be a figure in the public's consciousness. In April 2010, the movie *You Don't Know Jack,* directed by Barry Levinson and starring Al Pacino as the title character, was broadcast on HBO. The movie presented Kevorkian as a quirky but serious crusader for his ideas. Those sympathetic to the views espoused by Kevorkian believe he did more than anyone else to force society to face an issue that it has chosen to ignore. His critics believe he made a circus of what should be a serious and deliberative discussion.

Assisted Suicide: The Oregon Experience

On March 24, 1998, an anonymous woman in her mid-eighties became the first person known to choose physician-assisted suicide under an Oregon law authorizing physicians to prescribe drugs that terminally ill patients can use to end their lives.

The woman, who lived in Portland, died shortly after swallowing a lethal dose of barbiturates, which she washed down with a glass of brandy. She was suffering from metastatic breast cancer and had been given less than two months to live. In an audiotape she made two days before her death, she said she "looked forward" to her coming suicide, because "I will be relieved of all the stress I have." She said she had grown tired of fighting cancer and had trouble breathing and walking. "I can't see myself living a few more months like this," she said. She died about half an hour after taking the prescribed drugs.

She may not have been the first person to commit suicide under the provisions of the law. The law allows for strict privacy, and the woman's death was made public, with her consent, by an advocacy group that supports the law.

The Law

Oregon's 1994 "Written Request for Medication to End One's Life in a Humane and Dignified Manner," or Death With Dignity Act, is the first physician-assisted suicide measure passed by any state. The law does not permit a physician to play an active role in ending a patient's life. The major provision of the measure is that it allows physicians to prescribe lethal drugs for terminally ill patients without risking criminal prosecution.

The law spells out a set of conditions that must be met by patients and physicians:

1. A primary-care physician and a consulting physician must both agree that the patient has six months or less to live.

2. The patient must make two oral requests (at least forty-eight hours apart) for drugs to use to terminate his or her life.

3. The patient must wait at least fifteen days after the initial oral request, then make a written request to the physician.

4. If either physician thinks the patient has a mental disorder or is suffering from impaired judgment from depression, they must recommend the patient for counseling.

5. The patient can terminate the request at any time during the process.

6. The physician prescribing the drugs must inform the patient of such feasible alternatives as hospice care, comfort care, and pain control.

Under the law, a physician is not permitted to assist a patient to die by any means more active than prescribing a drug that can cause death and indicating the manner in which the drug can be used. Hence, such practices as lethal injections remain as illegal as before.

A Long Time Coming

In 1994, the Oregon law was approved by the slight margin of fifty-two to forty-eight percent of voters. Opponents of the law immediately challenged it in court. The legal wrangles took three years; then, in 1997, the opponents mounted an effort to have it repealed through a voter initiative. The effort failed, and the law was approved once more—this time by sixty percent of the voters.

Despite voter approval, physicians were uncertain about what might happen to them if they acted in accordance with the law and assisted a patient in killing himself. Thomas Constantine, then the head of the Drug Enforcement Administration, responding to pressure by two conservative members of Congress, announced that the agency would impose severe sanctions on any physician who prescribed lethal doses of drugs. Constantine claimed that prescribing drugs for use in suicide wasn't a legitimate medical use under the federal drug laws. The DEA cannot cancel a physician's license to practice medicine, but it can withdraw a physician's license to prescribe drugs. Thus, the DEA threat to physicians was very real.

The DEA warning kept the law from being implemented until June 1998. Attorney General Janet Reno said that the DEA threat to prosecute physicians had been issued without her knowledge or consent. Because the DEA is a branch of the Justice Department, Reno's statement removed a legal roadblock. Overruling Constantine, Reno said that the drug laws were intended to block illicit drug dealing and that there was no evidence that Congress ever meant for the DEA to play a role in resolving the moral problems presented by the Oregon law.

The law explicitly protects only physicians from prosecution. Hence, it leaves in doubt the legal status of nurses. Many terminally ill patients are paralyzed or too weak to take prescribed medications without assistance. Nurses typically help patients take prescribed medications, but what if they help the patient take a lethal dose of drugs? Does this make them liable for legal prosecution?

Also, from a moral point of view, if a nurse is opposed to euthanasia or suicide, does the general responsibility he has to assist a patient require him to help the patient take a lethal drug? Nurses in Oregon are facing these questions, although few (if any) have had to deal with them in a practical way.

Some Oregon pharmacists also have trouble with the physician-assisted suicide law. Because they must fill the prescriptions written by physicians, the law makes them, to an extent, participants in the suicide. Some have argued that drugs prescribed for potential use in a

suicide should be labeled as such on the prescription. That way pharmacists who object to assisted suicide can avoid becoming involved in one. The prescription could be filled by some other pharmacist.

Physicians object to this proposal, though. They point out that if prescriptions were labeled as potential suicide agents, the patient's confidentiality would be violated. Particularly in small towns, if word got out, the families of those who chose assisted suicide might become the targets of criticism or demonstrations by opponents of assisted suicide.

In March 1998, Oregon state officials decided to make physician-assisted suicide available to low-income residents under the state's Medicaid program. The state will have to bear the full cost, however, because, by law, federal funds cannot be used to pay for physician-assisted suicide.

Critics claim that this use of state funds is a tacit endorsement of suicide, but supporters claim that it is only an extension of the "comfort care" already covered by Medicaid. Many who believe state mental-health services are underfunded think that supporting physician-assisted suicide is a serious mistake. It suggests to patients that death is the only help available to them.

Is the Law Needed?

Proponents of the Oregon law would like to see other states pass similar legislation. They point out that terminally ill people who decide to end their lives are often frustrated in carrying out their wishes, even though the society has endorsed, in principle, a "right to die."

The federal Patient Self-Determination Act requires hospitals to inform patients that they have the right to refuse or discontinue treatment and that by means of living wills and powers of attorney for health care, they can put their decisions into practice. The Supreme Court in the *Cruzan* decision (see the Case Presentation "The Cruzan Case: The Supreme Court Upholds the Right to Die," in this chapter) implicitly acknowledged a "right to die," by allowing the withdrawal of life-sustaining treatment when "clear and compelling evidence" shows that this reflects an individual's wish. Yet, despite the legal possibility of exercising control over medical care during the last stages of one's life, various barriers stand in the way of actual control.

Right to Discontinue Care

Surveys of physicians and health care workers show that many are not aware of laws allowing them to withhold or discontinue such care as mechanical ventilation, kidney dialysis, and even feeding tubes. Many believe that once a treatment has been started, it is illegal to discontinue it. Courts have repeatedly upheld the right of individuals to decide that, at a certain point in their treatment, they do not want to be provided with food or water, yet in one survey forty-two percent of health care workers rejected this right as an option patients could choose.

Oral Instructions

Many physicians and hospitals simply ignore the oral instructions patients give them about discontinuing their care. In one study of more than 4000 seriously ill patients, researchers found that although a third of the patients asked not to be revived by cardiopulmonary resuscitation, fifty percent of the time "Do not resuscitate" was never written in their charts.

Advance Directives

The living wills or powers of attorney made out by patients may not be followed. In a 1997 study of 4804 terminally ill patients, only 688 had written directives, and just 22 of these contained instructions explicit enough to guide the care they received. Even these instructions were ignored about half the time, and physicians knew about the patient's instructions only about a quarter of the time.

Also, advance directives are sometimes not included among the documents constituting a patient's medical chart. In another study, when seventy-one patients were moved to a nursing home, twenty-five of them had living wills that were not sent with them.

As a result, despite the efforts patients may make to control what happens to them at the end of their lives, they may be forced to accept decisions about their care made by physicians or nurses in accordance with their own values or institutional policies.

Patient vs. Family

Families may override the wishes expressed by patients in their living wills. Even though the views of the patient take legal precedence over those of a relative, in practice a physician or hospital may do as the relative wishes. Families never sue because of the overtreatment of a patient, but they do because of withholding or discontinuing treatment.

Laws like the one in Oregon are viewed by many as the only way patients can be sure that they can exercise control in the final days of their lives. Many fear that if they enter a hospital, they won't be able to trust nurses and physicians to know their wishes and to respect them.

Various polls suggest that a majority of the American people favor a policy of voluntary physician-assisted suicide. When physicians have been charged with aiding the death of a terminally ill patient at the patient's request, they have typically been found not guilty or been given suspended sentences. People who cannot control their illness often take some comfort in being able to control their escape from it.

How Many Cases?

The Oregon law is written so that only Oregon residents can ask physicians to assist them in suicide under the stipulated conditions. Thus, sick people have not migrated to the state with the idea of getting a physician's help in killing themselves.

Although the way is clear for any terminally ill Oregon resident to seek help in dying,

PHYSICIAN-ASSISTED SUICIDE

When a person has a disease that cannot be cured and is living in severe pain, do you think that doctors should or should not be allowed to assist a patient to commit suicide if the patient requests it?

Support: 56%
Do Not Support: 38%

Based on national telephone survey of 1,003 adults conducted on May 10–13, 2007. Half were asked the question above. Gallup Organization, May 31, 2007.

relatively few people have done so. State officials reported that in 1998, the first year under the new law, fifteen people ended their lives with drugs legally prescribed for that purpose. (There were 29,000 deaths in Oregon that year.) The average age of the eight men and seven women was seventy.

The most recent figures available show that from 1998 to 2009 only 460 people ended their lives with assistance. The average age was seventy-one, but the range was from twenty-five to ninety-six. According to a state report, those choosing physician-assisted suicide were "not disproportionately poor, uneducated, uninsured, fearful of the financial consequences of their illnesses," or "lacking end-of-life care." The primary factor mentioned by individuals was "the importance of autonomy and personal control." Neither financial worries nor the pain of a long illness was mentioned by them as a decisive factor.

The average time to unconsciousness after taking the prescribed drugs was five minutes (with a range of one to thirty-eight), and the average time to death was twenty-five minutes.

That relatively few have taken advantage of the Oregon law may support the idea of those favoring it that most people simply want to know that if they are terminally ill and in pain, a way out is available to them. To this extent, then, the Oregon experience may encourage other states to allow physician-assisted suicide.

Supreme Court Leaves the Matter to the States

In November 2001, Attorney General John Ashcroft reversed the course taken by Janet Reno and sent a letter to the DEA authorizing agents to take legal action against physicians prescribing drugs for the purpose of ending the lives of terminally ill patients. Ashcroft held that "prescribing, dispensing or administering federally controlled substances to assist suicide" is "not a legitimate medical purpose." Ashcroft's successor, Alberto Gonzales, accepted the same view. Oregon filed suit against the Justice Department, and eventually the case went to the U.S. Supreme Court. In January 2006, the Court upheld the decisions of two lower courts and ruled six to nine that the Justice Department had acted without legal authority in attempting to restrict the actions of Oregon physicians.

The ruling was made on the narrow administrative ground that the regulation of medical practice is a state, not a federal, matter. The ruling left open the possibility that Congress could pass a law explicitly forbidding the use of drugs by physicians who are assisting in a suicide. However, because the ruling held that the regulation of medical practice is a state issue, it also opened the way for the states to pass assisted-suicide laws.

In March 2009, Washington became the second state to pass a ballot initiative allowing physician-assisted suicide. (The "Death with Dignity" law received sixty percent of the vote.) The law is modeled closely on the Oregon law, including the age requirement, waiting period, and certification by two physicians that the patient has no more than six months to live. Since the law went into effect, sixty-three people have filled prescriptions for lethal medication, but only thirty-six died as a result of taking the drugs.

In December 2009, a state court in Montana ruled that it was not illegal for a physician to prescribe lethal medications for terminally ill patients under certain conditions. The state, however, has neither passed any laws nor put into place the regulatory mechanisms that would allow physicians to escape legal challenges for assisting patients in ending their lives.

Other states are also struggling with the issue. Massachusetts is considering a measure allowing assisted suicide, but the bill is surrounded with controversy. A Connecticut physicians' group has filed a lawsuit to get the state to clarify the legal position of doctors who prescribe lethal drugs to terminally ill patients who request them.

CASE PRESENTATION
The Awakening: A Brief Miracle

In 1995, Donald Herbert was thirty-four years old and a member of the Buffalo, New York, fire rescue squad. On the morning of December 29 of that year, he raced into a burning apartment building and began searching the attic for potential victims. The smoke was thick, but he wore a breathing apparatus.

Suddenly, without warning, the roof of the burning building collapsed. Herbert's breathing mask was knocked off, and he was buried under flaming debris. His fellow firefighters realized what had happened, but by the time they could reach him, he had been without oxygen for at least six minutes. His rescuers pulled him through a window, then rushed him to the Erie County Medical Center.

Herbert's condition was critical. In addition to oxygen deprivation, he had suffered severe head trauma. He remained in a coma for two and a half months. He regained consciousness in 1996, but his speech was slurred, he couldn't feed himself, his vision appeared to be damaged, and he was confined to a bed or wheelchair. He didn't know his age or what his job had been. He seemed unable to recognize his wife and children or his relatives and old friends. Because he could not care for himself, Herbert was removed to Baker Manor, a nursing home in a Buffalo suburb.

Awakening

On a Saturday morning in May 2005, Donald Herbert suddenly recovered his memory. "I want to talk to my wife," Herbert said to a nursing home employee. The employee called his home, but it was his thirteen-year-old son

Nicholas who answered. "That can't be," Herbert said. "He can't talk, he's just a baby."

Herbert was soon surrounded by his wife Linda, his four sons, various relatives, and several old friends. For fourteen hours, they hugged and kissed him, talked to him, and rejoiced in his recovery. Herbert asked questions, especially about his sons. "He wouldn't go to sleep," his mother-in-law said. "He stayed up all night talking to his sons."

"How long have I been gone?" he asked.

"We told him almost ten years," his uncle Simon Manka recalled. "He said, 'Holy Cow!' He thought it had been three months." While Herbert was unconscious, cell phones became common, e-mail use spread worldwide, the attack of 9/11 occurred, and the United States went to war in Iraq. His oldest son turned twenty-four, and many of his fellow firefighters retired.

Mr. Manka told reporters that Herbert recognized several family members and friends and called them by name. He was completely different than he had been. "He was asking questions, and he'd recognize a voice." He recognized the voices of the members of the rescue crew he'd served with, even though he couldn't see the people.

Hearing her husband speak was "completely overwhelming," Linda Herbert said. "We are still trying to cope with this incredible experience."

A Change

Three days after his startling recovery, Donald Herbert began to become less animated. He still engaged in conversation, but his periods of clarity became less frequent.

He spent most of his time sleeping, and his family and friends made an effort not to tire him.

His doctor, Jamil Ahmed, said that Herbert's condition had been close to a persistent vegetative state, one in which he appeared to be awake but was unaware of what was going on around him. He seemed to have laid down some memories during this period, however, because he was able to recognize the names of some of the nursing home staff. The big change in Herbert took place three months after his medication was changed. The drug combination that he took had shown beneficial results in patients with more recent brain injuries. The combined drugs are more often used individually to treat patients with Parkinson's disease, attention deficit disorder, and depression.

On February 22, 2006, Donald Herbert died. He never left the nursing home, but he continued to interact to a limited degree with his family and friends until the end of his life. As recently as the week before his death, he was playing catch with his youngest son. Herbert developed pneumonia that weekend, and although he was treated with antibiotics, he failed to recover.

"He was never as good as he was when he first woke up," Michael Lombardo said. "But he was pretty good right up to the end."

Cases of people with severe brain damage making what seem to be miraculous recoveries of self-consciousness and memory occur from time to time, but they are extremely rare. When such cases are publicized, they encourage people who love someone diagnosed with a severe brain injury to believe that recovery is likely. Sadly, these hopes are almost never realized.

BRIEFING SESSION

Death comes to us all. We hope that when it comes it will be swift and allow us to depart without prolonged suffering, our dignity intact. We also hope that it will not force burdens on our family and friends, making them pay both financially and emotionally by our lingering and hopeless condition.

Such considerations give euthanasia a strong appeal. Should we not be able to snip the thread of life when the weight of suffering and hopelessness grows too heavy to bear? The answer to this question is not as easy as it may seem, for hidden within it are a number of complicated moral issues.

Just what is euthanasia? The word comes from the Greek for "good death," and in English it has come to have the meaning "easy death." But this does little to help us understand the concept. For consider these questions:

If we give ourselves an easy death, are we committing suicide? If we assist someone else to an easy death (with or without that person's permission), are we committing murder? Anyone who opposed killing (either of oneself or of others) on moral grounds might also consider it necessary to object to euthanasia.

It may be, however, that the answer to both questions is no. But if it is, then it is necessary to specify the conditions that distinguish euthanasia from both suicide and murder. Only then would it be possible to argue, without contradiction, that euthanasia is morally acceptable but the other two forms of killing are not.

Someone who believes that suicide is morally legitimate would not object to euthanasia carried out by the person herself, but he would still have to deal with the problem posed by the euthanasia/murder issue.

Active and Passive Euthanasia

We have talked of euthanasia as though it involved directly taking the life of a person, either one's own life or the life of another. However, some philosophers distinguish between "active euthanasia" and "passive euthanasia," which in turn rests on a distinction between killing and letting die.

To kill someone (including oneself) is to take a definite action to end his or her life (e.g., administering a lethal injection). To allow someone to die, by contrast, is to take no steps to prolong that person's life when those steps seem called for—failing to give a needed injection of antibiotics, for example. Active euthanasia, then, is direct killing and is an act of commission. Passive euthanasia is an act of omission.

This distinction is used in most contemporary codes of medical ethics (e.g., the American Medical Association's Code of Ethics) and is also recognized in the Anglo-American tradition of law. Except in special circumstances, it is illegal to deliberately cause the death of another person. It is not, however, illegal (except in special circumstances) to allow a person to die. Clearly, one might consider active euthanasia morally wrong while recognizing passive euthanasia as morally legitimate.

Some philosophers, however, have argued that the active–passive distinction is morally irrelevant with respect to euthanasia. Both are cases of causing death, and it is the circumstances in which death is caused, not the manner of causing it, that is of moral importance.

Furthermore, the active–passive distinction is not always clear cut. If a person dies after special life-sustaining equipment has been withdrawn, is this a case of active or passive euthanasia? Is it a case of euthanasia at all?

Voluntary, Involuntary, and Nonvoluntary Euthanasia

Writers on euthanasia have often thought it important to distinguish among voluntary, involuntary, and nonvoluntary euthanasia. *Voluntary euthanasia* includes cases in which a person takes his or her own life, either directly or by refusing treatment. But it also includes cases in which a person deputizes another to act in accordance with his wishes.

Thus, someone might instruct her family not to permit the use of artificial support systems should she become unconscious, suffer from brain damage, and be unable to speak for herself. Or someone might request that he be given a lethal injection after suffering third-degree burns over most of his body, suffering uncontrollable pain, and being told he has little hope of recovery.

Finally, assisted suicide, in which the individual requests the direct help of someone else in ending his life, falls into this category. (Some may think that one or more of the earlier examples are also cases of assisted suicide. What counts as assisted suicide is both conceptually and legally unclear.) That the individual explicitly consents to death is a necessary feature of voluntary euthanasia.

Involuntary euthanasia consists in ending the life of someone contrary to that person's wish. The person killed not only fails to give consent, but expresses the desire not to be killed. No one arguing in favor of nonvoluntary euthanasia holds that involuntary euthanasia is justifiable. Those who oppose both voluntary and nonvoluntary euthanasia often argue that to permit either runs the risk of opening the way for involuntary euthanasia.

Nonvoluntary euthanasia includes those cases in which the decision about death is not made by the person who is to die. Here the person gives no specific consent or instructions, and the decision is made by family, friends, or physicians. The distinction between voluntary and nonvoluntary euthanasia is not always a clear one. Physicians sometimes assume that people are "asking" to die even when no explicit request has been made. Also, the wishes and attitudes that people express when they are not in extreme life-threatening medical situations may be too vague for us to be certain that they would choose death when they are in such a situation. Is "I never want to be hooked up to one of those machines" an adequate indication that the person who says this does not want to be put on a respirator should she meet with an accident and fall into a comatose state?

If the distinctions made here are accepted as legitimate and relevant, we can distinguish eight cases in which euthanasia becomes a moral decision:

1. Self-administered euthanasia
   a. active
   b. passive

2. Other-administered euthanasia
   a. active and voluntary
   b. active and involuntary
   c. active and nonvoluntary
   d. passive and voluntary
   e. passive and involuntary
   f. passive and nonvoluntary

Even these possibilities don't exhaust the cases euthanasia presents us with. For example, notice that the voluntary–nonvoluntary distinction doesn't appear in connection with self-administered euthanasia in our scheme. Yet it might be argued that it should, for a person's decision to end his life (actively or passively) may well not be a wholly voluntary or free decision. People who are severely depressed by their illness and decide to end their lives, for example, might be thought of as not having made a voluntary choice.

Hence, one might approve of self-administered voluntary euthanasia, yet think that the nonvoluntary form should not be permitted. It should not be allowed not because it is necessarily morally wrong, but because it would not be a genuine decision by the person. The person might be thought to be suffering from a psychiatric disability. Indeed, the current debate about physician-assisted suicide turns, in part, on just this issue.

Defining "Death"

The advent of new medical technologies, pharmaceutical agents, and modes of treatment raises the question of when we should consider someone dead. Suppose someone's heartbeat, blood pressure, respiration, and liver and kidney functions can be maintained within the normal range of values by medical intervention. Should we still include this individual among living persons, even though she is in an irreversible coma or a chronic vegetative state?

If we consider the individual to be a living person, we need to decide how she ought to be treated. Should she be allowed to die or be maintained by medical means? This is the kind of question faced by families, physicians, and the courts in the *Quinlan* and *Cruzan* cases (see the Case Presentations "Karen Quinlan: The Debate Begins," and "The Cruzan Case: The Supreme Court Upholds the Right to Die," in this chapter), and it is one faced every day in dozens of unpublicized, though no less agonizing, cases.

But what if an unconscious individual lacking higher cortical functioning is no longer a living person? Could a physician who disconnected a respirator or failed to give an antibiotic be said to have killed a person? If nutrition and hydration are withheld from a brain-dead individual or even if the individual is given a lethal injection, is it reasonable to say that this is a case of killing? Perhaps the person died when her brain stopped functioning at a certain level. Or perhaps she died when she lapsed into coma.

A practical question that advances in medicine have made even more pressing is when or whether a comatose individual may be regarded as a source of transplant organs. If the individual remains a living person, it may be morally wrong (at least prima facie) to kill him to obtain organs for transplant. But what if the comatose individual is not really alive? What if he is dead already and no longer a person? Then there seem to be no reasonable grounds for objecting to removing his organs and using them to save the lives of those who need them. (See Chapter 7 for a discussion of organ donation.)

Questions like the ones raised here have prompted various attempts to define the notion of death. In the view of many commentators, the traditional notion of death is no longer adequate to serve as a guide to resolving issues about the treatment of individuals who, through disease or accident, have fallen into states in which many of their basic physiological functions can be maintained by medical means, although they remain comatose or lacking in higher-brain function.

Until recently, the traditional notion of death has been enshrined in laws defining crimes such as homicide and manslaughter. Given the change in medical technology, actions such as removing a respirator, which might once have been regarded as criminal for causing the death of a person, perhaps should now be viewed in a different way. Perhaps a person may be dead already, even though major physiological systems are still functioning.

Four major notions or concepts of death have emerged during the last two decades. We'll list each of them, but it's important to keep in mind that there is a difference between specifying the concept of death (or, as it is sometimes put, defining "death") and stating the criteria for determining that the concept fits in particular cases. The situation is analogous to defining "the best team" as the team winning the most games and then providing criteria for determining what counts as winning a game.

The concepts are merely sketched and the criteria for applying them only hinted at:

1. *Traditional.* A person is dead when he is no longer breathing and his heart is not beating. Hence, death may be defined as the permanent cessation of breathing and blood flow. This notion is sometimes known as the "cardiopulmonary" or "heart–lung criterion" for death.

2. *Whole brain.* Death is regarded as the irreversible cessation of all brain functions. Essentially, this means that there is no electrical activity in the brain, and even the brain stem is not functioning. Application of the concept depends on the use of electroencephalographic or imaging data.

3. *Higher brain.* Death is considered to involve the permanent loss of consciousness. Hence, someone in an irreversible coma or chronic vegetative state would

be considered dead, even though the brain stem continued to regulate breathing and heartbeat. Clinical, electroencephalographic, and imaging data are relevant to applying the concept. So, too, are statistics concerning the likelihood of the individual's regaining consciousness.

4. *Personhood.* Death occurs when an individual ceases to be a person. This may mean the loss of features that are essential to personal identity or (in some formulations) the loss of what is essential to being a person. Criteria for personal identity or for being a person are typically taken to include a complex of such activities as reasoning, remembering, feeling emotion, possessing a sense of the future, interacting with others, and so on. The criteria for applying this concept have more to do with the way an individual functions than with data about his brain.

Technology makes it necessary to take a fresh look at the traditional notion of death, but technology also provides data that have allowed for the development of new notions. It would be pointless, for example, to talk about brain death without having some means to determine when the concept might be satisfied.

The whole-brain concept of death was proposed in the 1981 *Report of the President's Commission for the Study of Ethical Problems in Medicine* and included in the Uniform Death Act. As a consequence, state laws employing the traditional concept of death generally have been modified in keeping with the whole-brain concept.

The whole-brain concept has the advantage of being relatively clear cut in application. However, applying the concept is not without difficulty and controversy. In the view of some, the concept is too restrictive and so fails to resolve some of the difficulties that prompted the need for a new concept. For example, both Karen Quinlan and Nancy Cruzan (see the Case Presentations "Karen Quinlan: The Debate Begins," and "The Cruzan Case: The Supreme Court Upholds the Right to Die," in this chapter) would have been considered alive by the whole-brain criteria. However, those who favor concepts of death based on the loss of higher brain function or the loss of personhood might argue that both cases were ones in which the affected individuals were, in the respective technical senses, dead.

Furthermore, critics charge, the whole-brain concept is not really as straightforward in its application as it might seem. Even when there appears to be a complete lack of cognitive functioning and even when basic brain-stem functions appear to have disappeared, a brain may remain electrically active to some degree. Isolated cells or groups of cells continue to be alive, and monitoring of the brain yields data that are open to conflicting interpretations.

The higher brain and personhood concepts face even greater difficulties. Each must formulate criteria that are accepted as nonarbitrary and as sufficient grounds for deciding that an individual is dead. No one has yet solved either of these problems for either of these concepts. The fact that there can be controversy over whole-brain death indicates how much harder it is to get agreement about when higher brain functions are lost. Also, securing agreement on criteria for determining when an entity either becomes or ceases to be a person is a conceptual difficulty far from being resolved to the satisfaction of most philosophers. (For more on this topic, see the discussion of defining death in the Social Context) "When the Diagnosis is Death," in this chapter.)

Advance Directives

Like so many issues in bioethics, euthanasia has traditionally been discussed only in the back rooms of medicine. Often, decisions about whether to allow a patient to die are made by physicians acting on their own authority. Such decisions do not represent so much an arrogant claim to godlike wisdom as an acknowledgment of the physician's obligation to do what is best for the patient.

Most physicians admit that allowing or helping a patient to die is sometimes the best assistance that can be given. Decisions made in this fashion depend on the beliefs and judgment of particular physicians. Because these may differ from those of the patient concerned, it is quite possible that the physician's decision may not reflect the wishes of the patient.

But covert decisions made by a physician acting alone are becoming practices of the past as euthanasia is discussed more widely and openly. Court cases, such as *Quinlan* and *Cruzan*, have both widened the scope of legally permissible actions and reinforced the notion that an individual has a right to refuse or discontinue life-sustaining medical treatment. Such cases have also made it clear that there are limits to the benefits that can be derived from medicine—that, under some conditions, individuals may be better off if everything that technologically can be done is not done. Increasingly, people want to be sure that they have some say in what happens to them should they fall victim to hopeless injury or illness.

One indication of this interest is that the number of states permitting individuals to sign "living wills" or advance directives has now increased to include all fifty states. The first living-will legislation was the "Natural Death Act" passed by the California legislature on August 30, 1977. The act is generally representative of all such legislation. It permits a competent adult to sign a directive that will authorize physicians to withhold or discontinue "mechanical" or "artificial" life-support equipment if the person is judged to be "terminal" and if "death is imminent."

The strength of advance directives is that they allow a person to express in an explicit manner how he or she wishes to be treated before treatment is needed. In this way, the autonomy of the individual is recognized. Even though unconscious or comatose, a person can continue to exert control over his or her life. This, in turn, means that physicians need not and should not be the decisive voice in determining the continuation or use of special medical equipment.

Critics of advance-directive legislation have claimed that it does not go far enough in

Whose Life Is It Anyway

A study published in the March 2002 issue of the *Journal of the American Geriatric Society* found that sixty percent of the 1185 Medicare patients surveyed at five teaching hospitals told their doctors to focus on making them comfortable rather than on extending their lives. Yet evidence indicated that more than one-third of the people expressing this wish had it ignored. They were treated more and lived longer than the two-thirds whose wishes were respected. Either their doctors forgot about their preferences, or they deliberately ignored them.

protecting autonomy and making death easier (where this is what is wanted). They point out that the directive specified in the California bill and most others would have made no difference in the case of Karen Quinlan. She had not been diagnosed as having a "terminal condition" at least two weeks prior to being put on a respirator, yet this is one of the requirements of the act. Consequently, the directive would have been irrelevant to her condition.

Nor, for that matter, would those people be allowed to die who wish to if their disease or injury does not involve treatment by "artificial" or "mechanical" means. Thus, a person suffering from throat cancer would simply have to bear the pain and wait for a "natural" death. Finally, at the moment, some states explicitly exclude nutrition and hydration as medical treatments that can be discontinued. The Supreme Court in the *Cruzan* case accepted the notion that the nutrition received by Nancy Cruzan through a feeding tube implanted in her stomach was a form of medical treatment that could be withdrawn. However, the Court did not rule on the Missouri law that forbids withdrawal. Until this law or some other like it is successfully challenged in court, an advance directive does not necessarily guarantee that such treatment will be discontinued, even when requested.

Limitations of such kinds on living wills have led some writers to recommend that individuals sign a legal instrument known as a durable power of attorney. In such a document,

an individual can name someone to act on his behalf should he become legally incompetent to act. Hence, unlike the advance directive, a durable power of attorney allows a surrogate to exercise control over novel and unanticipated situations. For example, the surrogate may order the discontinuation of artificial feeding, something that an advance directive might not permit.

The widespread wish to have some control over the end of one's life is reflected in a federal law that took effect in 1991. The Patient Self-Determination Act is sometimes referred to as a "medical Miranda warning."

The act requires that hospitals, nursing homes, and other health-care facilities receiving federal funding provide patients, at the time of admission, with written information about relevant state laws and the rights of citizens under those laws to refuse or discontinue treatment. Patients must also be told about the practices and policies at that particular institution so that they can choose a facility willing to abide by their decisions. The institutions must also record whether a patient has provided a written "advance directive" (e.g., a living will or power of attorney for health care) that will take effect should the patient become incapacitated.

Another sign of change is the recent concern with the medical circumstances in which people die. The medical ideal of a "hospital death," one in which the patient's temperature, pulse rate, and respiration are brought within normal limits by medication and machinery, is being severely challenged. This is reflected in the policy of the AMA which holds that it may be morally appropriate to withhold "all means of life-prolonging medical treatment," including artificial feeding, from patients in irreversible comas.

A new ideal of natural death also seems to be emerging. In this view, the kind of support a dying patient needs is psychological counseling and contact with family and friends rather than heroic medical efforts. An acceptance of death as a normal end of life and the development of new means of caring for the dying may ease the problem of euthanasia. If those who face imminent death are offered an alternative to either euthanasia or an all-out medical effort to preserve their lives, they may choose that alternative. "Death with dignity" need not always mean choosing a lethal injection.

Ethical Theories and Euthanasia

Roman Catholicism explicitly rejects all forms of euthanasia as being against the natural law duty to preserve life. The religion considers euthanasia as morally identical with either suicide or murder. This position is not so rigid as it may seem, however; the principle of double effect (see Part V, "Foundations of Bioethics") makes it morally acceptable to give medication for the relief of pain—even if the indirect result of the medication will be to shorten the life of the recipient. The intended result is not the death of the person but the relief of suffering. The difference in intention is thus considered to be a morally significant one. Those not accepting the principle of double effect would be likely to classify the administration of a substance that would relieve pain but also cause death as a case of euthanasia.

Furthermore, on the Catholic view there is no moral obligation to continue treatment when a person is medically hopeless. It is legitimate to allow people to die as a result of their illness or injury, even though their lives might be lengthened by the use of extraordinary means. In addition, we may legitimately make the same decisions about ourselves that we make about others who are in no condition to decide. Thus, without intending to kill ourselves, we may choose measures for the relief of pain that may secondarily hasten our end. Or we may refuse extraordinary treatment and let "nature" take its course—let "God's will" determine the outcome. (See Part V, "Foundations of Bioethics," for a fuller discussion of the Roman Catholic position on euthanasia and extraordinary means of sustaining life.)

At first sight, utilitarianism would seem to endorse euthanasia in all of its forms. Whenever suffering is great and the condition of the person is one without legitimate medical hope, the principle of utility might be invoked to approve putting the person to death. After all, in such a case we seem to be acting to end suffering and to bring about a state of affairs in which happiness exceeds unhappiness. Thus, whether the person concerned is ourself or another, euthanasia would seem to be a morally right action.

A utilitarian might argue in this way, but it is not the only way in which the principle of utility could be applied. It could be argued, for example, that since life is a necessary condition for happiness, it is wrong to destroy that condition because, by doing so, the possibility of all future happiness is lost. Furthermore, a rule utilitarian might well argue that a rule like "The taking of a human life is permissible when suffering is intense and the condition of the person permits no legitimate hope" would be open to abuse. Consequently, in the long run the rule would actually work to increase the amount of unhappiness in the world. Obviously, it is not possible to say that there is such a thing as "the utilitarian view of euthanasia." The principle of utility supplies a guide for an answer, but it is not itself an answer.

Euthanasia presents a considerable difficulty for Kant's ethics. For Kant, an autonomous rational being has a duty to preserve his or her life. Thus, one cannot rightly refuse needed medical care or commit suicide. Yet our status as autonomous rational beings also endows us with an inherent dignity. If that status is destroyed or severely compromised, as it is when people become comatose and unknowing because of illness or injury, then it is not certain that we have a duty to maintain our lives under such conditions. It may be more in keeping with our freedom and dignity for us to instruct others either to put us to death or to take no steps to keep us alive should we ever be in such a state. Voluntary euthanasia may be compatible with (if not required by) Kant's ethics.

By a similar line of reasoning, it may be that nonvoluntary euthanasia might be seen as a duty that we have to others. We might argue that by putting to death a comatose and hopeless person we are recognizing the dignity that person possessed in his or her previous state. It might also be argued that a human being in a vegetative state is not a person in the relevant moral sense. Thus, our ordinary duty to preserve life does not hold.

According to Ross, we have a strong prima facie obligation not to kill a person except in justifiable self-defense—unless we have an even stronger prima facie moral obligation to do something that cannot be done without killing. Since active euthanasia typically requires taking the life of an innocent person, there is a moral presumption against it. However, another of Ross's prima facie obligations is that we keep promises made to others. Accordingly, if someone who is now in an irreversible coma with no hope of recovery has left instructions that in case of such an event she wishes her life to be ended, then we are under a prima facie obligation to follow her instructions. Thus, in such a case we may be justified in overriding the presumption against taking an innocent life.

What if there are no such instructions? It could be argued that our prima facie obligation of acting beneficently toward others requires us to attempt to determine what someone's wishes would be from what we know about him as a person. We would then treat him the way that we believe that he would want us to. In the absence of any relevant information, we might make the decision on the basis of how a rational person would want to be treated in similar circumstances. Of course, if anyone has left instructions that his life is to be maintained, if possible, under any circumstances, then we have a prima facie obligation to respect this preference also.

READINGS

Section 1: The Killing–Letting-Die Distinction

Active and Passive Euthanasia

James Rachels

James Rachels challenges both the use and the moral significance of the distinction between active and passive euthanasia. Rachels argues that since both forms of euthanasia result in the death of a person, active euthanasia ought to be preferred to passive. Active euthanasia is more humane because it allows suffering to be brought to a speedy end. Furthermore, Rachels claims, the distinction itself can be shown to be morally irrelevant. Is there, he asks, any genuine moral difference between drowning a child and merely watching a child drown and doing nothing to save it?

Finally, Rachels attempts to show that the bare fact that there is a difference between killing and letting die doesn't make active euthanasia wrong. Killing of any kind is right and wrong depending on the intentions and circumstances in which it takes place; if the intentions and circumstances are of a certain kind, then active euthanasia can be morally right.

For these reasons, Rachels suggests that the approval given to the active–passive euthanasia distinction in the Code of Ethics of the American Medical Association is unwise. He encourages physicians to rely upon the distinction only to the extent that they are forced to do so by law but not to give it any significant moral weight. In particular, they should not make use of it when writing new policies or guidelines.

The distinction between active and passive euthanasia is thought to be crucial for medical ethics. The idea is that it is permissible, at least in some cases, to withhold treatment and allow a patient to die, but it is never permissible to take any direct action designed to kill the patient. This doctrine seems to be accepted by most doctors, and it is endorsed in a statement adopted by the House of Delegates of the American Medical Association on December 4, 1973:

> *The intentional termination of the life of one human being by another—mercy killing—is contrary to that for which the medical profession stands and is contrary to the policy of the American Medical Association.*
>
> *The cessation of the employment of extraordinary means to prolong the life of the body when there is irrefutable evidence that biological death is imminent is the decision of the patient and/or his immediate family. The advice and judgment of the physician should be freely available to the patient and/or his immediate family.*

However, a strong case can be made against this doctrine. In what follows I will set out some of the relevant arguments, and urge doctors to reconsider their views on this matter.

To begin with a familiar type of situation, a patient who is dying of incurable cancer of the throat is in terrible pain, which can no longer be satisfactorily alleviated. He is certain to die within a few days, even if present treatment is continued, but he does not want to

go on living for those days since the pain is unbearable. So he asks the doctor for an end to it, and his family joins in the request.

Suppose the doctor agrees to withhold treatment, as the conventional doctrine says he may. The justification for his doing so is that the patient is in terrible agony, and since he is going to die anyway, it would be wrong to prolong his suffering needlessly. But now notice this. If one simply withholds treatment, it may take the patient longer to die, and so he may suffer more than he would if more direct action were taken and a lethal injection given. This fact provides strong reason for thinking that, once the initial decision not to prolong his agony has been made, active euthanasia is actually preferable to passive euthanasia, rather than the reverse. To say otherwise is to endorse the option that leads to more suffering rather than less, and is contrary to the humanitarian impulse that prompts the decision not to prolong his life in the first place.

Part of my point is that the process of being "allowed to die" can be relatively slow and painful, whereas being given a lethal injection is relatively quick and painless. Let me give a different sort of example. In the United States about one in 600 babies is born with Down's syndrome. Most of these babies are otherwise healthy—that is, with only the usual pediatric care, they will proceed to an otherwise normal infancy. Some, however, are born with congenital defects such as intestinal obstructions that require operations if they are to live. Sometimes, the parents and the doctor will decide not to operate, and let the infant die. Anthony Shaw describes what happens then:

> . . . *When surgery is denied [the doctor] must try to keep the infant from suffering while natural forces sap the baby's life away. As a surgeon whose natural inclination is to use the scalpel to fight off death, standing by and watching a salvageable baby die is the most emotionally exhausting experience I know. It is easy at a conference, in a theoretical discussion, to decide that such infants should be allowed to die. It is altogether different to stand by in the nursery and watch as dehydration and infection wither a tiny being over hours and days. This is a terrible ordeal for me and the hospital staff—much more so than for the parents who never set foot in the nursery.*[1]

I can understand why some people are opposed to all euthanasia, and insist that such infants must be allowed to live. I think I can also understand why other people favor destroying these babies quickly and painlessly. But why should anyone favor letting "dehydration and infection wither a tiny being over hours and days"? The doctrine that says that a baby may be allowed to dehydrate and wither, but may not be given an injection that would end its life without suffering, seems so patently cruel as to require no further refutation. The strong language is not intended to offend, but only to put the point in the clearest possible way.

My second argument is that the conventional doctrine leads to decisions concerning life and death made on irrelevant grounds.

Consider again the case of the infants with Down's syndrome who need operations for congenital defects unrelated to the syndrome to live. Sometimes, there is no operation, and the baby dies, but when there is no such defect, the baby lives on. Now, an operation such as that to remove an intestinal obstruction is not prohibitively difficult. The reason why such operations are not performed in these cases is, clearly, that the child has Down's syndrome and the parents and doctor judge that because of that fact it is better for the child to die.

But notice that this situation is absurd, no matter what view one takes of the lives and potentials of such babies. If the life of such an infant is worth preserving, what does it matter if it needs a simple operation? Or, if one thinks it better that such a baby should not live on, what difference does it make that it happens to have an unobstructed intestinal tract? In either case,

the matter of life and death is being decided on irrelevant grounds. It is the Down's syndrome, and not the intestines, that is the issue. The matter should be decided, if at all, on that basis, and not be allowed to depend on the essentially irrelevant question of whether the intestinal tract is blocked.

What makes this situation possible, of course, is the idea that when there is an intestinal blockage, one can "let the baby die," but when there is no such defect there is nothing that can be done, for one must not "kill" it. The fact that this idea leads to such results as deciding life or death on irrelevant grounds is another good reason why the doctrine should be rejected.

One reason why so many people think that there is an important moral difference between active and passive euthanasia is that they think killing someone is morally worse than letting someone die. But is it? Is killing, in itself, worse than letting die? To investigate this issue, two cases may be considered that are exactly alike except that one involves killing whereas the other involves letting someone die. Then, it can be asked whether this difference makes any difference to the moral assessments. It is important that the cases be exactly alike, except for this one difference, since otherwise one cannot be confident that it is this difference and not some other that accounts for any variation in the assessments of the two cases. So, let us consider this pair of cases:

In the first, Smith stands to gain a large inheritance if anything should happen to his six-year-old cousin. One evening while the child is taking his bath, Smith sneaks into the bathroom and drowns the child, and then arranges things so that it will look like an accident.

In the second, Jones also stands to gain if anything should happen to his six-year-old cousin. Like Smith, Jones sneaks in planning to drown the child in his bath. However, just as he enters the bathroom Jones sees the child slip and hit his head, and fall face down in the water. Jones is delighted; he stands by, ready to push the child's head back under if it is necessary, but it is not necessary. With only a little thrashing about, the child drowns all by himself, "accidentally," as Jones watches and does nothing.

Now Smith killed the child, whereas Jones "merely" let the child die. That is the only difference between them. Did either man behave better, from a moral point of view? If the difference between killing and letting die were in itself a morally important matter, one should say that Jones's behavior was less reprehensible than Smith's. But does one really want to say that? I think not. In the first place, both men acted from the same motive, personal gain, and both had exactly the same end in view when they acted. It may be inferred from Smith's conduct that he is a bad man, although that judgment may be withdrawn or modified if certain further facts are learned about him—for example, that he is mentally deranged. But would not the very same thing be inferred about Jones from his conduct? And would not the same further considerations also be relevant to any modification of this judgment? Moreover, suppose Jones pleaded, in his own defense, "After all, I didn't do anything except just stand there and watch the child drown. I didn't kill him; I only let him die." Again, if letting die were in itself less bad than killing, this defense should have at least some weight. But it does not. Such a "defense" can only be regarded as a grotesque perversion of moral reasoning. Morally speaking, it is no defense at all.

Now, it may be pointed out, quite properly, that the cases of euthanasia with which doctors are concerned are not like this at all. They do not involve personal gain or the destruction of normal healthy children. Doctors are concerned only with cases in which the patient's life is of no further use to him, or in which the patient's life has become or will soon become a terrible burden. However, the point is the same in these cases: the bare difference between killing and letting die does not, in itself, make a moral difference. If a doctor lets a patient die, for humane reasons, he is in the same moral position as if he had given the patient a lethal injection for humane reasons. If his decision was wrong—if, for example, the patient's illness was in fact curable—the decision would be equally regrettable no matter which method was used to carry it out. And if the doctor's decision was the right one, the method used is not in itself important.

The AMA policy statement isolates the crucial issue very well; the crucial issue is "the intentional termination of the life of one human being by another." But after identifying this issue, and forbidding "mercy killing," the statement goes on to deny that the cessation of treatment is the intentional termination of a life. This is where the mistake comes in, for what is the cessation of treatment, in these circumstances, if it is not "the intentional termination of the life of one human being by another"? Of course it is exactly that, and if it were not, there would be no point to it.

Many people will find this judgment hard to accept. One reason, I think, is that it is very easy to conflate

the question of whether killing is, in itself, worse than letting die, with the very different question of whether most actual cases of killing are more reprehensible than most actual cases of letting die. Most actual cases of killing are clearly terrible (think, for example, of all the murders reported in the newspapers), and one hears of such cases every day. On the other hand, one hardly ever hears of a case of letting die, except for the actions of doctors who are motivated by humanitarian reasons. So one learns to think of killing in a much worse light than of letting die. But this does not mean that there is something about killing that makes it in itself worse than letting die, for it is not the bare difference between killing and letting die that makes the difference in the cases. Rather, the other factors—the murderer's motive of personal gain, for example, contrasted with the doctor's humanitarian motivation—account for different reactions to the different cases.

I have argued that killing is not in itself any worse than letting die; if my contention is right, it follows that active euthanasia is not any worse than passive euthanasia. What arguments can be given on the other side? The most common, I believe, is the following:

"The important difference between active and passive euthanasia is that, in passive euthanasia, the doctor does not do anything to bring about the patient's death. The doctor does nothing, and the patient dies of whatever ills already afflict him. In active euthanasia, however, the doctor does something to bring about the patient's death: he kills him. The doctor who gives the patient with cancer a lethal injection has himself caused his patient's death; whereas if he merely ceases treatment, the cancer is the cause of the death."

A number of points need to be made here. The first is that it is not exactly correct to say that in passive euthanasia the doctor does nothing, for he does do one thing that is very important: he lets the patient die. "Letting someone die" is certainly different, in some respects, from other types of action—mainly in that it is a kind of action that one may perform by way of not performing certain other actions. For example, one may let a patient die by way of not giving medication, just as one may insult someone by way of not shaking his hand. But for any purpose of moral assessment, it is a type of action nonetheless. The decision to let a patient die is subject to moral appraisal in the same way that a decision to kill him would be subject to moral appraisal: it may be assessed as wise or unwise, compassionate or sadistic, right or wrong. If a doctor deliberately let a patient die who was suffering from a routinely curable illness, the doctor would certainly be to blame for what he had done, just as he would be to blame if he had needlessly killed the patient. Charges against him would then be appropriate. If so, it would be no defense at all for him to insist that he didn't "do anything." He would have done something very serious indeed, for he let his patient die.

Fixing the cause of death may be very important from a legal point of view, for it may determine whether criminal charges are brought against the doctor. But I do not think that this notion can be used to show a moral difference between active and passive euthanasia. The reason why it is considered bad to be the cause of someone's death is that death is regarded as a great evil—and so it is. However, if it has been decided that euthanasia—even passive euthanasia—is desirable in a given case, it has also been decided that in this instance death is no greater an evil than the patient's continued existence. And if this is true, the usual reason for not wanting to be the cause of someone's death simply does not apply.

Finally, doctors may think that all of this is only of academic interest—the sort of thing that philosophers may worry about but that has no practical bearing on their own work. After all, doctors must be concerned about the legal consequences of what they do, and active euthanasia is clearly forbidden by the law. But even so, doctors should also be concerned with the fact that the law is forcing upon them a moral doctrine that may well be indefensible, and has a considerable effect on their practices. Of course, most doctors are not now in the position of being coerced in this matter, for they do not regard themselves as merely going along with what the law requires. Rather, in statements such as the AMA policy statement that I have quoted, they are endorsing this doctrine as a central point of medical ethics. In that statement, active euthanasia is condemned not merely as illegal but as "contrary to that for which the medical profession stands," whereas passive euthanasia is approved. However, the preceding considerations suggest that there is really no moral difference between the two, considered in themselves (there may be important moral differences in some cases in their *consequences*, but, as I pointed out, these differences may make active euthanasia, and not passive euthanasia, the morally preferable option). So, whereas doctors may have to discriminate between active and passive euthanasia to satisfy the law, they should not do any more than that. In particular, they should not give the distinction any added authority and weight by writing it into official statements of medical ethics.

Note

1. A. Shaw, "Doctor, Do We Have a Choice?" *The New York Times Magazine*, January 30, 1972, p. 54.

Is Killing No Worse than Letting Die?

Winston Nesbitt

Winston Nesbitt rejects the claim that there is no moral difference between killing and letting die. He holds that the pair of cases offered by Rachels (see previous article) to show that there is no difference, as well as the pair offered by Tooley described in the article, fail to demonstrate the claim. In both pairs, the agent is prepared to kill and fails to do so only because unexpected circumstances make it unnecessary. This feature, Nesbitt argues, makes both cases in each pair *equally* reprehensible. The examples used by Rachels and Tooley are flawed and cannot support the claim that because letting die is morally acceptable, so, too, is killing. Both, in their cases, are morally unacceptable.

Winston Nesbitt, From "Is Killing No Worse than Letting Die?," *Journal of Applied Philosophy*, Vol. 12, no. 1 (1995): 101–105. Copyright © 1995 Wiley-Blackwell Ltd. Reprinted by permission.

Nesbitt holds, finally, that there is a moral difference between killing and letting die. Letting die is *less* reprehensible than killing, because the kind of person who would let someone die poses a lesser danger than someone who would kill.

1

I want in this paper to consider a kind of argument sometimes produced against the thesis that it is worse to kill someone (that is, to deliberately take action that results in another's death) than merely to allow someone to die (that is, deliberately to fail to take steps which were available and which would have saved another's life). Let us, for brevity's sake, refer to this as the "difference thesis" since it implies that there is a moral difference between killing and letting die.

One approach commonly taken by opponents of the difference thesis is to produce examples of cases in which an agent does not kill, but merely lets someone die, and yet would be generally agreed to be just as morally reprehensible as if he had killed. This kind of appeal to common intuitions might seem an unsatisfactory way of approaching the issue. It has been argued[1] that what stance one takes concerning the difference thesis will depend on the ethical theory one holds, so that we cannot decide what stance is correct independently of deciding what is the correct moral theory. I do not, however, wish to object to the approach in question on these grounds. It may be true that different moral theories dictate different stances concerning the difference thesis, so that a theoretically satisfactory defence or refutation of the thesis requires a satisfactory defence of a theory which entails its soundness or unsoundness. However, the issue of its soundness or otherwise is a vital one in the attempt to decide some pressing moral questions,[2] and we cannot wait for a demonstration of the correct moral theory before taking up any kind of position with regard to it. Moreover, decisions on moral questions directly affecting practice are rarely derived from ethical first principles, but are usually based at some level on common intuitions, and it is arguable that at least where the question is one of public policy, this is as it should be.

2

It might seem at first glance a simple matter to show at least that common moral intuitions favour the difference thesis. Compare, to take an example of John Ladd's,[3] the case in which I push someone who I know cannot swim into a river, thereby killing her, with that in which I come across someone drowning and fail to rescue her, although I am able to do so, thereby letting her die. Wouldn't most of us agree that my behaviour is morally worse in the first case?

However, it would be generally agreed by those involved in the debate that nothing of importance for our issue, not even concerning common opinion, can be learned through considering such an example. As Ladd points out, without being told any more about the cases mentioned, we are inclined to assume that there are other morally relevant differences between them, because there usually would be. We assume, for example, some malicious motive in the case of killing, but perhaps only fear or indifference in the case of failing to save. James Rachels and Michael Tooley, both of whom argue against the difference thesis, make similar points,[4] as does Raziel Abelson, in a paper defending the thesis.[5] Tooley, for example, notes that as well as differences in motives, there are also certain other morally relevant differences between typical acts of killing and typical acts of failing to save which may make us judge them differently. Typically, saving someone requires more effort than refraining from killing someone. Again, an act of killing necessarily results in someone's death, but an act of failing to save does not—someone else may come to the rescue. Factors such as these, it is suggested, may account for our tendency to judge failure to save (i.e., letting die) less harshly than killing. Tooley concludes that if one wishes to appeal to intuitions here, "one must be careful to confine one's attention to pairs of cases that do not differ in these, or other significant respects."[6]

Accordingly, efforts are made by opponents of the difference thesis to produce pairs of cases which do not differ in morally significant respects (other than in one being a case of killing while the other is a case of letting die or failing to save). In fact, at least the major part of the case mounted by Rachels and Tooley against the difference thesis consists of the production of such examples. It is suggested that when we compare a case of killing with one which differs from it *only* in being a case of letting die, we will agree that either agent is as culpable as the other; and this is then taken to show that any inclination we ordinarily have to think killing worse than letting die is attributable to our tending, illegitimately, to think of typical cases of killing and of letting die, which differ in other morally relevant respects. I want now to examine the kind of example usually produced in these contexts.

3

I will begin with the examples produced by James Rachels in the article mentioned earlier, which is fast becoming one of the most frequently reprinted articles in the area.[7] Although the article has been the subject of a good deal of discussion, as far as I know the points which I will make concerning it have not been previously made. Rachels asks us to compare the following two cases. The first is that of Smith, who will gain a large inheritance should his six-year-old nephew die. With this in mind, Smith one evening sneaks into the bathroom where his nephew is taking a bath, and drowns him. The other case, that of Jones, is identical, except that as Jones is about to drown his nephew, the child slips, hits his head, and falls, face down and unconscious, into the bath-water. Jones, delighted at his good fortune, watches as his nephew drowns.

Rachels assumes that we will readily agree that Smith, who kills his nephew, is no worse, morally speaking, than Jones, who merely lets his nephew die. Do we really want to say, he asks, that either behaves better from the moral point of view than the other? It would, he suggests, be a "grotesque perversion of moral reasoning" for Jones to argue, "After all, I didn't do anything except just stand and watch the child drown. I didn't kill him; I only let him die."[8] Yet, Rachels says, if letting die were in itself less bad than killing, this defence would carry some weight.

There is little doubt that Rachels is correct in taking it that we will agree that Smith behaves no worse in his examples than does Jones. Before we are persuaded by this that killing someone is in itself morally no worse than letting someone die, though, we need to consider the examples more closely. We concede that Jones, who merely let his nephew die, is just as reprehensible as Smith, who killed his nephew. Let us ask, however, just what is the ground of our judgement of the agent in each case. In the case of Smith, this seems to be adequately captured by saying that Smith drowned his nephew for motives of personal gain. But can we say that the grounds on which we judge Jones to be reprehensible, and just as reprehensible as Smith, are that he let his nephew drown for motives of personal gain? I suggest not—for this neglects to mention a crucial fact about Jones, namely

that he was fully prepared to kill his nephew, and would have done so had it proved necessary. It would be generally accepted, I think, quite independently of the present debate, that someone who is fully prepared to perform a reprehensible action, in the expectation of certain circumstances, but does not do so because the expected circumstances do not eventuate, is just as reprehensible as someone who actually performs that action in those circumstances. Now this alone is sufficient to account for our judging Jones as harshly as Smith. He was fully prepared to do what Smith did, and would have done so if circumstances had not turned out differently from those in Smith's case. Thus, though we may agree that he is just as reprehensible as Smith, this cannot be taken as showing that his letting his nephew die is as reprehensible as Smith's killing his nephew—for we would have judged him just as harshly, given what he was prepared to do, even if he had not let his nephew die. To make this clear, suppose that we modify Jones' story along the following lines—as before, he sneaks into the bathroom while his nephew is bathing, with the intention of drowning the child in his bath. This time, however, just before he can seize the child, *he* slips and hits his head on the bath, knocking himself unconscious. By the time he regains consciousness, the child, unaware of his intentions, has called his parents, and the opportunity is gone. Here, Jones neither kills his nephew *nor* lets him die—yet I think it would be agreed that given his preparedness to kill the child for personal gain, he is as reprehensible as Smith.

The examples produced by Michael Tooley, in the book referred to earlier, suffer the same defect as those produced by Rachels. Tooley asks us to consider the following pair of scenarios, as it happens also featuring Smith and Jones. In the first, Jones is about to shoot Smith when he sees that Smith will be killed by a bomb unless Jones warns him, as he easily can. Jones does not warn him, and he is killed by the bomb—i.e., Jones lets Smith die. In the other, Jones wants Smith dead, and shoots him—i.e., he kills Smith.

Tooley elsewhere[9] produces this further example: two sons are looking forward to the death of their wealthy father, and decide independently to poison him. One puts poison in his father's whiskey, and is discovered doing so by the other, who was just about to do the same. The latter then allows his father to drink the poisoned whiskey, and refrains from giving him the antidote, which he happens to possess.

Tooley is confident that we will agree that in each pair of cases, the agent who kills is morally no worse than the one who lets die. It will be clear, however, that his examples are open to criticisms parallel to those just produced against Rachels. To take first the case where Jones is saved the trouble of killing Smith by the fortunate circumstance of a bomb's being about to explode near the latter: it is true that we judge Jones to be just as reprehensible as if he had killed Smith, but since he was fully prepared to kill him had he not been saved the trouble by the bomb, we would make the same judgement even if he had neither killed Smith nor let him die (even if, say, no bomb had been present, but Smith suffered a massive and timely heart attack). As for the example of the like-minded sons, here too the son who didn't kill was prepared to do so, and given this, would be as reprehensible as the other even if he had not let his father die (if, say, he did not happen to possess the antidote, and so was powerless to save him).

Let us try to spell out more clearly just where the examples produced by Rachels and Tooley fail. What both writers overlook is that what determines whether someone is reprehensible or not is not simply what he in fact does, but what he is prepared to do, perhaps as revealed by what he in fact does. Thus, while Rachels is correct in taking it that we will be inclined to judge Smith and Jones in his examples equally harshly, this is not surprising, since both are judged reprehensible for precisely the same reason, namely that they were fully prepared to kill for motives of personal gain. The same, of course, is true of Tooley's examples. In each example he gives of an agent who lets another die, the agent is fully prepared to kill (though in the event, he is spared the necessity). In their efforts to ensure that the members of each pair of cases they produce do not differ in any morally relevant respect (except that one is a case of killing and the other of letting die), Rachels and Tooley make them *too* similar—not only do Rachels' Smith and Jones, for example, have identical motives, but both are guilty of the same moral offence.

4

Given the foregoing account of the failings of the examples produced by Rachels and Tooley, what modifications do they require if they are to be legitimately used to gauge our attitudes towards killing and letting die, respectively? Let us again concentrate on Rachels' examples. Clearly, if his argument is to avoid the defect pointed out, we must stipulate that though Jones was prepared to let his nephew die once he saw that this would happen unless he intervened, he was not prepared to kill the child. The story

will now go something like this: Jones stands to gain considerably from his nephew's death, as before, but he is not prepared to kill him for this reason. However, he happens to be on hand when his nephew slips, hits his head, and falls face down in the bath. Remembering that he will profit from the child's death, he allows him to drown. We need, however, to make a further stipulation, regarding the explanation of Jones' not being prepared to kill his nephew. It cannot be that he fears untoward consequences for himself, such as detection and punishment, or that he is too lazy to choose such an active course, or that the idea simply had not occurred to him. I think it would be common ground in the debate that if the only explanation of his not being prepared to kill his nephew was one of these kinds, he would be morally no better than Smith, who differed only in being more daring, or more energetic, whether or not fate then happened to offer him the opportunity to let his nephew die instead. In that case, we must suppose that the reason Jones is prepared to let his nephew die, but not to kill him, is a moral one—not intervening to save the child, he holds, is one thing, but actually bringing about his death is another, and altogether beyond the pale.

I suggest, then, that the case with which we must compare that of Smith is this: Jones happens to be on hand when his nephew slips, hits his head, and falls unconscious into his bath-water. It is clear to Jones that the child will drown if he does not intervene. He remembers that the child's death would be greatly to his advantage, and does not intervene. Though he is prepared to let the child die, however, and in fact does so, he would not have been prepared to kill him, because, as he might put it, wicked though he is, he draws the line at killing for gain.

I am not entirely sure what the general opinion would be here as to the relative reprehensibility of Smith and Jones. I can only report my own, which is that Smith's behaviour is indeed morally worse than that of Jones. What I do want to insist on, however, is that, for the reasons I have given, we cannot take our reactions to the examples provided by Rachels and Tooley as an indication of our intuitions concerning the relative heinousness of killing and of letting die.

So far, we have restricted ourselves to discussion of common intuitions on our question, and made no attempt to argue for any particular answer. I will conclude by pointing out that, given the fairly common view that the *raison d'etre* of morality is to make it possible for people to live together in reasonable peace and security, it is not difficult to provide a rationale for the intuition that in our modified version of Rachels' examples, Jones is less reprehensible than Smith. For it is clearly preferable to have Jones-like persons around rather than Smith-like ones. We are not threatened by the former—such a person will not save me if my life should be in danger, but in this he is no more dangerous than an incapacitated person, or for that matter, a rock or tree (in fact he may be better, for he *might* save me as long as he doesn't think he will profit from my death). Smith-like persons, however, *are* a threat—if such a person should come to believe that she will benefit sufficiently from my death, then not only must I expect no help from her if my life happens to be in danger, but I must fear positive attempts on my life. In that case, given the view mentioned of the point of morality, people prepared to behave as Smith does are clearly of greater concern from the moral point of view than those prepared only to behave as Jones does; which is to say that killing is indeed morally worse than letting die.

Notes

1. See, for example, John Chandler (1990), "Killing and letting die—putting the debate in context," *Australasian Journal of Philosophy*, 68, no. 4, pp. 420–31.

2. It underlies, or is often claimed to underlie, for example, the Roman Catholic position on certain issues in the abortion debate, and the view that while "passive" euthanasia may sometimes be permissible, "active" euthanasia never is. It also seems involved in the common view that even if it is wrong to fail to give aid to the starving of the world, thereby letting them die, it is not as wrong as dropping bombs on them, thereby killing them.

3. John Ladd (1985), "Positive and negative euthanasia" in James E. White (ed.), *Contemporary Moral Problems* (St. Paul: West Publishing Co.), pp. 58–68.

4. James Rachels (1979), "Active and passive euthanasia" in James Rachels (ed.), *Moral Problems* (New York: Harper and Row), pp. 490–7; Michael Tooley (1983), *Abortion and Infanticide* (Oxford: Clarendon Press), pp. 187–8.

5. Raziel Abelson (1982), "There is a moral difference," in Raziel Abelson and Marie-Louise Friquegnon (eds.), *Ethics for Modern Life* (New York: St. Martin's Press), pp. 73–83.

6. Tooley, *Abortion and Infanticide*, p. 189.

7. Rachels, "Active and passive euthanasia."

8. Ibid., p. 494.

9. Michael Tooley (1980), "An irrelevant consideration: killing and letting die" in Bonnie Steinbeck (ed.), *Killing and Letting Die* (Englewood Cliffs, NJ: Prentice-Hall), pp. 56–62.

Section 2: The Case for Allowing Euthanasia and Assisted Suicide

The Wrongfulness of Euthanasia

J. Gay-Williams

J. Gay-Williams defines *euthanasia* as intentionally taking the life of a person who is believed to be suffering from some illness or injury from which recovery cannot reasonably be expected. Gay-Williams rejects passive euthanasia as a *name* for actions that are usually designated by the phrase but seems to approve of the actions themselves. He argues that euthanasia as intentional killing goes against natural law because it violates the natural inclination to preserve life. Furthermore, both self-interest and possible practical consequences of euthanasia provide reasons for rejecting it.

My impression is that euthanasia—the idea, if not the practice—is slowly gaining acceptance within our society. Cynics might attribute this to an increasing tendency to devalue human life, but I do not believe this is the major factor. The acceptance is much more likely to be the result of unthinking sympathy and

benevolence. Well-publicized, tragic stories like that of Karen Quinlan elicit from us deep feelings of compassion. We think to ourselves, "She and her family would be better off if she were dead." It is an easy step from this very human response to the view that if someone (and others) would be better off dead, then it might be all right to kill that person.[1] Although I respect the compassion that leads to this conclusion, I believe the conclusion is wrong. I want to show that euthanasia is wrong. It is inherently wrong, but it is also wrong judged from the standpoints of self-interest and of practical effects.

Before presenting my arguments to support this claim, it would be well to define "euthanasia." An essential aspect of euthanasia is that it involves taking a human life, either one's own or that of another. Also, the person whose life is taken must be someone who is believed to be suffering from some disease or injury from which recovery cannot reasonably be expected. Finally, the action must be deliberate and intentional. Thus, euthanasia is intentionally taking the life of a presumably hopeless person. Whether the life is one's own or that of another, the taking of it is still euthanasia.

It is important to be clear about the deliberate and intentional aspect of the killing. If a hopeless person is given an injection of the wrong drug by mistake and this causes his death, this is wrongful killing but not euthanasia. The killing cannot be the result of accident. Furthermore, if the person is given an injection of a drug that is believed to be necessary to treat his disease or better his condition and the person dies as a result, then this is neither wrongful killing nor euthanasia. The intention was to make the patient well, not kill him. Similarly, when a patient's condition is such that it is not reasonable to hope that any medical procedures or treatments will save his life, a failure to implement the procedures or treatments is not euthanasia. If the person dies, this will be as a result of his injuries or disease and not because of his failure to receive treatment.

The failure to continue treatment after it has been realized that the patient has little chance of benefiting from it has been characterized by some as "passive euthanasia." This phrase is misleading and mistaken.[2] In such cases, the person involved is not killed (the first essential aspect of euthanasia), nor is the death of the person intended by the withholding of additional treatment (the third essential aspect of euthanasia). The aim may be to spare the person additional and unjustifiable pain, to save him from the indignities of hopeless manipulations, and to avoid increasing the financial and emotional burden on his family. When I buy a pencil it is so that I can use it to write, not to contribute to an increase in the gross national product. This may be the unintended consequence of my action, but it is not the aim of my action. So it is with failing to continue the treatment of a dying person. I intend his death no more than I intend to reduce the GNP by not using medical supplies. His is an unintended dying, and so-called "passive euthanasia" is not euthanasia at all.

1. The Argument from Nature

Every human being has a natural inclination to continue living. Our reflexes and responses fit us to fight attackers, flee wild animals, and dodge out of the way of trucks. In our daily lives we exercise the caution and care necessary to protect ourselves. Our bodies are similarly structured for survival right down to the molecular level. When we are cut, our capillaries seal shut, our blood clots, and fibrogen is produced to start the process of healing the wound. When we are invaded by bacteria, antibodies are produced to fight against the alien organisms, and their remains are swept out of the body by special cells designed for clean-up work.

Euthanasia does violence to this natural goal of survival. It is literally acting against nature because all the processes of nature are bent towards the end of bodily survival. Euthanasia defeats these subtle mechanisms in a way that, in a particular case, disease and injury might not.

It is possible, but not necessary, to make an appeal to revealed religion in this connection.[3] Man as trustee of his body acts against God, its rightful possessor, when he takes his own life. He also violates the commandment to hold life sacred and never to take it without just and compelling cause. But since this appeal will persuade only those who are prepared to accept that religion has access to revealed truths, I shall not employ this line of argument.

It is enough, I believe, to recognize that the organization of the human body and our patterns of behavioral responses make the continuation of life a natural goal. By reason alone, then, we can recognize that euthanasia sets us against our own nature.[4] Furthermore, in doing so, euthanasia does violence to our dignity. Our dignity comes from seeking our ends. When one of our goals is survival, and actions are taken that eliminate that goal, then our natural dignity suffers. Unlike animals, we are conscious through reason of our nature and our ends. Euthanasia involves acting as if this dual nature—inclination towards survival and awareness of this as an end—did not exist. Thus, euthanasia denies our basic human character and requires that we regard ourselves or others as something less than fully human.

2. The Argument from Self-Interest

The above arguments are, I believe, sufficient to show that euthanasia is inherently wrong. But there are reasons for considering it wrong when judged by standards other than reason. Because death is final and irreversible, euthanasia contains within it the possibility that we will work against our own interest if we practice it or allow it to be practiced on us.

Contemporary medicine has high standards of excellence and a proven record of accomplishment, but it does not possess perfect and complete knowledge. A mistaken diagnosis is possible, and so is a mistaken prognosis. Consequently, we may believe that we are dying of a disease when, as a matter of fact, we may not be. We may think that we have no hope of recovery when, as a matter of fact, our chances are quite good. In such circumstances, if euthanasia were permitted, we would die needlessly. Death is final and the chance of error too great to approve the practice of euthanasia.

Also, there is always the possibility that an experimental procedure or a hitherto untried technique will pull us through. We should at least keep this option open, but euthanasia closes it off. Furthermore, spontaneous remission does occur in many cases. For no apparent reason, a patient simply recovers when those all around him, including his physicians, expected him to die. Euthanasia would just guarantee their expectations and leave no room for the "miraculous" recoveries that frequently occur.

Finally, knowing that we can take our life at any time (or ask another to take it) might well incline us to give up too easily. The will to live is strong in all of us, but it can be weakened by pain and suffering and feelings of hopelessness. If during a bad time we allow ourselves to be killed, we never have a chance to reconsider. Recovery from a serious illness requires that we fight for it, and anything that weakens our determination by suggesting that there is an easy way out is ultimately against our own interest. Also, we may be inclined towards euthanasia because of our concern for others. If we see our sickness and suffering as an emotional and financial burden on our family, we may feel that to leave our life is to make their lives easier.[5] The very presence of the possibility of euthanasia may keep us from surviving when we might.

3. The Argument from Practical Effects

Doctors and nurses are, for the most part, totally committed to saving lives. A life lost is, for them, almost a personal failure, an insult to their skills and knowledge. Euthanasia as a practice might well alter this. It could have a corrupting influence so that in any case that is severe doctors and nurses might not try hard enough to save the patient. They might decide that the patient would simply be "better off dead" and take the steps necessary to make that come about. This attitude could then carry over to their dealings with patients less seriously ill. The result would be an overall decline in the quality of medical care.

Finally, euthanasia as a policy is a slippery slope. A person apparently hopelessly ill may be allowed to take his own life. Then he may be permitted to deputize others to do it for him should he no longer be able to act. The judgment of others then becomes the ruling factor. Already at this point euthanasia is not personal and voluntary, for others are acting "on behalf of" the patient as they see fit. This may well incline them to act on behalf of other patients who have not authorized them to exercise their judgment. It is only a short step, then, from voluntary euthanasia (self-inflicted or authorized), to directed euthanasia administered to a patient who has given no authorization, to involuntary euthanasia conducted as part of a social policy.[6] Recently many psychiatrists and sociologists have argued that we define as "mental illness" those forms of behavior that we disapprove of.[7] This gives us license then to lock up those who display the behavior. The category of the "hopelessly ill" provides the possibility of even worse abuse. Embedded in a social policy, it would give society or its representatives the authority to eliminate all those who might be considered too "ill" to function normally any longer. The dangers of euthanasia are too great to all to run the risk of approving it in any form. The first slippery step may well lead to a serious and harmful fall.

I hope that I have succeeded in showing why the benevolence that inclines us to give approval of euthanasia is misplaced. Euthanasia is inherently wrong because it violates the nature and dignity of human beings. But even those who are not convinced by this must be persuaded that the potential personal and social dangers inherent in euthanasia are sufficient to forbid our approving it either as a personal practice or as a public policy.

Suffering is surely a terrible thing, and we have a clear duty to comfort those in need and to ease their suffering when we can. But suffering is also a natural part of life with values for the individual and for others that we should not overlook. We may legitimately seek for others and for ourselves an easeful death, as Arthur Dyck has pointed out.[8] Euthanasia, however, is not just an easeful death. It is a wrongful death. Euthanasia is not just dying. It is killing.

Notes

1. For a sophisticated defense of this position see Philippa Foot, "Euthanasia," *Philosophy and Public Affairs*, vol. 6 (1977), pp. 85–112. Foot does not endorse the radical conclusion that euthanasia, voluntary and involuntary, is always right.

2. James Rachels rejects the distinction between active and passive euthanasia as morally irrelevant in his "Active and Passive Euthanasia," *New England Journal of Medicine*, vol. 292, pp. 78–80. But see the criticism by Foot, pp. 100–103.

3. For a defense of this view see J. V. Sullivan, "The Immorality of Euthanasia," in *Beneficent Euthanasia*, ed. Marvin Kohl (Buffalo, N.Y.: Prometheus Books, 1975), pp. 34–44.

4. This point is made by Ray V. McIntyre in "Voluntary Euthanasia: The Ultimate Perversion," *Medical Counterpoint*, vol. 2, pp. 26–29.

5. See McIntyre, p. 28.

6. See Sullivan, "Immorality of Euthanasia," pp. 34–44, for a fuller argument in support of this view.

7. See, for example, Thomas S. Szasz, *The Myth of Mental Illness*, rev. ed. (New York: Harper & Row, 1974).

8. Arthur Dyck, "Beneficent Euthanasia and Benemortasia," Kohl, op. cit., pp. 117–129.

When Self-Determination Runs Amok

Daniel Callahan

Daniel Callahan argues against any social policy allowing voluntary euthanasia and assisted suicide. He maintains that self-determination and mercy (the two values supporting them) may become separated. When this happens, assisted suicide for any reason and nonvoluntary euthanasia for the incompetent will become acceptable.

Callahan rejects Rachels' claim that the difference between killing and letting die is morally irrelevant. He holds that the difference is fundamental and that the decision to terminate a life requires a judgment about meaning and quality that physicians are not competent to make.

In general, Callahan warns us, we must not allow physicians to move beyond the bounds of promoting health, and exercise the power of deciding questions about human happiness and well-being. Permitting them to make such decisions will lead to widespread abuse and destroy the integrity of the medical profession.

The euthanasia debate is not just another moral debate, one in a long list of arguments in our pluralistic society. It is profoundly emblematic of three important turning points in Western thought. The first is that of the legitimate conditions under which one person can kill another. The acceptance of voluntary active euthanasia would morally sanction what can only be called "consenting adult killing." By the term I mean the killing of one person by another in the name of their mutual right to be killer and killed if they freely agree to play those roles. This turn flies in the face of a long-standing effort to limit the circumstances under which one person can

Daniel Callahan, From "When Self-Determination Runs Amok," *Hastings Center Report*, Vol. 22, (March/April 1992): 52–55. Copyright © 1992 Hastings Center Report. All rights reserved. Reproduced by permission.

take the life of another, from efforts to control the free flow of guns and arms, to abolish capital punishment, and to more tightly control warfare. Euthanasia would add a whole new category of killing to a society that already has too many excuses to indulge itself in that way.

The second turning point lies in the meaning and limits of self-determination. The acceptance of euthanasia would sanction a view of autonomy holding that individuals may, in the name of their own private, idiosyncratic view of the good life, call upon others, including such institutions as medicine, to help them pursue that life, even at the risk of harm to the common good. This works against the idea that the meaning and scope of our own right to lead our own lives must be conditioned by, and be compatible with, the good of the community, which is more than an aggregate of self-directing individuals.

The third turning point is to be found in the claim being made upon medicine: it should be prepared to make its skills available to individuals to help them achieve their private vision of the good life. This puts medicine in the business of promoting the individualistic pursuit of general human happiness and well-being. It would overturn the traditional belief that medicine should limit its domain to promoting and preserving human health, redirecting it instead to the relief of that suffering which stems from life itself, not merely from a sick body.

I believe that, at each of these three turning points, proponents of euthanasia push us in the wrong direction. Arguments in favor of euthanasia fall into four general categories, which I will take up in turn: (1) the moral claim of individual self-determination and well-being; (2) the moral irrelevance of the difference between killing and allowing to die; (3) the supposed paucity of evidence to show likely harmful consequences of legalized euthanasia; and (4) the compatibility of euthanasia and medical practice.

Self-Determination

Central to most arguments for euthanasia is the principle of self-determination. People are presumed to have an interest in deciding for themselves, according to their own beliefs about what makes life good, how they will conduct their lives. That is an important value, but the question in the euthanasia context is, What does it mean and how far should it extend? If it were a question of suicide, where a person takes their own life without assistance from another, that principle might be pertinent, at least for debate. But euthanasia is not that limited a matter. The self-determination in that case can only be effected by the moral and physical assistance of another. Euthanasia is thus no longer a matter only of self-determination, but of a mutual, social decision between two people, the one to be killed and the other to do the killing.

How are we to make the moral move from my right of self-determination to some doctor's right to kill me—from *my* right to *his* right? Where does the doctor's moral warrant to kill come from? Ought doctors to be able to kill anyone they want as long as permission is given by competent persons? Is our right to life just like a piece of property, to be given away or alienated if the price (happiness, relief of suffering) is right? And then to be destroyed with our permission once alienated?

In answer to all those questions, I will say this: I have yet to hear a plausible argument why it should be permissible for us to put this kind of power in the hands of another, whether a doctor or anyone else. The idea that we can waive our right to life, and then give to another the power to take that life, requires a justification yet to be provided by anyone.

Slavery was long ago outlawed on the ground that one person should not have the right to own another, even with the other's permission. Why? Because it is a fundamental moral wrong for one person to give over his life and fate to another, whatever the good consequences, and no less a wrong for another person to have that kind of total, final power. Like slavery, dueling was long ago banned on similar grounds: even free, competent individuals should not have the power to kill each other, whatever their motives, whatever the circumstances. Consenting adult killing, like consenting adult slavery or degradation, is a strange route to human dignity.

There is another problem as well. If doctors, once sanctioned to carry out euthanasia, are to be themselves responsible moral agents—not simply hired hands with lethal injections at the ready—then they must have their own *independent* moral grounds to kill those who request such services. What do I mean? As those who favor euthanasia are quick to point out, some people want it because their life has become so burdensome it no longer seems worth living.

The doctor will have a difficulty at this point. The degree and intensity to which people suffer from their diseases and their dying, and whether they find life more of a burden than a benefit, has very little directly to do with the nature or extent of their actual physical condition. Three people can have the same condition, but only one will find the suffering unbearable. People suffer, but suffering is as much a function of the values of individuals as it is of the physical causes of that suffering. Inevitably in that circumstance, the doctor will in effect be treating the patient's values. To be responsible, the doctor would have to share those values. The doctor would have to decide, on her own, whether the patient's life was "no longer worth living."

But how could a doctor possibly know that or make such a judgment? Just because the patient said so? I raise this question because, while in Holland at the euthanasia conference reported by Maurice de Wachter . . . , the doctors present agreed that there is no objective way of measuring or judging the claims of patients that their suffering is unbearable. And if it is difficult to measure suffering, how much more difficult to determine the value of a patient's statement that her life is not worth living?

However one might want to answer such questions, the very need to ask them, to inquire into the physician's responsibility and grounds for medical and moral judgment, points out the social nature of the decision. Euthanasia is not a private matter of self-determination. It is an act that requires two people to make it possible, and a complicit society to make it acceptable.

Killing and Allowing to Die

Against common opinion, the argument is sometimes made that there is no moral difference between stopping life-sustaining treatment and more active forms of killing, such as lethal injection. Instead I would contend that the notion that there is no morally significant difference between omission and commission is just wrong. Consider in its broad implications what the eradication of the distinction implies: that death from disease has been banished, leaving only the actions of physicians in terminating treatment as the cause of death. Biology, which used to bring about death, has apparently been displaced by human agency. Doctors have finally, I suppose, thus genuinely become gods, now doing what nature and the deities once did.

What is the mistake here? It lies in confusing causality and culpability, and in failing to note the way in which human societies have overlaid natural causes with moral rules and interpretations. Causality (by which I mean the direct physical causes of death) and culpability (by which I mean our attribution of moral responsibility to human actions) are confused under three circumstances.

They are confused, first, when the action of a physician in stopping treatment of a patient with an underlying lethal disease is construed as *causing* death. On the contrary, the physician's omission can only bring about death on the condition that the patient's disease will kill him in the absence of treatment. We may hold the physician morally responsible for the death, if we have morally judged such actions wrongful omissions. But it confuses reality and moral judgment to see an omitted action as having the same causal status as one that directly kills. A lethal injection will kill both a healthy person and a sick person. A physician's omitted treatment will have no effect on a healthy person. Turn off the machine on me, a healthy person, and nothing will happen. It will only, in contrast, bring the life of a sick person to an end because of an underlying fatal disease.

Causality and culpability are confused, second, when we fail to note that judgments of moral responsibility and culpability are human constructs. By that I mean that we human beings, after moral reflection, have decided to call some actions right or wrong, and to devise moral rules to deal with them. When physicians could do nothing to stop death, they were not held responsible for it. When, with medical progress, they began to have some power over death—but only its timing and circumstances, not its ultimate inevitability—moral rules were devised to set forth their obligations. Natural causes of death were not thereby banished. They were, instead, overlaid with a medical ethics designed to determine moral culpability in deploying medical power.

To confuse the judgments of this ethics with the physical causes of death—which is the connotation of the word kill—is to confuse nature and human action. People will, one way or another, die of some disease; death will have dominion over all of us. To say that a doctor "kills" a patient by allowing this to happen should only be understood as a moral judgment about the licitness of his omission, nothing more. We can, as a fashion of speech only, talk about a doctor *killing* a patient by omitting treatment he should have provided. It is a fashion of speech precisely because it is the underlying disease that brings death when treatment is omitted; that is its cause, not the physician's omission. It is a misuse of the word *killing* to use it when a doctor stops a treatment he believes will no longer benefit the patient—when, that is, he steps aside to allow an eventually inevitable death to occur now rather than later. The only deaths that human beings invented are those that come from direct killing—when, with a lethal injection, we both cause death and are morally responsible for it. In the case of omissions, we do not cause death even if we may be judged morally responsible for it.

This difference between causality and culpability also helps us see why a doctor who has omitted a treatment he should have provided has "killed" that patient while another doctor—performing precisely the same act of omission on another patient in different circumstances—does not kill her, but only allows her to die. The difference is that we have come, by moral convention and conviction, to classify unauthorized or illegitimate omissions as acts of "killing." We call them "killing" in the expanded sense of the term: a culpable action that permits the real cause of death, the underlying disease, to proceed to its lethal conclusion. By contrast, the doctor who, at the patient's request, omits or terminates unwanted treatment does not kill at all. Her underlying disease, not his action, is the physical cause of death; and we have agreed to consider actions of that kind to be morally licit. He thus can truly be said to have "allowed" her to die.

If we fail to maintain the distinction between killing and allowing to die, moreover, there are some disturbing possibilities. The first would be to confirm many physicians in their already too-powerful belief that, when patients die or when physicians stop treatment because of the futility of continuing it, they are somehow both morally and physically responsible for the deaths that follow. That notion needs to be abolished, not strengthened. It needlessly and wrongly burdens the physician, to whom should not be attributed the powers of the gods. The second possibility would be that, in every case where a doctor judges medical treatment no longer effective in prolonging life, a quick and direct killing of the patient would be seen as the next, most reasonable step, on grounds of both humaneness and economics. I do not see how that logic could easily be rejected.

Calculating the Consequences

When concerns about the adverse social consequences of permitting euthanasia are raised, its advocates tend to dismiss them as unfounded and overly speculative. On the contrary, recent data about the Dutch experience suggests that such concerns are right on target. From my own discussions in Holland, and from the articles on that subject in this issue and elsewhere, I believe we can now fully see most of the *likely* consequences of legal euthanasia.

Three consequences seem almost certain, in this or any other country: the inevitability of some abuse of the law; the difficulty of precisely writing, and then enforcing, the law; and the inherent slipperiness of the moral reasons for legalizing euthanasia in the first place.

Why is abuse inevitable? One reason is that almost all laws on delicate, controversial matters are to some extent abused. This happens because not everyone will agree with the law as written and will bend it, or ignore it, if they can get away with it. From explicit admissions to me by Dutch proponents of euthanasia, and from the corroborating information provided by the Remmelink Report and the outside studies of Carlos Gomez and John Keown, I am convinced that in the Netherlands there are a substantial number of cases of nonvoluntary euthanasia, that is, euthanasia undertaken without the explicit permission of the person being killed. The other reason abuse is inevitable is that the law is likely to have a low enforcement priority in the criminal justice system. Like other laws of similar status, unless there is an unrelenting and harsh willingness to pursue abuse, violations will ordinarily be tolerated. The worst thing to me about my experience in Holland was the casual, seemingly indifferent attitude toward abuse. I think that would happen everywhere.

Why would it be hard to precisely write, and then enforce, the law? The Dutch speak about the requirement of "unbearable" suffering, but admit that such a term is just about indefinable, a highly subjective matter admitting of no objective standards. A requirement for outside opinion is nice, but it is easy to find complaisant colleagues. A requirement that a medical condition be "terminal" will run aground on the notorious difficulties of knowing when an illness is actually terminal.

Apart from those technical problems there is a more profound worry. I see no way, even in principle, to write or enforce a meaningful law that can guarantee effective procedural safeguards. The reason is obvious yet almost always overlooked. The euthanasia transaction will ordinarily take place within the boundaries of the private and confidential doctor–patient relationship. No one can possibly know what takes place in that context unless the doctor chooses to reveal it. In Holland, less than 10 percent of the physicians report their acts of euthanasia and do so with almost complete legal impunity. There is no reason why the situation should be any better elsewhere. Doctors will have their own reasons for keeping euthanasia secret, and some patients will have no less a motive for wanting it concealed.

I would mention, finally, that the moral logic of the motives for euthanasia contain within them the ingredients of abuse. The two standard motives for euthanasia and assisted suicide are said to be our right of self-determination, and our claim upon the mercy of others, especially doctors, to relieve our suffering. These two motives are typically spliced together and presented as a single justification. Yet if they are considered independently—and there is no inherent reason why they must be linked—they reveal serious problems. It is said that a competent, adult person should have a right to euthanasia for the relief of suffering. But why must the person be suffering? Does not that stipulation already compromise the principle of self-determination? How can self-determination have any limits? Whatever the person's motives may be, why are they not sufficient?

Consider next the person who is suffering but not competent, who is perhaps demented or mentally retarded. The standard argument would deny euthanasia to that person. But why? If a person is suffering but not competent, then it would seem grossly unfair to deny relief solely on the grounds of incompetence. Are the incompetent less entitled to relief from suffering than the competent? Will it only be affluent, middle-class people, mentally fit and savvy about working the medical system, who can qualify? Do the incompetent suffer less because of their incompetence?

Considered from these angles, there are no good moral reasons to limit euthanasia once the principle of taking life for that purpose has been legitimated. If we really believe in self-determination, then any competent person should have a right to be killed by a doctor for any reason that suits him. If we believe in the relief of suffering, then it seems cruel and capricious to deny it to the incompetent. There is, in short, no reasonable or logical stopping point once the turn has been made down the road to euthanasia, which could soon turn into a convenient and commodious expressway.

Euthanasia and Medical Practice

A fourth kind of argument one often hears both in the Netherlands and in this country is that euthanasia and assisted suicide are perfectly compatible with the aims of medicine. I would note at the very outset that a physician who participates in another person's suicide already abuses medicine. Apart from depression (the main statistical cause of suicide), people commit suicide because they find life empty, oppressive, or meaningless. Their judgment is a judgment about the value of continued life, not only about health (even if they are sick). Are doctors now to be given the right to make judgments about the kinds of life worth living and to give their blessing to suicide for those they judge wanting? What conceivable competence, technical or moral, could doctors claim to play such a role? Are we to medicalize suicide, turning judgments about its worth and value into one more clinical issue? Yes, those are rhetorical questions.

Yet they bring us to the core of the problem of euthanasia and medicine. The great temptation of modern medicine, not always resisted, is to move beyond the promotion and preservation of health into the boundless realm of general human happiness and well-being. The root problem of illness and mortality is both medical and philosophical or religious. "Why must I die?" can be asked as a technical, biological question or as a question about the meaning of life. When medicine tries to respond to the latter, which it is always under pressure to do, it moves beyond its proper role.

It is not medicine's place to lift from us the burden of that suffering which turns on the meaning we assign to the decay of the body and its eventual death. It is not medicine's place to determine when lives are not worth living or when the burden of life is too great to be borne. Doctors have no conceivable way of evaluating such claims on the part of patients, and they should have no right to act in response to them. Medicine should try to relieve human suffering, but only that suffering which is brought on by illness and dying as biological phenomena, not that suffering which comes from anguish or despair at the human condition.

Doctors ought to relieve those forms of suffering that medically accompany serious illness and the threat of death. They should relieve pain, do what they can to allay anxiety and uncertainty, and be a comforting presence. As sensitive human beings, doctors should be prepared to respond to patients who ask why they must die, or die in pain. But here the doctor and the patient are at the same level. The doctor may have no better an answer to those old questions than anyone else; and certainly no special insight from his training as a physician. It would be terrible for physicians to forget this, and to think that in a swift, lethal injection, medicine has found its own answer to the riddle of life. It would be a false answer, given by the wrong people. It would be no less a false answer for patients. They should neither ask medicine to put its own vocation at risk to serve their private interests, nor think that the answer to suffering is to be killed by another. The problem is precisely that, too often in human history, killing has seemed the quick, efficient way to put aside that which burdens us. It rarely helps, and too often simply adds to one evil still another. That is what I believe euthanasia would accomplish. It is self-determination run amok.

Section 3: The Case for Allowing Euthanasia and Physician-Assisted Suicide

When Abstract Moralizing Runs Amok

John Lachs

John Lachs claims that Callahan (see Section 1) fails to grasp the moral problems leading people to consider euthanasia. They are not interested in it as an escape from the suffering inherent in "the human condition," but as an end to pain and a burdensome life.

Callahan holds that even if we have the right to kill ourselves, it intrinsically cannot be transferred to others. But Lachs argues that the idea of a right that cannot be transferred makes no sense.

Callahan also claims that once the principle of taking life has been "legitimized," there can be no good moral reasons for not killing someone for any reason at all. Lachs argues that Callahan's claim rests on the view that judgments about our suffering and the value of our lives are subjective (and so not necessarily shared by others). Yet physicians are able to review objectively a patient's request to die with respect to the patient's condition and situation.

Contrary to Callahan's implication, no one has ever endorsed the principle of autonomy as absolute. It expresses one value among others. But it recognizes that our lives belong to ourselves and that society must justify infringements, and this is what the debate over euthanasia is about.

Moral reasoning is more objectionable when it is abstract than when it is merely wrong. For abstractness all but guarantees error by missing the human predicament that needs to be addressed, and worse, it is a sign that thought has failed to keep faith with its mission. The function of moral reflection is to shed light on the difficult problems we face; it cannot perform its job without a clear understanding of how and why certain of our practices come to seem no longer satisfactory.

It is just this grasp of the problem that is conspicuously lacking in Daniel Callahan's assault on euthanasia in "Self-Determination Run Amok."[1] The rhetoric Callahan unleashes gives not even a hint of the grave contemporary moral problems that euthanasia and assisted suicide, a growing number of people now think, promise to resolve.

John Lachs, From "When Abstract Moralizing Runs Amok," *The Journal of Clinical Ethics*, Vol 5, (1994): 10–13. Copyright © 1994 JCE. All rights reserved. Used with permission.

Instead, we are offered a set of abstract principles calculated to discredit euthanasia rather than to contribute to a sound assessment of it. Thus, Callahan informs us that suffering "brought on by illness and dying as biological phenomena"[2] is to be contrasted with suffering that comes from "anguish or despair at the human condition." The former constitutes the proper concern of medicine (so much for psychiatry!), the latter of religion and philosophy. Medication is the answer to physical pain; euthanasia can, therefore, be only a misconceived response to worries about the meaning of existence. Those who believe in it offer a "swift lethal injection" as the "answer to the riddle of life."

This way of putting the matter will come as a surprise to those who suffer from terrible diseases and who no longer find life worth living. It is grotesque to suppose that such individuals are looking for the meaning of existence and find it, absurdly, in a lethal injection. Their predicament is not intellectual but existential. They are not interested in the meaning of life but in acting on their belief that their own continued existence is, on balance, of no further benefit to them.

Those who advocate the legalization of euthanasia and the practice of assisted suicide propose them as answers to a serious and growing social problem. We now have the power to sustain the biological existence of large numbers of very sick people, and we use this power freely. Accordingly, individuals suffering from painful terminal diseases, Alzheimer's patients, and those in a persistent vegetative state are routinely kept alive long past the point where they can function as human beings. They must bear the pain of existence without the ability to perform the activities that give life meaning. Some of these people feel intensely that they are a burden to others, as well as to themselves, and that their speedy and relatively dignified departure would be a relief to all concerned. Many observers of no more than average sensitivity agree that the plight of these patients is severe enough to justify such desires.

Some of these sufferers are physically not in a position to end their lives. Others could do so if they had the necessary instruments. In our culture, however, few have a taste for blowing out their brains or jumping from high places. That leaves drugs, which almost everyone is accustomed to taking, and which everyone knows can ease one peacefully to the other side.

The medical profession has, however, acquired monopoly power over drugs. And the danger of legal entanglement has made physicians wary of helping patients hasten their deaths in the discreet, humane way that has been customary for centuries. The result is that people who want to die and for whom death has long ceased to be an evil can find no way out of their misery. Current and growing pressures on the medical profession to help such sufferers are, therefore, due at least partly to medicine itself. People want physicians to aid in their suicides because, without such help, they cannot end their lives. This restriction of human autonomy is due to the social power of medicine; it is neither surprising nor morally wrong, therefore, to ask those responsible for this limitation to undo some of its most noxious effects. If the medical profession relinquished its hold on drugs, people could make effective choices about their future without the assistance of physicians. Even limited access to deadly drugs, restricted to single doses for those who desire them and who are certified to be of sound mind and near the end of life, would keep physicians away from dealing in death.

Unfortunately, however, there is little sensible public discussion of such policy alternatives. And these policy alternatives may, in any case, not satisfy Callahan, who appears to believe that there is something radically wrong with anyone terminating a human life. Because he plays coy, his actual beliefs are difficult to make out. He says the notion that self-determination extends to suicide "might be pertinent, at least for debate."[3] But his argument against euthanasia sidesteps this issue: he maintains that even if there is a right to kill oneself, it is not one that can be transferred. The reason for this is that doing so would lead to "a fundamental moral wrong"—that of one person giving over "his life and fate to another."

One might wonder how we know that transferring power over oneself is "a fundamental moral wrong." Callahan appears to entertain the idea with intuitive certainty, which gives him the moral and the logical high ground and entitles him to demand a justification from whoever disagrees. But such intuitions are problematic themselves: is fervent embrace of them enough to guarantee their truth? Morality would be very distant from the concerns of life if it depended on such guideposts placed here and there in the desert of facts, unrelated to each other or to anything else. Their message, moreover, makes the guideposts suspect: it comes closer to being an echo of tradition or an expression of current views than a revelation of eternal moral truths.

Most important, the very idea of a right that intrinsically *cannot* be handed on is difficult to grasp. Under normal circumstances, to have a right is to be free or to be entitled to have or to do something. I have a right, for example, to clean my teeth. No one else has the right to do that without my consent. But I can authorize another, say my sweetheart or my dental hygienist, to do it for me. Similarly, I can assign my right to my house, my left kidney, to raising my children, to deciding when I rise, when I go to sleep, and what I do in between (by joining the Army), and by a power of attorney even to pursuing my own interest.

To be sure, the transfer of rights is not without limits. My wife and I can, for example, give over our right to our children, though we cannot do so for money. I can contract to slave away for ten hours a day cooking hamburgers, but I cannot sell myself to be, once and for all, a slave. This does not mean, however, that some rights are intrinsically nontransferable. If my right to my left kidney were nontransferable, I could neither sell it nor give it away. But I can give it away, and the only reason I cannot sell it is because sales of this sort were declared, at some point, to be against public policy. We cannot sell ourselves into slavery for the same reason: human societies set limits to the transfer of rights on account of its unacceptable costs.

The case is no different with respect to authorizing another to end my life. If I have a right to one of my kidneys, I have a right to both. And if I can tell a needy person to take one of them, I can tell two needy people to take one each. There is nothing *intrinsically* immoral about this, even though when the second helps himself I die. Yet, by dying too soon, I may leave opportunities unexplored and obligations unmet. Unscrupulous operators may take advantage of my goodwill or naiveté. The very possibility of such acts invites abuse. For these and similar reasons, we may decide that giving the first kidney is morally acceptable, but giving the second is not. The difference between the two acts, however, is not that the first is generous while the second is "a fundamental moral wrong," but that the second occurs in a context and has consequences and costs that the first does not.

Only in terms of context and cost, therefore, can we sensibly consider the issue of the morality of euthanasia. Moving on the level of abstract maxims, Callahan misses this point altogether. He declares: "There are no good moral reasons to limit euthanasia once the principle of taking life . . . has been legitimated."[4] Serious moral reflection, though it takes principles into account, is little interested in legitimating *them*. Its focus is on determining the moral acceptability of certain sorts of actions performed in complex contexts of life. Consideration of the circumstances is always essential: it is fatuous, therefore, to argue that if euthanasia is ever permissible, then "any competent person should have a right to be killed by a doctor for any reason that suits him."[5]

We can achieve little progress in moral philosophy without the ability and readiness to make relevant distinctions. Why, then, does Callahan refuse to acknowledge that there are important differences between the situation of a terminally ill patient in grave pain who wants to die and that of a young father in the dental chair who wishes, for a moment, that he were dead? Callahan's reason is that he thinks all judgments about the unbearability of suffering and the worthlessness of one's existence are subjective and, as such, parts of a "private, idiosyncratic view of the good life."[6] The amount of suffering "has very little directly to do" with our physical condition, and so the desire to end life is capricious and unreliable. If medicine honored such desires, it would "put its own vocation at risk" by serving "the private interests" of individuals.

I cannot imagine what the vocation of medicine might be if it is not to serve the private interests of individuals. It is, after all, my vision of the good life that accounts for my wish not to perish in a diabetic coma. And surgeons certainly pursue the private interests of their patients in removing cancerous growths and in providing face-lifts. Medicine does not surrender its vocation in serving the desires of individuals: since health and continued life are among our primary wishes, its career consists in just this service.

Nevertheless, Callahan is right that our judgments about the quality of our lives and about the level of our suffering have a subjective component. But so do the opinions of patients about their health and illness, yet physicians have little difficulty in placing these perceptions in a broader, objective context. Similarly, it is both possible and proper to take into account the objective circumstances that surround desires to terminate life. Physicians have developed considerable skill in relating subjective complaints to objective conditions; only by absurd exaggeration can we say that the doctor must accept either all or none of the patient's claims. The context of the young father in the dental chair makes it clear that only a madman would think of switching from novocaine to cyanide when he moans that he wants to be dead. Even people of ordinary sensitivity understand that the situation of an older person whose friends have all died and who now suffers the excruciating pain of terminal cancer is morally different.

The question of the justifiability of euthanasia, as all difficult moral questions, cannot be asked without specifying the details of context. Dire warnings of slippery slopes and of future large-scale, quietly conducted exterminations trade on overlooking differences of circumstance. They insult our sensitivity by the suggestion that a society of individuals of good will cannot recognize situations in which their fellows want and need help and cannot distinguish such situations from those in which the desire for death is rhetorical, misguided, temporary, or idiotic. It would indeed be tragic if medicine were to leap to the aid of lovelorn teenagers whenever they feel life is too much to bear. But it is just as lamentable to stand idly by and watch unwanted lives fill up with unproductive pain.

Callahan is correct in pointing out that, in euthanasia and in assisted suicide, the physician and the patient must have separate justifications for action. The patient's wish is defensible if it is the outcome of a sound reflective judgment. Such judgments take into account the current condition, pending projects, and long-term prospects of the individual and relate them to his or her permanent interests and established values. As all assessments, these can be in error. For this reason, persons soliciting help in dying must be ready to demonstrate that they are of sound mind and thus capable of making such choices, that their desire is enduring, and that both their subjective and their objective condition makes their wish sensible.

Physicians must first decide whether their personal values permit them to participate in such activities. If they do, they must diligently examine the justifiability of the patient's desire to die. Diagnosis and prognosis are often relatively easy to ascertain. But we are not without resources for a sound determination of the internal condition of individuals either: extensive questioning on multiple occasions, interviews with friends and loved ones, and exploration of life history and values of people contribute mightily to understanding their state of mind. Physicians who are prepared to aid individuals with this last need of their lives are not, therefore, in a position where they have to believe everything they hear and act on every request. They must make independent judgments instead of subordinating themselves as unthinking tools to the passing desires of those they wish to help. This does not attribute to doctors "the powers of the gods." It only requires that they be flexible in how they aid their patients and that they do so with due caution and on the basis of sound evaluation.

Callahan is once again right to be concerned that, if allowed, euthanasia will "take place within the boundaries of the private and confidential doctor–patient relationship."[7] This does, indeed, invite abuse and permit callous physicians to take a casual attitude to a momentous decision. Callahan is wrong, however, in supposing that this constitutes an argument against euthanasia. It is only a reason not to keep euthanasia secret, but to shed on it the wholesome light of publicity. Though the decision to terminate life is intensely private, no moral consideration demands that it be kept the confidential possession of two individuals. To the contrary, the only way we can minimize wrong decisions and abuse is to require scrutiny of the decision, prior to action on it, by a suitable social body. Such examination, including at least one personal interview with the patient, should go a long distance toward

relieving Callahan's concern that any law governing euthanasia would have "a low enforcement priority in the criminal justice system."[8] With formal social controls in place, there should be very little need for the involvement of courts and prosecutors.

To suppose, as Callahan does, that the principle of autonomy calls for us to stand idly by, or even to assist, whenever and for whatever reason people want to end their lives is calculated to discredit both euthanasia and autonomy. No serious moralist has ever argued that self-determination must be absolute. It cannot hold unlimited sway, as Mill and other advocates of the principle readily admit, if humans are to live in a society. And morally, it would cut no ice if murderers and rapists argued for the legitimacy of their actions by claiming that they flow naturally and solely from who they are.

The function of the principle of autonomy is to affirm *a* value and to shift the burden of justifying infringements of individual liberty to established social and governmental powers. The value it affirms is that of individual agency expressed in the belief that, through action and suffering and death, the life of each person enjoys a sort of private integrity. This means that, in the end, our lives belong to no one but ourselves. The limits to such self-determination or self-possession are set by the demands of social life. They can be discovered or decided upon in the process of moral reflection. A sensible approach to euthanasia can disclose how much weight autonomy carries in that context and how it can be balanced against other, equally legitimate but competing values.

In the hands of its friends, the principle of self-determination does not run amok. What runs amok in Callahan's version of autonomy and euthanasia is the sort of abstract moralizing that forgets the problem it sets out to address and shuts its eye to need and suffering.

Notes

1. D. Callahan, "Self-Determination Run Amok," *Hastings Center Report* 22 (March–April 1992): 52–55.
2. Ibid., 55.
3. Ibid., 52.
4. Ibid., 54.
5. Ibid.
6. Ibid., 52.
7. Ibid., 54.
8. Ibid.

Voluntary Euthanasia: A Utilitarian Perspective

Peter Singer

Singer asks what makes it wrong, from a nonreligious view, to kill *any* being, including a human. The utilitarian answer, which he accepts, is that killing ends the possibility that the being can experience whatever further good life holds. For a "hedonistic utilitarian" this means happiness, and for a "preference utilitarian" it means the satisfaction of preferences. Thus, when unhappiness or the frustration of preferences outweighs life's positive elements, killing is preferable to not killing.

Singer addresses only voluntary euthanasia (including assisted suicide) and accepts Mill's view that individuals are the best judges of their own interests and should be allowed to decide when the good things of life are outweighed by the bad, making death desirable. He argues that the right to life should be viewed as an option, not as inalienable, which would make life a duty. It is necessary to determine that candidates for voluntary euthanasia are competent to make decisions and have access to palliative care, but in some instances even depressed people may be acceptable candidates.

Finally, Singer asks whether allowing voluntary euthanasia would lead to the deaths of vulnerable individuals pressured into consenting to involuntary killing, then points to studies in the Netherlands and Oregon showing that the evidence does not support this view. He concludes that the utilitarian case for allowing patients to choose euthanasia is strong.

Utilitarianism

There is, of course, no single "utilitarian perspective" for there are several versions of utilitarianism and they differ on some aspects of euthanasia. Utilitarianism is a form of consequentialism. According to *act-utilitarianism*, the right action is the one that, of all the actions open to the agent, has consequences that are better than, or at least no worse than, any other action open to the agent. So the act-utilitarian judges the ethics of each act independently. According to *rule-utilitarianism*, the right action is the one that is in accordance with the rule that, if generally followed, would have consequences that are better than, or at least no worse than, any other rule that might be generally followed in the relevant situation. But if we are talking about changing laws to permit voluntary euthanasia, rather than about individual decisions to help someone to die, this distinction is not so relevant. Both act- and

Peter Singer, From "Voluntary Euthanasia: A Utilitarian Perspective," *Bioethics*, Vol. 17, no. 5–6, (2003): 526–541. Copyright © 2003 Wiley-Blackwell Ltd. Reproduced by permission of the author.

rule-utilitarians will base their judgements on whether changing the law will have better consequences than not changing it.

What consequences do we take into account? Here there are two possible views. Classical, or hedonistic, utilitarianism counts only pleasure and pain, or happiness and suffering, as intrinsically significant. Other goods are, for the hedonistic utilitarian, significant only in so far as they affect the happiness and suffering of sentient beings. That pleasure or happiness are good things and much desired, while pain and suffering are bad things that we want to avoid, is generally accepted. But are these the *only* things that are of intrinsic value? That is a more difficult claim to defend. Many people prefer to live a life with less happiness or pleasure in it, and perhaps even more pain and suffering, if they can thereby fulfil other important preferences. For example, they may choose to strive for excellence in art, or literature, or sport, even though they know that they are unlikely to achieve it, and may experience pain and suffering in the attempt. We could simply say that these people are making a mistake, if there is an alternative future open to them that would be likely to bring them a happier life. But on what grounds can we tell another person that her considered, well-informed, reflective choice is mistaken, even when she is in possession of all the same facts as we are? The difficulty of satisfactorily answering this question is one reason why I favour preference utilitarianism, rather than hedonistic utilitarianism. The right act is the one that will, in the long run, satisfy more preferences than it will thwart, when we weigh the preferences according to their importance for the person holding them.

There is of course a lot more to be said about questions internal to utilitarianism. But that is perhaps enough to provide a basis for our next topic.

When Killing Is, and Is Not, Wrong

Undoubtedly, the major objection to voluntary euthanasia is the rule that it is always wrong to kill an innocent human being. Anyone interested in an ethics that is free of religious commitments should be ready to ask sceptical questions about this view. Rule-utilitarians will not accept this rule without being persuaded that it will have better consequences than any other rule. Act-utilitarians will need to be assured that it will have the best consequences to follow the rule in *every* instance in which it applies.

The idea that it is always wrong to kill an innocent human being gains its strongest support from religious doctrines that draw a sharp distinction between human beings and other sentient beings. Without such religious ideas, it is difficult to think of any morally relevant properties that separate human beings with severe brain damage or other major intellectual disabilities from other beings at a similar mental level. For why should the fact that a being is a member of *our* species make it worse to kill that being than it is to kill a member of another species, if the two individuals have similar intellectual abilities, or if the non-human has superior intellectual abilities?

My claim that the wrongness of killing cannot rest on mere species membership is compatible with, but need not be based on, utilitarianism. Consider, for instance, the Kantian principle that it is always wrong to use someone merely as a means, and not as an end. Who is to count as "someone" for the purposes of applying such a principle? Kant's own argument in support of this principle depends on autonomy, and our autonomy, for Kant, depends on our ability to reason.[1] Hence, it is fallacious to treat Kant's principle as

equivalent to: "Never use a human being as means to an end." It would be better to read it as: "Never use an autonomous being merely as a means."

I can think of only one non-religious reason that has any plausibility at all, as a defence of the view that the boundary of our species also marks the boundary of those whom it is wrong to kill. This is a utilitarian argument, to the effect that the species boundary is sharp and clear, and if we allow it to be transgressed, we will slide down a slippery slope to widespread and unjustified killing. I will consider slippery slope arguments against allowing voluntary euthanasia towards the end of this paper. Here it is sufficient to note that this argument effectively admits that there is no intrinsic reason against attributing similar rights to life to humans and non-humans with similar intellectual capacities, but warns against the likely consequences of doing so. For our present inquiry into the underlying reasons against killing human beings, this is enough to show that one cannot simply assume that to be human is to give one a right to life. We need to ask, not: what is wrong with killing a human being; but rather, what makes it wrong to kill any being? A consequentialist might initially answer: whatever goods life holds, killing ends them. So if happiness is a good, as classical hedonistic utilitarians hold, then killing is bad because when one is dead one is no longer happy. Or if it is the satisfaction of preferences that is good, as modern preference utilitarians hold, then when one is dead, one's preferences can no longer be satisfied.

These answers suggest their own limits. First, if the future life of the being killed would hold more negative elements than positive ones—more unhappiness than happiness, more frustration of preferences than satisfaction of them—then we have a reason for killing, rather than against killing. Needless to say, this is highly relevant to the question of euthanasia.

At this point, however, some further questions arise that suggest the relevance of higher intellectual capacities. Among these questions are: who is to decide when a being's life contains, or is likely to contain, more positive characteristics than negative ones? And what further impact will the killing of a being have on the lives of others?

Regarding the first of these questions, the nineteenth century utilitarian John Stuart Mill argued that individuals are, ultimately, the best judges and guardians of their own interests. So, in a famous example, he said that if you see people about to cross a bridge you know to be unsafe, you may forcibly stop them in order to inform them of the risk that the bridge may collapse under them, but if they decide to continue, you must stand aside and let them cross, for only they know the importance to them of crossing, and only they know how to balance that against the possible loss of their lives.[2] Mill's example presupposes, of course, that we are dealing with beings who are capable of taking in information, reflecting and choosing. So here is the first point on which intellectual abilities are relevant. If beings are capable of making choices, we should, other things being equal, allow them to decide whether or not their lives are worth living. If they are not capable of making such choices, then someone else must make the decision for them, if the question should arise. (Since this paper focuses on voluntary euthanasia, I shall not go into details regarding life-and-death decisions for those who are not capable of exercising a choice. But to those who think that, in the absence of choice, the decision should always be "for life," I would add that even those who are most strongly against killing rarely insist on the use of every possible means of life-support, to draw life out to the last possible minute. In allowing life to end earlier than it might, they are effectively deciding for those who are not capable of making such decisions, and against life, not for it.[3])

The conclusion we can draw from this is as follows: if the goods that life holds are, in general, reasons against killing, those reasons lose all their force when it is clear that those killed will not have such goods, or that the goods they have will be outweighed by bad things that will happen to them. When we apply this reasoning to the case of someone who is capable of judging the matter, and we add Mill's view that individuals are the best judges of their own interests, we can conclude that this reason against killing does not apply to a person who, with unimpaired capacities for judgement, comes to the conclusion that his or her future is so clouded that it would be better to die than to continue to live. Indeed, the reason against killing is turned into its opposite, a reason for acceding to that person's request.

Now let us consider the second question: what impact does killing a being have on the lives of other beings? The answer will range from "none" to "devastating," depending on the particular circumstances. Even in the case of beings who are unable to comprehend the concept of death, there can be a great sense of loss, when a child or a parent, for example, is killed. But putting aside such cases of close relationship, there will be a difference between beings who are capable of feeling threatened by the deaths of others in circumstances similar to their own, and those who are not. This will provide an additional reason to think it wrong—normally—to kill those who can understand when their lives are at risk, that is, beings with higher intellectual capacities.

Once again, however, the fact that killing can lead to fear and insecurity in those who learn of the risk to their own lives, is transformed into a reason in favour of permitting killing, when people are killed only on their request. For then killing poses no threat. On the contrary, the possibility of receiving expert assistance when one wants to die relieves the fear that many elderly and ill people have, of dying in unrelieved pain and distress, or in circumstances that they regard as undignified and do not wish to live through.

Thus the usual utilitarian reasons against killing are turned around in the case of killing in the circumstances that apply in the case of voluntary euthanasia. But it is not only with utilitarian reasons that this happens. It is also true of the Kantian argument that to kill autonomous beings against their will shows a failure to respect them as autonomous beings. This is true, obviously, when they do not want to be killed; and it is equally obviously false when they have autonomously decided to hasten their death. In these circumstances, it is preventing others from assisting them in carrying out their considered desire that violates their autonomy. That Kant himself took the opposite view only shows that he was influenced more by the conventional Christian morality of his day than by a thorough-going application of his own fundamental principles.[4]

What of an argument based on a right to life? Here everything will depend on whether the right is treated as most other rights are, that is, as an option that one can choose to exercise or to give up, or if it is seen as "inalienable," as something that cannot be given up. I suggest that all rights should be seen as options. An "inalienable right" is not a right at all, but a duty. Hence the idea of a right to life does not provide a basis for opposing voluntary euthanasia. Just as my right to give you a book I own is the flip side of my right to keep my property if I choose to retain it, so here too, the right to end one's life, or to seek assistance in doing so, is the flip side of the right to life, that is, my right not to have my life taken against my will.

Against this, it will be said that we do not allow people to sell themselves into slavery. If, in a free society, people are not allowed to give up their freedom, why should they be able to give up their lives, which of course also ends their freedom?

It is true that the denial of the right of competent adults to sell themselves, after full consideration, into slavery creates a paradox for liberal theory. Can this denial be justified? There are two possible ways of justifying it, neither of which implies a denial of voluntary euthanasia. First, we might believe that to sell oneself into slavery—irrevocably to hand over control of your life to someone else—is such a crazy thing to do that the intention to do it creates an irrebuttable presumption that the person wishing to do it is not a competent rational being. In contrast, ending one's life when one is terminally or incurably ill is not crazy at all.

A second distinction between selling yourself into slavery and committing suicide can be appreciated by considering another apparently irrational distinction in a different situation. International law recognises a duty on nations to give asylum to genuine refugees who reach the nation's territory and claim asylum. Although the recent increase in asylum seekers has strained this duty, as yet no nation has openly rejected it. Instead, they seek to prevent refugees crossing their borders or landing on their shores.[5] Yet since the plight of the refugees is likely to be equally desperate, whether they succeed in setting foot on the nation's territory or not, this distinction seems arbitrary and morally untenable. The most plausible explanation is that it is abhorrent to forcibly send refugees back to a country that will persecute them. Preventing them from entering is slightly less abhorrent. Similarly, a law recognising a right to sell oneself into slavery would require an equivalent of America's notorious fugitive slave law; that is, those who sold themselves into slavery, and later, regretting their decision, ran away, would have to be forced to return to their "owners." The repugnance of doing this may be enough explanation for the refusal to permit people to sell themselves into slavery. Obviously, since no one changes their mind after voluntary euthanasia has been carried out, it could not lead to the state becoming involved in any similarly repugnant enforcement procedures.

Some will think that the fact that one cannot change one's mind after voluntary euthanasia is precisely the problem: if people might make mistakes about selling themselves into slavery, then they might also make mistakes about ending their lives. That has to be admitted. If voluntary euthanasia is permitted then some people will die who, if they had not opted for euthanasia, might have come to consider the remainder of their life worthwhile. But this has to be balanced against the presumably much larger number of people who, had voluntary euthanasia not been permitted, would have remained alive, in pain or distress and wishing that they had been able to die earlier. In such matters, there is no course of action that entirely excludes the possibility of a serious mistake. But should competent patients not be able to make their own judgements and decide what risks they prefer to take?

Competence, Mental Illness and Other Grounds for Taking Life

We have seen that Mill thought that individuals are the best judges and guardians of their own interests, and that this underlies his insistence that the state should not interfere with individuals for their own good, but only to prevent them harming others. This claim is not an implication of utilitarianism, and a utilitarian might disagree with it. But those who, whether for utilitarian or other reasons, support individual liberty, will be reluctant to interfere with individual freedom unless the case for doing so is very clear.

It is sometimes claimed that patients who are terminally ill cannot rationally or autonomously choose euthanasia, because they are liable to be depressed. The American writer Nat Hentoff, for example, has claimed that many physicians "are unable to recognize clinical depression, which, when treated successfully, removes the wish for death."[6] Even if this statement is true, it is not an argument against legalising voluntary euthanasia, but an argument for including in any legislation authorising voluntary euthanasia, a requirement that a psychiatrist, or someone else trained in recognising clinical depression, should examine any patient requesting voluntary euthanasia and certify that the patient is not suffering from a treatable form of clinical depression. Such a proposal is perfectly practicable, and when voluntary euthanasia was briefly legalised in Australia's Northern Territory a few years ago, the law did require that someone with a psychiatric qualification must certify that the patient was mentally competent to make the decision. Whether such a provision is necessary will depend on whether Hentoff's claim about the inability of physicians to recognise this condition is true.

In any case, not all clinical depression is susceptible to treatment. This leads to a different question, whether doctors should act on requests for euthanasia from patients who wish to die because they are suffering from clinical depression that has, over many years, proven unresponsive to treatment. This issue was raised in the Netherlands in 1991, when a psychiatrist,

Dr. Boudewijn Chabot, provided assistance in dying to a 50-year-old woman who was severely depressed, but suffered from no physical illness. When prosecuted, Chabot contended that the woman was suffering intolerably, and that several years of treatment had failed to alleviate her distress. He thus sought to bring the case under the then-accepted guidelines for voluntary euthanasia in the Netherlands. He was convicted, but only because no other doctor had examined the patient, as the guidelines required. The Supreme Court of the Netherlands accepted the more important claim that unbearable mental suffering could, if it was impossible to relieve by any other means, constitute a ground for acceptable voluntary euthanasia, and that a person suffering from this condition could be competent.[7]

From a utilitarian perspective, Chabot and the Dutch courts were correct. For the hedonistic utilitarian, what matters is not whether the suffering is physical or psychological, but how bad it is, whether it can be relieved, and—so that others will not be fearful of being killed when they want to live—whether the patient has clearly expressed a desire to die. Whether preference utilitarians would reach the same conclusion would depend on whether they are concerned with the satisfaction of actual preferences, or with the satisfaction of those preferences that people would have if they were thinking rationally and in a psychologically normal state of mind. It is easy to say: "If you were not depressed, you would not want to die." But why should we base our decision on the preferences a person would have if in a psychologically normal state of mind, even when it is extremely unlikely that the person in question will ever be in a psychologically normal state of mind?

Some cases of depression are episodic. A person can be depressed at times, and at other times normal. But if, having experienced many periods of depression, she knows how bad these periods are, and knows that they are very likely to recur, she may, while in a normal state of mind, desire to die rather than go through another period of depression. That could be a rational choice and one that a preference utilitarian should accept as providing a basis for assisted suicide or voluntary euthanasia. Given this, it seems possible to be rational about one's choice to die, even when depressed. The problem for the physician lies in recognising that the choice is one that would persist, even if the person were, temporarily, not depressed, but able to see that he would again become depressed. If this can be ascertained, a preference utilitarian should not dismiss such a preference.

The application of this view is probably more frequent than we realize. The World Health Organization estimates that there are about a million suicides a year and that depression or other forms of mental illness, including substance abuse, are involved in 90% of them. Moreover, the number of suicide attempts is said to be up to 20 times greater than the number of successful suicides.[8] The WHO and many other organisations focus on suicide prevention, and if by this is meant prevention of the causes that lead people to try to end their lives, then this focus is entirely sound. But if by "suicide prevention" is meant simply preventing people from succeeding in killing themselves, irrespective of whether it is possible to change the conditions that lead them to wish to kill themselves, then suicide prevention is not always the right thing to do. It is possible that in a significant number of cases, suicide is the only way of escaping from unbearable and unrelievable suffering due to mental illness, and is in accordance with the rational preferences of the person committing suicide.[9]

Richard Doerflinger has argued that those who invoke autonomy in order to argue for voluntary euthanasia or physician-assisted suicide are not being entirely straightforward, because they defend the autonomy of terminally ill or incurably ill patients, but not of people who are just bored with life.[10] A recent Dutch case raised that issue. Edward Brongersma, an 86-year-old former senator in the Dutch parliament, committed suicide with the assistance of a doctor, simply because he was elderly and tired of life. The doctor who assisted him was initially acquitted, but the Dutch Ministry of Justice appealed against the acquittal. This led to the doctor's conviction, on the grounds that what he did was outside the existing rules. Nevertheless, since the court recognised that the doctor had acted out of compassion, it did not impose any penalty.[11] A utilitarian should not find anything wrong in the doctor's action, either because the desire to die was Brongersma's considered preference, or because no one was in a better position than Brongersma to decide whether his life contains a positive or negative balance of experiences. Of course, it is relevant that Brongersma was 86 years old, and his life was unlikely to improve. We do not have to say the same about the situation of the lovesick teenager who thinks that without the girl he loves life can never again be worth living. Such cases are more akin to a temporary mental illness, or period of delusion. Neither a preference nor a hedonistic utilitarian would justify assisting a person in that state to end his life.

The reason that the focus of debate has been on people who are terminally or incurably ill, rather than on people who are simply tired of life, may just be political. Advocates of voluntary euthanasia and physician-assisted suicide find it difficult enough to persuade legislators or the public to change the law to allow doctors to help people who are terminally or incurably ill. To broaden the conditions still further would make the task impossible, in the present climate of opinion. Moreover, where terminally or incurably ill patients who want to die are concerned, both respect for the autonomy of the patients and a more objective standard of rational decision-making point in the same direction. If permissible assistance in dying is extended beyond this group it becomes more difficult to say whether a person's choice is persistent and based on good reasons, or would change over time. From a utilitarian perspective, this is a ground for saying, not that it is necessarily wrong to help those who are not terminally or incurably ill and yet want to die, but that it is more difficult to decide when the circumstances justify such assistance. This may be a ground against changing the law to allow assistance in those cases.

Palliative Care

I return now to another of Nat Hentoff's objections to the legalisation of voluntary euthanasia and physician-assisted suicide. Hentoff thinks that many physicians are not only unable to recognise depression, but also not good at treating pain, and that sometimes good pain relief can remove the desire for euthanasia. That is also true, but most specialists in palliative care admit that there is a small number of cases in which pain cannot be adequately relieved, short of making patients unconscious and keeping them that way until death ensues a few days later. That alternative—known as "terminal sedation"—is sometimes practised. Some ethicists, even non-religious ones, do not consider it equivalent to euthanasia, despite the fact that, since terminally sedated patients are not tube-fed, death always does ensue within a few days.[12]

From a utilitarian perspective, it is hard to see that terminal sedation offers any advantages over euthanasia. Since the unconscious patient has no experiences at all, and does not recover consciousness before dying, the hedonistic utilitarian will judge terminal sedation as identical, from the point of view of the patient, to euthanasia at the moment when the patient becomes unconscious. Nor will the preference utilitarian be able

to find a difference between the two states, unless the patient has, while still conscious, a preference for one rather than the other. Since additional resources are involved in caring for the terminally sedated patient, and the family is unable to begin the grieving process until death finally takes place, it seems that, other things being equal, voluntary euthanasia is better than voluntary terminal sedation.

But to return to the issue of whether better pain relief would eliminate the desire for euthanasia, there is again an obvious solution: ensure that candidates for euthanasia see a palliative care specialist. If every patient then ceases to ask for euthanasia, both proponents and opponents of voluntary euthanasia will be pleased. But that seems unlikely. Some patients who want euthanasia are not in pain at all. They want to die because they are weak, constantly tired, nauseous, or breathless. Or perhaps they just find the whole process of slowly wasting away undignified. These are reasonable grounds for wanting to die.

It is curious that those who argue against voluntary euthanasia on the grounds that terminally ill patients are often depressed, or have not received good palliative care, do not also argue against the right of terminally ill patients to refuse life-sustaining treatment or to receive pain relief that is liable to shorten life. Generally, they go out of their way to stress that they do not wish to interfere with the rights of patients to refuse life-sustaining treatment or to receive pain relief that is liable to shorten life. But the patients who make these decisions are also terminally ill, and are making choices that will, or may, end their lives earlier than they would have ended if the patient had chosen differently. To support the right of patients to make these decisions, but deny they should be allowed to choose physician-assisted suicide or voluntary euthanasia, is to assume that a patient can rationally refuse treatment (and that doctors ought, other things being equal, to co-operate with this decision) but that the patient cannot rationally choose voluntary euthanasia. This is implausible. There is no reason to believe that patients refusing life-sustaining treatment or receiving pain relief that will foreseeably shorten their lives, are less likely to be depressed, or clouded by medication, or receiving poor treatment for their pain, than patients who choose physician-assisted suicide or voluntary euthanasia. The question is whether a patient can rationally choose an earlier death over a later one (and whether doctors ought to co-operate with these kinds of end-of-life decisions), and that choice is made in either case. If patients can rationally opt for an earlier death by refusing life-supporting treatment or by accepting life-shortening palliative care, they must also be rational enough to opt for an earlier death by physician-assisted suicide or voluntary euthanasia.

The Slippery Slope Argument

Undoubtedly the most widely invoked secular argument against the legalisation of voluntary euthanasia is the slippery slope argument that legalising physician-assisted suicide or voluntary euthanasia will lead to vulnerable patients being pressured into consenting to physician-assisted suicide or voluntary euthanasia when they do not really want it. Or perhaps, as another version of the argument goes, they will simply be killed without their consent because they are a nuisance to their families, or because their healthcare provider wants to save money.

What evidence is there to support or oppose the slippery slope argument when applied to voluntary euthanasia? A decade ago, this argument was largely speculative. Now, however, we can draw on evidence from two jurisdictions where for several years it has been possible for doctors to practice voluntary euthanasia or physician-assisted suicide without fear of prosecution. These jurisdictions are Oregon and the Netherlands. According to Oregon officials, between 1997, when a law permitting physician-assisted suicide took effect, and 2001, 141 lethal prescriptions were issued, according to state records, and 91 patients used their prescriptions to end their lives. There are about 30,000 deaths in Oregon annually.[13] There have been no reports of the law being used to coerce patients to commit suicide against their will, and from all the evidence that is available, this does not appear to be a situation in which the law is being abused.

Opponents of voluntary euthanasia do contend, on the other hand, that the open practice of voluntary euthanasia in the Netherlands has led to abuse. In the early days of non-prosecution of doctors who carried out voluntary euthanasia, before full legalisation, a government-initiated study known as the Remmelink Report indicated that physicians occasionally—in roughly 1000 cases a year, or about 0.8% of all deaths—terminated the lives of their patients without their consent. This was, almost invariably, when the patients were very close to death and no longer capable of giving consent.[14] Nevertheless, the report gave

some grounds for concern. What it did not, and could not, have shown, however, is that the introduction of voluntary euthanasia has *led* to abuse. To show this one would need *either* two studies of the Netherlands, made some years apart and showing an increase in unjustified killings, *or* a comparison between the Netherlands and a similar country in which doctors practising voluntary euthanasia are liable to be prosecuted.

Such studies have become available since the publication of the Remmelink report. First, there was a second Dutch survey, carried out five years after the original one. It did not show any significant increase in the amount of non-voluntary euthanasia happening in the Netherlands, and thus dispelled fears that that country was sliding down a slippery slope.[15]

In addition, studies have been carried out in Australia and in Belgium to discover whether there was more abuse in the Netherlands than in other comparable countries where euthanasia was illegal and could not be practised openly. The Australian study used English translations of the survey questions in the Dutch studies to ask doctors about decisions involving both direct euthanasia and foregoing medical treatment (for example, withholding antibiotics or withdrawing artificial ventilation).[16] Its findings suggest that while the rate of active voluntary euthanasia in Australia is slightly lower than that shown in the most recent Dutch study (1.8% as against 2.3%), the rate of explicit *non-voluntary* euthanasia in Australia is, at 3.5%, much higher than the Dutch rate of 0.8%. Rates of other end-of-life decisions, such as withdrawing life-support or giving pain relief that was foreseen to be life shortening, were also higher than in the Netherlands.[17]

The Belgian study, which examined deaths in the country's northern, Flemish-speaking region, came to broadly similar conclusions. The rate of voluntary euthanasia was, at 1.3% of all deaths, again lower than in the Netherlands, but the proportion of patients given a lethal injection without having requested it was, at 3% of all deaths, similar to the Australian rate and like it, much higher than the rate in the Netherlands. The authors of the Belgian study, reflecting on their own findings and those of the Australian and Dutch study, concluded:

Perhaps less attention is given to the requirements of careful end-of-life practice in a society with a restrictive approach than in one with an open approach that tolerates and regulates euthanasia and PAS (Physician-Assisted Suicide).[18]

These two studies discredit assertions that the open practice of active voluntary euthanasia in the Netherlands had led to an increase in non-voluntary euthanasia. There is no evidence to support the claim that laws against physician-assisted suicide or voluntary euthanasia prevent harm to vulnerable people. It is equally possible that legalizing physician-assisted suicide or voluntary euthanasia will bring the issue out into the open, and thus make it easier to scrutinise what is actually happening, and to prevent harm to the vulnerable. If the burden of proof lies on those who defend a law that restricts individual liberty, then in the case of laws against physician-assisted suicide or voluntary euthanasia, that burden has not been discharged.

Those who, despite the studies cited, still seek to paint the situation in the Netherlands in dark colours, now need to explain the fact that its neighbour, Belgium, has chosen to follow that country's lead. The Belgian parliament voted, by large margins in both the upper and lower houses, to allow doctors to act on a patient's request for assistance in dying. The majority of Belgium's citizens are Flemish-speaking, and Flemish is so close to Dutch that they have no difficulty in reading Dutch newspapers and books, or watching Dutch television. If voluntary euthanasia in the Netherlands really was rife with abuses, why would the country that is better placed than all others to know what goes on in the Netherlands be keen to pass a similar law?

Conclusion

The utilitarian case for allowing patients to choose euthanasia, under specified conditions and safeguards, is strong. The slippery slope argument attempts to combat this case on utilitarian grounds. The outcomes of the open practice of voluntary euthanasia in the Netherlands, and of physician-assisted suicide in Oregon, do not, however, support the idea that allowing patients to choose euthanasia or physician-assisted suicide leads to a slippery slope. Hence it seems that, on utilitarian grounds, the legalisation of voluntary euthanasia or physician-assisted suicide would be a desirable reform.

Notes

1. See: I. Kant. *Groundwork of the Metaphysics of Morals*. First published 1785. Various editions: Part II.
2. John Stuart Mill. *On Liberty*. First published 1869. Various editions: Chapter 5.
3. For further discussion see: Peter Singer. 1993. *Practical Ethics*. Second edition. Cambridge. Cambridge University Press. Peter Singer. 1995. *Rethinking Life and Death*. New York. St Martin's Press.
4. See Kant's discussion of the "first example" in Part II of the *Groundwork of the Metaphysics of Morals*.
5. This distinction lies behind the deplorable *The Tampa* incident, in which the Australian government forcibly prevented refugees who had been picked up at sea by the Norwegian freighter *The Tampa* from landing in Australia. See: Refugees Stranded at Sea. *The Age* August 21, 2001. Available at: http://www.theage.com.au/news/national/2001/08/28/FFX71SRBVQC.html
6. Nat Hentoff. Challenging Singer. *Free Inquiry* 2002; 22: 1.
7. See: Arjan Schippers. How the Courts Allowed Euthanasia. http://www.rnw.nl/society/html/courts010723.html; and: Euthanasia in the Netherlands: Evidence of the Slippery Slope. http://www.nrlc.org/news/1999/NRL999/slope.html
8. World Health Organization. Updated April 2002. Prevention of Suicidal Behaviors: A Task for All. http://www5.who.int/mental_health/main.cfm?p = 0000000140
9. Relevant to this topic are: J. H. Groenewoud et al. Physician-Assisted Death in Psychiatric Practice in the Netherlands. *New England Journal of Medicine* 1997; 336: 1795–1801; V. G. Hardcastle & R. W. Stewart. Supporting Irrational Suicide. *Bioethics* 2002; 16; and J. Young. Morals, Suicide and Psychiatry: A View from Japan. *Bioethics* 2002; 16.
10. Richard Doerflinger. 2000. Assisted Suicide: Pro-Choice or Anti-Life, In *Contemporary Moral Issues*. Second edition. Lawrence Hinman, ed. Upper Saddle River, NJ. Prentice-Hall: 169–70.
11. Arjan Schippers. How the Courts Allowed Euthanasia. http://www.rnw.nl/society/html/courts010723.html
12. See: Törbjörn Tännsjo. Terminal Sedation—A Compromise in the Euthanasia Debate? *Bulletin of Medical Ethics* 2000; 163: 13–22.
13. Oregon Reporting 15 Deaths in 1998 under Suicide Law. *New York Times* February 18, 1999.
14. See: Ministry of Justice and Ministry of Welfare, Public Health and Culture. 1991. *Report of the Committee to Investigate Medical Practice Concerning Euthanasia. Medical Decisions about the End of Life (The "Remmelink Report")*. The Hague; P. J. van der Maas et al. 1992. *Euthanasia and Other Decisions Concerning the End of Life*. Amsterdam. Elsevier Science Publishers.
15. P. J. van der Maas, G. van der Waal et al. Euthanasia, Physician-Assisted Suicide, and other Medical Practices involving the End of Life in the Netherlands, 1990–1995. *New England Journal of Medicine* 1996; 335: 1699–1705.
16. Helga Kuhse, Peter Singer, Maurice Richard, Malcolm Clark & Peter Baume. End-of-Life Decisions in Australian Medical Practice. *Medical Journal of Australia* 1997; 166: 191–196.
17. For further evidence of the practice of illegal, and therefore uncontrolled, euthanasia in Australia, as well as in the United States, see: Roger Magnusson. 2002. *Angels of Death: Exploring the Euthanasia Underground*. Melbourne. Melbourne University Press.
18. L. Deliens, F. Mortier et al. End of Life Decisions in Medical Practice in Flanders, Belgium: A Nationwide Survey. *The Lancet* 200; 356: 1806–1811; see also: http://europe.cnn.com/2000/WORLD/europe/11/24/brussels.euthanasia

Section 4: Deciding for the Incompetent

In the Matter of Karen Quinlan, an Alleged Incompetent

Supreme Court of New Jersey

The 1976 decision of the New Jersey Supreme Court in the case of Karen Quinlan was significant in establishing that a legally based right of privacy permits a patient to decide to refuse medical treatment. The court also held that this right can be exercised by a parent or guardian when the patient herself is in no position to do so. Thus, in the opinion of the court removal of life-sustaining equipment would not be a case of homicide (or any other kind of wrongful killing), even if the patient should die as a result.

The ruling in the *Quinlan* case has had an enormous impact on decisions about discontinuing extraordinary medical measures. However, the ruling has generally been construed rather narrowly so as to apply only to mentally incompetent patients who are brain dead, comatose, or in an irreversible coma.

Constitutional and Legal Issues

I. The Free Exercise of Religion

Simply stated, the right to religious beliefs is absolute but conduct in pursuance thereof is not wholly immune from governmental restraint. So it is that, for the sake of life, courts sometimes (but not always) order blood transfusions for Jehovah's Witnesses (whose religious beliefs abhor such procedure), forbid exposure to death from handling virulent snakes or ingesting poison (interfering with deeply held religious sentiments in such regard), and protect the public health as in the case of compulsory vaccination (over the strongest of religious objections)....The Public interest is thus considered paramount, without essential dissolution of respect for religious beliefs.

We think, without further examples, that, ranged against the State's interest in the preservation of life, the impingement of religious belief, much less religious "neutrality" as here, does not reflect a constitutional

From *"In the Matter of Karen Quinlan,"* Supreme Court of New Jersey, 70 N.J. 10, 355 A. 2d 647.

Background Note: The decision of the court was issued on March 31, 1976. It was delivered by Chief Justice Hughes. The following abridgment omits references and case citations.

question, in the circumstances at least of the case presently before the Court. Moreover, like the trial court, we do not recognize an independent parental right of religious freedom to support the relief requested.

II. Cruel and Unusual Punishment

Similarly inapplicable to the case before us is the Constitution's Eighth Amendment protection against cruel and unusual punishment which, as held by the trial court, is not relevant to situations other than the imposition of penal sanctions. Historic in nature, it stemmed from punitive excesses in the infliction of criminal penalties. We find no precedent in law which would justify its extension to the correction of social injustice or hardship, such as, for instance, in the case of poverty. The latter often condemns the poor and deprived to horrendous living conditions which could certainly be described in the abstract as "cruel and unusual punishment." Yet the constitutional base of protection from "cruel and unusual punishment" is plainly irrelevant to such societal ills which must be remedied, if at all, under other concepts of constitutional and civil right.

So it is in the case of the unfortunate Karen Quinlan. Neither the State, nor the law, but the accident of fate and nature, has inflicted upon her conditions which though in essence cruel and most unusual, yet do not amount to "punishment" in any constitutional sense.

Neither the judgment of the court below, nor the medical decision which confronted it, nor the law and equity perceptions which impelled its action, nor the whole factual base upon which it was predicated, inflicted "cruel and unusual punishment" in the constitutional sense.

III. The Right of Privacy

It is the issue of the constitutional right of privacy that has given us most concern, in the exceptional circumstances of this case. Here a loving parent, *qua* parent and raising the rights of his incompetent and profoundly damaged daughter, probably irreversibly doomed to no more than a biologically vegetative remnant of life, is before the court. He seeks authorization to abandon specialized technological procedures which can only maintain for a time a body having no potential for resumption or continuance of other than a "vegetative" existence.

We have no doubt, in these unhappy circumstances, that if Karen were herself miraculously lucid for an interval (not altering the existing prognosis of the condition to which she would soon return) and perceptive of her irreversible condition, she could effectively decide upon discontinuance of the life-support apparatus, even if it meant the prospect of natural death. To this extent we may distinguish [a case] which concerned a severely injured young woman (Delores Heston), whose life depended on surgery and blood transfusion; and who was in such extreme shock that she was unable to express an informed choice (although the Court apparently considered the case as if the patient's own religious decision to resist transfusion were at stake), but most importantly a patient apparently salvable to long life and vibrant health—a situation not at all like the present case.

We have no hesitancy in deciding, in the instant diametrically opposite case, that no external compelling interest of the State could compel Karen to endure the unendurable, only to vegetate a few measurable months with no realistic possibility of returning to any semblance of cognitive or sapient life. We perceive no thread of logic distinguishing between such a choice on Karen's part and a similar choice which, under the evidence in this case, could be made by a competent patient terminally ill, riddled by cancer and suffering great pain; such a patient would not be resuscitated or put on a respirator in the example described by Dr. Korein, and *a fortiori* would not be kept *against his will* on a respirator.

Although the Constitution does not explicitly mention a right of privacy, Supreme Court decisions have recognized that a right of personal privacy exists and that certain areas of privacy are guaranteed under the Constitution. The Court has interdicted judicial intrusion into many aspects of personal decision, sometimes basing this restraint upon the conception of a limitation of judicial interest and responsibility, such as with regard to contraception and its relationship to family life and decision.

The Court in *Griswold* found the unwritten constitutional right of privacy to exist in the penumbra of specific guarantees of the Bill of Rights "formed by emanations from those guarantees that help give them life and substance." Presumably this right is broad enough to encompass a patient's decision to decline medical treatment under certain circumstances, in much the same way as it is broad enough to encompass a woman's decision to terminate pregnancy under certain conditions.

The claimed interests of the State in this case are essentially the preservation and sanctity of human life and defense to the right of the physician to administer medical treatment according to his best judgment. In this case the doctors say that removing Karen from the respirator will conflict with their professional judgment. The plaintiff answers that Karen's present treatment serves only a maintenance function; that the respirator cannot cure or improve her condition but at best can only prolong her inevitable slow deterioration and death; and that the interests of the patient, as seen by her surrogate, the guardian, must be evaluated by the court as predominant, even in the face of an option *contra* by the present attending physicians. Plaintiff's distinction is significant. The nature of Karen's care and the realistic chances of her recovery are quite unlike those of the patients discussed in many of the cases where treatments were ordered. In many of those cases the medical procedure required (usually a transfusion) constituted a minimal bodily invasion and the chances of recovery and return to functioning life were very good. We think that the State's interest *contra* weakens and the individual's right to privacy grows as the degree of bodily invasion increases and the prognosis dims. Ultimately there comes a point at which the individual's rights overcome the State interest. It is for that reason that we believe Karen's choice, if she were competent to make it, would be vindicated by the law. Her prognosis is extremely poor—she will never resume cognitive life. And the bodily invasion is very great—she requires

24-hour intensive nursing care, antibiotics, and the assistance of a respirator, a catheter and feeding tube.

Our affirmance of Karen's independent right of choice, however, would ordinarily be based upon her competency to assert it. The sad truth, however, is that she is grossly incompetent and we cannot discern her supposed choice based on the testimony of her previous conversation with friends, where such testimony is without sufficient probative weight. Nevertheless we have concluded that Karen's right of privacy may be asserted on her behalf by her guardian under the peculiar circumstances here present.

If a putative decision by Karen to permit this noncognitive, vegetative existence to terminate by natural forces is regarded as a valuable incident of her right of privacy, as we believe it to be, then it should not be discarded solely on the basis that her condition prevents her conscious exercise of the choice. The only practical way to prevent destruction of the right is to permit the guardian and family of Karen to render their best judgment, subject to the qualifications hereinafter stated, as to whether she would exercise it in these circumstances. If their conclusion is in the affirmative this decision should be accepted by a society the overwhelming majority of whose members would, we think, in similar circumstances, exercise such a choice in the same way for themselves or for those closest to them. It is for this reason that we determine that Karen's right of privacy may be asserted in her behalf, in this respect, by her guardian and family under the particular circumstances presented by this record. [Sections IV (Medical Factors), V (Alleged Criminal Liability), and VI (Guardianship of the Person) omitted.]

Declaratory Relief

We thus arrive at the formulation of the declaratory relief which we have concluded is appropriate to this case. Some time has passed since Karen's physical and mental condition was described to the Court. At that time her continuing deterioration was plainly projected. Since the record has not been expanded we assume that she is now even more fragile and nearer to death than she was then. Since her present treating physicians may give reconsideration to her present posture in the light of this opinion, and since we are transferring to the plaintiff as guardian the choice of the attending physician and therefore other physicians may be in charge of the case who may take a different view from that of the present attending physicians, we herewith declare the following affirmative relief on behalf of the plaintiff. Upon the concurrence of the guardian and family of Karen, should the responsible attending physicians conclude that there is no reasonable possibility of Karen's ever emerging from her present comatose condition to a cognitive, sapient state and that the life-support apparatus now being administered to Karen should be discontinued, they shall consult with the hospital "Ethics Committee" or like body of the institution in which Karen is then hospitalized. If that consultative body agrees that there is no reasonable possibility of Karen's ever emerging from her present comatose condition to a cognitive, sapient state, the present life-support system may be withdrawn and said action shall be without any civil or criminal liability therefore on the part of any participant, whether guardian, physician, hospital or others. We herewith specifically so hold.

DECISION SCENARIOS

The questions following each decision scenario are intended to prompt reflection and discussion. In deciding how to answer them, you should consider the information in the Briefing Session, the ethical theories and principles presented in Part V, "Foundations of Bioethics," and the arguments and criticisms offered in the relevant readings in this chapter.

DECISION SCENARIO 1

The Timothy Quill Case

In March 1991, Dr. Timothy Quill published an article in the *New England Journal of Medicine* in which he described how he had prescribed barbiturates for Patricia Diane Trumbull, a forty-five-year-old woman suffering from leukemia. In prescribing the medication,

Dr. Quill also informed Ms. Trumbull, who had been his patient for a long time, how much of the drug would constitute a lethal dose.

Ms. Trumbull later killed herself by taking an overdose of the barbiturate, and Dr. Quill was investigated by a Rochester, New York, grand jury. Although it is illegal in New York to assist someone in committing suicide, the grand jury decided not to indict Dr. Quill on the charge.

Dr. Quill's actions were later reviewed by the three-member New York State Board for Professional Medical Conduct to consider whether he should be charged with professional misconduct. The board arrived at the unanimous decision that "no charge of misconduct was warranted."

The board, in its report, distinguished between Dr. Quill's actions and those of Dr. Jack Kevorkian. (See the Case Presentation "Jack Kevorkian: Moral Leader or Dr. Death?" in this chapter.) The board pointed to Dr. Quill's long-term involvement in caring for

Ms. Trumbull and contrasted it with Dr. Kevorkian's lack of any prior involvement with those whom he assisted in killing themselves.

Moreoever, the board pointed out that Dr. Quill "did not directly participate in any taking of life," and this, too, made his actions different from those of Dr. Kevorkian. "One is legal and ethically appropriate, and the other, as reported, is not," the board concluded.

1. Does Dr. Quill's action fall within the scope of a physician's legitimate role?

2. Why might one view Dr. Quill's action as justifiable?

3. Was the action a case of active euthanasia?

DECISION SCENARIO **2**

What Would He Want?

Jeffry Box was eighty-one years old when he was brought to Doctor's Hospital. His right side was paralyzed, he spoke in a garbled way, and he had trouble understanding even the simplest matters. His only known relative was a sister four years younger, and she lived half a continent away. When a hospital social worker called to tell her about her brother's condition, she was quite uninterested. "I haven't seen him in fifteen years," she said. "I thought he might already be dead. Just do whatever you think best for him. I'm too old to worry about him."

Neurological tests and X-ray studies showed that Mr. Box was suffering from a brain hemorrhage caused by a ruptured blood vessel.

"Can you fix it?" asked Dr. Hollins. She was the resident responsible for Mr. Box's primary care. The man she addressed was Dr. Carl Oceana, the staff's only neurosurgeon.

"Sure," said Dr. Oceana. "I can repair the vessel and clean out the mess. But it won't do much good, you know."

"You mean he'll still be paralyzed?"

"And he'll still be mentally incoherent. After the operation he'll have to be put in a chronic-care place, because he won't be able to see to his own needs."

"And if you don't operate?" Dr. Hollins asked.

Dr. Oceana shrugged. "He'll be dead by tomorrow. Maybe sooner, depending on how long it takes for the pressure in his skull to build up."

"What would you do?"

"I know what I would want done to me if I were the patient," said Dr. Oceana. "I'd want people to keep their knives out of my head and let me die a nice, peaceful death."

"But we don't know what he would want," Dr. Hollins said. "He's never been our patient before, and the social worker hasn't been able to find any friends who might tell us what he'd want done."

"Let's just put ourselves in his place," said Dr. Oceana. "Let's do unto others what we would want done unto us."

"That means letting Mr. Box die."

"Exactly."

1. On what grounds might one object to Dr. Oceana's view?

2. Would active euthanasia be justified?

3. Would the natural law view make the operation discussed a moral mandate?

DECISION SCENARIO 3

The Bartling Case

On April 8, 1984, William Bartling was admitted to the Glendale Adventist Medical Center in Los Angeles. He was seventy years old and suffered from five ordinarily fatal diseases: emphysema, diffuse arteriosclerosis, coronary arteriosclerosis, an abdominal aneurysm, and inoperable lung cancer. During the performance of a biopsy to diagnose the lung cancer, Mr. Bartling's left lung collapsed. He was placed in the ICU, and a chest tube and mechanical respirator were used to assist his breathing.

Mr. Bartling complained about the pain the respirator caused him, and he repeatedly asked to have it removed. When his physician refused, he pulled out the chest tube himself. This happened so often that eventually Mr. Bartling's hands were tied to the bed to keep him from doing it. He had signed a living will in an attempt to avoid just such a situation.

Although after discussions with Richard Scott (Mr. Bartling's attorney), Mr. Bartling's physician and the hospital administration agreed to disconnect the respirator, the hospital's attorney refused to permit it. He argued that, since Mr. Bartling was not terminally ill, brain dead, or in a persistent vegetative state, the hospital might be open to legal action.

Mr. Scott took the case to Los Angeles Superior Court. He argued that Mr. Bartling was legally competent to make a decision about his welfare and that, although he did not want to die, he understood that disconnecting the respirator might lead to his death. The hospital's attorney took the position that Mr. Bartling was ambivalent on the question of his death. His statements "I don't want to die" and "I don't want to live on the respirator" were taken as inconsistent and so as evidence of ambivalence. Removing the respirator, the attorney argued, would be tantamount to aiding suicide or even committing homicide.

The court refused either to allow the respirator to be removed or to order that Mr. Bartling's hands be freed. To do so, the court ruled, would be to take a positive step to end treatment, and the only precedents for doing so were in cases in which the patients were comatose, brain dead, or in a chronic vegetative state.

The case was then taken to the California Court of Appeal, which ruled as follows: "If the right of a patient to self-determination as to his own medical treatment is to have any meaning at all, it must be paramount to the interests of the patient's hospitals and doctors. The right of a competent adult patient to refuse medical treatment is a constitutionally guaranteed right which must not be abridged."

The ruling came too late for Mr. Bartling. He died twenty-three hours before the court heard his appeal.

1. Is there any merit to the hospital's position that to remove Mr. Bartling's respirator or to free his hands would be equivalent to assisting suicide?

2. How can the reasoning in the *Quinlan* case be extended to Mr. Bartling's case?

3. What arguments can be used to support the view that it would be morally wrong even to untie Mr. Bartling's hands?

4. On what grounds might Mr. Bartling's request be honored?

DECISION SCENARIO 4

Angel of Mercy?

When two plainclothes detectives arrived at Virginia Crawford's suburban apartment at 6:30 on a Sunday morning to arrest her for murder, she was not surprised to see them.

She cried when they insisted on putting her in handcuffs before transporting her to the jail in the county court building. Yet she had more or less expected to be arrested eventually. For almost a month, a police investigation had been conducted at Mercy Hospital, where Ms. Crawford worked as a nurse in the intensive-care unit (ICU). The entire hospital staff knew about the investigation, and Ms. Crawford herself had been questioned on three occasions by officers conducting the inquiry. At the time, her answers had seemed to be satisfactory to the police, and there was no hint that she was under suspicion. Still, she always believed that eventually they would catch up with her.

The investigation centered on the deaths of four elderly patients during the period from February 1979 to March 1980. All of the patients were in the ICU at the times of their deaths. Each had been diagnosed as suffering from a terminal illness, and the chart notation on each case indicated that they had all suffered irreversible brain damage and were totally without higher brain functions.

The three women and one man were all unmarried and had no immediate family to take an interest in their welfare. All of them were being kept alive by respirators, and their deaths were caused directly by their respirators' being turned off. In each instance of death, Ms. Crawford had been the person in charge of the ICU.

After securing the services of an attorney, Ms. Crawford was released on bail and a time was set for her appearance in court. Through her attorney, Marvin Washington, she made a statement to the media:

"My client has asked me to announce that she fully and freely admits that she was the one who turned off the respirators of the four patients in question at Mercy Hospital. She acted alone and without the knowledge of any other individual. She is prepared to take full responsibility for her actions."

Mr. Washington went on to say that he would request a jury trial for his client. "I am sure," he said, "that no jury will convict Ms. Crawford of murder merely for turning off the life-support systems of people who were already dead."

When asked what he meant by that, Mr. Washington explained. "These patients were no longer people," he said. "Sometime during the course of the treatment, their brains simply stopped functioning in a way that we associate with human life."

Ms. Crawford was present during the reading of her statement, and after a whispered conversation with her attorney, she spoke once for herself. "I consider what I did an act of compassion and humanity," she said. "I consider it altogether moral, and I feel no guilt about it. I did for four people what they would have wanted done if they had only been in a condition to know."

1. Does the natural law view offer grounds for removing life-support systems from people who are beyond a reasonable hope of recovery? If so, what are they?

2. What arguments might lead us to condemn Ms. Crawford actions?

3. Can arguments favoring voluntary active euthanasia be extended to justify Ms. Crawford's actions?

4. Might Ms. Crawford be right about the patients' being dead according to some concept of death?

DECISION SCENARIO 5

Dutch Practices

In 1993, the Netherlands passed a law permitting physicians to assist in the suicide of terminally ill patients. The law requires that the patient's decision to die be informed and irrevocable and that there be no other solution acceptable to the patient that would improve the situation.

1. What arguments can be used to support a public policy of this kind?

2. Are the procedural safeguards adopted in the Netherlands adequate to prevent deliberate homicide? Are they adequate to prevent people who are temporarily depressed or irrational from killing themselves?

3. What dangers does such a policy pose?

4. Does the right of an individual to refuse life-sustaining medical treatment imply that an individual has a right to terminate his life by active means? If so, does this mean that society has a duty to provide assistance?

5. On what grounds might one object to the Dutch policy?

Chapter **11**

African Americans and Medicine

CHAPTER CONTENTS

CASES AND CONTEXTS

Bad Blood, Bad Faith: The Tuskegee Syphilis Study

The way the United States Public Health Service conducted the Tuskegee Study of Untreated Syphilis in the Negro Male probably did more than any other single event to promote suspicion and distrust of physicians, treatment, and the entire medical establishment in the African American community.

Ironically, the Tuskegee Study was the outgrowth of a program of deliberate efforts to improve the health of poor African Americans in the rural South. It is a story of good intentions paving the road to hell.

Medicine at the beginning of the twentieth century was in the process of becoming scientific, and thanks to the work of bacteriologists such as Pasteur, Koch, and Ehrlich in the preceding century, it was able to diagnose and treat a wide range of infectious diseases. Perhaps more important, it had acquired a good understanding of the ways in which such diseases spread, and public-health medicine had been founded to put the new knowledge into practice. The prevention of disease on a grand scale became a major goal of public health, and because preventing disease often meant treating those capable of spreading it, joint public programs of treatment and prevention became common.

Since its occurrence in Europe in the fifteenth century, syphilis had been viewed much the way AIDS was when it made its first appearance in the United States during the early 1980s. Syphilis was spread primarily by sexual contact and so could be passed on to sexual partners. Women could infect their children, and the children could be born dead or blind and diseased. Its association with sex, particularly illicit sex, turned it into a shameful disease for many and made its diagnosis and treatment difficult. In the Victorian age, mental hospitals housed many people suffering from the "insanity" marking the final stage of the disease, and this underscored the idea that syphilis was a disease affecting only people with loose moral conduct.

The causative agent of syphilis, a small corkscrew-shaped bacterium, was isolated in 1905, and a year later August Wassermann introduced a diagnostic blood test for the disease. In 1911, Paul Ehrlich (who coined the phrase "magic bullet") tested over six hundred chemical compounds before identifying one, salvarsan (number 606), that seemed effective in the treatment of syphilis. The hope of public-health officials in developed countries was that, armed with the Wassermann test and salvarsan, they could soon eradicate syphilis.

Macon County, Alabama

Salversan did not turn out to be the miracle drug public-health officials had hoped for, but even so, researchers soon discovered that injections of arsenic derivatives over a period of about eighteen months would halt the disease and render it noninfectious. This kept alive the dream of eliminating syphilis, and it was in pursuit of that dream that, in 1930 in Macon County, Alabama, the United States Public Health Service (PHS), building on experience recently acquired in Mississippi, initiated a program to diagnose and treat 10,000 African Americans for syphilis.

Sampling showed that thirty-five percent of the black population in Macon county was infected with syphilis, however, and the PHS soon realized that it had underestimated the costs of eradicating the disease in even one county. By 1931, in the midst of the Depression, the money for the program ran out, with only some 1400 people receiving even partial treatment. Additional money from the federal government or the Julius Rosenwald Fund, a Chicago charitable foundation that had supported the project, could not be expected.

Taliaferro Clark of the PHS was determined to salvage something from the Macon Project. He decided that even if there was no money for the extensive treatments, the Service could do a six-month study of the natural history of untreated syphilis at little cost. Did the disease behave the same in blacks as in whites, or did genetic differences make blacks more susceptible? Or were blacks, once infected, more resistant than whites to the effects of the disease?

The PHS accepted Clark's proposal and, in doing so, tacitly endorsed a research program that involved deceiving a group of people about the nature of their illness and deliberately withholding potentially effective treatments from them while giving them the impression that they were being appropriately treated. That the people were all rural, impoverished, and poorly educated black males makes it hard to avoid the conclusion that the PHS regarded the subjects as hardly more than experimental animals.

Representatives of the PHS approached the Tuskegee Institute with its research proposal, and in 1932 Tuskegee agreed to participate in the observational study. The institute would be paid for its participation, and its interns and nurses would have the opportunity to work for the government, a major incentive during the worst of the Depression in the rural South.

With the help of Tuskegee and black churches and community leaders, men were recruited for the study. They were promised free medical examinations, blood tests, and medicines. In rural Alabama, where few people, black or white, could afford to consult a physician even when sick, such an offer by an agency of the federal government seemed a golden opportunity.

No Diagnosis, No Treatment

What the subjects weren't told was that they wouldn't be given a more specific diagnosis than "bad blood" and would be treated only with placebos. The PHS doctors sometimes claimed that "bad blood" was the term used by rural blacks to mean syphilis. But the term was really a catchall category that could include anything from iron deficiency and sickle-cell disease to leukemia and syphilis. It was used to explain why people felt sluggish, tired easily, or had a low energy level.

In its primary stage, syphilis causes a genital, anal, or mouth ulcer. Known as a chancre, this is a pus-filled sore teeming with bacterial spirochetes that heals within a month or two. Six to twelve weeks after infection, the disease enters its secondary stage. It is marked by skin rashes that may last for months, swollen lymph nodes, headaches, bone pain, fever, loss of appetite, and fatigue. Sores that are highly infectious may develop on the skin. The secondary stage lasts for about a year; then the disease becomes latent. During this inactive stage, which may last for many years or even a lifetime, the person seems wholly normal.

About thirty percent of the time, however, people with untreated syphilis progress to the tertiary stage. One marked effect is the destruction of the tissues making up the bones, palate, nasal septum, tongue, skin, or almost any organ in the body. Infection of the heart may lead to the destruction of the valves or the aorta, causing aneurysms that can rupture and cause immediate death. Infection of the brain can lead to general paralysis and to progressive brain damage, which produces the "insanity" noted in the nineteenth century.

Study participants diagnosed with "bad blood" were given, at different times, vials of liquids, round pills, and capsules. But the drugs were nothing more than placebos, vitamins at best, and contained no ingredient active against syphilis. A sham diagnosis was matched by a sham treatment.

Unfortunately, despite the medical counterfeiting, the disease was real enough to maim and kill. At the end of the six-month study period, the data showed that untreated syphilis in blacks was just as deadly as in whites. This was seen as an important and exciting finding, because it contradicted the widely held opinion that blacks tolerated syphilis better and were less harmed by it.

Study Extended

Raymond A. Vonderlehr, a PHS officer, obtained permission to extend the study to collect more data. An African American nurse, Eunice Rivers, was added to the staff. She was assigned to recruit men to the study who were free of the disease and so could serve as a control group. The study came to involve 600 black men—399 diagnosed with syphilis and 201 free of the disease.

Nurse Rivers also had the job of keeping up with the study participants and making sure they showed up for their annual examinations and tests administered by the PHS physicians. She was given a government car, and it was a sign of pride in the black community of Macon County to be driven by Miss Rivers to the school where the exams were conducted. Because the study offered participants $50 for burial expenses if they agreed to an autopsy at their death, they spoke of themselves as belonging to Nurse Rivers's Burial Society.

Reports from the Tuskegee Study were published in peer-reviewed medical journals like the *Journal of the American Medical Association,* and from time to time PHS officers presented the study results to Congress. No one raised any questions about the ethics of the study or asked whether the men participating in it had been informed that they had syphilis and weren't being treated for it.

In 1938, the passage of the National Venereal Disease Control Act required the PHS to provide treatment for people suffering from syphilis or other venereal diseases, even if they couldn't afford to pay for it. Yet participants in the study were considered experimental subjects and not subject to the requirements of the law. Participants who sought treatment from venereal disease clinics were turned away.

At the outbreak of the Second World War, local draft boards were persuaded to exempt at least fifty participants from military service so their symptoms wouldn't be diagnosed and treated by military physicians. When penicillin, which is highly effective against the syphilis spirochete, became available in the mid-1940s, the PHS withheld it from the study participants. Even as participants became blind or insane, the study went on without any treatments being offered.

In 1947, Nazi physicians and scientists who had taken part in vicious, senseless, and often deadly human experiments were tried for war crimes at Nuremberg. One of the outcomes of the trial was the formulation of the Nuremberg Code to govern the participation of subjects in experimentation. (See the Briefing Session in Chapter 1.) The key element of the Code is the requirement that subjects give their free and informed consent before becoming participants. Although this requirement was consistently violated by the Tuskegee Study, even after the Nuremberg Code was enunciated, officials at the PHS failed to grasp its relevance to the research they were conducting.

Beginning of the End

In 1964, Irwin J. Schatz, a Detroit physician responding to an article, wrote to PHS researcher Anne Q. Yobs that he was "utterly astounded by the fact that physicians allow patients with a potentially fatal disease to remain untreated when effective therapy is available," but Schatz received no reply. Two years later, Peter Buxtun, a social worker hired by the PHS as a venereal disease investigator, heard rumors about the Tuskegee Study, and after reading the research publications based on it, sent a letter to the director of the Division of Venereal Disease, William J. Brown, to express his serious moral concerns about the experiment.

Buxtun received no response, but eventually he was invited to a meeting at the headquarters of the Centers for Disease Control, and there he was verbally attacked by John Cutler, a health officer knowledgeable about the study. "He was infuriated," Buxtun said. He "thought of me as some sort of lunatic who needed immediate chastisement." Cutler explained to Buxtun the importance the experiment would have in helping physicians treat black patients with syphilis.

Buxtun left the PHS voluntarily to go to law school, but he didn't forget about Tuskegee. In 1968, he wrote another letter to Brown. Pulling few punches, he pointed out that the racial makeup of the study supported "the thinking of Negro militants that Negroes have long been used for 'medical experiments' and 'teaching cases' in the emergency wards of county hospitals." He said they could hardly be regarded as volunteers and observed that whatever justification could have been offered for the experiment in 1932 was no longer relevant. He expressed the hope that the subjects in the study would be given appropriate treatments.

This time, Buxtun's letter produced action—but not much. In 1969, the Centers for Disease Control convened a panel to review the Tuskegee Study. With only one dissenting member, it concluded that the study should go on, because it had gone on so long already that treating the subjects with penicillin might cause them more harm than leaving them untreated would. (More than half of the patients treated for syphilis with penicillin suffer a severe reaction in response to the sudden killing of so many spirochetes.) In short, treatment might cause the participants more harm than doing nothing would.

Early in July 1972, Peter Buxtun turned over the materials he had accumulated on the Tuskegee Study to Associated Press reporter Jean Heller, and on July 25, after interviewing officials in the PHS, Heller broke the story nationally.

Public anger was swift in coming. The experiment was denounced by the Assistant Secretary of Health, Education, and Welfare, who launched an investigation into why study participants never received treatment for their disease. Congressional hearings were conducted, government research agencies reviewed their recruiting practices, and human subject committees were established to oversee all research involving people.

Most important, the Tuskegee Study came to an immediate halt. It had lasted for forty years, and twenty-eight of its participants had died by the time it ended. Since 1972, the federal government has paid out $10 million in out-of-court settlements to the subjects, their families, or heirs. Eight of the participants were still alive in 1998, but their number is dwindling.

On May 16, 1997, President Bill Clinton formally apologized to the survivors of the Tuskegee Study. "What is done cannot be undone, but we can end the silence," he said in a White House ceremony. "We can stop turning our heads away. We can look at you in the eye and finally say, on behalf of the American people, 'What the United States did was shameful, and I am sorry.'"

SOCIAL CONTEXT
Race-Based Medicine?

Heart failure is a disease in which, for reasons usually unknown, the heart begins to lose its capacity to pump blood effectively. The muscle of the heart grows weak and flaccid. The condition may start slowly and stabilize for a long time or get progressively worse.

When blood doesn't circulate adequately, fluid builds up in the lungs and body tissues. Heart-failure patients become short of breath, sometimes to the point of becoming bedridden, and their feet and ankles swell as the retained fluid accumulates. The heart itself, in an effort to compensate for its loss of normal pumping power, grows larger to maintain something like the normal amount of blood output. As the heart grows in size, it begins to fill the chest cavity and can press on the lungs, increasing breathing difficulties.

More than five million Americans suffer from heart failure. Drugs can be effective in eliminating some of the retained fluid and strengthening the heartbeat to improve circulation, but there is no cure for heart failure. When the hearts of those with the disease are finally unable to supply their bodies with an adequate amount of blood, they typically die. Those who are fortunate may be able to extend their lives with a heart transplant.

Search for a Drug

Because heart failure is so difficult to treat, during the 1970s J. N. Cohn, a cardiologist then at the University of Michigan, began to experiment with drugs that might expand the blood vessels (vasodilators) and allow more blood to leave the heart. An effective vasodilator, although it would not be a cure, would reduce some of the worst symptoms of heart failure, reduce the number of hospitalizations, and lengthen the lives of those with the disease.

The drug that Cohn experimented with that showed the most promise was a combination of the two generic drugs isosorbide dimitrate and hydralizine that he called BiDil. In the 1980s, he conducted a clinical trial of BiDil, using it to treat heart-failure patients in a Washington veterans' hospital, and concluded that the drug lowered the death rate. (The trial was called V-HeFt for "vasodilator heart-failure trial.") Cohn presented his findings to the FDA, but after reviewing the data, the FDA ruled in 1997 that the reduced mortality Cohn attributed to BiDil wasn't statistically significant. Thus, the FDA refused to approve the drug.

This would have been the end of the story for most drugs tested in a clinical trial, but the BiDil trial had produced one result Cohn saw as surprising. The trial involved 630 people, and 180 of them were African Americans. When only the black participants were considered, the data showed that BiDil reduced deaths to a degree that *was* statistically significant.

That this might happen made sense scientifically. Exactly how BiDil works is not certain, but it is known to increase the level of nitric oxide in the body. Nitric oxide, for its part, is known to cause smooth muscle tissue to relax, and it is this property that makes it a vasodilator. People with heart failure are often found deficient in nitric oxide, and African Americans tend to have lower nitric oxide levels than other groups. Almost a million of the five million people diagnosed with heart failure are black. Thus, if BiDil really was effective in treating heart failure in African Americans, they would have a great deal to gain if the FDA approved the drug.

Special Study Needed

In 2001, however, the FDA decided that although the data from Cohn's study were suggestive, they were not adequate to show that BiDil would benefit African Americans. The drug could be approved for this use only if researchers conducted a clinical trial limited to African Americans and the results demonstrated that the drug lowered the number of deaths due to heart failure than might statistically be expected.

NitroMed, the company holding the rights to market BiDil, realized that testing a drug using exclusively African American subjects might cause a controversy and trigger accusations of racism. The company began by talking with representatives of the Congressional Black Caucus and the NAACP, explaining the potential importance of BiDil, and securing their support. NitroMed then approached the Association of Black Cardiologists to ask for help in recruiting patients for the study.

The cardiologists debated the matter extensively. Eventually, they decided that testing a drug that promised to be of benefit primarily to African Americans was a way to redress decades of inequality in health care, particularly as symbolized by the unjust treatment of black men in the Tuskegee syphilis trials. (See the Social Context "Bad Blood, Bad Faith: The Tuskegee Syphilis Study," in this chapter.) At NitroMed's request, the cardiologists'

organization agreed to cosponsor and organize the study, for which it would receive $200,000 from NitroMed.

BiDil Study

The BiDil study enrolled 1,050 African American patients with heart failure. The results of the study, announced in 2005, showed that BiDil not only significantly reduced hospitalization and treatment costs, but also reduced the number of expected deaths by forty-three percent. Impressed by this outcome, the American Heart Association described BiDil as one of the most significant developments in cardiac care for the year. NitroMed presented the results to the FDA, and the drug continues to work its way through the approval process. (NitroMed will also get an extension on its patent protection for BiDil.)

A Drug for a Particular Race?

Not everyone has been pleased with the identification of a drug as effective for a particular race. Those who hold that race is a socially constructed category, one defined so as to reflect the interests of the dominant social group, see the idea of a drug as successful only within a race as implicitly supporting the notion that race is a biological category, not a social artifact.

Yet many, if not most, researchers don't consider the success of BiDil to have much to do with the debate about the biological or socially constructed status of races. They point out that an individual's race is, at best, a marker for the presence or absence of a gene. If black people in general and African Americans in particular lack a gene for producing nitric oxide in the most beneficial quantities, skin color is only an indicator of one element of their genetic makeup.

Without a doubt, some white, Hispanic, and Asian people also lack the gene for an abundance of nitric oxide, just not as large a percentage of them. Thus, being black, defenders of the view say, is no more than an indicator to a physician that someone with heart failure may be treated most effectively with BiDil. As soon as a gene is actually found and a test is available for its presence, the need to use race as a marker will disappear.

Self-Identification

A second difficulty with race is more practical. The FDA labeling will say that the drug is for use in people who "self-identify" as African Americans. The use of such language obviously allows physicians and insurance companies to avoid potentially explosive situations in which they decide that a patient is or is not black and the patient disagrees.

The problem with self-identification, though, is that it may not reveal much about the person's genetic background. Someone with a single distant black ancestor may self-identify as African American, although she may share few genes with many others who self-identify as African American. If she has heart failure, should her physician treat her with BiDil? Or should he take the controversial step of saying the equivalent of "I don't think you're black enough to benefit from BiDil" and offer her the treatment considered most effective for non-African Americans? Until a gene or set of genes is discovered that correlates with the effectiveness of BiDil, the self-identification requirement remains troublesome. (It shows, too, as critics charge, that skin color or racial identification is a very crude indicator of anyone's genetic makeup.)

Defenders of the use of race as a basis for prescribing a drug point out that African Americans are not the only group in the general population that has been discovered to have a different reaction to a drug: Crestor, a cholesterol-lowering drug, has such serious side effects for people of Asian ancestry that it's generally not prescribed for them.

Testing "Race-Based" Drugs

Another doubt about the wisdom of allowing the FDA to approve "race-based" drugs concerns testing them. To be approved, a drug usually must be tested in the general population and shown to be safe and effective. Subjects ordinarily must include both men and women, as well as representatives of minorities. Indeed, federal regulations require that special efforts be made to recruit African Americans and other minorities. But suppose a pharmaceutical company decides to follow the BiDil example and, to save money, decides to test a drug only in a special population, such as Asian Americans. Suppose also that the data show that the drug is safe and effective, and the FDA approves it as safe and effective for use in people of Asian ancestry.

This is good news for Asian Americans, but what about others? Will the drug work for them? We don't know. Once a drug is approved, a physician can prescribe it to anyone, but will a white woman taking the drug benefit as much as an Asian American woman? We have no data to form an answer to this question. A clinical trial is supposed to provide us with such information, but a trial limited to a special population deprives us of it. Thus, some say, race-based medicines may undercut the whole clinical-trial process.

Race and Risk

BiDil is not the only source of controversy about medicine and race. DeCode Genetics announced in 2005, that it had discovered a variant gene named DG031 that increases the risk of heart attacks in African Americans by more than 250 percent.

The gene was first discovered in people from Iceland. Then studies by DeCode of people in Philadelphia, Cleveland, and Atlanta identified the gene both in people of African ancestry and in people of European ancestry. However, for European Americans, possessing the gene increases the risk of heart attack by only about sixteen percent.

The gene discovered by DeCode is a more active variant of a gene named leukotriene A4 hydrolase, which plays a role in the body's inflammatory response to infection. The gene controls steps in the process of producing substances called leukotrienes that keep body tissue inflamed and thus fight infections by making conditions inhospitable to invading viruses or bacteria.

Some researchers believe the variant gene occurred as a mutation among Europeans and Asians in the very distant past, then was passed on through the generations because of its effectiveness in fighting off infectious diseases. The price for possessing the gene in the beginning was a greater risk of death due to heart disease because of plaque buildup in the arteries from the inflammation. The rupture of an artery or blockage due to plaque would trigger a heart attack. Yet, over the generations, selection pressures favored Europeans and Asians who possessed both the gene and other genes that compensated for its effects on the heart. Populations in Africa, according to this hypothesis, lacked the mutation for the variant gene, and it is only in recent times that it has spread into the African American population.

A drug being tested by DeCode Genetics acts on a part of the inflammation process not controlled by DG031, yet the drug promises to be of value to those who test positive for DG031. This means that if the drug is successful, it may reduce heart disease in a significant number of African Americans.

Should a clinical trial that consists of significant proportions of African Americans be conducted on DG031? Or should the trial reflect the general U.S. population, which contains only about fifteen percent African Americans? Views on this question are split.

Kari Stephansson, the president of DeCode Genetics, says, "It would make scientific, economic, and particularly political sense to have a significant part of the clinical trial done in an African American population." But Charles Rotimi, a genetic epidemiologist at Howard University, a leading African American institution, says that a separate clinical trial for African Americans wouldn't be sensible. The variant form of DG031 might be overactive in African Americans, he maintains, because of their greater exposure to deleterious environments. Thus, Rotimi seems to suggest, it is *not* genetic differences that are responsible for the different heart attack rates in European and African American segments of the population.

Genetics and Race

Assertions of genetic inferiority historically have been major components of racism and anti-Semitism. African Americans, given their history of unfair treatment by the dominant part of the population, have strong reasons to be suspicious of any effort to single them out as a group associated with disease. It could be only a short step from providing special treatments to African Americans because of a predisposition to certain genetic diseases to stigmatizing them as "diseased" and "naturally unhealthy." Anyone familiar with the background of the Tuskegee Syphilis study is aware that, even though it involved the most notorious abuse of medical trust in the history of the country, the study began with good intentions. Thus, some African Americans worry that singling them out to test them for certain genes or to use them as subjects to test the effectiveness of particular drugs may be the first step on a downhill slide leading to racial discrimination.

This is not a view universally shared by African Americans. In 2003, Howard University announced that it was initiating a program to collect the DNA of thousands of African Americans. The point of collecting the DNA is to look for genes for diseases like hypertension and diabetes, which occur with a higher frequency among black people than in the general population.

Ultimately, researchers at Howard hope, they will have enough genetic information about African Americans to warn particular people that they are predisposed to certain diseases, advise them how to avoid developing the diseases, and tailor treatments and drugs to fit their specific genetic profiles.

Genetic information has the power to heal and to hurt. This is true whether race is involved or not, but when race is added to genetics, the mixture can become explosive. Most researchers believe that it should be possible to work out ways to take advantage of new genetic information to help people of particular races without using that same information to harm them socially. The crucial task that has to be performed to bring this about is the working out of the necessary procedures and safeguards.

More Race-Based Drugs

The pharmaceutical Research Association reported in 2007 (the most recent figures), that more than seven hundred drugs targeted at African Americans are under development. Those who are involved in the research see the drugs as directed toward the unmet medical needs of the black population.

Yet, even while so many race-based drugs were under development, NitroMed announced in 2009 that it was suspending its marketing efforts for BiDil and was open to buyout offers for the drug. Sales for BiDil were poor, which some observers attribute to a reluctance on the part of physicians to prescribe a drug that is race targeted. Defenders of a race-based approach are critical of such reluctance, because, in their view, black people are being denied the best treatment available for their hypertension.

Yet even defenders of race-based medicine as currently practiced agree that it is no more than a brief stop on the road to the development of tests that will allow drugs to be tailored to the needs of individuals. When this can be done, race will become irrelevant.

SOCIAL CONTEXT
Is Health About Status, Not Race?

The Palace of Whitehall was a sprawling complex of buildings that became the center of English civil government in the thirteenth century. Fire destroyed most of it in 1698, but the street with its name remains the home of the British Civil Service. "Whitehall" refers to the Civil Service, just as "Capitol Hill" refers to Congress.

Sir Michael Marmot, an epidemiologist, saw Whitehall as an ideal place to study the relationship between social status and health. Civil servants in Britain (like those in the United States) are classified by grades in a hierarchical ranking. Thus, it is always clear whose status is higher, lower, or equivalent to another's. It is also possible to know how many grades higher or lower someone is than someone else.

Marmot realized that by employing the Whitehall grading scheme as a model of social status, he would avoid the problem of dealing with the uncertainties and vague boundaries of social class in Britain. Defining and distinguishing social classes involves complications associated with family background, education, income, race, religion, place of birth, and so on. Distinctions among different classes based on such factors could be criticized as arbitrary and irrelevant. The Civil Service grades, by contrast, are explicit and objective.

The Civil Service grades also have the advantage of allowing investigators to correct for differences in factors such as smoking, exercise, education, diet, and lack of medical care. These factors are most often mentioned to explain the differences between groups that develop particular diseases or are at greater risk for them. The United States, especially, is concerned with race as an indicator of health, as well as a risk factor for the development of particular diseases (e.g., African Americans are more at risk for hypertension and diabetes than are another ethnic groups). But, Marmot asked, is it these factors, or is it status, that is connected with health?

Whitehall civil servants as a group are more homogeneous than the general population. All have sedentary jobs, employment security, and access to good medical care. Yet they are sharply divided by differences of grade. Because Marmot wanted to focus on just one factor—social status—and ask whether it made a difference in the health of individuals, this translated into the question "Does a difference in Civil Service grade matter to the health of those at that grade?"

Marmot began his research in 1967. Whitehall I was limited to the study of mortality rates and the prevalence of cardiac and respiratory disease in males between the ages of 20 and 64. The study lasted for ten years and was followed by Whitehall II, which focused on the health of 10,308 civil servants aged 35 to 55. Two-thirds were men, one-third women. A third long-term follow-up study of the participants in the two original studies is still ongoing.

Whitehall Results

The Whitehall studies found that people in the bottom Civil Service grades are characterized by lower levels of physical activity, less leisure time, and more illnesses. They also tend to be shorter and exhibit more of the known risk factors for cardiac disease, such as smoking, high blood pressure, and obesity.

The surprise of the Whitehall study was that even when these risk factors are statistically controlled for, they can account for only one-third of the differences in health status between people at the highest grade and those at the lowest. Specifically, people at the lowest grade are three times more likely to die of a heart attack than those at the highest grade.

"A smoker who is low employment grade has a higher risk of heart disease than a smoker who is higher grade," Marmot writes. "A non-smoker who is lower grade has a higher risk of heart disease than a nonsmoker who is higher grade."

Stress?

The explanation for this and many similar differences, according to Marmot, is stress. "Sustained, chronic, and long-term stress is linked to low control over life circumstances," Marmot claims. Those at the lower levels in the Civil Service hierarchy experience more stress. They have little control over how they can arrange their lives. They must do the work assigned to them according to the instructions they are given. They must arrive at work at a specific time, take breaks of a set length at specific times, and quit work at a specific time. Within their day, those at the lower levels aren't free to vary much from a routine or to make decisions about what they are going to do with their day.

Those who are at the top levels of the hierarchy have much more control over their time. They may keep hours as predictable as those at the lower level, but they know they can vary them without suffering a reprimand or a penalty. They may skip lunch or take it early; they may spend two or three hours over lunch, talking business—or not. They initiate projects, assign projects to others, and generally arrange their lives and work as they see fit.

Stable Structures

Because those at the top control their lives to a greater degree than those at the bottom, they suffer less stress. The relationship between stress and health isn't completely understood, but we know that the release of stress hormones like epinephrine increases the heart rate, raises blood-glucose levels, and prepares the body to deal with an imminent threat. If stress continues over a long time, it can cause cardio-vascular harm and damage. As a result, people are more likely to develop high blood pressure, asthma, and diabetes, as well as suffer heart attacks and strokes. Prolonged stress can also cause immune system damage, and this makes people more vulnerable to a variety of viral and bacterial infections.

"Sustained chronic and long-term stress is linked to low control over life circumstances," Marmot writes. Stress of this sort is then linked to various diseases.

Of course, being at the top of a hierarchy, as writer Patricia Cohen observes, can be very stressful if the hierarchy is not stable and is under constant threat. She calls attention to the research of biologist Robert M. Sapolsky. His work with baboons, who live in a rigidly defined status structure, shows that high-status baboons have a lower incidence of stress-related diseases than low-status members of their group. However, if dominant baboons are challenged by aggressive, lower status baboons and have to fight to maintain their dominance, they start to display the physiological changes (hypertension, high blood-glucose levels, etc.) that are associated with disease.

Sapolsky's work suggests that social factors may moderate stress. Thus, baboons living in an uncontested, established order know their places, deal easily with one other, and avoid the stress of challenging a dominant animal and then dealing with the resulting conflict. Humans appear to behave in similar ways, and people who generally do best at maintaining their health, various studies show, are those who have a social-support network made up of friends and family. Similarly, married people have a lower mortality than those who are single, as do people who play active roles in their community.

Presumably, being in the upper levels of the British Civil Service would not be as conducive to the health of those in that position if the country were on the brink of revolution and revolutionaries were challenging the form of government that makes the bureaucracy such a stable structure.

The Oscar Advantage

A number of other studies have shown a link between status and health. One of the most striking is an analysis of Oscar winners by Canadian epidemiologist Donald Redelmeier. While watching the Academy Awards on TV, Redelmeier was struck by how healthy and robust the award nominees seemed to be.

"The people up on the stage didn't look anything like the patients I see at the hospital," he recalls. "It was the way they walked and gestured and talked. They just seemed so much more alive, for lack of a better word."

Redelmeier knew about the Whitehall stud-ies and others attempting to establish a link between social status and health. One of those that occurred to him was G. D. Smith's data correlating the size of the tombstones in Scot-tish cemeteries with the longevity of the people whose graves they marked. Smith had found that people with taller, larger tombstones had lived longer lives.

It's clear, Redelmeier thought, that overall success can extend lives, but what about a single, significant achievement? The lives of actors are very similar. They have about the same amount of education, have access to the same high-quality health care, and are subject to the same levels of stress in their work. But not all actors win an Academy Award. Could this single triumphal event make a difference in how long they live?

Redelmeier and his collaborator began to collect data about past Oscar winners and nom-inees for a leading or supporting role over the seventy years the Academy Awards have been given. They matched up each winner or nomi-nee in each relevant film with an actor of a sim-ilar age who had never been nominated. The list included actors like Jack Nicholson, who had won several Oscars, and ones like Richard Burton, who had been nominated many times but never won. It also included (for age matching) actors like Lorne Green, accomplished and respected performers never nominated for an Oscar. The researchers searched databases and record offices to establish the correct dates of birth and death for each of the 1649 performers on their final list.

The results of the statistical analysis of the list were as surprising as the findings of the Whitehall study. Redelmeier discovered that, with respect to longevity, being nominated for an Oscar made a difference, winning one made a bigger difference, and winning several made an even bigger difference.

Successful actors never nominated for an Academy Award, the data showed, lived an average of 75.8 years. Nominees lived 76.1 years, a modest increase over the unnominated. Oscar winners, by contrast, lived for 79.7 years, almost four years (3.9) longer than successful actors who were never nominated. The effect was extended for those winning multiple awards; they tended to live almost six years longer.

Redelmeier himself was stunned by the result. While, at first sight, a four-year increase in longevity for Oscar winners may seem relatively small, Redelmeier puts it in perspective. "If you were to cure all cancers of all people in North America for all time," he says, "you would add maybe 3.5 years to life expectancy." Statistically, then, a four-year extension of longevity in a population is a huge increase.

So why does giving an Academy Award to actors produce the effect of lengthening their lives? Redelmeier speculates that it may be the result of the prestige that the award bestows. Winning expresses an unambiguous recognition by their peers that they are at the top of the pyramid in their social structure. Moreover,

Redelmeier suggests, winning the award may produce peace of mind, reassuring the winners that they need not suffer from doubts resulting from bad reviews or cutting remarks by critics. This would have the consequence for winners of reducing the stress they might otherwise experience.

Relative Worth

Status matters to people. This is not surprising, because it is obvious to anyone with any experience of the world in school, business, sports, or any other sphere. What is surprising is that, at least when it comes to money, it is status itself, rather than an absolute amount of money that is more important.

Which of the two options would you choose: (A) an income of $125,000, when the average income of those around you is $100,000; or (B) an income of $175,000, when the average income of those around you is $200,000?

Surveys by economists such as Robert Evans show that the majority of people would choose option A. This means that, for most people, it isn't potential purchasing power alone that gives money its value. Otherwise, everyone would choose to have an additional $50,000 to spend. Survey findings indicate, instead, that most people are willing to sacrifice a significant sum of money to acquire a status superior to those around them.

Such surveys suggest that most people would prefer to be a big fish in a small pond, rather than a small fish in a big pond. If Marmot's Whitehall study and Redelmeier's Academy Award analysis are reliable guides, it may be that those who chose status over extra money are not being as irrational as might first appear. They may be making, quite unknowingly, a choice so beneficial to their health that it will lengthen their lives.

BRIEFING SESSION

Ethical and social issues connected with the health of minorities, particularly African Americans, have received little attention until recent decades.

Traditional Western medicine centered the great majority of its efforts on understanding and treating the disorders of the white male, who was implicitly taken as the standard patient and research subject. Perhaps this is not surprising, considering that the white male was also the standard physician and researcher.

Society has changed. A 2010 study showed that forty-eight percent of the children born in the United States were nonwhite, and by 2012 the number will have increased to more than fifty percent. The nation has become more diverse, and people of color in increasing numbers have become scientists and health care professionals. Even so, the past has left both thumbprints and bruises on the present. Social inequalities, including those connected with inequalities of income, are still with us, as are entrenched differences in the ways women and people belonging to ethnic minorities are dealt with, despite changed public policies. Clashes of cultures continue to occur, particularly as an increasing number of immigrants from a variety of non-European countries become residents and citizens.

All these factors have consequences for the health of individuals belonging to groups that to various degrees have been marginalized or neglected. As a result, decisions we make about health-care policy and the treatment of individuals must take into consideration both economic and cultural differences and the ways women and minorities have been dealt with in the past.

Special Claim by African Americans

African Americans can lay a strong claim to special attention in any discussion of social issues connected with health care. To a considerable extent, the black population continues to suffer from the effects of social prejudice, including an endemic distrust of physicians and hospitals that is rooted in historical and personal experience. Further, although African Americans no longer constitute the largest minority in the United States, they have the highest death rate of any group. Thus, we need to be particularly concerned about the impact of social practices and policies on the black community.

African Americans are not the only minorities with health problems, of course. American Indians have a higher level of diabetes, and Hispanic Americans suffer more from fatal and disabling strokes. Each ethnic group has its own health problems, and although problems can be connected with prejudice, negative attitudes, or flawed social policies, in some instances they may be the result of language difficulties or differences in cultural beliefs and patterns. In what follows, we will limit ourselves to examining medical care and medical research issues connected with African Americans, but this should not be taken to mean that similar issues could not be raised in connection with other racial and ethnic groups.

African Americans and Health Care

It is too soon to say to what extent the health care legislation passed in 2010 will make an impact on the health of African Americans by extending medical insurance coverage. Before the legislation, observers often pointed to the cost of hospitalization and treatment, the price of insurance, and the rise of managed care as reasons to worry that the United States was moving in the direction of a two-tier health care system: one for the rich and the other for everybody else. Yet some critics say even now that the United States already has a two-tier system—only the marker for separation isn't money alone. It's also race.

The gap between the health of African Americans and that of the general population is evident in the overall mortality and infant mortality and rates in most major chronic and fatal diseases. While heart attacks, strokes, and cancer have declined overall, blacks are still more likely to suffer them sooner than whites.

The situation is tellingly reflected in a comment by Donald Berwick, once a member of the President's Commission on Health Care Quality. "Tell me someone's race," says Dr. Berwick. "Tell me their income. And tell me whether they smoke. The answers to those three questions will tell me more about their longevity and health status than any other questions I could possibly ask. There's no genetic blood test that would have anything like that for predictive value."

Medicare and Medicaid, along with a variety of social programs, were expected to close the yawning gap between the health of African Americans and that of whites, but the results have been mixed.

Research by the National Institute for Aging shows that black people enjoy eight fewer years of relatively good health than do white people or Hispanic Americans. The Institute also found that while only one-fifth of whites from 51 to 61 described their health as fair to poor, one-third of blacks applied the description to themselves.

Moreover, far from having diminished, the incidence of asthma, obesity, maternal mortality, and fetal alcohol syndrome in the black population has increased. Further, the death rate for African Americans from stroke, cancer, respiratory disease, influenza, pneumonia, and HIV/AIDS is higher than that for whites.

In 2006, African Americans had the highest death rate from all leading causes of any racial or ethnic group.

African-Americans are 2.2 times more likely than whites to develop diabetes, thirty percent more likely to have a foot or leg amputated because of the disease, and 2.2 times more likely to die from the disease. Black men are twenty percent more likely than white men to suffer from heart disease and 1.5 times more likely to be diagnosed with lung or prostate cancer. Their five-year survival rate is lower than that of whites for lung, prostate, and pancreatic cancer.

Black women are almost twice as likely to be obese than white women, and this makes them more likely to develop diabetes and heart disease. Lupus, the chronic and potentially fatal autoimmune disease, is three times more common in black women than in white women.

Black women, beginning in their twenties and extending into their fifties, develop breast cancer earlier than white women. Their tumors are often more aggressive, and because a high percentage of the tumors lack estrogen and progesterone receptors on cell surfaces, they don't

---

10 LEADING CAUSES OF DEATH IN AFRICAN AMERICAN POPULATION

1. Heart disease
2. Cancer
3. Stroke
4. Unintentional injuries
5. Diabetes
6. Homicide
7. Nephritis, nephrotic syndrome, and nephrosis
8. Chronic lower respiratory disease
9. HIV/AIDS (from CDC factsheet)
10. Septicemia

Source: Centers for Disease Control. Figures are for 2006, the most recent available.

2006 AGE-ADJUSTED DEATH RATES FOR SELECTED CAUSES OF DEATH, PER 100,000 POPULATION

	All Populations	African Americans
All causes	776.5	982.0
Heart Disease	200.2	257.7
Cancer	180.7	217.4
Diabetes	23.3	45.1
Unintentional injury	39.8	38.3
HIV disease	4.0	18.6

Source: Health, United States, 2008, Table 28, updated November 2009.

tend [to] respond well to hormone treatments. The cells of the tumors are usually also negative for human epidermal growth factor receptor 2 (HER-2) and so can't be treated effectively with Herceptin, which blocks the growth of tumor cells. These are some of the factors that may explain why about twice as many black women as white women are likely to die of their disease.

HIV/AIDS

HIV/AIDS is a major health problem among African Americans. Although they make up only thirteen percent of the population, they account for more than fifty-one percent of new HIV/AIDS cases. Black women account for seventy-two percent of all new cases among women, and black women are eleven times more likely than white women to become HIV positive. Almost twice the number of blacks die of AIDS compared with whites, a gap that has been increasing since 1998. By one 2010 estimate, if African Americans constituted a separate country, they would have the sixth-highest rate of HIV/AIDS infection in the world.

Antiretroviral drugs are effective in reducing viral levels in people who are HIV positive, and when the drugs are used in combination with others, life-threatening or debilitating infections can often be brought under control. Yet the distrust of the medical establishment by African Americans hampers the efforts of the medical community to deliver appropriate care to many who are HIV positive or have developed AIDS.

Many African Americans delay seeking care until they are suffering from consequences of the disease that are harder to bring under control. Some begin treatment, only to drop out because they don't trust those involved in their care to be acting in their best interest. Some are afraid they are being used as subjects in life-threatening experiments about which they are told nothing.

Black–White Treatment Differences

A 2006 study found that African Americans with treatable lung cancers are less likely to get the best diagnostic tests and less likely to get the optimum treatment than whites. In a study of 21,219 patients sixty-five or older with small-cell lung cancer, researchers found that more whites than blacks received the diagnostic procedures mediastinoscopy (examining the tissues inside the chest) and thoroscopy (examining the pleural space around the lung). Blacks more frequently had only a bronchoscopy, a procedure in which a tube is inserted through the mouth or nose to examine the bronchial mucosa and to take biopsies.

The more elaborate procedures require incisions, so the patient must be referred to a surgeon. The advantage of these procedures is that they provide the physician with more information, permitting her to "stage" the patient's disease. Once she has a more exact sense of the extent and character of the disease, she can make decisions about the best way to treat it. Despite the advantage of this approach, blacks were only about seventy-five percent as likely as whites to undergo staging.

Even when black patients were referred to surgeons and had their disease staged, they were only a little more than half as likely as whites to have an operation for their cancer. That they did not is significant, because, in its earlier stages, small-cell lung cancer is curable by surgery and chemotherapy. Blacks who have the surgery do as well afterwards as whites.

Having the necessary insurance coverage or the ability to pay for the more advanced diagnostic tests was eliminated as a factor by the researchers. So what accounts for the difference? The lead investigator, Christopher S. Lathan, points out that "In our society it is always hard to rule out racism." Yet most physicians, he observes, want to do the best for their patients, and it may be that problems in communication lie at the base of the difference in treatment. Physicians may not succeed in making it as clear to black patients as to whites the importance of having the invasive, but more useful, diagnostic tests and the potential of surgery for extending their lives.

The lung-cancer study is similar to a 2001 heart-attack study in its picture of the way blacks and whites are treated differently. The heart-attack study showed that black people who have a heart attack are less likely than whites to undergo diagnostic cardiac catheterization, regardless of the race of their physicians. A review of the hospital records of 40,000 Medicare patients (35,675 whites, 4039 blacks) from various regions of the country who had experienced a heart attack showed that doctors referred white patients for catheterization forty percent more often than blacks, no matter what the physician's race.

What explains this difference? Perhaps whites have access to better medical care; or black patients may be more reluctant to agree to the procedure than white patients. Another possibility is that doctors may be more aggressive in treating white patients. Whatever the explanation, the findings, like those in the lung cancer study, support the general view that African Americans receive less care and less sophisticated care than whites get.

Why the Gap?

The failure of various educational and social programs to close the health gap between African Americans and whites is puzzling to public-health experts. Blacks have improved their status in American society over the last few decades. They have increased their educational level, found better jobs, raised their incomes, and moved into better housing. While prejudice and discrimination have not ended, many black people have become highly successful, and an even greater number have entered the mainstream of American life.

Despite such major changes, the health of African Americans has not improved. The gap between them and the rest of society has remained the same or even widened during the decades when so much else was getting better.

Evidence suggests that African Americans as a population have a genetic predisposition to develop diseases like sickle-cell anemia and perhaps prostate cancer; they may also have a predisposition to obesity and to the hazards

NOT ALL HEART ATTACKS ARE TREATED EQUALLY

Data presented by Jeffrey S. Berger and his colleagues at the 2006 meeting of the American College of Cardiology confirmed other studies showing that women, minorities, and the elderly are less likely to get the best care available after a heart attack.

People who have heart attacks are very often taken to community hospitals for immediate treatment. Such hospitals typically lack the facilities and staff required for such advanced treatments as coronary artery bypass surgery and coronary angiography. To receive them, patients have to be transferred to more comprehensive hospitals.

Berger's research showed that, compared with European Americans, African Americans were 69% as likely to be transferred and Hispanics were 53% as likely. Women were 84% as likely as men to be transferred. People aged 85 to 90 were only 25% as likely as those 65 to 69 to be transferred to a hospital where they could get advanced treatment.

that accompany it, such as high blood pressure, stroke, and diabetes. Yet even if all such predispositions were known to have a genetic basis (and most are still matters of scientific controversy or speculation), they would still not account for the large discrepancies between blacks and others in the incidence of diseases like cancer (all forms) and for the significant differences in life spans or in the number of well years of life. Other factors have to be involved.

African Americans generally receive less health care than whites, and often it is received later in an illness, when it is not as likely to be effective. Also, sometimes the care delivered is not as good as that delivered to whites. As the study mentioned above indicates, when white and black patients, both with insurance, are hospitalized for a heart attack, white patients receive more advanced care more often than black patients do.

A greater proportion of African Americans are poor and so are more likely to lack insurance or the ability to pay for medical care. This factor may keep more blacks out of doctor's offices or hospitals. Yet it can't be the whole explanation of the gap between the health of blacks and that of the rest of the population: Hispanic Americans are also poor and are even less likely to have health insurance, yet data from the Centers for Disease Control indicate that they stay healthy longer.

Also, even when blacks have adequate insurance, they don't always make use of it. A study carried out by Roshan Bastani, an expert on cancer and minorities, found that when white women were diagnosed with a breast abnormality, almost ninety-nine percent of them returned to their physicians for follow-up treatment. However, when the same diagnosis was made in a group of minority women who were predominantly black or Hispanic, only seventy-five percent returned. "Part of this has to do with attitude," according to Bastani. "Like, 'It may go away' or 'I don't have sick leave, so if I go in for this, I'm going to lose a day's pay.'"

Prejudice may also play a role not only in determining the quality of health care provided, but in directly affecting health. A study of hypertension found that it may be connected with the way black people respond to racial discrimination. When working-class blacks experienced two or more cases of discrimination (e.g., in looking for a job), they had higher baseline blood pressure than did working-class whites or black professionals. Interestingly, black professionals who were aware of experiencing cases of racial discrimination and who challenged them were at a lower risk of developing higher blood pressure. However, as the investigators acknowledged, the study, while suggestive, did not give a full account of why blacks are more likely to be hypertensive than other groups.

A 2002 study conducted by the Institute of Medicine found that members of minorities are less likely than whites to be treated appropriately for heart diseases, receive kidney transplants or dialysis, be tested and treated appropriately for cancer, and receive antiretroviral therapy for HIV/AIDS. Such findings lead some researchers to suspect that subtle or unconscious racism may be a factor affecting the health care of black people. More than eight years has passed since the study was published, and while it is possible that treatments provided to African Americans have improved, statistics about health disparities and comparative death rates suggest that they haven't made much difference.

The Tuskegee Effect

The medical establishment—physicians, nurses, therapists, clinics, and hospitals—is viewed with suspicion and distrust by millions of poor people in the United States Distrust is especially high among black people, but it extends to white, Hispanics and Indian people as well.

While public programs like Medicaid and Medicare now offer mostly equal care to all people, this was not the case in the past. Those unable to pay physicians avoided consulting them until their illness or that of a family member was so serious that desperation forced them to act. If they were hospitalized, it was most likely in a charity ward. They were dependent on the benevolence of their physicians and, given the paternalistic attitude prevalent in medicine until recent years, constrained to do what they were told without asking for information or explanations.

Further, the doctrine of informed consent had not yet achieved general acceptance in a form offering much protection to a patient's autonomy and well-being. Hence, the poor often received second-rate medical care and, without being told anything in useful detail, could become the subjects of medical or surgical experimentation.

The emblem of the way in which the trust of black patients was taken advantage of and betrayed by the biomedical establishment is the Tuskegee Study. (See the Case Presentation "Bad Blood, Bad Faith: The Tuskegee Syphilis Study," in this chapter.) But while Tuskegee illustrates the most flagrant abuse of medical authority, it was preceded by a more general pattern of abuse.

The distrust of physicians and hospitals was present before Tuskegee, which only confirmed and reinforced the fears and doubts of people in the black community. But all poor people knew you couldn't trust doctors and hospitals to look out for your interest. Thus, while we may talk of a "Tuskegee effect" to suggest why blacks are suspicious of medicine, the phrase isn't historically accurate. (Vanessa Gamble has documented the distrust as preceding Tuskegee by decades.)

Also, even now, those who have never heard of the Tuskegee study are distrustful. The distrust has been passed along to them as part of the lore of what's involved in coping with being poor. Years and perhaps decades must pass before the medical establishment can overcome the faults of its own past and earn the trust of all people, whatever their income or race. Perhaps the 2010 legislation that will allow millions more people to get the medical care they need will speed up the process of building trust.

Clinical Trials

African Ameircans participate in clinical trials of new drugs at a rate significantly below their number in the population. Some fear that they are being used as "guinea pigs" by physicians who will "poison" them with experimental drugs. The result is unfortunate both for individuals and for the group.

Without a representative number of black participants, it is impossible to acquire the data needed to determine whether blacks respond to drugs and drug regimens in the same way as the population in general. Not until ten years after the introduction of ACE inhibitor beta blockers and converting enzyme inhibitors were researchers able to compile enough data to realize that these groups of drugs are less effective in the treatment of hypertension among blacks than in whites.

By not participating in clinical trials, African Americans also miss the chance to benefit from experimental drugs. Until recently, promising drugs like taxol for breast cancer and antiretroviral drugs for HIV infection could be obtained by patients only through programs of experimental investigation. While receiving experimental drugs can be a mixed blessing

for patients, everyone should at least have the opportunity to decide whether to participate in a drug trial on the basis of relevant considerations. For many African Americans, distrust does not even permit them to get so far as to make an informed choice about participation.

Factors such as the costs of transportation and the difficulty of scheduling office visits also play a role in keeping African Americans from enrolling in clinical trials. Further, one study has shown that black women, in particular, tend to consider clinical trials unethical. They feel that researchers don't care about them and that, by participating in research, they would deprive themselves of the best treatment available.

The traditional underrepresentation of black people in clinical trials is likely to change eventually under the influence of federal policy. The National Institutes of Health now requires that all NIH-supported biomedical research include minorities and women, unless there are clear and compelling reasons to justify their exclusion. Implementing the mandate, however, as investigators know, often demands special recruitment efforts. Patients need to be educated about clinical trials, African American health care personnel need to be involved, and attempts need to be made to include community groups. Most of all, a strong and continuing effort must be made to earn and deserve the trust of the black community.

Organ Transplants

African Americans are at a higher risk for hypertension, diabetes, and kidney disease than the general population and this increases the chances that they will eventually suffer from kidney failure and need a transplant. Blacks make up thirteen percent of the population, but they constitute thirty-two percent of end-stage kidney disease patients needing dialysis. They also constitute more than thirty percent of those on the waiting list for a kidney transplant.

African Americans needing a kidney transplant are likely to do better with a kidney donated by someone of their own race. Kidneys are matched with patients not only by blood type, but by protein antigens, and the closer the match, the more likely the transplanted kidney will "take."

Despite having a greater need for donated kidneys, blacks donate at a significantly lower rate than do whites. Why don't African Americans donate organs as often as others? Some people don't donate for personal religious reasons (no organized religion in the United States objects to organ donation), but many are simply inadequately informed about how donated organs are distributed and they don't trust the system to be fair.

"There's a belief that only rich whites, especially those who are famous, become organ recipients," said Jackie Lynch, a recruiter of minorities for the Regional Organ Bank of Illinois. "They don't see a black role, other than as those who are dying and donating the organs." (Ironically, because of their relatively low rate of donation, it is blacks who receive a disproportionate number of organs.) Lynch said that black families sometimes ask his nonblack colleagues to leave the room so that they can ask him about the fairness of the organ distribution system.

Organ donation among African Americans has increased since the 1980s, and this suggests that it will continue to increase to at least the level of other ethnic groups. For that to happen, however, more public education about donation and the fairness of the system is needed. Black people will have to come to trust that the organs they donate will be used to save or extend the lives of people who may belong to any ethnic or racial group.

Closing the Gap?

In response to a presidential mandate, The Department of Health and Human Services initiated the project Healthy People: 2010 with the aim of improving the health status of minorities. HHS chose six areas in which to set goals to reduce the negative health differences between racial minorities and the general U.S. population. The data for 2010 are not complete, but a look

	United States	African Americans
Infant mortality	2.2	16.7
Cancer deaths	202.7	254.4
Heart disease deaths	204	250
Stroke deaths	62	82
Diabetes deaths	77	135
AIDs incidence	16.7	58.1

Infant mortality is per 1,000 births; other figures are per 100,000.

Source: Department of Health and Human Services (2010), *Healthy People: 2010: Selected Health Disparity Areas.*

at the available statistics indicates the size of the changes that need to take place before the health of African Americans becomes similar to that of the United States as a whole:

In all six areas of focus, black people are worse off than people in the general population. Discrimination, genetics, cultural patterns, education, and personal history are among the numerous factors that play a role in producing the relatively poor health of African Americans in the United States Yet there is no reason to believe that the impact of some of the factors on health cannot be reduced or even eventually eliminated.

Signs suggest that improvements are taking place. In 2006, the overall death rate for black was 982 per 100,000. For whites, the comparable figure was 765, but before 2006 the death rate for blacks was consistently in four figures. Thus, 2006 was the turning point, and the death rate for African Americans has remained at three figures since then.

New federal and state programs to assist children living in poverty and to provide prenatal care for expectant mothers should eventually be reflected in improved health statistics. New federal requirements that African Americans be included in clinical trials have been accompanied by discussions in the research community of ways to recruit blacks by providing them with information and transportation expenses and making it easier for them to become part of a study. Organ donations by African Americans have increased over the years, and as more black people come to have confidence in the integrity and fairness of the distribution system, donations should continue to rise.

Legislations to make medical insurance affordable for a greater number of people should do a great deal to improve the health of African Americans. Black people are more likely to be uninsured or underinsured than the general population. They are less likely to get preventive care and are more likely to delay seeking treatment. With more available medical advice, along with public education campaigns, blacks may begin to modify the sorts of individual behavior, like smoking, drinking, illicit drug use, and overeating, that have serious negative health consequences.

Undoing Tuskegee

Perhaps the most important change likely to lead to improvements in the health of African Americans is the development of trust in the black community for the medical establishment. The Tuskegee effect is likely to linger for years, and to overcome it the medical establishment must make a special effort to earn and deserve the trust of black patients.

Treating patients with respect, taking seriously their reservations about diagnostic tests or proposed treatments, and taking the time to educate them about their medical condition and the therapy for it are important in securing the trust of any group of patients. If African Americans are more distrustful, it's because they have more reason to be.

READINGS

Section 1: Race, Research, and Medicine

A Family Tree in Every Gene

Armand Marie Leroi

Armand Leroi rejects the idea that race is an exclusively social construct. If we look at correlations of genetic variants instead of single variants, he argues, populations sort into groups deriving from the five inhabited continents. When larger numbers of variants are considered, further subdivisions show up. Race is thus a shorthand way of talking about differences that are genetic rather than political or cultural. The notion of an "ethnic group," by contrast, conflates genetic, cultural, and political differences. Leroi believes that, until individual genome sequencing becomes possible, the best way to improve medical care is by employing the concept of race. It offers a more accurate way to assess a patient's risk for certain diseases and serves as a guide to select the best therapy.

Shortly after [the 2004] tsunami devastated the lands on the Indian Ocean, *The Times of India* ran an article with this headline: "Tsunami May Have Rendered Threatened Tribes Extinct." The tribes in question

were the Onge, Jarawa, Great Andamanese and Sentinelese—all living on the Andaman Islands—and they numbered some 400 people in all. The article, noting that several of the archipelago's islands were low-lying, in the direct path of the wave, and that casualties were expected to be high, said, "Some beads may have just gone missing from the Emerald Necklace of India."

The metaphor is as colorful as it is well intentioned. But what exactly does it mean? After all, in a catastrophe that cost more than 150,000 lives, why should the survival of a few hundred tribal people have any special claim on our attention? There are several possible answers to this question. The people of the Andamans have a unique way of life. True, their material culture does not extend beyond a few simple tools, and their visual art is confined to a few geometrical motifs, but they are hunter–gatherers and so a rarity in the modern world. Linguists, too, find them interesting since they collectively speak three languages seemingly unrelated to any others. But the *Times of India* took a slightly different track. These tribes are special, it said, because they are of "Negrito racial stocks" that are "remnants of the oldest human populations of Asia and Australia."

It's an old-fashioned, even Victorian, sentiment. Who speaks of "racial stocks" anymore? After all, to do so would be to speak of something that many scientists and scholars say does not exist. If modern anthropologists mention the concept of race, it is invariably only to warn against and dismiss it. Likewise many geneticists. "Race is social concept, not a scientific one," according to Dr. Craig Venter—and he should know, since he was first to sequence the human genome. The idea that human races are only social constructs has been the consensus for at least 30 years.

But now, perhaps, that is about to change. Last fall, the prestigious journal *Nature Genetics* devoted a large supplement to the question of whether human races exist and, if so, what they mean. The journal did this in part because various American health agencies are making race an important part of their policies to best protect the public—often over the protests of scientists. In the supplement, some two dozen geneticists offered their views. Beneath the jargon, cautious phrases and academic courtesies, one thing was clear: the consensus about social constructs was unraveling. Some even argued that, looked at the right way, genetic data show that races clearly do exist.

The dominance of the social construct theory can be traced to a 1972 article by Dr. Richard Lewontin, a Harvard geneticist, who wrote that most human genetic variation can be found within any given "race." If one looked at genes rather than faces, he claimed, the difference between an African and a European would be scarcely greater than the difference between any two Europeans. A few years later he wrote that the continued popularity of race as an idea was an "indication of the power of socioeconomically based ideology over the supposed objectivity of knowledge." Most scientists are thoughtful, liberal-minded and socially aware people. It was just what they wanted to hear.

Three decades later, it seems that Dr. Lewontin's facts were correct, and have been abundantly confirmed by ever better techniques of detecting genetic variety. His reasoning, however, was wrong. His error was an elementary one, but such was the appeal of his argument that it was only a couple of years ago that a Cambridge University statistician, A. W. F. Edwards, put his finger on it.

The error is easily illustrated. If one were asked to judge the ancestry of 100 New Yorkers, one could look at the color of their skin. That would do much to single out the Europeans, but little to distinguish the Senegalese from the Solomon Islanders. The same is true for any other feature of our bodies. The shapes of our eyes, noses and skulls; the color of our eyes and our hair; the heaviness, height and hairiness of our bodies are all, individually, poor guides to ancestry.

But this is not true when the features are taken together. Certain skin colors tend to go with certain kinds of eyes, noses, skulls and bodies. When we glance at a stranger's face we use those associations to infer what continent, or even what country, he or his ancestors came from—and we usually get it right. To put it more abstractly, human physical variation is correlated; and correlations contain information.

Genetic variants that aren't written on our faces, but that can be detected only in the genome, show similar correlations. It is these correlations that Dr. Lewontin seems to have ignored. In essence, he looked at one gene at a time and failed to see races. But if many—a few hundred—variable genes are considered simultaneously, then it is very easy to do so. Indeed, a 2002 study by scientists at the University of Southern California and Stanford showed that if a sample of people from around the world are sorted by computer into five groups on the basis of genetic similarity, the groups that emerge are native to Europe, East Asia, Africa, America and Australasia—more or less the major races of traditional anthropology.

One of the minor pleasures of this discovery is a new kind of genealogy. Today it is easy to find out where your ancestors came from—or even when they came, as with so many of us, from several different places. If you want to know what fraction of your genes are African, European or East Asian, all it takes is a mouth swab, a postage stamp and $400—though prices will certainly fall.

Yet there is nothing very fundamental about the concept of the major continental races; they're just the easiest way to divide things up. Study enough genes in enough people and one could sort the world's population into

10,100, perhaps 1,000 groups, each located somewhere on the map. This has not yet been done with any precision, but it will be. Soon it may be possible to identify your ancestors not merely as African or European, but Ibo or Yoruba, perhaps even Celt or Castilian, or all of the above.

The identification of racial origins is not a search for purity. The human species is irredeemably promiscuous. We have always seduced or coerced our neighbors even when they have a foreign look about them and we don't understand a word. If Hispanics, for example, are composed of a recent and evolving blend of European, American Indian and African genes, then the Uighurs of Central Asia can be seen as a 3,000-year-old mix of West European and East Asian genes. Even homogenous groups like native Swedes bear the genetic imprint of successive nameless migrations.

Some critics believe that these ambiguities render the very notion of race worthless. I disagree. The physical topography of our world cannot be accurately described in words. To navigate it, you need a map with elevations, contour lines and reference grids. But it is hard to talk in numbers, and so we give the world's more prominent features—the mountain ranges and plateaus and plains—names. We do so despite the inherent ambiguity of words. The Pennines of northern England are about one-tenth as high and long as the Himalayas, yet both are intelligibly described as mountain ranges.

So, too, it is with the genetic topography of our species. The billion or so of the world's people of largely European descent have a set of genetic variants in common that are collectively rare in everyone else; they are a race. At a smaller scale, three million Basques do as well; so they are a race as well. Race is merely a shorthand that enables us to speak sensibly, though with no great precision, about genetic rather than cultural or political differences.

But it is a shorthand that seems to be needed. One of the more painful spectacles of modern science is that of human geneticists piously disavowing the existence of races even as they investigate the genetic relationships between "ethnic groups." Given the problematic, even vicious, history of the word "race," the use of euphemisms is understandable. But it hardly aids understanding, for the term "ethnic group" conflates all the possible ways in which people differ from each other.

Indeed, the recognition that races are real should have several benefits. To begin with, it would remove the disjunction in which the government and public alike defiantly embrace categories that many, perhaps most, scholars and scientists say do not exist.

Second, the recognition of race may improve medical care. Different races are prone to different diseases. The risk that an African-American man will be afflicted with hypertensive heart disease or prostate cancer is nearly three times greater than that for a European-American man. On the other hand, the former's risk of multiple sclerosis is only half as great. Such differences could be due to socioeconomic factors. Even so, geneticists have started searching for racial differences in the frequencies of genetic variants that cause diseases. They seem to be finding them.

Race can also affect treatment. African-Americans respond poorly to some of the main drugs used to treat heart conditions—notably beta blockers and angiotensin-converting enzyme inhibitors. Pharmaceutical corporations are paying attention. Many new drugs now come labeled with warnings that they may not work in some ethnic or racial groups. Here, as so often, the mere prospect of litigation has concentrated minds.

Such differences are, of course, just differences in average. Everyone agrees that race is a crude way of predicting who gets some disease or responds to some treatment. Ideally, we would all have our genomes sequenced before swallowing so much as an aspirin. Yet until that is technically feasible, we can expect racial classifications to play an increasing part in health care.

The argument for the importance of race, however, does not rest purely on utilitarian grounds. There is also an aesthetic factor. We are a physically variable species. Yet for all the triumphs of modern genetics, we know next to nothing about what makes us so. We do not know why some people have prominent rather than flat noses, round rather than pointed skulls, wide rather than narrow faces, straight rather than curly hair. We do not know what makes blue eyes blue.

One way to find out, would be to study people of mixed race ancestry. In part, this is because racial differences in looks are the most striking that we see. But there is also a more subtle technical reason. When geneticists map genes, they rely on the fact that they can follow our ancestors' chromosomes as they get passed from one generation to the next, dividing and mixing in unpredictable combinations. That, it turns out, is much easier to do in people whose ancestors came from very different places.

The technique is called admixture mapping. Developed to find the genes responsible for racial differences in inherited disease, it is only just moving from theory to application. But through it, we may be able to write the genetic recipe for the fair hair of a Norwegian, the black-verging-on-purple skin of a Solomon Islander, the flat face of an Inuit, and the curved eyelid of a Han Chinese. We shall no longer gawp ignorantly at the gallery; we shall be able to name the painters.

There is a final reason race matters. It gives us reason—if there were not reason enough already—to value and protect some of the world's most obscure and marginalized people. When the *Times of India* article referred to the Andaman Islanders as being of ancient Negrito racial stock, the terminology was correct. Negrito is the name given by anthropologists to a people who once lived throughout Southeast Asia. They are very small, very dark, and have peppercorn hair. They look like African pygmies who have wandered away from Congo's jungles to take up life on a tropical isle. But they are not.

The latest genetic data suggest that the Negritos are descended from the first modern humans to have invaded Asia, some 100,000 years ago. In time they were overrun or absorbed by waves of Neolithic agriculturalists, and later nearly wiped out by British, Spanish and Indian colonialists. Now they are confined to the Malay Peninsula, a few islands in the Philippines and the Andamans.

Happily, most of the Andaman's Negritos seem to have survived December's tsunami. The fate of one tribe, the Sentinelese, remains uncertain, but an Indian coast guard helicopter sent to check up on them came under bow and arrow attack, which is heartening. Even so, Negrito populations, wherever they are, are so small, isolated and impoverished that it seems certain that they will eventually disappear.

Yet even after they have gone, the genetic variants that defined the Negritos will remain, albeit scattered, in the people who inhabit the littoral of the Bay of Bengal and the South China Sea. They will remain visible in the unusually dark skin of some Indonesians, the unusually curly hair of some Sri Lankans, the unusually slight frames of some Filipinos. But the unique combination of genes that makes the Negritos so distinctive, and that took tens of thousands of years to evolve, will have disappeared. A human race will have gone extinct, and the human species will be the poorer for it.

The Dangers of Difference: The Legacy of the Tuskegee Syphilis Study

Patricia A. King

Patricia King claims that recognizing racial differences in medicine poses a dilemma. Even when the intention is to help a stigmatized group or person, the result may be to cause harm.

King proposes that research always begin with the presumption that, with respect to disease, blacks and whites are biologically identical. While the presumption may be shown to be wrong in the course of the study, it acknowledges that, historically speaking, more harm has come from imputing racial differences than from ignoring them.

It has been sixty years since the beginning of the Tuskegee syphilis experiment and twenty years since its existence was disclosed to the American public. The social and ethical issues that the experiment poses for medicine, particularly for medicine's relationship with African Americans, are still not broadly understood, appreciated, or even remembered. Yet a significant aspect of the Tuskegee experiment's legacy is that in a

From Patricia A. King, "The Dangers of Difference," *Hastings Center Report*, Vol. 22, no. 6 (1992): 35–38. Reprinted by permission of the author and publisher. © The Hastings Center. (Most notes omitted.)

racist society that incorporates beliefs about the inherent inferiority of African Americans in contrast with the superior status of whites, any attention to the question of differences that may exist is likely to be pursued in a manner that burdens rather than benefits African Americans.

The Tuskegee experiment, which involved approximately 400 males with late-stage, untreated syphilis and approximately 200 controls free of the disease, is by any measure one of the dark pages in the history of American medicine. In this study of the natural course of untreated syphilis, the participants did not give informed consent. Stunningly, when penicillin was subsequently developed as a treatment for syphilis, measures were taken to keep the diseased participants from receiving it.

Obviously, the experiment provides a basis for the exploration of many ethical and social issues in medicine, including professional ethics, the limitations of informed consent as a means of protecting research subjects, and the motives and methods used to justify the exploitation of persons who live in conditions of severe economic and social disadvantage. At bottom, however, the Tuskegee experiment is different from other incidents of abuse in clinical research because all the participants were black males. The racism that played a central role in this tragedy continues to infect even our current well-intentioned efforts to reverse the decline in health status of African Americans. . . .

The Dilemma of Difference

In the context of widespread belief in the racial inferiority of blacks that surrounded the Tuskegee experiment, it should not come as a surprise that the experiment exploited its subjects. Recognizing and taking account of racial differences that have historically been utilized to burden and exploit African Americans poses a dilemma. Even in circumstances where the goal of a scientific study is to benefit a stigmatized group or person, such well-intentioned efforts may nevertheless cause harm. If the racial difference is ignored and all groups or persons are treated similarly, unintended harm may result from the failure to recognize racially correlated factors. Conversely, if differences among groups or persons are recognized and attempts are made to respond to past injustices or special burdens, the effort is likely to reinforce existing negative stereotypes that contributed to the emphasis on racial differences in the first place.

This dilemma about difference is particularly worrisome in medicine. Because medicine is pragmatic, it will recognize racial differences if doing so will promote health goals. As a consequence, potential harms that might result from attention to racial differences tend to be overlooked, minimized, or viewed as problems beyond the purview of medicine.

The question of whether (and how) to take account of racial differences has recently been raised in the context of the current AIDS epidemic. The participation of African Americans in clinical AIDS trials has been disproportionately small in comparison to the numbers of African Americans who have been infected

with the human immunodeficiency virus. Because of the possibility that African Americans may respond differently to drugs being developed and tested to combat AIDS, those concerned about the care and treatment of AIDS in the African American community have called for greater participation by African Americans in these trials. Ironically, efforts to address the problem of underrepresentation must cope with the enduring legacy of the Tuskegee experiment—the legacy of suspicion and skepticism toward medicine and its practitioners among African Americans.

In view of the suspicion Tuskegee so justifiably engenders, calls for increased participation by African Americans in clinical trials are worrisome. The question of whether to tolerate racially differentiated AIDS research testing of new or innovative therapies, as well as the question of what norms should govern participation by African Americans in clinical research, needs careful and thoughtful attention. A generic examination of the treatment of racial differences in medicine is beyond the scope of this article. However, I will describe briefly what has occurred since disclosure of the Tuskegee experiment to point out the dangers I find lurking in our current policies.

Inclusion and Exclusion

In part because of public outrage concerning the Tuskegee experiment, comprehensive regulations governing federal research using human subjects were revised and subsequently adopted by most federal agencies. An institutional review board (IRB) must approve clinical research involving human subjects, and IRB approval is made contingent on review of protocols for adequate protection of human subjects in accordance with federal criteria. These criteria require, among other things, that an IRB ensure that subject selection is "equitable." The regulations further provide that

> [i]n making this assessment the IRB should take into account the purposes of the research and the setting in which the research will be conducted, and should be particularly cognizant of the special problems of research involving vulnerable populations, such as women, mentally disabled persons, or economically or educationally disadvantaged persons.[1]

The language of the regulation makes clear that the concern prompting its adoption was the protection of vulnerable groups from exploitation. The obverse problem—that too much protection might promote the exclusion or underrepresentation of vulnerable groups, including African Americans—was not at issue. However, underinclusion can raise as much of a problem of equity as exploitation.

A 1990 General Accounting Office study first documented the extent to which minorities and women were underrepresented in federally funded research. In response, in December 1990 the National Institutes of Health, together with the Alcohol, Drug Abuse and Mental Health Administration, directed that minorities and women be included in study populations,

> *so that research findings can be of benefit to all persons at risk of the disease, disorder or condition under study; special emphasis should be placed on the need for inclusion of minorities and women in studies of diseases, disorders and conditions that disproportionately affect them.*[2]

If minorities are not included, a clear and compelling rationale must be submitted.

The new policy clearly attempts to avoid the perils of overprotection, but it raises new concerns. The policy must be clarified and refined if it is to meet the intended goal of ensuring that research findings are of benefit to all. There are at least three reasons for favoring increased representation of African Americans in clinical trials. The first is that there may be biological differences between blacks and whites that might affect the applicability of experimental findings to blacks, but these differences will not be noticed if blacks are not included in sufficient numbers to allow the detection of statistically significant racial differences. The second reason is that race is a reliable index for social conditions such as poor health and nutrition, lack of adequate access to health care, and economic and social disadvantage that might adversely affect potential benefits of new interventions and procedures. If there is indeed a correlation between minority status and these factors, then African Americans and all others with these characteristics will benefit from new information generated by the research. The third reason is that the burdens and benefits of research should be spread across the population regardless of racial or ethnic status. . . .

The third justification carries with it the obvious danger that the special needs or problems generated as a result of economic or social conditions associated with minority status may be overlooked and that, as a result, African Americans and other minorities will be further disadvantaged. The other two justifications are problematic and deserve closer examination. They each assume that there are either biological, social, economic, or cultural differences between blacks and whites. . . .

The Way Out of the Dilemma

Understanding how, or indeed whether, race correlates with disease is a very complicated problem. Race itself is a confusing concept with both biological and social connotations. Some doubt whether race has biological significance at all. Even if race is a biological fiction, however, its social significance remains.

In the wake of Tuskegee and, in more recent times, the stigma and discrimination that resulted from screening for sickle-cell trait (a genetic condition that occurs with greater frequency among African Americans), researchers have been reluctant to explore associations between race and disease. There is increasing recognition, however, of evidence of heightened resistance or vulnerability to disease along racial lines. Indeed, sickle-cell anemia itself substantiates the view that biological differences may exist. Nonetheless, separating myth from reality in determining the cause of disease and poor health status is not easy. Great caution should be exercised in attempting to validate biological differences in susceptibility to disease in light of this society's past experience with biological differences. Moreover, using race as an index for other conditions that might influence health and well-being is also dangerous. Such practices could emphasize social and economic differences that might also lead to stigma and discrimination.

If all the reasons for increasing minority participation in clinical research are flawed, how then can we promote improvement in health status of African Americans and other minorities through participation in clinical research, while simultaneously minimizing the harms that might flow from such participation? Is it possible to work our way out of this dilemma?

An appropriate strategy should have as its starting point the defeasible presumption that blacks and whites are biologically the same with respect to disease and treatment. Presumptions can be overturned of course, and the strategy should recognize the possibility that biological differences in some contexts are possible. But the presumption of equality acknowledges that historically the greatest harm has come from the willingness to impute biological differences rather than the willingness to overlook them. For some, allowing the presumption to be in any way defeasible is troubling. Yet I do not believe that fear should lead us to ignore the possibility of biologically differentiated responses to disease and treatment, especially when the goal is to achieve medical benefit.

It is well to note at this point the caution sounded by Hans Jonas. He wrote, "Of the new experimentation with man, medical is surely the most legitimate; psychological, the most dubious; biological (still to come), the most dangerous."[3] Clearly, priority should be given to exploring the possible social, cultural, and environmental determinants of disease before targeting the study of hypotheses that involve biological differences between blacks and whites. For example, rather than trying to determine whether blacks and whites respond differently to AZT, attention should first be directed to learning whether response to AZT is influenced by social, cultural, or environmental conditions. Only at the point where possible biological differences emerge should hypotheses that explore racial differences be considered.

A finding that blacks and whites are different in some critical aspect need not inevitably lead to increased discrimination or stigma for blacks. If there indeed had been a difference in the effects of untreated syphilis between blacks and whites such information might have been used to promote the health status of blacks. But the Tuskegee experiment stands as a reminder that such favorable outcomes rarely if ever occur. More often, either racist assumptions and stereotypes creep into the study's design, or findings broken down by race become convenient tools to support policies and behavior that further disadvantage those already vulnerable.

Notes

1. 45 *Code of Federal Regulations* §46.111 (a)(3).
2. National Institutes of Health and Alcohol, Drug Abuse and Mental Health Administration, "Special Instructions to Applicants Using Form PHS 398 Regarding Implementation of the NIH/ADAMHA Policy Concerning Inclusion of Women and Minorities in Clinical Research Study Populations," December 1990.
3. Hans Jonas, "Philosophical Reflections on Experimenting with Human Subjects," in *Experimentation with Human Subjects*, ed. Paul A. Freund (New York: George Braziller, 1970), p. 1.

Section 2:   Taking Race into Account

Bioethics: The Need for a Dialogue with African Americans

Annette Dula

Annette Dula argues for the importance of expanding bioethics to include the perspectives of various racial and ethnic groups. While she focuses on African Americans, she sees the points she makes as also applying to Hispanics, Native Americans, Asians, and other groups that have had health care experiences out of the mainstream.

The African American perspective, according to Dula, has been shaped by the experience of receiving poor-quality care (a situation mostly ignored as a problem by bioethics) and by the emphasis on action and social justice found in the work of black philosophers. By reviewing the history of the birth control movement and the Tuskegee experiment, Dula illustrates the need for an African American perspective on health care. She then uses the entrance of blacks into professional psychology and the "white women's movement" to illustrate how the introduction of a new perspective can change social perceptions of a group, weaken stereotypes, and promote justice.

Dula asks that bioethics recognize access to health care as a serious bioethical problem requiring debate and action. She ends by calling for the formation of a community of scholars who will "conduct research and articulate the perspectives of African Americans and other poor and underserved peoples."

Introduction

... I intend to show that the articulation and development of professional bioethics perspectives by minority academics are necessary to expand the narrow margins of debate. Without representation by every sector of society, the powerful and powerless alike, the discipline of bioethics is missing the opportunity to be enriched by the inclusion of a broader range of perspectives. Although I use African-American perspectives as an example, these points apply to other racial and ethnic groups—Hispanics, Native Americans, and Asians—who have suffered similar health care experiences.

In the first section of this chapter, I suggest that an African-American perspective on bioethics has two bases: (1) our health and medical experiences and (2) our tradition of black activist philosophy. In the second section, through examples, I show that an unequal power relationship has led to unethical medical behavior toward blacks, especially regarding reproductive issues. In the third section, I argue that developing a professional perspective not only gives voice to the concerns of those not in the power circle but also enriches the entire field of bioethics.

Medical and Health Experiences

The health of people and the quality of health care they receive reflect their status in society. It should come as little surprise, then, that the health experiences of African Americans differ vastly from those of white people. These differences are well documented. Compared to whites, more than twice as many black babies are born with low birthweight and over twice as many die before their first birthday. Fifty percent more blacks than whites are likely to regard themselves as being in fair or poor health. Blacks are included in fewer trials of new drugs—an inequity of particular importance for AIDS patients, who are disproportionately black and Hispanic. The mortality rate for heart disease in black males is twice that for white males;

research has shown that blacks tend to receive less aggressive treatment for this condition. More blacks die from cancer, which, unlike the situation in whites, is likely to be systemic by the time it is detected. African Americans live five fewer years than do whites. Indeed, if blacks had the same death rate as whites, 59,000 black deaths a year would not occur. Colin McCord and Harold P. Freeman, who reported that black men in Harlem are less likely to reach the age of 65 than are men in Bangladesh, conclude that the mortality rates of inner cities with largely black populations "justify special consideration analogous to that given to natural-disaster areas."

These health disparities are the result of at least three forces: institutional racism, economic inequality, and attitudinal barriers to access. Institutional racism has roots in the historically unequal power relations between blacks and the medical profession, and between blacks and the larger society. It has worked effectively to keep blacks out of the profession, even though a large percentage of those who manage to enter medicine return to practice in minority communities—where the need for medical professionals is greatest. Today, institutional racism in health care is manifested in the way African Americans and poor people are treated. They experience long waits, are unable to shop for services, and often receive poor quality and discontinuous health care. Moreover, many government programs do not target African Americans as a group. As a result, benefits to racially defined populations are diffused. There is hope: Healthy People 2000 complemented by the Clinton health care proposal can go a long way to reducing these problems.

Black philosopher W. E. B. Du Bois summed up the economic plight of African Americans: "To be poor is hard, but to be a poor race in a land of dollars is the very bottom of hardships." Poor people are more likely to have poor health, and a disproportionate number of poor people are black. African Americans tend to have lower paying jobs and fewer income-producing sources such as investments. Indeed, whites on average accumulate eleven times more wealth than do blacks. Less money also leads to substandard housing— housing that may contain unacceptable levels of lead paint, asbestos insulation, or other environmental hazards. Thus, both inadequate employment and subpar housing available to poor African Americans present health problems that wealthier people are able to avoid. In addition, going to the doctor may entail finding and paying for a babysitter and transportation, and taking time off from work at the risk of being fired, all of which the poor cannot afford.

Attitudinal barriers—perceived racism, different cultural perspectives on health and sickness, and beliefs about the health care system—are a third force that brings unequal health care. Seeking medical help may not have the same priority for poor people as it has for middle-class people. One study in the *Journal of the American Medical Association* revealed that, compared to whites, blacks are less likely to be satisfied with how their physicians treat them, more dissatisfied with their hospital care, and more likely to believe that their hospital stay was too short. In addition, many blacks, like people of other racial and ethnic groups, use home remedies and adhere to traditional theories of illness and healing that lie outside of the mainstream medical model. Institutional racism, economic inequality, and attitudinal barriers, then, contribute to inadequate access to health care for poor and minority peoples. These factors must be seen as bioethical concerns. Bioethics cannot be exclusively medical or even ethical. Rather, it must also deal with beliefs, values, cultural traditions, and the economic, political, and social order. A number of medical sociologists have severely criticized bioethicists for ignoring cultural and societal particularities that limit access to health care.

This inattention to cultural and societal aspects of health care may be attributed in part to the mainstream Western philosophy on which the field of bioethics is built. For example, renowned academic bioethicists such as Robert Veatch, Tom Beauchamp, and Alasdair MacIntyre rely on the philosophical works of Rawls, Kant, and Aristotle. In addition, until recently the mainstream Western philosophic method has been presented primarily as a thinking enterprise, rarely advocating change or societal transformation. Thus, for the most part, Western philosophers have either gingerly approached or neglected altogether to comment on such social injustices as slavery, poverty, racism, sexism, and classism. As pointed out in *Black Issues in Higher Education,* until recently mainstream philosophy was seen as above questions of history and culture.

Black Activist Philosophy

The second bias for an African-American perspective on bioethics is black activist philosophy. Black philosophy differs from mainstream philosophy in its emphasis on action and social justice. African-American philosophers view the world through a cultural and societal context of being an unequal partner. Many black philosophers believe that academic philosophy devoid of societal context is a luxury that black scholars can ill afford. Moreover, African-American philosophers have purposely elected to use philosophy as a tool not only for naming, defining, and analyzing social situations but also for recommending, advocating, and sometimes harassing for political and social empowerment—a stance contrary to mainstream philosophic methods. Even though all bioethicists would do well to examine the thinking of such philosophers as Alain Locke, Lucius Outlaw, Anita Allen, Leonard Harris, W. E. B. Du Bois, Bernard Boxill, Angela Davis, Cornel West, William Banner, and Jorge Garcia, references to the work of these African Americans are rarely seen in the bioethics literature.

Although the professionalization of bioethics has frequently bypassed African-American voices, there are a few notable exceptions. Mark Siegler, director of the Center for Clinical Medical Ethics at the University of Chicago, included three African-American fellows in the 1990–91 medical ethics training program; Edmund Pellegrino of the Kennedy Institute for Advanced Ethics co-sponsored three national conferences on African-American perspectives on bioethics; and Howard Brody at Michigan State University is attempting to diversify his medical ethics program. In addition, a number of current publications offer important information for bioethicists. For example, the National Research Council's *A Common Destiny: Blacks and American Society* provides a comprehensive analysis of the status of black Americans, including discussions on health, education, employment, and economic factors, as does the National Urban League's annual *The State of Black America;* Marlene Gerber Fried's *From Abortion to Reproductive Freedom* presents many ideas of women of color concerning abortion; and several journals (e.g., *Ethnicity and*

Disease, published by the Loyola University School of Medicine, and *The Journal of Health Care for the Poor and Underserved*) call particular attention to the health experiences of poor and undeserved people. Finally, literature and narrative as forms of presenting African-American perspectives on bioethics are now being explored.

Clearly, bioethics and African-American philosophy overlap. Both are concerned with distributive justice and fairness, with autonomy and paternalism in unequal relationships, and with both individual and societal ills. African-American philosophy, therefore, may have much to offer bioethics in general and African-American bioethics in particular.

Mainstream Issues Relevant to African Americans

A shocking history of medical abuse against unprotected people is also grounds for African-American perspectives in bioethics. In particular, reproductive rights issues—questions of family planning, sterilization, and genetic screening—are of special interest to black women.

A critical examination of the U.S. birth control movement reveals fundamental differences in perspectives, experiences, and interests between the white women who founded the movement and African-American women who were affected by it. Within each of three phases, the goals of the movement implicitly or explicitly served to exploit and subordinate African-American as well as poor white women.

The middle of the nineteenth century marked the beginning of the first phase of the birth control movement, characterized by the rallying cry "Voluntary Motherhood!" Advocates of voluntary motherhood asserted that women ought to say "no" to their husbands' sexual demands as a means of limiting the number of their children. The irony, of course, was that, while early white feminists were refusing their husbands' sexual demands, most black women did not have the same right to say "no" to these and other white women's husbands. Indeed, African-American women were exploited as breeding wenches in order to produce stocks of enslaved people for plantation owners. August Meier and Elliott Rudwick comment on slave-rearing as a major source of profit for nearly all slaveholding farmers and planters: "Though most Southern whites were scarcely likely to admit it, the rearing of slaves for profit was a common practice. [A] slave woman's proved or anticipated fecundity was an important factor in determining her market value; fertile females were often referred to as 'good breeders.'"

The second phase of the birth control movement gave rise to the actual phrase "birth control," coined by Margaret Sanger in 1915. Initially, this stage of the movement led to the recognition that reproductive rights and political rights were intertwined; birth control would give white women the freedom to pursue new opportunities made possible by the vote. This freedom allowed white women to go to work while black women cared for their children and did their housework.

This second stage coincided with the eugenics movement, which advocated improvement of the human race through selective breeding. When the white birth rate began to decline, eugenists chastised middle-class white women for contributing to the suicide of the white race: "Continued limitation of offspring in the white race simply invites the black, brown, and yellow races to finish work already begun by birth control, and reduce the whites to a subject race preserved merely for the sake of its skill."

Eugenists proposed a twofold approach for curbing "race suicide": imposing moral obligations on middle-class white women to have large families and on poor immigrant women and black women to restrict the size of theirs. For the second group, geneticists advocated birth control. The women's movement adopted the ideals of the eugenists regarding poor, immigrant, and minority women, and it even surpassed the rhetoric of the eugenists. Margaret Sanger described the relationship between the two groups: "The eugenists wanted to shift the birth-control emphasis from less children for the poor to more children for the rich. We went back of that [*sic*] and sought first to stop the multiplication of the unfit." Thus, while black women have historically practiced birth control, they learned to distrust the birth control movement as espoused by white feminists—a distrust that continues to the present day.

The third stage of the birth control movement began in 1942 with the establishment of the Planned Parenthood Federation of America. Although Planned Parenthood made valuable contributions to the independence, self-esteem, and aspirations of many women, it accepted existing power relations, continuing the eugenic tradition by defining undesirable "stock" by class or income level. Many blacks were suspicious of Planned Parenthood; men, particularly, viewed its policies as designed to weaken the black community politically or to wipe it out genetically. From the beginning of this century, both public and private institutions attempted to control the breeding of those deemed "undesirable." The first sterilization law was passed in Indiana in 1907, setting the stage for not only eugenic, but also punitive sterilization of criminals, the feebleminded, rapists, robbers, chicken thieves, drunkards, and drug addicts. By 1931 thirty states had passed sterilization laws, allowing more than 12,145 sterilizations. By the end of 1958, the sterilization total had risen to 60,926. In the 1950s several states attempted to extend sterilization laws to include compulsory sterilization of mothers of "illegitimate" children. As of 1991, sterilization laws were still in force in twenty-two states. They are seldom enforced, and where they have been, their eugenic significance has been negligible.

Numerous federal and state measures perpetuated a focus on poor women and women of color. Throughout the United States in the 1960s, the federal government began subsidizing family planning clinics designed to reduce the number of people on welfare by checking the transmission of poverty from generation to generation. The number of family planning clinics in a given geographical area was proportional to the number of black and Hispanic residents. In Puerto Rico, a massive federal birth control campaign introduced in 1937 was so successful that by the 1950s, the demand for sterilization exceeded facilities, and by 1965, one-third of the women in Puerto Rico had been sterilized.

In 1972 Los Angeles County Hospital, a hospital catering to large numbers of women of color, reported a sevenfold rise in hysterectomies. Between 1973 and 1976, almost 3,500 Native American women were sterilized at one Indian Health Service hospital in Oklahoma. In 1973 two black sisters from Montgomery, Alabama, 12-year-old Mary Alice Relf and 14-year-old Minnie Lee Relf, were reported to have been surgically sterilized without their parents' consent. An investigation revealed that in the same town, eleven other young girls of about the same age as the Relf sisters had also been sterilized; ten of them were black. During the early 1970s in Aiken, South Carolina, of thirty-four Medicaid-funded deliveries, eighteen included sterilizations, and all eighteen involved young black women. In 1972 Carl Schultz, director of the Department of Health, Education, and Welfare's Population Affairs Office, acknowledged that the government had funded between 100,000 and 200,000 sterilizations. These policies aroused black suspicions that family planning efforts were inspired by racist and eugenist motives.

The first phase of the birth control movement, then, completely ignored black women's sexual subjugation to white masters. In the second phase, the movement adopted the racist policies of the eugenics movement. The third stage saw a number of government-supported coercive measures to contain the population of poor people and people of color. While blacks perceive birth control per se as beneficial, blacks have historically objected to birth control as a method of dealing with poverty. Rather, most blacks believe that poverty can be remedied only by creating meaningful jobs, raising the minimum wage so that a worker can support a family, providing health care to working and nonworking people through their jobs or through universal coverage, instituting a high-quality day care system for low- or no-income people, and improving educational opportunities.

Informed Consent

Informed consent is one of the key ethical issues in bioethics. In an unequal patient–provider relationship, informed consent may not be possible. The weaker partner may consent because he or she is powerless, poor, or does not understand the implications of consent. And when members of subordinate groups are not awarded full respect as persons, those in positions of power then consider it unnecessary to obtain consent. The infamous Tuskegee experiment is a classic example. Starting in 1932, over 400 poor and uneducated syphilitic black men in Alabama were unwitting subjects in a Public Health Service experiment, condoned by the surgeon general, to study the course of untreated syphilis. Physicians told the men that they were going to receive special treatment, concealing the fact that the medical procedures were diagnostic rather than therapeutic. Although the effects of untreated syphilis were already known by 1936, the experiment continued for forty years. In 1969 a committee appointed by the Public Health Service to review the Tuskegee study decided to continue it. The Tuskegee experiment did not come to widespread public attention until 1972, when the *Washington Star* documented this breach of medical ethics. As a result, the experiment was halted. Unfortunately, however, the legacy of the experiment lingers on, as several chapters in this volume illustrate.

It may be tempting to assume that such medical abuses are part of the distant past. However, there is evidence that violations of informed consent persist. Of 52,000 Maryland women screened annually for sickle cell anemia between 1978 and 1980, 25 percent were screened without their consent, thus denying these women the benefit of prescreening education or followup counseling, or the opportunity to decline screening. A national survey conducted in 1986 found that 81 percent of women subjected to court-ordered obstetrical interventions (Caesarean section, hospital detention, or intrauterine transfusion) were black, Hispanic, or Asian; nearly half were unmarried; one-fourth did not speak English; and none were private patients. When in 1981, a Texas legislator asked his constituency whether they favored sterilization of women on welfare, a majority of the respondents said that welfare benefits should be tied to sterilizations.

How a Professional Perspective Makes a Difference

Thus far, I have shown some grounds for African-American perspectives on bioethics, based on black activist philosophy and the unequal health status of African Americans. I have also argued that a history of medical abuse and neglect toward people in an unequal power relationship commands our attention to African-American perspectives on bioethics issues. In this final section, I will argue that a professional perspective can voice the concerns of those not in the power circle. Two examples—black psychology and the white women's movement—illustrate that professional perspectives can make a difference in changing society's perceptions and, ultimately, policies regarding a particular population.

Black Psychology

Until recently, mainstream psychology judged blacks as genetically and mentally inferior, incapable of abstract reasoning, culturally deprived, passive, ugly, lazy, childishly happy, dishonest, and emotionally immature or disturbed. Mainstream psychology owned these definitions and viewed African Americans through a deficit–deficiency model—a model it had constructed to explain African-American behavior. When blacks entered the profession of psychology, they challenged

that deficit model by presenting an African-American perspective that addressed the dominant group's assessments and changed, to a certain extent, the way society views blacks. Real consequences of black psychologists' efforts to encourage self-definition, consciousness, and self-worth have been felt across many areas: professional training, intelligence and ability testing, criminal justice, and family counseling. Black psychologists have presented their findings before professional conferences, legislative hearings, and policy-making task forces. For example, black psychologists are responsible for the ban in California on using standardized intelligence tests as a criterion for placing black and other minority students in classes for the mentally retarded. The Association of Black Psychologists publishes the *Journal of Black Psychology*, and black psychologists contribute to a variety of other professional journals. As a result of these and other efforts, most respected psychologists no longer advocate the deficit–deficiency model.

The Women's Movement

The women's movement is another example of a subordinated group defining its own perspectives. The perspectives of white women have historically been defined largely by white men; white women's voices, like black voices, have traditionally been ignored or trivialized. A mere twenty years ago, the question, "Should there be a woman's perspective on health?" was emotionally debated. Although the question is still asked, a respected discipline of women's studies has emerged, with several journals devoted to women's health. Women in increasing numbers have been drawn to the field of applied ethics, specifically to bioethics, and they debate issues such as maternal and child health, rights of women versus rights of the fetus, unnecessary hysterectomies and Caesareans, the doctor–patient relationship, and the absence of women in clinical trials of new drugs. Unfortunately, however, the mainstream women's movement is largely the domain of white women. This, of course, does not mean that black women have not been activists for women's rights; on the contrary, African-American women historically have been deeply involved in fighting both racism and sexism, believing that the two are inseparable. Many black women distrust the movement, criticizing it as racist and self-serving, concerned only with white middle-class women's issues. Black feminists working within the abortion rights movement and with the National

Black Women's Health Project, an Atlanta-based self-help and health advocacy organization, are raising their voices to identify issues relevant to African-American women and men in general, and reproductive and health issues in particular. Like black psychologists, these black feminists are articulating a perspective that is effectively promoting pluralism.

Conclusion

The disturbing health inequities between blacks and whites—differences in infant mortality, average life span, chronic illnesses, and aggressiveness of treatment—suggest that minority access to health care should be recognized and accepted as a *bona fide* concern of bioethics. Opening the debate can only enrich this new field, thereby avoiding the moral difficulties of exclusion. Surely the serious and underaddressed health concerns of a large and increasing segment of our society are an ethical issue that is at least as important as such esoteric, high-visibility issues as the morality of gestational surrogacy. The front page of the August 5, 1991, *New York Times* headlined an article, "When Grandmother Is Mother, Until Birth." Although interesting and worthy of ethical comment, such sensational headlines undermine the moral seriousness of a situation in which over 37 million poor people do not have access to health care.

There is a basis for developing African-American perspectives on bioethics, and I have presented examples of medical abuse and neglect that suggest particular issues for consideration. Valuable as our advocacy has been, our perspectives have not gained full prominence in bioethics debates. Thus, it is necessary to form a community of scholars to conduct research on the contributions as well as the limitations of perspectives of African-American and other poor and underserved peoples in this important field.

The Demise of Affirmative Action and the Future of Health Care

H. Jack Geiger

Jack Geiger argues that the drop in medical school admissions of African Americans and other minorities, due to factors like the rollback of affirmative action and the underfunding of public schools, is the beginning of a "potential public health disaster."

By 2050, minority groups will make up the majority of the population, but who will be their physicians? A diverse population, Geiger says, "requires a diverse, culturally competent physician workforce" able to meet people's needs. Developing such a workforce requires recognizing that medical education is a social good and not merely a prize awarded to favored individuals. Yet our policies appear to be taking our society in the opposite direction. In 1998, two years after California voters outlawed the use of race in educational policies, minority enrollment in state medical schools had declined by 32 percent.

Just over 50 years ago, fewer than 4000 of the more than 200,000 American physicians were African American. More than a third of all US medical schools were closed to non-Whites. Only 8 graduates of Howard and

From Original title, "Ethnic Cleansing in the Groves of Academe," *American Journal of Public Health*, Vol. 88, No. 9 (1998), pp. 1299–1300. Reprinted by permission of the American Public Health Assn.

Meharry, the traditionally Black medical schools, were training in White hospitals. Only 20 predominantly White schools had any African American students. As recently as 30 years ago, 99% of the students in US medical schools other than Howard and Meharry were non-Hispanic Whites. The legacy of that era of injustice, racial segregation, and exclusion is with us now: White males constitute 37% of the US population—but more than 67% of all US physicians.[1]

Progress over the last 30 years has been substantial, but its course has been as erratic and fitful as the nation's overall commitment to racial justice and equity of opportunity. As a result of the civil rights movement and a concerted effort by medical schools,[2] underrepresented minorities (African Americans, Mexican Americans, mainland Puerto Ricans, and Native Americans) reached 10% of the total number of medical students by the mid-1970s, but then began to drop. (Ironically, minority population growth occurred much more rapidly during this period, so that minority underrepresentation in medical schools—despite the enrollment gains— actually increased.) A renewed intensive effort by the Association of American Medical Colleges[3] helped to produce a 36% increase in minority enrollment—to 12%—between 1990 and 1995. But then the assault on affirmative action, a backlash that had produced relatively modest limitations over the preceding 2 decades, resulted in the passage in California of Proposition 209, a voter initiative flatly barring so-called racial or ethnic preferences (even to pursue the goal of diversity) as a factor in admission to the University of California system. (Preferences for athletes, veterans, women, and the children of alumni were not addressed.) In Texas, the decision in *Hopwood v. Texas* had the same effect on admission to public universities in that state, Louisiana, and Mississippi.

The data presented by Carlisle et al.[4] in this issue of the Journal show that the damaging effect of such decisions on minority enrollment, while worse regionally, is national in scope. Overall, the admission of underrepresented minorities to the 1997 entering medical school class fell by 9.1%, on the heels of a 5.2% drop in 1996. The states of California, Texas, Mississippi, and Louisiana accounted for 44% of the decline. What is most ominous is that these reversals were concentrated in public institutions: minority enrollment declined at 61% of publicly funded schools, and 9 of the 10 schools with the biggest percentage drops were public. Yet two thirds of all underrepresented minority students attend such institutions. If these trends continue—and there are powerful reasons to believe that they will—we will return to the levels of the 1980s, or worse.

Not everyone, apparently, regards this as a bad thing. In a little-noted and blatantly racist remark to the *New York Times* in 1997, Ward Connerly, regent of the University of California, said, "If you're lying on a gurney, and a black doctor shows up, you're going

to get up and crawl out."[5] Such comments rest on an elaborate structure of myths, fallacies, and slurs: that quantitative instruments such as the Scholastic Achievement Test and the Medical College Admission Test are the only meaningful measures of applicant quality; that they are predictive of future clinical and professional performance; that they reflect only "innate ability" or "individual merit" and not, as well, the preparatory resources available to different groups of students; that it is only the playing field that need be level, and not the path that leads to it; that modest differences in mean scores justify an indelible label of "less qualified," even among those who successfully pass all subsequent educational and professional hurdles; and, in the racist extreme, that lower scores indicate genetic inferiority.[6] All of these allegations have been elegantly refuted;[7] still, they persist.

What is perhaps not fully recognized is that these reversals in minority admissions are merely the leading edge of a potential public health disaster. Application to medical school, after all, comes at the end of a long educational pipeline. The public school preparatory route, from kindergarten through high school and college, is equally under assault—most intensely where the majority of the students are minorities, or poor, or immigrants, or come from non-English-speaking homes, or all of the above.

Peter Schrag, in the recently published *Paradise Lost: California's Experience, America's Failure*,[8] offers that state's version of the savage inequalities in public education portrayed nationally by Jonathon Kozol.[9] As the state's demographics changed, Schrag points out, California's public schools, once the envy of the nation, have literally begun to rot. The state now spends $1000 less per child than the national median. It ranks 38th among the states in spending on library books and 45th in spending on computer software, and 54% of its high school teachers don't have enough textbooks for all their students. "There are schools," Schrag reports, "where ceilings are flaking, bare wiring hangs down, and floors buckle; where rotting planks make walkways dangerous. . . ."A million students are housed in "temporary" buildings "which now look more often like migrant camps."[8 (pp. 67–71)] And so, he reports, California public school students now rank 49th in reading and are tied for dead last in mathematics proficiency.

At the next level up, the combined effects of these levels of preparation and Proposition 209 can be seen in admission to the state university's elite campuses at Berkeley and Los Angeles (UCLA). Admission rates for African Americans and Hispanics were cut nearly in half, from 22% last year to 10.5% this year at Berkeley and from 22% to 14% at UCLA. Overall, the university system is now 85% White and Asian. Yet—to use the criteria so favored by affirmative action opponents—roughly 400 of the minority students who "failed to qualify" at Berkeley had perfect high school grade-point averages of 4.0 and Scholastic Achievement Test scores over 1200.

These are not just West Coast phenomena. The trustees of the City University of New York, where the student body is 70% non-White and heavily immigrant, recently voted to deny admission to students who failed any placement test in reading, writing, or mathematics and to prohibit the senior colleges from continuing to offer remediation courses. It is estimated that this change will bar 67% of African American applicants, 70% of Latinos, and 71% of Asians; overall, the senior colleges will lose 13,000 students a year and suffer crippling budget cuts in consequence. One trustee said, "We are *cleaning out* the four-year colleges, and putting remediation where it belongs [italics added]."[10] And at the same time, presumably, putting the minority students where they "belong." Whatever the intent, the effect will be clear. To use the trustee's metaphor, it will be the academic equivalent of ethnic cleansing.

What has all this to do with public health? We have only to look at the demographics. From 1980 to 1995 in the US, the White population increased by 12%, while African Americans increased by 24%, Hispanics by 83%, Native Americans by 57%, and Asians by 163%. By 2050, if not earlier, the members of these minority groups will make up the majority of Americans.[11] Who will provide their medical care—and that of the minority of Whites as well? If present patterns persist, access to care for those in greatest need and at greatest risk will worsen; what are now shameful disparities could become public health failures of staggering magnitude.

The argument is not that minority physicians must be the ones who care for the underserved, the people of color, the poorest and sickest of our populations, though the evidence is overwhelming that this is disproportionately the case at present.[12-14] The argument is, rather, that a diverse population in a democracy requires a diverse, culturally competent physician workforce that is fully prepared—by background, motivation, and training—to meet that population's unique needs. To achieve such a workforce, in turn, requires recognition that medical education—like all education—is a social good, an investment in the commonweal, and not merely a prize to be awarded to favored individual competitors. It is possible to be simultaneously excellent and inclusive. In a diverse and evolving democracy, it is essential.

The evidence presented by Carlisle et al. indicates that we are headed in the opposite direction. We continue in that direction at our own peril, and that of our children, and ultimately that of our society.

References

1. Nickens HW, Cohen JJ. On affirmative action. *JAMA.* 1996;275:572–574.

2. *Report of the Association of American Medical Colleges Task Force to the Inter-Association Committee on Expanding Education Opportunities for Blacks and Other Minority Students.* Washington, DC: Association of American Medical Colleges; 1970.

3. Nickens HW, Ready TP, Petersdorf RG. Project 3000 by 2000: racial and ethnic diversity in U.S. medical schools. *N Engl J Med.* 1994;331:472–476.

4. Carlisle DM, Gardiner JE, Liu H. The entry of underrepresented minority students into US medical schools: an evaluation of recent trends. *Am J Public Health.* 1998;88:1314–1318.

5. Bearak B. Questions of race run deep for foe of preferences. *New York Times.* July 17, 1997:A1.

6. Hernstein RJ, Murray C. *The Bell Curve: Intelligence and Class Structure in American Life.* New York, NY: Free Press; 1994.

7. *Questions and Answers on Affirmative Action in Medical Education.* Washington, DC: Association of American Medical Colleges; April 1995.

8. Schrag P. *Paradise Lost: California's Experience, America's Failure.* New York, NY: The New Press; 1998.

9. Kozol J. *Savage Inequalities: Children in America's Schools.* New York, NY: Crown Publishers, 1991.

10. Arenson KW. CUNY to tighten admissions policy at 4-year schools. *New York Times.* May 27, 1998:A1.

11. *Population Projections of the U.S. by Age, by Race, and Hispanic Origin: 1992–2050.* Washington, DC: Bureau of the Census; 1992:xviii Table 1.

12. Komaromy M, Grumbach K, Drake M, et al. The role of Black and Hispanic physicians in providing health care for underserved populations. *N Engl J Med.* 1996;334:1304–1328.

13. Cantor JC, Miles EL, Baker LC, Barker DC. Physician service to the underserved: implications for affirmative action in medical education. *Inquiry.* 1996;33(2):167–180.

14. Moy E, Bartman BA. Physician race and care of minority and medically indigent patients. *JAMA.* 1995;273:1515–1520.

DECISION SCENARIOS

The questions following each decision scenario are intended to prompt reflection and discussion. In considering how to answer them, you should consider the information in the Briefing Session, the ethical theories and principles presented in Part V, "Foundations of Bioethics," and the arguments and criticisms offered in the relevant readings in this chapter.

DECISION SCENARIO 1

Tuskegee Effect

Abner Sims is a forty-six-year-old African American who was diagnosed HIV positive three years ago. Although he did well when he was taking AZT (ZDV), his physician now wants to start him on a course of protease inhibitors. "Some people have done so well, it's no longer possible even to detect the virus in their blood," Sims's doctor tells him. "It's not a cure, but it's the next best thing."

Sims doesn't tell his doctor he won't take the new drug. Instead, he accepts the prescription, then doesn't get it filled. He also stops taking AZT when his supply runs out. When asked why he doesn't want to follow his physician's advice, Sims says, "A black man can't trust what a doctor tells him. If he wants to use that new drug on me, probably it's because he wants another guinea pig. That's what black people

are to doctors—guinea pigs." When asked, Sims says he has never heard of the Tuskegee syphilis study.

1. Why might Sims be said to be an example of the "Tuskegee effect"? How could he be an example if he has never heard of the Tuskegee syphilis study?

2. Would a nonhierarchical, nonauthoritarian approach to health care do a better job of gaining the trust of those like Abner Sims?

3. If the African American perspective is rooted in social action and a commitment to justice, how might that perspective help the medical establishment in dealing with those like Abner Sims?

4. What steps might be taken to encourage Sims and people like him to trust their physicians? What steps might be taken by physicians and the medical establishment to earn the trust of Sims and others?

DECISION SCENARIO 2

Racial-Differences Research

We know that African Americans are more prone to develop hypertension than are other ethnic or racial groups, that black women develop breast cancer at an earlier age, and that the incidence of prostate cancer is higher in black males. Some differences may be accounted for by differences in such social conditions as income, health insurance, access to medical care, and explicit or unintended racial prejudice.

Some researchers believe, however, that biological factors may also be involved. We know that some genetic diseases, such as sickle-cell disease, occur predominately among African Americans, just as other genetic diseases, such as cystic fibrosis, occur predominately among Caucasians. It seems reasonable to believe that genetic factors may predispose African Americans to develop a variety of medical problems,

like those just mentioned, at a greater frequency. If predisposing genes could be identified, tests for them could be developed and individuals could be informed about their risks. They might then be able to do more to prevent or delay the onset of the disease by changing their lifestyles or seeking medical treatment.

1. What social issues are raised by research programs that seek to identify genetic factors that may predispose African Americans to develop certain diseases?

2. In a society that is increasingly multiracial, does it make sense to try to identify predisposing genes in the African American population?

3. Is it possible to hold that race is a social construct while also advocating research into genetic factors associated with race?

DECISION SCENARIO 3

Designated Donor by Race

"We want to ask you to consider letting Mattie be an organ donor," Barbara Zepple said. She was the nurse assigned by the Transplant Service to talk with the families of patients who had been declared dead, but were good candidates for organ donation.

"Would they cut her up more?" Lilly Warder, Mattie's mother, asked.

"It's like an ordinary operation," Barbara said. "Once they remove the organs, they'll sew her up again. You won't be able to tell her organs have been donated."

"I don't know." Mrs. Warder shook her head. "It's like stealing from somebody's body. I don't like the idea."

"Do you know what Mattie would have wanted?" Barbara asked. "Did she like helping other people?"

"That's what she lived for." Mrs. Warder put her hand over her eyes for a moment. "Could you make sure they go to black people?"

"That's not something we can promise." Barbara shook her head. "Organs go to people who are most in need, no matter what race or gender or religion."

"Then I'm not sure I ought to give them away." Mrs. Warder shook her head. "Doctors took advantage of black folks in the past, and I'd like to try to make up for that."

1. Can Mrs. Warder's attempt to address wrongs done to black people by the medical community be defended on moral grounds?

2. Black people are kidney recipients significantly more often than they are kidney donors. Can an ethical case be made for a race-based organ distribution system?

DECISION SCENARIO 4

Social Construction

"Race is a socially constructed concept," Hee said. "We all belong to the human race, and our genes intermingle. It's the dominant group in a society that introduces racial distinctions so that it can exert social control over the 'inferior' races." Hee shook his head. "The idea of a drug for a specific race isn't just racist on its face; it's absurd."

"You're totally knee jerk when it comes to race," Al-Latha said. "Sure, there are no pure races. But, you know, some people share a lot more genes than others do." She smiled. "Maybe we all came from Africa thousands of years ago, but my grandfather came just twenty years ago."

"Yeah, but you've got at least one Hispanic grandparent," Hee shrugged. "That's my point."

"No, it's not," Al-Latha said. "It's mine. I'm holding a lot more African genes than Hispanic genes. And that means I'm more likely to develop some condition like high blood pressure than Asians or whites are." She held up a finger. "For the same reason, it's not absurd to think that some drugs might be more likely to benefit me more than they would whites or Asians."

1. Assume that race is defined by society. Does this mean that race has no connection with biological facts?

2. Suppose the (imaginary) drug Colow is tested in a clinical trial and found to be significantly more effective in lowering cholesterol in self-identified Chinese Americans than in any other segment of the population. Also, Colow is more effective for Chinese Americans than any other cholesterol-lowering drugs. Would it be morally legitimate to withhold Colow from everyone, including Chinese Americans, on the ground that it also works equally well for at least some whites and African Americans?

3. Making the same assumptions, would it be morally legitimate to deny everyone, including Chinese Americans, access to the drug on the ground that races do not exist and it is dangerous to society to act as if they did?

4. Is there a moral difference between identifying races or ethnic groups for the purpose of affirmative action or providing them with a more equitable share of resources (e.g., health care and housing) and identifying them for the purpose of testing whether a drug will be more effective in treating them for a particular disease?

DECISION SCENARIO 5

Cultural Competence

"Of course, he shouldn't have been admitted to medical school," Angela Forester said. "His grades were below the level of those admitted, and so were his MCAT scores."

"So what?" Brux Tai asked. "He's an African American, and there aren't many of those in med school nowadays."

"There would be more African Americans if those who wanted to go to medical school brought up their GPAs and test scores," Angela snapped. "As an African American, I'm not willing to see exceptions made on the basis of race. It's embarrassing."

1. Why might a decrease in the number of minorities in medical school be the start of a potential public health disaster?

2. Why might we want to downplay the importance of grades and test scores in determining admissions?

3. What factors might make it difficult for minorities to do as well academically as others?

4. Should we try to educate a group of diverse and "culturally competent" physicians?